Some Physical Constants

Quantity	Symbol	Value[a]
Atomic mass unit	u	$1.660\ 538\ 73\ (13) \times 10^{-27}$ kg
		$931.494\ 013\ (37)$ MeV/c^2
Avogadro's number	N_A	$6.022\ 141\ 99\ (47) \times 10^{23}$ particles/mol
Bohr magneton	$\mu_B = \dfrac{e\hbar}{2m_e}$	$9.274\ 008\ 99\ (37) \times 10^{-24}$ J/T
Bohr radius	$a_0 = \dfrac{\hbar^2}{m_e e^2 k_e}$	$5.291\ 772\ 083\ (19) \times 10^{-11}$ m
Boltzmann's constant	$k_B = \dfrac{R}{N_A}$	$1.380\ 650\ 3\ (24) \times 10^{-23}$ J/K
Compton wavelength	$\lambda_C = \dfrac{h}{m_e c}$	$2.426\ 310\ 215\ (18) \times 10^{-12}$ m
Coulomb constant	$k_e = \dfrac{1}{4\pi\epsilon_0}$	$8.987\ 551\ 788 \times 10^9$ N·m^2/C^2 (exact)
Deuteron mass	m_d	$3.343\ 583\ 09\ (26) \times 10^{-27}$ kg
		$2.013\ 553\ 212\ 71\ (35)$ u
Electron mass	m_e	$9.109\ 381\ 88\ (72) \times 10^{-31}$ kg
		$5.485\ 799\ 110\ (12) \times 10^{-4}$ u
		$0.510\ 998\ 902\ (21)$ MeV/c^2
Electron volt	eV	$1.602\ 176\ 462\ (63) \times 10^{-19}$ J
Elementary charge	e	$1.602\ 176\ 462\ (63) \times 10^{-19}$ C
Gas constant	R	$8.314\ 472\ (15)$ J/mol·K
Gravitational constant	G	$6.673\ (10) \times 10^{-11}$ N·m^2/kg^2
Josephson frequency–voltage ratio	$\dfrac{2e}{h}$	$4.835\ 978\ 98\ (19) \times 10^{14}$ Hz/V
Magnetic flux quantum	$\Phi_0 = \dfrac{h}{2e}$	$2.067\ 833\ 636\ (81) \times 10^{-15}$ T·m^2
Neutron mass	m_n	$1.674\ 927\ 16\ (13) \times 10^{-27}$ kg
		$1.008\ 664\ 915\ 78\ (55)$ u
		$939.565\ 330\ (38)$ MeV/c^2
Nuclear magneton	$\mu_n = \dfrac{e\hbar}{2m_p}$	$5.050\ 783\ 17\ (20) \times 10^{-27}$ J/T
Permeability of free space	μ_0	$4\pi \times 10^{-7}$ T·m/A (exact)
Permittivity of free space	$\epsilon_0 = \dfrac{1}{\mu_0 c^2}$	$8.854\ 187\ 817 \times 10^{-12}$ C^2/N·m^2 (exact)
Planck's constant	h	$6.626\ 068\ 76\ (52) \times 10^{-34}$ J·s
	$\hbar = \dfrac{h}{2\pi}$	$1.054\ 571\ 596\ (82) \times 10^{-34}$ J·s
Proton mass	m_p	$1.672\ 621\ 58\ (13) \times 10^{-27}$ kg
		$1.007\ 276\ 466\ 88\ (13)$ u
		$938.271\ 998\ (38)$ MeV/c^2
Rydberg constant	R_H	$1.097\ 373\ 156\ 854\ 9\ (83) \times 10^7$ m^{-1}
Speed of light in vacuum	c	$2.997\ 924\ 58 \times 10^8$ m/s (exact)

Note: These constants are the values recommended in 1998 by CODATA, based on a least-squares adjustment of data from different measurements. For a more complete list, see P. J. Mohr and B. N. Taylor, "CODATA recommended values of the fundamental physical constants: 1998." *Rev. Mod. Phys.* 72:351, 2000.

[a]The numbers in parentheses for the values represent the uncertainties of the last two digits.

Solar System Data

Body	Mass (kg)	Mean Radius (m)	Period (s)	Distance from the Sun (m)
Mercury	3.18×10^{23}	2.43×10^6	7.60×10^6	5.79×10^{10}
Venus	4.88×10^{24}	6.06×10^6	1.94×10^7	1.08×10^{11}
Earth	5.98×10^{24}	6.37×10^6	3.156×10^7	1.496×10^{11}
Mars	6.42×10^{23}	3.37×10^6	5.94×10^7	2.28×10^{11}
Jupiter	1.90×10^{27}	6.99×10^7	3.74×10^8	7.78×10^{11}
Saturn	5.68×10^{26}	5.85×10^7	9.35×10^8	1.43×10^{12}
Uranus	8.68×10^{25}	2.33×10^7	2.64×10^9	2.87×10^{12}
Neptune	1.03×10^{26}	2.21×10^7	5.22×10^9	4.50×10^{12}
Pluto	$\approx 1.4 \times 10^{22}$	$\approx 1.5 \times 10^6$	7.82×10^9	5.91×10^{12}
Moon	7.36×10^{22}	1.74×10^6	—	—
Sun	1.991×10^{30}	6.96×10^8	—	—

Physical Data Often Used

Average Earth–Moon distance	3.84×10^8 m
Average Earth–Sun distance	1.496×10^{11} m
Average radius of the Earth	6.37×10^6 m
Density of air (20°C and 1 atm)	1.20 kg/m^3
Density of water (20°C and 1 atm)	1.00×10^3 kg/m^3
Free-fall acceleration	9.80 m/s^2
Mass of the Earth	5.98×10^{24} kg
Mass of the Moon	7.36×10^{22} kg
Mass of the Sun	1.99×10^{30} kg
Standard atmospheric pressure	1.013×10^5 Pa

Note: These values are the ones used in the text.

Some Prefixes for Powers of Ten

Power	Prefix	Abbreviation	Power	Prefix	Abbreviation
10^{-24}	yocto	y	10^1	deka	da
10^{-21}	zepto	z	10^2	hecto	h
10^{-18}	atto	a	10^3	kilo	k
10^{-15}	femto	f	10^6	mega	M
10^{-12}	pico	p	10^9	giga	G
10^{-9}	nano	n	10^{12}	tera	T
10^{-6}	micro	μ	10^{15}	peta	P
10^{-3}	milli	m	10^{18}	exa	E
10^{-2}	centi	c	10^{21}	zetta	Z
10^{-1}	deci	d	10^{24}	yotta	Y

PRINCIPLES OF PHYSICS: A CALCULUS-BASED TEXT
Vol 2
Drexel University
Fourth Edition

SERWAY/JEWETT

THOMSON

BROOKS/COLE

Australia · Canada · Mexico · Singapore · Spain · United Kingdom · United States

THOMSON

BROOKS/COLE

PRINCIPLES OF PHYSICS:
A CALCULUS-BASED TEXT, 4e - Vol 2
Drexel University
SERWAY/JEWETT

Executive Editors:
Michele Baird, Maureen Staudt &
Michael Stranz

Project Development Manager:
Linda de Stefano

Marketing Coordinators:
Lindsay Annett and Sara Mercurio

**Production/Manufacturing
Supervisor:**
Donna M. Brown

Pre-Media Services Supervisor:
Dan Plofchan

Rights and Permissions Specialists:
Kalina Hintz and Bahman Naraghi

Cover Image
Getty Images*

The Adaptable Courseware Program
consists of products and additions to
existing Brooks/Cole products that are
produced from camera-ready copy.
Peer review, class testing, and
accuracy are primarily the responsibility
of the author(s).

ISBN 978-0-495-40711-9
(0-495-40711-9)

International Divisions List

Asia (Including India):
Thomson Learning
(a division of Thomson Asia Pte Ltd)
5 Shenton Way #01-01
UIC Building
Singapore 068808
Tel: (65) 6410-1200
Fax: (65) 6410-1208

Australia/New Zealand:
Thomson Learning Australia
102 Dodds Street
Southbank, Victoria 3006
Australia

Latin America:
Thomson Learning
Seneca 53
Colonia Polano
11560 Mexico, D.F., Mexico
Tel (525) 281-2906
Fax (525) 281-2656

Canada:
Thomson Nelson
1120 Birchmount Road
Toronto, Ontario
Canada M1K 5G4
Tel (416) 752-9100
Fax (416) 752-8102

UK/Europe/Middle East/Africa:
Thomson Learning
High Holborn House
50-51 Bedford Row
London, WC1R 4LS
United Kingdom
Tel 44 (020) 7067-2500
Fax 44 (020) 7067-2600

Spain (Includes Portugal):
Thomson Paraninfo
Calle Magallanes 25
28015 Madrid
España
Tel 34 (0)91 446-3350
Fax 34 (0)91 445-6218

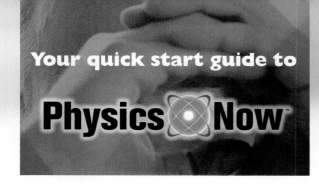

Your quick start guide to PhysicsNow™

Welcome to **PhysicsNow**, your fully integrated system for physics tutorials and self-assessment on the web. To get started, just follow these simple instructions.

Your first visit to PhysicsNow

1. Go to **http://www.pop4e.com** and click the **Register** button.

2. The first time you visit, you will be asked to select your school. Choose your state from the drop-down menu, then type in your school's name in the box provided and click **Search**. A list of schools with names similar to what you entered will show on the right. Find your school and click on it.

3. On the next screen, enter the access code from the card that came with your textbook in the "Content or Course Access Code" box*. Enter your email address in the next box and click **Submit.**

   * **PhysicsNow** access codes may be purchased separately. Should you need to purchase an access code, go back to **http://www.pop4e.com** and click the **Buy** button.

4. On the next screen, choose a password and click **Submit.**

5. Lastly, fill out the registration form and click **Register and Enter iLrn.** This information will only be used to contact you if there is a problem with your account.

6. You should now see the **PhysicsNow** homepage. Select a chapter and begin!

   Note: Your account information will be sent to the email address that you entered in Step 3, so be sure to enter a valid email address. You will use your email address as your username the next time you login.

Second and later visits

1. Go to **http://www.pop4e.com** and click the **Login** button.

2. Enter your user name (the email address you entered when you registered) and your password and then click **Login.**

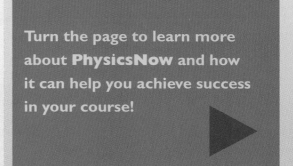

Turn the page to learn more about PhysicsNow and how it can help you achieve success in your course!

SYSTEM REQUIREMENTS:
(Please see the System Requirements link at www.ilrn.com for complete list.)
PC: Windows 98 or higher, Internet Explorer 5.5 or higher
Mac: OS X or higher, Mozilla browser 1.2.1 or higher

TECHNICAL SUPPORT:
For online help, click on **Technical Support** in the upper right corner of the screen, or contact us at:

1-800-423-0563 Monday–Friday • 8:30 A.M. to 6:00 P.M. EST
tl.support@thomson.com

THOMSON
BROOKS/COLE

What do you need to learn now?

Take charge of your learning with **PhysicsNow**™, a powerful student-learning tool for physics! This interactive resource helps you gauge your unique study needs, then gives you a *Personalized Learning Plan* that will help you focus in on the concepts and problems that will most enhance your understanding. With **PhysicsNow**, you have the resources you need to take charge of your learning!

The access code card included with this new copy of *Principles of Physics* is your ticket to all of the resources in **PhysicsNow.** (See the previous page for login instructions.)

Interact at every turn with the POWER and SIMPLICITY of PhysicsNow!

PhysicsNow combines Serway and Jewett's best-selling *Principles of Physics* with carefully crafted media resources that will help you learn. This dynamic resource and the Fourth Edition of the text were developed in concert, to enhance each other and provide you with a seamless, integrated learning system.

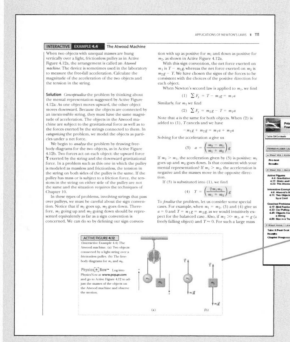

As you work through the text, you will see notes that direct you to the media-enhanced activities in **PhysicsNow**. This precise page-by-page integration means you'll spend less time flipping through pages or navigating websites looking for useful exercises. These multimedia exercises will make all the difference when you're studying and taking exams . . . after all, it's far easier to understand physics if it's seen in action, and **PhysicsNow** enables you to become a part of the action!

Begin at http://www.pop4e.com and build your own Personalized Learning Plan now!

Log into PhysicsNow at http://www.pop4e.com by using the free access code packaged with the text. You'll immediately notice the system's simple, browser-based format. You can build a complete *Personalized Learning Plan* for yourself by taking advantage of all three powerful components found on **PhysicsNow**:

▶ **What I Know**
▶ **What I Need to Learn**
▶ **What I've Learned**

The best way to maximize the system and optimize your time is to start by taking the *Pre-Test* ▶▶▶

What I Know

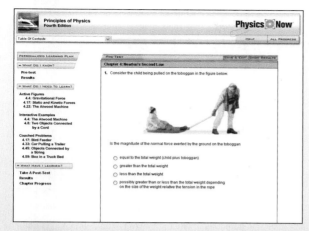

▲ You take a *Pre-Test* to measure your level of comprehension after reading a chapter. Each *Pre-Test* includes approximately 15 questions. The *Pre-Test* is your first step in creating your custom-tailored *Personalized Learning Plan*.

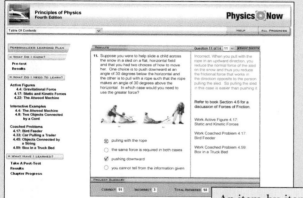

An item-by-item analysis gives you feedback on each of your answers.

▲ Once you've completed the "What I Know" *Pre-Test*, you are presented with a detailed *Personalized Learning Plan*, with text references that outline the elements you need to review in order to master the chapter's most essential concepts. This roadmap to concept mastery guides you to exercises designed to improve skills and to increase your understanding of the basic concepts.

At each stage, the *Personalized Learning Plan* refers to *Principles of Physics* to reinforce the connection between text and technology as a powerful learning tool.

What I Need to Learn

Once you've completed the *Pre-Test*, you're ready to work through tutorials and exercises that will help you master the concepts that are essential to your success in the course.

ACTIVE FIGURES

A remarkable bank of more than 200 animated figures helps you visualize physics in action. Taken straight from illustrations in the text, these *Active Figures* help you master key concepts from the book. By interacting with the animations and accompanying quiz questions, you come to an even greater understanding of the concepts you need to learn from each chapter. ▼

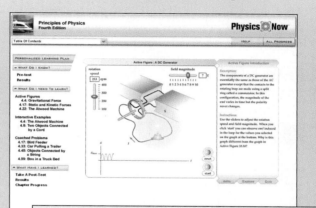

Each figure is titled so you can easily identify the concept you are seeing. The final tab features a *Quiz*. The *Explore* tab guides you through the animation so you understand what you should be seeing and learning.

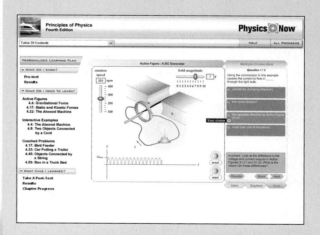

▲ The brief *Quiz* ensures that you mastered the concept played out in the animation—and gives you feedback on each response.

Continued on the next page ▶

COACHED PROBLEMS

Engaging *Coached Problems* reinforce the lessons in the text by taking a step-by-step approach to problem-solving methodology. Each *Coached Problem* gives you the option of breaking down a problem from the text into steps with feedback to 'coach' you toward the solution. There are approximately five *Coached Problems* per chapter.

You can choose to work through the *Coached Problems* by inputting an answer directly or working in steps with the program. If you choose to work in steps, the problem is solved with the same problem-solving methodology used in *Principles of Physics* to reinforce these critical skills. Once you've worked through the problem, you can click **Try Another** to change the variables in the problem for more practice.

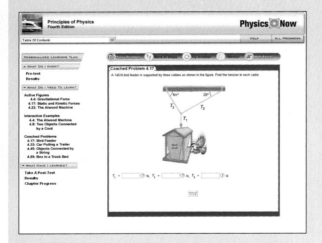

▲ Also built into each *Coached Problem* is a link to Brooks/Cole's exclusive **vMentor**™ web-based tutoring service site that lets you interact directly with a live physics tutor. If you're stuck on math, a *MathAssist* link on each *Coached Problem* launches tutorials on math specific to that problem.

INTERACTIVE EXAMPLES

You'll strengthen your problem-solving and visualization skills with *Interactive Examples*. Extending selected examples from the text, *Interactive Examples* utilize the proven and trusted problem-solving methodology presented in *Principles of Physics.* These animated learning modules give you all the tools you need to solve a problem type—you're then asked to apply what you have learned to different scenarios. You will find approximately two *Interactive Examples* for each chapter of the text.▼

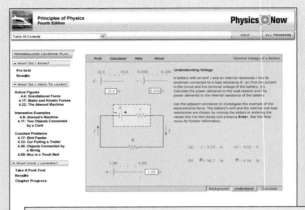

You're guided through the steps to solve the problem and then asked to input an answer in a simulation to see if your result is correct. Feedback is instantaneous.

What I've Learned

▶ After working through the problems highlighted in your *Personalized Learning Plan,* you move on to a *Post-Test,* about 15 questions per chapter.

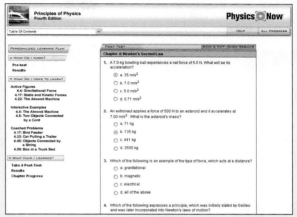

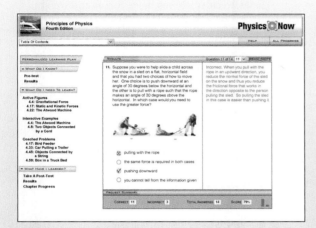

◀ Once you've completed the *Post-Test,* you receive your percentage score and specific feedback on each answer. The *Post-Tests* give you a new set of questions with each attempt, so you can take them over and over as you continue to build your knowledge and skills and master concepts.

Also available to help you succeed in your course

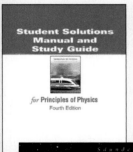

Student Solutions Manual and Study Guide
Volume I (Ch. 1–15) ISBN: 0-534-49145-6
Volume II (Ch. 16–31) ISBN: 0-534-49147-2
These manuals contain detailed solutions to approximately 20-percent of the end-of-chapter problems. These problems are indicated in the textbook with boxed problem numbers. Each manual also features a skills section, important notes from key sections of the text, and a list of important equations and concepts.

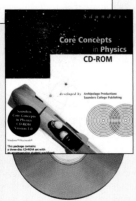

Core Concepts in Physics CD-ROM, Version 2.0
ISBN: 0-03-033731-3
Explore the core of physics with this powerful CD-ROM/workbook program! Content screens provide in-depth coverage of abstract and often difficult principles, building connections between physical concepts and mathematics. The presentation contains more than 350 movies—both animated and live video—including laboratory demonstrations, real-world examples, graphic models, and step-by-step explanations of essential mathematics. An accompanying workbook contains practical physics problems directly related to the presentation, along with worked solutions. Package includes three discs and a workbook.

Welcome to your MCAT Test Preparation Guide

The **MCAT Test Preparation Guide** makes your copy of *Principles of Physics,* **Fourth Edition,** the most comprehensive MCAT study tool and classroom resource in introductory physics. The grid, which begins below and continues on the next two pages, outlines twelve concept-based **study courses** for the physics part of your MCAT exam. Use it to prepare for the MCAT, class tests, and your homework assignments.

Vectors

Skill Objectives: To calculate distance, calculate angles between vectors, calculate magnitudes, and to understand vectors.

Review Plan:

Distance and Angles: Chapter 1
- Section 1.6
- Active Figure 1.4
- Chapter Problem 33

Using Vectors: Chapter 1
- Sections 1.7–1.9
- Quick Quizzes 1.4–1.8
- Examples 1.6–1.8
- Active Figures 1.9, 1.16
- Chapter Problems 37, 38, 45, 47, 51, 53

Motion

Skill Objectives: To understand motion in two dimensions, to calculate speed and velocity, to calculate centripetal acceleration, and acceleration in free fall problems.

Review Plan:

Motion in 1 Dimension: Chapter 2
- Sections 2.1, 2.2, 2.4, 2.6, 2.7
- Quick Quizzes 2.3–2.6
- Examples 2.1, 2.2, 2.4–2.10
- Active Figure 2.12
- Chapter Problems 3, 5, 13, 19, 21, 29, 31, 33

Motion in 2 Dimensions: Chapter 3
- Sections 3.1–3.3
- Quick Quizzes 3.2, 3.3
- Examples 3.1–3.4
- Active Figures 3.4, 3.5, 3.8
- Chapter Problems 1, 7, 15

Centripetal Acceleration: Chapter 3
- Sections 3.4, 3.5
- Quick Quizzes 3.4, 3.5
- Example 3.5
- Active Figure 3.12
- Chapter Problems 23, 31

Force

Skill Objectives: To know and understand Newton's Laws, to calculate resultant forces and weight.

Review Plan:

Newton's Laws: Chapter 4
- Sections 4.1–4.6
- Quick Quizzes 4.1–4.6
- Example 4.1
- Chapter Problem 7

Resultant Forces: Chapter 4
- Section 4.7
- Quick Quiz 4.7
- Example 4.6
- Chapter Problems 27, 35

Gravity: Chapter 11
- Section 11.1
- Quick Quiz 11.1
- Chapter Problem 3

Equilibrium

Skill Objectives: To calculate momentum and impulse, center of gravity, and torque.

Review Plan:

Momentum: Chapter 8
- Section 8.1
- Quick Quiz 8.2
- Examples 8.2, 8.3

Impulse: Chapter 8
- Sections 8.2, 8.3
- Quick Quizzes 8.3, 8.4
- Examples 8.4, 8.6
- Active Figures 8.8, 8.9
- Chapter Problems 7, 9, 15, 19, 21

Torque: Chapter 10
- Sections 10.5, 10.6
- Quick Quiz 10.7
- Example 10.8
- Chapter Problems 21, 27

Work

Skill Objectives: To calculate friction, work, kinetic energy, power, and potential energy.

Review Plan:

Friction: Chapter 5
- Section 5.1
- Quick Quizzes 5.1, 5.2

Work: Chapter 6
- Section 6.2
- Chapter Problems 1, 3

Kinetic Energy: Chapter 6
- Section 6.5
- Example 6.4

Power: Chapter 6
- Section 6.8
- Chapter Problem 35

Potential Energy: Chapter 7
- Sections 7.1, 7.2
- Quick Quizzes 7.1, 7.2
- Chapter Problem 5

Waves

Skill Objectives: To understand interference of waves, to calculate basic properties of waves, properties of springs, and properties of pendulums.

Review Plan:

Wave Properties: Chapters 12, 13
- Sections 12.1, 12.2, 13.1-13.3
- Quick Quiz 13.1
- Examples 12.1, 13.2
- Active Figures 12.1, 12.2, 12.4, 12.6, 12.10
Chapter 13
- Problem 9

Pendulum: Chapter 12
- Sections 12.4, 12.5
- Quick Quizzes 12.3, 12.4
- Examples 12.5, 12.6
- Active Figure 12.11
- Chapter Problem 23

Interference: Chapter 14
- Sections 14.1–14.3
- Quick Quiz 14.1
- Active Figures 14.1–14.3

Matter

Skill Objectives: To calculate density, pressure, specific gravity, and flow rates.

Review Plan:

Density: Chapters 1, 15
- Sections 1.1, 15.2

Pressure: Chapter 15
- Sections 15.1–15.4
- Quick Quizzes 15.1–15.4
- Examples 15.1, 15.3
- Chapter Problems 3, 7, 19, 23, 27

Flow rates: Chapter 15
- Section 15.6
- Quick Quiz 15.5

Sound

Skill Objectives: To understand interference of waves, calculate properties of waves, the speed of sound, Doppler shifts, and intensity.

Review Plan:

Sound Properties: Chapters 13, 14
- Sections 13.3, 13.4, 13.7, 13.8, 14.4
- Quick Quizzes 13.2, 13.3, 13.6
- Example 14.3
- Active Figures 13.6–13.8, 13.21, 13.22
Chapter 13
- Problems 3, 17, 23, 29, 35, 37
Chapter 14
- Problem 23

Interference/Beats: Chapter 14
- Sections 14.1, 14.2, 14.6
- Quick Quiz 14.6
- Active Figures 14.1–14.3, 14.12
- Chapter Problems 5, 39, 41

Light

Skill Objectives: To understand mirrors and lenses, to calculate the angles of reflection, to use the index of refraction, and to find focal lengths.

Review Plan:

Reflection: Chapter 25
- Sections 25.1–25.3
- Example 25.1
- Active Figure 25.5

Refraction: Chapter 25
- Sections 25.4, 25.5
- Quick Quizzes 25.2–25.5
- Example 25.2
- Chapter Problems 7, 13

Mirrors and Lenses: Chapter 26
- Sections 26.1–26.4
- Quick Quizzes 26.1–26.6
- Examples 26.1–26.7
- Active Figures 26.2, 26.24
- Chapter Problems 23, 27, 31, 35

Electrostatics

Skill Objectives: To understand and calculate the electric field, the electrostatic force, and the electric potential.

Review Plan:

Coulomb's Law: Chapter 19
- Section 19.2–19.4
- Quick Quiz 19.1–19.3
- Examples 19.1, 19.2
- Active Figure 19.7
- Chapter Problems 3, 5

Electric Field: Chapter 19
- Sections 19.5, 19.6
- Quick Quizzes 19.4, 19.5
- Active Figures 19.10, 19.19, 19.21

Potential: Chapter 20
- Sections 20.1–20.3
- Examples 20.1, 20.2
- Active Figure 20.6
- Chapter Problems 1, 5, 11, 13

Circuits

Skill Objectives: To understand and calculate current, resistance, voltage, and power, and to use circuit analysis.

Review Plan:

Ohm's Law: Chapter 21
- Sections 21.1, 21.2
- Quick Quizzes 21.1, 21.2
- Examples 21.1, 21.2
- Chapter Problem 7

Power and energy: Chapter 21
- Section 21.5
- Quick Quiz 21.4
- Example 21.5
- Active Figure 21.10
- Chapter Problems 17, 19, 23

Circuits: Chapter 21
- Section 21.6–21.8
- Quick Quizzes 21.5–21.8
- Example 21.7–21.9
- Active Figures 21.13, 21.14, 21.16
- Chapter Problems 25, 29, 35

Atoms

Skill Objectives: To understand decay processes and nuclear reactions and to calculate half-life.

Review Plan:

Atoms: Chapter 30
- Sections 30.1
- Quick Quizzes 30.1, 30.2
- Active Figure 30.1

Decays: Chapter 30
- Sections 30.3, 30.4
- Quick Quizzes 30.3–30.6
- Examples 30.3–30.6
- Active Figures 30.11–30.14, 30.16, 30.17
- Chapter Problems 13, 19, 23

Nuclear reactions: Chapter 30
- Sections 30.5
- Active Figure 30.21
- Chapter Problems 27, 29

DEDICATION

Emily and Fargo Serway

Two hard working and dedicated parents, for their unforgettable
love, vision, and wisdom.

John W. Jewett

Marvin V. Schober

These fathers and fathers-in-law provided models for hard work,
inspiration for creativity, and motivation for excellence.

They are sincerely missed.

BRIEF CONTENTS
VOLUME 2

CONTENTS

VOLUME 2

RAYMOND A. SERWAY received his doctorate at Illinois Institute of Technology and is Professor Emeritus at James Madison University. In 1990, he received the Madison Scholar Award at James Madison University, where he taught for 17 years. Dr. Serway began his teaching career at Clarkson University, where he conducted research and taught from 1967 to 1980. He was the recipient of the Distinguished Teaching Award at Clarkson University in 1977 and of the Alumni Achievement Award from Utica College in 1985. As Guest Scientist at the IBM Research Laboratory in Zurich, Switzerland, he worked with K. Alex Müller, 1987 Nobel Prize recipient. Dr. Serway also was a visiting scientist at Argonne National Laboratory, where he collaborated with his mentor and friend, Sam Marshall. In addition to earlier editions of this textbook, Dr. Serway is the co-author of *Physics for Scientists and Engineers,* Sixth Edition; *College Physics,* Seventh Edition; and *Modern Physics,* Third Edition. He also is the author of the high-school textbook *Physics,* published by Holt, Rinehart, & Winston. In addition, Dr. Serway has published more than 40 research papers in the field of condensed matter physics and has given more than 70 presentations at professional meetings. Dr. Serway and his wife Elizabeth enjoy traveling, golfing, and spending quality time with their four children and seven grandchildren.

JOHN W. JEWETT, JR. earned his doctorate at Ohio State University, specializing in optical and magnetic properties of condensed matter. Dr. Jewett began his academic career at Richard Stockton College of New Jersey, where he taught from 1974 to 1984. He is currently Professor of Physics at California State Polytechnic University, Pomona. Throughout his teaching career, Dr. Jewett has been active in promoting science education. In addition to receiving four National Science Foundation grants, he helped found and direct the Southern California Area Modern Physics Institute (SCAMPI). He also directed Science IMPACT (Institute for Modern Pedagogy and Creative Teaching), which works with teachers and schools to develop effective science curricula. Dr. Jewett's honors include the Stockton Merit Award at Richard Stockton College in 1980, the Outstanding Professor Award at California State Polytechnic University for 1991–1992, and the Excellence in Undergraduate Physics Teaching Award from the American Association of Physics Teachers (AAPT) in 1998. He has given over 80 presentations at professional meetings, including presentations at international conferences in China and Japan. In addition to his work on this textbook, he is co-author of *Physics for Scientists and Engineers,* Sixth Edition with Dr. Serway and author of *The World of Physics . . . Mysteries, Magic, and Myth.* Dr. Jewett enjoys playing keyboard with his all-physicist band, traveling, and collecting antiques that can be used as demonstration apparatus in physics lectures. Most importantly, he relishes spending time with his wife Lisa and their children and grandchildren.

Principles of Physics is designed for a one-year introductory calculus-based physics course for engineering and science students and for premed students taking a rigorous physics course. This fourth edition contains many new pedagogical features—most notably, an integrated Web-based learning system and a structured problem-solving strategy that uses a modeling approach. Based on comments from users of the third edition and reviewers' suggestions, a major effort was made to improve organization, clarity of presentation, precision of language, and accuracy throughout.

This project was conceived because of well-known problems in teaching the introductory calculus-based physics course. The course content (and hence the size of textbooks) continues to grow, while the number of contact hours with students has either dropped or remained unchanged. Furthermore, traditional one-year courses cover little if any physics beyond the 19th century.

In preparing this textbook, we were motivated by the spreading interest in reforming the teaching and learning of physics through physics education research. One effort in this direction was the Introductory University Physics Project (IUPP), sponsored by the American Association of Physics Teachers and the American Institute of Physics. The primary goals and guidelines of this project are to

- Reduce course content following the "less may be more" theme;
- Incorporate contemporary physics naturally into the course;
- Organize the course in the context of one or more "story lines";
- Treat all students equitably.

Recognizing a need for a textbook that could meet these guidelines several years ago, we studied the various proposed IUPP models and the many reports from IUPP committees. Eventually, one of us (RAS) became actively involved in the review and planning of one specific model, initially developed at the U.S. Air Force Academy, entitled "A Particles Approach to Introductory Physics." Part of the summer of 1990 was spent at the Academy working with Colonel James Head and Lt. Col. Rolf Enger, the primary authors of the Particles model, and other members of that department. This most useful collaboration was the starting point of this project.

The other author (JWJ) became involved with the IUPP model called "Physics in Context," developed by John Rigden (American Institute of Physics), David Griffiths (Oregon State University), and Lawrence Coleman (University of Arkansas at Little Rock). This involvement led to the contextual overlay that is used in this book and described in detail later in the Preface.

The combined IUPP approach in this book has the following features:

- It is an evolutionary approach (rather than a revolutionary approach), which should meet the current demands of the physics community.
- It deletes many topics in classical physics (such as alternating current circuits and optical instruments) and places less emphasis on rigid object motion, optics, and thermodynamics.
- Some topics in contemporary physics, such as special relativity, energy quantization, and the Bohr model of the hydrogen atom, are introduced early in the textbook.
- A deliberate attempt is made to show the unity of physics.
- As a motivational tool, the textbook connects physics principles to interesting social issues, natural phenomena, and technological advances.

OBJECTIVES

This introductory physics textbook has two main objectives: to provide the student with a clear and logical presentation of the basic concepts and principles of physics, and to strengthen an understanding of the concepts and principles through a broad range of interesting applications to the real world. To meet these objectives, we have emphasized sound physical arguments and problem-solving methodology. At the same time, we have attempted to motivate the student through practical examples that demonstrate the role of physics in other disciplines, including engineering, chemistry, and medicine.

CHANGES IN THE FOURTH EDITION

A number of changes and improvements have been made in the fourth edition of this text. Many of these are in response to recent findings in physics education research and to comments and suggestions provided by the reviewers of the manuscript and instructors using the first three editions. The following represent the major changes in the fourth edition:

New Context   The context overlay approach is described below under "Text Features." The fourth edition introduces a new Context for Chapters 2–7, "Alternative-Fuel Vehicles." This context addresses the current social issue of the depletion of our supply of petroleum and the efforts being made to develop new fuels and new types of automobiles to respond to this situation.

Active Figures   Many diagrams from the text have been animated to form **Active Figures,** part of the new *PhysicsNow*™ integrated Web-based learning system. There are over 150 Active Figures available at **www.pop4e.com.** By visualizing phenomena and processes that cannot be fully represented on a static page, students greatly increase their conceptual understanding. An addition to the figure caption, marked with the Physics⊗Now™ icon, describes briefly the nature and contents of the animation. In addition to viewing animations of the figures, students can change variables to see the effects, conduct suggested explorations of the principles involved in the figure, and take and receive feedback on quizzes related to the figure.

Interactive Examples   Sixty-seven of the worked examples have been identified as interactive. As part of the *PhysicsNow*™ Web-based learning system, students can engage in an extension of the problem solved in the example. This often includes elements of both visualization and calculation, and may also involve prediction and intuition-building. Interactive Examples are available at **www.pop4e.com.**

Quick Quizzes   Quick Quizzes have been cast in an objective format, including multiple choice, true-false, and ranking. Quick Quizzes provide students with opportunities to test their understanding of the physical concepts presented. The questions require students to make decisions on the basis of sound reasoning, and some of them have been written to help students overcome common misconceptions. Answers to all Quick Quiz questions are found at the end of each chapter. Additional Quick Quizzes that can be used in classroom teaching are available on the instructor's companion Web site. Many instructors choose to use such questions in a "peer instruction" teaching style, but they can be used in standard quiz format as well. To support the use of classroom response systems, we have coded the Quick Quiz questions so that they may be used within the response system of your choice.

General Problem-Solving Strategy   A general strategy to be followed by the student is outlined at the end of Chapter 1 and provides students with a structured process for solving problems. In the remaining chapters, the steps of the Strategy appear explicitly in one example per chapter so that students are encouraged throughout the course to follow the procedure.

Line-by-Line Revision   The text has been carefully edited to improve clarity of presentation and precision of language. We hope that the result is a book both accurate and enjoyable to read.

Problems   In an effort to improve variety, clarity and quality, the end-of-chapter problems were substantially revised. Approximately 15% of the problems (about 300) are new to this edition. The new problems especially are chosen to include interesting applications, notably biological applications. As in previous editions, many problems require students to make order-of-magnitude calculations. More problems now explicitly ask students to design devices and to change among different representations of a situation. All problems have been carefully edited and reworded where necessary. Solutions to approximately 20% of the end-of-chapter problems are included in the *Student Solutions Manual and Study Guide.* Boxed numbers identify these problems. A smaller subset of problems will be available with coached solutions as part of the *PhysicsNow*™ Web-based learning system and will be accessible to students and instructors using *Principles of Physics.* These coached problems are identified with the Physics⊗Now™ icon.

Biomedical Applications For biology and premed students, ◼ icons point the way to various practical and interesting applications of physical principles to biology and medicine. Where possible, an effort was made to include more problems that would be relevant to these disciplines.

TEXT FEATURES

Most instructors would agree that the textbook selected for a course should be the student's primary guide for understanding and learning the subject matter. Furthermore, the textbook should be easily accessible as well as styled and written to facilitate instruction and learning. With these points in mind, we have included many pedagogical features that are intended to enhance the textbook's usefulness to both students and instructors. These features are as follows:

Style To facilitate rapid comprehension, we have attempted to write the book in a clear, logical, and engaging style. The somewhat informal and relaxed writing style is intended to increase reading enjoyment. New terms are carefully defined, and we have tried to avoid the use of jargon.

Organization We have incorporated a "context overlay" scheme into the textbook, in response to the "Physics in Context" approach in the IUPP. This feature adds interesting applications of the material to real issues. We have developed this feature to be flexible, so that the instructor who does not wish to follow the contextual approach can simply ignore the additional contextual features without sacrificing complete coverage of the existing material. We believe, though, that the benefits students will gain from this approach will be many.

The context overlay organization divides the text into nine sections, or "Contexts," after Chapter 1, as follows:

Context Number	Context	Physics Topics	Chapters
1	Alternative-Fuel Vehicles	Classical mechanics	2–7
2	Mission to Mars	Classical mechanics	8–11
3	Earthquakes	Vibrations and waves	12–14
4	Search for the *Titanic*	Fluids	15
5	Global Warming	Thermodynamics	16–18
6	Lightning	Electricity	19–21
7	Magnetic Levitation Vehicles	Magnetism	22–23
8	Lasers	Optics	24–27
9	The Cosmic Connection	Modern physics	28–31

Each Context begins with an introduction, leading to a "central question" that motivates study within the Context. The final section of each chapter is a "Context Connection," which discusses how the material in the chapter relates to the Context and to the central question. The final chapter in each Context is followed by a "Context Conclusion." Each Conclusion uses the principles learned in the Context to respond fully to the central question. Each chapter, as well as the Context Conclusions, includes problems related to the context material.

Pitfall Prevention These features are placed in the margins of the text and address common student misconceptions and situations in which students often follow unproductive paths. Over 140 Pitfall Preventions are provided to help students avoid common mistakes and misunderstandings.

Modeling A modeling approach, based on four types of models commonly used by physicists, is introduced to help students understand they are solving problems that approximate reality. They must then learn how to test the validity of the model. This approach also helps students see the unity in physics, as a large fraction of problems can be solved with a small number of models. The modeling approach is introduced in Chapter 1.

Alternative Representations We emphasize alternative representations of information, including mental, pictorial, graphical, tabular, and mathematical representations. Many problems are easier to solve if the information is presented in alternative ways, to reach the many different methods students use to learn.

Problem-Solving Strategies We have included specific strategies for solving the types of problems featured both in the examples and in the end-of-chapter problems. These specific strategies are structured according to the steps in the General Problem-Solving Strategy introduced in Chapter 1. This feature helps students identify necessary steps in solving problems and eliminate any uncertainty they might have.

Worked Examples A large number of worked examples of varying difficulty are presented to promote students' understanding of concepts. In many cases, the examples serve as models for solving the end-of-chapter problems. Because of the increased emphasis on understanding physical concepts, many examples are conceptual in nature. The examples are set off in boxes, and the answers to examples with numerical solutions are highlighted with a tan screen.

Thinking Physics We have included many Thinking Physics examples throughout each chapter. These questions relate the physics concepts to common experiences or extend the concepts beyond what is discussed in the textual material. Immediately following each of these questions is a "Reasoning" section that responds to the question. Ideally, the student will use these features to better understand physical concepts before being presented with quantitative examples and working homework problems.

Previews Most chapters begin with a brief preview that includes a discussion of the particular chapter's objectives and content.

Important Statements and Equations Most important statements and definitions are set in boldface type or are highlighted with a blue outline for added emphasis and ease of review. Similarly, important equations are highlighted with a tan background screen to facilitate location.

Marginal Notes Comments and notes appearing in the margin can be used to locate important statements, equations, and concepts in the text.

Illustrations and Tables The readability and effectiveness of the text material and worked examples are enhanced by the large number of figures, diagrams, photographs, and tables. Full color adds clarity to the artwork and makes illustrations as realistic as possible. For example, vectors are color coded, and curves in graphs are drawn in color. The color photographs have been carefully selected, and their accompanying captions have been written to serve as an added instructional tool.

Mathematical Level We have introduced calculus gradually, keeping in mind that students often take introductory courses in calculus and physics concurrently. Most steps are shown when basic equations are developed, and reference is often made to mathematical appendices at the end of the textbook. Vector products are discussed in detail later in the text, where they are needed in physical applications. The dot product is introduced in Chapter 6, which addresses work and energy; the cross product is introduced in Chapter 10, which deals with rotational dynamics.

Significant Figures Significant figures in both worked examples and end-of-chapter problems have been handled with care. Most numerical examples and problems are worked out to either two or three significant figures, depending on the accuracy of the data provided.

Questions Questions requiring verbal responses are provided at the end of each chapter. Over 540 questions are included in the text. Some questions provide the student with a means of self-testing the concepts presented in the chapter. Others could serve as a basis for initiating classroom discussions. Answers to selected questions are included in the *Student Solutions Manual and Study Guide*.

Problems   The end-of-chapter problems are more numerous in this edition and more varied (in all, over 1980 problems are given throughout the text). For the convenience of both the student and the instructor, about two thirds of the problems are keyed to specific sections of the chapter, including Context Connection sections. The remaining problems, labeled "Additional Problems," are not keyed to specific sections. The ▨ icon identifies problems dealing with applications to the life sciences and medicine. One or more problems in each chapter ask students to make an order-of-magnitude calculation based on their own estimated data. Other types of problems are described in more detail below. Answers to odd-numbered problems are provided at the end of the book.

Usually, the problems within a given section are presented so that the straightforward problems (those with black problem numbers) appear first. For ease of identification, the numbers of intermediate-level problems are printed in blue, and those of challenging problems are printed in magenta.

Solutions to approximately 20% of the problems in each chapter are in the *Student Solutions Manual and Study Guide*. Among these, selected problems are identified with Physics⊗Now™ icons and have coached solutions available at **www.pop4e.com.**

Review Problems   Many chapters include review problems requiring the student to relate concepts covered in the chapter to those discussed in previous chapters. These problems can be used by students in preparing for tests and by instructors in routine or special assignments and for classroom discussions.

Paired Problems   As an aid for students learning to solve problems symbolically, paired numerical and symbolic problems are included in Chapters 1 through 4 and 16 through 21. Paired problems are identified by a common background screen.

Computer- and Calculator-Based Problems   Many chapters include one or more problems whose solution requires the use of a computer or graphing calculator. Modeling of physical phenomena enables students to obtain graphical representations of variables and to perform numerical analyses.

Units   The international system of units (SI) is used throughout the text. The U.S. customary system of units is used only to a limited extent in the chapters on mechanics and thermodynamics.

Summaries   Each chapter contains a summary that reviews the important concepts and equations discussed in that chapter.

Appendices and Endpapers   Several appendices are provided at the end of the textbook. Most of the appendix material represents a review of mathematical concepts and techniques used in the text, including scientific notation, algebra, geometry, trigonometry, differential calculus, and integral calculus. Reference to these appendices is made throughout the text. Most mathematical review sections in the appendices include worked examples and exercises with answers. In addition to the mathematical reviews, the appendices contain tables of physical data, conversion factors, atomic masses, and the SI units of physical quantities, as well as a periodic table of the elements and a list of Nobel Prize recipients. Other useful information, including fundamental constants and physical data, planetary data, a list of standard prefixes, mathematical symbols, the Greek alphabet, and standard abbreviations of units of measure, appears on the endpapers.

ANCILLARIES

The ancillary package has been updated substantially and streamlined in response to suggestions from users of the third edition. The most essential parts of the student package are the two-volume *Student Solutions Manual and Study Guide* with a tight focus on problem-solving and the Web-based *PhysicsNow*™ learning system. Instructors will find increased support for their teaching efforts with new electronic materials.

Student Ancillaries

Student Solutions Manual and Study Guide   by John R. Gordon, Ralph McGrew, and Raymond A. Serway. This two-volume manual features detailed solutions to approximately 20% of the end-of-chapter problems from the textbook. Boxed numbers identify those problems in the textbook whose complete solutions are found in the manual. The manual also features a summary of important chapter notes, a list of important equations and concepts, a short list of important study skills and strategies as well as answers to selected end-of-chapter conceptual questions.

Physics⊗Now™   Students log into *PhysicsNow™* at **www.pop4e.com** by using the free access code packaged with this text.* The *PhysicsNow™* system is made up of three interrelated parts:

- How much do you know?
- What do you need to learn?
- What have you learned?

Students maximize their success by starting with the Pre-Test for the relevant chapter. Each Pre-Test is a mix of conceptual and numerical questions. After completing the Pre-Test, each student is presented with a detailed Learning Plan. The Learning Plan outlines elements to review in the text and Web-based media (Active Figures, Interactive Examples, and Coached Problems) in order to master the chapter's most essential concepts. After working through these materials, students move on to a multiple-choice Post-Test presenting them with questions similar to those that might appear on an exam. Results can be e-mailed to instructors.

WebTutor™ on WebCT and Blackboard   WebTutor™ offers students real-time access to a full array of study tools, including a glossary of terms and a selection of animations.

The Brooks/Cole Physics Resource Center   You'll find additional online quizzes, Web links, and animations at **http://physics.brookscole.com.**

Instructor's Ancillaries

The following ancillaries are available to qualified adopters. Please contact your local Brooks/Cole • Thomson sales representative for details.

Instructor's Solutions Manual   by Ralph McGrew. This single manual contains worked solutions to all the problems in the textbook (Volumes 1 and 2) and answers to the end-of-chapter questions. The solutions to problems new to the fourth edition are marked for easy identification by the instructor.

Test Bank   by Edward Adelson. Contains approximately 2,000 multiple-choice questions. It is provided in print form for the instructor who does not have access to a computer. The questions in the *Test Bank* are also available in electronic format with complete answers and solutions in iLrn Computerized Testing. The number of conceptual questions has been increased for the 4th edition.

Multimedia Manager   This easy-to-use multimedia lecture tool allows you to quickly assemble art and database files with notes to create fluid lectures. The CD-ROM set (Volume 1, Chapters 1–15; Volume 2, Chapters 16–31) includes a database of animations, video clips, and digital art from the text as well as PowerPoint lectures and electronic files of the *Instructor's Solutions Manual* and *Test Bank.*

Physics⊗Now™ *PhysicsNow™* **Course Management Tools**   This extension to the student tutorial environment of *PhysicsNow™* allows instructors to deliver online assignments in an environment that is familiar to students. This powerful system is your gateway to managing on-line homework, testing, and course administration all in one shell with the proven content to make your course a success. *PhysicsNow™* is a fully integrated testing, tutorial, and course management software accessible by instructors and students anytime, anywhere. To see a demonstration of this powerful system, contact your Thomson representative or go to **www.pop4e.com**.

Physics⊗Now™ *PhysicsNow™* **Homework Management**   *PhysicsNow™* gives you a rich array of problem types and grading options. Its library of assignable questions includes all of the end-of-chapter problems from the text so that you can select the problems you want to

*Free access codes are only available with new copies of *Principles of Physics,* 4th edition.

include in your online homework assignments. These well-crafted problems are algorithmically generated so that you can assign the same problem with different variables for each student. A flexible grading tolerance feature allows you to specify a percentage range of correct answers so that your students are not penalized for rounding errors. You can give students the option to work an assignment multiple times and record the highest score or limit the times they are able to attempt it. In addition, you can create your own problems to complement the problems from the text. Results flow automatically to an exportable grade book so that instructors are better able to assess student understanding of the material, even prior to class or to an actual test.

iLrn Computerized Testing Extend the student experience with **PhysicsNow™** into a testing or quizzing environment. The test item file from the text is included to give you a bank of well-crafted questions that you can deliver online or print out. As with the homework problems, you can use the program's friendly interface to craft your own questions to complement the Serway/Jewett questions. You have complete control over grading, deadlines, and availability and can create multiple tests based on the same material.

WebTutor™ on WebCT and Blackboard With **WebTutor™**'s text-specific, pre-formatted content and total flexibility, instructors can easily create and manage their own personal Web site. **WebTutor™**'s course management tool gives instructors the ability to provide virtual office hours, post syllabi, set up threaded discussions, track student progress with the quizzing material, and much more. **WebTutor™** also provides robust communication tools, such as a course calendar, asynchronous discussion, real-time chat, a whiteboard, and an integrated e-mail system.

Additional Options for Online Homework

WebAssign: A Web-Based Homework System WebAssign is the most utilized homework system in physics. Designed by physicists for physicists, this system is a trusted companion to your teaching. An enhanced version of WebAssign is available for *Principles of Physics*. This enhanced version includes animations with conceptual questions and tutorial problems with feedback and hints to guide student content mastery. Take a look at this new innovation from the most trusted name in physics homework at **www.webassign.net.**

LON-CAPA: A Computer-Assisted Personalized Approach LON-CAPA is a Web-based course management system. For more information, visit the LON-CAPA Web site at **www.lon-capa.org.**

University of Texas Homework Service With this service, instructors can browse problem banks, select those problems they wish to assign to their students, and then let the Homework Service take over the delivery and grading. Details about and a demonstration of this service are available at **http://hw.ph.utexas.edu/hw.html.**

TEACHING OPTIONS

Although some topics found in traditional textbooks have been omitted from this textbook, instructors may find that the current text still contains more material than can be covered in a two-semester sequence. For this reason, we would like to offer the following suggestions. If you wish to place more emphasis on contemporary topics in physics, you should consider omitting parts or all of Chapters 15, 16, 17, 18, 24, 25, and 26. On the other hand, if you wish to follow a more traditional approach that places more emphasis on classical physics, you could omit Chapters 9, 11, 28, 29, 30, and 31. Either approach can be used without any loss in continuity. Other teaching options would fall somewhere between these two extremes by choosing to omit some or all of the following sections, which can be considered optional:

3.6 Relative Velocity
7.7 Energy Diagrams and Stability of Equilibrium
9.9 General Relativity
10.11 Rolling Motion of Rigid Objects
12.6 Damped Oscillations
12.7 Forced Oscillations
14.7 Nonsinusoidal Wave Patterns

ACKNOWLEDGMENTS

The fourth edition of this textbook was prepared with the guidance and assistance of many professors who reviewed part or all of the manuscript, the pre-revision text, or both. We wish to acknowledge the following scholars and express our sincere appreciation for their suggestions, criticisms, and encouragement:

Anthony Aguirre, *University of California at Santa Cruz*

Royal Albridge, *Vanderbilt University*

Billy E. Bonner, *Rice University*

Richard Cardenas, *St. Mary's University*

Christopher R. Church, *Miami University (Ohio)*

Athula Herat, *Northern Kentucky University*

Huan Z. Huang, *University of California at Los Angeles*

George Igo, *University of California at Los Angeles*

Edwin Lo

Michael J. Longo, *University of Michigan*

Rafael Lopez-Mobilia, *University of Texas at San Antonio*

Ian S. McLean, *University of California at Los Angeles*

Richard Rolleigh, *Hendrix College*

Gregory Severn, *University of San Diego*

Satinder S. Sidhu, *Washington College*

Fiona Waterhouse, *University of California at Berkeley*

Principles of Physics, fourth edition was carefully checked for accuracy by James E. Rutledge (University of California at Irvine), Harry W. K. Tom (University of California at Riverside), Gregory Severn (University of San Diego), Bruce Mason (University of Oklahoma at Norman), and Ralf Rapp (Texas A&M University). We thank them for their dedication and vigilance.

We thank the following people for their suggestions and assistance during the preparation of earlier editions of this textbook:

Edward Adelson, *Ohio State University;* Yildirim M. Aktas, *University of North Carolina—Charlotte;* Alfonso M. Albano, *Bryn Mawr College;* Subash Antani, *Edgewood College;* Michael Bass, *University of Central Florida;* Harry Bingham, *University of California, Berkeley;* Anthony Buffa, *California Polytechnic State University, San Luis Obispo;* James Carolan, *University of British Columbia;* Kapila Clara Castoldi, *Oakland University;* Ralph V. Chamberlin, *Arizona State University;* Gary G. DeLeo, *Lehigh University;* Michael Dennin, *University of California, Irvine;* Alan J. DeWeerd, *Creighton University;* Madi Dogariu, *University of Central Florida;* Gordon Emslie, *University of Alabama at Huntsville;* Donald Erbsloe, *United States Air Force Academy;* William Fairbank, *Colorado State University;* Marco Fatuzzo, *University of Arizona;* Philip Fraundorf, *University of Missouri—St. Louis;* Patrick Gleeson, *Delaware State University;* Christopher M. Gould, *University of Southern California;* James D. Gruber, *Harrisburg Area Community College;* John B. Gruber, *San Jose State University;* Todd Hann, *United States Military Academy;* Gail Hanson, *Indiana University;* Gerald Hart, *Moorhead State University;* Dieter H. Hartmann, *Clemson University;* Richard W. Henry, *Bucknell University;* Laurent Hodges, *Iowa State University;* Michael J. Hones, *Villanova University;* Joey Huston, *Michigan State University;* Herb Jaeger, *Miami University;* David Judd, *Broward Community College;* Thomas H. Keil, *Worcester Polytechnic Institute;* V. Gordon Lind, *Utah State University;* Roger M. Mabe, *United States Naval Academy;*

David Markowitz, *University of Connecticut;* Thomas P. Marvin, *Southern Oregon University;* Martin S. Mason, *College of the Desert;* Wesley N. Mathews, Jr., *Georgetown University;* John W. McClory, *United States Military Academy;* L. C. McIntyre, Jr., *University of Arizona;* Alan S. Meltzer, *Rensselaer Polytechnic Institute;* Ken Mendelson, *Marquette University;* Roy Middleton, *University of Pennsylvania;* Allen Miller, *Syracuse University;* Clement J. Moses, *Utica College of Syracuse University;* John W. Norbury, *University of Wisconsin—Milwaukee;* Anthony Novaco, *Lafayette College;* Romulo Ochoa, *The College of New Jersey;* Melvyn Oremland, *Pace University;* Desmond Penny, *Southern Utah University;* Steven J. Pollock, *University of Colorado—Boulder;* Prabha Ramakrishnan, *North Carolina State University;* Rex D. Ramsier, *The University of Akron;* Rogers Redding, *University of North Texas;* Charles R. Rhyner, *University of Wisconsin—Green Bay;* Perry Rice, *Miami University;* Dennis Rioux, *University of Wisconsin—Oshkosh;* Janet E. Seger, *Creighton University;* Gregory D. Severn, *University of San Diego;* Antony Simpson, *Dalhousie University;* Harold Slusher, *University of Texas at El Paso;* J. Clinton Sprott, *University of Wisconsin at Madison;* Shirvel Stanislaus, *Valparaiso University;* Randall Tagg, *University of Colorado at Denver;* Cecil Thompson, *University of Texas at Arlington;* Chris Vuille, *Embry–Riddle Aeronautical University;* Robert Watkins, *University of Virginia;* James Whitmore, *Pennsylvania State University*

We are indebted to the developers of the IUPP models, "A Particles Approach to Introductory Physics" and "Physics in Context," upon which much of the pedagogical approach in this textbook is based.

Ralph McGrew coordinated the end-of-chapter problems. Problems new to this edition were written by Edward Adelson, Michael Browne, Andrew Duffy, Robert Forsythe, Perry Ganas, John Jewett, Randall Jones, Boris Korsunsky, Edwin Lo, Ralph McGrew, Clement Moses, Raymond Serway, and Jerzy Wrobel. Daniel Fernandez, David Tamres, and Kevin Kilty made corrections in problems from the previous edition.

We are grateful to John R. Gordon and Ralph McGrew for writing the *Student Solutions Manual and Study Guide,* to Ralph McGrew for preparing an excellent *Instructor's Solutions Manual,* and to Edward Adelson of Ohio State University for preparing the *Test Bank.* We thank M & N Toscano for the attractive layout of these volumes. During the development of this text, the authors benefited from many useful discussions with colleagues and other physics instructors, including Robert Bauman, William Beston, Don Chodrow, Jerry Faughn, John R. Gordon, Kevin Giovanetti, Dick Jacobs, Harvey Leff, Clem Moses, Dorn Peterson, Joseph Rudmin, and Gerald Taylor.

Special thanks and recognition go to the professional staff at the Brooks/Cole Publishing Company—in particular, Susan Pashos, Jay Campbell, Sarah Lowe, Seth Dobrin, Teri Hyde, Michelle Julet, David Harris, and Chris Hall—for their fine work during the development and production of this textbook. We are most appreciative of Sam Subity's masterful management of the *PhysicsNow*™ media program. Julie Conover is our enthusiastic Marketing Manager, and Stacey Purviance coordinates our marketing communications. We recognize the skilled production service provided by Donna King and the staff at Progressive Publishing Alternatives and the dedicated photo research efforts of Dena Betz.

Finally, we are deeply indebted to our wives and children for their love, support, and long-term sacrifices.

RAYMOND A. SERWAY
St. Petersburg, Florida

JOHN W. JEWETT, JR.
Pomona, California

TO THE STUDENT

It is appropriate to offer some words of advice that should benefit you, the student. Before doing so, we assume you have read the Preface, which describes the various features of the text that will help you through the course.

HOW TO STUDY

Very often instructors are asked, "How should I study physics and prepare for examinations?" There is no simple answer to this question, but we would like to offer some suggestions based on our own experiences in learning and teaching over the years.

First and foremost, maintain a positive attitude toward the subject matter, keeping in mind that physics is the most fundamental of all natural sciences. Other science courses that follow will use the same physical principles, so it is important that you understand and are able to apply the various concepts and theories discussed in the text.

The Contexts in the text will help you understand how the physical principles relate to real issues, phenomena, and applications. Be sure to read the Context Introductions, Context Connection sections in each chapter, and Context Conclusions. These will be most helpful in motivating your study of physics.

CONCEPTS AND PRINCIPLES

It is essential that you understand the basic concepts and principles before attempting to solve assigned problems. You can best accomplish this goal by carefully reading the textbook before you attend your lecture on the covered material. When reading the text, you should jot down those points that are not clear to you. We've purposely left wide margins in the text to give you space for doing this. Also be sure to make a diligent attempt at answering the questions in the Quick Quizzes as you come to them in your reading. We have worked hard to prepare questions that help you judge for yourself how well you understand the material. Pay careful attention to the many Pitfall Preventions throughout the text. These will help you avoid misconceptions, mistakes, and misunderstandings as well as maximize the efficiency of your time by minimizing adventures along fruitless paths. During class, take careful notes and ask questions about those ideas that are unclear to you. Keep in mind that few people are able to absorb the full meaning of scientific material after only one reading.

After class, several readings of the text and your notes may be necessary. Be sure to take advantage of the features available in the *PhysicsNow*™ learning system, such as the Active Figures, Interactive Examples, and Coached Problems. Your lectures and laboratory work supplement your reading of the textbook and should clarify some of the more difficult material. You should minimize your memorization of material. Successful memorization of passages from the text, equations, and derivations does not necessarily indicate that you understand the material.

Your understanding of the material will be enhanced through a combination of efficient study habits, discussions with other students and with instructors, and your ability to solve the problems presented in the textbook. Ask questions whenever you feel clarification of a concept is necessary.

STUDY SCHEDULE

It is important for you to set up a regular study schedule, preferably a daily one. Make sure you read the syllabus for the course and adhere to the schedule set by your instructor. The lectures will be much more meaningful if you read the corresponding textual material before attending them. As a general rule, you should devote about two hours of study time for every hour you are in class. If you are having trouble with the course, seek the advice of the instructor or other students who have taken the course. You may find it necessary to seek further instruction from experienced students. Very often, instructors offer review sessions in addition to regular class periods. It is important that you avoid the practice of delaying study until a day or two before an exam. More often than not, this approach has disastrous results. Rather than undertake an all-night study session, briefly review the basic concepts and equations and get a good night's rest. If you feel you need additional help in understanding the concepts, in preparing for exams, or in problem-solving, we suggest that you acquire a copy of the *Student Solutions Manual and Study Guide* that accompanies this textbook; this manual should be available at your college bookstore.

USE THE FEATURES

You should make full use of the various features of the text discussed in the preface. For example, marginal notes are useful for locating and describing important equations and concepts, and **boldfaced** type indicates important statements and definitions. Many useful tables are contained in the Appendices, but most tables are incorporated in the text where they are most often referenced. Appendix B is a convenient review of mathematical techniques.

Answers to odd-numbered problems are given at the end of the textbook, answers to Quick Quizzes are located at the end of each chapter, and answers to selected end-of-chapter questions are provided in the *Student Solutions Manual and Study Guide*. Problem-Solving Strategies are included in selected chapters throughout the text and give you additional information about how you should solve problems. The Table of Contents provides an overview of the entire text, while the Index enables you to locate specific material quickly. Footnotes sometimes are used to supplement the text or to cite other references on the subject discussed.

After reading a chapter, you should be able to define any new quantities introduced in that chapter and to discuss the principles and assumptions used to arrive at certain key relations. The chapter summaries and the review sections of the *Student Solutions Manual and Study Guide* should help you in this regard. In some cases, it may be necessary for you to refer to the index of the text to locate certain topics. You should be able to correctly associate with each physical quantity the symbol used to represent that quantity and the unit in which the quantity is specified. Furthermore, you should be able to express each important relation in a concise and accurate prose statement.

PROBLEM-SOLVING

R. P. Feynman, Nobel laureate in physics, once said, "You do not know anything until you have practiced." In keeping with this statement, we strongly advise that you develop the skills necessary to solve a wide range of problems. Your ability to solve problems will be one of the main tests of your knowledge of physics; therefore, you should try to solve as many problems as possible. It is essential that you understand basic concepts and principles before attempting to solve problems. It is good practice to try to find alternative solutions to the same problem. For example, you can solve problems in mechanics using Newton's laws, but very often an alternative method that draws on energy considerations is more direct. You should not deceive yourself into thinking you understand a problem merely because you have seen it solved in class. You must be able to solve the problem and similar problems on your own.

The approach to solving problems should be carefully planned. A systematic plan is especially important when a problem involves several concepts. First, read the problem several times until you are confident you understand what is being asked. Look for any key words that will help you interpret the problem and perhaps allow you to make certain assumptions. Your ability to interpret a question properly is an integral part of problem-solving. Second, you should acquire the habit of writing down the information given in a problem and those quantities that need to be found; for example, you might construct a table listing both the quantities given and the quantities to be found. This procedure is sometimes used in the worked examples of the textbook. After you have decided on the method you feel is appropriate for a given problem, proceed with your solution. Finally, check your results to see if they are reasonable and consistent with your initial understanding of the problem. General problem-solving strategies of this type are included in the text and are set off in their own boxes. We have also developed a General Problem-Solving Strategy, making use of models, to help guide you through complex problems. This strategy is located at the end of Chapter 1. If you follow the steps of this procedure, you will find it easier to come up with a solution and also gain more from your efforts.

Often, students fail to recognize the limitations of certain equations or physical laws in a particular situation. It is very important that you understand and remember the assumptions underlying a particular theory or formalism. For example, certain equations in kinematics apply only to a particle moving with constant acceleration. These equations are not valid for describing motion whose acceleration is not constant, such as the motion of an object connected to a spring or the motion of an object through a fluid.

EXPERIMENTS

Physics is a science based on experimental observations. In view of this fact, we recommend that you try to supplement the text by performing various types of "hands-on" experiments, either at home or in the laboratory. For example, the common Slinky™ toy is excellent for studying traveling waves; a ball swinging on the end of a long string can be used to investigate pendulum motion; various masses attached to the end of a vertical spring or rubber band can be used to determine their elastic nature; an old pair of Polaroid sunglasses and some discarded lenses and a magnifying glass are the components of various experiments in optics; and the approximate measure of the free-fall acceleration can be determined simply by measuring with a stopwatch the time it takes for a ball to drop from a known height. The list of such experiments is endless. When physical models are not available, be imaginative and try to develop models of your own.

NEW MEDIA

We strongly encourage you to use the *PhysicsNow*™ Web-based learning system that accompanies this textbook. It is far easier to understand physics if you see it in action, and these new materials will enable you to become a part of that action. *PhysicsNow*™ media described in the Preface are accessed at the URL **www.pop4e.com,** and feature a three-step learning process consisting of a Pre-Test, a personalized learning plan, and a Post-Test.

In addition to the Coached Problems identified with icons, *PhysicsNow*™ includes the following Active Figures and Interactive Examples:

Chapter 1
Active Figures 1.4, 1.9, and 1.16
Interactive Example 1.8

Chapter 2
Active Figures 2.1, 2.2, 2.8, 2.11, and 2.12
Interactive Examples 2.8 and 2.10

Chapter 3
Active Figures 3.4, 3.5, 3.8, and 3.12
Interactive Examples 3.2 and 3.6

Chapter 4
Active Figures 4.12 and 4.13
Interactive Examples 4.4 and 4.5

Chapter 5
Active Figures 5.1, 5.9, 5.15, and 5.18
Interactive Examples 5.7 and 5.8

Chapter 6
Active Figure 6.8
Interactive Examples 6.6 and 6.7

Chapter 7
Active Figures 7.3, 7.6, and 7.15
Interactive Examples 7.1 and 7.2

Chapter 8
Active Figures 8.8, 8.9, 8.11, 8.13, and 8.14
Interactive Examples 8.2 and 8.8

Chapter 9
Active Figures 9.3, 9.5, and 9.8
Interactive Example 9.5

Chapter 10
Active Figures 10.4, 10.11, 10.12, 10.21, and 10.28
Interactive Examples 10.5, 10.8, and 10.9

Chapter 11
Active Figures 11.1, 11.5, 11.7, 11.19, and 11.20
Interactive Examples 11.1 and 11.3

Chapter 12
Active Figures 12.1, 12.2, 12.4, 12.6, 12.9, 12.10, 12.11, and 12.14
Interactive Example 12.1

Chapter 13
Active Figures 13.6, 13.7, 13.8, 13.14, 13.15, 13.21, 13.22, and 13.24
Interactive Examples 13.5 and 13.7

Chapter 14

Active Figures 14.1, 14.2, 14.3, 14.8, 14.9, 14.12, 14.15, and 14.16

Interactive Examples 14.1 and 14.3

Chapter 15

Active Figures 15.9 and 15.10

Interactive Examples 15.4 and 15.7

Chapter 16

Active Figures 16.9, 16.14, 16.16, 16.17, and 16.18

Interactive Example 16.4

Chapter 17

Active Figures 17.5, 17.6, 17.8, and 17.13

Interactive Example 17.9

Chapter 18

Active Figures 18.1, 18.5, 18.6, and 18.7

Interactive Example 18.3

Chapter 19

Active Figures 19.7, 19.10, 19.19, 19.21, 19.26, and 19.31

Interactive Examples 19.1, 19.7, and 19.10

Chapter 20

Active Figures 20.6, 20.20, 20.23, and 20.24

Interactive Examples 20.2, 20.3, 20.8, and 20.9

Chapter 21

Active Figures 21.4, 21.10, 21.13, 21.14, 21.16, 21.25, and 21.27

Interactive Examples 21.2, 21.6, 21.8, and 21.9

Chapter 22

Active Figures 22.1, 22.7, 22.8, 22.11, 22.12, 22.20, 22.27, and 22.28

Interactive Examples 22.3 and 22.6

Chapter 23

Active Figures 23.2, 23.3, 23.11, 23.14, 23.23, 23.24, 23.26, and 23.27

Interactive Examples 23.3, 23.4 and 23.8

Chapter 24

Active Figures 24.3, 24.8, 24.14, and 24.16

Interactive Examples 24.1 and 24.4

Chapter 25

Active Figures 25.2, 25.5, 25.8, 25.9, 25.16, 25.22, 25.28, and 25.30

Interactive Examples 25.1 and 25.3

Chapter 26

Active Figures 26.2, 26.12, 26.17, and 26.24

Interactive Examples 26.2, 26.3, 26.7 and 26.8

Chapter 27

Active Figures 27.2, 27.14, 27.21, and 27.22

Interactive Examples 27.1, 27.3, 27.5, and 27.7

Chapter 28

Active Figures 28.2, 28.7, 28.8, 28.9, 28.16, 28.17, 28.19, 28.23 and 28.24

Interactive Examples 28.3, 28.4, 28.9, and 28.12

Chapter 29

Active Figure 29.6

Interactive Example 29.6

Chapter 30

Active Figures 30.1, 30.11, 30.12, 30.13, 30.14, 30.16, 30.17, and 30.21

Interactive Examples 30.3 and 30.6

Chapter 31

Active Figure 31.11

Interactive Example 31.2

It is our sincere hope that you too will find physics an exciting and enjoyable experience and that you will profit from this experience, regardless of your chosen profession. Welcome to the exciting world of physics!

The scientist does not study nature because it is useful; he studies it because he delights in it, and he delights in it because it is beautiful. If nature were not beautiful, it would not be worth knowing, and if nature were not worth knowing, life would not be worth living.

Henri Poincaré

List of Life Science Applications and Problems

CHAPTER 19

Electric Forces and Electric Fields

Mother and daughter are both enjoying the effects of electrically charging their bodies. Each individual hair on their heads becomes charged and exerts a repulsive force on the other hairs, resulting in the "stand-up" hairdos that you see here.

(Courtesy of Resonance Research Corporation)

This chapter is the first of three on *electricity*. You are probably familiar with electrical effects, such as the static cling between articles of clothing removed from the dryer. You may also be familiar with the spark that jumps from your finger to a doorknob after you have walked across a carpet. Much of your daily experience involves working with devices that operate on energy transferred to the device by means of electrical transmission and provided by the electric power company. Even your own body is an electrochemical machine that uses electricity extensively. Nerves carry impulses as electrical signals, and electric forces are involved in the flow of materials across cell membranes.

This chapter begins with a review of some of the basic properties of the electrostatic force that we introduced in Chapter 5 as well as some properties of the electric field associated with stationary charged particles. Our study of electrostatics then continues with the concept of an electric field that is associated with a continuous charge distribution and the effect of this field on other charged particles. In these studies, we shall apply the models of a particle in a field and a particle under a net force that we have seen in earlier chapters.

19.1 | HISTORICAL OVERVIEW

The laws of electricity and magnetism play a central role in the operation of devices such as radios, televisions, electric motors, computers, high-energy particle accelerators, and a host of electronic devices used in medicine. More fundamental, however, is that the interatomic and intermolecular forces responsible for the formation of solids and liquids are electric in origin. Furthermore, such forces as the pushes and pulls between objects in contact and the elastic force in a spring arise from electric forces at the atomic level.

Chinese documents suggest that magnetism was recognized as early as about 2000 B.C. The ancient Greeks observed electric and magnetic phenomena possibly as early as 700 B.C. They found that a piece of amber, when rubbed, attracted pieces of straw or feathers. The existence of magnetic forces was known from observations that pieces of a naturally occurring stone called *magnetite* (Fe_3O_4) were attracted to iron. (The word *electric* comes from the Greek word for amber, *elektron*. The word *magnetic* comes from *Magnesia,* a city on the coast of Turkey where magnetite was found.)

In 1600, Englishman William Gilbert discovered that electrification was not limited to amber but was a general phenomenon. Scientists went on to electrify a variety of objects, including people!

It was not until the early part of the 19th century that scientists established that electricity and magnetism are related phenomena. In 1820, Hans Oersted discovered that a compass needle, which is magnetic, is deflected when placed near an electric current. In 1831, Michael Faraday in England and, almost simultaneously, Joseph Henry in the United States showed that when a wire loop is moved near a magnet (or, equivalently, when a magnet is moved near a wire loop) an electric current is observed in the wire. In 1873, James Clerk Maxwell used these observations and other experimental facts as a basis for formulating the laws of electromagnetism as we know them today. Shortly thereafter (around 1888), Heinrich Hertz verified Maxwell's predictions by producing electromagnetic waves in the laboratory. This achievement was followed by such practical developments as radio and television.

Maxwell's contributions to the science of electromagnetism were especially significant because the laws he formulated are basic to *all* forms of electromagnetic phenomena. His work is comparable in importance to Newton's discovery of the laws of motion and the theory of gravitation.

19.2 | PROPERTIES OF ELECTRIC CHARGES

A number of simple experiments demonstrate the existence of electrostatic forces. For example, after running a comb through your hair, you will find that the comb attracts bits of paper. The attractive electrostatic force is often strong enough to suspend the bits. The same effect occurs with other rubbed materials, such as glass or rubber.

Another simple experiment is to rub an inflated balloon with wool or across your hair (Fig. 19.1). On a dry day, the rubbed balloon will stick to the wall of a room, often for hours. When materials behave this way, they are said to have become electrically charged. You can give your body an electric charge by walking across a wool rug or by sliding across a car seat. You can then feel, and remove, the charge on your body by lightly touching another person or object. Under the right conditions, a visible spark is seen when you touch and a slight tingle is felt by both parties. (Such an experiment works best on a dry day

(Charles D. Winters)

FIGURE 19.1 Rubbing a balloon against your hair on a dry day causes the balloon and your hair to become electrically charged.

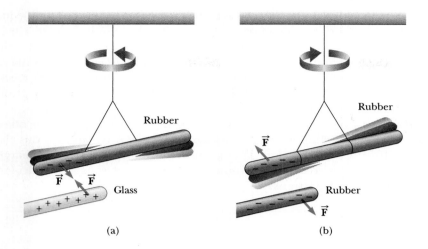

(a)   (b)

because excessive moisture in the air can provide a pathway for charge to leak off a charged object.)

Experiments also demonstrate that there are two kinds of **electric charge,** given the names **positive** and **negative** by Benjamin Franklin (1706–1790). Figure 19.2 illustrates the interactions of the two kinds of charge. A hard rubber (or plastic) rod that has been rubbed with fur (or an acrylic material) is suspended by a piece of thread. When a glass rod that has been rubbed with silk is brought near the rubber rod, the rubber rod is attracted toward the glass rod (Fig. 19.2a). If two charged rubber rods (or two charged glass rods) are brought near each other, as in Figure 19.2b, the force between them is repulsive. This observation demonstrates that the rubber and glass have different kinds of charge. We use the convention suggested by Franklin; the electric charge on the glass rod is called positive and that on the rubber rod is called negative. On the basis of such observations, we conclude that **charges of the same sign repel each other and charges with opposite signs attract each other.**

We know that only two kinds of electric charge exist because any unknown charge that is found experimentally to be attracted to a positive charge is also repelled by a negative charge. No one has ever observed a charged object that is repelled by both a positive and a negative charge or that is attracted to both.

Attractive electric forces are responsible for the behavior of a wide variety of commercial products. For example, the plastic in many contact lenses, *etafilcon,* is made up of molecules that electrically attract the protein molecules in human tears. These protein molecules are absorbed and held by the plastic so that the lens ends up being primarily composed of the wearer's tears. Therefore, the lens does not behave as a foreign object to the wearer's eye and can be worn comfortably. Many cosmetics also take advantage of electric forces by incorporating materials that are electrically attracted to skin or hair, causing the pigments or other chemicals to stay put once they are applied.

 Electrical attraction of contact lenses

Another important characteristic of electric charge is that **the net charge in an isolated system is always conserved.** This represents the electric charge version of the isolated system model. We first introduced isolated system models in Chapter 7 when we discussed conservation of energy; we now see a principle of **conservation of electric charge** for an isolated system. When two initially neutral objects are charged by being rubbed together, charge is not created in the process. The objects become charged because *electrons are transferred* from one object to the other. One object gains some amount of negative charge from the electrons transferred to it while the other loses an equal amount of negative charge and hence is left with a positive charge. For the isolated system of the two objects, no transfer of charge occurs across the boundary of the system. The only change is that charge has been transferred between two members of the system. For example, when a glass rod is

FIGURE 19.3 When a glass rod is rubbed with silk, electrons are transferred from the glass to the silk. Because of conservation of charge, each electron adds negative charge to the silk, and an equal positive charge is left behind on the rod. Also, because the charges are transferred in discrete bundles, the charges on the two objects are $\pm e$ or $\pm 2e$ or $\pm 3e$, and so on.

rubbed with silk, as in Figure 19.3, the silk obtains a negative charge that is equal in magnitude to the positive charge on the glass rod as negatively charged electrons are transferred from the glass to the silk. Likewise, when rubber is rubbed with fur, electrons are transferred from the fur to the rubber. An *uncharged object* contains an enormous number of electrons (on the order of 10^{23}). For every negative electron, however, a positively charged proton is also present; hence, an uncharged object has no net charge of either sign.

Another property of electric charge is that the total charge on an object is quantized as integral multiples of the elementary charge e. We first saw this charge $e = 1.60 \times 10^{-19}$ C in Chapter 5. The quantization results because the charge on an object must be due to an integral number of excess electrons or a deficiency of an integral number of electrons.

QUICK QUIZ 19.1 Three objects are brought close to one another, two at a time. When objects A and B are brought together, they repel. When objects B and C are brought together, they also repel. Which of the following statements are true? **(a)** Objects A and C possess charges of the same sign. **(b)** Objects A and C possess charges of opposite sign. **(c)** All three objects possess charges of the same sign. **(d)** One of the objects is neutral. **(e)** We need to perform additional experiments to determine the signs of the charges.

19.3 | INSULATORS AND CONDUCTORS

We have discussed the transfer of charge from one object to another. It is also possible for electric charges to move from one location to another within an object; such motion of charge is called **electrical conduction.** It is convenient to classify substances in terms of the ability of charges to move within the substance:

Conductors are materials in which electric charges move relatively freely and **insulators** are materials in which electric charges do not move freely.

Materials such as glass, rubber, and Lucite are insulators. When such materials are charged by rubbing, only the rubbed area becomes charged; the charge does not tend to move to other regions of the material. In contrast, materials such as copper, aluminum, and silver are good conductors. When such materials are charged in some small region, the charge readily distributes itself over the entire surface of the material. If you hold a copper rod in your hand and rub it with wool or fur, it will not attract a small piece of paper, which might suggest that a metal cannot be charged. If you hold the copper rod by an insulating handle and then rub, however, the rod remains charged and attracts the piece of paper. In the first case, the electric charges produced by rubbing readily move from the copper through your body, which is a conductor, and finally to the Earth. In the second case, the insulating handle prevents the flow of charge to your hand.

Semiconductors are a third class of materials, and their electrical properties are somewhere between those of insulators and those of conductors. Charges can move somewhat freely in a semiconductor, but far fewer charges are moving through a semiconductor than in a conductor. Silicon and germanium are well-known examples of semiconductors that are widely used in the fabrication of a variety of electronic devices. The electrical properties of semiconductors can be changed over many orders of magnitude by adding controlled amounts of certain foreign atoms to the materials.

Charging by Induction

When a conductor is connected to the Earth by means of a conducting wire or pipe, it is said to be **grounded.** For present purposes, the Earth can be modeled as an infinite reservoir for electrons, which means that it can accept or supply an unlimited number of electrons. In this context, the Earth serves a purpose similar to our energy reservoirs introduced in Chapter 17. With that in mind, we can understand how to charge a conductor by a process known as **charging by induction.**

To understand how to charge a conductor by induction, consider a neutral (uncharged) metallic sphere insulated from the ground as shown in Figure 19.4a. There are an equal number of electrons and protons in the sphere if the charge on the sphere is exactly zero. When a negatively charged rubber rod is brought near the sphere, electrons in the region nearest the rod experience a repulsive force and migrate to the opposite side of the sphere. This migration leaves the side of the sphere near the rod with an effective positive charge because of the diminished number of electrons as in Figure 19.4b. (The left side of the sphere in Figure 19.4b is positively charged *as if* positive charges moved into this region, but in a metal it is only electrons that are free to move.) This migration occurs even if the rod never actually touches the sphere. If the same experiment is performed with a conducting wire connected from the sphere to the Earth (Fig. 19.4c), some of the electrons in the conductor are so strongly repelled by the presence of the negative charge in the rod that they move out of the sphere through the wire and into the Earth. The symbol ⏚ at the end of the wire in Figure 19.4c indicates that the wire is connected to **ground,** which means a reservoir such as the Earth. If the wire to ground is then removed (Fig. 19.4d), the conducting sphere contains an excess of *induced* positive charge because it has fewer electrons than it needs to cancel out the positive charge of the protons. When the rubber rod is removed from the vicinity of the sphere (Fig. 19.4e), this induced positive charge remains on the ungrounded sphere. Note that the rubber rod loses none of its negative charge during this process.

Charging an object by induction requires no contact with the object inducing the charge. This behavior is in contrast to charging an object by rubbing, which does require contact between the two objects.

A process similar to the first step in charging by induction in conductors takes place in insulators. In most neutral atoms and molecules, the average position of the positive charge coincides with the average position of the negative charge. In the presence of a charged object, however, these positions may shift slightly because of the attractive and repulsive forces from the charged object, resulting in more positive charge on one side of the molecule than on the other. This effect is known as **polarization.** The polarization of individual molecules produces a layer of charge on the surface of the insulator as shown in Figure 19.5a, in which a charged balloon on the left is placed against a wall on the right. In the figure, the negative charge layer in the wall is closer to the positively charged balloon than the positive

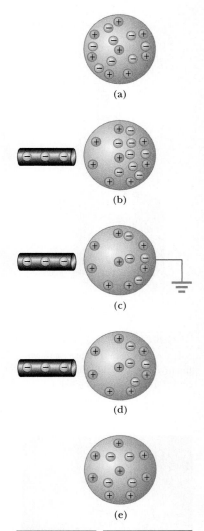

FIGURE 19.4 Charging a metallic object by *induction;* that is, the two objects never touch each other. (a) A neutral metallic sphere, with equal numbers of positive and negative charges. (b) The electrons on the neutral sphere are redistributed when a charged rubber rod is placed near the sphere. (c) When the sphere is grounded, some of its electrons leave through the ground wire. (d) When the ground connection is removed, the sphere has excess positive charge that is nonuniformly distributed. (e) When the rod is removed, the remaining electrons redistribute uniformly and there is a net uniform distribution of positive charge on the sphere.

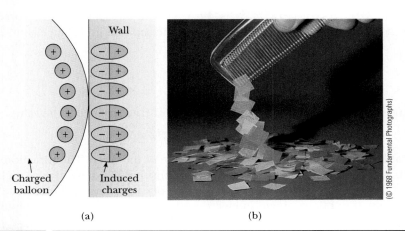

FIGURE 19.5 (a) The charged balloon on the left induces a charge distribution on the wall's surface due to realignment of charges in the molecules. (b) A charged comb attracts bits of paper because charges in the paper's molecules are realigned.

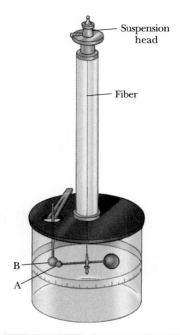

Suspension head

Fiber

B

A

Coulomb's torsion balance, which was used to establish the inverse-square law for the electrostatic force between two charges.

CHARLES COULOMB (1736–1806)

French physicist Coulomb's major contributions to science were in the areas of electrostatics and magnetism. During his lifetime, he also investigated the strengths of materials and determined the forces that affect objects on beams, thereby contributing to the field of structural mechanics. In the field of ergonomics, his research provided a fundamental understanding of the ways in which people and animals can best do work.

charges at the other ends of the molecules. Therefore, the attractive force between the positive and negative charges is larger than the repulsive force between the positive charges. The result is a net attractive force between the charged balloon and the neutral insulator. It is this polarization effect that explains why a comb that has been rubbed through hair attracts bits of neutral paper (Fig. 19.5b) or why a balloon that has been rubbed against your hair can stick to a neutral wall.

QUICK QUIZ 19.2 Three objects are brought close to one another, two at a time. When objects A and B are brought together, they attract. When objects B and C are brought together, they repel. From this experiment, what can we conclude? **(a)** Objects A and C possess charges of the same sign. **(b)** Objects A and C possess charges of opposite sign. **(c)** All three of the objects possess charges of the same sign. **(d)** One of the objects is neutral. **(e)** We need to perform additional experiments to determine information about the charges on the objects.

19.4 COULOMB'S LAW

Electric forces between charged objects were measured quantitatively by Charles Coulomb using the torsion balance, which he invented (Fig. 19.6). Coulomb confirmed that the electric force between two small charged spheres is proportional to the inverse square of their separation distance r, that is, $F_e \propto 1/r^2$. The operating principle of the torsion balance is the same as that of the apparatus used by Sir Henry Cavendish to measure the gravitational constant (Section 11.1), with the electrically neutral spheres replaced by charged ones. The electric force between charged spheres A and B in Figure 19.6 causes the spheres to either attract or repel each other, and the resulting motion causes the suspended fiber to twist. Because the restoring torque of the twisted fiber is proportional to the angle through which it rotates, a measurement of this angle provides a quantitative measure of the electric force of attraction or repulsion. Once the spheres are charged by rubbing, the electric force between them is very large compared with the gravitational attraction, and so the gravitational force can be ignored.

In Chapter 5, we introduced **Coulomb's law,** which describes the magnitude of the electrostatic force between two charged particles with charges q_1 and q_2 and separated by a distance r:

$$F_e = k_e \frac{|q_1||q_2|}{r^2} \qquad [19.1]$$

where k_e ($= 8.99 \times 10^9 \ \text{N} \cdot \text{m}^2/\text{C}^2$) is the **Coulomb constant** and the force is in newtons if the charges are in coulombs and if the separation distance is in meters. The constant k_e is also written as

$$k_e = \frac{1}{4\pi\epsilon_0}$$

where the constant ϵ_0, known as the **permittivity of free space,** has the value

$$\epsilon_0 = 8.854\,2 \times 10^{-12} \ \text{C}^2/\text{N} \cdot \text{m}^2$$

Note that Equation 19.1 gives only the magnitude of the force. The direction of the force on a given particle must be found by considering where the particles are located with respect to one another and the sign of each charge. Therefore, a pictorial representation of a problem in electrostatics is very important in analyzing the problem.

The charge of an electron is $q = -e = -1.60 \times 10^{-19}$ C, and the proton has a charge of $q = +e = 1.60 \times 10^{-19}$ C; therefore, 1 C of charge is equal to the

TABLE 19.1	Charge and Mass of the Electron, Proton, and Neutron	
Particle	Charge (C)	Mass (kg)
Electron (e)	$-1.602\ 176\ 5 \times 10^{-19}$	$9.109\ 38 \times 10^{-31}$
Proton (p)	$+1.602\ 176\ 5 \times 10^{-19}$	$1.672\ 62 \times 10^{-27}$
Neutron (n)	0	$1.674\ 93 \times 10^{-27}$

magnitude of the charge of $(1.60 \times 10^{-19})^{-1} = 6.25 \times 10^{18}$ electrons. (The elementary charge e was introduced in Section 5.5.) Note that 1 C is a substantial amount of charge. In typical electrostatic experiments, where a rubber or glass rod is charged by friction, a net charge on the order of 10^{-6} C ($= 1\ \mu$C) is obtained. In other words, only a very small fraction of the total available electrons (on the order of 10^{23} in a 1-cm^3 sample) are transferred between the rod and the rubbing material. The experimentally measured values of the charges and masses of the electron, proton, and neutron are given in Table 19.1.

When dealing with Coulomb's law, remember that force is a *vector* quantity and must be treated accordingly. Furthermore, **Coulomb's law applies exactly only to particles.**[1] The electrostatic force exerted by q_1 on q_2, written $\vec{\mathbf{F}}_{12}$, can be expressed in vector form as[2]

$$\vec{\mathbf{F}}_{12} = k_e \frac{q_1 q_2}{r^2} \hat{\mathbf{r}}_{12} \qquad [19.2]$$

where $\hat{\mathbf{r}}_{12}$ is a unit vector directed from q_1 toward q_2 as in Active Figure 19.7a. Equation 19.2 can be used to find the direction of the force in space, although a carefully drawn pictorial representation is needed to clearly identify the direction of $\hat{\mathbf{r}}_{12}$. From Newton's third law, we see that the electric force exerted by q_2 on q_1 is equal in magnitude to the force exerted by q_1 on q_2 and in the opposite direction; that is, $\vec{\mathbf{F}}_{21} = -\vec{\mathbf{F}}_{12}$. From Equation 19.2, we see that if q_1 and q_2 have the same sign, the product $q_1 q_2$ is positive and the force is repulsive as in Active Figure 19.7a. The force on q_2 is in the same direction as $\hat{\mathbf{r}}_{12}$ and is directed away from q_1. If q_1 and q_2 are of opposite sign as in Active Figure 19.7b, the product $q_1 q_2$ is negative and the force is attractive. In this case, the force on q_2 is in the direction opposite to $\hat{\mathbf{r}}_{12}$, directed toward q_1.

When more than two charged particles are present, the force between any pair is given by Equation 19.2. Therefore, **the resultant force on any one particle equals the *vector* sum of the individual forces due to all other particles.** This **principle of superposition** as applied to electrostatic forces is an experimentally observed fact and simply represents the traditional vector sum of forces introduced in Chapter 4. As an example, if four charged particles are present, the resultant force on particle 1 due to particles 2, 3, and 4 is given by the vector sum

$$\vec{\mathbf{F}}_1 = \vec{\mathbf{F}}_{21} + \vec{\mathbf{F}}_{31} + \vec{\mathbf{F}}_{41}$$

QUICK QUIZ 19.3 (i) Object A has a charge of $+2\ \mu$C, and object B has a charge of $+6\ \mu$C. Which of the following statements is true about the electric forces on the objects? (a) $F_{AB} = -3F_{BA}$ (b) $F_{AB} = -F_{BA}$ (c) $3F_{AB} = -F_{BA}$ (d) $F_{AB} = 3F_{BA}$ (e) $F_{AB} = F_{BA}$ (f) $3F_{AB} = F_{BA}$ (ii) Which of the following statements is true about the electric forces on the objects? (a) $\vec{\mathbf{F}}_{AB} = -3\vec{\mathbf{F}}_{BA}$ (b) $\vec{\mathbf{F}}_{AB} = -\vec{\mathbf{F}}_{BA}$ (c) $3\vec{\mathbf{F}}_{AB} = -\vec{\mathbf{F}}_{BA}$ (d) $\vec{\mathbf{F}}_{AB} = 3\vec{\mathbf{F}}_{BA}$ (e) $\vec{\mathbf{F}}_{AB} = \vec{\mathbf{F}}_{BA}$ (f) $3\vec{\mathbf{F}}_{AB} = \vec{\mathbf{F}}_{BA}$

---

[1]Coulomb's law can also be used for larger objects to which the particle model can be applied.
[2]Notice that we use "q_2" as shorthand notation for "the particle with charge q_2." This usage is common when discussing charged particles, similar to the use in mechanics of "m_2" for "the particle with mass m_2." The context of the sentence will tell you whether the symbol represents an amount of charge or a particle with that charge.

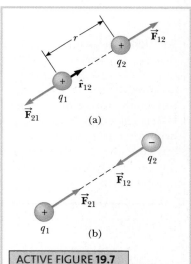

ACTIVE FIGURE 19.7

Two point charges separated by a distance r exert a force on each other given by Coulomb's law. Note that the force $\vec{\mathbf{F}}_{21}$ exerted by q_2 on q_1 is equal in magnitude and opposite in direction to the force $\vec{\mathbf{F}}_{12}$ exerted by q_1 on q_2. (a) When the charges are of the same sign, the force is repulsive. (b) When the charges are of opposite signs, the force is attractive.

Physics⊗Now™ Log into PhysicsNow at **www.pop4e.com** and go to Active Figure 19.7 to move the charges to any position in two-dimensional space and observe the electric forces on them.

INTERACTIVE   EXAMPLE 19.1   Where Is the Resultant Force Zero?

Three charged particles lie along the x axis as in Figure 19.8. The particle with charge $q_1 = +15.0 \ \mu C$ is at $x = 2.00$ m, and the particle with charge $q_2 = +6.00 \ \mu C$ is at the origin. Where on the x axis can a particle with negative charge q_3 be placed such that the resultant force on it is zero?

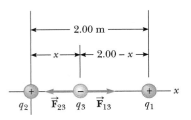

FIGURE 19.8   (Interactive Example 19.1) Three point charges are placed along the x axis. If the net force on q_3 is zero, the force $\vec{F}_{13}$ exerted by q_1 on q_3 must be equal in magnitude and opposite in direction to the force $\vec{F}_{23}$ exerted by q_2 on q_3.

Solution The requested resultant force of zero indicates that q_3 is a particle in equilibrium, so the two forces on q_3 cancel. Because q_3 is negative and both q_1 and q_2 are positive, the forces $\vec{F}_{13}$ and $\vec{F}_{23}$ are both attractive. To cancel, the forces on q_3 must be in opposite directions. If q_3 is placed to the left of q_2 or to the right of q_1, the two forces on q_3 will be in the same direction. Therefore, the only possibility of having forces in opposite directions is to place q_3 between q_1 and q_2, as indicated in Figure 19.8.

If we let x be the coordinate of q_3, the forces $\vec{F}_{13}$ and $\vec{F}_{23}$ can be written as

$$\vec{F}_{13} = k_e \frac{q_1 q_3}{(2.00 - x)^2} \hat{r}_{13} = -k_e \frac{q_1 q_3}{(2.00 - x)^2} \hat{i}$$

$$\vec{F}_{23} = k_e \frac{q_2 q_3}{x^2} \hat{r}_{23} = k_e \frac{q_2 q_3}{x^2} \hat{i}$$

where we have recognized that $\hat{r}_{13} = -\hat{i}$ for the force due to q_1 because q_1 is to the right of q_3. (Remember that q_3 is negative, so $\vec{F}_{13}$ will be in the positive direction as shown in Figure 19.8 and $\vec{F}_{23}$ will be in the negative direction.) We now add these two forces and set the resultant equal to zero:

$$\sum \vec{F} = \vec{F}_{13} + \vec{F}_{23} = -k_e \frac{q_1 q_3}{(2.00 - x)^2} \hat{i} + k_e \frac{q_2 q_3}{x^2} \hat{i} = 0$$

Because k_e and q_3 are common to both terms, they cancel, and we can solve for x:

$$\frac{q_1}{(2.00 - x)^2} = \frac{q_2}{x^2}$$

$$(4.00 - 4.00x + x^2)(6.00 \times 10^{-6} \text{ C}) = x^2 (15.0 \times 10^{-6} \text{ C})$$

which simplifies to

$$9.00x^2 + 24.0x - 24.0 = 0$$

Solving this quadratic equation for x, we find that $x = \boxed{0.775 \text{ m.}}$ Why is the negative root not acceptable?

Physics⊗Now™ By logging into PhysicsNow at **www.pop4e.com** and going to Interactive Example 19.1, you can predict where on the x axis the electric force is zero for random values of q_1 and q_2.

EXAMPLE 19.2   The Hydrogen Atom

The electron and proton of a hydrogen atom are separated (on average) by a distance of approximately 5.3×10^{-11} m. Find the magnitudes of the electrostatic force and the gravitational force that either particle exerts on the other.

Solution From Coulomb's law, we find that the magnitude of the attractive electrostatic force is

$$F_e = k_e \frac{e^2}{r^2} = (8.99 \times 10^9 \text{ N} \cdot \text{m}^2/\text{C}^2) \frac{(1.60 \times 10^{-19} \text{ C})^2}{(5.3 \times 10^{-11} \text{ m})^2}$$

$$= \boxed{8.2 \times 10^{-8} \text{ N}}$$

Using Newton's law of universal gravitation (Section 5.5) and Table 19.1 for the particle masses, we find that the magnitude of the gravitational force is

$$F_g = G \frac{m_e m_p}{r^2}$$

$$= (6.67 \times 10^{-11} \text{ N} \cdot \text{m}^2/\text{kg}^2) \frac{(9.11 \times 10^{-31} \text{ kg})(1.67 \times 10^{-27} \text{ kg})}{(5.3 \times 10^{-11} \text{ m})^2}$$

$$= \boxed{3.6 \times 10^{-47} \text{ N}}$$

The ratio $F_g/F_e \approx 4 \times 10^{-40}$. Therefore, the gravitational force between charged atomic particles is negligible compared with the electric force.

19.5 ELECTRIC FIELDS

The gravitational field $\vec{\mathbf{g}}$ at a point in space was defined in Section 11.1 to be equal to the gravitational force $\vec{\mathbf{F}}_g$ acting on a test particle of mass m_0 divided by the mass of the test particle: $\vec{\mathbf{g}} = \vec{\mathbf{F}}_g/m_0$. It represents the gravitational version of the model of a particle in a field. In a similar manner, an electric field at a point in space can be defined in terms of the electric force acting on a test particle with charge q_0 placed at that point. Because charge exists in two varieties, we must choose a convention for our test particle. We choose the convention that **a test particle always carries a positive electric charge.** With this convention, we can introduce the electric version of the particle in a field model. The **electric field $\vec{\mathbf{E}}$** at a point in space is defined as **the electric force $\vec{\mathbf{F}}_e$ acting on a test particle placed at that point divided by the charge q_0 of the test particle:**

$$\vec{\mathbf{E}} \equiv \frac{\vec{\mathbf{F}}_e}{q_0} \qquad [19.3]$$

Therefore, **an electric field exists at a point if a charged test particle placed at rest at that point experiences an electric force.** Because force is a vector, the electric field is also a vector. Note that $\vec{\mathbf{E}}$ is the field produced by some charged particle(s) separate from the test particle; it is *not* the field produced by the test particle. We call the particle(s) creating the electric field the **source particle(s).** The electric field set up by a source charge is analogous to the gravitational field set up by some massive object such as the Earth. This gravitational field exists whether a test particle of mass m_0 is present or not. Similarly, the electric field of the source particles is present whether or not we introduce a test particle into the field. The test particle is used only to measure the force and thus detect the existence of the field and evaluate its strength.

When using Equation 19.3, we must assume that the test charge q_0 is small enough that it does not disturb the charge distribution responsible for the electric field. If a vanishingly small test charge q_0 is placed near a uniformly charged metallic sphere as in Figure 19.9a, the charge on the metallic sphere remains uniformly distributed. If the test charge is large enough ($q_0' \gg q_0$) as in Figure 19.9b, the charge on the metallic sphere is redistributed and the ratio of the force to the test charge is different: ($F_e'/q_0' \neq F_e/q_0$). That is, because of this redistribution of charge on the metallic sphere, the electric field it sets up is different from the field it sets up in the presence of the much smaller q_0.

The vector $\vec{\mathbf{E}}$ has the SI units of newtons per coulomb (N/C), analogous to the units newtons per kilogram (N/kg) for the gravitational field. The direction of $\vec{\mathbf{E}}$ is the same as the direction of $\vec{\mathbf{F}}_e$ because we have used the convention of a positive charge on the test particle.

Once the electric field is known at some point, the force on *any* particle with charge q placed at that point can be calculated from a rearrangement of Equation 19.3:

$$\vec{\mathbf{F}}_e = q\vec{\mathbf{E}} \qquad [19.4]$$

Once the electric force on a particle is evaluated, its motion can be determined from the particle under a net force model or the particle in equilibrium model (the electric force may have to be combined with other forces acting on the particle), and the techniques of earlier chapters can be used to find the motion of the particle.

Consider a point charge[3] q located a distance r from a test particle with charge q_0. According to Coulomb's law, the force exerted on the test particle by q is

■ **Definition of electric field**

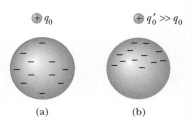

(a) (b)

FIGURE 19.9 (a) For a small enough test charge q_0, the charge distribution on the sphere is undisturbed. (b) If the test charge q_0' were larger, the charge distribution on the sphere would be disturbed as a result of the proximity of q_0'.

⊞ **PITFALL PREVENTION 19.1**

PARTICLES ONLY Keep in mind that Equation 19.4 is only valid for a charged *particle,* an object of zero size. For a charged object of finite size in an electric field, the field may vary in magnitude and direction over the size of the object, so the corresponding force equation would be more complicated.

---

[3]We have used the phrase "charged particle" so far. The phrase "point charge" is somewhat misleading because charge is a property of a particle, not a physical entity. It is similar to misleading phrasing in mechanics such as "a mass m is placed . . ." (which we have avoided) rather than "a particle with mass m is placed. . . ." This phrase is so ingrained in physics usage, however, that we will use it and hope that this footnote suffices to clarify its use.

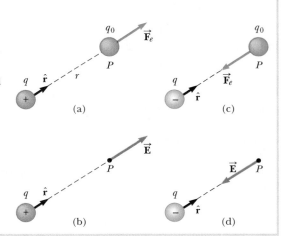

ACTIVE FIGURE 19.10

A test charge q_0 at point P is a distance r from a point charge q. (a) If q is positive, the force on the test charge is directed away from q. (b) For the positive source charge, the electric field at P points radially outward from q. (c) If q is negative, the force on the test charge is directed toward q. (d) For the negative source charge, the electric field at P points radially inward toward q.

Physics⊗Now™ Log into PhysicsNow at **www.pop4e.com** and go to Active Figure 19.10 to move point P to any position in two-dimensional space and observe the electric field due to q.

$$\vec{\mathbf{F}}_e = k_e \frac{q q_0}{r^2} \hat{\mathbf{r}}$$

where $\hat{\mathbf{r}}$ is a unit vector directed from q toward q_0. This force in Active Figure 19.10a is directed away from the source charge q. Because the electric field at P, the position of the test charge, is defined by $\vec{\mathbf{E}} = \vec{\mathbf{F}}_e / q_0$, we find that at P, the electric field created by q is

■ **Electric field due to a point charge**

$$\vec{\mathbf{E}} = k_e \frac{q}{r^2} \hat{\mathbf{r}} \qquad [19.5]$$

If the source charge q is positive, Active Figure 19.10b shows the situation with the test charge removed; the source charge sets up an electric field at point P, directed away from q. If q is negative as in Active Figure 19.10c, the force on the test charge is toward the source charge, so the electric field at P is directed toward the source charge as in Active Figure 19.10d.

To calculate the electric field at a point P due to a group of point charges, we first calculate the electric field vectors at P individually using Equation 19.5 and then add them vectorially. In other words, **the total electric field at a point in space due to a group of charged particles equals the vector sum of the electric fields at that point due to all the particles.** This superposition principle applied to fields follows directly from the vector addition property of forces. Therefore, the electric field at point P of a group of source charges can be expressed as

■ **Electric field due to a finite number of point charges**

$$\vec{\mathbf{E}} = k_e \sum_i \frac{q_i}{r_i^2} \hat{\mathbf{r}}_i \qquad [19.6]$$

where r_i is the distance from the ith charge q_i to the point P (the location at which the field is to be evaluated) and $\hat{\mathbf{r}}_i$ is a unit vector directed from q_i toward P.

QUICK QUIZ 19.4 A test charge of $+ 3 \ \mu C$ is at a point P where an external electric field is directed to the right and has a magnitude of $4 \times 10^6 \ N/C$. If the test charge is replaced with another charge of $- 3 \ \mu C$, the external electric field at P **(a)** is unaffected, **(b)** reverses direction, or **(c)** changes in a way that cannot be determined.

EXAMPLE 19.3 Electric Field of a Dipole

An **electric dipole** consists of a point charge q and a point charge $- q$ separated by a distance of $2a$ as in Figure 19.11. As we shall see in later chapters, neutral atoms and molecules behave as dipoles when placed in an external electric field. Furthermore, many molecules, such as HCl, are permanent dipoles. (HCl can be effectively modeled as an H^+ ion combined with a Cl^- ion.) The effect of such dipoles on the behavior of materials subjected to electric fields is discussed in Chapter 20.

A Find the electric field $\vec{E}$ due to the dipole along the y axis at the point P, which is a distance y from the origin.

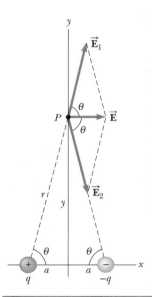

FIGURE 19.11 (Example 19.3) The total electric field $\vec{E}$ at P due to two equal and opposite charges (an electric dipole) equals the vector sum $\vec{E}_1 + \vec{E}_2$. The field $\vec{E}_1$ is due to the positive charge q, and $\vec{E}_2$ is the field due to the negative charge $-q$.

Solution At P, the fields $\vec{E}_1$ and $\vec{E}_2$ due to the two particles are equal in magnitude because P is equidistant from the two charges. The total field at P is $\vec{E} = \vec{E}_1 + \vec{E}_2$, where the magnitudes of the fields are

$$E_1 = E_2 = k_e \frac{q}{r^2} = k_e \frac{q}{y^2 + a^2}$$

The y components of $\vec{E}_1$ and $\vec{E}_2$ are equal in magnitude and opposite in sign, so they cancel. The x components are equal and add because they have the same sign. The total field $\vec{E}$ is therefore parallel to the x axis and has a magnitude

$$E = 2k_e \frac{q}{y^2 + a^2} \cos \theta$$

From the geometry in Figure 19.11 we see that $\cos \theta = a/r = a/(y^2 + a^2)^{1/2}$. Therefore,

$$E = 2k_e \frac{q}{y^2 + a^2} \cos \theta = 2k_e \frac{q}{(y^2 + a^2)} \frac{a}{(y^2 + a^2)^{1/2}}$$

$$= k_e \frac{2qa}{(y^2 + a^2)^{3/2}}$$

B Find the electric field for points $y \gg a$ far from the dipole.

Solution The preceding equation gives the value of the electric field on the y axis at all values of y. For points far from the dipole, for which $y \gg a$, we can ignore a^2 in the denominator and write

$$E \approx k_e \frac{2qa}{y^3}$$

Therefore, we see that along the y axis the field of a dipole at a distant point varies as $1/r^3$, whereas the more slowly varying field of a point charge varies as $1/r^2$. (*Note:* In the geometry of this example, $r = y$.) At distant points, the fields of the two charges in the dipole almost cancel each other. The $1/r^3$ variation in E for the dipole is also obtained for a distant point along the x axis (Problem 19.16) and for a general distant point.

Electric Field Due to Continuous Charge Distributions

In most practical situations (e.g., an object charged by rubbing), the average separation between source charges is small compared with their distances from the point at which the field is to be evaluated. In such cases, the system of source charges can be modeled as *continuous*. That is, we imagine that the system of closely spaced charges is equivalent to a total charge that is continuously distributed through some volume or over some surface.

To evaluate the electric field of a continuous charge distribution, the following procedure is used. First, we divide the charge distribution into small elements, each of which contains a small amount of charge Δq as in Figure 19.12. Next, modeling the element as a point charge, we use Equation 19.5 to calculate the electric field $\Delta \vec{E}$ at a point P due to one of these elements. Finally, we evaluate the total field at P due to the charge distribution by performing a vector sum of the contributions of all the charge elements (i.e., by applying the superposition principle).

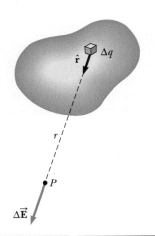

FIGURE 19.12 The electric field $\vec{\mathbf{E}}$ at P due to a continuous charge distribution is the vector sum of the fields $\Delta\vec{\mathbf{E}}$ due to all the elements Δq of the charge distribution.

The electric field at P due to one element of charge Δq_i is given by

$$\Delta\vec{\mathbf{E}}_i = k_e \frac{\Delta q_i}{r_i^2} \hat{\mathbf{r}}_i$$

where the index i refers to the ith element in the distribution, r_i is the distance from the element to point P, and $\hat{\mathbf{r}}_i$ is a unit vector directed from the element toward P. The total electric field $\vec{\mathbf{E}}$ at P due to all elements in the charge distribution is approximately

$$\vec{\mathbf{E}} \approx k_e \sum_i \frac{\Delta q_i}{r_i^2} \hat{\mathbf{r}}_i$$

Now, we apply the model in which the charge distribution is continuous, and we let the elements of charge become infinitesimally small. With this model, the total field at P in the limit $\Delta q_i \rightarrow 0$ becomes

$$\vec{\mathbf{E}} = \lim_{\Delta q_i \to 0} k_e \sum_i \frac{\Delta q_i}{r_i^2} \hat{\mathbf{r}}_i = k_e \int \frac{dq}{r^2} \hat{\mathbf{r}} \qquad [19.7]$$

where dq is an infinitesimal amount of charge and the integration is over all the charge creating the electric field. The integration is a *vector* operation and must be treated with caution. It can be evaluated in terms of individual components, or perhaps symmetry arguments can be used to reduce it to a scalar integral. We shall illustrate this type of calculation with several examples in which we assume that the charge is *uniformly* distributed on a line or a surface or throughout some volume. When performing such calculations, it is convenient to use the concept of a *charge density* along with the following notations:

- If a total charge Q is uniformly distributed throughout a volume V, the **volume charge density** ρ is defined by

▪ Volume charge density

$$\rho \equiv \frac{Q}{V} \qquad [19.8]$$

where ρ has units of coulombs per cubic meter.

- If Q is uniformly distributed on a surface of area A, the **surface charge density** σ is defined by

▪ Surface charge density

$$\sigma \equiv \frac{Q}{A} \qquad [19.9]$$

where σ has units of coulombs per square meter.

- If Q is uniformly distributed along a line of length ℓ, the **linear charge density** λ is defined by

▪ Linear charge density

$$\lambda \equiv \frac{Q}{\ell} \qquad [19.10]$$

where λ has units of coulombs per meter.

PROBLEM-SOLVING STRATEGY **Calculating the Electric Field**

The following procedure is recommended for solving problems that involve the determination of an electric field due to individual charges or a charge distribution:

1. Conceptualize Think carefully about the individual charges or the charge distribution that you have in the problem. Imagine what type of electric field they would create and

establish the mental representation. Appeal to any symmetry in the arrangement of charges to help you visualize the electric field.

2. Categorize Are you analyzing a group of individual charges or a continuous charge distribution? The answer to this question will tell you how to proceed in the *Analyze* step.

3. Analyze

(a) *If you are analyzing a group of individual charges,* use the superposition principle. When several point charges are present, the resultant field at a point in space is the *vector sum* of the individual fields due to the individual charges (Eq. 19.6). Example 19.3 demonstrated this procedure. Be very careful in the manipulation of vector quantities. It may be useful to review the material on vector addition in Chapter 1.

(b) *If you are analyzing a continuous charge distribution,* replace the vector sums for evaluating the total electric field from individual charges by vector integrals. The charge distribution is divided into infinitesimal pieces, and the vector sum is carried out by integrating over the entire charge distribution (Eq. 19.7). Examples 19.4 and 19.5 demonstrate such procedures.

Symmetry. Whenever dealing with either a distribution of point charges or a continuous charge distribution, take advantage of any symmetry in the system that you observed in the *Conceptualize* step to simplify your calculations. The cancellation of field components parallel to the *y* axis in Example 19.3 and perpendicular to the axis in Example 19.5 is an example of the application of symmetry.

4. Finalize
Once you have determined your result, check to see if your field is consistent with the mental representation and that it reflects any symmetry that you noted previously. Imagine varying parameters such as the distance of the observation point from the charges or the radius of any circular or spherical objects to see if the mathematical result changes in a reasonable way.

EXAMPLE 19.4 | **The Electric Field Due to a Charged Rod**

A rod of length ℓ has a uniform linear charge density λ and a total charge Q. Calculate the electric field at a point P along the axis of the rod, a distance a from one end (Fig. 19.13).

Solution Figure 19.13 helps us visualize the source of the electric field and conceptualize what the field might look like. We expect the field to be symmetric around the horizontal dimension of the rod and would expect the field to decrease for increasing values of a. We categorize this problem as one involving a continuous distribution of charge on the rod rather than a collection of individual charges. To analyze the problem, we choose an infinitesimal element of the charge distribution as indicated by the blue portion in Figure 19.13. Let us use dx to represent the length of one small segment of the rod and let dq be the charge on the segment. We express the charge dq of the element in terms of the other variables within the integral (in this example, there is one variable, x). The charge dq on the small segment is $dq = \lambda\, dx$.

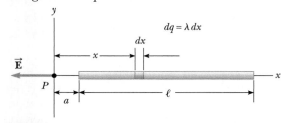

FIGURE 19.13 | (Example 19.4) The electric field at P due to a uniformly charged rod lying along the x axis. The field at P due to the segment of charge dq is $k_e\, dq/x^2$. The total field at P is the vector sum over all segments of the rod.

The field $d\vec{\mathbf{E}}$ due to this segment at the point P is in the negative x direction, and its magnitude is

$$dE = k_e \frac{dq}{x^2} = k_e \frac{\lambda\, dx}{x^2}$$

Each element of the charge distribution produces a field at P in the negative x direction, so the vector sum of their contributions reduces to an algebraic sum. The total field at P due to all segments of the rod, which are at different distances from P, is given by Equation 19.7, which in this case becomes

$$E = \int_a^{\ell + a} k_e \lambda \frac{dx}{x^2}$$

where the limits on the integral extend from one end of the rod ($x = a$) to the other ($x = \ell + a$). Because k_e and λ are constants, they can be removed from the integral. Therefore, we find that

$$E = k_e \lambda \int_a^{\ell + a} \frac{dx}{x^2} = k_e \lambda \left[-\frac{1}{x} \right]_a^{\ell + a}$$

$$= k_e \lambda \left(\frac{1}{a} - \frac{1}{\ell + a} \right) = \boxed{\frac{k_e Q}{a(\ell + a)}}$$

where we have used that the linear charge density is $\lambda = Q/\ell$.

To finalize, note that E decreases as a increases, as we expected from our mental representation. If point P is very far from the rod ($a \gg \ell$), we can ignore the ℓ in the denominator, and $E \approx k_e Q/a^2$. This result is just the form you would expect for a point charge. Therefore, at large values of a, the charge distribution appears to be a point charge of magnitude Q as you should expect.

EXAMPLE 19.5 | The Electric Field of a Uniform Ring of Charge

A ring of radius a has a uniform positive charge per unit length, with a total charge Q. Calculate the electric field at a point P on the axis of the ring at a distance x from the center of the ring (Fig. 19.14a).

Solution The magnitude of the electric field at P due to the segment of charge dq is

$$dE = k_e \frac{dq}{r^2}$$

This field has an x component $dE_x = dE \cos \theta$ along the axis of the ring and a component $dE_\perp$ perpendicular to the axis. The perpendicular component of any element is canceled by the perpendicular component of an element on the opposite side of the ring, as for the elements 1 and 2 in Figure 19.14b. Therefore, the perpendicular components of the field for the entire ring sum to zero and the resultant field at P must lie along the x axis. Because $r = (x^2 + a^2)^{1/2}$ and $\cos \theta = x/r$, we find that

$$dE_x = dE \cos \theta = \left(k_e \frac{dq}{r^2} \right) \left(\frac{x}{r} \right) = \frac{k_e x}{(x^2 + a^2)^{3/2}} dq$$

We integrate this expression to find the total field at P. In this case, all segments of the ring give the same contribution to the field at P because they are all equidistant from this point. Therefore,

$$E_x = \int \frac{k_e x}{(x^2 + a^2)^{3/2}} dq = \frac{k_e x}{(x^2 + a^2)^{3/2}} \int dq$$

$$= \frac{k_e x}{(x^2 + a^2)^{3/2}} Q$$

This result shows that the field is zero at the center point of the ring, $x = 0$. Does that surprise you?

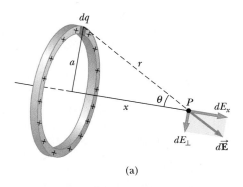 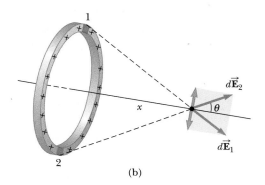

(a)   (b)

FIGURE 19.14 | (Example 19.5) A uniformly charged ring of radius a. (a) The field at P on the x axis due to an element of charge dq. (b) The total electric field at P is along the x axis. The perpendicular component of the electric field at P due to segment 1 is canceled by the perpendicular component due to segment 2.

19.6 | ELECTRIC FIELD LINES

A convenient specialized pictorial representation for visualizing electric field patterns is created by drawing lines showing the direction of the electric field vector at any point. These lines, called **electric field lines,** are related to the electric field in any region of space in the following manner:

- The electric field vector $\vec{\mathbf{E}}$ is *tangent* to the electric field line at each point.
- The number of electric field lines per unit area through a surface that is perpendicular to the lines is proportional to the magnitude of the electric field in that region. Therefore, E is large where the field lines are close together and small where they are far apart.

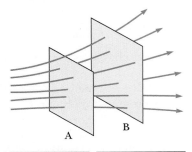

FIGURE 19.15 | Electric field lines penetrating two surfaces. The magnitude of the field is greater on surface A than on surface B.

These properties are illustrated in Figure 19.15. The density of lines through surface A is greater than the density of lines through surface B. Therefore, the magnitude of the electric field on surface A is larger than on surface B. Furthermore, the field drawn in Figure 19.15 is nonuniform because the lines at different locations point in different directions.

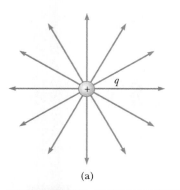
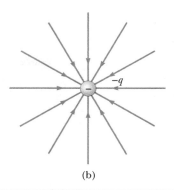
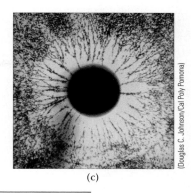

(a)   (b)   (c)

(Douglas C. Johnson/Cal Poly Pomona)

FIGURE 19.16 The electric field lines for a point charge. (a) For a positive point charge, the lines are directed radially outward. (b) For a negative point charge, the lines are directed radially inward. Note that the figures show only those field lines that lie in the plane containing the charge. (c) The dark areas are small particles suspended in oil, which align with the electric field produced by a small charged conductor at the center.

Some representative electric field lines for a single positive point charge are shown in Figure 19.16a. Note that in this two-dimensional drawing we show only the field lines that lie in the plane of the page. The lines are actually directed radially outward in *all* directions from the charge, somewhat like the needles of a porcupine. Because a positively charged test particle placed in this field would be repelled by the charge q, the lines are directed radially away from q. Similarly, the electric field lines for a single negative point charge are directed toward the charge (Fig. 19.16b). In either case, the lines are radial and extend to infinity. Note that the lines are closer together as they come nearer to the charge, indicating that the magnitude of the field is increasing.

Is this visualization of the electric field in terms of field lines consistent with Equation 19.5? To answer this question, consider an imaginary spherical surface of radius r, concentric with the charge. From symmetry, we see that the magnitude of the electric field is the same everywhere on the surface of the sphere. The number of lines N emerging from the charge is equal to the number penetrating the spherical surface. Hence, the number of lines per unit area on the sphere is $N/4\pi r^2$ (where the surface area of the sphere is $4\pi r^2$). Because E is proportional to the number of lines per unit area, we see that E varies as $1/r^2$. This result is consistent with that obtained from Equation 19.5; that is, $E = k_e q/r^2$.

The rules for drawing electric field lines for any charge distribution are as follows:

- The lines for a group of point charges must begin on positive charges and end on negative ones. In the case of an excess of one type of charge, some lines will begin or end infinitely far away.
- The number of lines drawn beginning on a positive charge or ending on a negative one is proportional to the magnitude of the charge.
- Field lines cannot intersect.

Because charge is quantized, the number of lines leaving any positively charged object must be 0, ae, $2ae$, ..., where a is an arbitrary (but fixed) proportionality constant chosen by the person drawing the lines. Once a is chosen, the number of lines is no longer arbitrary. For example, if object 1 has charge Q_1 and object 2 has charge Q_2, the ratio of the number of lines connected to object 2 to those connected to object 1 is $N_2/N_1 = Q_2/Q_1$.

The electric field lines for two point charges of equal magnitude but opposite signs (the electric dipole) are shown in Figure 19.17. In this case, the number of lines that begin at the positive charge must equal the number that terminate at the negative charge. At points very near the charges, the lines are nearly radial. The

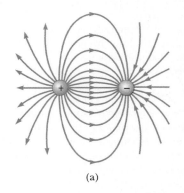

(a)

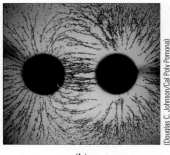

(b)

(Douglas C. Johnson/Cal Poly Pomona)

FIGURE 19.17 (a) The electric field lines for two charges of equal magnitude and opposite sign (an electric dipole). Note that the number of lines leaving the positive charge equals the number terminating at the negative charge. (b) Small particles suspended in oil align with the electric field.

(Douglas C. Johnson/Cal Poly Pomona)

FIGURE 19.18 (a) The electric field lines for two positive point charges. (The locations A, B, and C are discussed in Quick Quiz 19.5.) (b) Small particles suspended in oil align with the electric field.

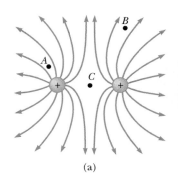
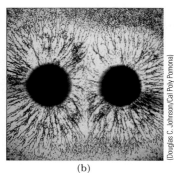

(a)   (b)

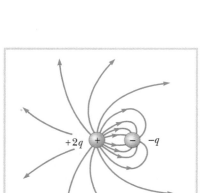

ACTIVE FIGURE 19.19

The electric field lines for a point charge $+2q$ and a second point charge $-q$. Note that two lines leave the charge $+2q$ for every one that terminates on $-q$.

Physics⊗Now™ Log into PhysicsNow at **www.pop4e.com** and go to Active Figure 19.19 to choose the values and signs for the two charges and observe the electric field lines for the configuration that you have chosen.

PITFALL PREVENTION 19.3

ELECTRIC FIELD LINES ARE NOT REAL
Electric field lines are not material objects. They are used only as a pictorial representation to provide a qualitative description of the electric field. One problem with this representation is that one always draws a finite number of lines from each charge, which makes it appear as if the field were quantized and exists only in certain parts of space. The field, in fact, is continuous, existing at every point. Another problem with this representation is the danger of obtaining the wrong impression from a two-dimensional drawing of field lines used to describe a three-dimensional situation.

high density of lines between the charges indicates a region of strong electric field. The attractive nature of the force between the particles is also suggested by Figure 19.17, with the lines from one particle ending on the other particle.

Figure 19.18 shows the electric field lines in the vicinity of two equal positive point charges. Again, close to either charge the lines are nearly radial. The same number of lines emerges from each particle because the charges are equal in magnitude. At great distances from the particles, the field is approximately equal to that of a single point charge of magnitude $2q$. The repulsive nature of the electric force between particles of like charge is suggested in the figure in that no lines connect the particles and that the lines bend away from the region between the charges.

Finally, we sketch the electric field lines associated with a positive point charge $+2q$ and a negative point charge $-q$ in Active Figure 19.19. In this case, the number of lines leaving $+2q$ is twice the number terminating on $-q$. Hence, only half the lines that leave the positive charge end at the negative charge. The remaining half terminate on hypothetical negative charges we assume to be located infinitely far away. At large distances from the particles (large compared with the particle separation), the electric field lines are equivalent to those of a single point charge $+q$.

QUICK QUIZ 19.5 Rank the magnitudes of the electric field at points A, B, and C in Figure 19.18a, largest magnitude first.

19.7 ▌ MOTION OF CHARGED PARTICLES IN A UNIFORM ELECTRIC FIELD

When a particle of charge q and mass m is placed in an electric field $\vec{\mathbf{E}}$, the electric force exerted on the charge is given by Equation 19.4, $\vec{\mathbf{F}}_e = q\vec{\mathbf{E}}$. If this force is the only force exerted on the particle, it is the net force. According to the particle under a net force model from Chapter 4, the net force causes the particle to accelerate. In this case, Newton's second law applied to the particle gives

$$\vec{\mathbf{F}}_e = q\vec{\mathbf{E}} = m\vec{\mathbf{a}}$$

The acceleration of the particle is therefore

$$\vec{\mathbf{a}} = \frac{q\vec{\mathbf{E}}}{m} \qquad [19.11]$$

If $\vec{\mathbf{E}}$ is uniform (i.e., constant in magnitude and direction), the acceleration is constant. If the particle has a positive charge, its acceleration is in the direction of the electric field. If the particle has a negative charge, its acceleration is in the direction opposite the electric field.

EXAMPLE 19.6	An Accelerating Positive Charge

A particle with positive charge q and mass m is released from rest in a uniform electric field $\vec{\mathbf{E}}$ directed along the x axis as in Figure 19.20. Describe its motion.

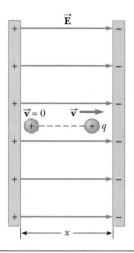

FIGURE **19.20**	(Example 19.6) A positive point charge q in a uniform electric field $\vec{\mathbf{E}}$ undergoes constant acceleration in the direction of the field.

Solution The acceleration is constant and is given by $q\,\vec{\mathbf{E}}/m$ (Eq. 19.11). The motion is simple linear motion along the x axis. We can therefore apply the model of a particle under constant acceleration and use the equations of kinematics in one dimension (from Chapter 2):

$$x_f = x_i + v_i t + \tfrac{1}{2}at^2$$

$$v_f = v_i + at$$

$$v_f{}^2 = v_i{}^2 + 2a(x_f - x_i)$$

Choosing $x_i = 0$ and $v_i = 0$ gives

$$x_f = \tfrac{1}{2}at^2 = \frac{qE}{2m}\,t^2$$

$$v_f = at = \frac{qE}{m}\,t$$

$$v_f{}^2 = 2ax_f = \left(\frac{2qE}{m}\right)x_f$$

The kinetic energy of the particle after it has moved a distance $x = x_f - x_i$ is

$$K = \tfrac{1}{2}mv^2 = \tfrac{1}{2}m\left(\frac{2qE}{m}\right)x = qEx$$

This result can also be obtained by identifying the particle as a nonisolated system and applying the nonisolated system model. Energy is transferred from the environment (the electric field) by work, so the work–kinetic energy theorem gives the same result as the calculation above. Try it!

The electric field in the region between two oppositely charged flat metal plates is approximately uniform (Active Fig. 19.21). Suppose an electron of charge $-e$ is projected horizontally into this field with an initial velocity $v_i\hat{\mathbf{i}}$. Because the electric field $\vec{\mathbf{E}}$ in Active Figure 19.21 is in the positive y direction, the acceleration of the electron is in the negative y direction. That is,

$$\vec{\mathbf{a}} = -\frac{eE}{m_e}\,\hat{\mathbf{j}} \qquad\qquad [19.12]$$

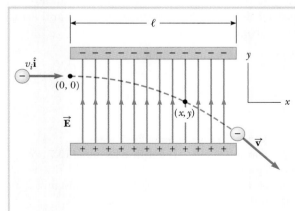

ACTIVE FIGURE 19.21

An electron is projected horizontally into a uniform electric field produced by two charged plates. The electron undergoes a downward acceleration (opposite $\vec{\mathbf{E}}$), and its motion is parabolic while it is between the plates.

Physics⊗Now™ Log into Physics-Now at **www.pop4e.com** and go to Active Figure 19.21 to choose the magnitude of the electric field and the mass and charge of the projected particle.

Because the acceleration is constant, we can apply the kinematic equations from Chapter 3 with $v_{xi} = v_i$ and $v_{yi} = 0$. At time t, the components of the velocity of the electron are

$$v_x = v_i = \text{constant} \qquad [19.13]$$

$$v_y = a_y t = -\frac{eE}{m_e} t \qquad [19.14]$$

Its position coordinates at time t are

$$x_f = v_i t \qquad [19.15]$$

$$y_f = \tfrac{1}{2} a_y t^2 = -\tfrac{1}{2} \frac{eE}{m_e} t^2 \qquad [19.16]$$

Substituting the value $t = x_f/v_i$ from Equation 19.15 into Equation 19.16, we see that y_f is proportional to $x_f{}^2$. Hence, the trajectory of the electron is a parabola. The trajectory of the electron in a uniform electric field $\vec{\mathbf{E}}$ under the action of a constant force of magnitude qE has the same shape as that of a particle in a uniform gravitational field $\vec{\mathbf{g}}$ under the action of a constant force of magnitude mg. After the electron leaves the field, it continues to move in a straight line, obeying Newton's first law, with a speed $v > v_i$.

Note that we have ignored the gravitational force on the electron. This approximation is valid when dealing with atomic particles. For an electric field of 10^4 N/C, the ratio of the magnitude of the electric force eE to the magnitude of the gravitational force mg is on the order of 10^{14} for an electron and on the order of 10^{11} for a proton.

INTERACTIVE **EXAMPLE 19.7** **An Accelerated Electron**

An electron enters the region of a uniform electric field as in Active Figure 19.21, with $v_i = 3.00 \times 10^6$ m/s and $E = 200$ N/C. The horizontal length of the plates is $\ell = 0.100$ m.

A Find the acceleration of the electron while it is in the electric field.

Solution The charge on the electron is $-e$ and its mass is $m_e = 9.11 \times 10^{-31}$ kg. Therefore, Equation 19.12 gives

$$\vec{\mathbf{a}} = -\frac{eE}{m_e}\hat{\mathbf{j}} = -\frac{(1.60 \times 10^{-19}\ \text{C})(200\ \text{N/C})}{9.11 \times 10^{-31}\ \text{kg}}\hat{\mathbf{j}}$$

$$= -3.51 \times 10^{13}\hat{\mathbf{j}}\ \text{m/s}^2$$

B Find the time interval required for the electron to travel through the field.

Solution The horizontal distance through the field is $\ell = 0.100$ m. Modeling the electron as a particle under constant velocity in the horizontal direction,

we find that the time interval spent in the electric field is

$$\Delta t = \frac{\ell}{v_i} = \frac{0.100\ \text{m}}{3.00 \times 10^6\ \text{m/s}} = 3.33 \times 10^{-8}\ \text{s}$$

C What is the vertical displacement Δy of the electron while it is in the field?

Solution Modeling the electron as a particle under constant acceleration in the vertical direction and using the results from parts A and B, we find that

$$\Delta y = y_f - y_i = \tfrac{1}{2} a_y t^2$$

$$= -\tfrac{1}{2}(3.51 \times 10^{13}\ \text{m/s}^2)(3.33 \times 10^{-8}\ \text{s})^2$$

$$= -0.0195\ \text{m} = -1.95\ \text{cm}$$

Physics⊗Now™ By logging into PhysicsNow at **www.pop4e.com** and going to Interactive Example 19.7, you can predict, for random values of the electric field, the required initial velocity for the exiting electron to just miss the right edge of the lower plate in Active Figure 19.21.

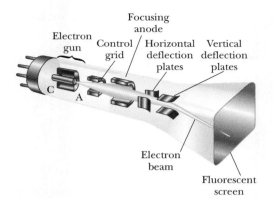

FIGURE 19.22 Schematic diagram of a cathode-ray tube. Electrons leaving the hot cathode C are accelerated to the anode A. In addition to accelerating electrons, the electron gun is also used to focus the beam of electrons, and the plates deflect the beam.

The Cathode-Ray Tube

The previous example describes a portion of a cathode-ray tube (CRT). This tube, illustrated in Figure 19.22, is commonly used to obtain a visual display of electronic information in oscilloscopes, radar systems, television receivers, and computer monitors. The CRT is a vacuum tube in which a beam of electrons is accelerated and deflected under the influence of electric or magnetic fields. The electron beam is produced by an *electron gun* located in the neck of the tube. The electrons travel through the *control grid,* which determines the number of electrons passing through (and therefore the brightness of the display). The focusing anode focuses the beam of electrons to a small spot on the display screen. The fluorescent screen is coated with a material that emits visible light when bombarded with electrons.

In an oscilloscope, the electrons are deflected in various directions by two sets of plates placed perpendicularly to each other in the neck of the tube. (A television CRT steers the beam with a magnetic field, which we will discuss in Chapter 22.) An external electric circuit is used to control the amount of charge present on the plates. Placing positive charge on one horizontal deflection plate and negative charge on the other creates an electric field between the plates and allows the beam to be steered from side to side. The vertical deflection plates act in the same way, except that changing the charge on them deflects the beam vertically.

19.8 ELECTRIC FLUX

Now that we have described the concept of electric field lines qualitatively, let us use a new concept, *electric flux,* to approach electric field lines on a quantitative basis. Electric flux is a quantity proportional to the number of electric field lines penetrating some surface. (We can define only a proportionality because the number of lines we choose to draw is arbitrary.)

First consider an electric field that is uniform in both magnitude and direction as in Figure 19.23. The field lines penetrate a plane rectangular surface of area A, which is perpendicular to the field. Recall that the number of lines per unit area is proportional to the magnitude of the electric field. The number of lines penetrating the surface of area A is therefore proportional to the product EA. The product of the electric field magnitude E and a surface area A perpendicular to the field is called the **electric flux** Φ_E:

$$\Phi_E = EA \qquad [19.17]$$

From the SI units of E and A, we see that electric flux has the units $N \cdot m^2/C$.

If the surface under consideration is not perpendicular to the field, the number of lines through it must be less than that given by Equation 19.17. This concept can

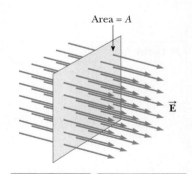

FIGURE 19.23 Field lines of a uniform electric field penetrating a plane of area A perpendicular to the field. The electric flux Φ_E through this area is equal to EA.

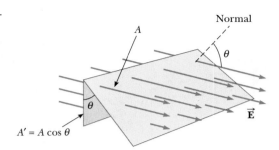

FIGURE 19.24 Field lines for a uniform electric field through an area A whose normal is at an angle θ to the field. Because the number of lines that go through the shaded area A' is the same as the number that go through A, we conclude that the total flux through A' is equal to the flux through A and is given by $\Phi_E = EA \cos \theta$.

be understood by considering Figure 19.24, where the normal to the surface of area A is at an angle of θ to the uniform electric field. Note that the number of lines that cross this area is equal to the number that cross the projected area A', which is perpendicular to the field. From Figure 19.24, we see that the two areas are related by $A' = A \cos \theta$. Because the flux through area A equals the flux through A', we conclude that the desired flux is

$$\Phi_E = EA \cos \theta \qquad [19.18]$$

From this result, we see that the flux through a surface of fixed area has the maximum value EA when the angle θ between the normal to the surface and the electric field is zero. This situation occurs when the normal is parallel to the field and the surface is perpendicular to the field. The flux is zero when the surface is parallel to the field because the angle θ in Equation 19.18 is then 90°.

In more general situations, the electric field may vary in both magnitude and direction over the surface in question. Unless the field is uniform, our definition of flux given by Equation 19.18 therefore has meaning only over a small element of area. Consider a general surface divided up into a large number of small elements, each of area ΔA. The variation in the electric field over the element can be ignored if the element is small enough. It is convenient to define a vector $\Delta \vec{\mathbf{A}}_i$ whose magnitude represents the area of the ith element and whose direction is defined to be perpendicular to the surface as in Figure 19.25. The electric flux $\Delta \Phi_E$ through this small element is

$$\Delta \Phi_E = E_i \Delta A_i \cos \theta_i = \vec{\mathbf{E}}_i \cdot \Delta \vec{\mathbf{A}}_i$$

where we have used the definition of the scalar product of two vectors $(\vec{\mathbf{A}} \cdot \vec{\mathbf{B}} = AB \cos \theta)$. By summing the contributions of all elements, we obtain the total flux through the surface. If we let the area of each element approach zero, the number of elements approaches infinity and the sum is replaced by an integral. The general definition of electric flux is therefore

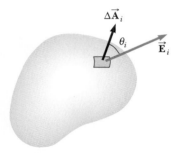

FIGURE 19.25 A small element of a surface of area ΔA_i. The electric field makes an angle θ_i with the normal to the surface (the direction of $\Delta \vec{\mathbf{A}}_i$), and the flux through the element is equal to $E_i \Delta A_i \cos \theta_i$.

❚ Electric flux

$$\Phi_E \equiv \lim_{\Delta A_i \to 0} \sum \vec{\mathbf{E}}_i \cdot \Delta \vec{\mathbf{A}}_i = \int_{\text{surface}} \vec{\mathbf{E}} \cdot d\vec{\mathbf{A}} \qquad [19.19]$$

Equation 19.19 is a surface integral, which must be evaluated over the surface in question. In general, the value of Φ_E depends both on the field pattern and on the specified surface.

We shall often be interested in evaluating electric flux through a *closed surface*. A closed surface is defined as one that completely divides space into an inside region and an outside region so that movement cannot take place from one region to the other without penetrating the surface. This definition is similar to that of the system boundary in system models, in which the boundary divides space into a region inside the system and the outer region, the environment. The surface of a sphere is an example of a closed surface, whereas a drinking glass is an open surface.

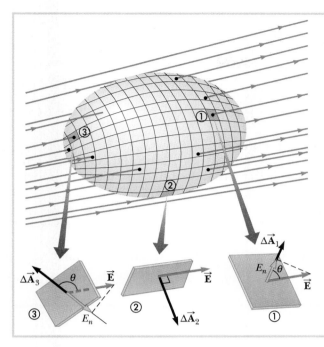

A closed surface in an electric field. The area vectors $\Delta \vec{A}_i$ are, by convention, normal to the surface and point outward. The flux through an area element can be positive (element ①), zero (element ②), or negative (element ③).

Physics⊗Now™ Log into PhysicsNow at **www.pop4e.com** and go to Active Figure 19.26 to select a segment on the surface and see the relationship between the electric field vector $\vec{E}$ and the area vector $\Delta \vec{A}_i$.

Consider the closed surface in Active Figure 19.26. Note that the vectors $\Delta \vec{A}_i$ point in different directions for the various surface elements. At each point, these vectors are *perpendicular* to the surface and, by convention, always point *outward* from the inside region. At the element labeled ①, $\vec{E}$ is outward and $\theta_i < 90°$; hence, the flux $\Delta \Phi_E = \vec{E} \cdot \Delta \vec{A}_i$ through this element is positive. For element ②, the field lines graze the surface (perpendicular to the vector $\Delta \vec{A}_i$); therefore, $\theta_i = 90°$ and the flux is zero. For elements such as ③, where the field lines are crossing the surface from the outside to the inside, $180° > \theta_i > 90°$ and the flux is negative because $\cos \theta_i$ is negative. The net flux through the surface is proportional to the net number of lines penetrating the surface, where the net number means **the number leaving the volume surrounded by the surface minus the number entering the volume.** If more lines are leaving the surface than entering, the net flux is positive. If more lines enter than leave the surface, the net flux is negative. Using the symbol $\oint$ to represent an integral over a closed surface, we can write the net flux Φ_E through a closed surface as

$$\Phi_E = \oint \vec{E} \cdot d\vec{A} = \oint E_n \, dA \qquad [19.20]$$

where E_n represents the component of the electric field normal to the surface.

Evaluating the net flux through a closed surface can be very cumbersome. If the field is perpendicular or parallel to the surface at each point and constant in magnitude, however, the calculation is straightforward. The following example illustrates this point.

EXAMPLE 19.8　　Flux Through a Cube

Consider a uniform electric field $\vec{E}$ directed along the $+x$ axis. Find the net electric flux through the surface of a cube of edges ℓ oriented as shown in Figure 19.27.

Solution The net flux can be evaluated by summing up the fluxes through each face of the cube. First, note that the flux through four of the faces is zero because $\vec{E}$

is perpendicular to $d\vec{A}$ on these faces. In particular, the orientation of $d\vec{A}$ is perpendicular to $\vec{E}$ for the faces labeled ③ and ④ in Figure 19.27. Therefore, $\theta = 90°$, so $\vec{E} \cdot d\vec{A} = E \, dA \cos 90° = 0$. The flux through each face parallel to the xy plane is also zero for the same reason.

Now consider the faces labeled ① and ②. The net flux through these faces is

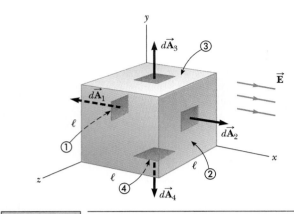

FIGURE 19.27 (Example 19.8) A hypothetical surface in the shape of a cube in a uniform electric field parallel to the *x* axis. The net flux through the surface is zero. Side ④ is the bottom of the cube and side ① is opposite side ②.

$$\Phi_E = \int_1 \vec{E} \cdot d\vec{A} + \int_2 \vec{E} \cdot d\vec{A}$$

For face ①, $\vec{E}$ is constant and inward, whereas $d\vec{A}$ is outward ($\theta = 180°$), so the flux through this face is

$$\int_1 \vec{E} \cdot d\vec{A} = \int_1 E\, dA \cos 180° = -E \int_1 dA = -EA = -E\ell^2$$

because the area of each face is $A = \ell^2$.

Likewise, for ②, $\vec{E}$ is constant and outward and in the same direction as $d\vec{A}$ ($\theta = 0°$), so the flux through this face is

$$\int_2 \vec{E} \cdot d\vec{A} = \int_2 E\, dA \cos 0° = E \int_2 dA = +EA = E\ell^2$$

Hence, the net flux over all faces is zero because

$$\Phi_E = -E\ell^2 + E\ell^2 = \boxed{0}$$

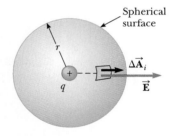

FIGURE 19.28 A spherical surface of radius *r* surrounding a point charge *q*. When the charge is at the center of the sphere, the electric field is normal to the surface and constant in magnitude everywhere on the surface.

19.9 GAUSS'S LAW

In this section, we describe a general relation between the net electric flux through a closed surface and the charge *enclosed* by the surface. This relation, known as **Gauss's law,** is of fundamental importance in the study of electrostatic fields.

First, let us consider a positive point charge *q* located at the center of a spherical surface of radius *r* as in Figure 19.28. The field lines radiate outward and hence are perpendicular (or normal) to the surface at each point. That is, at each point on the surface, $\vec{E}$ is parallel to the vector $\Delta\vec{A}_i$ representing the local element of area ΔA_i. Therefore, at all points on the surface,

$$\vec{E} \cdot \Delta\vec{A}_i = E_n \Delta A_i = E \Delta A_i$$

and, from Equation 19.20, we find that the net flux through the surface is

$$\Phi_E = \oint E_n\, dA = \oint E\, dA = E \oint dA = EA$$

because *E* is constant over the surface. From Equation 19.5, we know that the magnitude of the electric field everywhere on the surface of the sphere is $E = k_e q/r^2$. Furthermore, for a spherical surface, $A = 4\pi r^2$ (the surface area of a sphere). Hence, the net flux through the surface is

$$\Phi_E = EA = \left(\frac{k_e q}{r^2}\right)(4\pi r^2) = 4\pi k_e q$$

Recalling that $k_e = 1/4\pi\epsilon_0$, we can write this expression in the form

$$\Phi_E = \frac{q}{\epsilon_0} \qquad [19.21]$$

This result, which is independent of *r*, says that the net flux through a spherical surface is proportional to the charge *q* at the center *inside* the surface. This result mathematically represents that (1) the net flux is proportional to the number of field lines, (2) the number of field lines is proportional to the charge inside the surface, and (3) every field line from the charge must pass through the surface. That the net flux is independent of the radius is a consequence of the inverse-square dependence of the electric field given by Equation 19.5. That is, E varies as $1/r^2$, but the area of the sphere varies as r^2. Their combined effect produces a flux that is independent of r.

Now consider several closed surfaces surrounding a charge q as in Figure 19.29. Surface S_1 is spherical, whereas surfaces S_2 and S_3 are nonspherical. The flux that passes through surface S_1 has the value q/ϵ_0. As we discussed in Section 19.8, the flux is proportional to the number of electric field lines passing through that surface. The construction in Figure 19.29 shows that the number of electric field lines through the spherical surface S_1 is equal to the number of electric field lines through the nonspherical surfaces S_2 and S_3. It is therefore reasonable to conclude that the net flux through any closed surface is independent of the shape of that surface. (One can prove that conclusion using $E \propto 1/r^2$.) In fact, **the net flux through any closed surface surrounding the point charge q is given by q/ϵ_0.** Because we could choose a spherical surface surrounding the charge such that the charge is *not* at the center of the surface, **the flux through the surface is independent of the position of the charge within the surface.**

Now consider a point charge located *outside* a closed surface of arbitrary shape as in Figure 19.30. As you can see from this construction, electric field lines enter the surface and then leave it. Therefore, the number of electric field lines entering the surface equals the number leaving the surface. Consequently, we conclude that **the net electric flux through a closed surface that surrounds no net charge is zero.** If we apply this result to Example 19.8, we see that the net flux through the cube is zero because there was no charge inside the cube. If there were charge in the cube, the electric field could not be uniform throughout the cube as specified in the example.

Let us extend these arguments to the generalized case of many point charges. We shall again make use of the superposition principle. That is, we can express the net flux through any closed surface as

$$\oint \vec{E} \cdot d\vec{A} = \oint (\vec{E}_1 + \vec{E}_2 + \cdots) \cdot d\vec{A}$$

where $\vec{E}$ is the total electric field at any point on the surface and $\vec{E}_1, \vec{E}_2, \ldots$ are the fields produced by the individual charges at that point. Consider the system of charges shown in Active Figure 19.31. The surface S surrounds only one charge, q_1; hence, the net flux through S is q_1/ϵ_0. The flux through S due to the charges outside it is zero because each electric field line from these charges that enters S at one point leaves it at another. The surface S' surrounds charges q_2 and q_3; hence, the net flux through S' is $(q_2 + q_3)/\epsilon_0$. Finally, the net flux through surface S'' is zero because no charge exists inside this surface. That is, *all* electric field lines that enter S'' at one point leave S'' at another. Notice that charge q_4 does not contribute to the net flux through any of the surfaces because it is outside all the surfaces.

Gauss's law, which is a generalization of the foregoing discussion, states that the net flux through *any* closed surface is

$$\Phi_E = \oint \vec{E} \cdot d\vec{A} = \frac{q_{in}}{\epsilon_0} \qquad [19.22]$$

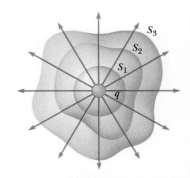

FIGURE 19.29 Closed surfaces of various shapes surrounding a charge q. The net electric flux through each surface is the same.

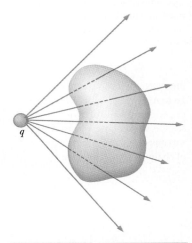

FIGURE 19.30 A point charge located *outside* a closed surface. The number of lines entering the surface equals the number leaving the surface.

PITFALL PREVENTION 19.4

ZERO FLUX IS NOT ZERO FIELD
In this discussion, we see two possibilities in which there is zero flux through a closed surface: either no charged particles are enclosed by the surface, or charged particles are enclosed but the net charge is zero. For either possibility, *do not* fall into the trap of saying that because the flux is zero, the electric field is zero at the surfaces. Remember that Gauss's law states that the electric *flux* is proportional to the enclosed charge, not the electric *field*.

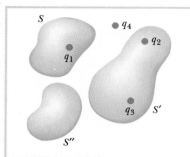

ACTIVE FIGURE 19.31

The net electric flux through any closed surface depends only on the charge *inside* that surface. The net flux through surface *S* is q_1/ϵ_0, the net flux through surface *S′* is $(q_2 + q_3)/\epsilon_0$, and the net flux through surface *S″* is zero. Charge q_4 does not contribute to the flux through any surface because it is outside all surfaces.

Physics⊗Now™ Log into PhysicsNow at **www.pop4e.com** and go to Active Figure 19.31 to change the size and shape of the surface and see the effect on the electric flux of surrounding different combinations of charge with a gaussian surface.

where q_{in} represents the *net charge inside the surface* and $\vec{\mathbf{E}}$ represents the electric field at any point on the surface. In words, Gauss's law states that **the net electric flux through any closed surface is equal to the net charge inside the surface divided by ϵ_0.** The closed surface used in Gauss's law is called a **gaussian surface.**

Gauss's law is valid for the electric field of any system of charges or continuous distribution of charge. In practice, however, **the technique is useful for calculating the electric field only in situations where the degree of symmetry is high.** As we shall see in the next section, **Gauss's law can be used to evaluate the electric field for charge distributions that have spherical, cylindrical, or plane symmetry.** We do so by choosing an appropriate gaussian surface that allows $\vec{\mathbf{E}}$ to be removed from the integral in Gauss's law and performing the integration. Note that a gaussian surface is a mathematical surface and need not coincide with any real physical surface.

QUICK QUIZ 19.6 For a gaussian surface through which the net flux is zero, the following four statements *could be true*. Which of the statements *must be true*? **(a)** No charges are inside the surface. **(b)** The net charge inside the surface is zero. **(c)** The electric field is zero everywhere on the surface. **(d)** The number of electric field lines entering the surface equals the number leaving the surface.

QUICK QUIZ 19.7 Consider the charge distribution shown in Active Figure 19.31. **(i)** What are the charges contributing to the total electric *flux* through surface *S′*? **(a)** q_1 only **(b)** q_4 only **(c)** q_2 and q_3 **(d)** all four charges **(e)** none of the charges **(ii)** What are the charges contributing to the total electric *field* at a chosen point on the surface *S′*? **(a)** q_1 only **(b)** q_4 only **(c)** q_2 and q_3 **(d)** all four charges **(e)** none of the charges

■ Thinking Physics 19.1

A spherical gaussian surface surrounds a point charge q. Describe what happens to the net flux through the surface if (a) the charge is tripled, (b) the volume of the sphere is doubled, (c) the surface is changed to a cube, and (d) the charge is moved to another location *inside* the surface.

Reasoning (a) If the charge is tripled, the flux through the surface is also tripled because the net flux is proportional to the charge inside the surface. (b) The net flux remains constant when the volume changes because the surface surrounds the same amount of charge, regardless of its volume. (c) The net flux does not change when the shape of the closed surface changes. (d) The net flux through the closed surface remains unchanged as the charge inside the surface is moved to another location as long as the new location remains inside the surface. ■

19.10 APPLICATION OF GAUSS'S LAW TO SYMMETRIC CHARGE DISTRIBUTIONS

As mentioned earlier, Gauss's law is useful in determining electric fields when the charge distribution has a high degree of symmetry. The following examples show ways of choosing the gaussian surface over which the surface integral given by Equation 19.22 can be simplified and the electric field determined. The surface should always be chosen to take advantage of the symmetry of the charge distribution so that we can remove E from the integral and solve for it. The crucial step in applying Gauss's law is to determine a useful gaussian surface. Such a surface should be a closed surface for which each portion of the surface satisfies one or more of the following conditions:

1. The value of the electric field can be argued by symmetry to be constant over the portion of the surface.
2. The dot product in Equation 19.22 can be expressed as a simple algebraic product $E \, dA$ because $\vec{\mathbf{E}}$ and $d\vec{\mathbf{A}}$ are parallel.
3. The dot product in Equation 19.22 is zero because $\vec{\mathbf{E}}$ and $d\vec{\mathbf{A}}$ are perpendicular.
4. The field can be argued to be zero everywhere on the portion of the surface.

Note that different portions of the gaussian surface can satisfy different conditions as long as every portion satisfies at least one condition. We will see all four of these conditions used in the examples through the remainder of this chapter.

EXAMPLE 19.9   **The Electric Field Due to a Point Charge**

Starting with Gauss's law, calculate the electric field due to an isolated point charge q.

Solution A single charge is the simplest possible charge distribution, and we will use this familiar example to show the technique of solving for the electric field with Gauss's law. We choose a spherical gaussian surface of radius r centered on the point charge as in Figure 19.32.

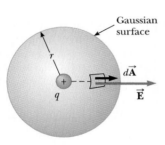

Gaussian surface

r

$d\vec{\mathbf{A}}$

q

$\vec{\mathbf{E}}$

FIGURE 19.32   (Example 19.9) The point charge q is at the center of the spherical gaussian surface, and $\vec{\mathbf{E}}$ is parallel to $d\vec{\mathbf{A}}$ at every point on the surface.

The electric field of a positive point charge is radial outward by symmetry and is therefore normal to the surface at every point. As in condition 2, $\vec{\mathbf{E}}$ is therefore parallel to $d\vec{\mathbf{A}}$ at each point on the surface, so $\vec{\mathbf{E}} \cdot d\vec{\mathbf{A}} = E \, dA$ and Gauss's law gives

$$\Phi_E = \oint \vec{\mathbf{E}} \cdot d\vec{\mathbf{A}} = \oint E \, dA = \frac{q}{\epsilon_0}$$

By symmetry, E is constant everywhere on the surface, which satisfies condition 1, and so it can be removed from the integral. Therefore,

$$\oint E \, dA = E \oint dA = E(4\pi r^2) = \frac{q}{\epsilon_0}$$

where we have used that the surface area of a sphere is $4\pi r^2$. We now solve for the electric field:

$$E = \frac{q}{4\pi\epsilon_0 r^2} = \boxed{k_e \frac{q}{r^2}}$$

which is the familiar electric field of a point charge that we developed from Coulomb's law earlier in this chapter.

INTERACTIVE   EXAMPLE 19.10   **A Spherically Symmetric Charge Distribution**

An insulating solid sphere of radius a has a uniform volume charge density ρ and carries a total positive charge Q (Fig. 19.33).

A Calculate the magnitude of the electric field at a point outside the sphere.

Solution Because the charge distribution is spherically symmetric, we again select a spherical gaussian surface of radius r, concentric with the sphere, as in Figure 19.33a. For this choice, conditions 1 and 2 are satisfied,

as they were for the point charge in Example 19.9. Following the line of reasoning given in Example 19.9, we find that

$$E = \boxed{k_e \frac{Q}{r^2}} \qquad \text{(for } r > a\text{)}$$

Note that this result is identical to that obtained for a point charge. We therefore conclude that, for a uniformly charged sphere, the field in the region external to the sphere is *equivalent* to that of a point charge located at the center of the sphere.

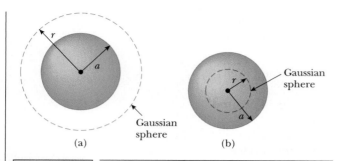

FIGURE 19.33 (Interactive Example 19.10) A uniformly charged insulating sphere of radius a and total charge Q. (a) For points outside the sphere, a large, spherical gaussian surface is drawn concentric with the sphere. In diagrams such as this one, the dotted line represents the intersection of the gaussian surface with the plane of the page. (b) For points inside the sphere, a spherical gaussian surface smaller than the sphere is drawn.

B Find the magnitude of the electric field at a point inside the sphere.

Solution In this case, we select a spherical gaussian surface having radius $r < a$, concentric with the insulating sphere (Fig. 19.33b). Let us denote the volume of this smaller sphere by V'. To apply Gauss's law in this situation, it is important to recognize that the charge q_{in} within the gaussian surface of volume V' is less than Q. To calculate q_{in}, we use that $q_{in} = \rho V'$:

$$q_{in} = \rho V' = \rho(\tfrac{4}{3}\pi r^3)$$

By symmetry, the magnitude of the electric field is constant everywhere on the spherical gaussian surface and the field is normal to the surface at each point, so both conditions 1 and 2 are satisfied. Gauss's law in the region $r < a$ therefore gives

$$\oint E\, dA = E \oint dA = E(4\pi r^2) = \frac{q_{in}}{\epsilon_0}$$

Solving for E gives

$$E = \frac{q_{in}}{4\pi\epsilon_0 r^2} = \frac{\rho(\tfrac{4}{3}\pi r^3)}{4\pi\epsilon_0 r^2} = \frac{\rho}{3\epsilon_0} r$$

Because $\rho = Q/\tfrac{4}{3}\pi a^3$ by definition and $k_e = 1/4\pi\epsilon_0$, this expression for E can be written as

$$E = \frac{Qr}{4\pi\epsilon_0 a^3} = \boxed{\frac{k_e Q}{a^3} r} \qquad \text{(for } r < a\text{)}$$

This result for E differs from that obtained in part A. It shows that $E \to 0$ as $r \to 0$. A plot of E versus r is shown in Figure 19.34. Note that the expressions for parts A and B match when $r = a$.

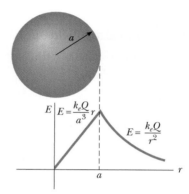

FIGURE 19.34 (Interactive Example 19.10) A plot of E versus r for a uniformly charged insulating sphere. The electric field inside the sphere ($r < a$) varies linearly with r. The electric field outside the sphere ($r > a$) is the same as that of a point charge Q located at $r = 0$.

Physics Now™ By logging into PhysicsNow at **www.pop4e.com** and going to Interactive Example 19.10, you can investigate the electric field inside and outside the sphere.

EXAMPLE 19.11 A Cylindrically Symmetric Charge Distribution

Find the electric field a distance r from a line of positive charge of infinite length and constant charge per unit length ℓ (Fig. 19.35a).

Solution The symmetry of the charge distribution requires that $\vec{E}$ must be perpendicular to the line charge and directed outward as in Figure 19.35. To reflect the symmetry of the charge distribution, we select a cylindrical gaussian surface of radius r and length ℓ that is coaxial with the line charge. For the curved part of this surface, $\vec{E}$ is constant in magnitude and perpendicular to the surface at each point (conditions 1 and 2).

Furthermore, the flux through the ends of the gaussian cylinder is zero because $\vec{E}$ is parallel to these surfaces (and therefore perpendicular to $d\vec{A}$), which is the first application we have seen of condition 3.

The surface integral in Gauss's law is taken over the entire gaussian surface. Because of the zero value of $\vec{E} \cdot d\vec{A}$ for the ends of the cylinder, however, we can restrict our attention to only the curved surface of the cylinder.

The total charge inside our gaussian surface is $q_{in} = \lambda \ell$. Applying Gauss's law and applying conditions 1 and 2, we find, for the curved surface, that

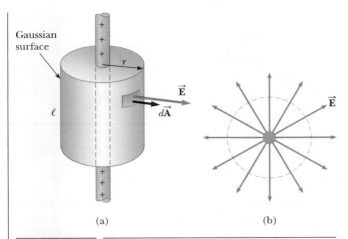

Gaussian surface

(a)   (b)

FIGURE 19.35 (Example 19.11) (a) An infinite line of charge surrounded by a cylindrical gaussian surface concentric with the line charge. (b) An end view shows that the electric field on the cylindrical surface is constant in magnitude and perpendicular to the surface.

$$\Phi_E = \oint \vec{\mathbf{E}} \cdot d\vec{\mathbf{A}} = E \oint dA = EA = \frac{q_{in}}{\epsilon_0} = \frac{\lambda \ell}{\epsilon_0}$$

The area of the curved surface is $A = 2\pi r \ell$. Therefore,

$$E(2\pi r \ell) = \frac{\lambda \ell}{\epsilon_0}$$

$$E = \frac{\lambda}{2\pi \epsilon_0 r} = \boxed{2k_e \frac{\lambda}{r}} \qquad [19.23]$$

Therefore, we see that the electric field of a cylindrically symmetric charge distribution varies as $1/r$, whereas the field external to a spherically symmetric charge distribution varies as $1/r^2$. Equation 19.23 can also be obtained using Equation 19.7; the mathematical techniques necessary for this calculation, however, are more cumbersome.

If the line charge in this example were of finite length, the result for E is not that given by Equation 19.23. A finite line charge does not possess sufficient symmetry to use Gauss's law because the magnitude of the electric field is no longer constant over the surface of the gaussian cylinder; the field near the ends of the line would be different from that far from the ends. Therefore, condition 1 is not satisfied in this situation. Furthermore, $\vec{\mathbf{E}}$ is not perpendicular to the cylindrical surface at all points; the field vectors near the ends would have a component parallel to the line. Condition 2 is not satisfied. When the symmetry in the charge distribution is insufficient, as in this situation, it is necessary to calculate $\vec{\mathbf{E}}$ using Equation 19.7.

For points close to a finite line charge and far from the ends, Equation 19.23 gives a good approximation of the value of the field.

It is left as a problem (Problem 19.39) to show that the electric field inside a uniformly charged rod of finite thickness and infinite length is proportional to r.

EXAMPLE 19.12 A Nonconducting Plane Sheet of Charge

Find the electric field due to a nonconducting, infinite plane with uniform surface charge density σ.

Solution Symmetry tells us that $\vec{\mathbf{E}}$ must be perpendicular to the plane and that the field will have the same magnitude at points on opposite sides of the plane and equidistant from it. That the direction of $\vec{\mathbf{E}}$ is away from positive charges tells us that the direction of $\vec{\mathbf{E}}$ on one side of the plane must be opposite its direction on the other side as in Figure 19.36. A gaussian surface that reflects the symmetry is a small cylinder whose axis is perpendicular to the plane and whose ends each have an area A and are equidistant from the plane. Because $\vec{\mathbf{E}}$ is parallel to the curved surface and therefore perpendicular to $d\vec{\mathbf{A}}$ everywhere on the surface, condition 3 is satisfied and the curved surface makes no contribution to the surface integral. For the flat ends of the cylinder, conditions 1 and 2 are satisfied. The flux through each end of the cylinder is EA; hence, the total flux through the entire gaussian surface is just that through the ends, $\Phi_E = 2EA$.

Noting that the total charge inside the surface is $q_{in} = \sigma A$, we use Gauss's law to obtain

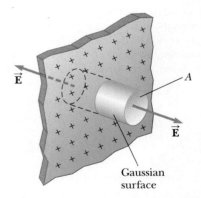

Gaussian surface

FIGURE 19.36 (Example 19.12) A cylindrical gaussian surface penetrating an infinite sheet of charge. The flux is EA through each end of the gaussian surface and zero through its curved surface.

$$\Phi_E = 2EA = \frac{q_{in}}{\epsilon_0} = \frac{\sigma A}{\epsilon_0}$$

$$E = \boxed{\frac{\sigma}{2\epsilon_0}} \qquad [19.24]$$

Because the distance of the flat end of the cylinder from the plane does not appear in Equation 19.24, we conclude that $E = \sigma/2\epsilon_0$ at *any* distance from the plane. That is, the field is uniform everywhere.

An important charge configuration related to this example is two parallel planes each with a surface charge density σ, with one plane positively charged and the other negatively charged (Problem 19.62). In this situation, the electric fields from the two planes add in the region between the planes, resulting in a field with a magnitude of σ/ϵ_0, and cancel to give a field of zero elsewhere.

19.11 CONDUCTORS IN ELECTROSTATIC EQUILIBRIUM

A good electrical conductor, such as copper, contains charges (electrons) that are not bound to any atom and are free to move about within the material. When no motion of charge occurs within the conductor, the conductor is in **electrostatic equilibrium.** In this situation, *every* charge in the conductor is a particle in equilibrium, experiencing zero net force. As we shall see, an isolated conductor (one that is insulated from ground) in electrostatic equilibrium has the following properties:

1. The electric field is zero everywhere inside the conductor.
2. If the isolated conductor carries a net charge, the net charge resides entirely on its surface.
3. The electric field just outside the charged conductor is perpendicular to the conductor surface and has a magnitude σ/ϵ_0, where σ is the surface charge density at that point.
4. On an irregularly shaped conductor, the surface charge density is highest at locations where the radius of curvature of the surface is smallest.

We will verify the first three properties in the following discussion. The fourth property is presented here so that we have a complete list of properties for conductors in electrostatic equilibrium. The verification of it, however, requires concepts from Chapter 20, so we will postpone its verification until then.

The first property can be understood by considering a conducting slab placed in an external field $\vec{E}$ (Fig. 19.37). The electric field inside the conductor *must* be zero under the assumption that we have electrostatic equilibrium. If the field were not zero, free charges in the conductor would accelerate under the action of the electric force. This motion of electrons, however, would mean that the conductor is not in electrostatic equilibrium. Therefore, the existence of electrostatic equilibrium is consistent only with a zero field in the conductor.

Let us investigate how this zero field is accomplished. Before the external field is applied, free electrons are uniformly distributed throughout the conductor. When the external field is applied, the free electrons accelerate to the left in Figure 19.37, causing a plane of negative charge to be present on the left surface. The movement of electrons to the left results in a plane of positive charge on the right surface. These planes of charge create an additional electric field inside the conductor that opposes the external field. As the electrons move, the surface charge density increases until the magnitude of the internal field equals that of the external field, giving a net field of zero inside the conductor.

We can use Gauss's law to verify the second property of a conductor in electrostatic equilibrium. Figure 19.38 shows an arbitrarily shaped conductor. A gaussian surface is drawn just inside the conductor and can be as close to the surface as we wish. As we have just shown, the electric field everywhere inside a conductor in electrostatic equilibrium is zero. Therefore, the electric field must be zero at every point on the gaussian surface (condition 4 in Section 19.10). From this result and Gauss's law, we conclude that the net charge inside the gaussian surface is zero. Because there can be no net charge inside the gaussian surface (which is arbitrarily close to the conductor's surface), any net charge on the conductor must reside on

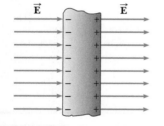

FIGURE 19.37 A conducting slab in an external electric field $\vec{E}$. The charges induced on the surfaces of the slab produce an electric field that opposes the external field, giving a resultant field of zero *inside* the conductor.

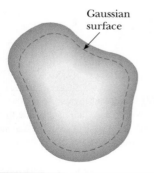

Gaussian surface

FIGURE 19.38 An isolated conductor of arbitrary shape. The broken line represents a gaussian surface just inside the physical surface of the conductor.

its surface. Gauss's law does not tell us how this excess charge is distributed on the surface, only that it must reside on the surface.

Conceptually, we can understand the location of the charges on the surface by imagining placing many charges at the center of the conductor. The mutual repulsion of the charges causes them to move apart. They will move as far as they can, which is to various points on the surface.

To verify the third property, we can also use Gauss's law. We draw a gaussian surface in the shape of a small cylinder having its end faces parallel to the surface (Fig. 19.39). Part of the cylinder is just outside the conductor and part is inside. The field is normal to the surface because the conductor is in electrostatic equilibrium. If $\vec{E}$ had a component parallel to the surface, an electric force would be exerted on the charges parallel to the surface, free charges would move along the surface, and so the conductor would not be in equilibrium. Therefore, we satisfy condition 3 in Section 19.10 for the curved part of the cylinder in that no flux exists through this part of the gaussian surface because $\vec{E}$ is parallel to this part of the surface. No flux exists through the flat face of the cylinder inside the conductor because $\vec{E} = 0$ (condition 4). Hence, the net flux through the gaussian surface is the flux through the flat face outside the conductor where the field is perpendicular to the surface. Using conditions 1 and 2 for this face, the flux is EA, where E is the electric field just outside the conductor and A is the area of the cylinder's face. Applying Gauss's law to this surface gives

$$\Phi_E = \oint E\, dA = EA = \frac{q_{in}}{\epsilon_0} = \frac{\sigma A}{\epsilon_0}$$

where we have used that $q_{in} = \sigma A$. Solving for E gives

$$E = \frac{\sigma}{\epsilon_0} \qquad\qquad [19.25]$$

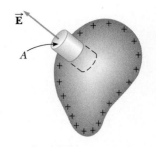

FIGURE 19.39 A gaussian surface in the shape of a small cylinder is used to calculate the electric field just outside a charged conductor. The flux through the gaussian surface is EA.

∎ Thinking Physics 19.2

Suppose a point charge $+Q$ is in empty space. We surround the charge with a spherical, uncharged conducting shell so that the charge is at the center of the shell. What effect does that have on the field lines from the charge?

Reasoning When the spherical shell is placed around the charge, the free charges in the shell adjust so as to satisfy the rules for a conductor in equilibrium and Gauss's law. A net charge of $-Q$ moves to the interior surface of the conductor, so the electric field within the conductor is zero (a spherical gaussian surface totally within the shell encloses no *net* charge). A net charge of $+Q$ resides on the outer surface, so a gaussian surface outside the sphere encloses a net charge of $+Q$, just as if the shell were not there. Therefore, the only change in the field lines from the initial situation is the absence of field lines over the thickness of the conducting shell. ∎

19.12 THE ATMOSPHERIC ELECTRIC FIELD

CONTEXT CONNECTION

In this chapter, we discussed the electric field due to various charge distributions. On the surface of the Earth and in the atmosphere, a number of processes create charge distributions, resulting in an electric field in the atmosphere. These processes include cosmic rays entering the atmosphere, radioactive decay at the Earth's surface, and lightning, the focus of our study in this Context.

The result of these processes is an average negative charge distributed over the surface of the Earth of about 5×10^5 C, which is a tremendous amount of charge. (The Earth is neutral overall; the positive charges corresponding to this negative surface charge are spread through the atmosphere, as we shall discuss in

Chapter 20.) We can calculate the average surface charge density over the surface of the Earth:

$$\sigma_{avg} = \frac{Q}{A} = \frac{Q}{4\pi r^2} = \frac{5 \times 10^5 \, \text{C}}{4\pi(6.37 \times 10^6 \, \text{m})^2} \sim 10^{-9} \, \text{C/m}^2$$

Throughout this Context, we will be adopting a number of simplification models. Consequently, we will consider our calculations to be order-of-magnitude estimates of the actual values, as suggested by the $\sim$ sign above.

The Earth is a good conductor. Therefore, we can use the third property of conductors in Section 19.11 to find the average magnitude of the electric field at the surface of the Earth:

$$E_{avg} = \frac{\sigma_{avg}}{\epsilon_0} = \frac{10^{-9} \, \text{C/m}^2}{8.85 \times 10^{-12} \, \text{C}^2/\text{N} \cdot \text{m}^2} \sim 10^2 \, \text{N/C}$$

which is a typical value of the **fair-weather electric field** that exists in the absence of a thunderstorm. The direction of the field is downward because the charge on the Earth's surface is negative. During a thunderstorm, the electric field under the thundercloud is significantly higher than the fair-weather electric field, because of the charge distribution in the thundercloud.

Figure 19.40 shows a typical charge distribution in a thundercloud. The charge distribution can be modeled as a *tripole,* although the positive charge at the bottom of the cloud tends to be smaller than the other two charges. The mechanism of charging in thunderclouds is not well understood and continues to be an active area of research.

It is this high concentration of charge in the thundercloud that is responsible for the very strong electric fields that cause lightning discharge between the cloud and the ground. Typical electric fields during a thunderstorm are as high as 25 000 N/C. The distribution of negative charges in the center of the cloud in Figure 19.40 is the source of negative charge that moves downward in a lightning strike.

Atmospheric electric fields can be measured with an instrument called a **field mill.** Figure 19.41 shows the operation of the field mill. In Figure 19.41a, a metallic

FIGURE 19.40 A typical tripolar charge distribution in a thundercloud. The amounts of positive charge at the top and negative charge in the middle are approximately the same, but the amount of positive charge at the bottom is less. The dots indicate the average position of each charge distribution.

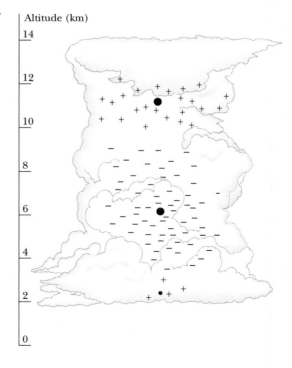

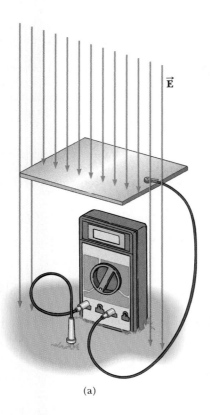

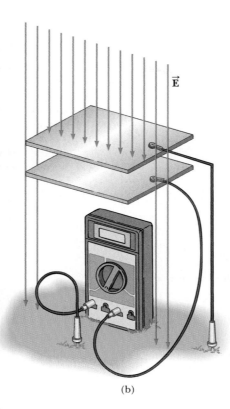

FIGURE 19.41 A field mill for measuring the atmospheric electric field. When the upper plate is moved over the lower plate, charges move through the meter.

(a)   (b)

plate is connected to the ground by a wire. A meter measures the flow of charge through the wire. Because the ground is negatively charged, electrons will flow from the ground into the metal plate. These electrons represent the ends of some of the electric field lines in the atmosphere.

Now, as shown in Figure 19.41b, this plate is covered with a second plate also attached to the ground. The electric field lines that previously ended on the lower plate now end on the upper plate. The charges on the lower plate are repelled by those in the upper plate and pass through the meter into the ground. The meter measures the amount of charge flowing through the wire. This charge is related to how much charge is on the lower plate, which, in turn, is related to the magnitude of the electric field. Therefore, the meter can be calibrated to measure the atmospheric electric field. In operation, the plates are similar to the blades of a fan. As one set of blades rotates over a second stationary set, charge pulses back and forth through the meter.

In this chapter, we have analyzed the atmosphere in terms of the electric field. In Chapter 20, we shall learn about electric potential and analyze the atmosphere again in terms of this new parameter. ■

SUMMARY

Physics⊗Now™ Take a practice test by logging into Physics-Now at **www.pop4e.com** and clicking on the Pre-Test link for this chapter.

Electric charges have the following important properties:

1. Two kinds of charges exist in nature, **positive** and **negative,** with the property that charges of opposite sign attract each other and charges of the same sign repel each other.

2. The force between charged particles varies as the inverse square of their separation distance.
3. Charge is conserved.
4. Charge is quantized.

Conductors are materials in which charges move relatively freely. **Insulators** are materials in which charges do not move freely.

Coulomb's law states that the electrostatic force between two stationary, charged particles separated by a distance r has the magnitude

$$F_e = k_e \frac{|q_1||q_2|}{r^2} \qquad [19.1]$$

where the Coulomb constant $k_e = 8.99 \times 10^9 \ \text{N} \cdot \text{m}^2/\text{C}^2$. The vector form of Coulomb's law is

$$\vec{\mathbf{F}}_{12} = k_e \frac{q_1 q_2}{r^2} \hat{\mathbf{r}}_{12} \qquad [19.2]$$

An **electric field** exists at a point in space if a positive test charge q_0 placed at that point experiences an electric force. The electric field is defined as

$$\vec{\mathbf{E}} \equiv \frac{\vec{\mathbf{F}}_e}{q_0} \qquad [19.3]$$

The force on a particle with charge q placed in an electric field $\vec{\mathbf{E}}$ is

$$\vec{\mathbf{F}}_e = q\vec{\mathbf{E}} \qquad [19.4]$$

The electric field due to the point charge q at a distance r from the charge is

$$\vec{\mathbf{E}} = k_e \frac{q}{r^2} \hat{\mathbf{r}} \qquad [19.5]$$

where $\hat{\mathbf{r}}$ is a unit vector directed from the charge toward the point in question. The electric field is directed radially outward from a positive charge and is directed toward a negative charge.

The electric field due to a group of charges can be obtained using the superposition principle. That is, the total electric field equals the vector sum of the electric fields of all the charges at some point:

$$\vec{\mathbf{E}} = k_e \sum_i \frac{q_i}{r_i^2} \hat{\mathbf{r}}_i \qquad [19.6]$$

Similarly, the electric field of a continuous charge distribution at some point is

$$\vec{\mathbf{E}} = k_e \int \frac{dq}{r^2} \hat{\mathbf{r}} \qquad [19.7]$$

where dq is the charge on one element of the charge distribution and r is the distance from the element to the point in question.

Electric field lines are useful for describing the electric field in any region of space. The electric field vector $\vec{\mathbf{E}}$ is always tangent to the electric field lines at every point. Furthermore, the number of lines per unit area through a surface perpendicular to the lines is proportional to the magnitude of $\vec{\mathbf{E}}$ in that region.

Electric flux is proportional to the number of electric field lines that penetrate a surface. If the electric field is uniform and makes an angle of θ with the normal to the surface, the electric flux through the surface is

$$\Phi_E = EA \cos \theta \qquad [19.18]$$

In general, the electric flux through a surface is defined by the expression

$$\Phi_E \equiv \int_{\text{surface}} \vec{\mathbf{E}} \cdot d\vec{\mathbf{A}} \qquad [19.19]$$

Gauss's law says that the net electric flux Φ_E through any closed gaussian surface is equal to the *net* charge *inside* the surface divided by ϵ_0:

$$\Phi_E = \oint \vec{\mathbf{E}} \cdot d\vec{\mathbf{A}} = \frac{q_{\text{in}}}{\epsilon_0} \qquad [19.22]$$

Using Gauss's law, one can calculate the electric field due to various symmetric charge distributions.

A conductor in **electrostatic equilibrium** has the following properties:

1. The electric field is zero everywhere inside the conductor.
2. If the isolated conductor carries a net charge, the net charge resides entirely on its surface.
3. The electric field just outside the charged conductor is perpendicular to the conductor surface and has a magnitude σ/ϵ_0, where σ is the surface charge density at that point.
4. On an irregularly shaped conductor, the surface charge density is highest at locations where the radius of curvature of the surface is smallest.

QUESTIONS

☐ = answer available in the *Student Solutions Manual and Study Guide*

1. Explain what is meant by the term "a neutral atom." Explain what "a negatively charged atom" means.

2. Sparks are often seen or heard on a dry day when fabrics are removed from a clothes dryer in dim light. Explain.

3. 🦓 Hospital personnel must wear special conducting shoes while working around oxygen in an operating room. Why? Contrast with what might happen if people wore rubber-soled shoes.

4. Explain the similarities and differences between Newton's law of universal gravitation and Coulomb's law.

5. A balloon is negatively charged by rubbing and then clings to a wall. Does that mean that the wall is positively charged? Why does the balloon eventually fall?

6. Is it possible for an electric field to exist in empty space? Explain. Consider point A in Figure 19.18a. Does charge exist at this point? Does a force exist at this point? Does a field exist at this point?

7. When is it valid to approximate a charge distribution by a point charge?

8. Figure 19.11 shows three electric field vectors at the same point. With a little extrapolation, Figure 19.16a would show many electric field lines at the same point. Is it really

true that "no two field lines can cross"? Are the diagrams drawn correctly? Explain your answers.

9. Would life be different if the electron were positively charged and the proton were negatively charged? Does the choice of signs have any bearing on physical and chemical interactions? Explain.

10. Consider two equal point charges separated by some distance d. At what point (other than ∞) would a third test charge experience no net force?

11. Consider two electric dipoles in empty space. Each dipole has zero net charge. Does an electric force exist between the dipoles? That is, can two objects with zero net charge exert electric forces on each other? If so, is the force one of attraction or of repulsion?

12. A particle with negative charge $-q$ is placed at the point P near the positively charged ring shown in Figure 19.14 (Example 19.5). Assuming that x is much less than a, describe the motion of the point charge after it is released from rest.

13. If more electric field lines leave a gaussian surface than enter it, what can you conclude about the net charge enclosed by that surface?

14. A uniform electric field exists in a region of space in which there are no charges. What can you conclude about the net electric flux through a gaussian surface placed in this region of space?

15. If the total charge inside a closed surface is known but the distribution of the charge is unspecified, can you use Gauss's law to find the electric field? Explain.

16. On the basis of the repulsive nature of the force between like charges and the freedom of motion of charge within a conductor, explain why excess charge on an isolated conductor must reside on its surface.

17. A person is placed in a large, hollow, metallic sphere that is insulated from ground. If a large charge is placed on the sphere, will the person be harmed upon touching the inside of the sphere? Explain what will happen if the person also has an initial charge whose sign is opposite that of the charge on the sphere.

18. Two solid spheres, both of radius R, carry identical total charges Q. One sphere is a good conductor, whereas the other is an insulator. If the charge on the insulating sphere is uniformly distributed throughout its interior volume, how do the electric fields outside these two spheres compare? Are the fields identical inside the two spheres?

19. A common demonstration involves charging a rubber balloon, which is an insulator, by rubbing it on your hair and then touching the balloon to a ceiling or wall, which is also an insulator. The electrical attraction between the charged balloon and the neutral wall results in the balloon sticking to the wall. Imagine now that we have two infinitely large, flat sheets of insulating material. One is charged and the other is neutral. If these sheets are brought into contact, will an attractive force exist between them, as there was for the balloon and the wall?

PROBLEMS

1, 2, 3 = straightforward, intermediate, challenging
☐ = full solution available in the *Student Solutions Manual and Study Guide*

Physics⊗Now™ = coached problem with hints available at www.pop4e.com

🖥 = computer useful in solving problem
▨ = paired numerical and symbolic problems
🐌 = biomedical application

Section 19.2 ∎ Properties of Electric Charges

1. (a) Find to three significant digits the charge and the mass of an ionized hydrogen atom, represented as H^+. (*Suggestion:* Begin by looking up the mass of a neutral atom on the periodic table of the elements in Appendix C.) (b) Find the charge and the mass of Na^+, a singly ionized sodium atom. (c) Find the charge and the average mass of a chloride ion Cl^- that joins with the Na^+ to make one molecule of table salt. (d) Find the charge and the mass of $Ca^{++} = Ca^{2+}$, a doubly ionized calcium atom. (e) You can model the center of an ammonia molecule as an N^{3-} ion. Find its charge and mass. (f) The plasma in a hot star contains quadruply ionized nitrogen atoms, N^{4+}. Find

their charge and mass. (g) Find the charge and the mass of the nucleus of a nitrogen atom. (h) Find the charge and the mass of the molecular ion H_2O^-.

2. (a) Calculate the number of electrons in a small, electrically neutral silver pin that has a mass of 10.0 g. Silver has 47 electrons per atom, and its molar mass is 107.87 g/mol. (b) Electrons are added to the pin until the net negative charge is 1.00 mC. How many electrons are added for every 10^9 electrons already present?

Section 19.4 ∎ Coulomb's Law

3. Nobel laureate Richard Feynman once said that if two persons stood at arm's length from each other and each person had 1% more electrons than protons, the force of repulsion between them would be enough to lift a "weight" equal to that of the entire Earth. Carry out an order-of-magnitude calculation to substantiate this assertion.

4. Two protons in an atomic nucleus are typically separated by a distance of 2×10^{-15} m. The electric repulsion force between the protons is huge, but the attractive nuclear force is even stronger and keeps the nucleus from bursting apart. What is the magnitude of the electric force between two protons separated by 2.00×10^{-15} m?

5. Three point charges are located at the corners of an equilateral triangle as shown in Figure P19.5. Calculate the resultant electric force on the 7.00-μC charge.

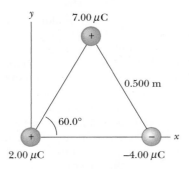

FIGURE **P19.5**

6. A charged particle A exerts a force of 2.62 μN to the right on charged particle B when the particles are 13.7 mm apart. Particle B moves straight away from A to make the distance between them 17.7 mm. What vector force does it then exert on A?

7. Two identical conducting small spheres are placed with their centers 0.300 m apart. One is given a charge of 12.0 nC and the other a charge of -18.0 nC. (a) Find the electric force exerted by one sphere on the other. (b) Next, the spheres are connected by a conducting wire. Find the electric force between the two after they have come to equilibrium.

8. Two small beads having positive charges $3q$ and q are fixed at the opposite ends of a horizontal, insulating rod, extending from the origin to the point $x = d$. As shown in Figure P19.8, a third small, charged bead is free to slide on the rod. At what position is the third bead in equilibrium? Can it be in stable equilibrium?

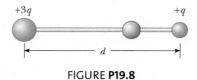

FIGURE **P19.8**

9. **Review problem.** In the Bohr theory of the hydrogen atom, an electron moves in a circular orbit about a proton, where the radius of the orbit is 0.529×10^{-10} m. (a) Find the magnitude of the electric force each exerts on the other. (b) If this force causes the centripetal acceleration of the electron, what is the speed of the electron?

Section 19.5 ▪ Electric Fields

10. What are the magnitude and direction of the electric field that will balance the weight of (a) an electron and (b) a proton? (You may use the data in Table 19.1.)

11. In Figure P19.11, determine the point (other than infinity) at which the electric field is zero.

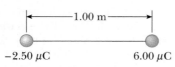

FIGURE **P19.11**

12. Two point charges are located on the x axis. The first is a charge $+Q$ at $x = -a$. The second is an unknown charge located at $x = +3a$. The net electric field these charges produce at the origin has a magnitude of $2k_eQ/a^2$. What are the two possible values of the unknown charge?

13. Three point charges are arranged as shown in Figure P19.13. (a) Find the vector electric field that the 6.00-nC and -3.00-nC charges together create at the origin. (b) Find the vector force on the 5.00-nC charge.

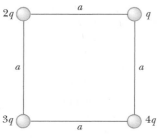

FIGURE **P19.13**

14. Two 2.00-μC point charges are located on the x axis. One is at $x = 1.00$ m, and the other is at $x = -1.00$ m. (a) Determine the electric field on the y axis at $y = 0.500$ m. (b) Calculate the electric force on a -3.00-μC charge placed on the y axis at $y = 0.500$ m.

15. Four point charges are at the corners of a square of side a as shown in Figure P19.15. (a) Determine the magnitude and direction of the electric field at the location of charge q. (b) What is the resultant force on q?

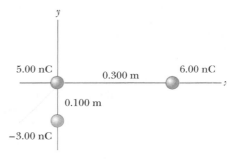

FIGURE **P19.15**

16. Consider the electric dipole shown in Figure P19.16. Show that the electric field at a *distant* point on the $+x$ axis is $E_x \approx 4k_eqa/x^3$.

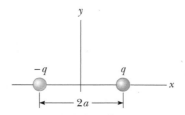

FIGURE **P19.16**

17. A rod 14.0 cm long is uniformly charged and has a total charge of -22.0 μC. Determine the magnitude and

direction of the electric field along the axis of the rod at a point 36.0 cm from its center.

18. A continuous line of charge lies along the x axis, extending from $x = +x_0$ to positive infinity. The line carries charge with a uniform linear charge density λ_0. What are the magnitude and direction of the electric field at the origin?

19. A uniformly charged ring of radius 10.0 cm has a total charge of 75.0 μC. Find the electric field on the axis of the ring at (a) 1.00 cm, (b) 5.00 cm, (c) 30.0 cm, and (d) 100 cm from the center of the ring.

20. Show that the maximum magnitude E_{max} of the electric field along the axis of a uniformly charged ring occurs at $x = a/\sqrt{2}$ (see Fig. 19.14) and has the value $Q/(6\sqrt{3}\pi\epsilon_0 a^2)$.

21. **Physics⊗Now™** A uniformly charged insulating rod of length 14.0 cm is bent into the shape of a semicircle as shown in Figure P19.21. The rod has a total charge of -7.50 μC. Find the magnitude and direction of the electric field at O, the center of the semicircle.

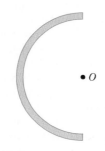

FIGURE **P19.21**   Problems 19.21 and 20.27.

22. A thin rod of length ℓ and uniform charge per unit length λ lies along the x axis as shown in Figure P19.22. (a) Show that the electric field at P, a distance y from the rod along its perpendicular bisector, has no x component and is given by $E = 2k_e\lambda \sin\theta_0/y$. (b) Using your result to part (a), show that the field of a rod of infinite length is $E = 2k_e\lambda/y$. (*Suggestion:* First, calculate the field at P due to an element of length dx, which has a charge $\lambda\,dx$. Then, change variables from x to θ, using the relationships $x = y\tan\theta$ and $dx = y\sec^2\theta\,d\theta$, and integrate over θ.)

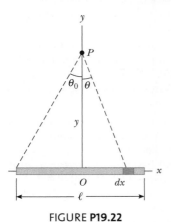

FIGURE **P19.22**

23. Three solid plastic cylinders all have radius 2.50 cm and length 6.00 cm. One (a) carries charge with uniform density 15.0 nC/m^2 everywhere on its surface. Another

(b) carries charge with the same uniform density on its curved lateral surface only. The third (c) carries charge with uniform density 500 nC/m^3 throughout the plastic. Find the charge of each cylinder.

Section 19.6 ■ Electric Field Lines

24. Figure P19.24 shows the electric field lines for two point charges separated by a small distance. (a) Determine the ratio q_1/q_2. (b) What are the signs of q_1 and q_2?

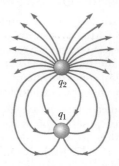

FIGURE **P19.24**

25. A negatively charged rod of finite length carries charge with a uniform charge per unit length. Sketch the electric field lines in a plane containing the rod.

26. Three equal positive charges q are at the corners of an equilateral triangle of side a as shown in Figure P19.26. (a) Assume that the three charges together create an electric field. Sketch the field lines in the plane of the charges. Find the location of a point (other than ∞) where the electric field is zero. (b) What are the magnitude and direction of the electric field at P due to the two charges at the base?

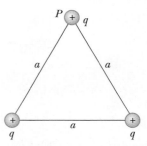

FIGURE **P19.26**   Problems 19.26 and 20.17.

Section 19.7 ■ Motion of Charged Particles in a Uniform Electric Field

27. A proton accelerates from rest in a uniform electric field of 640 N/C. At some later instant, its speed is 1.20×10^6 m/s (nonrelativistic, because v is much less than the speed of light). (a) Find the acceleration of the proton. (b) After what time interval does the proton reach this speed? (c) How far does the proton move in this time interval? (d) What is its kinetic energy at the end of this time interval?

28. The electrons in a particle beam each have a kinetic energy K. What are the magnitude and direction of the electric field that will stop these electrons in a distance d?

29. A proton moves at 4.50×10^5 m/s in the horizontal direction. It enters a uniform vertical electric field with a magnitude of 9.60×10^3 N/C. Ignoring any gravitational effects, find (a) the time interval required for the proton to travel 5.00 cm horizontally, (b) its vertical displacement during the time interval in which it travels 5.00 cm horizontally, and (c) the horizontal and vertical components of its velocity after it has traveled 5.00 cm horizontally.

Section 19.8 ▪ Electric Flux

30. A vertical electric field of magnitude 2.00×10^4 N/C exists above the Earth's surface on a day when a thunderstorm is brewing. A car covers a rectangle measuring 6.00 m by 3.00 m on the roadway below it, which is built on dry fill. The roadway slopes downward at $10.0°$. Determine the electric flux through the bottom of the car.

31. A 40.0-cm-diameter loop is rotated in a uniform electric field until the position of maximum electric flux is found. The flux in this position is measured to be 5.20×10^5 N·m²/C. What is the magnitude of the electric field?

Section 19.9 ▪ Gauss's Law

32. The electric field everywhere on the surface of a thin spherical shell of radius 0.750 m is measured to be 890 N/C and points radially toward the center of the sphere. (a) What is the net charge within the sphere's surface? (b) What can you conclude about the nature and distribution of the charge inside the spherical shell?

33. Physics⊗Now™ A point charge Q is located just above the center of the flat face of a hemisphere of radius R as shown in Figure P19.33. What is the electric flux (a) through the curved surface and (b) through the flat face?

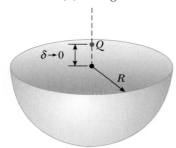

FIGURE **P19.33**

34. A charge of 170 μC is at the center of a cube of edge 80.0 cm. (a) Find the total flux through each face of the cube. (b) Find the flux through the whole surface of the cube. (c) Would your answers to parts (a) or (b) change if the charge were not at the center? Explain.

Section 19.10 ▪ Application of Gauss's Law to Symmetric Charge Distributions

35. A solid sphere of radius 40.0 cm has a total positive charge of 26.0 μC uniformly distributed throughout its volume. Calculate the magnitude of the electric field (a) 0 cm, (b) 10.0 cm, (c) 40.0 cm, and (d) 60.0 cm from the center of the sphere.

36. A 10.0-g piece of Styrofoam carries a net charge of -0.700 μC and floats above the center of a large horizontal sheet of plastic that has a uniform charge density on its surface. What is the charge per unit area on the plastic sheet?

37. A cylindrical shell of radius 7.00 cm and length 240 cm has its charge uniformly distributed on its curved surface. The magnitude of the electric field at a point 19.0 cm radially outward from its axis (measured from the midpoint of the shell) is 36.0 kN/C. Find (a) the net charge on the shell and (b) the electric field at a point 4.00 cm from the axis, measured radially outward from the midpoint of the shell.

38. Consider a thin spherical shell of radius 14.0 cm with a total charge of 32.0 μC distributed uniformly on its surface. Find the electric field (a) 10.0 cm and (b) 20.0 cm from the center of the charge distribution.

39. Physics⊗Now™ Consider a long cylindrical charge distribution of radius R with a uniform charge density ρ. Find the electric field at distance r from the axis where $r < R$.

40. An insulating solid sphere of radius a has a uniform volume charge density and carries a total positive charge Q. A spherical gaussian surface of radius r, which shares a common center with the insulating sphere, is inflated starting from $r = 0$. (a) Find an expression for the electric flux passing through the surface of the gaussian sphere as a function of r for $r < a$. (b) Find an expression for the electric flux for $r > a$. (c) Plot the flux versus r.

41. In nuclear fission, a nucleus of uranium-238, which contains 92 protons, can divide into two smaller spheres, each having 46 protons and a radius of 5.90×10^{-15} m. What is the magnitude of the repulsive electric force pushing the two spheres apart?

Section 19.11 ▪ Conductors in Electrostatic Equilibrium

42. A long, straight metal rod has a radius of 5.00 cm and a charge per unit length of 30.0 nC/m. Find the electric field (a) 3.00 cm, (b) 10.0 cm, and (c) 100 cm from the axis of the rod, where distances are measured perpendicular to the rod.

43. A very large, thin, flat plate of aluminum of area A has a total charge Q uniformly distributed over its surfaces. Assuming that the same charge is spread uniformly over the *upper* surface of an otherwise identical glass plate, compare the electric fields just above the center of the upper surface of each plate.

44. A square plate of copper with 50.0-cm sides has no net charge and is placed in a region of uniform electric field of 80.0 kN/C directed perpendicularly to the plate. Find (a) the charge density of each face of the plate and (b) the total charge on each face.

45. A solid conducting sphere of radius 2.00 cm has a charge 8.00 μC. A conducting spherical shell of inner radius 4.00 cm and outer radius 5.00 cm is concentric with the solid sphere and has a total charge -4.00 μC. Find the electric field at (a) $r = 1.00$ cm, (b) $r = 3.00$ cm, (c) $r = 4.50$ cm, and (d) $r = 7.00$ cm from the center of this charge configuration.

46. The electric field on the surface of an irregularly shaped conductor varies from 56.0 kN/C to 28.0 kN/C. Calculate the local surface charge density at the point on the surface where the radius of curvature of the surface is (a) greatest and (b) smallest.

47. A long, straight wire is surrounded by a hollow metal cylinder whose axis coincides with that of the wire. The wire has a charge per unit length of λ, and the cylinder has a net charge per unit length of 2λ. From this information, use Gauss's law to find (a) the charge per unit length on the inner and outer surfaces of the cylinder and (b) the electric field outside the cylinder, a distance r from the axis.

48. Consider an electric field that is uniform in direction throughout a certain volume. Can it be uniform in magnitude? Must it be uniform in magnitude? Answer these questions (a) assuming that the volume is filled with an insulating material carrying charge described by a volume charge density and (b) assuming the volume is empty space. State reasoning to prove your answers.

49. **Physics⊗Now™** A thin, square conducting plate 50.0 cm on a side lies in the xy plane. A total charge of 4.00×10^{-8} C is placed on the plate. Find (a) the charge density on the plate, (b) the electric field just above the plate, and (c) the electric field just below the plate. You may assume that the charge density is uniform.

Section 19.12 ■ Context Connection—The Atmospheric Electric Field

50. In fair weather, the electric field in the air at a particular location just above the Earth's surface is 120 N/C directed downward. (a) What is the surface charge density on the ground surface? Is it positive or negative? (b) If the weather were fair everywhere and the surface charge density were uniform, what would be the charge of the whole surface of the Earth? How many excess electrons (or protons) would be on the entire surface of the Earth to produce an atmospheric field of 120 N/C down?

51. In the air over a particular region, at an altitude of 500 m above the ground, the electric field is 120 N/C directed downward. At 600 m above the ground, the electric field is 100 N/C downward. What is the average volume charge density in the layer of air between these two elevations? Is it positive or negative?

52. The electric field in the Earth's atmosphere suggests that the solid and liquid surface of the Earth has a charge of about -5×10^5 C. Imagine that the planet as a whole had a charge of -5.00×10^5 C and that the Moon, with 27.3% of the radius of the Earth, had a charge of -1.37×10^5 C. (a) Find the electric force that the Earth would then exert on the Moon. (b) Compare the answer to part (a) with the gravitational force that the Earth exerts on the Moon. As your calculation suggests, for the purpose of accounting for astronomical motions, we may treat the actual forces as purely gravitational. We may say that astronomical objects have negligible total charges.

Additional Problems

53. Two known charges, $-12.0\ \mu\text{C}$ and $45.0\ \mu\text{C}$, and an unknown charge are located on the x axis. The charge $-12.0\ \mu\text{C}$ is at the origin, and the charge $45.0\ \mu\text{C}$ is at $x = 15.0$ cm. The unknown charge is to be placed so that each charge is in equilibrium under the action of the electric forces exerted by the other two charges. Is this situation possible? Is it possible in more than one way? Find the required location, magnitude, and sign of the unknown charge.

54. A small, 2.00-g plastic ball is suspended by a 20.0-cm-long string in a uniform electric field as shown in Figure P19.54. If the ball is in equilibrium when the string makes a 15.0° angle with the vertical, what is the net charge on the ball?

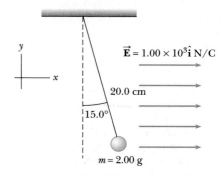

FIGURE **P19.54**

55. Four identical point charges ($q = +10.0\ \mu\text{C}$) are located on the corners of a rectangle as shown in Figure P19.55. The dimensions of the rectangle are $L = 60.0$ cm and $W = 15.0$ cm. Calculate the magnitude and direction of the resultant electric force exerted on the charge at the lower left corner by the other three charges.

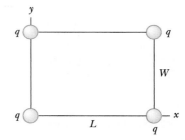

FIGURE **P19.55** Problems 19.55 and 20.10.

56. Inez is putting up decorations for her sister's quinceañera (fifteenth birthday party). She ties three light silk ribbons together to the top of a gateway and hangs a rubber balloon from each ribbon (Fig. P19.56). To include the effects of

FIGURE **P19.56**

the gravitational and buoyant forces on it, each balloon can be modeled as a particle of mass 2.00 g, with its center 50.0 cm from the point of support. Inez wishes to show off the colors of the balloons. She rubs the whole surface of each balloon with her woolen scarf to make them hang separately with gaps between them. The centers of the hanging balloons form a horizontal equilateral triangle with sides 30.0 cm long. What is the common charge each balloon carries?

57. Two identical metallic blocks resting on a frictionless horizontal surface are connected by a light metallic spring having the spring constant 100 N/m and an unstretched length of 0.300 m as shown in Figure P19.57a. A total charge of Q is slowly placed on the system, causing the spring to stretch to an equilibrium length of 0.400 m as shown in Figure P19.57b. Determine the value of Q, assuming that all the charge resides on the blocks and modeling the blocks as point charges.

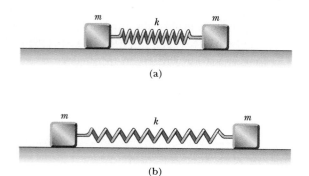

(a)

(b)

FIGURE **P19.57** Problems 19.57 and 19.58.

58. Two identical metallic blocks resting on a frictionless horizontal surface are connected by a light metallic spring having a spring constant k and an unstretched length L_i as shown in Figure P19.57a. A total charge Q is slowly placed on the system, causing the spring to stretch to an equilibrium length L as shown in Figure P19.57b. Determine the value of Q, assuming that all the charge resides on the blocks and modeling the blocks as point charges.

59. Two small spheres of mass m are suspended from strings of length ℓ that are connected at a common point. One sphere has charge Q, and the other has charge $2Q$. The strings make angles θ_1 and θ_2 with the vertical. (a) How are θ_1 and θ_2 related? (b) Assume that θ_1 and θ_2 are small. Show that the distance r between the spheres is given by

$$r \approx \left(\frac{4k_e Q^2 \ell}{mg}\right)^{1/3}$$

60. ▢ Three charges of equal magnitude q are fixed in position at the vertices of an equilateral triangle (Fig. P19.60). A fourth charge Q is free to move along the positive x axis under the influence of the forces exerted by the three fixed charges. Find a value for s for which Q is in equilibrium. You will need to solve a transcendental equation.

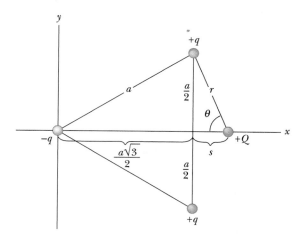

FIGURE **P19.60**

61. Consider the charge distribution shown in Figure P19.61. (a) Show that the magnitude of the electric field at the center of any face of the cube has a value of $2.18 k_e q/s^2$. (b) What is the direction of the electric field at the center of the top face of the cube?

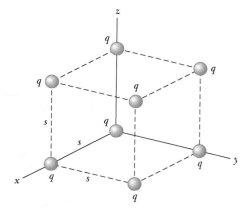

FIGURE **P19.61**

62. Two infinite, nonconducting sheets of charge are parallel to each other as shown in Figure P19.62. The sheet on the left has a uniform surface charge density σ, and the one on the right has a uniform charge density $-\sigma$. Calculate the electric field at points (a) to the left of, (b) in between, and (c) to the right of the two sheets.

FIGURE **P19.62**

63. Repeat the calculations for Problem 19.62 when both sheets have *positive* uniform surface charge densities of value σ.

64. A line of charge with uniform density 35.0 nC/m lies along the line $y = -15.0$ cm, between the points with coordinates $x = 0$ and $x = 40.0$ cm. Find the electric field it creates at the origin.

65. **Physics⊗Now™** A solid, insulating sphere of radius a has a uniform charge density ρ and a total charge Q. Concentric with this sphere is an uncharged, conducting hollow sphere whose inner and outer radii are b and c as shown in Figure P19.65. (a) Find the magnitude of the electric field in the regions $r < a$, $a < r < b$, $b < r < c$, and $r > c$. (b) Determine the induced charge per unit area on the inner and outer surfaces of the hollow sphere.

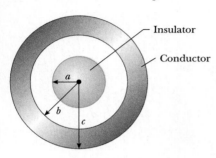

Insulator

Conductor

a

b

c

FIGURE P19.65

66. **Review problem.** A negatively charged particle $-q$ is placed at the center of a uniformly charged ring, where the ring has a total positive charge Q as shown in Example 19.5. The particle, confined to move along the x axis, is displaced a small distance x along the axis (where $x \ll a$) and released. Show that the particle oscillates in simple harmonic motion with a frequency given by

$$f = \frac{1}{2\pi}\left(\frac{k_e qQ}{ma^3}\right)^{1/2}$$

67. A sphere of radius $2a$ is made of a nonconducting material that has a uniform volume charge density ρ. (Assume that the material does not affect the electric field.) A spherical cavity of radius a is now removed from the sphere as shown in Figure P19.67. Show that the electric field within the cavity is uniform and is given by $E_x = 0$ and $E_y = \rho a/3\epsilon_0$. (*Suggestion:* The field within the cavity is the superposition of the field due to the original uncut sphere plus the field due to a sphere the size of the cavity with a uniform negative charge density $-\rho$.)

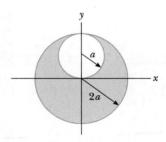

y

a

x

$2a$

FIGURE P19.67

ANSWERS TO QUICK QUIZZES

19.1 (a), (c), and (e). The experiment shows that objects A and B have charges of the same sign, as do objects B and C. Therefore, all three objects have charges of the same sign. We cannot determine from this information, however, whether the charges are positive or negative.

19.2 (e). In the first experiment, objects A and B may have charges with opposite signs or one of the objects may be neutral. The second experiment shows that objects B and C have charges with opposite signs, so object B must be charged. We still do not know if object A is charged or neutral, however.

19.3 (i), (e). From Newton's third law, the electric force exerted by object B on object A is equal in magnitude to the force exerted by object A on object B. (ii), (b). From Newton's third law, the electric force exerted by object B on object A is equal in magnitude to the force exerted by object A on object B and in the opposite direction.

19.4 (a). There is no effect on the electric field if we assume that the source charge producing the field is not disturbed by our actions. Remember that the electric field is created by source charge(s) (unseen in this case), not the test charge(s).

19.5 A, B, and C. The field is greatest at point A because that is where the field lines are closest together. The absence of lines near point C indicates that the electric field there is zero.

19.6 (b) and (d). Statement (a) is not necessarily true because an equal number of positive and negative charges could be present inside the surface. Statement (c) is not necessarily true as can be seen from Figure 19.30 because a nonzero electric field exists everywhere on the surface, but the charge is not enclosed within the surface. Thus, the net flux is zero.

19.7 (i), (c). The charges q_1 and q_4 are outside the surface and contribute zero net flux through S'. (ii), (d). We don't need the surfaces to realize that any given point in space will experience an electric field due to all local source charges.

Electric Potential and Capacitance

This device is a *variable capacitor*, used to tune radios to a selected station. When one set of metal plates is rotated so as to lie between a fixed set of plates, the *capacitance* of the device changes. Capacitance is a parameter that depends on *electric potential*, the primary topic of this chapter.

(George Semple)

CHAPTER OUTLINE

The concept of potential energy was introduced in Chapter 7 in connection with such conservative forces as gravity and the elastic force of a spring. By using the principle of conservation of mechanical energy in an isolated system, we are often able to avoid working directly with forces when solving mechanical problems. In this chapter, we shall use the energy concept in our study of electricity. Because the electrostatic force (given by Coulomb's law) is conservative, electrostatic phenomena can conveniently be described in terms of an *electric* potential energy function. This concept enables us to define a quantity called *electric potential*, which is a scalar quantity and which therefore leads to a simpler means of describing some electrostatic phenomena than the electric field method. As we shall see in subsequent chapters, the concept of electric potential is of great practical value in many applications.

This chapter also addresses the properties of capacitors, devices that store charge. The ability of a capacitor to store charge is measured by its *capacitance*. Capacitors are used in common applications such as frequency tuners in radio receivers, filters in power supplies, dampers to eliminate unwanted sparking in automobile ignition systems, and energy-storing devices in electronic flash units.

20.1 POTENTIAL DIFFERENCE AND ELECTRIC POTENTIAL

When a point charge q_0 is placed in an electric field $\vec{\mathbf{E}}$, the electric force on the particle is $q_0\vec{\mathbf{E}}$ (Eq. 19.4). This force is the vector sum of the individual forces exerted on q_0 by the various source charges producing the field $\vec{\mathbf{E}}$. It follows that the force $q_0\vec{\mathbf{E}}$ is conservative because the individual forces governed by Coulomb's law are conservative. (See Section 7.3 for a review of conservative forces.) Let us consider a system consisting of the point charge and all the source charges creating the electric field. Because the field represents the effect of the source charges, we can also consider the system to be the electric field and the charge q_0 that we place in the field, without referring specifically to the source charges. When the point charge moves in response to the electric force within the electric field, work is done on the particle by the field. For an infinitesimal displacement $d\vec{\mathbf{s}}$ of a point charge q_0, the work done by the electric field on the charge is $\vec{\mathbf{F}}_e \cdot d\vec{\mathbf{s}} = q_0\vec{\mathbf{E}} \cdot d\vec{\mathbf{s}}$.

The work done by the field on a point charge is similar to the work done by a gravitational field on a falling object. We found in Chapter 7 that the gravitational potential energy of an isolated object–field system changes by an amount equal to the negative of the work done within the system by the field on the object (Eq. 7.3). Similarly, the work done within the system by the electric field on a charged particle changes the potential energy of the isolated charge–field system by an amount $dU = -dW = -q_0\vec{\mathbf{E}} \cdot d\vec{\mathbf{s}}$. For a finite displacement of a test particle of charge q_0 between points A and B, the **change in potential energy** of the charge–field system is

$$\Delta U = U_B - U_A = -q_0 \int_A^B \vec{\mathbf{E}} \cdot d\vec{\mathbf{s}} \qquad [20.1]$$

■ Change in potential energy for a charge–field system

The integral in Equation 20.1 is performed over the path along which the particle moves from A to B. It is called either a **path integral** or a **line integral**. Because the force $q_0\vec{\mathbf{E}}$ is conservative, **this integral does not depend on the path taken between A and B.**

In Chapter 19, we recognized that the force between a test charge and a distribution of source charges depends on all the charges, whereas the electric field is defined as a quantity established only by the source charges. We do something similar in this discussion. The potential energy of the system of a test charge q_0 in an electric field $\vec{\mathbf{E}}$ depends on the test charge and all the source charges establishing the electric field. Let us remove the effect of the test charge by dividing the potential energy of the system by the test charge. The potential energy U of the system per unit charge q_0 is independent of the value of q_0 and has a unique value at every point in an electric field. The quantity U/q_0 is called the **electric potential** V (or simply the **potential**):

$$V \equiv \frac{U}{q_0} \qquad [20.2]$$

■ Definition of electric potential

Because potential energy is a scalar, electric potential is also a scalar quantity. Note that potential is not a property of the charge–field system because we have divided the potential energy of the system by the charge. It is a property only of the field. Therefore, in the physical situation, we can imagine removing the test charge from the field. The potential still exists at the point the test charge occupied and is due to the source charges that establish the electric field.

The **potential difference** $\Delta V = V_B - V_A$ between the points A and B is defined as the change in potential energy of the charge–field system when the test particle is

▦ PITFALL PREVENTION 20.1

POTENTIAL AND POTENTIAL ENERGY *The potential is characteristic of the field only*, independent of a charged test particle that may be placed in the field. *Potential energy is characteristic of the charge–field system* due to an interaction between the field and a charged particle placed in the field.

moved between the points divided by the charge q_0 on the test particle:

■ **Potential difference between two points in an electric field**

$$\Delta V = \frac{\Delta U}{q_0} = -\int_A^B \vec{\mathbf{E}} \cdot d\vec{\mathbf{s}} \qquad [20.3]$$

Potential difference should not be confused with potential energy difference. The potential difference between two points in an electric field is *proportional* to the potential energy difference of the charge–field system when the charge is at the two points, and we see from Equation 20.3 that the two are related by $\Delta U = q_0 \, \Delta V$.

Equation 20.3 defines potential difference only. The potential is often taken to be zero at some convenient point, sometimes called a *ground*. We usually set the potential due to one or more source charges at zero for a point at infinity (i.e., a point infinitely remote from the source charges producing the electric field). With this choice, we can say that **the electric potential at an arbitrary point due to source charges equals the work required by an external agent to bring a test particle from infinity to that point divided by the charge on the test particle.** Therefore, if we take $V_A = 0$ at infinity in Equation 20.3, the potential at any point P is

$$V_P = -\int_\infty^P \vec{\mathbf{E}} \cdot d\vec{\mathbf{s}} \qquad [20.4]$$

where $\vec{\mathbf{E}}$ is the electric field established by the source charges. In reality, V_P represents the potential difference between the point P and a point at infinity. (Note that Eq. 20.4 is a special case of Eq. 20.3.) When discussing potentials in an electric circuit, we shall set $V = 0$ at some selected point in the circuit.

Because potential is a measure of energy per unit charge, the SI units of potential are joules per coulomb, called the **volt** (V):

$$1\,\text{V} \equiv 1\,\text{J/C}$$

PITFALL PREVENTION 20.2

VOLTAGE In practice, a variety of phrases are used to describe the potential difference between two points, the most common being **voltage**, arising from the unit for potential. A voltage *applied* to a device, such as a television, or *across* a device has the same meaning as the potential difference across the device. For example, if we say that the voltage applied to a lightbulb is 120 V, we mean that the potential difference between the two electrical contacts on the lightbulb is 120 V.

That is, if we release a particle with a charge of 1 C in an electric field and it moves from a point of high potential to a point of low potential through a potential difference of $-1\,\text{V}$, it will have 1 J of work done on it by the field and therefore will attain a kinetic energy of 1 J. (From the continuity equation for energy, Eq. 6.20, for the system of the particle, $W = \Delta K$.) Alternatively, 1 J of work must be done by an external agent to take a particle with a charge of 1 C through a potential difference of $+1\,\text{V}$ at constant velocity. (From the continuity equation for energy, for the particle–field system, $W = \Delta U$.) Equation 20.3 shows that the potential difference also has the same units as the product of electric field and displacement. It therefore follows that the SI units of electric field, newtons per coulomb, can be expressed as volts per meter:

$$1\,\text{N/C} = 1\,\text{V/m}$$

which suggests that the electric field can be interpreted as the rate of change in space of the electric potential. A strong electric field corresponds to a potential that changes rapidly in space, whereas a weak field represents a slowly changing potential.

As we learned in Section 9.7, a unit of energy commonly used in physics is the **electron volt** (eV):

■ **The electron volt**

$$1\,\text{eV} = (1e)(1\,\text{V}) = (1.60 \times 10^{-19}\,\text{C})(1\,\text{J/C}) = 1.60 \times 10^{-19}\,\text{J} \qquad [20.5]$$

One eV is the kinetic energy gained by a particle with charge e being accelerated by an electric field through a potential difference of magnitude 1 V. Equation 20.5 can be used to convert any energy in joules to electron volts. For instance, an electron in the beam of a typical TV picture tube may have a speed of 3.0×10^7 m/s. This speed corresponds to a kinetic energy of 4.1×10^{-16} J, which is equivalent to 2.6×10^3 eV. Such an electron has to be accelerated from rest through a potential difference of 2.6 kV to reach this speed.

20.2 POTENTIAL DIFFERENCES IN A UNIFORM ELECTRIC FIELD

In this section, we describe the potential difference between any two points in a *uniform* electric field. Consider a uniform electric field directed along the negative y axis as in Figure 20.1a. Let us calculate the potential difference between two points A and B, separated by a distance d, where d is measured parallel to the field lines. If we apply Equation 20.3 to this situation, we have

$$V_B - V_A = \Delta V = -\int_A^B \vec{\mathbf{E}} \cdot d\vec{\mathbf{s}} = -\int_A^B E \cos 0° \, ds = -\int_A^B E \, ds$$

Because the field is uniform, the magnitude E of the field is a constant and can be removed from the integral, giving

$$\Delta V = -E \int_A^B ds = -Ed \qquad [20.6]$$

▪ **Potential difference between two points in a uniform electric field**

The negative sign results because point B is at a lower potential than point A; that is, $V_B < V_A$. In general, electric field lines always point in the direction of decreasing electric potential.

Now suppose a test particle with charge q_0 moves from A to B. The change in the electric potential energy of the charge–field system can be found from Equations 20.3 and 20.6:

$$\Delta U = q_0 \, \Delta V = -q_0 E d \qquad [20.7]$$

From this result, we see that if q_0 is positive, ΔU is negative. Thus, **when a positive charge moves in the direction of the electric field, the electric potential energy of the charge–field system decreases.** This situation is analogous to the change in gravitational potential energy $-mgd$ of an object–field system when an object with mass m falls through a height d in a uniform gravitational field, as suggested in Figure 20.1b. If a particle with a positive charge q_0 is released from rest in the electric field, it experiences an electric force $q_0 \vec{\mathbf{E}}$ in the direction of $\vec{\mathbf{E}}$ (downward in Fig. 20.1a). Therefore, it accelerates downward, gaining kinetic energy. **As the charged particle gains kinetic energy, the charge–field system loses an equal amount of potential energy.** This familiar result is similar to what we have seen for gravitational situations (Fig. 20.1b). The statement is simply the principle of conservation of mechanical energy in the isolated system model for electric fields.

If q_0 is negative, ΔU in Equation 20.7 is positive and the situation is reversed. If a negatively charged particle is released from rest in the field $\vec{\mathbf{E}}$, it accelerates in a direction opposite the electric field. **The charge–field system loses electric potential**

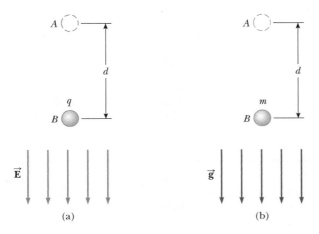

(a) (b)

FIGURE 20.1 (a) When the electric field $\vec{\mathbf{E}}$ is directed downward, point B is at a lower electric potential than point A. When a positive test charge moves from A to B, the charge–field system loses electric potential energy. (b) A gravitational analogy: When an object with mass m moves downward in the direction of the gravitational field $\vec{\mathbf{g}}$, the object–field system loses gravitational potential energy.

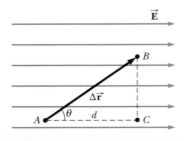

FIGURE 20.2 A particle is moved in a uniform electric field. Point B is at a lower potential than point A. Points B and C are at the *same* potential.

energy when a negative charge moves in the direction opposite to the electric field. We have no analog for this situation in the gravitational case because no negative mass has been observed.

Now consider the more general case of a charged particle moving between any two points in a uniform electric field as in Figure 20.2. If $\Delta\vec{r}$ represents the displacement vector between points A and B, Equation 20.3 gives

$$\Delta V = -\int_A^B \vec{E} \cdot d\vec{s} = -\vec{E} \cdot \int_A^B d\vec{s} = -\vec{E} \cdot \Delta\vec{r} \qquad [20.8]$$

where again we are able to remove $\vec{E}$ from the integral because the electric field is uniform. Furthermore, the change in electric potential energy of the charge–field system is

$$\Delta U = q_0 \Delta V = -q_0 \vec{E} \cdot \Delta\vec{r} \qquad [20.9]$$

Finally, our results show that all points in a plane *perpendicular* to a uniform electric field are at the same potential as can be seen in Figure 20.2, where the potential difference $V_B - V_A = -\vec{E} \cdot \Delta\vec{r} = -E\Delta r\cos\theta = -Ed = V_C - V_A$. Therefore, $V_B = V_C$. The name **equipotential surface** is given to any surface consisting of a continuous distribution of points having the same electric potential. Note that because $\Delta U = q_0 \Delta V$, no work is required to move a test particle between any two points on an equipotential surface. The equipotential surfaces of a uniform electric field consist of a family of planes, all perpendicular to the field. Equipotential surfaces for fields with other symmetries will be described in later sections.

EXAMPLE 20.1 **The Electric Field Between Two Parallel Plates of Opposite Charge**

A 12-V battery is connected between two parallel plates as in Figure 20.3. The separation between the plates is 0.30 cm, and the electric field is assumed to be uniform. (This simplification model is reasonable if the plate separation is small relative to the plate size and if

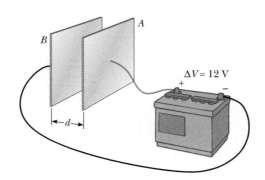

FIGURE 20.3 (Example 20.1) A 12-V battery connected to two parallel plates. The electric field between the plates has a magnitude given by the potential difference ΔV divided by the plate separation d.

we do not consider points near the edges of the plates.) Find the magnitude of the electric field between the plates.

Solution The electric field is directed from the positive plate A toward the negative plate B. The positive plate is at a higher potential than the negative plate. Note that the potential difference between plates must equal the potential difference between the battery terminals. This requirement can be understood by recognizing that all points on a conductor in equilibrium are at the same potential.[1] Hence, no potential difference occurs between a terminal of the battery and any portion of the plate to which it is connected. The magnitude of the uniform electric field between the plates is therefore

$$E = \frac{|V_B - V_A|}{d} = \frac{12\text{ V}}{0.30 \times 10^{-2}\text{ m}} = \boxed{4.0 \times 10^3\text{ V/m}}$$

This configuration, which is called a *parallel-plate capacitor*, is examined in more detail later in this chapter.

---

[1]The electric field vanishes within a conductor in electrostatic equilibrium, and so the path integral $\int \vec{E} \cdot d\vec{s}$ between any two points within the conductor must be zero. A fuller discussion of this point is given in Section 20.6.

| INTERACTIVE | EXAMPLE 20.2 | **Motion of a Proton in a Uniform Electric Field** |

A proton is released from rest in a uniform electric field of magnitude 8.0×10^4 V/m directed along the positive x axis (Fig. 20.4). The proton undergoes a displacement of magnitude $d = 0.50$ m in the direction of $\vec{E}$.

A Find the difference in the electric potential between the points A and B.

Solution The difference in electric potential does not depend on the presence of the proton. From Equation 20.6, we have

$$\Delta V = -Ed = -(8.0 \times 10^4 \text{ V/m})(0.50 \text{ m})$$

$$= -4.0 \times 10^4 \text{ V}$$

This negative result tells us that the electric potential decreases between points A and B.

B Find the change in potential energy of the charge–field system for this displacement.

Solution From Equation 20.3, we have

$$\Delta U = q\,\Delta V = e\,\Delta V$$
$$= (1.6 \times 10^{-19} \text{ C})(-4.0 \times 10^4 \text{ V}) = -6.4 \times 10^{-15} \text{ J}$$

The negative sign here means that the potential energy of the system decreases as the proton moves in the direction

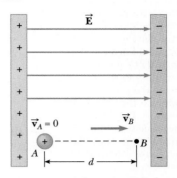

| FIGURE **20.4** | (Interactive Example 20.2) A proton accelerates from A to B in the direction of the electric field. |

of the electric field. This decrease is consistent with conservation of energy in an isolated system: as the proton accelerates in the direction of the field, it gains kinetic energy and at the same time the system loses electric potential energy. The increase in kinetic energy of a charged particle in an electric field is exploited in many devices, including electron guns for TV picture tubes and particle accelerators for research in particle physics.

Physics⊗Now™ Log into PhysicsNow at **www.pop4e.com** and go to Interactive Example 20.2 to predict and observe the speed of the proton as it arrives at the negative plate for random values of the electric field.

20.3 ELECTRIC POTENTIAL AND ELECTRIC POTENTIAL ENERGY DUE TO POINT CHARGES

In establishing the concept of electric potential, we imagined placing a test particle in an electric field set up by some undescribed source charges. As a simplification model, the field was assumed to be uniform in Section 20.2 so as to firmly plant the idea of electric potential in our minds. Let us now focus our attention on point charges, which we know set up electric fields that are not uniform.

Consider an isolated positive point charge q (Fig. 20.5). Recall that such a charge is a source of an electric field that is directed radially outward from the charge. To find the electric potential at a distance of r from the charge, we begin with the general expression for potential difference, Equation 20.3:

$$V_B - V_A = -\int_A^B \vec{E} \cdot d\vec{s}$$

Because the electric field due to the point charge is given by $\vec{E} = k_e q \hat{r}/r^2$ (Eq. 19.5), where $\hat{r}$ is a unit vector directed from the charge toward the field point, the quantity $\vec{E} \cdot d\vec{s}$ can be expressed as

$$\vec{E} \cdot d\vec{s} = k_e \frac{q}{r^2} \hat{r} \cdot d\vec{s}$$

The dot product $\hat{r} \cdot d\vec{s} = ds \cos \theta$, where θ is the angle between $\hat{r}$ and $d\vec{s}$ as in Figure 20.5. Furthermore, note that $ds \cos \theta$ is the projection of $d\vec{s}$ onto $\vec{r}$, so

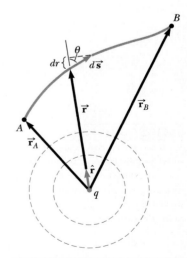

FIGURE **20.5** The potential difference between points A and B due to a point charge q depends *only* on the initial and final radial coordinates r_A and r_B. The two dashed circles represent cross-sections of spherical equipotential surfaces.

SIMILAR EQUATION WARNING Be sure to avoid confusion between Equation 20.11 for the electric potential of a point charge and Equation 19.5 for the electric field of a point charge. The equations look very similar, but potential is proportional to $1/r$, whereas the field is proportional to $1/r^2$. The effect of a charge on the space surrounding it can be described in two ways. The charge sets up a vector electric field $\vec{\mathbf{E}}$, which is related to the force experienced by a test charge placed in the field. It also sets up a scalar potential V, which is related to the potential energy of the two-charge system when a test charge is placed in the field.

$ds \cos \theta = dr$. With these substitutions, we find that $\vec{\mathbf{E}} \cdot d\vec{\mathbf{s}} = (k_e q / r^2)\, dr$, so the expression for the potential difference becomes

$$V_B - V_A = -\int_{r_A}^{r_B} k_e \frac{q}{r^2}\, dr = -k_e q \int_{r_A}^{r_B} \frac{dr}{r^2} = \left. \frac{k_e q}{r} \right|_{r_A}^{r_B}$$

$$= k_e q \left[\frac{1}{r_B} - \frac{1}{r_A} \right] \qquad [20.10]$$

The line integral of $\vec{\mathbf{E}} \cdot d\vec{\mathbf{s}}$ is *independent* of the path between A and B, as it must be, because the electric field of a point charge is conservative.[2] Furthermore, Equation 20.10 expresses the important result that the potential difference between any two points A and B depends *only* on the *radial* coordinates r_A and r_B. As we learned in Section 20.1, it is customary to choose the reference of potential to be zero at $r_A = \infty$. With this choice, the electric potential due to a point charge at any distance r from the charge is

$$V = k_e \frac{q}{r} \qquad [20.11]$$

From this expression we see that V is constant on a spherical surface of radius r centered on the point charge. Hence, we conclude that **the equipotential surfaces for an isolated point charge consist of a family of spheres concentric with the charge** as shown in Figure 20.5. Note that the equipotential surfaces are perpendicular to the electric field lines, as is the case for a uniform electric field.

The electric potential at a point in space due to two or more point charges is obtained by applying the superposition principle. That is, the total potential at some point P due to multiple point charges is the sum of the potentials at P due to the individual charges. For a group of charges, we can write the total potential at P in the form

$$V = k_e \sum_i \frac{q_i}{r_i} \qquad [20.12]$$

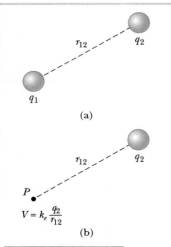

(a)

$V = k_e \dfrac{q_2}{r_{12}}$

(b)

ACTIVE FIGURE 20.6

(a) If two point charges are separated by a distance r_{12}, the potential energy of the pair of charges is given by $k_e q_1 q_2 / r_{12}$. (b) If charge q_1 is removed, a potential $k_e q_2 / r_{12}$ exists at point P due to charge q_2.

Physics⊗Now™ Log into PhysicsNow at **www.pop4e.com** and go to Active Figure 20.6. You can move charge q_1 or point P and see the result on the electric potential energy of the system for part (a) and the electric potential due to charge q_2 for part (b).

where the potential is again taken to be zero at infinity and r_i is the distance from point P to the charge q_i. Note that the sum in Equation 20.12 is an *algebraic* sum of scalars rather than a *vector* sum (which is used to calculate the electric field of a group of charges, as in Eq. 19.6). Therefore, it is much easier to evaluate V for multiple charges than to evaluate $\vec{\mathbf{E}}$.

We now consider the potential energy of a system of two charged particles. If V_2 is the electric potential at a point P due to charge q_2, the work an external agent must do to bring a second charge q_1 from infinity to P without acceleration is $q_1 V_2$. This work represents a transfer of energy into the system, and the energy appears in the system as potential energy U when the particles are separated by a distance r_{12} (Active Fig. 20.6a). We can therefore express the **electric potential energy of a pair of point charges** as

$$U = q_1 V_2 = k_e \frac{q_1 q_2}{r_{12}} \qquad [20.13]$$

Note that if the charges are of the same sign, U is positive, which is consistent because positive work must be done by an external agent on the system to bring the two charges near one another (because charges of the same sign repel). If the charges are of opposite sign, U is negative. Therefore, negative work is done by an external agent against the attractive force between the charges of opposite sign as they are brought near each other because a force must be applied opposite to the displacement to prevent q_1 from accelerating toward q_2.

---

[2] A conservative field is one that exerts a conservative force on an object placed within it. Both gravitational and electric fields are conservative.

In Active Figure 20.6b, we have removed the charge q_1. At the position that this charge previously occupied, point P, we can use Equations 20.2 and 20.13 to define a potential due to charge q_2 as $V = U/q_1 = k_e q_2/r_{12}$.

If the system consists of more than two charged particles, the total electric potential energy can be obtained by calculating U for every pair of charges and summing the terms algebraically. The total electric potential energy of a system of point charges is equal to the work required to bring the charges, one at a time, from an infinite separation to their final positions.

QUICK QUIZ 20.1 A spherical balloon contains a positively charged object at its center. **(i)** As the balloon is inflated to a greater volume while the charged object remains at the center, does the electric potential at the surface of the balloon **(a)** increase, **(b)** decrease, or **(c)** remain the same? **(ii)** Does the electric flux through the surface of the balloon **(a)** increase, **(b)** decrease, or **(c)** remain the same?

QUICK QUIZ 20.2 In Active Figure 20.6a, take q_1 to be a negative source charge and q_2 to be the test charge. **(i)** If q_2 is initially positive and is replaced with a charge of the same magnitude but negative, does the potential at the position of q_2 due to q_1 **(a)** increase, **(b)** decrease, or **(c)** remain the same? **(ii)** When q_2 is changed from positive to negative, does the potential energy of the two-charge system **(a)** increase, **(b)** decrease, or **(c)** remain the same?

INTERACTIVE **EXAMPLE 20.3** **The Electric Potential Due to Two Point Charges**

A 2.00-μC point charge is located at the origin, and a second point charge of -6.00 μC is located on the y axis at the position $(0, 3.00)$ m as in Figure 20.7a.

A Find the total electric potential due to these charges at point P, whose coordinates are $(4.00, 0)$ m.

Solution For two point charges, the sum in Equation 20.12 gives

$$V_P = k_e \left(\frac{q_1}{r_1} + \frac{q_2}{r_2} \right)$$

In this example, $q_1 = 2.00$ μC, $r_1 = 4.00$ m, $q_2 = -6.00$ μC, and $r_2 = 5.00$ m. Therefore, V_P reduces to

$$V_P = (8.99 \times 10^9 \, \text{N} \cdot \text{m}^2/\text{C}^2)$$

$$\times \left(\frac{2.00 \times 10^{-6} \, \text{C}}{4.00 \, \text{m}} + \frac{-6.00 \times 10^{-6} \, \text{C}}{5.00 \, \text{m}} \right)$$

$$= -6.29 \times 10^3 \, \text{V}$$

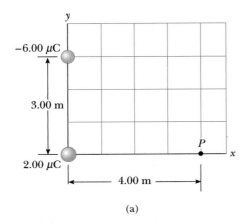

(a)

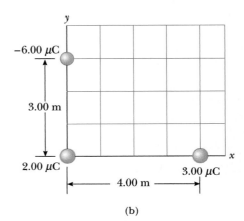

(b)

FIGURE 20.7 (Interactive Example 20.3) (a) The electric potential at point P due to the two point charges q_1 and q_2 is the algebraic sum of the potentials due to the individual charges. (b) How much work is done to bring a 3.00-μC charge from infinity to point P?

B How much work is required to bring a 3.00-μC point charge from infinity to the point P (Fig. 20.7b)?

Solution The work done is equal to the change in the system potential energy given by Equation 20.3:

$$W = \Delta U = q_3 \, \Delta V = q_3(V_P - 0)$$
$$= (3.00 \times 10^{-6} \, \text{C})(-6.29 \times 10^3 \, \text{V})$$
$$= \boxed{-18.9 \times 10^{-3} \, \text{J}}$$

The negative sign is because the 3.00-μC charge is attracted to the combination of q_1 and q_2, which has a net negative charge. The 3.00-μC charge would naturally move toward the other charges if released from

infinity, so the external agent does not have to do anything to cause them to move together. To keep the charge from accelerating, however, the agent must apply a force *away* from point P. Therefore, the force exerted by the agent is opposite the displacement of the charge, leading to a negative value of the work. Positive work would have to be done by an external agent to remove the charge from P back to infinity.

Physics⊗Now™ Log into PhysicsNow at **www.pop4e.com** and go to Interactive Example 20.3 to explore the value of the electric potential at point P and the electric potential energy of the system in Figure 20.7b.

20.4 OBTAINING ELECTRIC FIELD FROM ELECTRIC POTENTIAL

The electric field $\vec{\mathbf{E}}$ and the electric potential V are related by Equation 20.4, which shows how to find the potential if the electric field is known. We now show how to calculate the electric field if the electric potential is known in a certain region.

From Equation 20.3, we can express the potential difference dV between two points a distance ds apart as

$$dV = -\vec{\mathbf{E}} \cdot d\vec{\mathbf{s}} \qquad [20.14]$$

If the electric field has only *one* component—E_x, for example—then $\vec{\mathbf{E}} \cdot d\vec{\mathbf{s}} = E_x \, dx$. Therefore, Equation 20.14 becomes $dV = -E_x \, dx$, or

$$E_x = -\frac{dV}{dx}$$

■ Relation between electric field and electric potential

That is, the electric field is equal to the negative of the derivative of the electric potential with respect to some coordinate. The potential change is zero for any displacement perpendicular to the electric field, which is consistent with the notion that equipotential surfaces are perpendicular to the field as in Figure 20.8a.

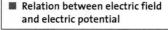

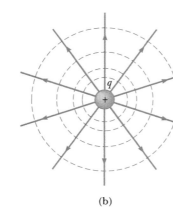

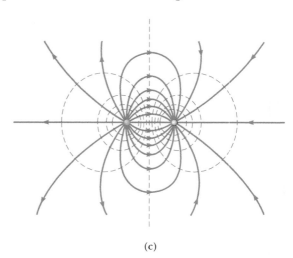

(a)   (b)   (c)

FIGURE **20.8** Equipotential surfaces (dashed blue lines) and electric field lines (brown lines) for (a) a uniform electric field produced by an infinite sheet of charge, (b) a point charge, and (c) an electric dipole. In all cases, the equipotential surfaces are *perpendicular* to the electric field lines at every point.

If the charge distribution has spherical symmetry such that the charge density depends only on the radial distance r, the electric field is radial. In this case, $\vec{\mathbf{E}} \cdot d\vec{\mathbf{s}} = E_r \, dr$, and we can express dV as $dV = -E_r \, dr$. Therefore,

$$E_r = -\frac{dV}{dr} \qquad\qquad [20.15]$$

For example, the potential of a point charge is $V = k_e q/r$. Because V is a function of r only, the potential function has spherical symmetry. Applying Equation 20.15, we find that the magnitude of the electric field due to the point charge is $E_r = k_e q/r^2$, a familiar result. Note that the potential changes only in the radial direction, not in a direction perpendicular to r. Therefore, V (like E_r) is a function only of r. Again, that is consistent with the idea that equipotential surfaces are perpendicular to field lines. In this case, the equipotential surfaces are a family of spheres concentric with the spherically symmetric charge distribution (Fig. 20.8b). The equipotential surfaces for the electric dipole are sketched in Figure 20.8c.

In general, the electric potential is a function of all three spatial coordinates. If V is given in terms of rectangular coordinates, the electric field components E_x, E_y, and E_z can be found from $V(x, y, z)$ as the partial derivatives

$$E_x = -\frac{\partial V}{\partial x} \qquad E_y = -\frac{\partial V}{\partial y} \qquad E_z = -\frac{\partial V}{\partial z} \qquad [20.16]$$

For example, if $V = 3x^2 y + y^2 + yz$,

$$E_x = -\frac{\partial V}{\partial x} = -\frac{\partial}{\partial x}(3x^2 y + y^2 + yz) = -\frac{\partial}{\partial x}(3x^2 y) = -3y\frac{d}{dx}(x^2) = -6xy$$

$$E_y = -\frac{\partial V}{\partial y} = -\frac{\partial}{\partial y}(3x^2 y + y^2 + yz) = -\left[3x^2\frac{d}{dy}(y) + \frac{d}{dy}(y^2) + z\frac{d}{dy}(y)\right]$$

$$= -3x^2 - 2y - z$$

$$E_z = -\frac{\partial V}{\partial z} = -\frac{\partial}{\partial z}(3x^2 y + y^2 + yz) = -\frac{\partial}{\partial z}(yz) = -y\frac{d}{dz}(z) = -y$$

QUICK QUIZ 20.3 **(i)** In a certain region of space, the electric potential is zero everywhere along the x axis. From this information, we can conclude that the x component of the electric field in this region is **(a)** zero, **(b)** in the $+x$ direction, or **(c)** in the $-x$ direction. **(ii)** In a certain region of space, the electric field is zero. From this information, we can conclude that the electric potential in this region is **(a)** zero, **(b)** constant, **(c)** positive, or **(d)** negative.

EXAMPLE 20.4 **The Electric Potential of a Dipole**

An electric dipole consists of two charges of opposite sign but equal magnitude separated by a distance $2a$ as

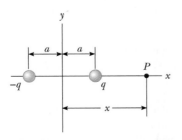

FIGURE 20.9 (Example 20.4) An electric dipole located on the x axis.

in Figure 20.9. The dipole is along the x axis and is centered at the origin.

A Calculate the electric potential at any point P along the x axis.

Solution Using Equation 20.12, we have

$$V = k_e \sum_i \frac{q_i}{r_i} = k_e\left(\frac{q}{x-a} + \frac{-q}{x+a}\right) = \frac{2k_e qa}{x^2 - a^2}$$

B Calculate the electric field on this axis at points very far from the dipole.

Solution Using Equation 20.16 and the result from part A, we calculate the electric field at P:

$$E_x = -\frac{\partial V}{\partial x} = -\frac{d}{dx}\left(\frac{2k_e qa}{x^2 - a^2}\right) = -2k_e qa \frac{d}{dx}(x^2 - a^2)^{-1}$$

$$= (-2k_e qa)(-1)(x^2 - a^2)^{-2}(2x)$$

$$= \frac{4k_e qax}{(x^2 - a^2)^2}$$

If P is far from the dipole so that $x \gg a$, then a^2 can be ignored in the term $x^2 - a^2$ and E_x becomes

$$E_x \approx \frac{4k_e qax}{x^4} = \frac{4k_e qa}{x^3} \quad (x \gg a)$$

Comparing this result to that from Example 19.3, we see a factor of 2 difference between the results for the field far from the dipole. In the previous example, we were looking at the field along a line perpendicular to the line connecting the charges. As we see in Figure 19.11, the vertical components of the field cancel because the point at which we evaluate the field is equidistant from both charges. Therefore, only the very small horizontal components of the individual fields contribute to the total field. In this example, we are looking at the field along an extension of the line connecting the charges. For points along this line, the field vectors have components only along the line and the field vectors are in opposite directions. The point at which we evaluate the field, however, is necessarily closer to one charge than the other. As a result, the field is larger than that along the perpendicular direction by a factor of 2.

20.5 ELECTRIC POTENTIAL DUE TO CONTINUOUS CHARGE DISTRIBUTIONS

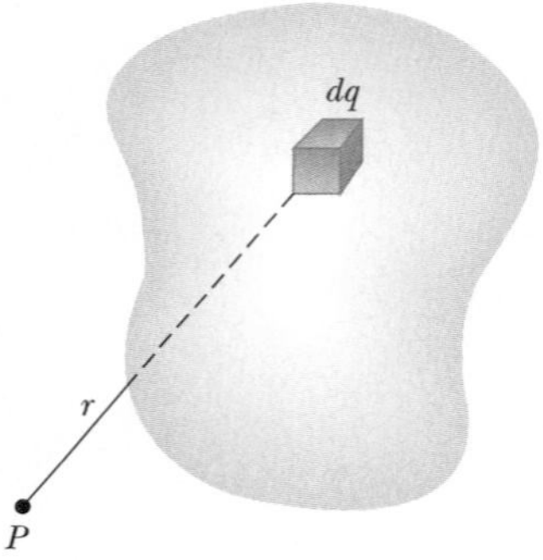

FIGURE 20.10 The electric potential at point P due to a continuous charge distribution can be calculated by dividing the charge distribution into elements of charge dq and summing the potential contributions over all elements.

The **electric potential due to a continuous charge distribution** can be calculated in two ways. If the charge distribution is known, we can start with Equation 20.11 for the potential of a point charge. We then consider the potential due to a small charge element dq, modeling this element as a point charge (Fig. 20.10). The potential dV at some point P due to the charge element dq is

$$dV = k_e \frac{dq}{r} \qquad [20.17]$$

where r is the distance from the charge element to P. To find the total potential at P, we integrate Equation 20.17 to include contributions from all elements of the charge distribution. Because each element is, in general, at a different distance from P and because k_e is a constant, we can express V as

$$V = k_e \int \frac{dq}{r} \qquad [20.18]$$

In effect, we have replaced the sum in Equation 20.12 with an integral.

The second method for calculating the potential of a continuous charge distribution makes use of Equation 20.3. This procedure is useful when the electric field is already known from other considerations, such as Gauss's law. In this case, we substitute the electric field into Equation 20.3 to determine the potential difference between any two points. We then choose V to be zero at some convenient point. We shall illustrate both methods with examples.

PROBLEM-SOLVING STRATEGY **Calculating Electric Potential**

The following procedure is recommended for solving problems that involve the determination of an electric potential due to a charge distribution:

1. Conceptualize Think carefully about the individual charges or the charge distribution that you have in the problem and imagine what type of potential they would create so that you can establish the mental representation. Appeal to any symmetry in the arrangement of charges to help you visualize the potential.

2. Categorize Are you analyzing a group of individual charges or a continuous charge distribution? The answer to this question will tell you how to proceed in the *Analyze* step.

3. Analyze When working problems involving electric potential, remember that potential is a *scalar quantity*, so there are no vector components to consider. Therefore, when using the superposition principle to evaluate the electric potential at a point, simply take the algebraic sum of the potentials due to each charge. You must keep track of signs, however.

As with potential energy in mechanics, only *changes* in electric potential are significant; hence, the point where the potential is set at zero is arbitrary. When dealing with point charges or a finite-sized charge distribution, we usually define $V = 0$ to be at a point infinitely far from the charges. If the charge distribution itself extends to infinity, however, some other nearby point must be selected as the reference point.

(a) *If you are analyzing a group of individual charges:* Use the superposition principle. When several point charges are present, the resultant potential at a point in space is the *algebraic sum* of the individual potentials due to the individual charges (Eq. 20.12). Example 20.4 demonstrated this procedure.

(b) *If you are analyzing a continuous charge distribution:* Replace the sums for evaluating the total potential at some point P from individual charges by integrals (Eq. 20.18). The charge distribution is divided into infinitesimal elements of charge

dq located at a distance of r from point P, and the sum is carried out by integrating over the entire charge distribution. An element is then treated as a point charge, so the potential at P due to the element is $dV = k_e (dq/r)$. The total potential at P is obtained by integrating dV over the entire charge distribution. For many problems, it is possible in performing the integration to express dq and r in terms of a single variable. To simplify the integration, it is important to give careful consideration to the geometry involved in the problem. Example 20.5 demonstrates such a procedure.

Another method that can be used to obtain the potential due to a finite continuous charge distribution is to start with the definition of the potential difference given by Equation 20.3. If $\vec{E}$ is known or can be obtained easily (e.g., from Gauss's law), the line integral of $\vec{E} \cdot d\vec{s}$ can be evaluated. Example 20.6 uses this method.

4. Finalize Once you have determined your result, check to see if your potential is consistent with the mental representation and that it reflects any symmetry that you noted previously. Imagine varying parameters such as the distance of the observation point from the charges or the radius of any circular or spherical objects to see if the mathematical result changes in a reasonable way.

EXAMPLE 20.5 **Potential Due to a Uniformly Charged Ring**

Find the electric potential and electric field at a point P located on the axis of a uniformly charged ring of radius a and total charge Q. The plane of the ring is chosen perpendicular to the x axis (Fig. 20.11).

Solution Figure 20.11 helps us visualize the source of the potential and conceptualize what the potential might look like. We expect the potential to be symmetric around the x axis and to decrease for increasing values of x. We categorize this problem as one involving a continuous distribution of charge on the ring rather than a collection of individual charges. To analyze the

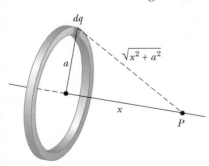

FIGURE 20.11 (Example 20.5) A uniformly charged ring of radius a, whose plane is perpendicular to the x axis. All elements dq of the ring are at the same distance from any point P on the x axis.

problem, let us take P to be at a distance x from the center of the ring as in Figure 20.11. The charge element dq is at a distance equal to $r = \sqrt{x^2 + a^2}$ from point P. Hence, using Equation 20.18, we can express V as

$$V = k_e \int \frac{dq}{r} = k_e \int \frac{dq}{\sqrt{x^2 + a^2}}$$

In this case, each element dq is at the same distance from P. The term $\sqrt{x^2 + a^2}$ can therefore be removed from the integral, and V reduces to

$$V = \frac{k_e}{\sqrt{x^2 + a^2}} \int dq = \boxed{\frac{k_e Q}{\sqrt{x^2 + a^2}}}$$

Let us now address the electric field. The only variable in the expression for V is x. From the symmetry, we see that along the x axis $\vec{E}$ can have only an x component. We can therefore use Equation 20.16 to find the magnitude of the electric field at P:

$$E_x = -\frac{\partial V}{\partial x} = -k_e Q \frac{d}{dx} (x^2 + a^2)^{-1/2}$$

$$= -k_e Q(-\tfrac{1}{2})(x^2 + a^2)^{-3/2}(2x)$$

$$= \boxed{\frac{k_e Q x}{(x^2 + a^2)^{3/2}}}$$

To finalize, note that V decreases as x increases, as we expected from our mental representation. If the point P is very far from the ring ($x \gg a$), then a in the denominator of the expression for V can be ignored and $V \approx k_e Q/x$. This expression is just the one you would expect for a point charge. At large values of x, therefore, the charge distribution appears to be a point charge of magnitude Q as you should expect. Also notice that this result for the electric field agrees with that obtained by direct integration (see Example 19.5).

EXAMPLE 20.6 | **Potential of a Uniformly Charged Sphere**

An insulating solid sphere of radius R has a total charge of Q, which is distributed uniformly throughout the volume of the sphere (Fig. 20.12a).

A Find the electric potential at a point outside the sphere, that is, for $r > R$. Take the potential to be zero at $r = \infty$.

Solution In Example 19.8, we found from Gauss's law that the magnitude of the electric field outside a spherically symmetric charge distribution is

$$E_r = k_e \frac{Q}{r^2} \quad \text{(for } r > R)$$

where the field is directed radially outward when Q is positive. To obtain the potential at an exterior point, such as B in Figure 20.12a, we substitute this expression

for E into Equation 20.4. Because $\vec{E} \cdot d\vec{s} = E_r\, dr$ in this case, we have

$$V_B = -\int_\infty^r E_r\, dr = -k_e Q \int_\infty^r \frac{dr}{r^2}$$

$$= k_e \frac{Q}{r} \quad \text{(for } r > R)$$

Note that the result is identical to that for the electric potential due to a point charge. Because the potential must be continuous at $r = R$, we can use this expression to obtain the potential at the surface of the sphere. That is, the potential at a point such as C in Figure 20.12a is

$$V_C = k_e \frac{Q}{R} \quad \text{(for } r = R)$$

B Find the potential at a point inside the charged sphere, that is, for $r < R$.

Solution In Example 19.8, we found that the electric field inside a uniformly charged sphere is

$$E_r = k_e \frac{Q}{R^3} r \quad \text{(for } r < R)$$

We can use this result and Equation 20.3 to evaluate the potential difference $V_D - V_C$, where D is an interior point:

$$V_D - V_C = -\int_R^r E_r\, dr = -\frac{k_e Q}{R^3} \int_R^r r\, dr = \frac{k_e Q}{2R^3}(R^2 - r^2)$$

Substituting $V_C = k_e Q/R$ into this expression and solving for V_D, we find that

$$V_D = \frac{k_e Q}{2R}\left(3 - \frac{r^2}{R^2}\right) \quad \text{(for } r < R)$$

At $r = R$, this expression gives a result for the potential that agrees with the potential V_C at the surface. A plot of V versus r for this charge distribution is given in Figure 20.12b.

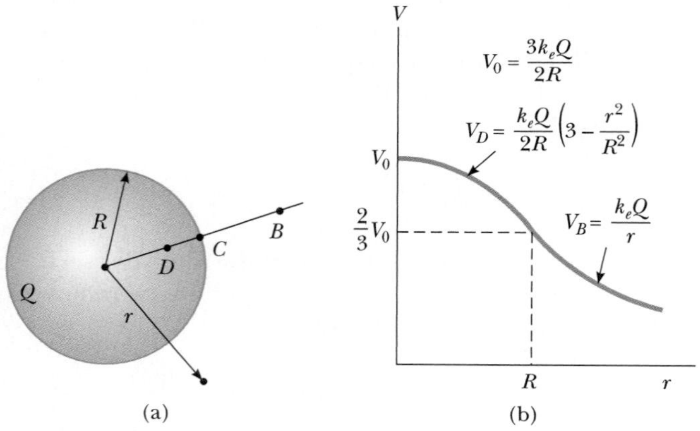

FIGURE 20.12 (Example 20.6) (a) A uniformly charged insulating sphere of radius R and total charge Q. The electric potential at points B and C is equivalent to that of a point charge Q located at the center of the sphere. (b) A plot of the electric potential V versus the distance r from the center of a uniformly charged, insulating sphere of radius R. The curve for V_D inside the sphere is parabolic and joins smoothly with the curve for V_B outside the sphere, which is a hyperbola. The potential has a maximum value V_0 at the center of the sphere.

20.6 ELECTRIC POTENTIAL OF A CHARGED CONDUCTOR

In Chapter 19, we found that when a solid conductor in electrostatic equilibrium carries a net charge, the charge resides on the outer surface of the conductor. Furthermore, we showed that the electric field just outside the surface of a conductor in equilibrium is perpendicular to the surface, whereas the field *inside* the conductor is zero.

We shall now show that **every point on the surface of a charged conductor in electrostatic equilibrium is at the same electric potential.** Consider two points A and B on the surface of a charged conductor as in Figure 20.13. Along a surface path connecting these points, $\vec{\mathbf{E}}$ is always perpendicular to the displacement $d\vec{\mathbf{s}}$; therefore, $\vec{\mathbf{E}} \cdot d\vec{\mathbf{s}} = 0$. Using this result and Equation 20.3, we conclude that the potential difference between A and B is necessarily zero. That is,

$$V_B - V_A = -\int_A^B \vec{\mathbf{E}} \cdot d\vec{\mathbf{s}} = 0$$

This result applies to *any* two points on the surface. Therefore, V is constant everywhere on the surface of a charged conductor in equilibrium, so such a surface is an equipotential surface. Furthermore, because the electric field is zero inside the conductor, we conclude that the potential is constant everywhere inside the conductor and equal to its value at the surface. It follows that no work is required to move a test charge from the interior of a charged conductor to its surface.

For example, consider a solid metal sphere of radius R and total positive charge Q as in Figure 20.14a. The electric field outside the sphere has magnitude $k_e Q/r^2$ and points radially outward. Following Example 20.6, we see that the potential at the interior and surface of the sphere must be $k_e Q/R$ relative to infinity. The potential outside the sphere is $k_e Q/r$. Figure 20.14b is a plot of the potential as a function of r, and Figure 20.14c shows the variations of the electric field with r.

When a net charge resides on a spherical conductor, the surface charge density is uniform as indicated in Figure 20.14a. If, however, the conductor is nonspherical as in Figure 20.13, the surface charge density is not uniform. To determine how the charge distributes on a nonspherical conductor, imagine a simplification model in which a nonspherical conductor is represented by the system shown in Figure 20.15. The system consists of two charged conducting spheres of radii r_1 and r_2, where $r_1 > r_2$, connected by a thin conducting wire. Imagine that the spheres are so far apart that the electric field of one does not influence the other (much farther apart than shown in Fig. 20.15). As a result, the electric field of each sphere can be modeled as that due to a spherically symmetric distribution of charge, which is the same as that due to a point charge.

Because the spheres are connected by a conducting wire, the entire system is a single conductor and all points must be at the same potential. In particular, the potentials at the surfaces of the two spheres must be equal. Using Equation 20.11 for the potential of a point charge, we set the potentials at the surfaces of the spheres equal:

$$k_e \frac{q_1}{r_1} = k_e \frac{q_2}{r_2} \quad \rightarrow \quad \frac{q_1}{q_2} = \frac{r_1}{r_2}$$

Therefore, the larger sphere has the larger amount of charge. Let us compare the surface charge densities on the two spheres, however:

$$\frac{\sigma_2}{\sigma_1} = \frac{\left(\dfrac{q_2}{4\pi r_2^2}\right)}{\left(\dfrac{q_1}{4\pi r_1^2}\right)} = \frac{q_2}{q_1}\frac{r_1^2}{r_2^2} = \frac{r_2}{r_1}\frac{r_1^2}{r_2^2} = \frac{r_1}{r_2}$$

Therefore, although the larger sphere has the larger total charge, the smaller sphere has the larger surface charge density, which leads to the fourth property

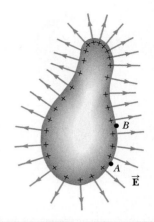

FIGURE **20.13** An arbitrarily shaped conductor with an excess positive charge. When the conductor is in electrostatic equilibrium, all the charge resides at the surface, $\vec{\mathbf{E}} = 0$ inside the conductor, and the electric field just outside the conductor is perpendicular to the surface. The potential is constant inside the conductor and is equal to the potential at the surface. The surface charge density is nonuniform.

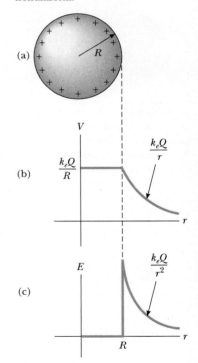

FIGURE **20.14** (a) The excess charge on a conducting sphere of radius R is uniformly distributed on its surface. (b) Electric potential versus distance r from the center of the charged conducting sphere. (c) Electric field versus distance r from the center of the charged conducting sphere.

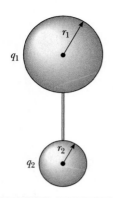

FIGURE 20.15 Two charged spherical conductors connected by a conducting wire. The spheres are at the same potential V.

listed in Section 19.11. Equation 19.25 tells us that the electric field near the surface of a conductor is proportional to the surface charge density. Therefore, the field near the smaller sphere is larger than the field close to the larger sphere.

We generalize this result by stating that **the electric field due to a charged conductor is large near convex surfaces of the conductor having small radii of curvature and is small near convex surfaces of the conductor having large radii of curvature.** A sharp point on a conductor is a region with an extremely small radius of curvature, so the field is very high near points on conductors.

■ Thinking Physics 20.1

Why is the end of a lightning rod pointed?

Reasoning The role of a lightning rod is to serve as a location at which the lightning strikes so that the charge delivered by the lightning will pass safely to the ground. If the lightning rod is pointed, the electric field due to charges moving between the rod and the ground is very strong near the point because the radius of curvature of the conductor is very small. This large electric field will greatly increase the likelihood that the return stroke will occur near the tip of the lightning rod rather than elsewhere. ■

A Cavity Within a Conductor in Equilibrium

Now consider a conductor of arbitrary shape containing a cavity as in Figure 20.16. Let us assume that no charges are inside the cavity. We shall show that **the electric field inside the cavity must be zero,** regardless of the charge distribution on the outside surface of the conductor. Furthermore, the field in the cavity is zero even if an electric field exists outside the conductor.

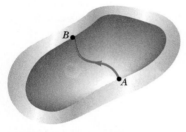

FIGURE 20.16 A conductor in electrostatic equilibrium containing an empty cavity. The electric field in the cavity is zero, regardless of the charge on the conductor.

To prove this point, we remember that every point on the conductor is at the same potential and therefore any two points A and B on the surface of the cavity must be at the same potential. Now imagine that a field $\vec{\mathbf{E}}$ exists in the cavity and evaluate the potential difference $V_B - V_A$, defined by the expression

$$V_B - V_A = -\int_A^B \vec{\mathbf{E}} \cdot d\vec{\mathbf{s}}$$

where the path from A to B is within the cavity. Because $V_B - V_A = 0$, however, the integral must be zero regardless of the path chosen for the integration from A to B. The only way that the integral on the right side of the equation can be equal to zero for *all* possible paths within the cavity is for $\vec{\mathbf{E}}$ to be equal to zero at all points inside the cavity. Therefore, we conclude that a cavity surrounded by conducting walls is a field-free region as long as no charges are inside the cavity.

This result has some interesting applications. For example, it is possible to shield an electronic device or even an entire laboratory from external fields by surrounding it with conducting walls. Shielding is often necessary during highly sensitive electrical measurements. During a thunderstorm, the safest location is inside an automobile. Even if lightning strikes the car, the metal body guarantees that you will not receive a shock inside, where $\vec{\mathbf{E}} = 0$.

20.7 | CAPACITANCE

As we continue with our discussion of electricity and, in later chapters, magnetism, we shall build *circuits* consisting of *circuit elements*. A circuit generally consists of a number of electrical components (circuit elements) connected together by conducting wires and forming one or more closed loops. These circuits can be considered as systems that exhibit a particular type of behavior. The first circuit element we shall consider is a **capacitor.**

In general, a capacitor consists of two conductors of any shape. Consider two conductors having a potential difference of ΔV between them. Let us assume that the conductors have charges of equal magnitude and opposite sign as in Figure 20.17. This situation can be accomplished by connecting two uncharged conductors to the terminals of a battery. Once that is done and the battery is disconnected, the charges remain on the conductors. We say that **the capacitor stores charge.**

The potential difference ΔV *across* the capacitor is the magnitude of the potential difference between the two conductors. This potential difference is proportional to the charge Q on the capacitor, which is defined as the magnitude of the charge on *either* of the two conductors. The **capacitance** C of a capacitor is defined as the ratio of the charge on the capacitor to the magnitude of the potential difference across the capacitor:

$$C \equiv \frac{Q}{\Delta V} \qquad [20.19]$$

By definition, **capacitance is always a positive quantity.** Because the potential difference is proportional to the charge, the ratio $Q/\Delta V$ is constant for a given capacitor. Equation 20.19 tells us that the capacitance of a system is a measure of the amount of charge that can be stored on the capacitor for a given potential difference.

From Equation 20.19, we see that capacitance has the SI units coulombs per volt, which is called a **farad** (F) in honor of Michael Faraday. The farad is a very large unit of capacitance. In practice, typical devices have capacitances ranging from microfarads to picofarads.

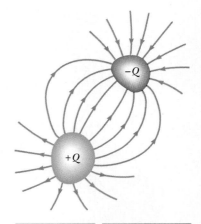

FIGURE 20.17 A capacitor consists of two conductors electrically isolated from each other and their surroundings. Once the capacitor is charged, the two conductors carry charges of equal magnitude but opposite sign.

QUICK QUIZ 20.4 A capacitor stores charge Q at a potential difference ΔV. If the voltage applied by a battery to the capacitor is doubled to $2\,\Delta V$, **(a)** the capacitance falls to half its initial value and the charge remains the same, **(b)** the capacitance and the charge both fall to half their initial values, **(c)** the capacitance and the charge both double, or **(d)** the capacitance remains the same and the charge doubles.

The capacitance of a device depends on the geometric arrangement of the conductors. To illustrate this point, let us calculate the capacitance of an isolated spherical conductor of radius R and charge Q. (Based on the shape of the field lines from a single spherical conductor, we can model the second conductor as a concentric spherical shell of infinite radius.) Because the potential of the sphere is simply $k_e Q/R$ (and $V = 0$ for the shell of infinite radius), the capacitance of the sphere is

$$C = \frac{Q}{\Delta V} = \frac{Q}{k_e Q/R} = \frac{R}{k_e} = 4\pi\epsilon_0 R \qquad [20.20]$$

(Remember from Section 19.4 that the Coulomb constant $k_e = 1/4\pi\epsilon_0$.) Equation 20.20 shows that the capacitance of an isolated charged sphere is proportional to the sphere's radius and is independent of both the charge and the potential difference.

The capacitance of a pair of oppositely charged conductors can be calculated in the following manner. A convenient charge of magnitude Q is assumed, and the potential difference is calculated using the techniques described in Section 20.5. One then uses $C = Q/\Delta V$ to evaluate the capacitance. As you might expect, the calculation is relatively straightforward if the geometry of the capacitor is simple.

Let us illustrate with two familiar geometries: parallel plates and concentric cylinders. In these examples, we shall assume that the charged conductors are separated by a vacuum. (The effect of a material between the conductors will be treated in Section 20.10.)

▦ PITFALL PREVENTION 20.4

CAPACITANCE IS A CAPACITY To help you understand the concept of capacitance, think of similar notions that use a similar word. The *capacity* of a milk carton is the volume of milk it can store. The *heat capacity* of an object is the amount of energy an object can store per unit of temperature difference. The *capacitance* of a capacitor is the amount of charge the capacitor can store per unit of potential difference.

▦ PITFALL PREVENTION 20.5

POTENTIAL DIFFERENCE IS ΔV, NOT V We use the symbol ΔV for the potential difference across a circuit element or a device because this notation is consistent with our definition of potential difference and with the meaning of the delta sign. It is a common but confusing practice to use the symbol V without the delta sign for a potential difference. Keep that in mind if you consult other texts.

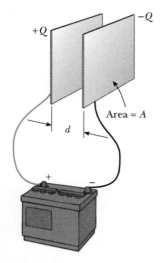

FIGURE 20.18 A parallel-plate capacitor consists of two parallel conducting plates, each of area A, separated by a distance d. When the capacitor is charged by connecting the plates to the terminals of a battery, the plates carry charges of equal magnitude but opposite sign.

The Parallel-Plate Capacitor

A parallel-plate capacitor consists of two parallel plates of equal area A separated by a distance d as in Figure 20.18. If the capacitor is charged, one plate has charge Q and the other, charge $-Q$. The magnitude of the charge per unit area on either plate is $\sigma = Q/A$. If the plates are very close together (compared with their length and width), we adopt a simplification model in which the electric field is uniform between the plates and zero elsewhere, as we discussed in Example 19.12. According to Example 19.12, the magnitude of the electric field between the plates is

$$E = \frac{\sigma}{\epsilon_0} = \frac{Q}{\epsilon_0 A}$$

Because the field is uniform, the potential difference across the capacitor can be found from Equation 20.6. Therefore,

$$\Delta V = Ed = \frac{Qd}{\epsilon_0 A}$$

Substituting this result into Equation 20.19, we find that the capacitance is

$$C = \frac{Q}{\Delta V} = \frac{Q}{Qd/\epsilon_0 A}$$

$$C = \frac{\epsilon_0 A}{d} \qquad [20.21]$$

That is, **the capacitance of a parallel-plate capacitor is proportional to the area of its plates and inversely proportional to the plate separation.**

As you can see from the definition of capacitance, $C = Q/\Delta V$, the amount of charge a given capacitor can store for a given potential difference across its plates increases as the capacitance increases. It therefore seems reasonable that a capacitor constructed from plates having large areas should be able to store a large charge.

A careful inspection of the electric field lines for a parallel-plate capacitor reveals that the field is uniform in the central region between the plates, but is nonuniform at the edges of the plates. Figure 20.19 shows a drawing and a photograph of the electric field pattern of a parallel-plate capacitor, showing the nonuniform field lines at the plates' edges. As long as the separation between the plates is small compared with the dimensions of the plates (unlike Fig. 20.19b), the edge effects can be ignored and we can use the simplification model in which the electric field is uniform everywhere between the plates.

⊞ **PITFALL PREVENTION 20.6**

Too many Cs Be sure not to confuse italic C for capacitance with regular C for the unit coulomb.

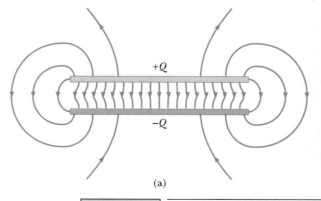

(a)

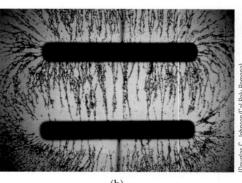

(b)

(Douglas C. Johnson/Cal Poly Pomona)

FIGURE 20.19 (a) The electric field between the plates of a parallel-plate capacitor is uniform near the center but nonuniform near the edges. (b) Electric field pattern of two oppositely charged conducting parallel plates. Small particles on an oil surface align with the electric field.

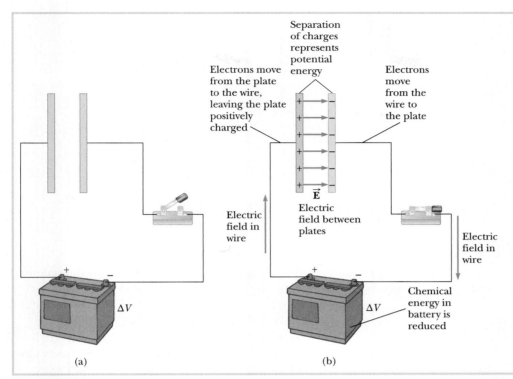

ACTIVE FIGURE 20.20

(a) A circuit consisting of a capacitor, a battery, and a switch. (b) When the switch is closed, the battery establishes an electric field in the wire that causes electrons to move from the left plate into the wire and into the right plate from the wire. As a result, a separation of charge exists on the plates, which represents an increase in electric potential energy of the system. This energy in the system of the circuit has been transformed from chemical energy in the battery.

Physics⊗Now™ Log into PhysicsNow at **www.pop4e.com** and go to Active Figure 20.20 to adjust the battery voltage and see the result on the charge on the plates and the electric field between the plates.

Separation of charges represents potential energy

Electrons move from the plate to the wire, leaving the plate positively charged

Electrons move from the wire to the plate

$\vec{E}$

Electric field in wire

Electric field between plates

Electric field in wire

ΔV

ΔV

Chemical energy in battery is reduced

(a)

(b)

Active Figure 20.20 shows a battery connected to a single parallel-plate capacitor with a switch in the circuit. Let us identify the circuit as a system. When the switch is closed, the battery establishes an electric field in the wires and charges flow between the wires and the capacitor. As that occurs, energy is transformed within the system. Before the switch is closed, energy is stored as chemical energy in the battery. This type of energy is associated with chemical bonds and is transformed during the chemical reaction that occurs within the battery when it is operating in an electric circuit. When the switch is closed, some of the chemical energy in the battery is converted to electric potential energy related to the separation of positive and negative charges on the plates. As a result, we can describe a capacitor as a device that stores energy as well as charge. We will explore this energy storage in more detail in Section 20.9.

EXAMPLE 20.7 **Parallel-Plate Capacitor**

A parallel-plate capacitor has an area $A = 2.00 \times 10^{-4} \text{ m}^2$ and a plate separation $d = 1.00$ mm. Find its capacitance.

Solution From Equation 20.21, we find that

$$C = \frac{\epsilon_0 A}{d} = (8.85 \times 10^{-12} \text{ C}^2/\text{N} \cdot \text{m}^2)\left(\frac{2.00 \times 10^{-4} \text{ m}^2}{1.00 \times 10^{-3} \text{ m}}\right)$$

$$= 1.77 \times 10^{-12} \text{ F} = \boxed{1.77 \text{ pF}}$$

The Cylindrical Capacitor

A cylindrical capacitor consists of a cylindrical conductor of radius a and charge Q coaxial with a larger cylindrical shell of radius b and charge $-Q$ (Fig. 20.21a). Let us find the capacitance of this device if its length is ℓ. If we assume that ℓ is large compared with a and b, we can adopt a simplification model in which we ignore end effects. In this case, the field is perpendicular to the axis of the cylinders and is

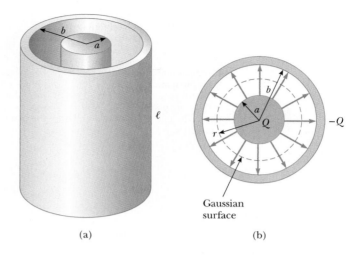

FIGURE 20.21 (a) A cylindrical capacitor consists of a solid cylindrical conductor of radius a and length ℓ surrounded by a coaxial cylindrical shell of radius b. (b) End view. The dashed line represents the end of the cylindrical gaussian surface of radius r.

(a)

(b)

confined to the region between them (Fig. 20.21b). We first calculate the potential difference between the two cylinders, which is given in general by

$$V_b - V_a = -\int_a^b \vec{\mathbf{E}} \cdot d\vec{\mathbf{s}}$$

where $\vec{\mathbf{E}}$ is the electric field in the region $a < r < b$. In Chapter 19, using Gauss's law, we showed that the electric field of a cylinder with charge per unit length λ has the magnitude $E = 2k_e\lambda/r$. The same result applies here because the outer cylinder does not contribute to the electric field inside it. Using this result and noting that the direction of $\vec{\mathbf{E}}$ is radially away from the inner cylinder in Figure 20.21b, we find that

$$V_b - V_a = -\int_a^b E_r\, dr = -2k_e\lambda \int_a^b \frac{dr}{r} = -2k_e\lambda \ln\left(\frac{b}{a}\right)$$

Substituting this result into Equation 20.19 and using that $\lambda = Q/\ell$, we find that

$$C = \frac{Q}{\Delta V} = \frac{Q}{\dfrac{2k_eQ}{\ell}\ln\left(\dfrac{b}{a}\right)} = \frac{\ell}{2k_e\ln\left(\dfrac{b}{a}\right)} \qquad [20.22]$$

where the magnitude of the potential difference between the cylinders is $\Delta V = |V_a - V_b| = 2k_e\lambda \ln(b/a)$, a positive quantity. Our result for C shows that the capacitance is proportional to the length of the cylinders. As you might expect, the capacitance also depends on the radii of the two cylindrical conductors. As an example, a coaxial cable consists of two concentric cylindrical conductors of radii a and b separated by an insulator. The cable carries currents in opposite directions in the inner and outer conductors. Such a geometry is especially useful for shielding an electrical signal from external influences. From Equation 20.22, we see that the capacitance per unit length of a coaxial cable is

$$\frac{C}{\ell} = \frac{1}{2k_e\ln\left(\dfrac{b}{a}\right)}$$

20.8 COMBINATIONS OF CAPACITORS

Two or more capacitors are often combined in electric circuits in different ways. The equivalent capacitance of certain combinations can be calculated using methods described in this section.

In studying electric circuits, we use a specialized simplified pictorial representation called a **circuit diagram**. Such a diagram uses **circuit symbols** to represent various circuit elements. The circuit symbols are connected by straight lines that represent the wires between the circuit elements. Figure 20.22 shows the circuit symbols for a capacitor, a battery, and an open switch. Notice that the circuit symbol for a capacitor consists of two parallel lines of equal length, representing the plates in a parallel-plate capacitor, and the lines in the battery symbol are of different lengths. The positive terminal of the battery is at the higher potential and is represented by the longer line in the battery symbol.

Parallel Combination

Two capacitors connected as shown in the pictorial representation in Active Figure 20.23a are known as a **parallel combination** of capacitors. Active Figure 20.23b shows the circuit diagram for this configuration. The left plates of both capacitors are connected by a conducting wire to the positive terminal of the battery, and both plates are therefore at the same potential as that of the battery terminal. Likewise, the right plates are connected to the negative terminal of the battery and are at the same potential as that terminal. The voltage applied across the combination is therefore the terminal voltage of the battery.[3] Furthermore, the voltage across *each capacitor* is the same as the terminal voltage of the battery.

When the capacitors are first connected in the circuit, electrons are transferred between the wires and the plates, causing the left plates to become positively charged and the right plates to become negatively charged. The flow of charge ceases when the voltage across the capacitors is equal to that across the battery terminals. At this point, the capacitors have reached their maximum charge. Let us call the maximum charges on the two capacitors Q_1 and Q_2. Then the *total charge Q* stored by the two capacitors is

$$Q = Q_1 + Q_2 \qquad [20.23]$$

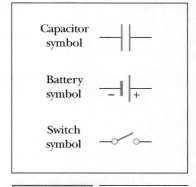

FIGURE 20.22 Circuit symbols for a capacitor, a battery, and an open switch. Note that capacitors are in blue, and batteries and switches are in red.

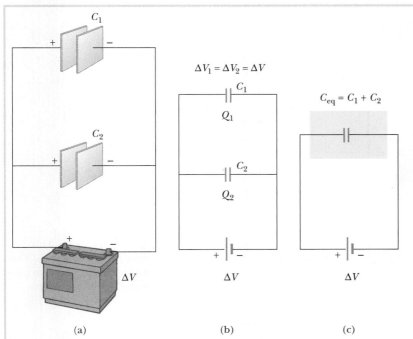

(a) (b) (c)

ACTIVE FIGURE 20.23

(a) A parallel combination of two capacitors connected to a battery. (b) The circuit diagram for the parallel combination. The potential difference is the same across each capacitor. (c) The equivalent capacitance is $C_{eq} = C_1 + C_2$.

Physics⊗Now™ Log into PhysicsNow at **www.pop4e.com** and go to Active Figure 20.23 to adjust the battery voltage and the individual capacitances and see the resulting charges and voltages on the capacitors. You can combine up to four capacitors in parallel.

---

[3]In some situations, the parallel combination may be in a circuit with other circuit elements so that the potential difference across the combination is not that of a battery in the circuit, but must be determined by analyzing the entire circuit.

Suppose we wish to replace the two capacitors in Active Figure 20.23b with one equivalent capacitor having the capacitance C_{eq}. This equivalent capacitor (Active Fig. 20.23c) must have exactly the same result in the circuit as the original two. That is, it must store charge Q when connected to the battery. From Active Figure 20.23c, we see that the voltage across the equivalent capacitor is ΔV. Therefore, we have

$$Q = C_{eq}\,\Delta V$$

and, for the individual capacitors,

$$Q_1 = C_1\,\Delta V \qquad Q_2 = C_2\,\Delta V$$

Substitution of these relations into Equation 20.23 gives

$$C_{eq}\,\Delta V = C_1\,\Delta V + C_2\,\Delta V$$

or

$$C_{eq} = C_1 + C_2 \qquad \text{(parallel combination)} \qquad [20.24]$$

If we extend this treatment to three or more capacitors connected in parallel, the equivalent capacitance is

■ **Equivalent capacitance of several capacitors in parallel**

$$C_{eq} = C_1 + C_2 + C_3 + \cdots \qquad \text{(parallel combination)} \qquad [20.25]$$

Therefore, we see that **the equivalent capacitance of a parallel combination of capacitors is the algebraic sum of the individual capacitances and is larger than any of the individual capacitances.**

Series Combination

Now consider two capacitors connected in **series** as illustrated in Active Figure 20.24a. Active Figure 20.24b shows the circuit diagram. For this series combination of capacitors, **the magnitude of the charge is the same on all the plates.**

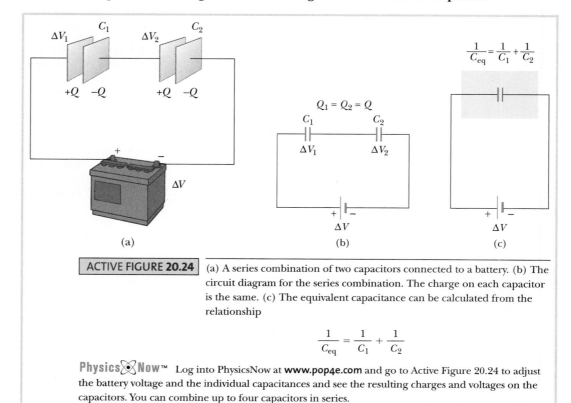

ACTIVE FIGURE 20.24 (a) A series combination of two capacitors connected to a battery. (b) The circuit diagram for the series combination. The charge on each capacitor is the same. (c) The equivalent capacitance can be calculated from the relationship

$$\frac{1}{C_{eq}} = \frac{1}{C_1} + \frac{1}{C_2}$$

Physics⚛Now™ Log into PhysicsNow at **www.pop4e.com** and go to Active Figure 20.24 to adjust the battery voltage and the individual capacitances and see the resulting charges and voltages on the capacitors. You can combine up to four capacitors in series.

To see why that is true, let us consider the charge transfer process in some detail. We start with uncharged capacitors and follow what happens just after a battery is connected to the circuit. When the connection is made, the right plate of C_1 and the left plate of C_2 form an isolated conductor. Therefore, whatever negative charge enters one plate from the connecting wire must be equal to the positive charge of the other plate so as to maintain neutrality of the isolated conductor: that is the electric charge version of the isolated system model. As a result, both capacitors must have the same charge Q.

Suppose we wish to determine the capacitance of an equivalent capacitor that has the same effect in the circuit as the series combination. That is, as the equivalent capacitor is being charged, charge $-Q$ must enter its right plate from the wires and the charge on its left plate must be $+Q$. By applying the definition of capacitance to the circuit shown in Active Figure 20.24c, we have

$$\Delta V = \frac{Q}{C_{eq}} \qquad [20.26]$$

where ΔV is the potential difference between the terminals of the battery and C_{eq} is the equivalent capacitance.

Because the right plate of C_1 and the left plate of C_2 in Active Figure 20.24a form an isolated conductor, both plates are at the same potential V_i, where the i stands for the isolated conductor. The notation V_{left} represents the potential of the left plate of C_1, and V_{right} represents the potential of the right plate of C_2. Because these latter two plates are connected directly to the battery, the potential difference between them must be

$$\Delta V = V_{left} - V_{right}$$

If we add and subtract V_i to this equation, we have

$$\Delta V = (V_{left} - V_i) + (V_i - V_{right})$$

which we can write as

$$\Delta V = \Delta V_1 + \Delta V_2 \qquad [20.27]$$

where ΔV_1 and ΔV_2 are the potential differences across capacitors C_1 and C_2. In general, the potential difference across any number of capacitors in series is equal to the sum of the potential differences across the individual capacitors. Because $Q = C\,\Delta V$ can be applied to each capacitor, the potential difference across each is

$$\Delta V_1 = \frac{Q}{C_1} \qquad \Delta V_2 = \frac{Q}{C_2}$$

Substituting these expressions into Equation 20.27 and using Equation 20.26 to replace ΔV, we have

$$\frac{Q}{C_{eq}} = \frac{Q}{C_1} + \frac{Q}{C_2}$$

Canceling Q, we arrive at the relationship

$$\frac{1}{C_{eq}} = \frac{1}{C_1} + \frac{1}{C_2} \qquad \text{(series combination)} \qquad [20.28]$$

If this analysis is applied to three or more capacitors connected in series, the equivalent capacitance is found to be given by

$$\frac{1}{C_{eq}} = \frac{1}{C_1} + \frac{1}{C_2} + \frac{1}{C_3} + \cdots \qquad \text{(series combination)} \qquad [20.29]$$

▪ Equivalent capacitance of several capacitors in series

which shows that **the inverse of the equivalent capacitance is the algebraic sum of the inverses of the individual capacitances and that the equivalent capacitance of a series combination is always less than any individual capacitance in the combination.**

QUICK QUIZ 20.5 Two capacitors are identical. They can be connected in series or in parallel. **(i)** If you want the *smallest* equivalent capacitance for the combination, **(a)** do you connect them in series, **(b)** do you connect them in parallel, or **(c)** do the combinations have the same capacitance? **(ii)** Each capacitor is charged to a voltage of 10 V. If you want the largest combined potential difference across the combination, **(a)** do you connect them in series, **(b)** do you connect them in parallel, or **(c)** do the combinations have the same potential difference?

INTERACTIVE **EXAMPLE 20.8** **Equivalent Capacitance**

Find the equivalent capacitance between a and b for the combination of capacitors shown in Figure 20.25a. All capacitances are in microfarads.

Solution Using Equations 20.25 and 20.29, we reduce the combination step by step as indicated in the figure. The 1.0-μF and 3.0-μF capacitors are in parallel and combine according to $C_{eq} = C_1 + C_2$. Their equivalent capacitance is 4.0 μF. Likewise, the 2.0-μF and 6.0-μF capacitors are also in parallel and have an equivalent capacitance of 8.0 μF. The upper branch in Figure 20.25b now consists of two 4.0-μF capacitors in series, which combine according to

$$\frac{1}{C_{eq}} = \frac{1}{C_1} + \frac{1}{C_2} = \frac{1}{4.0\ \mu F} + \frac{1}{4.0\ \mu F} = \frac{1}{2.0\ \mu F}$$

$$C_{eq} = 2.0\ \mu F$$

Likewise, the lower branch in Figure 20.25b consists of two 8.0-μF capacitors in series, which give an equivalent of 4.0 μF. Finally, the 2.0-μF and 4.0-μF capacitors in Figure 20.25c are in parallel and have an equivalent capacitance of 6.0 μF. Hence, the equivalent capacitance of the circuit is **6.0 μF** as shown in Figure 20.25d.

Physics⊗Now™ Log into PhysicsNow at **www.pop4e.com** and go to Interactive Example 20.8 to practice reducing a combination of capacitors to a single equivalent capacitor.

FIGURE 20.25 (Interactive Example 20.8) To find the equivalent combination of the capacitors in (a), the various combinations are reduced in steps as indicated in (b), (c), and (d), using the series and parallel rules described in the text. All capacitance values are in microfarads.

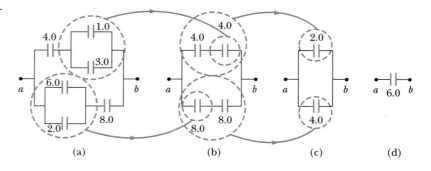

(a)   (b)   (c)   (d)

20.9 | ENERGY STORED IN A CHARGED CAPACITOR

Almost everyone who works with electronic equipment has at some time verified that a capacitor can store energy. If the plates of a charged capacitor are connected by a conductor, such as a wire, charge transfers between the plates and the wire until the two plates are uncharged. The discharge can often be observed as a visible spark. If you accidentally touch the opposite plates of a charged capacitor, your fingers act as pathways by which the capacitor discharges, resulting in an electric shock. The degree of shock depends on the capacitance and the voltage applied to the capacitor. When high voltages are present, such as in the power supply of a television set, the shock can be fatal.

Consider a parallel-plate capacitor that is initially uncharged so that the initial potential difference across the plates is zero. Now imagine that the capacitor is connected to a battery and develops a charge of Q. The final potential difference across the capacitor is $\Delta V = Q/C$.

To calculate the energy stored in the capacitor, imagine charging the capacitor in a different way that achieves the same result. An external agent reaches in and grabs small bits of charge and transfers them from one plate to the other. Suppose q is the charge on the capacitor at some instant during this charging process. At the same instant, the potential difference across the capacitor is $\Delta V = q/C$. Now imagine that the external agent transfers an additional increment of charge dq from the plate of charge $-q$ to the plate of charge q (which is at the higher potential) by applying a force on the charge dq to move it through the electric field between the plates. The work required to transfer an increment of charge dq from one plate to the other is

$$dW = \Delta V \, dq = \frac{q}{C} \, dq$$

Therefore, the total work required to charge the capacitor from $q = 0$ to the final charge $q = Q$ is

$$W = \int_0^Q \frac{q}{C} \, dq = \frac{Q^2}{2C}$$

The capacitor can be modeled as a nonisolated system for this discussion. The work done by the external agent on the system in charging the capacitor appears as potential energy U stored in the capacitor. In reality, of course, this energy is not the result of mechanical work done by an external agent moving charge from one plate to the other, but is due to transformation of chemical energy in the battery. We have used a model of work done by an external agent that gives us a result that is also valid for the actual situation. Using $Q = C\Delta V$, the energy stored in a charged capacitor can be expressed in the following alternative forms:

$$U = \frac{Q^2}{2C} = \tfrac{1}{2}Q\,\Delta V = \tfrac{1}{2}C(\Delta V)^2 \qquad [20.30]$$

▪ **Energy stored in a charged capacitor**

This result applies to *any* capacitor, regardless of its geometry. In practice, the maximum energy (or charge) that can be stored is limited because electric discharge ultimately occurs between the plates of the capacitor at a sufficiently large value of ΔV. For this reason, capacitors are usually labeled with a maximum operating voltage.

For an object on an extended spring, the elastic potential energy can be modeled as being stored *in the spring*. Internal energy of a substance associated with its temperature is located *throughout the substance*. Where is the energy in a capacitor located? The energy stored in a capacitor can be modeled as being stored *in the electric field between the plates of the capacitor*. For a parallel-plate capacitor, the potential difference is related to the electric field through the relationship $\Delta V = Ed$. Furthermore, the capacitance is $C = \epsilon_0 A/d$. Substituting these expressions into Equation 20.30 gives

$$U = \tfrac{1}{2}\left(\frac{\epsilon_0 A}{d}\right)(Ed)^2 = \tfrac{1}{2}(\epsilon_0 Ad)E^2 \qquad [20.31]$$

Because the volume of a parallel-plate capacitor that is occupied by the electric field is Ad, the energy per unit volume $u = U/Ad$, called the **energy density,** is

$$u = \tfrac{1}{2}\epsilon_0 E^2 \qquad [20.32]$$

▪ **Energy density in an electric field**

Although Equation 20.32 was derived for a parallel-plate capacitor, the expression is generally valid. That is, **the energy density in any electric field is proportional to the square of the magnitude of the electric field at a given point.**

▮ Thinking Physics 20.2

You charge a capacitor and then remove it from the battery. The capacitor consists of large movable plates, with air between them. You pull the plates farther apart a small distance. What happens to the charge on the capacitor? To the potential difference? To the energy stored in the capacitor? To the capacitance? To the electric field between the plates? Is work done in pulling the plates apart?

Reasoning Because the capacitor is removed from the battery, charges on the plates have nowhere to go. Therefore, the charge on the capacitor remains the same as the plates are pulled apart. Because the electric field of large plates is independent of distance for uniform fields, the electric field remains constant. Because the electric field is a measure of the rate of change of potential with distance, the potential difference between the plates increases as the separation distance increases. Because the same charge is stored at a higher potential difference, the capacitance decreases. Because energy stored is proportional to both charge and potential difference, the energy stored in the capacitor increases. This energy must be transferred into the system from somewhere; the plates attract each other, so work is done by you on the system of two plates when you pull them apart. ▮

INTERACTIVE EXAMPLE 20.9 **Rewiring Two Charged Capacitors**

Two capacitors with capacitances C_1 and C_2 (where $C_1 > C_2$) are charged to the same potential difference ΔV_i. The charged capacitors are removed from the battery, and their plates are connected as shown in Figure 20.26a. The switches S_1 and S_2 are then closed as in Figure 20.26b.

A Find the final potential difference ΔV_f between a and b after the switches are closed.

Solution Let us identify the left-hand plates of the capacitors as an isolated system because they are not connected to the right-hand plates by conductors. The

charges on the left-hand plates before the switches are closed are

$$Q_{1i} = C_1 \Delta V_i \quad \text{and} \quad Q_{2i} = -C_2 \Delta V_i$$

The negative sign for Q_{2i} is necessary because the charge on the left plate of capacitor C_2 is negative. The total charge Q in the system is

$$(1) \quad Q = Q_{1i} + Q_{2i} = (C_1 - C_2)\Delta V_i$$

After the switches are closed, the electric charge version of the isolated system model tells us that the total charge on the left-hand plates remains the same:

$$(2) \quad Q = Q_{1f} + Q_{2f}$$

The charges will redistribute on the left-hand plates until the entire conductor in the system is at the same potential V_{left}. Similarly, charges will distribute on the two right-hand plates until the entire conductor in this system is at the same potential V_{right}. Therefore, the final potential difference $\Delta V_f = |V_{left} - V_{right}|$ across both capacitors is the same. To satisfy this requirement, the charges on the capacitors after the switches are closed are

$$(3) \quad Q_{1f} = C_1 \Delta V_f$$

$$(4) \quad Q_{2f} = C_2 \Delta V_f$$

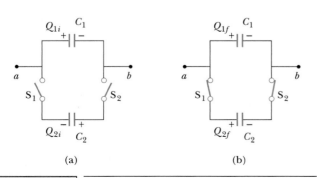

(a)   (b)

FIGURE 20.26 (Interactive Example 20.9) Two capacitors are connected with plates of opposite charge in contact.

Dividing these equations, we have

$$(5) \quad \frac{Q_{1f}}{Q_{2f}} = \frac{C_1 \Delta V_f}{C_2 \Delta V_f} = \frac{C_1}{C_2} \rightarrow Q_{1f} = \frac{C_1}{C_2} Q_{2f}$$

Combining (2) and (5) gives

$$Q = \frac{C_1}{C_2} Q_{2f} + Q_{2f} = Q_{2f}\left(1 + \frac{C_1}{C_2}\right)$$

$$(6) \quad Q_{2f} = Q\left(\frac{C_2}{C_1 + C_2}\right)$$

Using (5) and (6) to find Q_{1f}, we have

$$Q_{1f} = \frac{C_1}{C_2}\left[Q\left(\frac{C_2}{C_1 + C_2}\right)\right] = Q\left(\frac{C_1}{C_1 + C_2}\right)$$

Finally, we use (3) and (4) to find the voltage across each capacitor:

$$\Delta V_{1f} = \frac{Q_{1f}}{C_1} = \frac{Q\left(\dfrac{C_1}{C_1 + C_2}\right)}{C_1} = \frac{Q}{C_1 + C_2}$$

$$\Delta V_{2f} = \frac{Q_{2f}}{C_2} = \frac{Q\left(\dfrac{C_2}{C_1 + C_2}\right)}{C_2} = \frac{Q}{C_1 + C_2}$$

Notice that $\Delta V_{1f} = \Delta V_{2f} = \Delta V_f$, which is the expected result.

B Find the total energy stored in the capacitors before and after the switches are closed and the ratio of the final energy to the initial energy.

Solution Before the switches are closed, the total energy stored in the capacitors is

$$U_i = \tfrac{1}{2}C_1(\Delta V_i)^2 + \tfrac{1}{2}C_2(\Delta V_i)^2 = \tfrac{1}{2}(C_1 + C_2)(\Delta V_i)^2$$

After the switches are closed, the total energy stored in the capacitors is

$$U_f = \tfrac{1}{2}C_1(\Delta V_f)^2 + \tfrac{1}{2}C_2(\Delta V_f)^2 = \tfrac{1}{2}(C_1 + C_2)(\Delta V_f)^2$$

$$= \tfrac{1}{2}(C_1 + C_2)\left(\frac{Q}{C_1 + C_2}\right)^2 = \tfrac{1}{2}\frac{Q^2}{C_1 + C_2}$$

Using (1), this expression can be written as

$$U_f = \tfrac{1}{2}\frac{(C_1 - C_2)^2(\Delta V_i)^2}{C_1 + C_2}$$

Therefore, the ratio of the final energy stored to the initial energy stored is

$$\frac{U_f}{U_i} = \frac{\left(\tfrac{1}{2}\dfrac{(C_1 - C_2)^2(\Delta V_i)^2}{C_1 + C_2}\right)}{\tfrac{1}{2}(C_1 + C_2)(\Delta V_i)^2} = \left(\frac{C_1 - C_2}{C_1 + C_2}\right)^2$$

which shows that the final energy is less than the initial energy. Therefore, even though we correctly used an isolated system model for electric charge in this problem, we see that it is *not* an isolated system for energy. That begs the question as to how energy is transferred out of the system. The transfer mechanism is electromagnetic radiation, which may not be clear to you at this point but which will become clearer once we study the material in Chapter 24.

Physics⊗Now™ Log into PhysicsNow at **www.pop4e.com** and go to Interactive Example 20.9 to explore this situation for various initial values of the voltage and the capacitance.

20.10 CAPACITORS WITH DIELECTRICS

A **dielectric** is an insulating material such as rubber, glass, or waxed paper. When a dielectric material is inserted between the plates of a capacitor, the capacitance increases. If the dielectric completely fills the space between the plates, the capacitance increases by the dimensionless factor κ, called the **dielectric constant** of the material.

The following experiment can be performed to illustrate the effect of a dielectric in a capacitor. Consider a parallel-plate capacitor of charge Q_0 and capacitance C_0 in the absence of a dielectric. The potential difference across the capacitor as measured by a voltmeter is $\Delta V_0 = Q_0/C_0$ (Fig. 20.27a). Notice that the capacitor circuit is *open;* that is, the plates of the capacitor are *not* connected to a battery and charge cannot flow through an ideal voltmeter. Hence, there is *no* path by which charge can flow and alter the charge on the capacitor. If a dielectric is now inserted between the plates as in Figure 20.27b, it is found that the voltmeter reading *decreases* by a factor of κ to the value ΔV, where

$$\Delta V = \frac{\Delta V_0}{\kappa}$$

Because $\Delta V < \Delta V_0$, we see that $\kappa > 1$.

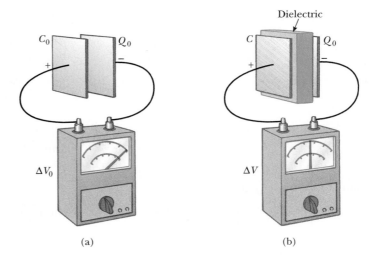

Because the charge Q_0 on the capacitor *does not change*, we conclude that the capacitance must change to the value

$$C = \frac{Q_0}{\Delta V} = \frac{Q_0}{\Delta V_0/\kappa} = \kappa \frac{Q_0}{\Delta V_0}$$

$$C = \kappa C_0 \qquad [20.33]$$

where C_0 is the capacitance in the absence of the dielectric. That is, the capacitance *increases* by the factor κ when the dielectric completely fills the region between the plates.[4] For a parallel-plate capacitor, where $C_0 = \epsilon_0 A/d$, we can express the capacitance when the capacitor is filled with a dielectric as

$$C = \kappa \frac{\epsilon_0 A}{d} \qquad [20.34]$$

PITFALL PREVENTION 20.7

IS THE CAPACITOR CONNECTED TO A BATTERY? In problems in which you are modifying a capacitor (by insertion of a dielectric, for example), you must note whether modifications to the capacitor are being made while the capacitor is connected to a battery or after it is disconnected. If the capacitor remains connected to the battery, the voltage across the capacitor necessarily remains the same. If you disconnect the capacitor from the battery before making any modifications to the capacitor, the capacitor is an isolated system and its charge remains the same.

From this result, it would appear that the capacitance could be made very large by decreasing d, the distance between the plates. In practice, however, the lowest value of d is limited by the electric discharge that could occur through the dielectric medium separating the plates. For any given separation d, the maximum voltage that can be applied to a capacitor without causing a discharge depends on the **dielectric strength** (maximum electric field) of the dielectric, which for dry air is equal to 3×10^6 V/m. If the electric field in the medium exceeds the dielectric strength, the insulating properties break down and the medium begins to conduct. Most insulating materials have dielectric strengths and dielectric constants greater than those of air, as Table 20.1 indicates. Therefore, we see that a dielectric provides the following advantages:

• It increases the capacitance of a capacitor.
• It increases the maximum operating voltage of a capacitor.
• It may provide mechanical support between the conducting plates.

We can understand the effects of a dielectric by considering the polarization of molecules that we discussed in Section 19.3. Figure 20.28a shows polarized molecules of a dielectric in random orientations in the absence of an electric field. Figure 20.28b shows the polarization of the molecules when the dielectric is placed between the plates of the charged capacitor and the polarized molecules tend to line up parallel to the field lines. The plates set up an electric field $\vec{\mathbf{E}}_0$ in a direction to

---

[4]If another experiment is performed in which the dielectric is introduced while the potential difference is held constant by means of a battery, the charge increases to the value $Q = \kappa Q_0$. The additional charge is transferred from the connecting wires, and the capacitance still increases by the factor κ.

TABLE **20.1**	Approximate Dielectric Constants and Dielectric Strengths of Various Materials at Room Temperature	
Material	**Dielectric Constant κ**	**Dielectric Strength[a] (10^6 V/m)**
Air (dry)	1.000 59	3
Bakelite	4.9	24
Fused quartz	3.78	8
Mylar	3.2	7
Neoprene rubber	6.7	12
Nylon	3.4	14
Paper	3.7	16
Paraffin-impregnated paper	3.5	11
Polystyrene	2.56	24
Polyvinyl chloride	3.4	40
Porcelain	6	12
Pyrex glass	5.6	14
Silicone oil	2.5	15
Strontium titanate	233	8
Teflon	2.1	60
Vacuum	1.000 00	—
Water	80	—

[a]The dielectric strength equals the maximum electric field that can exist in a dielectric without electrical breakdown. Note that these values depend strongly on the presence of impurities and flaws in the materials.

the right in Figure 20.28b. In the body of the dielectric, a general homogeneity of charge exists, but look along the edges. There is a layer of negative charge along the left edge of the dielectric and a layer of positive charge along the right edge. These layers of charge can be modeled as additional charged parallel plates, as in Figure 20.28c. Because the polarity is opposite that of the real plates, these charges set up an induced electric field $\vec{\mathbf{E}}_{ind}$ directed to the left in the diagram that partially cancels the electric field due to the real plates. Therefore, for the charged capacitor removed from a battery, the electric field and hence the voltage between the plates is reduced by the introduction of the dielectric. The charge on the plates is stored at a lower potential difference, so the capacitance increases.

Types of Capacitors

Commercial capacitors are often made using metal foil interlaced with a dielectric such as thin sheets of paraffin-impregnated paper. These alternating layers of metal foil and dielectric are then rolled into the shape of a cylinder to form a small package (Fig. 20.29a). High-voltage capacitors commonly consist of interwoven metal plates immersed in silicone oil (Fig. 20.29b). Small capacitors are often constructed from ceramic materials. Variable capacitors (typically 10–500 pF) usually consist of

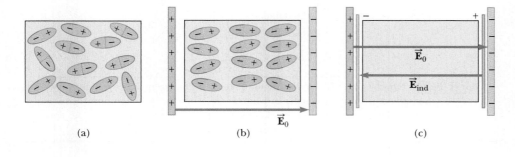

(a) (b) (c)

FIGURE **20.28** (a) Polar molecules are randomly oriented in the absence of an external electric field. (b) When an external electric field is applied, the molecules partially align with the field. (c) The charged edges of the dielectric can be modeled as an additional pair of parallel plates establishing an electric field $\vec{\mathbf{E}}_{ind}$ in the direction opposite to that of $\vec{\mathbf{E}}_0$.

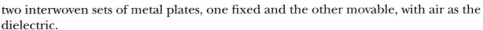

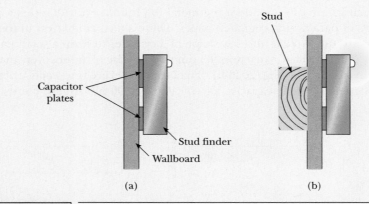

FIGURE 20.29 Three commercial capacitor designs. (a) A tubular capacitor whose plates are separated by paper and then rolled into a cylinder. (b) A high-voltage capacitor consists of many parallel plates separated by insulating oil. (c) An electrolytic capacitor.

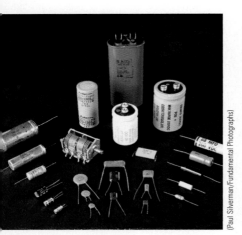

A collection of capacitors used in a variety of applications. ∎

two interwoven sets of metal plates, one fixed and the other movable, with air as the dielectric.

An *electrolytic capacitor* is often used to store large amounts of charge at relatively low voltages. This device, shown in Figure 20.29c, consists of a metal foil in contact with an electrolyte, a solution that conducts electricity by virtue of the motion of ions contained in the solution. When a voltage is applied between the foil and the electrolyte, a thin layer of metal oxide (an insulator) is formed on the foil, and this layer serves as the dielectric. Very large capacitance values can be attained because the dielectric layer is very thin.

When electrolytic capacitors are used in circuits, they must be installed with the proper polarity. If the polarity of the applied voltage is opposite what is intended, the oxide layer will be removed and the capacitor will not be able to store charge.

QUICK QUIZ 20.7 If you have ever tried to hang a picture, you know it can be difficult to locate a wooden stud in which to anchor your nail or screw. A carpenter's electric stud finder will locate the studs in a wall. It consists of a parallel-plate capacitor, with the plates next to each other, as shown in Figure 20.30. Does the capacitance increase or decrease when the device is moved over a stud?

FIGURE 20.30 (Quick Quiz 20.7) An electric stud finder. (a) The materials between the plates of the capacitor are the wallboard and air. (b) When the capacitor moves across a stud in the wall, the materials between the plates are wallboard and wood. The change in the dielectric constant causes a signal light to illuminate.

EXAMPLE 20.10 | A Paper-Filled Capacitor

A parallel-plate capacitor has plates of dimensions 2.0 cm × 3.0 cm separated by a 1.0-mm thickness of paper.

A | Find the capacitance of this device.

Solution Because $\kappa = 3.7$ for paper (see Table 20.1), we have

$$C = \kappa \frac{\epsilon_0 A}{d}$$

$$= 3.7(8.85 \times 10^{-12} \text{ C}^2/\text{N} \cdot \text{m}^2) \left(\frac{6.0 \times 10^{-4} \text{ m}^2}{1.0 \times 10^{-3} \text{ m}} \right)$$

$$= 20 \times 10^{-12} \text{ F} = \boxed{20 \text{ pF}}$$

B | What is the maximum charge that can be placed on the capacitor?

Solution From Table 20.1, we see that the dielectric strength of paper is 16×10^6 V/m. Because the thickness of the paper is 1.0 mm, the maximum voltage that can be applied before breakdown is

$$\Delta V_{max} = E_{max} d = (16 \times 10^6 \text{ V/m})(1.0 \times 10^{-3} \text{ m})$$

$$= 16 \times 10^3 \text{ V}$$

Hence, the maximum charge is

$$Q_{max} = C \, \Delta V_{max} = (20 \times 10^{-12} \text{ F})(16 \times 10^3 \text{ V}) = \boxed{0.32 \ \mu\text{C}}$$

EXAMPLE 20.11 | Energy Stored Before and After

A parallel-plate capacitor is charged with a battery to a charge Q_0 as in Figure 20.31a. The battery is then removed and a slab of material that has a dielectric constant κ is inserted between the plates as in Figure 20.31b. Find the energy stored in the capacitor before and after the dielectric is inserted.

Solution From Equation 20.30, the energy stored in the capacitor in the absence of the dielectric is

$$U_0 = \frac{Q_0^2}{2C_0}$$

After the battery is removed and the dielectric is inserted between the plates, the charge on the capacitor remains the same because the unconnected capacitor is an isolated system. Hence, the energy stored in the presence of the dielectric is

$$U = \frac{Q_0^2}{2C}$$

The capacitance in the presence of the dielectric, however, is given by $C = \kappa C_0$, so U becomes

$$U = \frac{Q_0^2}{2\kappa C_0} = \frac{U_0}{\kappa}$$

Because $\kappa > 1$, we see that the final energy is less than the initial energy by the factor $1/\kappa$.

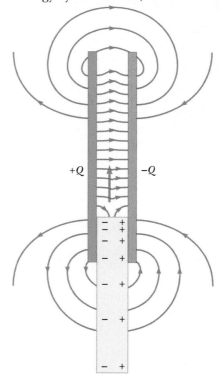

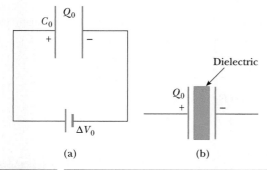

FIGURE 20.31 | (Example 20.11) (a) A battery charges up a parallel-plate capacitor. (b) The battery is removed and a slab of dielectric material is inserted between the plates.

FIGURE 20.32 | (Example 20.11) When a dielectric approaches an empty capacitor, the charge distributions induced on the edges cause an attraction between the dielectric and the capacitor.

This missing energy can be accounted for as follows. We identify the system as the capacitor and the dielectric. As the dielectric is brought near the capacitor so that electric field lines from the plates pass through the dielectric, the molecules of the dielectric become polarized. The edges of the dielectric take on a charge opposite to the plate nearest the edge as in Figure 20.32. Therefore, an attractive force exists between the dielectric and the plates. If the dielectric were released, it would be pulled into the plates and would pass through the plates with a kinetic energy, emerging on the other side and exhibiting oscillatory motion. If an external agent such as your hand holds the dielectric, allowing it to move into the plates at constant speed, the agent is doing negative work on the system. The displacement of the dielectric is into the plates, but the applied force is away from the plates. This work represents a decrease in energy for the system, so the energy change is $\Delta U = U - U_0$. Therefore, the unconnected capacitor and dielectric form an isolated system for electric charge, but when considering energy, it is a nonisolated system.

20.11 THE ATMOSPHERE AS A CAPACITOR

CONTEXT CONNECTION

In the Context Connection of Chapter 19, we mentioned some processes occurring on the surface of the Earth and in the atmosphere that result in charge distributions. These processes result in a negative charge on the Earth's surface and positive charges distributed throughout the air.

This separation of charge can be modeled as a capacitor. The surface of the Earth is one plate and the positive charge in the air is the other plate. The positive charge in the atmosphere is not all located at one height but is spread throughout the atmosphere. Therefore, the position of the upper plate must be modeled, based on the charge distribution. Models of the atmosphere show that an appropriate effective height of the upper plate is about 5 km from the surface. The model atmospheric capacitor is shown in Figure 20.33.

Considering the charge distribution on the surface of the Earth to be spherically symmetric, we can use the result from Example 20.6 to claim that the potential at a point above the Earth's surface is

$$V = k_e \frac{Q}{r}$$

where Q is the charge on the surface. The potential difference between the plates of our atmospheric capacitor is

$$\Delta V = \frac{Q}{4\pi\epsilon_0}\left(\frac{1}{r_{\text{surface}}} - \frac{1}{r_{\text{upper plate}}}\right)$$

$$= \frac{Q}{4\pi\epsilon_0}\left(\frac{1}{R_E} - \frac{1}{R_E + h}\right) = \frac{Q}{4\pi\epsilon_0}\left(\frac{h}{R_E(R_E + h)}\right)$$

where R_E is the radius of the Earth and $h = 5$ km. From this expression, we can calculate the capacitance of the atmospheric capacitor:

$$C = \frac{Q}{\Delta V} = \frac{Q}{\dfrac{Q}{4\pi\epsilon_0}\left[\dfrac{h}{R_E(R_E + h)}\right]} = \frac{4\pi\epsilon_0 R_E(R_E + h)}{h}$$

Substituting the numerical values, we have

$$C = \frac{4\pi\epsilon_0 R_E(R_E + h)}{h}$$

$$= \frac{4\pi(8.85 \times 10^{-12}\ \text{C}^2/\text{N·m}^2)(6.4 \times 10^3\ \text{km})(6.4 \times 10^3\ \text{km} + 5\ \text{km})}{5\ \text{km}}\left(\frac{1000\ \text{m}}{1\ \text{km}}\right)$$

$$\approx 0.9\ \text{F}$$

FIGURE 20.33 The atmospheric capacitor. The Earth's surface serves as the negative plate, and the positive plate is modeled at a height in the atmosphere that represents positive charges spread through the atmosphere.

Negative plate (Earth's surface)

Positive plate (charges in atmosphere)

This result is extremely large, compared with the *picofarads* and *microfarads* that are typical values for capacitors in electrical circuits, especially for a capacitor having plates that are 5 km apart! We shall use this model of the atmosphere as a capacitor in our Context Conclusion, in which we calculate the number of lightning strikes on the Earth in one day.

SUMMARY

Physics⊗Now™ Take a practice test by logging into Physics-Now at **www.pop4e.com** and clicking on the Pre-Test link for this chapter.

When a positive test charge q_0 is moved between points A and B in an electric field $\vec{E}$, the **change in potential energy** of the charge–field system is

$$\Delta U = -q_0 \int_A^B \vec{E} \cdot d\vec{s} \qquad [20.1]$$

The **potential difference** ΔV between points A and B in an electric field $\vec{E}$ is defined as the change in potential energy divided by the test charge q_0:

$$\Delta V = \frac{\Delta U}{q_0} = -\int_A^B \vec{E} \cdot d\vec{s} \qquad [20.3]$$

where **electric potential** V is a scalar and has the units joules per coulomb, defined as 1 **volt** (V).

The potential difference between two points A and B in a uniform electric field $\vec{E}$ is

$$\Delta V = -\vec{E} \cdot \Delta\vec{r} \qquad [20.8]$$

where $\Delta\vec{r}$ is the displacement vector between A and B.

Equipotential surfaces are surfaces on which the electric potential remains constant. Equipotential surfaces are *perpendicular* to electric field lines.

The electric potential due to a point charge q at a distance r from the charge is

$$V = k_e \frac{q}{r} \qquad [20.11]$$

The electric potential due to a group of point charges is obtained by summing the potentials due to the individual charges. Because V is a scalar, the sum is a simple algebraic operation.

The **electric potential energy of a pair of point charges** separated by a distance r_{12} is

$$U = k_e \frac{q_1 q_2}{r_{12}} \qquad [20.13]$$

which represents the work required to bring the charges from an infinite separation to the separation r_{12}. The potential energy of a distribution of point charges is obtained by summing terms like Equation 20.13 over *all pairs* of particles.

If the electric potential is known as a function of coordinates x, y, and z, the components of the electric field can be obtained by taking the negative derivative of the potential with respect to the coordinates. For example, the x component of an electric field in the x direction is

$$E_x = -\frac{\partial V}{\partial x} \qquad [20.16]$$

The **electric potential due to a continuous charge distribution** is

$$V = k_e \int \frac{dq}{r} \qquad [20.18]$$

Every point on the surface of a charged conductor in electrostatic equilibrium is at the same potential. Furthermore, the potential is constant everywhere inside the conductor and is equal to its value at the surface.

A capacitor is a device for storing charge. A charged capacitor consists of two equal and oppositely charged conductors with a potential difference ΔV between them. The **capacitance** C of any capacitor is defined as the ratio of the magnitude of the charge Q on either conductor to the magnitude of the potential difference ΔV:

$$C \equiv \frac{Q}{\Delta V} \qquad [20.19]$$

The SI units of capacitance are coulombs per volt, or the **farad** (F), and 1 F = 1 C/V.

If two or more capacitors are connected in parallel, the potential differences across them must be the same. The equivalent capacitance of a parallel combination of capacitors is

$$C_{eq} = C_1 + C_2 + C_3 + \cdots \qquad [20.25]$$

If two or more capacitors are connected in series, the charges on them are the same and the equivalent capacitance of the series combination is given by

$$\frac{1}{C_{eq}} = \frac{1}{C_1} + \frac{1}{C_2} + \frac{1}{C_3} + \cdots \qquad [20.29]$$

Energy is required to charge a capacitor because the charging process is equivalent to transferring charges from one conductor at a lower potential to another conductor at a higher potential. The electric potential energy U stored in the capacitor is

$$U = \frac{Q^2}{2C} = \tfrac{1}{2} Q\,\Delta V = \tfrac{1}{2} C(\Delta V)^2 \qquad [20.30]$$

When a dielectric material is inserted between the plates of a capacitor, the capacitance generally increases by the dimensionless factor κ, called the **dielectric constant.** That is,

$$C = \kappa C_0 \qquad [20.33]$$

where C_0 is the capacitance in the absence of the dielectric.

QUESTIONS

□ = answer available in the *Student Solutions Manual and Study Guide*

1. Distinguish between electric potential and electric potential energy.

2. A negative charge moves in the direction of a uniform electric field. Does the potential energy of the charge–field system increase or decrease? Does the charge move to a position of higher or lower potential?

3. Give a physical explanation showing that the potential energy of a pair of charges with the same sign is positive, whereas the potential energy of a pair of charges with opposite signs is negative.

4. Explain why, under static conditions, all points in a conductor must be at the same electric potential.

5. Why is it important to avoid sharp edges or points on conductors used in high-voltage equipment?

6. How would you shield an electronic circuit or laboratory from stray electric fields? Why does that method work?

7. Study Figure 19.4 and the accompanying text discussion of charging by induction. When the grounding wire is touched to the rightmost point on the sphere in Figure 19.4c, electrons are drained away from the sphere to leave the sphere positively charged. Instead, suppose the grounding wire is touched to the leftmost point on the sphere. Will electrons still drain away, moving closer to the negatively charged rod as they do so? What kind of charge, if any, will remain on the sphere?

8. The plates of a capacitor are connected to a battery. What happens to the charge on the plates if the connecting wires are removed from the battery? What happens to the charge if the wires are removed from the battery and connected to each other?

9. One pair of capacitors is connected in parallel, whereas an identical pair is connected in series. Which pair would be more dangerous to handle after being connected to the same battery? Explain.

10. If you are given three different capacitors C_1, C_2, C_3, how many different combinations of capacitance can you produce?

11. If the potential difference across a capacitor is doubled, by what factor does the energy stored change?

12. Because the charges on the plates of a parallel-plate capacitor are opposite in sign, they attract each other. Hence, it would take positive work to increase the plate separation. What type of energy in the system changes due to the external work done in this process?

13. It is possible to obtain large potential differences by first charging a group of capacitors connected in parallel and then activating a switch arrangement that in effect disconnects the capacitors from the charging source and from each other and reconnects them in a series arrangement. The group of charged capacitors is then discharged in series. What is the maximum potential difference that can be obtained in this manner by using ten capacitors each of 500 μF and a charging source of 800 V?

14. Assume that you want to increase the maximum operating voltage of a parallel-plate capacitor. Describe how you can do so for a fixed plate separation.

15. If you were asked to design a capacitor in which small size and large capacitance were required, what factors would be important in your design?

16. Explain why a dielectric increases the maximum operating voltage of a capacitor although the physical size of the capacitor does not change.

PROBLEMS

1, 2, 3 = straightforward, intermediate, challenging
□ = full solution available in the *Student Solutions Manual and Study Guide*

Physics⊗Now™ = coached problem with hints available at www.pop4e.com

🖥 = computer useful in solving problem

▬ = paired numerical and symbolic problems

📑 = biomedical application

Section 20.1 ▪ Potential Difference and Electric Potential

1. (a) Calculate the speed of a proton that is accelerated from rest through a potential difference of 120 V. (b) Calculate the speed of an electron that is accelerated through the same potential difference.

2. How much work is done (by a battery, generator, or some other source of potential difference) in moving Avogadro's number of electrons from an initial point where the electric potential is 9.00 V to a point where the potential is − 5.00 V? (The potential in each case is measured relative to a common reference point.)

Section 20.2 ▪ Potential Differences in a Uniform Electric Field

3. A uniform electric field of magnitude 250 V/m is directed in the positive x direction. A + 12.0-μC charge moves from the origin to the point $(x, y) = (20.0$ cm, 50.0 cm). (a) What is the change in the potential energy of the charge–field system? (b) Through what potential difference does the charge move?

4. The difference in potential between the accelerating plates in the electron gun of a TV picture tube is about

25 000 V. If the distance between these plates is 1.50 cm, what is the magnitude of the uniform electric field in this region?

5. **Physics⊗Now™** An electron moving parallel to the x axis has an initial speed of 3.70×10^6 m/s at the origin. Its speed is reduced to 1.40×10^5 m/s at the point $x = 2.00$ cm. Calculate the potential difference between the origin and that point. Which point is at the higher potential?

6. Review problem. A block having mass m and positive charge Q is connected to an insulating spring having constant k. The block lies on a frictionless, insulating horizontal track, and the system is immersed in a uniform electric field of magnitude E, directed as shown in Figure P20.6. If the block is released from rest when the spring is unstretched (at $x = 0$), (a) by what maximum amount does the spring expand? (b) What is the equilibrium position of the block? (c) Show that the block's motion is simple harmonic and determine its period. (d) Repeat part (a), assuming that the coefficient of kinetic friction between block and surface is μ_k.

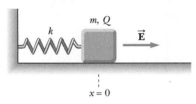

FIGURE P20.6

Section 20.3 ▪ Electric Potential and Electric Potential Energy Due to Point Charges

Note: Unless stated otherwise, assume that the reference level of potential is $V = 0$ at $r = \infty$.

7. (a) Find the potential at a distance of 1.00 cm from a proton. (b) What is the potential difference between two points that are 1.00 cm and 2.00 cm from a proton? (c) Repeat parts (a) and (b) for an electron.

8. Given two 2.00-μC charges as shown in Figure P20.8 and a positive test charge $q = 1.28 \times 10^{-18}$ C at the origin, (a) what is the net force exerted by the two 2.00-μC charges on the test charge q? (b) What is the electric field at the origin due to the two 2.00-μC charges? (c) What is the electrical potential at the origin due to the two 2.00-μC charges?

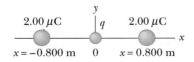

FIGURE P20.8

9. A charge $+q$ is at the origin. A charge $-2q$ is at $x = 2.00$ m on the x axis. (a) For what finite value(s) of x is the electric field zero? (b) For what finite value(s) of x is the electric potential zero?

10. *Compare this problem with Problem 19.55.* Four identical point charges ($q = +10.0\ \mu$C) are located on the corners of a rectangle as shown in Figure P19.55. The dimensions of the rectangle are $L = 60.0$ cm and $W = 15.0$ cm. Calculate the change in electric potential energy of the system as the charge at the lower left corner in Figure P19.55 is brought to this position from infinitely far away. Assume that the other three charges remain fixed in position.

11. The three charges in Figure P20.11 are at the vertices of an isosceles triangle. Calculate the electric potential at the midpoint of the base, taking $q = 7.00\ \mu$C.

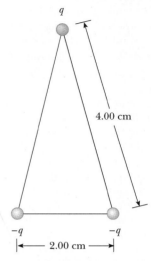

FIGURE P20.11

12. *Compare this problem with Problem 19.14.* Two point charges each of magnitude 2.00 μC are located on the x axis. One is at $x = 1.00$ m and the other is at $x = -1.00$ m. (a) Determine the electric potential on the y axis at $y = 0.500$ m. (b) Calculate the change in electric potential energy of the system as a third charge of $-3.00\ \mu$C is brought from infinitely far away to a position on the y axis at $y = 0.500$ m.

13. **Physics⊗Now™** Show that the amount of work required to assemble four identical point charges of magnitude Q at the corners of a square of side s is $5.41 k_e Q^2/s$.

14. Two charged particles create influences at the origin, described by the expressions

$$8.99 \times 10^9\ \text{N} \cdot \text{m}^2/\text{C}^2 \left[-\frac{7.00 \times 10^{-9}\ \text{C}}{(0.070\ 0\ \text{m})^2} \cos 70.0° \hat{\mathbf{i}} \right.$$
$$\left. -\frac{7.00 \times 10^{-9}\ \text{C}}{(0.070\ 0\ \text{m})^2} \sin 70.0° \hat{\mathbf{j}} + \frac{8.00 \times 10^{-9}\ \text{C}}{(0.030\ 0\ \text{m})^2} \hat{\mathbf{j}} \right]$$

and

$$8.99 \times 10^9\ \text{N} \cdot \text{m}^2/\text{C}^2 \left[\frac{7.00 \times 10^{-9}\ \text{C}}{0.070\ 0\ \text{m}} - \frac{8.00 \times 10^{-9}\ \text{C}}{0.030\ 0\ \text{m}} \right]$$

(a) Identify the locations of the particles and the charges on them. (b) Find the force on a -16.0-nC charge placed at the origin and (c) the work required to move this third charge to the origin from a very distant point.

15. Review problem. Two insulating spheres have radii 0.300 cm and 0.500 cm, masses 0.100 kg and 0.700 kg, and uniformly distributed charges $-2.00\ \mu$C and 3.00 μC. They are released from rest when their centers are separated by

1.00 m. (a) How fast will each be moving when they collide? (*Suggestion:* Consider conservation of energy and of linear momentum.) (b) If the spheres were conductors, would the speeds be greater or less than those calculated in part (a)? Explain.

16. **Review problem.** Two insulating spheres have radii r_1 and r_2, masses m_1 and m_2, and uniformly distributed charges $-q_1$ and q_2. They are released from rest when their centers are separated by a distance d. (a) How fast is each moving when they collide? (*Suggestion:* Consider conservation of energy and conservation of linear momentum.) (b) If the spheres were conductors, would their speeds be greater or less than those calculated in part (a)? Explain.

17. *Compare this problem with Problem 19.26.* Three equal positive charges q are at the corners of an equilateral triangle of side a as shown in Figure P19.26. (a) At what point, if any, in the plane of the charges is the electric potential zero? (b) What is the electric potential at the point P due to the two charges at the base of the triangle?

18. Two particles, with charges of 20.0 nC and −20.0 nC, are placed at the points with coordinates (0, 4.00 cm) and (0, −4.00 cm) as shown in Figure P20.18. A particle with charge 10.0 nC is located at the origin. (a) Find the electric potential energy of the configuration of the three fixed charges. (b) A fourth particle, with a mass of 2.00×10^{-13} kg and a charge of 40.0 nC, is released from rest at the point (3.00 cm, 0). Find its speed after it has moved freely to a very large distance away.

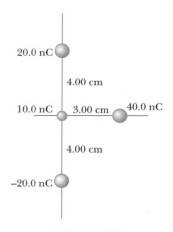

FIGURE **P20.18**

19. **Review problem.** A light, unstressed spring has length d. Two identical particles, each with charge q, are connected to the opposite ends of the spring. The particles are held stationary a distance d apart and are then released at the same time. The system then oscillates on a horizontal frictionless table. The spring has a bit of internal kinetic friction, so the oscillation is damped. The particles eventually stop vibrating when the distance between them is $3d$. Find the increase in internal energy that appears in the spring during the oscillations. Assume that the system of the spring and two charges is isolated.

20. In 1911, Ernest Rutherford and his assistants Hans Geiger and Ernest Marsden conducted an experiment in which they scattered alpha particles from thin sheets of gold. An alpha particle, having charge $+2e$ and mass 6.64×10^{-27} kg, is a product of certain radioactive decays. The results of the experiment led Rutherford to the idea that most of the mass of an atom is in a very small nucleus, with electrons in orbit around it, in his planetary model of the atom. Assume that an alpha particle, initially very far from a gold nucleus, is fired with a velocity of 2.00×10^7 m/s directly toward the nucleus (charge $+79e$). How close does the alpha particle get to the nucleus before turning around? Assume that the gold nucleus remains stationary.

Section 20.4 ▪ Obtaining Electric Field From Electric Potential

21. The potential in a region between $x = 0$ and $x = 6.00$ m is $V = a + bx$, where $a = 10.0$ V and $b = -7.00$ V/m. Determine (a) the potential at $x = 0$, 3.00 m, and 6.00 m; and (b) the magnitude and direction of the electric field at $x = 0$, 3.00 m, and 6.00 m.

22. The electric potential inside a charged spherical conductor of radius R is given by $V = k_e Q/R$ and outside the potential is given by $V = k_e Q/r$. Using $E_r = -dV/dr$, derive the electric field (a) inside and (b) outside this charge distribution.

23. **Physics⊗Now™** Over a certain region of space, the electric potential is $V = 5x - 3x^2y + 2yz^2$. Find the expressions for the x, y, and z components of the electric field over this region. What is the magnitude of the field at the point P that has coordinates $(1, 0, -2)$ m?

Section 20.5 ▪ Electric Potential Due to Continuous Charge Distributions

24. Consider a ring of radius R with the total charge Q spread uniformly over its perimeter. What is the potential difference between the point at the center of the ring and a point on its axis a distance $2R$ from the center?

25. A rod of length L (Fig. P20.25) lies along the x axis with its left end at the origin. It has a nonuniform charge density $\lambda = \alpha x$, where α is a positive constant. (a) What are the units of α? (b) Calculate the electric potential at A.

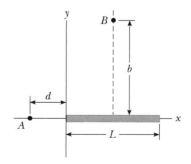

FIGURE **P20.25** Problems 20.25 and 20.26.

26. For the arrangement described in Problem 20.25, calculate the electric potential at point B that lies on the perpendicular bisector of the rod a distance b above the x axis.

27. *Compare this problem with Problem 19.21.* A uniformly charged insulating rod of length 14.0 cm is bent into the shape of a

semicircle as shown in Figure P19.21. The rod has a total charge of $-7.50\ \mu C$. Find the electric potential at O, the center of the semicircle.

Section 20.6 ▪ Electric Potential of a Charged Conductor

28. How many electrons should be removed from an initially uncharged spherical conductor of radius 0.300 m to produce a potential of 7.50 kV at the surface?

29. **Physics⊗Now**™ A spherical conductor has a radius of 14.0 cm and charge of 26.0 μC. Calculate the electric field and the electric potential (a) $r = 10.0$ cm, (b) $r = 20.0$ cm, and (c) $r = 14.0$ cm from the center.

30. Electric charge can accumulate on an airplane in flight. You may have observed needle-shaped metal extensions on the wing tips and tail of an airplane. Their purpose is to allow charge to leak off before much of it accumulates. The electric field around the needle is much larger than around the body of the airplane and can become large enough to produce dielectric breakdown of the air, discharging the airplane. To model this process, assume that two charged spherical conductors are connected by a long conducting wire and that a charge of 1.20 μC is placed on the combination. One sphere, representing the body of the airplane, has a radius of 6.00 cm, and the other, representing the tip of the needle, has a radius of 2.00 cm. (a) What is the·electric potential of each sphere? (b) What is the electric field at the surface of each sphere?

Section 20.7 ▪ Capacitance

31. (a) How much charge is on each plate of a 4.00-μF capacitor when it is connected to a 12.0-V battery? (b) If this same capacitor is connected to a 1.50-V battery, what charge is stored?

32. Two conductors having net charges of $+10.0\ \mu C$ and $-10.0\ \mu C$ have a potential difference of 10.0 V between them. (a) Determine the capacitance of the system. (b) What is the potential difference between the two conductors if the charges on each are increased to $+100\ \mu C$ and $-100\ \mu C$?

33. An isolated charged conducting sphere of radius 12.0 cm creates an electric field of 4.90×10^4 N/C at a distance 21.0 cm from its center. (a) What is its surface charge density? (b) What is its capacitance?

34. A variable air capacitor used in a radio tuning circuit is made of N semicircular plates each of radius R and positioned a distance d from its neighbors, to which it is electrically connected. As shown in the opening photograph on page 642 and modeled in Figure P20.34, a second identical set of plates is enmeshed with its plates halfway between those of the first set. The second set can rotate as a unit. Determine the capacitance as a function of the angle of rotation θ, where $\theta = 0$ corresponds to the maximum capacitance.

35. An air-filled capacitor consists of two parallel plates, each with an area of 7.60 cm^2, separated by a distance of 1.80 mm. A 20.0-V potential difference is applied to these plates. Calculate (a) the electric field between the plates, (b) the surface charge density, (c) the capacitance, and (d) the charge on each plate.

36. A 50.0-m length of coaxial cable has an inner conductor that has a diameter of 2.58 mm and carries a charge of 8.10 μC. The surrounding conductor has an inner diameter of 7.27 mm and a charge of $-8.10\ \mu C$. (a) What is the capacitance of this cable? (b) What is the potential difference between the two conductors? Assume that the region between the conductors is air.

37. A small object of mass m carries a charge q and is suspended by a thread between the vertical plates of a parallel-plate capacitor. The plate separation is d. If the thread makes an angle θ with the vertical, what is the potential difference between the plates?

38. A *spherical capacitor* consists of a spherical conducting shell of radius b and charge $-Q$ that is concentric with a smaller conducting sphere of radius a and charge $+Q$ (Fig. P20.38). (a) Show that its capacitance is

$$C = \frac{ab}{k_e(b - a)}$$

(b) Show that as b approaches infinity, the capacitance approaches the value $a/k_e = 4\pi\epsilon_0 a$.

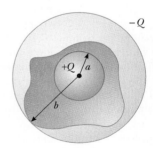

FIGURE **P20.38**

Section 20.8 ▪ Combinations of Capacitors

39. Two capacitors, $C_1 = 5.00\ \mu F$ and $C_2 = 12.0\ \mu F$, are connected in parallel, and the resulting combination is connected to a 9.00-V battery. (a) What is the equivalent capacitance of the combination? What are (b) the potential difference across each capacitor and (c) the charge stored on each capacitor?

40. The two capacitors of Problem 20.39 are now connected in series and to a 9.00-V battery. Find (a) the equivalent capacitance of the combination, (b) the potential difference across each capacitor, and (c) the charge on each capacitor.

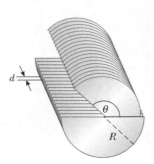

FIGURE **P20.34**

41. **Physics⊗Now™** Four capacitors are connected as shown in Figure P20.41. (a) Find the equivalent capacitance between points a and b. (b) Calculate the charge on each capacitor, taking $\Delta V_{ab} = 15.0$ V.

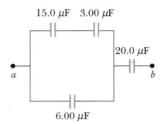

15.0 μF   3.00 μF

20.0 μF

a b

6.00 μF

FIGURE **P20.41**

42. Two capacitors when connected in parallel give an equivalent capacitance of C_p and an equivalent capacitance of C_s when connected in series. What is the capacitance of each capacitor?

43. Consider the circuit shown in Figure P20.43, where $C_1 = 6.00$ μF, $C_2 = 3.00$ μF, and $\Delta V = 20.0$ V. Capacitor C_1 is first charged by the closing of switch S_1. Switch S_1 is then opened, and the charged capacitor is connected to the uncharged capacitor by the closing of S_2. Calculate the initial charge acquired by C_1 and the final charge on each capacitor.

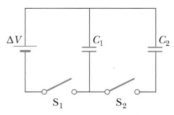

ΔV C_1 C_2

S_1 S_2

FIGURE **P20.43**

44. Three capacitors are connected to a battery as shown in Figure P20.44. Their capacitances are $C_1 = 3C$, $C_2 = C$, and $C_3 = 5C$. (a) What is the equivalent capacitance of this set of capacitors? (b) State the ranking of the capacitors according to the charge they store, from largest to smallest. (c) Rank the capacitors according to the potential differences across them, from largest to smallest. (d) If now C_3 is increased, what happens to the charge stored by each of the capacitors?

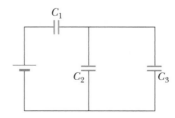

C_1

C_2 C_3

FIGURE **P20.44**

45. According to its design specification, the timer circuit delaying the closing of an elevator door is to have a capacitance of 32.0 μF between two points A and B. (a) When one circuit is being constructed, the inexpensive but durable capacitor installed between these two points is found to have capacitance 34.8 μF. To meet the specification, one additional capacitor can be placed between the two points. Should it be in series or in parallel with the 34.8-μF capacitor? What should be its capacitance? (b) The next circuit comes down the assembly line with capacitance 29.8 μF between A and B. What additional capacitor should be installed in series or in parallel in that circuit to meet the specification?

46. Find the equivalent capacitance between points a and b in the combination of capacitors shown in Figure P20.46.

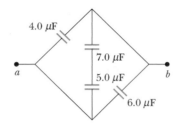

4.0 μF

7.0 μF

a b

5.0 μF

6.0 μF

FIGURE **P20.46**

Section 20.9 ■ Energy Stored in a Charged Capacitor

47. (a) A 3.00-μF capacitor is connected to a 12.0-V battery. How much energy is stored in the capacitor? (b) If the capacitor had been connected to a 6.00-V battery, how much energy would have been stored?

48. The immediate cause of many deaths is ventricular fibrillation, an uncoordinated quivering of the heart as opposed to proper beating. An electric shock to the chest can cause momentary paralysis of the heart muscle, after which the heart will sometimes start organized beating again. A *defibrillator* (Fig. P20.48) is a device that applies a strong electric shock to the chest over a time interval of a few milliseconds. The device contains a capacitor of several microfarads, charged to several thousand volts. Electrodes called paddles, about 8 cm across and coated with conducting paste, are held against the chest on both sides of the heart.

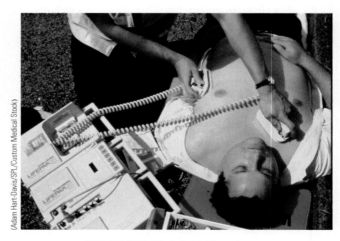

(Adam Hart-Davis/SPL/Custom Medical Stock)

FIGURE **P20.48** A defibrillator in use.

Their handles are insulated to prevent injury to the operator, who calls "Clear!" and pushes a button on one paddle to discharge the capacitor through the patient's chest. Assume that an energy of 300 J is to be delivered from a 30.0-μF capacitor. To what potential difference must it be charged?

49. Two capacitors, $C_1 = 25.0 \ \mu$F and $C_2 = 5.00 \ \mu$F, are connected in parallel and charged with a 100-V power supply. (a) Draw a circuit diagram and calculate the total energy stored in the two capacitors. (b) What potential difference would be required across the same two capacitors connected in series so that the combination stores the same energy as in part (a)? Draw a circuit diagram of this circuit.

50. ▨ As a person moves about in a dry environment, electric charge accumulates on the person's body. Once it is at high voltage, either positive or negative, the body can discharge via sometimes noticeable sparks and shocks. Consider a human body well separated from ground, with the typical capacitance 150 pF. (a) What charge on the body will produce a potential of 10.0 kV? (b) Sensitive electronic devices can be destroyed by electrostatic discharge from a person. A particular device can be destroyed by a discharge releasing an energy of 250 μJ. To what voltage on the body does this energy correspond?

51. A parallel-plate capacitor has a charge Q and plates of area A. What force acts on one plate to attract it toward the other plate? Because the electric field between the plates is $E = Q/A\epsilon_0$, you might think that the force is $F = QE = Q^2/A\epsilon_0$. This conclusion is wrong because the field E includes contributions from both plates, and the field created by the positive plate cannot exert any force on the positive plate. Show that the force exerted on each plate is actually $F = Q^2/2\epsilon_0 A$. (*Suggestion:* Let $C = \epsilon_0 A/x$ for an arbitrary plate separation x; then require that the work done in separating the two charged plates be $W = \int F \, dx$.) The force exerted by one charged plate on another is sometimes used in a machine shop to hold a workpiece stationary.

52. A uniform electric field $E = 3\,000$ V/m exists within a certain region. What volume of space contains an energy equal to 1.00×10^{-7} J? Express your answer in cubic meters and in liters.

Section 20.10 ▮ Capacitors with Dielectrics

53. Determine (a) the capacitance and (b) the maximum potential difference that can be applied to a Teflon-filled parallel-plate capacitor having a plate area of 1.75 cm^2 and plate separation of 0.040 0 mm.

54. (a) How much charge can be placed on a capacitor with air between the plates before it breaks down if the area of each of the plates is 5.00 cm^2? (b) Find the maximum charge assuming polystyrene is used between the plates instead of air.

55. A commercial capacitor is to be constructed as shown in Figure 20.29a. This particular capacitor is made from two strips of aluminum foil separated by a strip of paraffin-coated paper. Each strip of foil and paper is 7.00 cm wide. The foil is 0.004 00 mm thick, and the paper is 0.025 0 mm thick and has a dielectric constant of 3.70. What length

should the strips have if a capacitance of 9.50×10^{-8} F is desired before the capacitor is rolled up? (Adding a second strip of paper and rolling the capacitor effectively doubles its capacitance by allowing charge storage on both sides of each strip of foil.)

56. The supermarket sells rolls of aluminum foil, of plastic wrap, and of waxed paper. Describe a capacitor made from supermarket materials. Compute order-of-magnitude estimates for its capacitance and its breakdown voltage.

57. A parallel-plate capacitor in air has a plate separation of 1.50 cm and a plate area of 25.0 cm^2. The plates are charged to a potential difference of 250 V and disconnected from the source. The capacitor is then immersed in distilled water. Determine (a) the charge on the plates before and after immersion, (b) the capacitance and potential difference after immersion, and (c) the change in energy of the capacitor. Assume that the liquid is an insulator.

Section 20.11 ▮ Context Connection—The Atmosphere as a Capacitor

58. Lightning can be studied with a Van de Graaff generator, essentially consisting of a spherical dome on which charge is continuously deposited by a moving belt. Charge can be added until the electric field at the surface of the dome becomes equal to the dielectric strength of air (3×10^6 V/m). Any more charge leaks off in sparks as shown in Figure P20.58. Assume that the dome has a diameter of 30.0 cm and is surrounded by dry air. (a) What is the maximum potential of the dome? (b) What is the maximum charge on the dome?

FIGURE **P20.58**

59. **Review problem.** A certain storm cloud has a potential of 1.00×10^8 V relative to a tree. If, during a lightning storm, 50.0 C of charge is transferred through this potential difference and 1.00% of the energy is absorbed by the tree, how much sap in the tree can be boiled away? Model the sap as water initially at 30.0° C. Water has a specific heat of

4 186 J/kg · °C, a boiling point of 100 °C, and a latent heat of vaporization of 2.26×10^6 J/kg.

Additional Problems

60. **Review problem.** From a large distance away, a particle of mass 2.00 g and charge 15.0 μC is fired at 21.0$\hat{\textbf{i}}$ m/s straight toward a second particle, originally stationary but free to move, with mass 5.00 g and charge 8.50 μC. (a) At the instant of closest approach, both particles will be moving at the same velocity. Explain why. (b) Find this velocity. (c) Find the distance of closest approach. (d) Find the velocities of both particles after they separate again.

61. The liquid-drop model of the atomic nucleus suggests that high-energy oscillations of certain nuclei can split the nucleus into two unequal fragments plus a few neutrons. The fission products acquire kinetic energy from their mutual Coulomb repulsion. Calculate the electric potential energy (in electron volts) of two spherical fragments from a uranium nucleus having the following charges and radii: $38e$ and 5.50×10^{-15} m; $54e$ and 6.20×10^{-15} m. Assume that the charge is distributed uniformly throughout the volume of each spherical fragment and that just before separating each fragment is at rest and their surfaces are in contact. The electrons surrounding the nucleus can be ignored.

62. The Bohr model of the hydrogen atom states that the single electron can exist only in certain allowed orbits around the proton. The radius of each Bohr orbit is $r = n^2(0.052\ 9\ \text{nm})$ where $n = 1, 2, 3, \ldots$. Calculate the electric potential energy of a hydrogen atom when the electron is in the (a) first allowed orbit, with $n = 1$; (b) second allowed orbit, with $n = 2$; and (c) when the electron has escaped from the atom, with $r = \infty$. Express your answers in electron volts.

63. Calculate the work that must be done to charge a spherical shell of radius R to a total charge Q.

64. A Geiger–Mueller tube is a radiation detector that essentially consists of a closed, hollow metal cylinder (the cathode) of inner radius r_a and a coaxial cylindrical wire (the anode) of radius r_b (Fig. P20.64). The charge per unit length on the anode is λ, and the charge per unit length on the cathode is $-\lambda$. A gas fills the space between the electrodes. When a high-energy elementary particle passes through this space, it can ionize an atom of the gas. The strong electric field makes the resulting ion and electron accelerate in opposite directions. They strike other molecules of the gas to ionize them, producing an avalanche of electrical discharge. The pulse of electric current between the wire and the cylinder is counted by an external circuit. (a) Show that the magnitude of the potential difference between the wire and the cylinder is

$$\Delta V = 2k_e\lambda \ln\left(\frac{r_a}{r_b}\right)$$

(b) Show that the magnitude of the electric field in the space between cathode and anode is given by

$$E = \frac{\Delta V}{\ln(r_a/r_b)}\left(\frac{1}{r}\right)$$

where r is the distance from the axis of the anode to the point where the field is to be calculated.

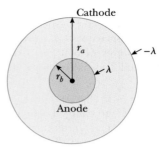

FIGURE P20.64 Problems 20.64, 20.65, and 20.66.

65. Assume that the internal diameter of the Geiger–Mueller tube described in Problem 20.64 is 2.50 cm and that the wire along the axis has a diameter of 0.200 mm. The dielectric strength of the gas between the central wire and the cylinder is 1.20×10^6 V/m. Use the result of Problem 20.64 to calculate the maximum potential difference that can be applied between the wire and the cylinder before breakdown occurs in the gas.

66. ⌨ The results of Problem 20.64 apply also to an electrostatic precipitator (Figs. P20.64 and P20.66). This pollution-control device consists of a vertical cylindrical duct with a wire along its axis at a high negative voltage. Corona discharge ionizes the air around the wire to produce free electrons and positive and negative molecular ions. The electrons and negative ions accelerate outward. As air passes through the cylinder, the dirt particles become electrically charged by collisions and ion capture. They are then swept out of the air by the horizontal electric field between the wire and the cylinder. In a particular case, an applied voltage $\Delta V = V_a - V_b = 50.0$ kV is to produce an electric field of magnitude 5.50 MV/m at the surface of the central wire. Assume that the outer cylindrical wall has uniform radius $r_a = 0.850$ m. (a) What should be the radius r_b of the central wire? You will need to solve a transcendental equation. (b) What is the magnitude of the electric field at the outer wall?

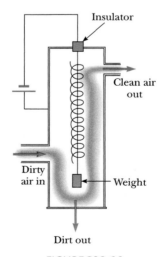

FIGURE P20.66

67. 🖌 A model of a red blood cell portrays the cell as a capacitor with two spherical plates. It is a positively charged conducting liquid sphere of area A, separated by an insulating membrane of thickness t from the surrounding neg-

atively charged conducting fluid. Tiny electrodes introduced into the cell show a potential difference of 100 mV across the membrane. Take the membrane's thickness as 100 nm and its dielectric constant as 5.00. (a) Assume that a typical red blood cell has a mass of 1.00×10^{-12} kg and density 1 100 kg/m³. Calculate its volume and its surface area. (b) Find the capacitance of the cell. (c) Calculate the charge on the surfaces of the membrane. How many electronic charges does this charge represent? (*Suggestion:* The chapter text models the Earth's atmosphere as a capacitor with two spherical plates.)

68. Four balls, each with mass m, are connected by four non-conducting strings to form a square with side a as shown in Figure P20.68. The assembly is placed on a horizontal, nonconducting, frictionless surface. Balls 1 and 2 each have charge q, and balls 3 and 4 are uncharged. Find the maximum speed of balls 3 and 4 after the string connecting balls 1 and 2 is cut.

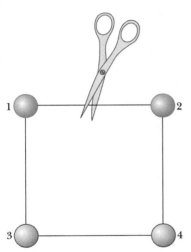

FIGURE **P20.68**

69. The x axis is the symmetry axis of a stationary, uniformly charged ring of radius R and charge Q (Fig. P20.69). A particle with charge Q and mass M is located at the center of the ring. When it is displaced slightly, the point charge accelerates along the x axis to infinity. Show that the ultimate speed of the point charge is

$$v = \left(\frac{2k_e Q^2}{MR} \right)^{1/2}$$

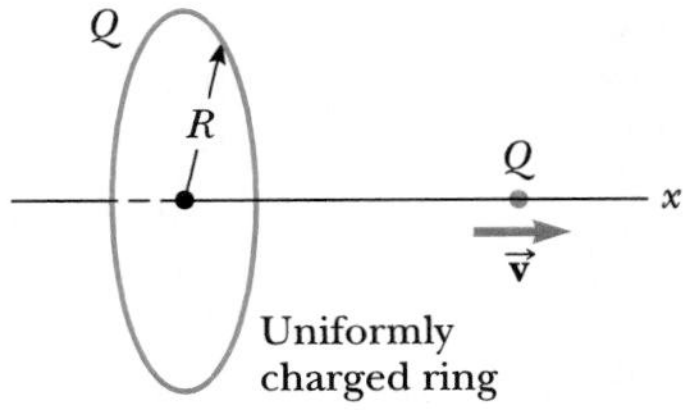

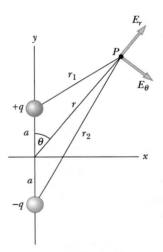

FIGURE **P20.69**

70. An electric dipole is located along the y axis as shown in Figure P20.70. The magnitude of its electric dipole moment is defined as $p = 2qa$. (a) At a point P, which is far from the dipole $(r \gg a)$, show that the electric potential is

$$V = \frac{k_e p \cos \theta}{r^2}$$

(b) Calculate the radial component E_r and the perpendicular component E_θ of the associated electric field. Note that $E_\theta = -(1/r)(\partial V / \partial \theta)$. Do these results seem reasonable for $\theta = 90°$ and $0°$? for $r = 0$? (c) For the dipole arrangement shown, express V in terms of Cartesian coordinates using $r = (x^2 + y^2)^{1/2}$ and

$$\cos \theta = \frac{y}{(x^2 + y^2)^{1/2}}$$

Using these results and again taking $r \gg a$, calculate the field components E_x and E_y.

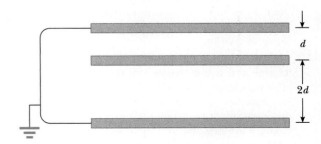

FIGURE **P20.70**

71. Two large, parallel metal plates are oriented horizontally and separated by a distance $3d$. A grounded conducting wire joins them, and initially each plate carries no charge. Now a third identical plate carrying charge Q is inserted between the two plates, parallel to them and located a distance d from the upper plate, as shown in Figure P20.71. (a) What induced charge appears on each of the two original plates? (b) What potential difference appears between the middle plate and each of the other plates? Let A represent the area of each plate.

FIGURE **P20.71**

72. A 2.00-nF parallel-plate capacitor is charged to an initial potential difference $\Delta V_i = 100$ V and then isolated. The dielectric material between the plates is mica, with a dielectric constant of 5.00. (a) How much work is required to withdraw the mica sheet? (b) What is the potential difference of the capacitor after the mica is withdrawn?

73. A parallel-plate capacitor is constructed using a dielectric material whose dielectric constant is 3.00 and whose dielectric strength is 2.00×10^8 V/m. The desired capacitance is 0.250 μF, and the capacitor must withstand a maximum potential difference of 4 000 V. Find the minimum area of the capacitor plates.

74. A 10.0-μF capacitor is charged to 15.0 V. It is next connected in series with an uncharged 5.00-μF capacitor. The series combination is finally connected across a 50.0-V battery as diagrammed in Figure P20.74. Find the new potential differences across the 5.00-μF and 10.0-μF capacitors.

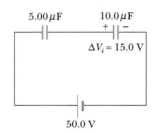

FIGURE **P20.74**

75. A capacitor is constructed from two square metallic plates of sides ℓ and separation d. Charges $+ Q$ and $- Q$ are placed on the plates and the power supply is then removed. A material of dielectric constant κ is inserted a distance x into the capacitor as shown in Figure P20.75. Assume that d is much smaller than x. (a) Find the equivalent capacitance of the device. (b) Calculate the energy stored in the capacitor. (c) Find the direction and magnitude of the force exerted by the plates on the dielectric. (d) Obtain a numerical value for the force when $x = \ell/2$, assuming that $\ell = 5.00$ cm, $d = 2.00$ mm, the dielectric is glass ($\kappa = 4.50$), and the capacitor was charged to 2 000 V before the dieletric was inserted. (*Suggestion:* The system can be considered as two capacitors connected in parallel.)

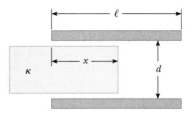

FIGURE **P20.75** Problems 20.75 and 20.76.

76. Two square plates of sides ℓ are placed parallel to each other with separation d as suggested in Figure P20.75. You may assume that d is much less than ℓ. The plates carry uniformly distributed static charges $+ Q_0$ and $- Q_0$. A block of metal has width ℓ, length ℓ, and thickness slightly less than d. It is inserted a distance x into the space between the plates. The charges on the plates are not disturbed as the block slides in. In a static situation, a metal prevents an electric field from penetrating inside it. The metal can be thought of as a perfect dielectric, with $\kappa \rightarrow \infty$. (a) Calculate the stored energy as a function of x. (b) Find the direction and magnitude of the force that acts on the metallic block. (c) The area of the advancing front face of the block is essentially equal to ℓd. Considering the force on the block as acting on this face, find the stress (force per area) on it. (d) For comparison, express the energy density in the electric field between the capacitor plates in terms of Q_0, ℓ, d, and ϵ_0.

77. Determine the equivalent capacitance of the combination shown in Figure P20.77. (*Suggestion:* Consider the symmetry involved.)

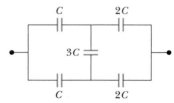

FIGURE **P20.77**

ANSWERS TO QUICK QUIZZES

20.1 (i), (b). The electric potential is inversely proportion to the radius (see Eq. 20.11). (ii), (c). Because the same number of field lines passes through a closed surface of any shape or size, the electric flux through the surface remains constant.

20.2 (i), (c). The potential is established only by the source charge and is independent of the test charge. (ii), (a). The potential energy of the two-charge system is initially negative due to the products of charges of opposite sign in Equation 20.13. When the sign of q_2 is changed, both charges are negative and the potential energy of the system is positive.

20.3 (i), (a). If the potential is constant (zero in this case), its derivative along this direction is zero. (ii), (b). If the electric field is zero, there is no change in the electric potential and it must be constant. This constant value *could* be zero, but it does not *have to be* zero.

20.4 (d). The capacitance is a property of the physical system and does not vary with applied voltage. According to Equation 20.19, if the voltage is doubled, the charge is doubled.

20.5 (i), (a). When connecting capacitors in series, the inverse of the capacitances add, resulting in a smaller overall equivalent capacitance. (ii), (a). When capacitors are connected in series, the voltages add, for a total of 20 V in this case. If they are combined in parallel, the voltage across the combination is still 10 V.

20.6 (b). For a given voltage, the energy stored in a capacitor is proportional to C: $U = C(\Delta V)^2/2$. Therefore, you want to maximize the equivalent capacitance. You do so by connecting the three capacitors in parallel so that the capacitances add.

20.7 Increase. The dielectric constant of wood (and of all other insulating materials, for that matter) is greater than 1; therefore, the capacitance increases (Eq. 20.33). This increase is sensed by the stud finder's special circuitry, which causes an indicator on the device to light up.

CHAPTER 21

Current and Direct Current Circuits

These power lines transfer energy from the electrical power company to homes and businesses. The energy is transferred at a very high voltage, possibly hundreds of thousands of volts in some cases. Even though that makes power lines very dangerous, the high voltage results in less loss of power due to resistance in the wires. We will study both resistance and power in this chapter.

(© Lester Lefkowitz/Image Bank/Getty Images)

CHAPTER OUTLINE

Thus far, our discussion of electrical phenomena has focused on charges at rest, or the study of *electrostatics*. We shall now consider situations involving electric charges in motion. The term *electric current,* or simply *current,* is used to describe the flow of charge through some region of space. Most practical applications of electricity involve electric currents. For example, in a flashlight, charges flow in the filament of the lightbulb after the switch is turned on. In most common situations, the flow of charge takes place in a conductor, such as a copper wire. It is also possible, however, for currents to exist outside a conductor. For instance, a beam of electrons in a TV picture tube constitutes a current in which charge flows through a vacuum.

In Chapter 20, we introduced the notion of a *circuit*. As we continue our investigations into circuits in this chapter, we introduce the *resistor* as a new circuit element.

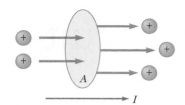

FIGURE 21.1 Charges in motion through an area A. The time rate at which charge flows through the area is defined as the current I. The direction of the current is the direction in which positive charges flow when free to do so.

■ Electric current

PITFALL PREVENTION 21.1

CURRENT FLOW IS REDUNDANT The phrase *current flow* is commonly used, although it is strictly incorrect, because current *is* a flow (of charge). This terminology is similar to the phrase *heat transfer,* which is also redundant because heat *is* a transfer (of energy). We will avoid the phrase *current flow* and speak of *charge flow* or *flow of charge.*

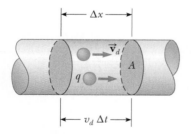

FIGURE 21.2 A section of a uniform conductor of cross-sectional area A. The mobile charge carriers move with an average speed v_d along the wire, and the displacement they experience in this direction in a time interval Δt is $\Delta x = v_d \Delta t$. If we choose Δt to be the time interval during which the charges are displaced, on the average, by the length of the cylinder, the number of carriers in the section of length Δx is $nAv_d \Delta t$, where n is the number of carriers per unit volume.

21.1 | ELECTRIC CURRENT

Whenever charge is flowing, an **electric current** is said to exist. To define current mathematically, suppose charged particles are moving perpendicular to a surface of area A as in Figure 21.1. (This area could be the cross-sectional area of a wire, for example.) The current is defined as **the rate at which electric charge flows through this surface.** If ΔQ is the amount of charge that passes through this area in a time interval Δt, the average current I_{avg} over the time interval is the ratio of the charge to the time interval:

$$I_{avg} = \frac{\Delta Q}{\Delta t} \qquad [21.1]$$

It is possible for the rate at which charge flows to vary in time. We define the **instantaneous current** I as the limit of the preceding expression as Δt goes to zero:

$$I \equiv \lim_{\Delta t \to 0} \frac{\Delta Q}{\Delta t} = \frac{dQ}{dt} \qquad [21.2]$$

The SI unit of current is the **ampere** (A):

$$1\,\text{A} = 1\,\text{C/s} \qquad [21.3]$$

That is, 1 A of current is equivalent to 1 C of charge passing through a surface in 1 s.

The particles flowing through a surface as in Figure 21.1 can be charged positively or negatively, or we can have two or more types of particles moving, with charges of both signs in the flow. **Conventionally, we define the direction of the current as the direction of flow of positive charge,** regardless of the sign of the actual charged particles in motion.[1] In a common conductor such as copper, the current is physically due to the motion of the negatively charged electrons. Therefore, when we speak of current in such a conductor, **the direction of the current is opposite the direction of flow of electrons.** On the other hand, if one considers a beam of positively charged protons in a particle accelerator, the current is in the direction of motion of the protons. In some cases—gases and electrolytes, for example—the current is the result of the flow of both positive and negative charged particles. It is common to refer to a moving charged particle (whether it is positive or negative) as a mobile **charge carrier.** For example, the charge carriers in a metal are electrons.

We now build a structural model that will allow us to relate the macroscopic current to the motion of the charged particles. Consider identical charged particles moving in a conductor of cross-sectional area A (Fig. 21.2). The volume of a section of the conductor of length Δx (the gray region shown in Fig. 21.2) is $A \Delta x$. If n represents the number of mobile charge carriers per unit volume (in other words, the charge carrier density), the number of carriers in the gray section is $nA \Delta x$. Therefore, the total charge ΔQ in this section is

$$\Delta Q = \text{number of carriers in section} \times \text{charge per carrier} = (nA \Delta x)q$$

where q is the charge on each carrier. If the carriers move with an average velocity component v_d in the x direction (along the wire), the displacement they experience in this direction in a time interval Δt is $\Delta x = v_d \Delta t$. The speed v_d of the charge carrier along the wire is an average speed called the **drift speed.** Let us choose Δt to be the time interval required for the charges in the cylinder to move through a displacement whose magnitude is equal to the length of the cylinder. This time

[1]Even though we discuss a direction for current, current is not a vector. As we shall see later in the chapter, currents add algebraically and not vectorially.

interval is also that required for all the charges in the cylinder to pass through the circular area at one end. With this choice, we can write ΔQ in the form

$$\Delta Q = (nAv_d\,\Delta t)\,q$$

If we divide both sides of this equation by Δt, we see that the average current in the conductor is

$$I_{avg} = \frac{\Delta Q}{\Delta t} = nqv_dA \qquad [21.4]$$

■ **Current in terms of microscopic parameters**

Equation 21.4 relates a macroscopically measured average current to the microscopic origin of the current: the density of charge carriers n, the charge per carrier q, and the drift speed v_d.

> **QUICK QUIZ 21.1** Consider positive and negative charges moving horizontally through the four regions shown in Figure 21.3. Rank the currents in these four regions, from lowest to highest.

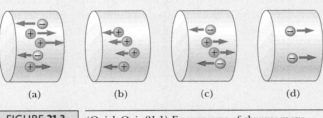

(a)   (b)   (c)   (d)

FIGURE 21.3   (Quick Quiz 21.1) Four groups of charges move through a region.

Let us investigate further the notion of drift speed. We have identified drift speed as an average speed along the wire, but the charge carriers are by no means moving in a straight line with speed v_d. Consider a conductor in which the charge carriers are free electrons. In the absence of a potential difference across the conductor, these electrons undergo random motion similar to that of gas molecules in the structural model of kinetic theory that we studied in Chapter 16. This random motion is related to the temperature of the conductor. The electrons undergo repeated collisions with the metal atoms, and the result is a complicated zigzag motion (Active Fig. 21.4). When a potential difference is applied across the conductor, an electric field is established in the conductor. The electric field exerts an electric force on the electrons (Eq. 19.4). This force accelerates the electrons and hence produces a current. The motion of the electrons due to the electric force is superimposed on their random motion to provide an average velocity whose magnitude is the drift speed.

When electrons make collisions with metal atoms during their motion, they transfer energy to the atoms. This energy transfer causes an increase in the vibrational energy of the atoms and a corresponding increase in the temperature of the conductor.[2] This process involves all three types of energy storage in the continuity equation for energy, Equation 6.20. If we consider the system to be the electrons, the metal atoms, and the electric field (which is established by an external source such as a battery), the energy at the instant when the potential difference is applied across the conductor is electric potential energy associated with the field and the electrons. This energy is transformed by work done by the field on the electrons to kinetic energy of electrons. When the electrons strike the metal atoms, some of the kinetic energy is transferred to the atoms, which adds to the internal energy of the system.

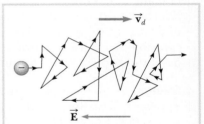

ACTIVE FIGURE 21.4

A schematic representation of the zigzag motion of a charge carrier in a conductor. The changes in direction are due to collisions with atoms in the conductor. Note that the net motion of electrons is opposite the direction of the electric field. Because of the acceleration of the charge carriers due to the electric force, the paths are actually parabolic. The drift speed, however, is much smaller than the average speed, so the parabolic shape is not visible on this scale.

Physics⊗Now™ Log into PhysicsNow at **www.pop4e.com** and go to Active Figure 21.4 to adjust the electric field to see the resulting effect on the motion of an electron.

---

[2]This increase in temperature is sometimes called *Joule heating*, but that term is a misnomer because there is no heat involved. We will not use this wording.

The **current density** J in the conductor is defined as the current per unit area. From Equation 21.4, the current density is

$$J \equiv \frac{I}{A} = nq v_d \qquad [21.5]$$

where J has the SI units amperes per square meter.

■ Thinking Physics 21.1

In Chapter 19, we claimed that the electric field inside a conductor is zero. In the preceding discussion, however, we have used the notion of an electric field in a conducting wire that exerts electric forces on electrons, causing them to move with a drift velocity. Is this notion inconsistent with Chapter 19?

Reasoning The electric field is zero only in a conductor in *electrostatic equilibrium,* that is, a conductor in which the charges are at rest after having moved to equilibrium positions. In a current-carrying conductor, the charges are not at rest, so the requirement for a zero field is not imposed. The electric field in a conductor in a circuit is due to a distribution of charge over the surface of the conductor that can be quite complicated.[3] ■

EXAMPLE 21.1   Drift Speed in a Copper Wire

The 12-gauge copper wire in a typical residential building has a cross-sectional area of 3.31×10^{-6} m^2. If it carries a current of 10.0 A, what is the drift speed of the electrons? Assume that each copper atom contributes one free electron to the current. Take the density of copper as 8.95 g/cm^3.

Solution From the periodic table of the elements in Appendix C, we find that the molar mass of copper is 63.5 g/mol. Knowing the density of copper enables us to calculate the volume occupied by 1 mol of copper:

$$V = \frac{M}{\rho} = \frac{63.5 \text{ g/mol}}{8.95 \text{ g/cm}^3} = 7.09 \text{ cm}^3/\text{mol}$$

Recall that one mole of any substance contains Avogadro's number of atoms, 6.02×10^{23} atoms. Because each copper atom contributes one free electron to the current, the density of charge carriers is

$$n = \frac{6.02 \times 10^{23} \text{ electrons}}{7.09 \text{ cm}^3} \left(\frac{1.00 \times 10^6 \text{ cm}^3}{1 \text{ m}^3} \right)$$
$$= 8.49 \times 10^{28} \text{ electrons/m}^3$$

From Equation 21.4, we find that the drift speed is

$$v_d = \frac{I}{nqA}$$
$$= \frac{10.0 \text{ C/s}}{(8.49 \times 10^{28} \text{ m}^{-3})(1.60 \times 10^{-19} \text{ C})(3.31 \times 10^{-6} \text{ m}^2)}$$
$$= 2.22 \times 10^{-4} \text{ m/s}$$

⊞ PITFALL PREVENTION 21.2

ELECTRONS ARE AVAILABLE EVERY-WHERE Let us emphasize the point being made here: *Electrons do not have to travel from the light switch to the light for the light to operate.* Electrons already in the filament of the light-bulb move in response to the electric field set up by the battery. Note also that the role of a battery is not to provide electrons to the circuit. It establishes the electric field that exerts a force on electrons already in the wires and elements of the circuit.

Example 21.1 shows that typical drift speeds in conductors are very small. In fact, the drift speed is much smaller than the average speed between collisions. For instance, electrons traveling with the drift speed calculated in Example 21.1 would take about 75 min to travel 1 m! In view of this low speed, you might wonder why a light turns on almost instantaneously when a switch is thrown. In a conductor, the electric field that drives the free electrons is established in the conductor almost instantaneously. Therefore, when you flip a light switch, the electric force that causes the electrons to start moving in the wire with a drift speed begins immediately. Electrons already in the filament of the lightbulb begin to move in response to this force, and the lightbulb begins to emit light.

---

[3]See Chapter 6 in R. Chabay and B. Sherwood, *Electric and Magnetic Interactions,* (New York: Wiley, 1995) for details on this charge distribution.

21.2 RESISTANCE AND OHM'S LAW

The drift speed of electrons in a current-carrying wire is related to the electric field in the wire. If the field is increased, the electric force on the electrons is stronger and the drift speed increases. We shall show in Section 21.4 that this relationship is linear and that the drift speed is directly proportional to the electric field. For a uniform field in a conductor of uniform cross-section, the potential difference across the conductor is proportional to the electric field as in Equation 20.6. Therefore, when a potential difference ΔV is applied across the ends of a metallic conductor as in Figure 21.5, the current in the conductor is found to be proportional to the applied voltage; that is, $I \propto \Delta V$. We can write this proportionality as $\Delta V = IR$, where R is called the **resistance** of the conductor. We define this resistance according to the equation we have just written, as the ratio of the voltage across the conductor to the current it carries:

$$R \equiv \frac{\Delta V}{I}$$ [21.6]

Resistance has the SI units volts per ampere, called **ohms** (Ω). Therefore, if a potential difference of 1 V across a conductor produces a current of 1 A, the resistance of the conductor is 1 Ω. As another example, if an electrical appliance connected to a 120-V source carries a current of 6.0 A, its resistance is 20 Ω.

Resistance is the quantity that determines the current that results due to a voltage in a simple circuit. For a fixed voltage, if the resistance increases, the current decreases. If the resistance decreases, the current increases.

It might be useful for you to build a mental model for current, voltage, and resistance by comparing these concepts to analogous concepts for the flow of water in a river. As water flows downhill in a river of constant width and depth, the rate of flow of water (analogous to current) depends on the angle that the river bottom makes with the horizontal (analogous to voltage) and on the width and depth as well as on the effects of rocks, the riverbank, and other obstructions (analogous to resistance). Likewise, electric current in a uniform conductor depends on the applied voltage and the resistance of the conductor is caused by collisions of the electrons with atoms in the conductor.

For many materials, including most metals, experiments show that the resistance is constant over a wide range of applied voltages. This behavior is known as **Ohm's law** after Georg Simon Ohm (1787–1854), who was the first to conduct a systematic study of electrical resistance.

Many individuals call Equation 21.6 Ohm's law, but this terminology is incorrect. This equation is simply the definition of resistance, and it provides an important relationship between voltage, current, and resistance. Ohm's law is *not* a fundamental law of nature, but a behavior that is valid only for certain materials and devices, and only over a limited range of conditions. Materials or devices that obey Ohm's law, and hence that have a constant resistance over a wide range of voltages, are said to be **ohmic** (Fig. 21.6a). Materials or devices that do not obey Ohm's law are

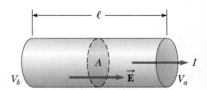

FIGURE 21.5 A uniform conductor of length ℓ and cross-sectional area A. A potential difference $V_b - V_a$ is maintained across the conductor so that an electric field $\vec{\mathbf{E}}$ exists in the conductor, and this field produces a current I that is proportional to the potential difference.

■ Definition of resistance

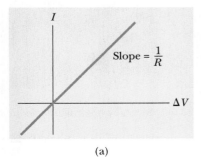

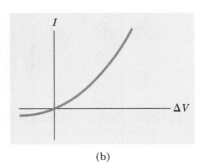

(a)   (b)

FIGURE 21.6 (a) The current–potential difference curve for an ohmic material. The curve is linear, and the slope is equal to the inverse of the resistance of the conductor. (b) A nonlinear current–potential difference curve for a semiconducting diode. This device does not obey Ohm's law.

nonohmic. One common semiconducting device that is nonohmic is the *diode,* a circuit element that acts like a one-way valve for current. Its resistance is small for currents in one direction (positive ΔV) and large for currents in the reverse direction (negative ΔV) as shown in Figure 21.6b. Most modern electronic devices have nonlinear current–voltage relationships; their operation depends on the particular ways they violate Ohm's law.

> **QUICK QUIZ 21.2** In Figure 21.6b, as the applied voltage increases, does the resistance of the diode **(a)** increase, **(b)** decrease, or **(c)** remain the same?

A **resistor** is a simple circuit element that provides a specified resistance in an electrical circuit. The symbol for a resistor in circuit diagrams is a zigzag red line (—WW—). We can express Equation 21.6 in the form

$$\Delta V = IR \tag{21.7}$$

This equation tells us that the voltage across a resistor is the product of the resistance and the current in the resistor.

The resistance of an ohmic conducting wire is found to be proportional to its length ℓ and inversely proportional to its cross-sectional area A. That is,

■ Resistance of a uniform material of resistivity ρ along a length ℓ

$$R = \rho \frac{\ell}{A} \tag{21.8}$$

where the constant of proportionality ρ is called the **resistivity** of the material,[4] which has the unit ohm meter ($\Omega \cdot m$). To understand this relationship between resistance and resistivity, note that every ohmic material has a characteristic resistivity, a parameter that depends on the properties of the material and on temperature. On the other hand, as you can see from Equation 21.8, the resistance of a particular conductor depends on its size and shape as well as on the resistivity of the material. Table 21.1 provides a list of resistivities for various materials measured at 20°C.

The inverse of the resistivity is defined[5] as the **conductivity** σ. Hence, the resistance of an ohmic conductor can be expressed in terms of its conductivity as

PITFALL PREVENTION 21.4

RESISTANCE AND RESISTIVITY
Resistivity is a property of a *substance,* whereas resistance is a property of an *object.* We have seen similar pairs of variables before. For example, density is a property of a substance, whereas mass is a property of an object. Equation 21.8 relates resistance to resistivity, and we have seen a previous equation (Eq. 1.1) that relates mass to density.

$$R = \frac{\ell}{\sigma A} \tag{21.9}$$

where $\sigma = 1/\rho$.

Equation 21.9 shows that the resistance of a conductor is proportional to its length and inversely proportional to its cross-sectional area, similar to the flow of

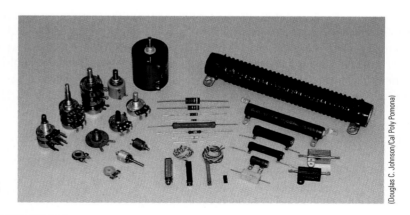

An assortment of resistors used in electric circuits. ■

---

[4]The symbol ρ used for resistivity should not be confused with the same symbol used earlier in the text for mass density and volume charge density.
[5]Do not confuse the symbol σ for conductivity with the same symbol used earlier for the Stefan–Boltzmann constant and surface charge density.

TABLE 21.1	Resistivities and Temperature Coefficients of Resistivity for Various Materials	
Material	**Resistivity^a ($\Omega \cdot$ m)**	**Temperature Coefficient α [($^\circ$C)$^{-1}$]**
Silver	1.59×10^{-8}	3.8×10^{-3}
Copper	1.7×10^{-8}	3.9×10^{-3}
Gold	2.44×10^{-8}	3.4×10^{-3}
Aluminum	2.82×10^{-8}	3.9×10^{-3}
Tungsten	5.6×10^{-8}	4.5×10^{-3}
Iron	10×10^{-8}	5.0×10^{-3}
Platinum	11×10^{-8}	3.92×10^{-3}
Lead	22×10^{-8}	3.9×10^{-3}
Nichrome^b	1.50×10^{-6}	0.4×10^{-3}
Carbon	3.5×10^{-5}	-0.5×10^{-3}
Germanium	0.46	-48×10^{-3}
Silicon	640	-75×10^{-3}
Glass	10^{10} to 10^{14}	
Hard rubber	$\sim 10^{13}$	
Sulfur	10^{15}	
Quartz (fused)	75×10^{16}	

^{a}All values are at 20°C.
^{b}Nichrome is a nickel–chromium alloy commonly used in heating elements.

liquid through a pipe. As the length of the pipe is increased and the pressure difference between the ends of the pipe is held constant, the pressure difference between any two points separated by a fixed distance decreases and there is less force pushing the element of fluid between these points through the pipe. As its cross-sectional area is increased, the pipe can transport more fluid in a given time interval, so its resistance drops.

As another analogy between electrical circuits and our previous studies, let us combine Equations 21.6 and 21.9:

$$R = \frac{\ell}{\sigma A} = \frac{\Delta V}{I} \quad \rightarrow \quad I = \sigma A \frac{\Delta V}{\ell} \quad \rightarrow \quad \frac{q}{\Delta t} = \sigma A \frac{\Delta V}{\ell}$$

where q is the amount of charge transferred in a time interval Δt. Let us compare this equation to Equation 17.35 for conduction of energy through a slab of material of area A, length ℓ, and thermal conductivity k, which we reproduce below:

$$\mathcal{P} = kA \frac{(T_h - T_c)}{L} \quad \rightarrow \quad \frac{Q}{\Delta t} = kA \frac{\Delta T}{L}$$

In this equation, Q is the amount of energy transferred by heat in a time interval Δt.

Another analogy arises in an example that is important in biochemical applications. *Fick's law* describes the rate of transfer of a chemical solute through a solvent by the process of *diffusion*. This transfer occurs because of a difference in concentration of the solute (mass of solute per volume) between the two locations. Fick's law is as follows:

$$\frac{n}{\Delta t} = DA \frac{\Delta C}{L}$$

 Diffusion in biological systems

where $n/\Delta t$ is the rate of flow of the solute in moles per second, A is the area through which the solute moves, and L is the length over which the concentration difference is ΔC. The concentration is measured in moles per cubic meter. The parameter D is a diffusion constant (with units of meters squared per second) that describes the rate of diffusion of a solute through the solvent and is similar in nature to electrical or thermal conductivity. Fick's law has important applications in describing the transport of molecules across biological membranes.

(SuperStock)

FIGURE 21.7 The colored bands on a resistor represent a code for determining resistance. The first two colors give the first two digits in the resistance value. The third color represents the power of ten for the multiplier of the resistance value. The last color is the tolerance of the resistance value. As an example, the four colors on the circled resistors are red (= 2), black (= 0), orange (= 10^3), and gold (= 5%), and so the resistance value is $20 \times 10^3 \ \Omega = 20$ kΩ with a tolerance value of 5% = 1 kΩ. (The values for the colors come from Table 21.2.)

TABLE 21.2	Color Code for Resistors		
Color	**Number**	**Multiplier**	**Tolerance**
Black	0	1	
Brown	1	10^1	
Red	2	10^2	
Orange	3	10^3	
Yellow	4	10^4	
Green	5	10^5	
Blue	6	10^6	
Violet	7	10^7	
Gray	8	10^8	
White	9	10^9	
Gold		10^{-1}	5%
Silver		10^{-2}	10%
Colorless			20%

All three of the preceding equations have exactly the same mathematical form. Each has a time rate of change on the left, and each has the product of a conductivity, an area, and a ratio of a difference in a variable to a length on the right. This type of equation is a *transport equation* used when we transport energy, charge, or moles of matter. The difference in the variable on the right side of each equation is what drives the transport. A temperature difference drives energy transfer by heat, a potential difference drives a transfer of charge, and a concentration difference drives a transfer of matter.

Most electric circuits use resistors to control the current level in the various parts of the circuit. Two common types of resistors are the *composition* resistor containing carbon and the *wire-wound* resistor, which consists of a coil of wire. Resistors are normally color-coded to give their values in ohms, as shown in Figure 21.7 and Table 21.2.

INTERACTIVE EXAMPLE 21.2 The Resistance of Nichrome Wire

A Calculate the resistance per unit length of a 22-gauge Nichrome wire, which has a radius of 0.321 mm.

Solution The cross-sectional area of this wire is

$$A = \pi r^2 = \pi (0.321 \times 10^{-3} \ \text{m})^2 = 3.24 \times 10^{-7} \ \text{m}^2$$

The resistivity of Nichrome is $1.50 \times 10^{-6} \ \Omega \cdot \text{m}$ (Table 21.1). We use Equation 21.8 to find the resistance per unit length:

$$\frac{R}{\ell} = \frac{\rho}{A} = \frac{1.50 \times 10^{-6} \ \Omega \cdot \text{m}}{3.24 \times 10^{-7} \ \text{m}^2} = \boxed{4.63 \ \Omega/\text{m}}$$

B If a potential difference of 10 V is maintained across a 1.0-m length of the Nichrome wire, what is the current in the wire?

Solution Because a 1.0-m length of this wire has a resistance of 4.63 Ω, we have

$$I = \frac{\Delta V}{R} = \frac{10 \ \text{V}}{4.63 \ \Omega} = \boxed{2.2 \ \text{A}}$$

Note from Table 21.1 that the resistivity of Nichrome wire is two orders of magnitude larger than that of copper. A copper wire of the same radius would have a resistance per unit length of only 0.052 Ω/m. A 1.0-m length of copper wire of the same radius would carry the same current (2.2 A) with an applied voltage of only 0.11 V.

Because of its high resistivity and its resistance to oxidation, Nichrome is often used for heating elements in toasters, irons, and electric heaters.

Physics⊗Now™ Explore the resistance of different materials by logging into PhysicsNow at **www.pop4e.com** and going to Interactive Example 21.2.

Change in Resistivity with Temperature

Resistivity depends on a number of factors, one of which is temperature. For most metals, resistivity increases approximately linearly with increasing temperature over a limited temperature range according to the expression

$$\rho = \rho_0[1 + \alpha(T - T_0)] \tag{21.10}$$

■ Variation of resistivity with temperature

where ρ is the resistivity at some temperature T (in degrees Celsius), ρ_0 is the resistivity at some reference temperature T_0 (usually 20°C), and α is called the **temperature coefficient of resistivity** (not to be confused with the average coefficient of linear expansion α in Chapter 16). From Equation 21.10, we see that α can be expressed as

$$\alpha = \frac{1}{\rho_0}\frac{\Delta\rho}{\Delta T} \tag{21.11}$$

■ Temperature coefficient of resistivity

where $\Delta\rho = \rho - \rho_0$ is the change in resistivity in the temperature interval $\Delta T = T - T_0$.

The resistivities and temperature coefficients of certain materials are listed in Table 21.1. Note the enormous range in resistivities, from very low values for good conductors, such as copper and silver, to very high values for good insulators, such as glass and rubber. An ideal, or "perfect," conductor would have zero resistivity, and an ideal insulator would have infinite resistivity.

Because resistance is proportional to resistivity according to Equation 21.8, the temperature variation of the resistance can be written as

$$R = R_0[1 + \alpha(T - T_0)] \tag{21.12}$$

■ Variation of resistance with temperature

Precise temperature measurements are often made using this property, as shown in Example 21.3.

> **QUICK QUIZ 21.3** When does a lightbulb carry more current: **(a)** just after it is turned on and the glow of the metal filament is increasing or **(b)** after it has been on for a few seconds and the glow is steady?

EXAMPLE 21.3 A Platinum Resistance Thermometer

A resistance thermometer, which measures temperature by measuring the change in resistance of a conductor, is made from platinum and has a resistance of 50.0 Ω at 20.0°C. When immersed in a vessel containing melting indium, its resistance increases to 76.8 Ω. Assuming that the resistance varies linearly with temperature over the temperature range in question, what is the melting point of indium?

Solution Solving Equation 21.12 for ΔT and obtaining α from Table 21.1, we have

$$\Delta T = \frac{R - R_0}{\alpha R_0} = \frac{76.8\ \Omega - 50.0\ \Omega}{[3.92 \times 10^{-3}\ (°C)^{-1}](50.0\ \Omega)}$$
$$= 137°C$$

Because $T_0 = 20.0°C$, we find that $T = \boxed{157°C}$.

21.3 SUPERCONDUCTORS

For several metals, resistivity is nearly proportional to temperature as shown in Figure 21.8. In reality, however, there is always a nonlinear region at very low temperatures, and the resistivity usually approaches some finite value near absolute zero (see the magnified inset in Fig. 21.8). This residual resistivity near absolute zero is due primarily to collisions of electrons with impurities and to imperfections in the metal. In contrast, the high temperature resistivity (the linear region) is dominated

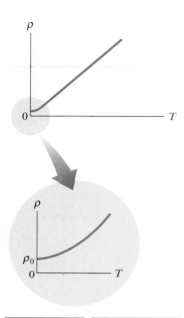

FIGURE 21.8 Resistivity versus temperature for a normal metal, such as copper. The curve is linear over a wide range of temperatures, and ρ increases with increasing temperature. As T approaches absolute zero (inset), the resistivity approaches a finite value ρ_0.

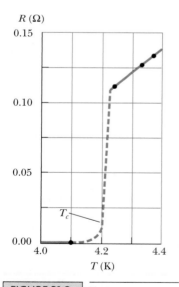

FIGURE 21.9 Resistance versus temperature for a sample of mercury. The graph follows that of a normal metal above the critical temperature T_c. The resistance drops to zero at T_c, which is 4.2 K for mercury.

by collisions of electrons with the vibrating metal atoms. We shall describe this process in more detail in Section 21.4.

There is a class of metals and compounds for which the resistivity goes to zero below a certain **critical temperature** T_c. These materials are known as **superconductors.** The resistance–temperature graph for a superconductor follows that of a normal metal at temperatures above T_c. When the temperature reaches T_c, the resistance of the sample drops suddenly to zero (Fig. 21.9). This phenomenon was discovered by Dutch physicist Heike Kamerlingh Onnes in 1911 as he worked with mercury, which is a superconductor below 4.2 K. Recent measurements have shown that the resistivities of superconductors below T_c are less than $4 \times 10^{-25} \ \Omega \cdot m$, which is about 10^{17} times smaller than the resistivity of copper and considered to be zero in practice.

Today, thousands of superconductors are known. Such common metals as aluminum, tin, lead, zinc, and indium are superconductors. Table 21.3 lists the critical temperatures of several superconductors. The value of T_c is sensitive to chemical composition, pressure, and crystalline structure. It is interesting to note that copper, silver, and gold, which are excellent conductors at room temperatures, do not exhibit superconductivity.

One truly remarkable feature of superconductors is that once a current is set up in them, it persists *without any applied voltage* (because $R = 0$). In fact, steady currents have been observed to persist in superconducting loops for several years with no apparent decay!

An important development in physics that created much excitement in the scientific community in the latter part of the twentieth century is the discovery of high-temperature copper-oxide-based superconductors. The excitement began with a 1986 publication by J. Georg Bednorz and K. Alex Müller, scientists at the IBM Zurich Research Laboratory in Switzerland, in which they reported evidence for superconductivity at a temperature near 30 K in an oxide of barium, lanthanum, and copper. Bednorz and Müller were awarded the Nobel Prize in Physics in 1987 for their remarkable discovery. Shortly thereafter, a new family of compounds was open for investigation, and research activity in the field of superconductivity proceeded vigorously. In early 1987, groups at the University of Alabama at Huntsville and the University of Houston announced the discovery of superconductivity at about 92 K in an oxide of yttrium, barium, and copper ($YBa_2Cu_3O_7$). Late in 1987, teams of scientists from Japan and the United States reported superconductivity at 105 K in an oxide of bismuth, strontium, calcium, and copper. More recently, scientists have reported superconductivity at temperatures as high as 134 K in a compound containing mercury. At this point, one cannot rule out the possibility of room-temperature superconductivity, and the search for novel superconducting materials continues. It is an important search both for scientific reasons and because practical applications become more probable and widespread as the critical temperature is raised.

An important and useful application is superconducting magnets in which the magnetic field magnitudes are about ten times greater than those of the best normal electromagnets. (We will study magnetism in Chapter 22.) Such superconducting magnets are being considered as a means of storing energy. The idea of using superconducting power lines for transmitting power efficiently is also receiving some consideration. Modern superconducting electronic devices consisting of two thin-film superconductors separated by a thin insulator have been constructed. They include magnetometers (magnetic-field measuring devices) and various microwave devices.

21.4 ▌ A STRUCTURAL MODEL FOR ELECTRICAL CONDUCTION

In Section 21.1, a structural model of electrical conduction was developed by relating the macroscopic current to the drift speed of microscopic charge carriers in a material. This section expands that model by introducing the microscopic origin of resistance. Once the model is completed, we shall compare its predictions to experimental measurements.

Consider a conductor as a regular array of atoms containing free electrons (sometimes called *conduction* electrons). Such electrons are free to move through the conductor (as we learned in our discussion of drift speed in Section 21.1) and are approximately equal in number to the number of atoms in the conductor. In the absence of an electric field, the free electrons move in random directions with average speeds on the order of 10^6 m/s. The situation is similar to the motion of gas molecules confined in a vessel that we studied in kinetic theory in Chapter 16. In fact, the conduction electrons in a metal are often called an *electron gas*.

Conduction electrons are not totally free because they are confined to the interior of the conductor and undergo frequent collisions with the array of atoms. The collisions are the predominant mechanism contributing to the resistivity of a metal at normal temperatures. Note that there is no current in a conductor in the absence of an electric field because the average velocity of the free electrons is zero. On the average, just as many electrons move in one direction as in the opposite direction, so there is no net flow of charge.

The situation is modified, however, when an electric field is applied to the metal. In addition to random thermal motion, the free electrons drift slowly in a direction opposite that of the electric field, with an average drift speed of v_d, which is much less (typically 10^{-4} m/s; see Example 21.1) than the average speed between collisions (typically 10^6 m/s).

In our structural model, we shall assume that the excess kinetic energy acquired by the electrons in the electric field is lost to the conductor in the collision process. The energy given up to the atoms in the collisions increases the total vibrational energy of the atoms, causing the conductor to warm up. The model also assumes that an electron's motion after a collision is independent of its motion before the collision.

Given this basis for our model, we now take the first step toward obtaining an expression for the drift speed. When a mobile, charged particle of mass m and charge q is subjected to an electric field $\vec{\mathbf{E}}$, it experiences a force $q\vec{\mathbf{E}}$ (Eq. 19.4). For electrons in a metal, $\vec{\mathbf{F}}_e = -e\vec{\mathbf{E}}$. The motion of the electron can be determined from Newton's second law, $\sum \vec{\mathbf{F}} = m_e \vec{\mathbf{a}}$. The acceleration of the electron is

$$\vec{\mathbf{a}} = \frac{\sum \vec{\mathbf{F}}}{m_e} = \frac{\vec{\mathbf{F}}_e}{m_e} = \frac{-e\vec{\mathbf{E}}}{m_e} \qquad [21.13]$$

The acceleration, which occurs for only a short time interval between collisions, changes the velocity of the electron. Because the force is constant, the acceleration is constant, and we can model the electron as a particle under constant acceleration. If $\vec{\mathbf{v}}_0$ is the velocity of the electron just after a collision, at which we define the time as $t = 0$, the velocity of the electron at time t is

$$\vec{\mathbf{v}} = \vec{\mathbf{v}}_0 + \vec{\mathbf{a}}t = \vec{\mathbf{v}}_0 - \frac{e\vec{\mathbf{E}}}{m_e} t \qquad [21.14]$$

The motion of the electron through the metal is characterized by a very large number of collisions per second. Consequently, we consider the average value of $\vec{\mathbf{v}}$ over a time interval long compared with the time interval between collisions, which gives us the drift velocity $\vec{\mathbf{v}}_d$. Because the velocity of the electron after a collision is assumed to be independent of its velocity before the collision, the initial velocities are randomly distributed in direction, so the average value of $\vec{\mathbf{v}}_0$ is zero. In the second term on the right of Equation 21.14, the charge, electric field, and mass are all constant. Therefore, the only factor affected by the averaging process is the time t. The average value of this term is $(-e\vec{\mathbf{E}}/m_e)\tau$, where τ is the *average time interval between collisions*. Therefore, Equation 21.14 becomes, after the averaging process,

$$\vec{\mathbf{v}}_d = \frac{-e\vec{\mathbf{E}}}{m_e} \tau \qquad [21.15]$$

∎ Drift velocity

TABLE 21.3
Critical Temperatures for Various Superconductors

Material	T_c (K)
$HgBa_2Ca_2Cu_3O_8$	134
Tl–Ba–Ca–Cu–O	125
Bi–Sr–Ca–Cu–O	105
$YBa_2Cu_3O_7$	92
Nb_3Ge	23.2
Nb_3Sn	18.05
Nb	9.46
Pb	7.18
Hg	4.15
Sn	3.72
Al	1.19
Zn	0.88

(Courtesy of IBM Research Laboratory)

A small, permanent magnet levitated above a disk of the superconductor $YBa_2Cu_3O_7$, which is at 77 K. This levitation is one the phenomena related to the lack of resistance in the superconductor. ∎

Substituting the magnitude of this drift velocity (the drift speed) into Equation 21.4, we have

$$I = nev_d A = ne\left(\frac{eE}{m_e}\tau\right)A = \frac{ne^2 E}{m_e}\tau A \qquad [21.16]$$

According to Equation 21.6, the current is related to the macroscopic variables of potential difference and resistance:

$$I = \frac{\Delta V}{R}$$

Incorporating Equation 21.8, we can write this expression as

$$I = \frac{\Delta V}{\left(\rho\dfrac{\ell}{A}\right)} = \frac{\Delta V}{\rho\ell}A$$

In the conductor, the electric field is uniform, so we use Equation 20.6, $\Delta V = E\ell$, to substitute for the magnitude of the potential difference across the conductor:

$$I = \frac{E\ell}{\rho\ell}A = \frac{E}{\rho}A \qquad [21.17]$$

Setting the two expressions for the current, Equations 21.16 and 21.17, equal, we solve for the resistivity:

■ Resistivity in terms of micro-scopic parameters

$$I = \frac{ne^2 E}{m_e}\tau A = \frac{E}{\rho}A \quad \rightarrow \quad \rho = \frac{m_e}{ne^2\tau} \qquad [21.18]$$

According to this structural model, resistivity does not depend on the electric field or, equivalently, on the potential difference, but depends only on fixed parameters associated with the material and the electron. This feature is characteristic of a conductor obeying Ohm's law. The model shows that the resistivity can be calculated from a knowledge of the density of the electrons, their charge and mass, and the average time interval τ between collisions. This time interval is related to the average distance between collisions ℓ_{avg} (the *mean free path*) and the average speed v_{avg} through the expression[6]

$$\tau = \frac{\ell_{avg}}{v_{avg}} \qquad [21.19]$$

EXAMPLE 21.4   Electron Collisions in Copper

A Using the data and results from Example 21.1 and the structural model of electron conduction, estimate the average time interval between collisions for electrons in copper at 20°C.

Solution From Equation 21.18 we see that

$$\tau = \frac{m_e}{ne^2\rho}$$

where $\rho = 1.7 \times 10^{-8}\ \Omega\cdot\text{m}$ for copper and the carrier density $n = 8.49 \times 10^{28}$ electrons/m³ for the wire described in Example 21.1. Substitution of these values into the expression above gives

$$\tau = \frac{9.11 \times 10^{-31}\ \text{kg}}{(8.49 \times 10^{28}\ \text{m}^{-3})(1.6 \times 10^{-19}\ \text{C})^2(1.7 \times 10^{-8}\ \Omega\cdot\text{m})}$$

$$= 2.5 \times 10^{-14}\ \text{s}$$

Note that this result is a very short time interval and that the electrons make a very large number of collisions per second.

B Assuming that the average speed for free electrons in copper is 1.6×10^6 m/s and using the result from part A, calculate the mean free path for electrons in copper.

---

[6]Recall that the average speed of a group of particles depends on the temperature of the group (Chapter 16) and is not the same as the drift speed v_d.

Solution Using Equation 21.19, we find

$$\ell_{\text{avg}} = v_{\text{avg}}\tau = (1.6 \times 10^6 \, \text{m/s})(2.5 \times 10^{-14} \, \text{s})$$

$$= 4.0 \times 10^{-8} \, \text{m}$$

which is equivalent to 40 nm (compared with atomic spacings of about 0.2 nm). Therefore, although the time interval between collisions is very short, the electrons travel about 200 atomic distances before colliding with an atom.

Although this structural model of conduction is consistent with Ohm's law, it does not correctly predict the values of resistivity or the behavior of the resistivity with temperature. For example, the results of classical calculations for v_{avg} using the ideal gas model for the electrons are about a factor of ten smaller than the actual values, which results in incorrect predictions of values of resistivity from Equation 21.18. Furthermore, according to Equations 21.18 and 21.19, the temperature variation of the resistivity is predicted to vary as v_{avg}, which according to an ideal-gas model (Chapter 16, Eq. 16.22) is proportional to $\sqrt{T}$. This behavior is in disagreement with the linear dependence of resistivity with temperature for pure metals (Fig. 21.8a). Because of these incorrect predictions, we must modify our structural model. We shall call the model that we have developed so far the *classical* model for electrical conduction. To account for the incorrect predictions of the classical model, we will develop it further into a *quantum mechanical* model, which we shall describe briefly.

We discussed two important simplification models in earlier chapters, the particle model and the wave model. Although we discussed these two simplification models separately, quantum physics tells us that this separation is not so clear-cut. As we shall discuss in detail in Chapter 28, particles have wave-like properties. The predictions of some models can only be matched to experimental results if the model includes the wave-like behavior of particles. The structural model for electrical conduction in metals is one of these cases.

Let us imagine that the electrons moving through the metal have wave-like properties. If the array of atoms in a conductor is regularly spaced (that is, periodic), the wave-like character of the electrons makes it possible for them to move freely through the conductor and a collision with an atom is unlikely. For an idealized conductor, no collisions would occur, the mean free path would be infinite, and the resistivity would be zero. Electrons are scattered only if the atomic arrangement is irregular (not periodic), as a result of structural defects or impurities, for example. At low temperatures, the resistivity of metals is dominated by scattering caused by collisions between the electrons and impurities. At high temperatures, the resistivity is dominated by scattering caused by collisions between the electrons and the atoms of the conductor, which are continuously displaced as a result of thermal agitation, destroying the perfect periodicity. The thermal motion of the atoms makes the structure irregular (compared with an atomic array at rest), thereby reducing the electron's mean free path.

Although it is beyond the scope of this text to show this modification in detail, the classical model modified with the wave-like character of the electrons results in predictions of resistivity values that are in agreement with measured values and predicts a linear temperature dependence. When discussing the hydrogen atom in Chapter 11, we had to introduce some quantum notions to understand experimental observations such as atomic spectra. Likewise, we had to introduce quantum notions in Chapter 17 to understand the temperature behavior of molar specific heats of gases. Here we have another case in which quantum physics is necessary for the model to agree with experiment. Although classical physics can explain a tremendous range of phenomena, we continue to see hints that quantum physics must be incorporated into our models. We shall study quantum physics in detail in Chapters 28 through 31.

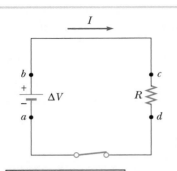

ACTIVE FIGURE 21.10

A circuit consisting of a resistor of resistance *R* and a battery having a potential difference Δ*V* across its terminals. Positive charge flows in the clockwise direction.

Physics☒Now™ Log into PhysicsNow at **www.pop4e.com** and go to Active Figure 21.10 to adjust the battery voltage and the resistance to see the resulting current in the circuit and power delivered to the resistor.

▄▄ **PITFALL PREVENTION 21.5**

MISCONCEPTIONS ABOUT CURRENT
Several common misconceptions are associated with current in a circuit like that in Active Figure 21.10. One is that current comes out of one terminal of the battery and is then "used up" as it passes through the resistor. According to this approach, there is current in only one part of the circuit. The correct understanding, however, is that the current is the same *everywhere* in the circuit. A related misconception has the current coming out of the resistor being smaller than that going in because some of the current is "used up." Another misconception has current coming out of both terminals of the battery, in opposite directions, and then "clashing" in the resistor, delivering the energy in this manner. We know that is not the case because the charges flow in the same rotational sense at *all* points in the circuit. Be sure your conceptual understanding of current is valid.

21.5 ELECTRIC ENERGY AND POWER

In Section 21.1, we discussed the energy transformations occurring in a circuit. If a battery is used to establish an electric current in a conductor, there is a continuous transformation of chemical energy in the battery to kinetic energy of the electrons to internal energy in the conductor, resulting in an increase in the temperature of the conductor.

In typical electric circuits, energy is transferred from a source, such as a battery, to some device, such as a lightbulb or a radio receiver by electrical transmission (T_{ET} in Eq. 6.20). Let us determine an expression that will allow us to calculate the rate of this energy transfer. First, consider the simple circuit in Active Figure 21.10, where we imagine that energy is being delivered to a resistor. Because the connecting wires also have resistance, some energy is delivered to the wires and some energy to the resistor. Unless noted otherwise, we will adopt a simplification model in which the resistance of the wires is so small compared with the resistance of the circuit element that we ignore the energy delivered to the wires.

Let us now analyze the energetics of the circuit in which a battery is connected to a resistor of resistance *R* as in Active Figure 21.10. Imagine following a positive quantity of charge *Q* around the circuit from point *a* through the battery and resistor and back to *a*. Point *a* is a reference point at which the potential is defined as zero. We identify the entire circuit as our system. As the charge moves from *a* to *b* through the battery whose potential difference is Δ*V*, the electrical potential energy of the system increases by the amount *Q* Δ*V*, whereas the chemical energy in the battery decreases by the same amount. (Recall from Chapter 20 that Δ*U* = *q* Δ*V*.) As the charge moves from *c* to *d* through the resistor, however, the system loses this electrical potential energy during collisions with atoms in the resistor. In this process, the energy is transformed to internal energy corresponding to increased vibrational motion of the atoms in the resistor. Because we have neglected the resistance of the interconnecting wires, no energy transformation occurs for paths *bc* and *da*. When the charge returns to point *a*, the net result is that some of the chemical energy in the battery has been delivered to the resistor and resides in the resistor as internal energy associated with molecular vibration.

The resistor is normally in contact with air, so its increased temperature results in a transfer of energy by heat into the air. In addition, there will be thermal radiation from the resistor, representing another means of escape for the energy. After some time interval has passed, the resistor remains at a constant temperature because the input of energy from the battery is balanced by the output of energy by heat and radiation. Some electrical devices include *heat sinks*[7] connected to parts of the circuit to prevent these parts from reaching dangerously high temperatures. Heat sinks are pieces of metal with many fins. The high thermal conductivity of the metal provides a rapid transfer of energy by heat away from the hot component and the large number of fins provides a large surface area in contact with the air, so energy can transfer by radiation and into the air by heat at a high rate.

Let us consider now the rate at which the system loses electric potential energy as the charge *Q* passes through the resistor:

$$\frac{dU}{dt} = \frac{d}{dt}(Q\,\Delta V) = \frac{dQ}{dt}\,\Delta V = I\,\Delta V$$

where *I* is the current in the circuit. Of course, the system regains this potential energy when the charge passes through the battery, at the expense of chemical energy in the battery. The rate at which the system loses potential energy as the charge passes through the resistor is equal to the rate at which the system gains internal energy in the resistor. Therefore, the **power** 𝒫, representing the rate at which energy

---

[7]This terminology is another misuse of the word *heat* that is ingrained in our common language.

is delivered to the resistor, is

$$\mathcal{P} = I\,\Delta V \qquad\qquad [21.20]$$

We have developed this result by considering a battery delivering energy to a resistor. Equation 21.20, however, can be used to determine the power transferred from a voltage source to *any* device carrying a current I and having a potential difference ΔV between its terminals.

Using Equation 21.20 and that $\Delta V = IR$ for a resistor, we can express the power delivered to the resistor in the alternative forms

$$\mathcal{P} = I^2 R = \frac{(\Delta V)^2}{R} \qquad\qquad [21.21]$$

The SI unit of power is the watt, introduced in Chapter 6. If you analyze the units in Equations 21.20 and 21.21, you will see that the result of the calculation provides a watt as the unit. The power delivered to a conductor of resistance R is often referred to as an I^2R *loss*.

As we learned in Section 6.8, the unit of energy your electric company uses to calculate energy transfer, the kilowatt-hour, is the amount of energy transferred in 1 h at the constant rate of 1 kW. Because 1 W = 1 J/s, we have

$$1 \text{ kWh} = (1.0 \times 10^3 \text{ W})(3\,600 \text{ s}) = 3.6 \times 10^6 \text{ J} \qquad [21.22]$$

QUICK QUIZ 21.4 For the two lightbulbs shown in Figure 21.11, rank the currents at points *a* through *f*, from largest to smallest.

▪ Thinking Physics 21.2

Two lightbulbs A and B are connected across the same potential difference as in Figure 21.11. The electric input powers to the lightbulbs are shown. Which lightbulb has the higher resistance? Which carries the greater current?

Reasoning Because the voltage across each lightbulb is the same and the rate of energy delivered to a resistor is $\mathcal{P} = (\Delta V)^2/R$, the lightbulb with the lower resistance exhibits the higher rate of energy transfer. In this case, the resistance of A is larger than that for B. Furthermore, because $\mathcal{P} = I\,\Delta V$, we see that the current carried by B is larger than that of A. ▪

▪ Thinking Physics 21.3

When is a lightbulb more likely to fail, just after it is turned on or after it has been on for a while?

Reasoning When the switch is closed, the source voltage is immediately applied across the lightbulb. As the voltage is applied across the cold filament when the lightbulb is first turned on, the resistance of the filament is low. Therefore, the current is high and a relatively large amount of energy is delivered to the bulb per unit time interval. This causes the temperature of the filament to rise rapidly, resulting in thermal stress on the filament that makes it likely to fail at that moment. As the filament warms up in the absence of failure, its resistance rises and the current falls. As a result, the rate of energy delivered to the lightbulb falls. The thermal stress on the filament is reduced so that the failure is less likely to occur after the bulb has been on for a while. ▪

▪ **Power delivered to a device**

▦ **PITFALL PREVENTION 21.6**

CHARGES DO NOT MOVE ALL THE WAY AROUND A CIRCUIT The movement of a charge around the circuit is not what happens in a circuit, unless you wait for a very long time. Due to the very low magnitude of the drift velocity, it might take *hours* for a single electron to make one complete trip around the circuit. In terms of understanding the energy transfer in a circuit, however, it is useful to *imagine* a charge moving all the way around the circuit.

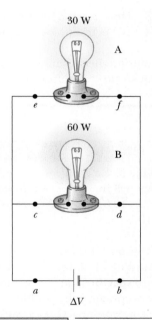

FIGURE 21.11 (Quick Quiz 21.4 and Thinking Physics 21.2) Two lightbulbs connected across the same potential difference.

▦ **PITFALL PREVENTION 21.7**

ENERGY IS NOT "DISSIPATED" In some books, you may see Equation 21.20 described as the power "dissipated in" a resistor, suggesting that energy disappears. Instead, we say energy is "delivered to" a resistor. The notion of *dissipation* arises because a warm resistor will expel energy by radiation and heat, and energy delivered by the battery leaves the circuit. (It does not disappear!)

EXAMPLE 21.5   **Electrical Rating of a Lightbulb**

A lightbulb is rated at 120 V/75 W, which means that at its intended operating voltage of 120 V it has energy delivered to it at a rate of 75.0 W. The lightbulb is powered by a 120-V direct-current power supply.

A Find the current in the lightbulb and its resistance.

Solution Because the power rating of the lightbulb is 75.0 W and the operating voltage is 120 V, we can use $\mathcal{P} = I\,\Delta V$ to find the current:

$$I = \frac{\mathcal{P}}{\Delta V} = \frac{75.0 \text{ W}}{120 \text{ V}} = \boxed{0.625 \text{ A}}$$

Using $\Delta V = IR$, the resistance is calculated to be

$$R = \frac{\Delta V}{I} = \frac{120 \text{ V}}{0.625 \text{ A}} = \boxed{192 \ \Omega}$$

B How much does it cost to operate the lightbulb for 24 h if electricity costs 12¢ per kilowatt-hour?

Solution Because the energy delivered to the lightbulb equals power multiplied by time interval, the amount of

energy you must pay for, expressed in kWh, is

$$\text{Energy} = (0.075 \text{ kW})(24 \text{ h}) = 1.8 \text{ kWh}$$

If energy is purchased at 12¢ per kWh, the cost is

$$\text{Cost} = (1.8 \text{ kWh})(\$0.12/\text{kWh}) = \boxed{\$0.22}$$

That is, it costs 22¢ to operate the lightbulb for one day. This cost is a small amount, but when larger and more complex devices are used, the costs go up rapidly.

Demands on energy supplies have made it necessary to be aware of the energy requirements of electric devices, not only because they are becoming more expensive to operate but also because, with the dwindling of the coal and oil resources that ultimately supply us with electrical energy, increased awareness of conservation becomes necessary. Every electric appliance has a label that contains the information needed to calculate the power requirements of the appliance. The power consumption in watts is often stated directly, as on a lightbulb. In other cases, the amount of current in the device and the voltage at which it operates are given. This information and Equation 21.20 are sufficient to calculate the operating cost of any electric device.

INTERACTIVE   **EXAMPLE 21.6**   **Linking Electricity and Thermodynamics**

What is the required resistance of an immersion heater that will increase the temperature of 1.50 kg of water from 10.0°C to 50.0°C in 10.0 min while operating at 110 V?

Solution This example allows us to link our new understanding of power in electricity with our experience with specific heat in thermodynamics in Chapter 17. To conceptualize the problem, we need to realize that an immersion heater is a resistor that is inserted into a container of water. As energy is delivered to the immersion heater, raising its temperature, energy leaves the surface of the resistor by heat, going into the water. When the immersion heater reaches a constant temperature, the rate of energy delivered to the resistance by electrical transmission is equal to the rate of energy delivered by heat to the water.

As a simplification model, we ignore the initial time interval during which the temperature of the resistor increases, and we also ignore any variation of resistance with temperature. Therefore, we imagine a constant rate of energy transfer for the entire 10.0 min. We categorize this problem as one in which energy is delivered to the resistor by electrical transmission and then to the water by heat. To analyze the problem, we set the rate of energy delivered to the resistor equal to the rate of

energy entering the water:

$$\mathcal{P} = \frac{(\Delta V)^2}{R} = \frac{Q}{\Delta t}$$

where Q represents an amount of energy transfer by heat into the water and Equation 21.21 expresses the electrical power. The amount of energy transfer by heat necessary to raise the temperature of the water is given by Equation 17.3, $Q = mc\,\Delta T$. Therefore,

$$\frac{(\Delta V)^2}{R} = \frac{mc\,\Delta T}{\Delta t} \quad \rightarrow \quad R = \frac{(\Delta V)^2\,\Delta t}{mc\,\Delta T}$$

Substituting the values given in the statement of the problem gives

$$R = \frac{(110 \text{ V})^2(600 \text{ s})}{(1.50 \text{ kg})(4\,186 \text{ J/kg}\cdot{}^\circ\text{C})(50.0{}^\circ\text{C} - 10.0{}^\circ\text{C})}$$

$$= \boxed{28.9 \ \Omega}$$

To finalize this problem, let us compare the power and the cost of operation of the immersion heater to the lightbulb in Example 21.5. The power of the immersion heater is found from Equation 21.21:

$$\mathcal{P} = \frac{(\Delta V)^2}{R} = \frac{(110 \text{ V})^2}{28.9 \ \Omega} = 419 \text{ W}$$

which is significantly larger than the power of the light-bulb in Example 21.5. The energy transferred to the heater during the operation time of 10.0 min is

$$\Delta E = \mathcal{P} \, \Delta t = (419 \text{ W})(10.0 \text{ min})\left(\frac{1 \text{ h}}{60.0 \text{ min}}\right)$$

$$= 69.8 \text{ Wh} = 0.069 \text{ 8 kWh}$$

If the energy is purchased at an estimated price of 12.0¢ per kilowatt-hour, the cost is

$$\text{Cost} = (0.069 \text{ 8 kWh})(\$0.120/\text{kWh})$$

$$= \$0.008 \text{ 38} = 0.838¢$$

Even though the power rating is higher for the heater than for the lightbulb, it costs much less to operate the heater. Of course, the primary factor in this comparison is that the heater is operated for 10.0 min, whereas the lightbulb in Example 21.5 is operated for 24 h.

Physics⊗Now™ Explore the heating of water by logging into PhysicsNow at **www.pop4e.com** and going to Interactive Example 21.6.

21.6 | SOURCES OF emf

The entity that maintains the constant voltage in Figure 21.12 is called a **source of emf**.[8] Sources of emf are any devices (such as batteries and generators) that increase the potential energy of a circuit system by maintaining a potential difference between points in the circuit while charges move through the circuit. One can think of a source of emf as a "charge pump." The emf $\mathcal{E}$ of a source describes the work done per unit charge, and hence the SI unit of emf is the volt.

At this point, you may wonder why we need to define a second quantity, emf, with the volt as a unit when we have already defined the potential difference. To see the need for this new quantity, consider the circuit shown in Figure 21.12, consisting of a battery connected to a resistor. We shall assume that the connecting wires have no resistance. We might be tempted to claim that the potential difference across the battery terminals (the terminal voltage) equals the emf of the battery. A real battery, however, always has some **internal resistance** r. As a result, the terminal voltage is not equal to the emf, as we shall show.

The circuit shown in Figure 21.12 can be described by the circuit diagram in Active Figure 21.13a. The battery within the dashed rectangle is modeled as an ideal, zero-resistance source of emf $\mathcal{E}$ in series with the internal resistance r. Now imagine moving from a to b in Active Figure 21.13a. As you pass from the negative to the positive terminal within the source of emf the potential increases by $\mathcal{E}$. As you move through the resistance r, however, the potential decreases by an amount Ir, where I is the current in the circuit. Therefore, the terminal voltage $\Delta V = V_b - V_a$ of the battery is[9]

$$\Delta V = \mathcal{E} - Ir \qquad [21.23]$$

Note from this expression that $\mathcal{E}$ is equivalent to the **open-circuit voltage, that is, the terminal voltage when the current is zero.** Active Figure 21.13b is a graphical representation of the changes in potential as the circuit is traversed clockwise. By inspecting Active Figure 21.13a, we see that the terminal voltage ΔV must also equal the potential difference across the external resistance R, often called the **load resistance**; that is, $\Delta V = IR$. Combining this expression with Equation 21.23, we see that

$$\mathcal{E} = IR + Ir \qquad [21.24]$$

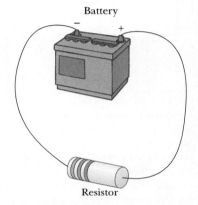

Battery

Resistor

FIGURE 21.12 A circuit consisting of a resistor connected to the terminals of a battery.

---

[8]The term *emf* was originally an abbreviation for *electromotive force,* but it is not a force, so the long form is discouraged. The name electromotive force was used early in the study of electricity before the understanding of batteries was as sophisticated as it is today.

[9]The terminal voltage in this case is less than the emf by the amount Ir. In some situations, the terminal voltage may *exceed* the emf by the amount Ir. Such a situation occurs when the direction of the current is *opposite* that of the emf, as when a battery is being charged by another source of emf.

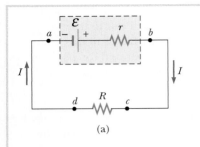

(a)

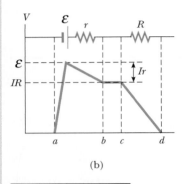

(b)

ACTIVE FIGURE 21.13

(a) Circuit diagram of a source of emf $\mathcal{E}$ (in this case, a battery) with internal resistance r, connected to an external resistor of resistance R. (b) Graphical representation showing how the potential changes as the circuit in (a) is traversed clockwise.

Physics⊗Now™ Log into Physics-Now at **www.pop4e.com** and go to Active Figure 21.13 to adjust the emf and resistances r and R to see the effect on the current and on the graph in (b).

⊞ **PITFALL PREVENTION 21.8**

WHAT IS CONSTANT IN A BATTERY? Notice that Equation 21.25 shows us that the current in the circuit depends on the resistance connected to the battery. It is a common misconception that a battery is a source of constant current. Equation 21.25 clearly shows that to be not true. It is also not true that a battery is a source of constant terminal voltage. Equation 21.23 shows that to be not true. **A battery is a source of constant emf.**

■ Equivalent resistance of resistors in series

Solving for the current gives

$$I = \frac{\mathcal{E}}{R + r} \qquad [21.25]$$

which shows that the current in this simple circuit depends on both the resistance R external to the battery and the internal resistance r. If R is much greater than r, we can adopt a simplification model in which we neglect r in our analysis. In many circuits, we shall adopt this simplification model.

If we multiply Equation 21.24 by the current I, we have

$$I\mathcal{E} = I^2R + I^2r$$

This equation tells us that the total power output $I\mathcal{E}$ of the source of emf is equal to the rate I^2R at which energy is delivered to the load resistance plus the rate I^2r at which energy is delivered to the internal resistance. If $r \ll R$, much more of the energy from the battery is delivered to the load resistance than stays in the battery, although the amount of energy is relatively small because the load resistance is large, resulting in a small current. If $r \gg R$, a significant fraction of the energy from the source of emf stays in the battery package because it is delivered to the internal resistance. For example, if a wire is simply connected between the terminals of a flashlight battery, the battery becomes warm. This warming represents the transfer of energy from the source of emf to the internal resistance, where it appears as internal energy associated with temperature. Problem 21.57 explores the conditions under which the largest amount of energy is transferred from the battery to the load resistor.

21.7 ❘ RESISTORS IN SERIES AND IN PARALLEL

When two or more resistors are connected together end to end as in Active Figure 21.14a, they are said to be in **series.** (Compare this configuration to capacitors in series in Active Figure 20.24.) In a series connection, if an amount of charge Q exits resistor R_1, charge Q must also enter the second resistor R_2. Otherwise, charge will accumulate on the wire between the resistors. Therefore, the same amount of charge passes through both resistors in a given time interval and the currents are the same in both resistors.

Because the potential difference between a and b in the circuit diagram of Active Figure 21.14b equals IR_1 and the potential difference between b and c equals IR_2, the potential difference between a and c is

$$\Delta V = IR_1 + IR_2 = I(R_1 + R_2)$$

The potential difference across the battery is also applied to the equivalent resistance in Active Figure 21.14c:

$$\Delta V = IR_{\text{eq}}$$

where we have indicated that the equivalent resistance has the same effect on the circuit because it results in the same current in the battery as the combination of resistors. Combining these equations, we see that we can replace the two resistors in series with a single equivalent resistance whose value is the *sum* of the individual resistances:

$$\Delta V = IR_{\text{eq}} = I(R_1 + R_2) \quad \rightarrow \quad R_{\text{eq}} = R_1 + R_2 \qquad [21.26]$$

The equivalent resistance of three or more resistors connected in series is simply

$$R_{\text{eq}} = R_1 + R_2 + R_3 + \cdots \qquad [21.27]$$

Therefore, **the equivalent resistance of a series connection of resistors is the algebraic sum of the individual resistances and is always greater than any individual resistance.**

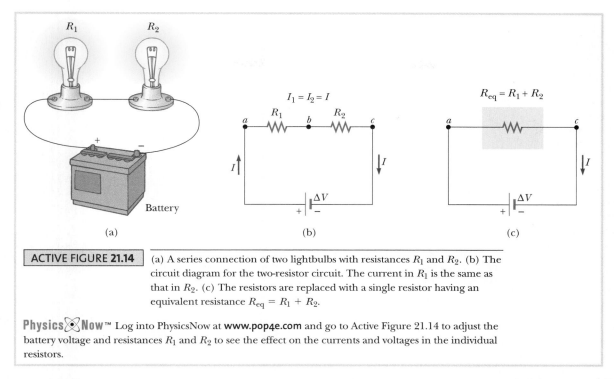

(a)   (b)   (c)

ACTIVE FIGURE 21.14 | (a) A series connection of two lightbulbs with resistances R_1 and R_2. (b) The circuit diagram for the two-resistor circuit. The current in R_1 is the same as that in R_2. (c) The resistors are replaced with a single resistor having an equivalent resistance $R_{eq} = R_1 + R_2$.

Physics⊗Now™ Log into PhysicsNow at **www.pop4e.com** and go to Active Figure 21.14 to adjust the battery voltage and resistances R_1 and R_2 to see the effect on the currents and voltages in the individual resistors.

Looking back at Equation 21.25, the denominator is the simple algebraic sum of the external and internal resistances, which is consistent with the internal and external resistances being in series in Active Figure 21.13a.

Note that if the filament of one lightbulb in Active Figure 21.14a were to fail,[10] the circuit would no longer be complete (an open-circuit condition would exist) and the second bulb would also go out.

QUICK QUIZ 21.5 | If a piece of wire were used to connect points b and c in Active Figure 21.14b, does the brightness of lightbulb R_1 **(a)** increase, **(b)** decrease, or **(c)** remain the same?

QUICK QUIZ 21.6 | With the switch in the circuit of Figure 21.15a closed, there is no current in R_2 because the current has an alternate zero-resistance path through the switch. There is current in R_1, and this current is measured with the ammeter (a device for measuring current) at the right side of the circuit. If the switch is opened (Fig. 21.15b), current exists in R_2. What happens to the reading on the ammeter when the switch is opened? **(a)** The reading goes up. **(b)** The reading goes down. **(c)** The reading does not change.

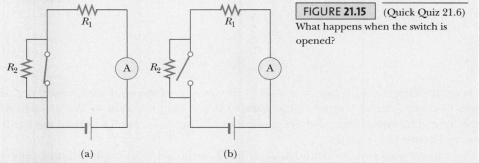

(a)   (b)

FIGURE 21.15 | (Quick Quiz 21.6) What happens when the switch is opened?

> **⊞ PITFALL PREVENTION 21.9**
>
> LOCAL AND GLOBAL CHANGES A local change in one part of a circuit may result in a global change throughout the circuit. For example, if a single resistance is changed in a circuit containing several resistors and batteries, the currents in all resistors and batteries, the terminal voltages of all batteries, and the voltages across all resistors may change as a result.

---

[10]We will describe the end of the life of a lightbulb by saying that *the filament fails* rather than by saying that the lightbulb "burns out." The word *burn* suggests a combustion process, which is not what occurs in a lightbulb. When a filament fails, it breaks, so that the bulb can no longer carry a current.

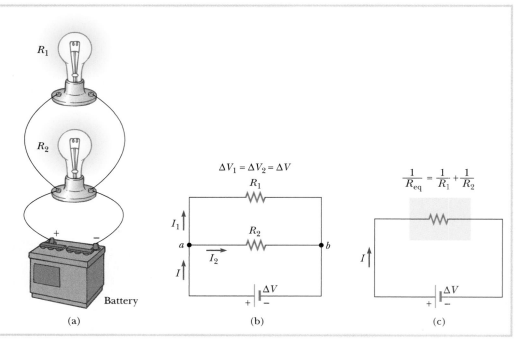

ACTIVE FIGURE 21.16

(a) A parallel connection of two light-bulbs with resistances R_1 and R_2. (b) The circuit diagram for the two-resistor circuit. The potential difference across R_1 is the same as that across R_2. (c) The resistors are replaced with a single resistor having an equivalent resistance given by Equation 21.29.

Physics⊗Now™ Log into Physics-Now at **www.pop4e.com** and go to Active Figure 21.16 to adjust the battery voltage and resistances R_1 and R_2 to see the effect on the currents and voltages in the individual resistors.

⊞ **PITFALL PREVENTION 21.10**

CURRENT DOES NOT TAKE THE PATH OF LEAST RESISTANCE You may have heard a phrase like "current takes the path of least resistance." This wording is a reference to a parallel combination of current paths such that there are two or more paths for the current to take. The phrase is incorrect, however. The current takes *all* paths. Those paths with lower resistance will have large currents, but even very high-resistance paths will carry *some* of the current.

▮ Equivalent resistance of resistors in parallel

Now consider two resistors connected in **parallel** as shown in Active Figure 21.16a. In this case, the potential differences across the resistors are equal because each resistor is connected directly across the battery terminals. The currents are generally not the same, however. When the charges reach point a (called a *junction*) in the circuit diagram in Active Figure 21.16b, the current splits into two parts, with I_1 in R_1 and I_2 in R_2. If R_1 is greater than R_2, then I_1 is less than I_2. Because charge must be conserved, the current I that enters point a must equal the total current leaving point a:

$$I = I_1 + I_2$$

Because the potential differences across the resistors are the same, $I = \Delta V/R$ gives

$$I = I_1 + I_2 = \frac{\Delta V}{R_1} + \frac{\Delta V}{R_2} = \Delta V \left(\frac{1}{R_1} + \frac{1}{R_2} \right) = \frac{\Delta V}{R_{eq}}$$

where R_{eq} is an equivalent single resistance that has the same effect on the circuit; that is, it causes the same current in the battery (Active Fig. 21.16c). From this result, we see that the equivalent resistance of two resistors in parallel is given by

$$\frac{1}{R_{eq}} = \frac{1}{R_1} + \frac{1}{R_2} \qquad [21.28]$$

An extension of this analysis to three or more resistors in parallel yields the following general expression:

$$\frac{1}{R_{eq}} = \frac{1}{R_1} + \frac{1}{R_2} + \frac{1}{R_3} + \cdots \qquad [21.29]$$

From this expression, it can be seen that **the inverse of the equivalent resistance of two or more resistors connected in parallel is the algebraic sum of the inverses of the individual resistances, and the equivalent resistance is always less than the smallest resistance in the group.**

A circuit consisting of resistors can often be reduced to a simple circuit containing only one resistor. To do so, examine the initial circuit and replace any resistors in series or any in parallel with equivalent resistances using Equations 21.27 and 21.29. Draw a sketch of the new circuit after these changes have been made. Examine the new circuit and replace any new series or parallel combinations that now exist. Continue this process until a single equivalent resistance is found for the entire circuit. (That may not be possible; if not, see the techniques of Section 21.8.)

If the current in or the potential difference across a resistor in the initial circuit is to be found, start with the final circuit and gradually work your way back through the equivalent circuits. Find currents and voltages across resistors using $\Delta V = IR$ and your understanding of series and parallel combinations.

Household circuits are always wired so that the electrical devices are connected in parallel as in Active Figure 21.16a. In this manner, each device operates independently of the others so that if one is switched off, the others remain on. For example, if one of the lightbulbs in Active Figure 21.16a were removed from its socket, the other would continue to operate. Equally important, each device operates on the same voltage. If devices were connected in series, the voltage applied to the combination would divide among the devices, so the voltage applied to any one device would depend on how many devices were in the combination.

In many household circuits, circuit breakers are used in series with other circuit elements for safety purposes. A circuit breaker is designed to switch off and open the circuit at some maximum current (typically 15 A or 20 A) whose value depends on the nature of the circuit. If a circuit breaker were not used, excessive currents caused by turning on many devices could result in excessive temperatures in wires and, perhaps, cause a fire. In older home construction, fuses were used in place of circuit breakers. When the current in a circuit exceeds some value, the conductor in a fuse melts and opens the circuit. The disadvantage of fuses is that they are destroyed in the process of opening the circuit, whereas circuit breakers can be reset.

> **QUICK QUIZ 21.7** With the switch in the circuit of Figure 21.17a open, no current exists in R_2. Current does exist in R_1, and this current is measured with the ammeter at the right side of the circuit. If the switch is closed (Fig. 21.17b), current exists in R_2. What happens to the reading on the ammeter when the switch is closed? **(a)** The reading goes up. **(b)** The reading goes down. **(c)** The reading does not change.

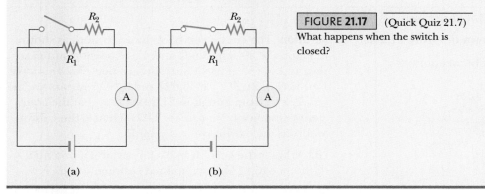

FIGURE 21.17 (Quick Quiz 21.7) What happens when the switch is closed?

(a)   (b)

> **QUICK QUIZ 21.8** **(i)** In Active Figure 21.14b, imagine that we add a third resistor in series with the first two. Does the current in the battery **(a)** increase, **(b)** decrease, or **(c)** remain the same? Does the terminal voltage of the battery **(d)** increase, **(e)** decrease, or **(f)** remain the same? **(ii)** In Active Figure 21.16b, imagine that we add a third resistor in parallel with the first two. Does the current in the battery **(a)** increase, **(b)** decrease, or **(c)** remain the same? Does the terminal voltage of the battery **(d)** increase, **(e)** decrease, or **(f)** remain the same?

■ Thinking Physics 21.4

Compare the brightnesses of the four identical lightbulbs in Figure 21.18. What happens if bulb A fails so that it cannot conduct? What if bulb C fails? What if bulb D fails ?

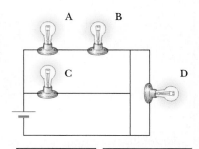

FIGURE 21.18 (Thinking Physics 21.4) What happens to the lightbulbs if one fails?

Reasoning Bulbs A and B are connected in series across the battery, whereas bulb C is connected by itself. Therefore, the terminal voltage of the battery is split between bulbs A and B. As a result, bulb C will be brighter than bulbs A and B, which should be equally as bright as each other. Bulb D has a wire connected across it. Therefore, there is no potential difference across bulb D and it does not glow at all. If bulb A fails, bulb B goes out but bulb C stays lit. If bulb C fails, there is no effect on the other bulbs. If bulb D fails, the event is undetectable because bulb D was not glowing initially. ▪

▪ Thinking Physics 21.5

Figure 21.19 illustrates how a three-way lightbulb is constructed to provide three levels of light intensity. The socket of the lamp is equipped with a three-way switch for selecting different light intensities. The bulb contains two filaments. Why are the filaments connected in parallel? Explain how the two filaments are used to provide three different light intensities.

Reasoning If the filaments were connected in series and one of them were to fail, there would be no current in the bulb and the bulb would give no illumination, regardless of the switch position. When the filaments are connected in parallel, however, and one of them (say the 75-W filament) fails, the bulb still operates in some switch positions because there is current in the other (100-W) filament. The three light intensities are made possible by selecting one of three values of filament resistance, using a single value of 120 V for the applied voltage. The 75-W filament offers one value of resistance, the 100-W filament offers a second value, and the third resistance is obtained by combining the two filaments in parallel. When switch S_1 is closed and switch S_2 is opened, only the 75-W filament carries current. When switch S_1 is open and switch S_2 is closed, only the 100-W filament carries current. When both switches are closed, both filaments carry current, and a total illumination corresponding to 175 W is obtained. ▪

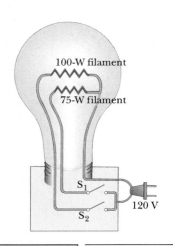

100-W filament

75-W filament

S_1

S_2

120 V

FIGURE 21.19 (Thinking Physics 21.5) A three-way lightbulb.

EXAMPLE 21.7 Find the Equivalent Resistance

Four resistors are connected as shown in Figure 21.20a.

A Find the equivalent resistance between *a* and *c*.

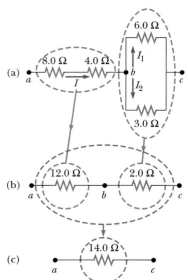

(a)

6.0 Ω

8.0 Ω   4.0 Ω

a I b I_1 c

I_2

3.0 Ω

(b)

12.0 Ω   2.0 Ω

a b c

(c)

14.0 Ω

a c

FIGURE 21.20 (Example 21.7) The four resistors shown in (a) can be reduced in steps to an equivalent 14.0-Ω resistor shown in (c).

Solution The circuit can be reduced in steps as shown in Figure 21.20. The 8.0-Ω and 4.0-Ω resistors are in series, and so the equivalent resistance between *a* and *b* is 12.0 Ω (Eq. 21.27). The 6.0-Ω and 3.0-Ω resistors are in parallel, so from Equation 21.29 we find that the equivalent resistance from *b* to *c* is 2.0 Ω. Hence, the equivalent resistance from *a* to *c* is 14.0 Ω.

B What is the current in each resistor if a potential difference of 42 V is maintained between *a* and *c*?

Solution Using $\Delta V = IR$ and the results from part A, we have

$$I = \frac{\Delta V_{ac}}{R_{eq}} = \frac{42 \text{ V}}{14.0 \text{ } \Omega} = 3.0 \text{ A}$$

The current I in the 8.0-Ω and 4.0-Ω resistors is the same because the resistors are in series. At the junction at *b*, the current splits. Part of it (I_1) is in the 6.0-Ω resistor, and part (I_2) is in the 3.0-Ω resistor. Because the potential differences ΔV_{bc} across these resistors are the same (they are in parallel), we see that $\Delta V_{bc} = IR = (6.0 \text{ } \Omega)I_1 = (3.0 \text{ } \Omega)I_2$, or $I_2 = 2.0I_1$. Using this result and that $I_1 + I_2 = 3.0$ A, we find that $I_1 = 1.0$ A and $I_2 = 2.0$ A. We could have guessed this result by noting that the current in the 3.0-Ω resistor has to be twice the current in the 6.0-Ω resistor in view of their relative resistances and that the same potential difference appears across each of them.

As a final check, note that $\Delta V_{bc} = (6.0\ \Omega)I_1 = (3.0\ \Omega)I_2 = 6.0$ V and $\Delta V_{ab} = (12.0\ \Omega)I = 36$ V; therefore, $\Delta V_{ac} = \Delta V_{ab} + \Delta V_{bc} = 42$ V, as it must.

INTERACTIVE EXAMPLE 21.8   **Three Resistors in Parallel**

Three resistors are connected in parallel as in Figure 21.21. A potential difference of 18.0 V is maintained between points *a* and *b*.

A Find the current in each resistor.

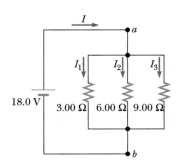

FIGURE 21.21   (Interactive Example 21.8) Three resistors connected in parallel. The voltage across each resistor is 18.0 V.

Solution The resistors are in parallel, and the potential difference across each is 18.0 V. Applying $\Delta V = IR$ to each resistor gives

$$I_1 = \frac{\Delta V}{R_1} = \frac{18.0\ \text{V}}{3.00\ \Omega} = \boxed{6.00\ \text{A}}$$

$$I_2 = \frac{\Delta V}{R_2} = \frac{18.0\ \text{V}}{6.00\ \Omega} = \boxed{3.00\ \text{A}}$$

$$I_3 = \frac{\Delta V}{R_3} = \frac{18.0\ \text{V}}{9.00\ \Omega} = \boxed{2.00\ \text{A}}$$

B Calculate the power delivered to each resistor and the total power delivered to the three resistors.

Solution Applying $\mathcal{P} = I^2R$ to each resistor gives

3.00-Ω: $\mathcal{P}_1 = I_1^2R_1 = (6.00\ \text{A})^2(3.00\ \Omega) = \boxed{108\ \text{W}}$

6.00-Ω: $\mathcal{P}_2 = I_2^2R_2 = (3.00\ \text{A})^2(6.00\ \Omega) = \boxed{54.0\ \text{W}}$

9.00-Ω: $\mathcal{P}_3 = I_3^2R_3 = (2.00\ \text{A})^2(9.00\ \Omega) = \boxed{36.0\ \text{W}}$

which shows that the smallest resistor receives the most power. You can also use $\mathcal{P} = (\Delta V)^2/R$ to find the power delivered to each resistor. Summing the three quantities gives a total power of 198 W.

C Calculate the equivalent resistance of the combination of three resistors.

Solution We can use Equation 21.29 to find R_{eq}:

$$\frac{1}{R_{\text{eq}}} = \frac{1}{3.00\ \Omega} + \frac{1}{6.00\ \Omega} + \frac{1}{9.00\ \Omega} = \frac{11}{18.0\ \Omega}$$

$$R_{\text{eq}} = \frac{18.0\ \Omega}{11} = \boxed{1.64\ \Omega}$$

We can check this answer using the battery voltage and the total current from part A:

$$R_{\text{eq}} = \frac{\Delta V}{I_{\text{tot}}} = \frac{18.0\ \text{V}}{6.00\ \text{A} + 3.00\ \text{A} + 2.00\ \text{A}} = 1.64\ \Omega$$

Physics⊗Now™ By logging into PhysicsNow at **www.pop4e.com** and going to Interactive Example 21.8, you can explore different configurations of the battery and resistors.

21.8 KIRCHHOFF'S RULES

As indicated in the preceding section, some simple circuits can be analyzed using $\Delta V = IR$ and the rules for series and parallel combinations of resistors. Resistors, however, can be connected so that the circuits formed cannot be reduced to a single equivalent resistor. Consider the circuit in Figure 21.22, for example. If either battery were removed from this circuit, the resistors could be combined with the techniques of Section 21.7. With both batteries present, however, that cannot be done.

The procedure for analyzing such circuits is greatly simplified by the use of two simple rules called **Kirchhoff's rules**:

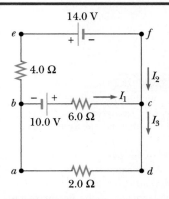

FIGURE 21.22 A circuit that cannot be simplified by using the rules for series and parallel resistors.

GUSTAV KIRCHHOFF (1824–1887)

Kirchhoff, a professor at Heidelberg, Germany, and Robert Bunsen invented the spectroscope and founded the science of spectroscopy, which led to atomic spectra such as those seen in Chapter 11. They discovered the elements cesium and rubidium and invented astronomical spectroscopy. Kirchhoff formulated another Kirchhoff's rule, namely, "a cool substance will absorb light of the same wavelengths that it emits when hot."

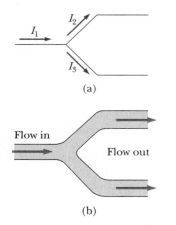

FIGURE 21.23 (a) A schematic diagram illustrating Kirchhoff's junction rule. Conservation of charge requires that the sum of the currents at a junction must equal zero. Therefore, in this case, $I_1 - I_2 - I_3 = 0$. (b) A mechanical analog of the junction rule. Water does not accumulate at the junction, so the amount of water flowing out of the branches on the right must equal the amount flowing into the single branch on the left.

- At any junction, the sum of the currents must equal zero:

$$\sum_{\text{junction}} I = 0$$

This rule is often referred to as the **junction rule.** In Figure 21.22, there are junctions at b and c.

- The sum of the potential differences across each element around any closed circuit loop must be zero:

$$\sum_{\text{loop}} \Delta V = 0$$

This rule is usually called the **loop rule.** In Figure 21.22, we can identify three loops: *abcda, aefda,* and *befcb.*

Kirchhoff's rules are generally used to determine the current in each element in the circuit. In using these rules, we first draw the circuit diagram and assume a direction for the current in each device in the circuit. We draw an arrow representing that direction next to the device and assign a symbol to each independent current, such as I_1, I_2, and so on. Figure 21.22 shows the three different currents that exist in this circuit. Keep in mind that currents in devices connected in series are the same, so the currents in these devices will have the same assigned symbol.

The junction rule is a statement of **conservation of charge.** The amount of charge that enters a given point in a circuit in a time interval must also leave that point in the same time interval because charge cannot build up or disappear at a point. Currents with a direction into the junction are entered into the junction rule as $+I$, whereas currents with a direction out of a junction are entered as $-I$. If we apply the rule to the junction in Figure 21.23a, we have

$$I_1 - I_2 - I_3 = 0$$

Figure 21.23b represents a hydraulic analog to this situation in which water flows through a branched pipe with no leaks. The flow rate into the pipe equals the total flow rate out of the two branches.

The loop rule is equivalent to the law of **conservation of energy.** Suppose a charge moves around any closed loop in a circuit[11] (the charge starts and ends at the same point). In this case, the circuit must gain as much energy as it loses. In this isolated system model for the system of the circuit, no energy is transferred across the boundary of the system (ignoring energy transfer by radiation and heat into the air from warm circuit elements), but energy transformations do occur within the system. The energy of the circuit may decrease due to a potential drop $-IR$ as a charge moves through a resistor or as a result of having the charge move in the reverse direction through an emf. In the latter case, electric potential energy is converted to chemical energy as the battery is charged. The potential energy increases when the charge moves through a battery in the same direction as the emf.

Another approach to understanding the loop rule is to remember the definition of a conservative force from Chapter 7. One of the mathematical behaviors of a conservative force is that the work done by a such a force when a member of the system moves around a closed path is zero. A loop in a circuit is a closed path. If we imagine moving a charge around a loop, the total work done by the conservative electric force must be zero. The total work is the sum of positive and negative works as the charge passes through various circuit elements. Because work is related

---

[11]Remember that this situation is *not* what happens; a charge might take hours to traverse a loop. In terms of analyzing the circuit in terms of energy, however, we can build a mental model in which we *imagine* taking a charge all the way around the circuit.

to potential energy changes and because potential energy changes are related to potential differences (Eq. 20.3), that the sum of all the works is zero is equivalent to the sum of all the potential differences being zero, which is Kirchhoff's loop rule.

As an aid in applying the loop rule, the following sign conventions are used. We have already drawn arrows for currents on our diagram and have assigned symbols to the currents to apply the junction rule. To set up the sign conventions, we choose a direction around each loop that we imagine carrying a positive charge, clockwise or counterclockwise. Therefore, for any device, there will be two directions that we need to consider, one for our chosen current and one for our chosen travel through the device. The sign conventions for potential differences for resistors and batteries based on these two directions are summarized in Figure 21.24, where it is assumed that travel is from point a toward point b:

- If a resistor is traversed in the direction of the current, the potential difference across the resistor is $-IR$ (Fig. 21.24a).
- If a resistor is traversed in the direction *opposite* the current, the potential difference across the resistor is $+IR$ (Figure 21.24b).
- If a source of emf is traversed in the direction of the emf (from $-$ to $+$ on the terminals), the potential difference is $+\mathcal{E}$ (Fig. 21.24c).
- If a source of emf is traversed in the direction opposite the emf (from $+$ to $-$ on the terminals), the potential difference is $-\mathcal{E}$ (Fig. 21.24d).

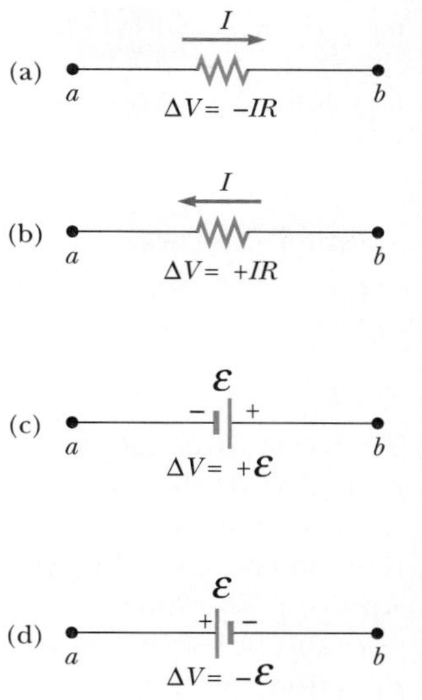

There are limitations on the use of the junction rule and the loop rule. You may use the junction rule as often as needed, as long as each time you write an equation you include in it a current that has not been used in a previous junction rule equation. In general, the number of times the junction rule can be used is one fewer than the number of junction points in the circuit. The loop rule can be used as often as needed, as long as a new circuit element (a resistor or battery) or a new current appears in each new equation. In general, **the number of independent equations you need must equal the number of unknown currents to solve a particular circuit problem.**

FIGURE 21.24 Rules for determining the potential differences across a resistor and a battery. (The battery is assumed to have no internal resistance.) Each circuit element is traversed from a to b.

PROBLEM-SOLVING STRATEGY **Kirchhoff's Rules**

The following procedure is recommended for solving problems that involve circuits that cannot be reduced by the rules for combining resistors in series or parallel.

1. Conceptualize Study the circuit diagram and make sure that you recognize all elements in the circuit. Identify the polarity of each battery and try to imagine the directions in which the current would exist through the batteries.

2. Categorize Determine whether the circuit can be reduced by means of combining series and parallel resistors. If so, use the techniques of Section 21.7. If not, apply Kirchhoff's rules according to step 3 below.

3. Analyze Assign labels to all the known quantities and assign symbols to all the unknown quantities. You must assign *directions* to the currents in each part of the circuit. Although the assignment of current directions is arbitrary, you must adhere

rigorously to the directions you assign when you apply Kirchhoff's rules.

Apply the junction rule (Kirchhoff's first rule) to all junctions in the circuit except one. Now apply the loop rule (Kirchhoff's second rule) to as many loops in the circuit as are needed to obtain, in combination with the equations from the junction rule, as many equations as there are unknowns. To apply this rule, you must choose a direction in which to travel around the loop (either clockwise or counterclockwise) and correctly identify the change in potential as you cross each element. Watch out for signs!

Solve the equations simultaneously for the unknown quantities.

4. Finalize Check your numerical answers for consistency. Do not be alarmed if any of the resulting currents have a negative value; if so, you have guessed the direction of that current incorrectly, but *its magnitude will be correct.*

| INTERACTIVE EXAMPLE 21.9 | Applying Kirchhoff's Rules |

A Find the currents I_1, I_2, and I_3 in the circuit shown in Figure 21.22.

Solution We choose the directions of the currents as in Figure 21.22. Applying Kirchhoff's first rule to junction c gives

$$(1) \quad I_1 + I_2 - I_3 = 0$$

There are three loops in the circuit: *abcda, befcb,* and *aefda* (the outer loop). We need only two loop equations to determine the unknown currents. The third loop equation would give no new information. Applying Kirchhoff's second rule to loops *abcda* and *befcb* and traversing these loops in the clockwise direction, we obtain the expressions

$$(2) \quad \text{Loop } abcda: \quad 10.0\,\text{V} - (6.0\,\Omega)I_1 - (2.0\,\Omega)I_3 = 0$$

$$(3) \quad \text{Loop } befcb: \quad -14.0\,\text{V} - 10.0\,\text{V} + (6.0\,\Omega)I_1 - (4.0\,\Omega)I_2 = 0$$

Note that in loop *befcb*, a positive sign is obtained when traversing the 6.0-Ω resistor because the direction of the path is opposite the direction of I_1. Loop *aefda* gives $-14.0\,\text{V} - (2.0\,\Omega)I_3 - (4.0\,\Omega)I_2 = 0$, which is just the sum of (2) and (3).

Expressions (1), (2), and (3) represent three independent equations with three unknowns. We can solve the problem as follows. Dropping the units for simplicity and substituting I_3 from (1) into (2) gives

$$10.0 - 6.0I_1 - 2.0(I_1 + I_2) = 0$$

$$10.0 = 8.0I_1 + 2.0I_2 \quad (4)$$

Dividing each term in (3) by 2 and rearranging the equation gives

$$-12.0 = -3.0I_1 + 2.0I_2 \quad (5)$$

Subtracting (5) from (4) eliminates I_2, giving

$$22.0 = 11.0I_1$$

$$I_1 = 2.0\,\text{A}$$

Using this value of I_1 in (5) gives a value for I_2:

$$2.0I_2 = 3.0I_1 - 12.0 = 3.0(2.0) - 12.0 = -6.0$$

$$I_2 = -3.0\,\text{A}$$

Finally, $I_3 = I_1 + I_2 = -1.0\,\text{A}$. Hence, the currents have the values

$$I_1 = \boxed{2.0\,\text{A}} \qquad I_2 = \boxed{-3.0\,\text{A}} \qquad I_3 = \boxed{-1.0\,\text{A}}$$

That I_2 and I_3 are negative indicates only that we chose the wrong directions for these currents. The numerical values, however, are correct.

B Find the potential difference between points b and c.

Solution In traversing the path from b to c along the central branch, we have

$$V_c - V_b = +10.0\,\text{V} - (6.0\,\Omega)I_1$$

$$= +10.0\,\text{V} - (6.0\,\Omega)(2.0\,\text{A}) = \boxed{-2.0\,\text{V}}$$

Physics⊗Now™ By logging into PhysicsNow at **www.pop4e.com** and going to Interactive Example 21.9, you can practice applying Kirchhoff's rules.

21.9 ┃ *RC* CIRCUITS

So far, we have been concerned with circuits with constant currents, or *steady-state circuits*. We now consider circuits containing capacitors in which the currents may vary in time.

Charging a Capacitor

Consider the series circuit shown in Active Figure 21.25a. Let us assume that the capacitor is initially uncharged. No current exists when switch S is open (Active Fig. 21.25b). If the switch is thrown closed at $t = 0$, charges begin to flow, setting up a current in the circuit,[12] and the capacitor begins to charge (Active Fig. 21.25c). Note that during the charging, charges do not jump across the plates of the capacitor because the gap between the plates represents an open circuit. Instead, due to the electric field in the wires established by the battery, electrons move into the top plate from the wires and out of the bottom plate into the wires until the capacitor is

---

[12]By "a current in the circuit," we mean current in all parts of the circuit *except* for the region between the plates of the capacitor.

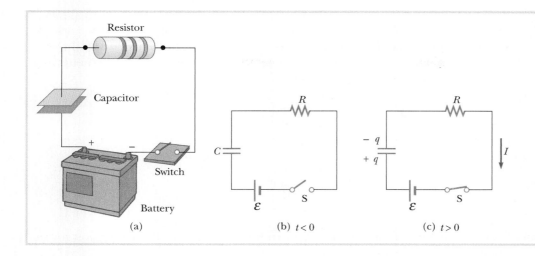

ACTIVE FIGURE 21.25
(a) A capacitor in series with a resistor, switch, and battery. (b) Circuit diagram representing this system at time $t < 0$, before the switch is closed. (c) Circuit diagram at time $t > 0$, after the switch has been closed.

Physics⊗Now™ Log into PhysicsNow at **www.pop4e.com** and go to Active Figure 21.25 to adjust the values of R and C to see the effect on the charging of the capacitor.

fully charged. The value of the maximum charge depends on the emf of the battery. Once the maximum charge is reached, the current in the circuit is zero.

To put this discussion on a quantitative basis, let us apply Kirchhoff's second rule to the circuit after the switch is closed. In our sign conventions, we did not specify a convention for the potential difference across a capacitor. From our study of capacitors in Chapter 20, however, it should be clear that carrying a positive charge across a capacitor from − to + would represent an increase in potential energy for the circuit, a positive potential difference. Traversing the capacitor in the opposite direction would correspond to a decrease in potential energy, a negative potential difference.

Choosing clockwise as our direction around the circuit in Active Figure 21.25 and applying the sign convention for capacitors that we have just discussed, we have

$$\mathcal{E} - \frac{q}{C} - IR = 0 \qquad [21.30]$$

where $-q/C$ is the potential difference across the capacitor and $-IR$ is the potential difference across the resistor consistent with our direction of travel. Note that q and I are *instantaneous* values of the charge and current, respectively, as the capacitor is charged.

We can use Equation 21.30 to find the initial current in the circuit and the maximum charge on the capacitor. At $t = 0$, when the switch is closed, the charge on the capacitor is zero, and from Equation 21.30, we find that the initial current in the circuit I_0 is a maximum and equal to

$$I_0 = \frac{\mathcal{E}}{R} \qquad [21.31]$$

At this time, **the potential difference is entirely across the resistor.** Later, when the capacitor is charged to its maximum value Q, charges cease to flow, the current in the circuit is zero, and **the potential difference is entirely across the capacitor.** Substituting $I = 0$ into Equation 21.30 yields the following expression for Q:

$$Q = C\mathcal{E} \qquad \text{(maximum charge)} \qquad [21.32]$$

To determine analytical expressions for the time dependence of the charge and current, we must solve Equation 21.30. To do so, let us substitute $I = dq/dt$ and rearrange the equation:

$$\frac{dq}{dt} = \frac{\mathcal{E}}{R} - \frac{q}{RC} = \frac{C\mathcal{E} - q}{RC}$$

This expression is a differential equation whose solution is the time-dependent charge on the capacitor. An expression for q may be found in the following way. We rearrange the equation by placing terms involving q on the left side and those involving t on the right side. Then we integrate both sides from the moment when the switch is closed to an arbitrary later instant:

$$\frac{dq}{(q - C\mathcal{E})} = -\frac{1}{RC}\,dt$$

$$\int_0^q \frac{dq}{(q - C\mathcal{E})} = -\frac{1}{RC}\int_0^t dt$$

$$\ln\left(\frac{q - C\mathcal{E}}{-C\mathcal{E}}\right) = -\frac{t}{RC}$$

Using the definition of the natural logarithm, we can solve this expression for the charge on the capacitor as a function of time:

$$\frac{q - C\mathcal{E}}{-C\mathcal{E}} = e^{-t/RC}$$

$$q(t) = C\mathcal{E}[1 - e^{-t/RC}] = Q[1 - e^{-t/RC}] \qquad [21.33]$$

where e is the base of the natural logarithm (*not* the charge on the electron!) and $Q = C\mathcal{E}$ is the maximum charge on the capacitor.

An expression for the current as a function of time may be found by differentiating Equation 21.33 with respect to time. Using $I = dq/dt$, we obtain

$$I(t) = \frac{\mathcal{E}}{R}\,e^{-t/RC} \qquad [21.34]$$

where $\mathcal{E}/R$ is the initial current in the circuit.

Plots of charge and current versus time are shown in Figure 21.26. Note that the charge is zero at $t = 0$ and approaches the maximum value of $C\mathcal{E}$ as $t \to \infty$ (Fig. 21.26a). Furthermore, the current has its maximum value of $I_0 = \mathcal{E}/R$ at $t = 0$ and decays exponentially to zero as $t \to \infty$ (Fig. 21.26b). The quantity RC that appears in the exponential of Equations 21.33 and 21.34 is called the **time constant** τ of the circuit. It represents the time interval during which the current decreases to $1/e$ of its initial value; that is, at the end of the time interval τ, $I = e^{-1}I_0 = 0.368I_0$. After the time interval 2τ, $I = e^{-2}I_0 = 0.135I_0$, and so forth. Likewise, in a time interval τ the charge increases from zero to $C\mathcal{E}[1 - e^{-1}] = 0.632C\mathcal{E}$.

The energy decrease of the battery during the charging process is the product of the total charge and the emf, $Q\mathcal{E} = C\mathcal{E}^2$. After the capacitor is fully charged, the energy stored in it is $\frac{1}{2}Q\mathcal{E} = \frac{1}{2}C\mathcal{E}^2$, which is just half the energy decrease of the battery. It is left to an end-of-chapter problem to show that the remaining half of the energy supplied by the battery appears as internal energy in the resistor (Problem 21.58).

■ Charge versus time for a charging capacitor

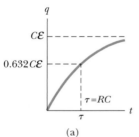
(a)

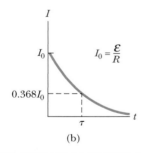
(b)

FIGURE 21.26 (a) Plot of capacitor charge versus time for the circuit shown in Active Figure 21.25. After a time interval equal to one time constant τ has passed, the charge is 63.2% of the maximum value $C\mathcal{E}$. The charge approaches its maximum value as t approaches infinity. (b) Plot of current versus time for the RC circuit shown in Active Figure 21.25. The current has its maximum value $I_0 = \mathcal{E}/R$ at $t = 0$ and decays to zero exponentially as t approaches infinity. After a time interval equal to one time constant τ has passed, the current is 36.8% of its initial value.

Discharging a Capacitor

Now consider the circuit in Active Figure 21.27, consisting of a capacitor with an initial charge Q, a resistor, and a switch. When the switch is open (Active Fig. 21.27a), a potential difference of Q/C exists across the capacitor and zero potential difference exists across the resistor because $I = 0$. If the switch is thrown closed at $t = 0$, the capacitor begins to discharge through the resistor. At some time during the discharge, the current in the circuit is I and the charge on the capacitor is q (Active Fig. 21.27b).

The circuit of Active Figure 21.27 is the same as the circuit of Active Figure 21.25 except for the absence of the battery. Therefore, we modify the Kirchhoff's rule expression in Equation 21.30 by dropping the emf from the equation:

$$-\frac{q}{C} - IR = 0 \qquad [21.35]$$

Because $I = dq/dt$, Equation 21.35 becomes

$$-R\frac{dq}{dt} = \frac{q}{C}$$

$$\frac{dq}{q} = -\frac{1}{RC}\,dt$$

In $I = dq/dt$, dq is negative, because the charge on the discharging capacitor is decreasing; therefore, I has a negative value. This is indicated in Active Figure 21.27 by the reversal of the current arrow compared to Active Figure 21.25. Furthermore, in Equation 21.37 below, the current will come out to have an explicit negative value. Integrating this expression from the moment the switch is closed, at which time $q = Q$, to an arbitrary later instant gives

$$\int_Q^q \frac{dq}{q} = -\frac{1}{RC}\int_0^t dt$$

$$\ln\left(\frac{q}{Q}\right) = -\frac{t}{RC}$$

$$q(t) = Qe^{-t/RC} \qquad [21.36]$$

Differentiating Equation 21.36 with respect to time gives the current as a function of time:

$$I(t) = \frac{dq}{dt} = -I_0 e^{-t/RC} \qquad [21.37]$$

where the initial current is $I_0 = Q/RC$. Therefore, we see that both the charge on the capacitor and the current decay exponentially at a rate characterized by the time constant $\tau = RC$. The negative sign in Equation 21.37 indicates the direction of the current, which is opposite to the direction during the charging process.

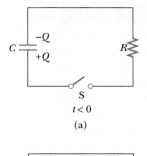
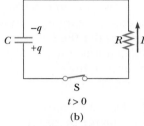

ACTIVE FIGURE 21.27
(a) A charged capacitor connected to a resistor and a switch, which is open for $t < 0$. (b) After the switch is closed at $t = 0$, a current that decreases in magnitude with time is set up in the direction shown and the charge on the capacitor decreases exponentially with time.

Physics⊗Now™ Log into Physics-Now at **www.pop4e.com** and go to Active Figure 21.27 to adjust the values of R and C to see the effect on the discharging of the capacitor.

QUICK QUIZ 21.9 Consider the circuit in Active Figure 21.25a and assume that the battery has no internal resistance. **(i)** Just after the switch is closed, the potential difference across which of the following is equal to the emf of the battery? **(a)** C **(b)** R **(c)** neither C nor R **(ii)** After a very long time, the potential difference across which of the following is equal to the emf of the battery? **(a)** C **(b)** R **(c)** neither C nor R

∎ Thinking Physics 21.6

Many roadway construction sites have flashing yellow lights to warn motorists of possible dangers. What causes the lightbulbs to flash?

Reasoning A typical circuit for such a flasher is shown in Figure 21.28. The lamp L is a gas-filled lamp that acts as an open circuit until a large potential difference causes an electrical discharge in the gas, which gives off a bright light. During this discharge, charges flow through the gas between the electrodes of the lamp. After switch S is closed, the battery charges up the capacitor of capacitance C. At the beginning, the current is high and the charge on the capacitor is low, so most of the potential difference appears across the resistance R. As the capacitor charges, more potential difference appears across it, reflecting the lower current and therefore lower potential difference across the resistor. Eventually, the potential difference across the capacitor reaches a value at which the lamp will conduct, causing a flash. This discharges the capacitor through the lamp and the process of charging begins again. The period between flashes can be adjusted by changing the time constant of the RC circuit. ∎

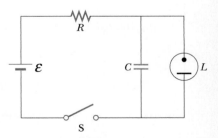

FIGURE 21.28 (Thinking Physics 21.6) The RC circuit in a roadway construction flasher. When the switch is closed, the charge on the capacitor increases until the voltage across the capacitor (and across the flash lamp) is high enough for the lamp to flash, discharging the capacitor.

EXAMPLE 21.10   Charging a Defibrillator

A *defibrillator* (see Fig. P20.48 on page 678) can store energy in the electric field of a large capacitor. Under the proper conditions, the defibrillator can be used to stop cardiac fibrillation (random contractions) in heart attack victims. When fibrillation occurs, the heart produces a rapid, irregular pattern of beats. A fast discharge of energy through the heart can return the organ to its normal beat pattern. Emergency medical teams use portable defibrillators that contain batteries capable of charging a capacitor to a high voltage.

Consider the following parameters for the RC circuit in a defibrillator: $C = 32.0\ \mu F$ and $R = 47.0\ k\Omega$. The circuitry in the charging system applies 5 000 V to the RC circuit to charge it.

A Find the time constant of the circuit, the maximum charge on the capacitor, the maximum current in the circuit during the charging process, and the charge and current as a function of time.

Solution The time constant of the circuit is
$\tau = RC = (47.0 \times 10^3\ \Omega)(32.0 \times 10^{-6}\ F) = \boxed{1.50\ s}$.
The maximum charge on the capacitor is

$Q = C\mathcal{E} = (32.0 \times 10^{-6}\ F)(5\ 000\ V) = \boxed{0.160\ C}$.
The maximum current in the circuit is
$I_0 = \mathcal{E}/R = (5\ 000\ V)/(47.0 \times 10^3\ \Omega) = \boxed{0.106\ A}$.
Using these values and Equations 21.33 and 21.34, we find that

$$q(t) = \boxed{(0.160\ C)\ [1 - e^{-t/1.50}]}$$

$$I(t) = \boxed{(0.106\ A)\ e^{-t/1.50}}$$

B Find the energy stored in the capacitor when it is fully charged.

Solution Using Equation 20.30, we have

$$U = \tfrac{1}{2}C(\Delta V)^2 = \tfrac{1}{2}(32.0 \times 10^{-6}\ C)(5\ 000\ V)^2 = \boxed{400\ J}$$

Note that the time constant τ of 1.50 s means that several seconds are required until the capacitor is close to fully charged. Therefore, after an unsuccessful attempt to defibrillate a patient's heart by delivering the stored energy to the chest, the emergency personnel must wait several seconds for the capacitor to charge before trying again.

EXAMPLE 21.11   Discharging a Capacitor in an *RC* Circuit

Consider a capacitor C being discharged through a resistor R as in Active Figure 21.27.

A After how many time constants is the charge on the capacitor one fourth of its initial value?

Solution The charge on the capacitor varies with time according to Equation 21.36, $q(t) = Qe^{-t/RC}$. To find the time at which the charge q has dropped to one fourth of its initial value, we substitute $q(t) = Q/4$ into this expression and solve for t:

$$\tfrac{1}{4}Q = Qe^{-t/RC}$$

$$\tfrac{1}{4} = e^{-t/RC}$$

Taking the natural logarithm of both sides, we find that

$$-\ln 4 = -\frac{t}{RC}$$

$$t = RC\ln 4 = \boxed{1.39RC}$$

B The energy stored in the capacitor decreases with time as it discharges. After how many time constants is this stored energy one fourth of its initial value?

Solution Using Equations 20.30 and 21.36, we can express the energy stored in the capacitor at any time t as

$$U = \frac{q^2}{2C} = \frac{Q^2}{2C}e^{-2t/RC} = U_0 e^{-2t/RC}$$

where U_0 is the initial energy stored in the capacitor. Similar to part A, we now set $U = U_0/4$ and solve for t:

$$\tfrac{1}{4}U_0 = U_0 e^{-2t/RC}$$

$$\tfrac{1}{4} = e^{-2t/RC}$$

Again, taking the natural logarithm of both sides and solving for t gives

$$t = \tfrac{1}{2}RC\ln 4 = \boxed{0.693RC}$$

21.10   THE ATMOSPHERE AS A CONDUCTOR

CONTEXT CONNECTION

When discussing capacitors with air between the plates in Chapter 20, we adopted the simplification model that air was a perfect insulator. Although that was a good model for typical potential differences encountered in capacitors, we know that it is possible for a current to exist in air. Lightning is a dramatic example of this possibility, but a more mundane example is the common spark that you might receive upon bringing your finger near a doorknob after rubbing your feet across a carpet.

Let us analyze the process that occurs in electrical discharge, which is the same for lightning and the doorknob spark except for the size of the current. Whenever a strong electric field exists in air, it is possible for the air to undergo electrical breakdown in which the effective resistivity of the air drops dramatically and the air becomes a conductor. At any given time, due to cosmic ray collisions and other events, air contains a number of ionized molecules (Fig. 21.29a). For a relatively weak electric field, such as the fair-weather electric field, these ions and freed electrons accelerate slowly due to the electric force. They collide with other molecules with no effect and eventually neutralize as a freed electron ultimately finds an ion and combines with it. In a strong electric field such as that associated with a thunderstorm, however, the freed electrons can accelerate to very high speeds (Fig. 21.29b) before making a collision with a molecule (Fig. 21.29c). If the field is strong enough, the electron may have enough energy to ionize the molecule in this collision (Fig. 21.29d). Now there are two electrons to be accelerated by the field, and each can strike another molecule at high speed (Fig. 21.29e). The result is a very rapid increase in the number of charge carriers available in the air and a corresponding decrease in resistance of the air. Therefore, there can be a large current in the air that tends to neutralize the charges that established the initial potential difference, such as the charges in the cloud and on the ground. When that happens, we have lightning.

Typical currents during lightning strikes can be very high. While the stepped leader is making its way toward the ground, the current is relatively modest, in the range of 200 to 300 A. This current is large compared with typical household currents but small compared with peak currents in lightning discharges. Once the connection is made between the stepped leader and the return stroke, the current rises rapidly to a typical value of 5×10^4 A. Considering that typical potential differences between cloud and ground in a thunderstorm can be measured in hundreds of thousands of volts, the power during a lightning stroke is measured in billions of watts. Much of the energy in the stroke is delivered to the air, resulting in a rapid temperature increase and the resultant flash of light and sound of thunder.

Even in the absence of a thundercloud, there is a flow of charge through the air. The ions in the air make the air a conductor, although not a very good one. Atmospheric measurements indicate a typical potential difference across our atmospheric capacitor (Section 20.11) of about 3×10^5 V. As we shall show in the Context 6 Conclusion, the total resistance of the air between the plates in the atmospheric capacitor is about 300 Ω. Therefore, the average fair-weather current in the air is

$$I = \frac{\Delta V}{R} = \frac{3 \times 10^5 \,\text{V}}{300 \,\Omega} \approx 1 \times 10^3 \,\text{A}$$

A number of simplifying assumptions were made in these calculations, but this result is on the right order of magnitude for the global current. Although the result might seem surprisingly large, remember that this current is spread out over the entire surface area of the Earth. Therefore, the average fair-weather current density is

$$J = \frac{I}{A} = \frac{I}{4\pi r^2} = \frac{1 \times 10^3 \,\text{A}}{4\pi (6.4 \times 10^6 \,\text{m})^2} \approx 2 \times 10^{-12} \,\text{A/m}^2$$

In comparison, the current density in a lightning strike is on the order of 10^5 A/m^2.

The fair-weather current and the lightning current are in opposite directions. The fair-weather current delivers positive charge to the ground, whereas lightning delivers negative charge. These two effects are in balance,[13] which is the principle that we shall use to estimate the average number of lightning strikes on the Earth in the Context Conclusion.

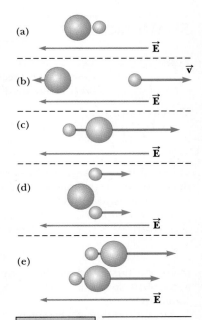

FIGURE 21.29 The anatomy of a spark. (a) A molecule is ionized as a result of a random event. (b) The ion accelerates slowly and the electron accelerates rapidly due to the force from the electric field. (c) The accelerated electron approaches another molecule at high speed. (d) The new molecule is ionized, and the original electron and the new electron accelerate rapidly. (e) These electrons approach other molecules, freeing two more electrons, and an avalanche of ionization proceeds.

[13]There are a number of other effects, too, but we will adopt a simplification model in which these are the only two effects. For more information, see E. A. Bering, A. A. Few, and J. R. Benbrook, "The Global Electric Circuit," *Physics Today,* October 1998, pp. 24–30.

SUMMARY

The **electric current** I in a conductor is defined as

$$I \equiv \frac{dQ}{dt} \qquad [21.2]$$

where dQ is the charge that passes through a cross-section of the conductor in the time interval dt. The SI unit of current is the ampere (A); $1 \text{ A} = 1 \text{ C/s}$.

The current in a conductor is related to the motion of the charge carriers through the relationship

$$I_{\text{avg}} = nqv_d A \qquad [21.4]$$

where n is the density of charge carriers, q is their charge, v_d is the **drift speed,** and A is the cross-sectional area of the conductor.

The **resistance** R of a conductor is defined as the ratio of the potential difference across the conductor to the current:

$$R \equiv \frac{\Delta V}{I} \qquad [21.6]$$

The SI units of resistance are volts per ampere, defined as ohms (Ω); $1 \ \Omega = 1 \text{ V/A}$.

If the resistance is independent of the applied voltage, the conductor obeys **Ohm's law,** and conductors that have a constant resistance over a wide range of voltages are said to be **ohmic.**

If a conductor has a uniform cross-sectional area A and a length ℓ, its resistance is

$$R = \rho \frac{\ell}{A} \qquad [21.8]$$

where ρ is called the **resistivity** of the material from which the conductor is made. The inverse of the resistivity is defined as the **conductivity** $\sigma = 1/\rho$.

The resistivity of a conductor varies with temperature in an approximately linear fashion; that is,

$$\rho = \rho_0[1 + \alpha(T - T_0)] \qquad [21.10]$$

where ρ_0 is the resistivity at some reference temperature T_0 and α is the **temperature coefficient of resistivity.**

In a classical model of electronic conduction in a metal, the electrons are treated as molecules of a gas. In the absence of an electric field, the average velocity of the electrons is zero. When an electric field is applied, the electrons move (on the average) with a drift velocity $\vec{\mathbf{v}}_d$, which is opposite the electric field:

$$\vec{\mathbf{v}}_d = \frac{-e\vec{\mathbf{E}}}{m_e} \tau \qquad [21.15]$$

where τ is the average time interval between collisions with the atoms of the metal. The resistivity of the material according to this model is

$$\rho = \frac{m_e}{ne^2\tau} \qquad [21.18]$$

where n is the number of free electrons per unit volume.

If a potential difference ΔV is maintained across a circuit element, the **power,** or the rate at which energy is delivered to the circuit element, is

$$\mathcal{P} = I\,\Delta V \qquad [21.20]$$

Because the potential difference across a resistor is $\Delta V = IR$, we can express the power delivered to a resistor in the form

$$\mathcal{P} = I^2R = \frac{(\Delta V)^2}{R} \qquad [21.21]$$

The **emf** of a battery is the voltage across its terminals when the current is zero. Because of the voltage drop across the **internal resistance** r of a battery, the **terminal voltage** of the battery is less than the emf when a current exists in the battery.

The **equivalent resistance** of a set of resistors connected in **series** is

$$R_{\text{eq}} = R_1 + R_2 + R_3 + \cdots \qquad [21.27]$$

The **equivalent resistance** of a set of resistors connected in **parallel** is given by

$$\frac{1}{R_{\text{eq}}} = \frac{1}{R_1} + \frac{1}{R_2} + \frac{1}{R_3} + \cdots \qquad [21.29]$$

Circuits involving more than one loop are analyzed using two simple rules called **Kirchhoff's rules:**

- At any junction, the sum of the currents must equal zero:

$$\sum_{\text{junction}} I = 0$$

- The sum of the potential differences across each element around any closed circuit loop must be zero:

$$\sum_{\text{loop}} \Delta V = 0$$

For the junction rule, current in a direction into a junction is $+ I$, whereas current with a direction away from a junction is $- I$.

For the loop rule, when a resistor is traversed in the direction of the current, the change in potential ΔV across the resistor is $- IR$. If a resistor is traversed in the direction opposite the current, $\Delta V = + IR$.

If a source of emf is traversed in the direction of the emf (negative to positive), the change in potential is $+ \varepsilon$. If it is traversed opposite the emf (positive to negative), the change in potential is $- \varepsilon$.

If a capacitor is charged with a battery of emf ε through a resistance R, the charge on the capacitor and the current in the circuit vary in time according to the expressions

$$q(t) = Q[1 - e^{-t/RC}] \qquad [21.33]$$

$$I(t) = \frac{\varepsilon}{R} e^{-t/RC} \qquad [21.34]$$

where $Q = C\varepsilon$ is the maximum charge on the capacitor. The product RC is called the **time constant** of the circuit.

If a charged capacitor is discharged through a resistance R, the charge and current decrease exponentially in time according to the expressions

$$q(t) = Qe^{-t/RC} \qquad [21.36]$$

$$I(t) = -I_0 e^{-t/RC} \qquad [21.37]$$

where $I_0 = Q/RC$ is the initial current in the circuit and Q is the initial charge on the capacitor.

QUESTIONS

☐ = answer available in the *Student Solutions Manual and Study Guide*

1. In an analogy between electric current and automobile traffic flow, what would correspond to charge? What would correspond to current?

2. What factors affect the resistance of a conductor?

3. Two wires A and B of circular cross-section are made of the same metal and have equal lengths, but the resistance of wire A is three times greater than that of wire B. What is the ratio of their cross-sectional areas? How do their radii compare?

4. What would happen to the drift velocity of the electrons in a wire and to the current in the wire if the electrons could move freely without resistance through the wire?

5. Use the atomic theory of matter to explain why the resistance of a material should increase as its temperature increases.

6. Explain how a current can persist in a superconductor without any applied voltage.

7. If charges flow very slowly through a metal, why does it not require several hours for a light to come on when you throw a switch?

8. Two lightbulbs both operate from 120 V. One has a power of 25 W and the other 100 W. Which lightbulb has higher resistance? Which lightbulb carries more current?

9. Car batteries are often rated in ampere-hours. Does this rating designate the amount of current, power, energy, or charge that can be drawn from the battery?

10. When resistors are connected in series, which of the following would be the same for each resistor: potential difference, current, power?

11. When resistors are connected in parallel, which of the following would be the same for each resistor: potential difference, current, power?

12. A *short circuit* is a path of very low resistance in a circuit in parallel with some other part of the circuit. Discuss the effect of the short circuit on the portion of the circuit it parallels. Use a lamp with a frayed cord as an example.

13. Why is it possible for a bird to sit on a high-voltage wire without being electrocuted?

14. If electric power is transmitted over long distances, the resistance of the wires becomes significant. Why? Which method of transmission would result in less energy wasted: high current and low voltage or low current and high voltage? Explain your answer.

15. Referring to Figure Q21.15, describe what happens to the lightbulb after the switch is closed. Assume that the capacitor has a large capacitance and is initially uncharged, and assume that the lightbulb illuminates when connected directly across the battery terminals.

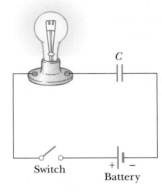

FIGURE Q21.15

16. Are the two headlights of a car wired in series or in parallel? How can you tell?

17. Embodied in Kirchhoff's rules are two conservation laws. What are they?

18. Figure Q21.18 shows a series combination of three lightbulbs, each rated at 120 V. From top to bottom, their power ratings are 60 W, 75 W, and 200 W. Why is the 60-W bulb the brightest and the 200-W bulb the dimmest? Which bulb has the greatest resistance? How would their intensities differ if they were connected in parallel?

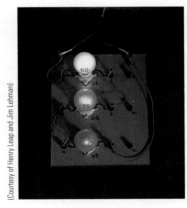

(Courtesy of Henry Leap and Jim Lehman)

FIGURE Q21.18

19. A student claims that the second lightbulb in series is less bright than the first because the first lightbulb uses up some of the current. How would you respond to this statement?

20. So that your grandmother can listen to *A Prairie Home Companion*, you take her bedside radio to the hospital where she is staying. You are required to have a maintenance

worker test it for electrical safety. Finding that it develops 120 V on one of its knobs, he does not let you take it up to your grandmother's room. She complains that she has had the radio for many years and that nobody has ever gotten a shock from it. You end up having to buy a new plastic radio. Is that fair? Will the old radio be safe back in her bedroom?

21. A series circuit consists of three identical lamps connected to a battery as shown in Figure Q21.21. When the switch S is closed, what happens (a) to the intensities of lamps A and B, (b) to the intensity of lamp C, (c) to the current in the circuit, and (d) to the voltage across the three lamps? (e) Does the power delivered to the circuit increase, decrease, or remain the same?

22. A ski resort consists of a few chairlifts and several interconnected downhill runs on the side of a mountain, with a lodge at the bottom. The chairlifts are analogous to batteries, and the runs are analogous to resistors. Describe how two runs can be in series. Describe how three runs can be in parallel. Sketch a junction of one chairlift and two runs.

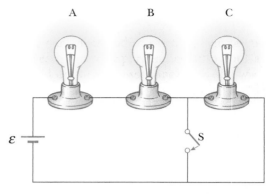

FIGURE **Q21.21**

State Kirchhoff's junction rule for ski resorts. One of the skiers happens to be carrying a sky-diver's altimeter. She never takes the same set of chairlifts and runs twice, but keeps passing you at the fixed location where you are working. State Kirchhoff's loop rule for ski resorts.

PROBLEMS

> 1, 2, 3 = straightforward, intermediate, challenging
> ☐ = full solution available in the *Student Solutions Manual and Study Guide*
> Physics⊗Now™ = coached problem with hints available at **www.pop4e.com**
> 💻 = computer useful in solving problem
> ▬ = paired numerical and symbolic problems
> 🦓 = biomedical application

Section 21.1 ▮ Electric Current

1. In a particular cathode-ray tube, the measured beam current is 30.0 μA. How many electrons strike the tube screen every 40.0 s?

2. A small sphere that carries a charge q is whirled in a circle at the end of an insulating string. The angular frequency of revolution is ω. What average current does this revolving charge represent?

3. Physics⊗Now™ Suppose the current in a conductor decreases exponentially with time according to the equation $I(t) = I_0 e^{-t/\tau}$, where I_0 is the initial current (at $t = 0$) and τ is a constant having dimensions of time. Consider a fixed observation point within the conductor. (a) How much charge passes this point between $t = 0$ and $t = \tau$? (b) How much charge passes this point between $t = 0$ and $t = 10\tau$? (c) How much charge passes this point between $t = 0$ and $t = \infty$?

4. The quantity of charge q (in coulombs) that has passed through a surface of area 2.00 cm^2 varies with time according to the equation $q = 4t^3 + 5t + 6$, where t is in seconds. (a) What is the instantaneous current across the surface at $t = 1.00$ s? (b) What is the value of the current density?

5. An aluminum wire having a cross-sectional area of 4.00×10^{-6} m^2 carries a current of 5.00 A. Find the drift speed of the electrons in the wire. The density of aluminum is 2.70 g/cm^3. Assume that one conduction electron is supplied by each atom.

Section 21.2 ▮ Resistance and Ohm's Law

6. A lightbulb has a resistance of 240 Ω when operating with a potential difference of 120 V across it. What is the current in the lightbulb?

7. Physics⊗Now™ A 0.900-V potential difference is maintained across a 1.50-m length of tungsten wire that has a cross-sectional area of 0.600 mm^2. What is the current in the wire?

8. Suppose you wish to fabricate a uniform wire out of 1.00 g of copper. If the wire is to have a resistance of $R = 0.500$ Ω and if all the copper is to be used, what will be (a) the length and (b) the diameter of this wire?

9. An aluminum wire with a diameter of 0.100 mm has a uniform electric field of 0.200 V/m imposed along its entire length. The temperature of the wire is 50.0°C. Assume one free electron per atom. (a) Use the information in Table 21.1 and determine the resistivity. (b) What is the current density in the wire? (c) What is the total current in the wire? (d) What is the drift speed of the conduction electrons? (e) What potential difference must exist between the ends of a 2.00-m length of the wire to produce the stated electric field?

10. While taking photographs in Death Valley on a day when the temperature is 58.0°C, Bill Hiker finds that a certain voltage applied to a copper wire produces a current of 1.000 A. Bill then travels to Antarctica and applies the

same voltage to the same wire. What current does he register there if the temperature is $-88.0°C$? Assume that no change occurs in the wire's shape and size.

11. **Review problem.** An aluminum rod has a resistance of 1.234 Ω at 20.0°C. Calculate the resistance of the rod at 120°C by accounting for the changes in both the resistivity and the dimensions of the rod.

Section 21.4 ∎ A Structural Model for Electrical Conduction

12. If the current carried by a conductor is doubled, what happens to (a) the charge carrier density, (b) the current density, (c) the electron drift velocity, and (d) the average time interval between collisions?

13. If the magnitude of the drift velocity of free electrons in a copper wire is 7.84×10^{-4} m/s, what is the electric field in the conductor?

Section 21.5 ∎ Electric Energy and Power

14. A toaster is rated at 600 W when connected to a 120-V source. What current does the toaster carry, and what is its resistance?

15. In a hydroelectric installation, a turbine delivers 1 500 hp to a generator, which in turn transfers 80.0% of the mechanical energy out by electrical transmission. Under these conditions, what current does the generator deliver at a terminal potential difference of 2 000 V?

16. One rechargeable battery of mass 15.0 g delivers to a CD player an average current of 18.0 mA at 1.60 V for 2.40 h before the battery needs to be recharged. The recharger maintains a potential difference of 2.30 V across the battery and delivers a charging current of 13.5 mA for 4.20 h. (a) What is the efficiency of the battery as an energy storage device? (b) How much internal energy is produced in the battery during one charge–discharge cycle? (c) If the battery is surrounded by ideal thermal insulation and has an overall effective specific heat of 975 J/kg·°C, by how much will its temperature increase during the cycle?

17. Suppose a voltage surge produces 140 V for a moment. By what percentage does the power output of a 120-V, 100-W lightbulb increase? Assume that its resistance does not change.

18. An 11.0-W energy-efficient fluorescent lamp is designed to produce the same illumination as a conventional 40.0-W incandescent lightbulb. How much money does the user of the energy-efficient lamp save during 100 h of use? Assume a cost of $0.080 0/kWh for energy from the electric company.

19. A certain toaster has a heating element made of Nichrome wire. When the toaster is first connected to a 120-V source (and the wire is at a temperature of 20.0°C), the initial current is 1.80 A. The current begins to decrease as the heating element warms up, however. When the toaster reaches its final operating temperature, the current drops to 1.53 A. (a) Find the power delivered to the toaster when it is at its operating temperature. (b) What is the final temperature of the heating element?

20. We estimate that 270 million plug-in electric clocks are in the United States, approximately one clock for each person. The clocks convert energy at the average rate 2.50 W. To supply this energy, how many metric tons of coal are burned per hour in coal-fired electric generating plants that are, on average, 25.0% efficient? The heat of combustion for coal is 33.0 MJ/kg.

21. The cost of electricity varies widely through the United States; $0.120/kWh is one typical value. At this unit price, calculate the cost of (a) leaving a 40.0-W porch light on for two weeks while you are on vacation, (b) making a piece of dark toast in 3.00 min with a 970-W toaster, and (c) drying a load of clothes in 40.0 min in a 5 200-W dryer.

22. An office worker uses an immersion heater to warm 250 g of water in a light, covered insulated cup from 20°C to 100°C in 4.00 min. In electrical terms, the heater is a Nichrome resistance wire connected to a 120-V power supply. Specify a diameter and a length that the wire can have. Can it be made from less than 0.5 cm³ of Nichrome? You may assume that the wire is at 100°C throughout the time interval.

23. An electric car is designed to run off a bank of 12.0-V batteries with total energy storage of 2.00×10^7 J. (a) If the electric motor draws 8.00 kW, what is the current delivered to the motor? (b) If the electric motor draws 8.00 kW as the car moves at a steady speed of 20.0 m/s, how far will the car travel before it is "out of juice"?

24. Make an order-of-magnitude estimate of the cost of one person's routine use of a hair dryer for 1 yr. If you do not use a hair dryer yourself, observe or interview someone who does. State the quantities you estimate and their values.

Section 21.6 ∎ Sources of emf

25. A battery has an emf of 15.0 V. The terminal voltage of the battery is 11.6 V when it is delivering 20.0 W of power to an external load resistor R. (a) What is the value of R? (b) What is the internal resistance of the battery?

26. Two 1.50-V batteries—with their positive terminals in the same direction—are inserted in series into the barrel of a flashlight. One battery has an internal resistance of 0.255 Ω and the other an internal resistance of 0.153 Ω. When the switch is closed, a current of 600 mA occurs in the lamp. (a) What is the lamp's resistance? (b) What fraction of the chemical energy transformed appears as internal energy in the batteries?

Section 21.7 ∎ Resistors in Series and in Parallel

27. (a) Find the equivalent resistance between points a and b in Figure P21.27. (b) A potential difference of 34.0 V is applied between points a and b. Calculate the current in each resistor.

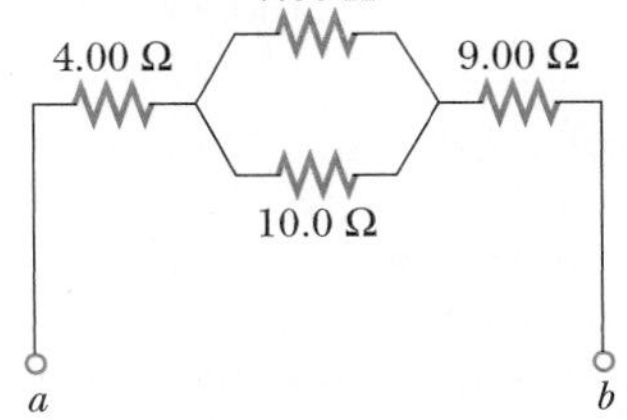

FIGURE **P21.27**

28. 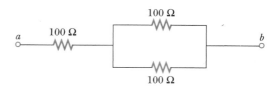 For the purpose of measuring the electric resistance of shoes through the body of the wearer to a metal ground plate, the American National Standards Institute (ANSI) specifies the circuit shown in Figure P21.28. The potential difference ΔV across the 1.00-MΩ resistor is measured with a high-resistance voltmeter. The resistance of the person's body is negligible by comparison. (a) Show that the resistance of the footwear is given by

$$R_{\text{shoes}} = 1.00 \text{ M}\Omega \left(\frac{50.0 \text{ V} - \Delta V}{\Delta V} \right)$$

(b) In a medical test, a current through the human body should not exceed 150 μA. Can the current delivered by the ANSI-specified circuit exceed 150 μA? To decide, consider a person standing barefoot on the ground plate.

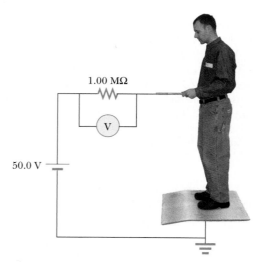

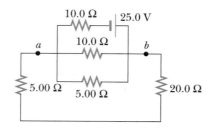

FIGURE **P21.28**

29. **Physics⊗Now™** Consider the circuit shown in Figure P21.29. Find (a) the current in the 20.0-Ω resistor and (b) the potential difference between points a and b.

FIGURE **P21.29**

30. Three 100-Ω resistors are connected as shown in Figure P21.30. The maximum power that can safely be delivered to any one resistor is 25.0 W. (a) What is the maximum voltage that can be applied to the terminals a and b? (b) For the voltage determined in part (a), what is the power delivered to each resistor? What is the total power delivered?

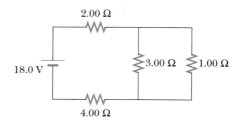

FIGURE **P21.30**

31. Calculate the power delivered to each resistor in the circuit shown in Figure P21.31.

FIGURE **P21.31**

32. Four resistors are connected to a battery as shown in Figure P21.32. The current in the battery is I, the battery emf is $\mathcal{E}$, and the resistor values are $R_1 = R$, $R_2 = 2R$, $R_3 = 4R$, and $R_4 = 3R$. (a) Rank the resistors according to the potential difference across them, from largest to smallest. Note any cases of equal potential differences. (b) Determine the potential difference across each resistor in terms of $\mathcal{E}$. (c) Rank the resistors according to the current in them, from largest to smallest. Note any cases of equal currents. (d) Determine the current in each resistor in terms of I. (e) If R_3 is increased, what happens to the current in each of the resistors? (f) In the limit that $R_3 \rightarrow \infty$, what are the new values of the current in each resistor in terms of I, the original current in the battery?

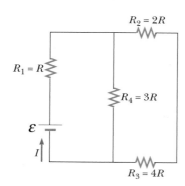

FIGURE **P21.32**

33. A young man has moved into his own apartment. His possessions include a canister vacuum cleaner marked 535 W at 120 V and a Volkswagen Beetle, which he wishes to clean. He must leave the car in a parking lot far from the building, so he needs an extension cord 15.0 m long to plug in the vacuum cleaner. You may assume that the vacuum cleaner has constant resistance. (a) If the resistance of each of the two conductors in an inexpensive cord is 0.900 Ω, what is the actual power delivered to the vacuum cleaner? (b) If instead the power is to be at least 525 W,

what must be the diameter of each of two identical copper conductors in the cord he buys? (c) Repeat part (b) if the power is to be at least 532 W. (*Suggestion:* A symbolic solution can simplify the calculations.)

Section 21.8 ∎ Kirchhoff's Rules

Note: The currents are not necessarily in the direction shown for some circuits.

34. The ammeter shown in Figure P21.34 reads 2.00 A. Find I_1, I_2, and $\mathcal{E}$.

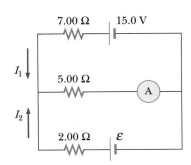

FIGURE P21.34

35. **Physics⊗Now™** Determine the current in each branch of the circuit shown in Figure P21.35.

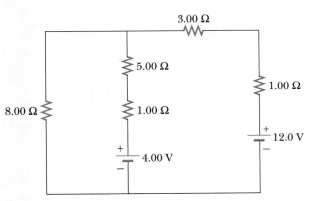

FIGURE P21.35 Problems 21.35, 21.36, and 21.37.

36. In Figure P21.35, show how to add just enough ammeters to measure every different current. Show how to add just enough voltmeters to measure the potential difference across each resistor and across each battery.

37. The circuit considered in Problem 21.35 and shown in Figure P21.35 is connected for 2.00 min. (a) Find the energy delivered by each battery. (b) Find the energy delivered to each resistor. (c) Identify the net energy transformation that occurs in the operation of the circuit and the total amount of energy transformed.

38. The following equations describe an electric circuit:

$$-(220\ \Omega)I_1 + 5.80\ \text{V} - (370\ \Omega)I_2 = 0$$
$$+(370\ \Omega)I_2 + (150\ \Omega)I_3 - 3.10\ \text{V} = 0$$
$$I_1 + I_3 - I_2 = 0$$

(a) Draw a diagram of the circuit. (b) Calculate the unknowns and identify the physical meaning of each unknown.

39. Taking $R = 1.00$ kΩ and $\mathcal{E} = 250$ V in Figure P21.39, determine the direction and magnitude of the current in the horizontal wire between a and e.

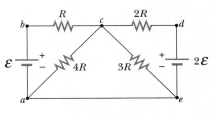

FIGURE P21.39

40. A dead battery is charged by connecting it to the live battery of another car with jumper cables (Fig. P21.40). Determine the current in the starter and in the dead battery.

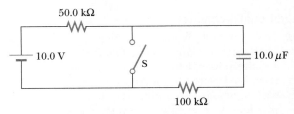

FIGURE P21.40

Section 12.9 ∎ RC Circuits

41. **Physics⊗Now™** Consider a series *RC* circuit (see Fig. 21.25) for which $R = 1.00$ MΩ, $C = 5.00$ μF, and $\mathcal{E} = 30.0$ V. Find (a) the time constant of the circuit and (b) the maximum charge on the capacitor after the switch is closed. (c) Find the current in the resistor 10.0 s after the switch is closed.

42. A 2.00-nF capacitor with an initial charge of 5.10 μC is discharged through a 1.30-kΩ resistor. (a) Calculate the current in the resistor 9.00 μs after the resistor is connected across the terminals of the capacitor. (b) What charge remains on the capacitor after 8.00 μs? (c) What is the maximum current in the resistor?

43. In the circuit of Figure P21.43, the switch S has been open for a long time. It is then suddenly closed. Determine the time constant (a) before the switch is closed and (b) after the switch is closed. (c) Let the switch be closed at $t = 0$. Determine the current in the switch as a function of time.

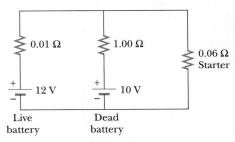

FIGURE P21.43

44. In places such as a hospital operating room and a factory for electronic circuit boards, electric sparks must be avoided. A person standing on a grounded floor and touching nothing else can typically have a body capacitance of 150 pF, in parallel with a foot capacitance of 80.0 pF produced by the dielectric soles of his or her shoes. The person acquires static electric charge from interactions with furniture, clothing, equipment, packaging materials, and essentially everything else. The static charge is conducted to ground through the equivalent resistance of the two shoe soles in parallel with each other. A pair of rubber-soled street shoes can present an equivalent resistance of 5 000 MΩ. A pair of shoes with special static-dissipative soles can have an equivalent resistance of 1.00 MΩ. Consider the person's body and shoes as forming an RC circuit with the ground. (a) How long does it take the rubber-soled shoes to reduce a 3 000-V static charge to 100 V? (b) How long does it take the static-dissipative shoes to do the same thing?

45. The circuit in Figure P21.45 has been connected for a long time. (a) What is the voltage across the capacitor? (b) If the battery is disconnected, how long does it take the capacitor to discharge to one tenth of its initial voltage?

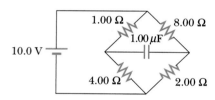

FIGURE P21.45

46. A 10.0-μF capacitor is charged by a 10.0-V battery through a resistance R. The capacitor reaches a potential difference of 4.00 V at the instant 3.00 s after charging begins. Find R.

Section 12.10 ▪ Context Connection—The Atmosphere as a Conductor

47. A current density of 6.00×10^{-13} A/m^2 exists in the atmosphere at a location where the electric field is 100 V/m. Calculate the electrical conductivity of the Earth's atmosphere in this region.

48. Assume that global lightning on the Earth constitutes a constant current of 1.00 kA between the ground and an atmospheric layer at potential 300 kV. (a) Find the power of terrestrial lightning. (b) For comparison, find the power of sunlight falling on the Earth. Sunlight has an intensity of 1 370 W/m^2 above the atmosphere. Sunlight falls perpendicularly on the circular projected area that the Earth presents to the Sun.

Additional Problems

49. One lightbulb is marked "25 W 120 V" and another "100 W 120 V," which means that each lightbulb has its respective power delivered to it when plugged into a constant 120-V potential difference. (a) Find the resistance of each lightbulb. (b) During what time interval does 1.00 C pass into the dim lightbulb? Is the charge different in any way upon its exit from the lightbulb versus its entry? (c) In what time interval does 1.00 J pass into the dim lightbulb? By what mechanisms does this energy enter and exit the lightbulb? (d) Find how much it costs to run the dim lightbulb continuously for 30.0 days, assuming that the electric company sells its product at $0.070 0 per kWh. What product *does* the electric company sell? What is its price for one SI unit of this quantity?

50. An experiment is conducted to measure the electrical resistivity of Nichrome in the form of wires with different lengths and cross-sectional areas. For one set of measurements, a student uses 30-gauge wire, which has a cross-sectional area of 7.30×10^{-8} m^2. The student measures the potential difference across the wire and the current in the wire with a voltmeter and an ammeter, respectively. For each of the measurements given in the table taken on wires of three different lengths, calculate the resistance of the wires and the corresponding values of the resistivity. What is the average value of the resistivity? How does this value compare with the value given in Table 21.1?

L (m)	ΔV (V)	I (A)	R (Ω)	ρ (Ω·m)
0.540	5.22	0.500		
1.028	5.82	0.276		
1.543	5.94	0.187		

51. A straight cylindrical wire lying along the x axis has a length of 0.500 m and a diameter of 0.200 mm. It is made of a material described by Ohm's law with a resistivity of $\rho = 4.00 \times 10^{-8}$ Ω·m. Assume that a potential of 4.00 V is maintained at $x = 0$ and that $V = 0$ at $x = 0.500$ m. Find (a) the electric field $\vec{E}$ in the wire, (b) the resistance of the wire, (c) the electric current in the wire, and (d) the current density $\vec{J}$ in the wire. Express vectors in vector notation. (e) Show that $\vec{E} = \rho\vec{J}$.

52. A straight cylindrical wire lying along the x axis has a length L and a diameter d. It is made of a material described by Ohm's law with a resistivity ρ. Assume that potential V is maintained at $x = 0$ and that the potential is zero at $x = L$. In terms of L, d, V, ρ, and physical constants, derive expressions for (a) the electric field in the wire, (b) the resistance of the wire, (c) the electric current in the wire, and (d) the current density in the wire. Express vectors in vector notation. (e) Prove that $\vec{E} = \rho\vec{J}$.

53. An electric heater is rated at 1 500 W, a toaster at 750 W, and an electric grill at 1 000 W. The three appliances are connected to a common 120-V household circuit. (a) How much current does each draw? (b) Is a circuit with a 25.0-A circuit breaker sufficient in this situation? Explain your answer.

54. An oceanographer is studying how the ion concentration in sea water depends on depth. She does so by lowering into the water a pair of concentric metallic cylinders (Fig. P21.54) at the end of a cable and taking data to determine the resistance between these electrodes as a function of depth. The water between the two cylinders forms a cylindrical shell of inner radius r_a, outer radius r_b, and length L much larger than r_b. The scientist applies a potential difference ΔV between the inner and outer surfaces,

producing an outward radial current I. Let ρ represent the resistivity of the water. (a) Find the resistance of the water between the cylinders in terms of L, ρ, r_a, and r_b. (b) Express the resistivity of the water in terms of the measured quantities L, r_a, r_b, ΔV, and I.

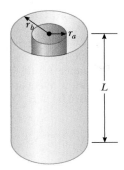

FIGURE **P21.54**

55. Four 1.50-V AA batteries in series are used to power a transistor radio. If the batteries can move a charge of 240 C, how long will they last if the radio has a resistance of 200 Ω?

56. A battery has an emf of 9.20 V and an internal resistance of 1.20 Ω. What resistance across the battery will extract from it (a) a power of 12.8 W and (b) a power of 21.2 W?

57. A battery has an emf $\mathcal{E}$ and internal resistance r. A variable load resistor R is connected across the terminals of the battery. (a) Determine the value of R such that the potential difference across the terminals is a maximum. (b) Determine the value of R so that the current in the circuit is a maximum. (c) Determine the value of R so that the power delivered to the load resistor is a maximum. Choosing the load resistance for maximum power transfer is a case of what is called *impedance matching* in general. Impedance matching is important in shifting gears on a bicycle, in connecting a loudspeaker to an audio amplifier, in connecting a battery charger to a bank of solar photoelectric cells, and in many other applications.

58. A battery is used to charge a capacitor through a resistor as shown in Figure 21.25. Show that half the energy supplied by the battery appears as internal energy in the resistor and that half is stored in the capacitor.

59. The values of the components in a simple series RC circuit containing a switch (Fig. 21.25) are $C = 1.00 \ \mu F$, $R = 2.00 \times 10^6 \ \Omega$, and $\mathcal{E} = 10.0$ V. At the instant 10.0 s after the switch is closed, calculate (a) the charge on the capacitor, (b) the current in the resistor, (c) the rate at which energy is being stored in the capacitor, and (d) the rate at which energy is being delivered by the battery.

60. The switch in Figure P21.60a closes when $\Delta V_c > 2\Delta V/3$ and opens when $\Delta V_c < \Delta V/3$. The voltmeter reads a voltage as plotted in Figure P21.60b. What is the period T of the waveform in terms of R_A, R_B, and C?

61. Switch S has been closed for a long time, and the electric circuit shown in Figure P21.61 carries a constant current. Take $C_1 = 3.00 \ \mu F$, $C_2 = 6.00 \ \mu F$, $R_1 = 4.00$ kΩ, and $R_2 = 7.00$ kΩ. The power delivered to R_2 is 2.40 W. (a) Find the charge on C_1. (b) Now the switch is opened. After many milliseconds, by how much has the charge on C_2 changed?

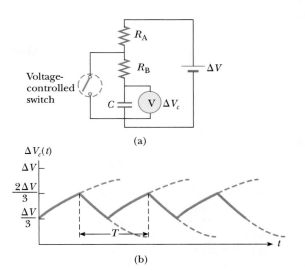

(a)

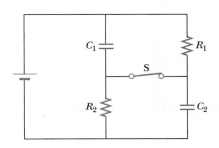

(b)

FIGURE **P21.60**

FIGURE **P21.61**

62. The circuit shown in Figure P21.62 is set up in the laboratory to measure an unknown capacitance C with the use of a voltmeter of resistance $R = 10.0$ MΩ and a battery whose emf is 6.19 V. The data given in the table are the measured voltages across the capacitor as a function of time, where $t = 0$ represents the instant at which the switch is opened. (a) Construct a graph of $\ln(\mathcal{E}/\Delta V)$ versus t and perform a linear least-squares fit to the data. (b) From the slope of your graph, obtain a value for the time constant of the circuit and a value for the capacitance.

ΔV (V)	t (s)	$\ln(\mathcal{E}/\Delta V)$
6.19	0	
5.55	4.87	
4.93	11.1	
4.34	19.4	
3.72	30.8	
3.09	46.6	
2.47	67.3	
1.83	102.2	

63. Four resistors are connected in parallel across a 9.20-V battery. They carry currents of 150 mA, 45.0 mA, 14.00 mA, and 4.00 mA. (a) If the resistor with the largest resistance is replaced with one having twice the resistance, what is the ratio of the new current in the battery to the original current? (b) If instead the resistor with the smallest

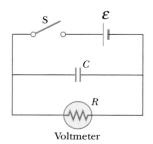

FIGURE **P21.62**

resistance is replaced with one having twice the resistance, what is the ratio of the new total current to the original current? (c) On a February night, energy leaves a house by several energy leaks, including the following: 1 500 W by conduction through the ceiling, 450 W by infiltration (air flow) around the windows, 140 W by conduction through the basement wall above the foundation sill, and 40.0 W by conduction through the plywood door to the attic. To produce the biggest saving in heating bills, which one of these energy transfers should be reduced first?

64. The student engineer of a campus radio station wishes to verify the effectiveness of the lightning rod on the antenna mast (Fig. P21.64). The unknown resistance R_x is between points C and E. Point E is a true ground but is inaccessible for direct measurement because this stratum is several meters below the Earth's surface. Two identical rods are driven into the ground at A and B, introducing an unknown resistance R_y. The procedure is as follows. Measure resistance R_1 between points A and B, then connect A and B with a heavy conducting wire and measure resistance R_2 between points A and C. (a) Derive an equation for R_x in terms of the observable resistances, R_1 and R_2. (b) A satisfactory ground resistance would be $R_x < 2.00 \ \Omega$. Is the grounding of the station adequate if measurements give $R_1 = 13.0 \ \Omega$ and $R_2 = 6.00 \ \Omega$?

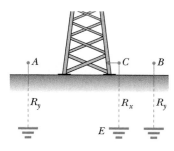

FIGURE **P21.64**

ANSWERS TO QUICK QUIZZES

21.1. (d), (b) = (c), (a). The current in part (d) is equivalent to two positive charges moving to the left. Parts (b) and (c) each represent four charges moving in the same direction because negative charges moving to the left are equivalent to positive charges moving to the right. The current in part (a) is equivalent to five positive charges moving to the right.

21.2. (b). According to Equation 21.6, resistance is the ratio of voltage across a device to current in the device. In Figure 21.6b, a line drawn from the origin to a point on the curve will have a slope equal to $I/\Delta V$, which is the inverse of resistance. As ΔV increases, the slope of this line also increases, so the resistance decreases.

21.3. (a). When the filament is at room temperature, its resistance is low and hence the current is relatively large. As the filament warms up, its resistance increases and the current decreases.

21.4. $I_a = I_b > I_c = I_d > I_e = I_f$. Charge constituting the current I_a leaves the positive terminal of the battery and then splits to flow through the two lightbulbs; therefore, $I_a = I_c + I_e$. Because the potential difference ΔV is the same across the two lightbulbs and because the power delivered to a device is $\mathcal{P} = I \Delta V$, the 60-W lightbulb with the higher power rating must carry the greater current. Because charge does not accumulate in the lightbulbs, we know that the same amount of charge flowing into a lightbulb from the left has to flow out on the right; consequently $I_c = I_d$ and $I_e = I_f$. The two currents leaving the lightbulbs recombine to form the current back into the battery, $I_f + I_d = I_b$.

21.5. (a). Connecting b to c "shorts out" lightbulb R_2 and changes the total resistance of the circuit from $R_1 + R_2$ to just R_1. Because the resistance of the circuit has decreased (and the potential difference supplied by the battery does not change), the current in the circuit increases.

21.6 (b). When the switch is opened, resistors R_1 and R_2 are in series, so the total circuit resistance is larger than when the switch was closed. As a result, the current drops.

21.7 (a). When the switch is closed, resistors R_1 and R_2 are in parallel, so the total circuit resistance is smaller than when the switch was open. As a result, the current increases.

21.8 (i), (b), (d). Adding another series resistor increases the total resistance of the circuit and therefore reduces the current in the circuit. The potential difference across the battery terminals increases because the reduced current results in a smaller voltage decrease across the internal resistance. (ii), (a), (e). If a third resistor were connected in parallel, the total resistance of the circuit would decrease and the current in the battery would increase. The potential difference across the terminals would decrease because the increased current results in a greater voltage drop across the internal resistance.

21.9 (i), (b). Just after the switch is closed, there is no charge on the capacitor, so there is no voltage across it. Charges begin to flow in the circuit to charge up the capacitor, so all the voltage $\Delta V = IR$ appears across the resistor. (ii), (a). After a long time, the capacitor is fully charged and the current drops to zero. Therefore, the battery voltage is now entirely across the capacitor.

Determining the Number of Lightning Strikes

Now that we have investigated the principles of electricity, let us respond to our central question for the *Lightning* Context:

How can we determine the number of lightning strikes on the Earth in a typical day?

We must combine several ideas from our knowledge of electricity to perform this calculation. In Chapter 20, the atmosphere was modeled as a capacitor. Such modeling was first done by Lord Kelvin, who modeled the ionosphere as the positive plate several tens of kilometers above the Earth's surface. More sophisticated models have shown the effective height of the positive plate to be the 5 km that we used in our earlier calculation.

The Atmospheric Capacitor Model

The plates of the atmospheric capacitor are separated by a layer of air containing a large number of free ions that can carry current. Air is a good insulator; measurements show that the resistivity of air is about $3 \times 10^{13}\ \Omega \cdot m$. Let us calculate the resistance of the air between our capacitor plates. The shape of the resistor is that of a spherical shell between the plates of the atmospheric capacitor. The length of 5 km, however, is very short compared with the radius of 6 400 km. Therefore, we can ignore the spherical shape and approximate the resistor as a 5-km slab of flat material whose area is the surface area of the Earth. Using Equation 21.8,

$$R = \rho \frac{\ell}{A} = (3 \times 10^{13}\ \Omega \cdot m)\ \frac{5 \times 10^3\ m}{4\pi(6.4 \times 10^6\ m)^2} \approx 3 \times 10^2\ \Omega$$

The charge on the atmospheric capacitor can pass from the upper plate to the ground by electric current in the air between the plates. Thus, we can model the atmosphere as an *RC* circuit, using the capacitance found in Chapter 20, and the resistance connecting the plates calculated above (Fig. 1). The time constant for this *RC* circuit is

$$\tau = RC = (0.9\ F)(3 \times 10^2\ \Omega) \approx 3 \times 10^2\ s = 5\ min$$

Thus, the charge on the atmospheric capacitor should fall to $e^{-1} = 37\%$ of its original value after only 5 min! After 30 min, less than 0.3% of the charge would remain! Why doesn't that happen? What keeps the atmospheric capacitor charged? The answer is *lightning*. The processes occurring in cloud charging result in lightning strikes that deliver negative charge to the ground to replace that neutralized by the flow of charge through the air. On the average, a net charge on the atmospheric capacitor results from a balance between these two processes.

Now, let's use this balance to numerically answer our central question. We first address the charge on the atmospheric capacitor. In Chapter 19, we mentioned a

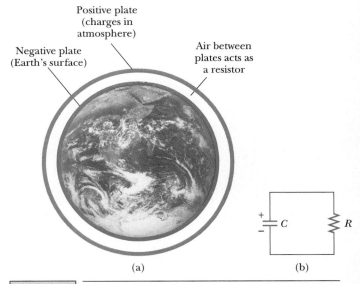

FIGURE 1 (a) The atmosphere can be modeled as a capacitor, with conductive air between the plates. (b) We can imagine an equivalent *RC* circuit for the atmosphere, with the natural discharge of the capacitor in balance with the charging of the capacitor by lightning.

charge of 5×10^5 C that is spread over the surface of the Earth, which is the charge on the atmospheric capacitor.

A typical lightning strike delivers about 25 C of negative charge to the ground in the process of charging the capacitor. Dividing the charge on the capacitor by the charge per lightning strike tells us the number of lightning strikes required to charge the capacitor:

$$\text{Number of lightning strikes} = \frac{\text{total charge}}{\text{charge per lightning strike}}$$

$$= \frac{5 \times 10^5 \text{ C}}{25 \text{ C per strike}} \approx 2 \times 10^4 \text{ lightning strikes}$$

According to our calculation for the RC circuit, the atmospheric capacitor almost completely discharges through the air in about 30 min. Thus, 2×10^4 lightning strikes must occur every 30 min, or 4×10^4/h, to keep the charging and discharging processes in balance. Multiplying by the number of hours in a day gives us

$$\text{Number of lightning strikes per day} = (4 \times 10^4 \text{ strikes/h})\left(\frac{24 \text{ h}}{1 \text{ d}}\right)$$

$$\approx 1 \times 10^6 \text{ strokes/day}$$

Despite the simplifications that we have adopted in our calculations, this number is on the right order of magnitude for the actual number of lightning strikes on the Earth in a typical day: 1 million!

Problems

1. Consider the atmospheric capacitor described in the text, with the ground as one plate and positive charges in the atmosphere as the other. On one particular day, the capacitance of the atmospheric capacitor is 0.800 F. The effective plate separation distance is 4.00 km, and the resistivity of the air between the plates is 2.00×10^{13} $\Omega \cdot$m. If no lightning events occur, the capacitor will discharge through the air. If a charge of 4.00×10^4 C is on the atmospheric capacitor at time $t = 0$, at what later time is the charge reduced (a) to 2.00×10^4 C, (b) to 5.00×10^3 C, and (c) to zero?

2. Consider this alternative line of reasoning to estimate the number of lightning strikes on the Earth in one day. Using the charge on the Earth of 5.00×10^5 C and the atmospheric capacitance of 0.9 F, we find that the potential difference across the capacitor is $\Delta V = Q/C = 5.00 \times 10^5$ C/0.9 F $\approx 6 \times 10^5$ V. The leakage current in the air is $I = \Delta V/R = 6 \times 10^5$ V/300 $\Omega \approx 2$ kA. To keep the capacitor charged, lightning should deliver the same net current in the opposite direction. (a) If each lightning strike delivers 25 C of charge to the ground, what is the average time interval between lightning strikes so that the average current due to lightning is 2 kA? (b) Using this average time interval between lightning strikes, calculate the number of lightning strikes in one day.

3. Consider again the atmospheric capacitor discussed in the text. (a) Assume that atmospheric conditions are such that, for one complete day, the lower 2.50 km of the air between the capacitor plates has resistivity 2.00×10^{13} $\Omega \cdot$m and the upper 2.50 km has resistivity 0.500×10^{13} $\Omega \cdot$m. How many lightning strikes occur on this day? (b) Assume that atmospheric conditions are such that, for one complete day, resistivity of the air between the plates in the southern hemisphere is 2.00×10^{13} $\Omega \cdot$m and the resistivity between the plates in the northern hemisphere is 0.200×10^{13} $\Omega \cdot$m. How many lightning strikes occur on this day?

Magnetic Levitation Vehicles

All commercial long-distance ground transportation currently operating in the United States is subject to the force of friction between wheels and a roadway or a track. Recall that friction is a nonconservative force that transforms kinetic energy into internal energy. As discussed in Chapters 16 through 18 on thermodynamics, this internal energy is wasted.

Magnetic levitation (maglev) vehicles are suspended by magnetic forces and therefore do not make physical contact with a roadway or track. This suspension eliminates mechanical friction with the track, the primary cause of transformation of kinetic energy to internal energy. There is still a friction force from the surrounding air that will transform some of the kinetic energy.

Robert Goddard, of rocket fame, published a story in 1907 that describes many features of magnetic levitation. He also published a paper in *Scientific American* in 1909 describing a magneti-cally levitated vehicle operating in a tunnel between Boston and New York City. Emile Bachelet, a French engineer, published a paper in 1912 describing a magnetically levitated vehicle for delivering mail. He received a patent for his invention, but it required far too much power to be practical.

After these early ideas, no significant progress in magnetic levitation was made until the 1960s. At that time, advances in superconducting magnets spurred new interest in magnetic levitation because of the possible savings in energy costs over previous designs such as Bachelet's. In 1963, a physicist at Brookhaven National Laboratory proposed a system using superconducting magnets. Within a few years, projects were underway at Stanford University, MIT, Raytheon, Ford Motor Company, the University of Toronto, and McGill University. Projects were also initiated shortly thereafter in Japan, Germany, and England.

© Transrapid International, Berlin, Germany)

FIGURE 1   Because a magnetic levitation (maglev) vehicle is not subject to mechanical friction with rails, it can reach very high speeds. This photo shows the German Transrapid maglev vehicle in operation. Of all proposed models of maglev, the Transrapid is furthest along in its development.

Despite this promising start by several U.S. companies and universities, federal funding for maglev research in the United States ended in 1975. Research in other countries continued, primarily in Germany and Japan. These studies and a variety of full-scale test vehicles have shown that maglev technology is very successful. Research in maglev has seen a modest revival in the United States following the National Maglev Initiative signed into law in 1991, but the United States remains far behind Germany and Japan.

The German maglev project is called the Transrapid. It has undergone extensive testing in Germany. In December 2003, it realized a major milestone in having the first commercial Transrapid line open for business in Shanghai,

FIGURE 2   The German Transrapid in commercial operation in Shanghai, China. Recent tests have shown that this vehicle can travel at speeds of more than 500 km/h.

China. Additional proposals call for the Transrapid to be incorporated into transportation projects in Pittsburgh; Los Angeles; between Baltimore and Washington, D.C.; and between Anaheim, California, and Las Vegas, Nevada.

The Japanese maglev vehicle is dubbed the MLX01 (ML for maglev, X for "experimental"). This vehicle holds the world speed record for a maglev ve-

hicle at 581 km/h, achieved in December 2003 with technicians on board. The MLX01 is currently in the final phase of testing before the Japanese Ministry of Transport decides whether to proceed with commercial development.

In addition to the energy savings in a maglev vehicle associated with the re-

FIGURE 3   The Japanese MLX01 test vehicle. Although this vehicle differs in technology from the German maglev vehicles, it also can travel at very high speeds and currently holds the world record for a maglev vehicle.

duction of friction, there are other benefits. One is reduced environmental impact compared with a traditional railroad because of the absence of emissions. Furthermore, the reliability under various weather conditions such as snow and rain is enhanced because the motion is not dependent on a coefficient of friction. In this Context, we shall investigate the physics of magnetic fields and electromagnetism and apply these principles to understanding the processes of lifting, propelling, and braking a maglev vehicle. Two primary mechanisms—the *attractive* and *repulsive* models—are the basis of current research and development efforts. We shall study each of these models so we can respond to our central question:

How can we lift, propel, and brake a vehicle with magnetic forces?

CHAPTER 22

Magnetic Forces and Magnetic Fields

Magnetic fingerprinting allows fingerprints to be seen on surfaces that otherwise would not allow prints to be lifted. The powder spread on the surface is coated with an organic material that adheres to the greasy residue in a fingerprint. A magnetic "brush" removes the excess powder and makes the fingerprint visible.

(James King-Holmes/Photo Researchers, Inc.)

The list of technological applications of magnetism is very long. For instance, large electromagnets are used to pick up heavy loads in scrap yards. Magnets are used in such devices as meters, motors, and loudspeakers. Magnetic tapes are routinely used in sound and video recording equipment and for computer data storage. Intense magnetic fields generated by superconducting magnets are currently being used as a means of containing plasmas at temperatures on the order of 10^8 K used in controlled nuclear fusion research.

As we investigate magnetism in this chapter, we shall find that the subject cannot be divorced from electricity. For example, magnetic fields affect moving electric charges, and moving charges produce magnetic fields. This close association between electricity and magnetism will justify their union into *electromagnetism* that we explore in this chapter and the next.

22.1 │ HISTORICAL OVERVIEW

Many historians of science believe that the compass, which uses a magnetic needle, was used in China as early as the 13th century B.C., its invention being of Arab or Indian origin. The phenomenon of magnetism was known to the Greeks as early as about 800 B.C. They discovered that certain stones, made of a material now called *magnetite* (Fe_3O_4), attracted pieces of iron.

In 1269, Pierre de Maricourt (c. 1220–?) mapped out the directions taken by a magnetized needle when it was placed at various points on the surface of a spherical natural magnet. He found that the directions formed lines that encircled the sphere and passed through two points diametrically opposite each other, which he called the **poles** of the magnet. Subsequent experiments have shown that every magnet, regardless of its shape, has two poles, called **north** (N) and **south** (S), that exhibit forces on each other in a manner analogous to electric charges. That is, similar poles (N–N or S–S) repel each other and dissimilar poles (N–S) attract each other. The poles received their names because of the behavior of a magnet in the presence of the Earth's magnetic field. If a bar magnet is suspended from its midpoint by a piece of string so that it can swing freely in a horizontal plane, it rotates until its "north" pole points to the north geographic pole of the Earth (which is a south magnetic pole) and its "south" pole points to the Earth's south geographic pole. (The same idea is used to construct a simple compass.)

In 1600, William Gilbert (1544–1603) extended these experiments to a variety of materials. Using the fact that a compass needle orients in preferred directions, Gilbert suggested that magnets are attracted to land masses. In 1750, John Michell (1724–1793) used a torsion balance to show that magnetic poles exert attractive or repulsive forces on each other and that these forces vary as the inverse square of their separation. Although the force between two magnetic poles is similar to the force between two electric charges, an important difference exists. Electric charges can be isolated (witness the electron and proton), whereas magnetic poles cannot be isolated. That is, **magnetic poles are always found in pairs.** No matter how many times a permanent magnet is cut, each piece always has a north pole and a south pole. (Some theories speculate that magnetic monopoles—isolated north or south poles—may exist in nature, and attempts to detect them currently make up an active experimental field of investigation. None of these attempts has yet proven successful, however.)

The relationship between magnetism and electricity was discovered in 1819 when, while preparing for a lecture demonstration, Danish scientist Hans Christian Oersted found that an electric current in a wire deflected a nearby compass needle. Shortly thereafter, André-Marie Ampère (1775–1836) deduced quantitative laws of magnetic force between current-carrying conductors. He also suggested that electric current loops of molecular size are responsible for *all* magnetic phenomena.

In the 1820s, Faraday and, independently, Joseph Henry (1797–1878) identified further connections between electricity and magnetism. They showed that an electric current could be produced in a circuit either by moving a magnet near the circuit or by changing the current in a nearby circuit. Their observations demonstrated that a changing magnetic field produces an electric field. Years later, theoretical work by James Clerk Maxwell showed that the reverse is also true: a changing electric field gives rise to a magnetic field.

In this chapter, we shall investigate the effects of constant magnetic fields on charges and currents, and study the sources of magnetic fields. In the next chapter, we shall explore the effects of magnetic fields that vary in time.

22.2 │ THE MAGNETIC FIELD

In earlier chapters, we described the interaction between charged objects in terms of electric fields. Recall that an electric field surrounds any stationary electric charge. The region of space surrounding a *moving* charge includes a **magnetic field**

(North Wind Picture Archives)

HANS CHRISTIAN OERSTED
(1777–1851)

Oersted, a Danish physicist, is best known for observing that a compass needle deflects when placed near a wire carrying a current. This important discovery was the first evidence of the connection between electric and magnetic phenomena. Oersted was also the first to prepare pure aluminum.

in addition to the electric field. A magnetic field also surrounds any material with permanent magnetism. We find that the magnetic field is a vector field, as is the electric field.

To describe any type of vector field, we must define its magnitude and its direction. The direction of the magnetic field vector $\vec{\mathbf{B}}$ at any location is the direction in which the north pole of a compass needle points at that location. Active Figure 22.1 shows how the magnetic field of a bar magnet can be traced with the aid of a compass, defining a **magnetic field line,** similar in many ways to the electric field lines we studied in Chapter 19. Several magnetic field lines of a bar magnet traced out in this manner are shown in the two-dimensional pictorial representation in Active Figure 22.1. Magnetic field patterns can be displayed by small iron filings placed in the vicinity of a magnet, as in Figure 22.2.

We can quantify the magnetic field $\vec{\mathbf{B}}$ by using our model of a particle in a field. The existence of a magnetic field at some point in space can be determined by measuring the **magnetic force** $\vec{\mathbf{F}}_B$ exerted on an appropriate test particle placed at that point. This process is the same one we followed in defining the electric field in Chapter 19. Our test particle will be an electrically charged particle such as a proton. If we perform such an experiment, we find the following results:

- The magnetic force $\vec{\mathbf{F}}_B$ is proportional to the charge q of the particle as well as to the speed v of the particle.
- When a charged particle moves parallel to the magnetic field vector, the magnetic force $\vec{\mathbf{F}}_B$ on the charge is zero.
- When the velocity vector makes an angle θ with the magnetic field, the magnetic force acts in a direction perpendicular to both $\vec{\mathbf{v}}$ and $\vec{\mathbf{B}}$; that is, the magnetic force is perpendicular to the plane formed by $\vec{\mathbf{v}}$ and $\vec{\mathbf{B}}$ (Fig. 22.3a).
- The magnetic force on a negative charge is directed opposite to the force on a positive charge moving in the same direction (Fig. 22.3b).
- If the velocity vector makes an angle θ with the magnetic field, the magnitude of the magnetic force is proportional to sin θ.

These results show that the magnetic force on a particle is more complicated than the electric force. The magnetic force is distinctive because it depends on the

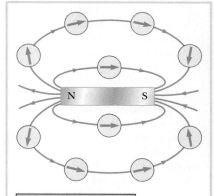

ACTIVE FIGURE 22.1

A small compass can be used to trace the magnetic field lines of a bar magnet.

Physics ⊗ Now™ Log into Physics-Now at **www.pop4e.com** and go to Active Figure 22.1 to move the compass around and trace the field lines for yourself.

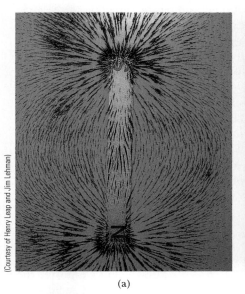
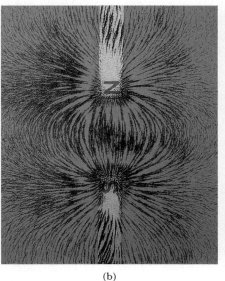

(a) (b) (c)

(Courtesy of Henry Leap and Jim Lehman)

FIGURE 22.2 (a) Magnetic field patterns surrounding a bar magnet as displayed with iron filings. (b) Magnetic field patterns between *dissimilar* poles of two bar magnets. (c) Magnetic field pattern between *similar* poles of two bar magnets.

FIGURE 22.3 The direction of
the magnetic force on a charged
particle moving with a velocity $\vec{v}$ in
the presence of a magnetic field $\vec{B}$.
(a) When $\vec{v}$ is at an angle θ to $\vec{B}$, the
magnetic force is perpendicular to
both $\vec{v}$ and $\vec{B}$. (b) Oppositely
directed magnetic forces are exerted
on two oppositely charged particles
moving with the same velocity in a
magnetic field. The broken lines
suggest the paths followed by the
particles after the instant shown in
the figure.

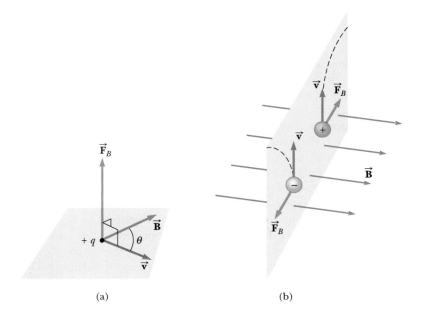

(a)   (b)

velocity of the particle and because its direction is perpendicular to both $\vec{v}$ and $\vec{B}$. Despite this complicated behavior, these observations can be summarized in a compact way by writing the magnetic force in the form

■ Magnetic force on a charged particle moving in a magnetic field

$$\vec{F}_B = q\vec{v} \times \vec{B} \qquad [22.1]$$

where the direction of the magnetic force is that of $\vec{v} \times \vec{B}$, which, by definition of the cross product, is perpendicular to both $\vec{v}$ and $\vec{B}$. Equation 22.1 is analogous to Equation 19.4, $\vec{F}_e = q\vec{E}$, but is clearly more complicated. We can regard Equation 22.1 as an operational definition of the magnetic field at a point in space. The SI unit of magnetic field is the **tesla** (T), where

$$1\ T = 1\ N \cdot s/C \cdot m$$

Figure 22.4 reviews two right-hand rules for determining the direction of the cross product $\vec{v} \times \vec{B}$ and determining the direction of $\vec{F}_B$. The rule in Figure 22.4a depends on our right-hand rule for the cross product in Figure 10.13. You point the four fingers of your right hand along the direction of $\vec{v}$ with the palm facing $\vec{B}$ and curl them toward $\vec{B}$. The extended thumb, which is at a right angle to the fingers, points in the direction of $\vec{v} \times \vec{B}$. Because $\vec{F}_B = q\vec{v} \times \vec{B}$, $\vec{F}_B$ is in the direction of your thumb if q is positive and opposite the direction of your thumb if q is negative.

A second rule is shown in Figure 22.4b. Here the thumb points in the direction of $\vec{v}$ and the extended fingers in the direction of $\vec{B}$. Now, the force $\vec{F}_B$ on a positive charge extends outward from your palm. The advantage of this rule is that the force on the charge is in the direction that you would push on something with your hand, outward from your palm. The force on a negative charge is in the opposite direction. Feel free to use either of these two right-hand rules.

The magnitude of the magnetic force is

$$F_B = |q|vB \sin \theta \qquad [22.2]$$

where θ is the angle between $\vec{v}$ and $\vec{B}$. From this expression, we see that F_B is zero when $\vec{v}$ is either parallel or antiparallel to $\vec{B}$ ($\theta = 0$ or $180°$). Furthermore, the force has its maximum value $F_B = |q|vB$ when $\vec{v}$ is perpendicular to $\vec{B}$ ($\theta = 90°$).

There are important differences between electric and magnetic forces on charged particles:

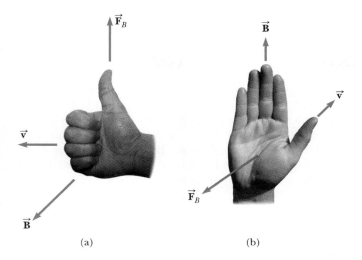

(a)   (b)

FIGURE 22.4 Two right-hand rules for determining the direction of the magnetic force $\vec{F}_B = q\vec{v} \times \vec{B}$ acting on a particle with charge q moving with a velocity $\vec{v}$ in a magnetic field $\vec{B}$. (a) In this rule, the fingers point in the direction of $\vec{v}$, with $\vec{B}$ coming out of your palm, so that you can curl your fingers in the direction of $\vec{B}$. The direction of $\vec{v} \times \vec{B}$, and the force on a positive charge, is the direction in which the thumb points. (b) In this rule, the vector $\vec{v}$ is in the direction of your thumb and $\vec{B}$ is in the direction of your fingers. The force $\vec{F}_B$ on a positive charge is in the direction of your palm, as if you are pushing the particle with your hand.

- The electric force is always parallel or antiparallel to the direction of the electric field, whereas the magnetic force is perpendicular to the magnetic field.
- The electric force acts on a charged particle independent of the particle's velocity, whereas the magnetic force acts on a charged particle only when the particle is in motion and the force is proportional to the velocity.
- The electric force does work in displacing a charged particle, whereas the magnetic force associated with a constant magnetic field does *no* work when a charged particle is displaced.

This last statement is true because when a charge moves in a constant magnetic field, the magnetic force is always *perpendicular* to the displacement. That is, for a small displacement $d\vec{s}$ of a particle, the work done by the magnetic force on the particle is $dW = \vec{F}_B \cdot d\vec{s} = (\vec{F}_B \cdot \vec{v})\,dt = 0$ because the magnetic force is a vector perpendicular to $\vec{v}$. From this property and the work–kinetic energy theorem, we conclude that the kinetic energy of a charged particle *cannot* be altered by a constant magnetic field alone. In other words, when a charge moves with a velocity of $\vec{v}$, an applied magnetic field can alter the direction of the velocity vector, but it cannot change the speed of the particle.

In Figures 22.3 and 22.4, we used green arrows to represent magnetic field vectors, which will be the convention in this book. In Active Figure 22.1, we represented the magnetic field of a bar magnet with green field lines. Studying magnetic fields presents a complication that we avoided in electric fields. In our study of electric fields, we drew all electric field vectors in the plane of the page or used perspective to represent them directed at an angle to the page. The cross product in Equation 22.1 requires us to think in three dimensions for problems in magnetism. Thus, in addition to drawing vectors pointing left or right and up or down, we will need a method of drawing vectors into or out of the page. These methods of representing the vectors are illustrated in Figure 22.5. A vector coming out of the page is represented by a dot, which we can think of as the tip of the arrowhead representing the vector coming through the paper toward us (Fig. 22.5a). A vector going into the page is represented by a cross, which we can think of as the tail feathers of an arrow going into the page (Fig. 22.5b). This depiction can be used for any type of vector we will encounter: magnetic field, velocity, force, and so on.

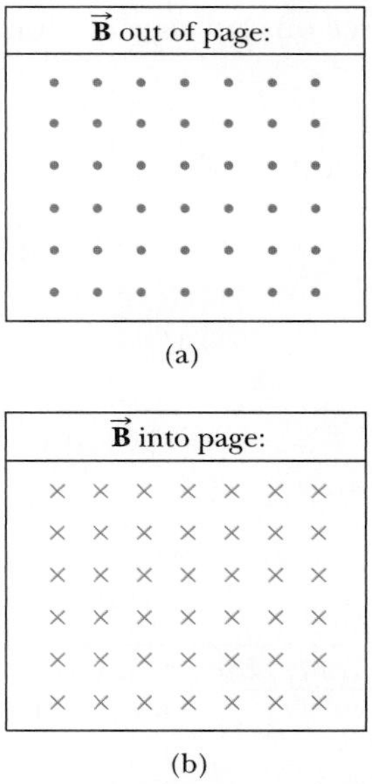

$\vec{B}$ out of page:
. . . .
. . . .
. . . .
. . . .
. . . .
. . . .

(a)

$\vec{B}$ into page:
× × × × × × × ×
× × × × × × × ×
× × × × × × × ×
× × × × × × × ×
× × × × × × × ×
× × × × × × × ×

(b)

FIGURE 22.5 (a) Magnetic field lines coming out of the paper are indicated by dots, representing the tips of arrows coming outward. (b) Magnetic field lines going into the paper are indicated by crosses, representing the feathers of arrows going inward.

QUICK QUIZ 22.1 An electron moves in the plane of this paper toward the top of the page. A magnetic field is also in the plane of the page and directed toward the right. What is the direction of the magnetic force on the electron? **(a)** toward the top of the page **(b)** toward the bottom of the page **(c)** toward the left edge of the page **(d)** toward the right edge of the page **(e)** upward out of the page **(f)** downward into the page

■ Thinking Physics 22.1

On a business trip to Australia, you take along your U.S.-made compass that you used in your Boy Scout days. Does this compass work correctly in Australia?

Reasoning Using the compass in Australia presents no problem. The north pole of the magnet in the compass will be attracted to the south magnetic pole near the north geographic pole, just as it was in the United States. The only difference in the magnetic field lines is that they have an upward component in Australia, whereas they have a downward component in the United States. When you hold the compass in a horizontal plane, it cannot detect the vertical component of the field, however; it only displays the direction of the horizontal component of the magnetic field. ■

EXAMPLE 22.1 **An Electron Moving in a Magnetic Field**

An electron in a television picture tube moves toward the front of the tube with a speed of 8.0×10^6 m/s along the x axis (Fig. 22.6). The neck of the tube is surrounded by a coil of wire that creates a magnetic field of magnitude 0.025 T, directed at an angle of 60° to the x axis and lying in the xy plane. Calculate the magnetic force on and acceleration of the electron.

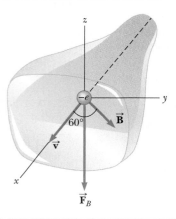

FIGURE 22.6 (Example 22.1) The magnetic force $\vec{F}_B$ on the electron is in the negative z direction when $\vec{v}$ and $\vec{B}$ lie in the xy plane.

Solution Using Equation 22.2, we find the magnitude of the magnetic force:

$$F_B = |q|vB \sin \theta$$
$$= (1.60 \times 10^{-19} \text{ C})(8.0 \times 10^6 \text{ m/s})(0.025 \text{ T})(\sin 60°)$$
$$= 2.8 \times 10^{-14} \text{ N}$$

Because $\vec{v} \times \vec{B}$ is in the positive z direction (from the right-hand rule) and the charge is negative, $\vec{F}_B$ is in the negative z direction.

Once we have determined the magnetic force, we have a Chapter 4 problem because the electron is a particle under a net force and the acceleration is determined from Newton's second law. The mass of the electron is $m_e = 9.1 \times 10^{-31}$ kg, and so its acceleration is

$$a = \frac{F_B}{m_e} = \frac{2.8 \times 10^{-14} \text{ N}}{9.1 \times 10^{-31} \text{ kg}} = 3.1 \times 10^{16} \text{ m/s}^2$$

in the negative z direction.

22.3 | MOTION OF A CHARGED PARTICLE IN A UNIFORM MAGNETIC FIELD

In Section 22.2, we found that the magnetic force acting on a charged particle moving in a magnetic field is perpendicular to the velocity of the particle and that, consequently, the work done on the particle by the magnetic force is zero. Consider now the special case of a positively charged particle moving in a uniform magnetic field when the initial velocity vector of the particle is perpendicular to the field. Let us assume that the direction of the magnetic field is into the page. Active Figure 22.7 shows that the particle moves in a circular path whose plane is perpendicular to the magnetic field.

The particle moves in this way because the magnetic force $\vec{\mathbf{F}}_B$ is perpendicular to $\vec{\mathbf{v}}$ and $\vec{\mathbf{B}}$ and has a constant magnitude qvB. As the force changes the direction of $\vec{\mathbf{v}}$, the direction of $\vec{\mathbf{F}}_B$ changes continuously as in Active Figure 22.7. Because $\vec{\mathbf{F}}_B$ always points toward the center of the circle, the particle can be modeled as being in uniform circular motion. As Active Figure 22.7 shows, the rotation is counterclockwise for a positive charge in a magnetic field directed into the page. If q were negative, the rotation would be clockwise. We can use Newton's second law to determine the radius of the circular path:

$$\sum F = F_B = ma$$

$$qvB = \frac{mv^2}{r}$$

$$r = \frac{mv}{qB} \qquad [22.3]$$

That is, the radius of the path is proportional to the linear momentum mv of the particle and inversely proportional to the magnitude of the charge on the particle and to the magnitude of the magnetic field. The angular speed of the particle is (from Eq. 10.10)

$$\omega = \frac{v}{r} = \frac{qB}{m} \qquad [22.4]$$

The period of the motion (the time interval required for the particle to complete one revolution) is equal to the circumference of the circular path divided by the speed of the particle:

$$T = \frac{2\pi r}{v} = \frac{2\pi}{\omega} = \frac{2\pi m}{qB} \qquad [22.5]$$

These results show that the angular speed of the particle and the period of the circular motion do not depend on the translational speed of the particle or the radius of the orbit for a given particle in a given uniform magnetic field. The angular speed ω is often referred to as the **cyclotron frequency** because charged particles circulate at this angular speed in one type of accelerator called a *cyclotron*, discussed in Section 22.4.

If a charged particle moves in a uniform magnetic field with its velocity at some arbitrary angle to $\vec{\mathbf{B}}$, its path is a helix. For example, if the field is in the x direction as in Active Figure 22.8, there is no component of force on the particle in the x direction. As a result, $a_x = 0$, and so the x component of velocity of the particle remains constant. The magnetic force $q\vec{\mathbf{v}} \times \vec{\mathbf{B}}$ causes the components v_y and v_z to change in time, however, and the resulting motion of the particle is a helix having its axis parallel to the magnetic field. The projection of the path onto the yz plane (viewed along the x axis) is a circle. (The projections of the path onto the xy and xz planes are sinusoids!) Equations 22.3 to 22.5 still apply provided that v is replaced by $v_\perp = \sqrt{v_y^2 + v_z^2}$.

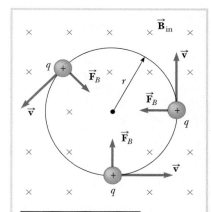

ACTIVE FIGURE 22.7

When the velocity of a charged particle is perpendicular to a uniform magnetic field, the particle moves in a circular path in a plane perpendicular to $\vec{\mathbf{B}}$. The magnetic force $\vec{\mathbf{F}}_B$ acting on the charge is always directed toward the center of the circle.

Physics Now™ Log into Physics-Now at **www.pop4e.com** and go to Active Figure 22.7. You can adjust the mass, speed, and charge of the particle and the magnitude of the magnetic field to observe the resulting circular motion.

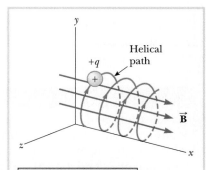

ACTIVE FIGURE 22.8

A charged particle having a velocity vector with a component parallel to a uniform magnetic field moves in a helical path.

Physics Now™ Log into Physics-Now at **www.pop4e.com** and go to Active Figure 22.8. You can adjust the x component of the velocity of the particle and observe the resulting helical motion.

QUICK QUIZ 22.2 **(i)** A charged particle is moving perpendicular to a magnetic field in a circle with a radius r. The magnitude of the magnetic field is increased. Compared with the initial radius of the circular path, is the radius of the new path **(a)** smaller, **(b)** larger, or **(c)** equal in size? **(ii)** An identical particle enters the field, with $\vec{\mathbf{v}}$ perpendicular to $\vec{\mathbf{B}}$, but with a higher speed v than the first particle. Compared with the radius of the circle for the first particle in the same magnetic field, is the radius of the circle for the second particle **(a)** smaller, **(b)** larger, or **(c)** equal in size?

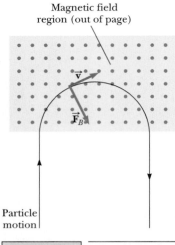

Magnetic field
region (out of page)

$\vec{v}$

$\vec{F}_B$

Particle
motion

FIGURE 22.9 (Thinking Physics
22.2) A positively charged particle
enters a region of magnetic field
directed out of the page.

■ Thinking Physics 22.2

Suppose a uniform magnetic field exists in a finite region of space as in Figure 22.9. Can you inject a charged particle into this region and have it stay trapped in the region by the magnetic force?

Reasoning Consider separately the components of the particle velocity parallel and perpendicular to the field lines in the region. For the component parallel to the field lines, no force is exerted on the particle and it continues to move with the parallel component until it leaves the region of the magnetic field. Now consider the component perpendicular to the field lines. This component results in a magnetic force that is perpendicular to both the field lines and the velocity component. As discussed earlier, if the force acting on a charged particle is always perpendicular to its velocity, the particle moves in a circular path. Thus, the particle follows half of a circular arc and exits the field on the other side of the circle, as shown in Figure 22.9. Therefore, a particle injected into a uniform magnetic field cannot stay trapped in the field region. ■

EXAMPLE 22.2 **A Proton Moving Perpendicular to a Uniform Magnetic Field**

A proton is moving in a circular orbit of radius 14.0 cm in a uniform 0.350-T magnetic field directed perpendicular to the velocity of the proton.

[A] Find the translational speed of the proton.

Solution From Equation 22.3, we find that

$$v = \frac{qBr}{m_p} = \frac{(1.60 \times 10^{-19}\ \text{C})(0.350\ \text{T})(14.0 \times 10^{-2}\ \text{m})}{1.67 \times 10^{-27}\ \text{kg}}$$

$$= 4.69 \times 10^6\ \text{m/s}$$

[B] Find the period of the circular motion of the proton.

Solution From Equation 22.5,

$$T = \frac{2\pi m_p}{qB} = \frac{2\pi(1.67 \times 10^{-27}\ \text{kg})}{(1.60 \times 10^{-19}\ \text{C})(0.350\ \text{T})}$$

$$= 1.87 \times 10^{-7}\ \text{s}$$

INTERACTIVE EXAMPLE 22.3 **Bending an Electron Beam**

In an experiment designed to measure the strength of a uniform magnetic field, electrons are accelerated from rest (by means of an electric field) through a potential difference of 350 V. After leaving the region of the electric field, the electrons enter a magnetic field and travel along a curved path because of the magnetic force exerted on them. The radius of the path is measured to be 7.50 cm. Figure 22.10 shows such a curved beam of electrons.

[A] Assuming that the magnetic field is perpendicular to the beam, what is the magnitude of the field?

Solution The drawing in Active Figure 22.7 and the photograph in Figure 22.10 help us conceptualize the circular motion of the electrons. We categorize this

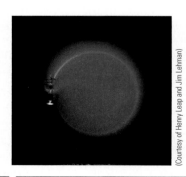

(Courtesy of Henry Leap and Jim Lehman)

FIGURE 22.10 (Interactive Example 22.3) The bending of an electron beam in a magnetic field.

problem as one in which we will use our understanding of uniform circular motion along with our knowledge of the magnetic force. Looking at Equation 22.3, we see that we need the speed v of the electron if we are to find the magnetic field magnitude, and v is not given. Consequently, we must find the speed of the electron based on the potential difference through which it is accelerated. We can therefore also categorize this problem as one in which we must apply conservation of mechanical energy for an isolated system. We begin to analyze the problem by finding the electron speed. For the isolated electron–electric field system, the loss of potential energy as the electron moves through the 350-V potential difference appears as an increase in the kinetic energy of the electron. Because $K_i = 0$ and $K_f = \frac{1}{2}m_e v^2$, we have

$$\Delta K + \Delta U = 0 \quad \rightarrow \quad \tfrac{1}{2}m_e v^2 + (-e)\,\Delta V = 0$$

$$v = \sqrt{\frac{2e\,\Delta V}{m_e}} = \sqrt{\frac{2(1.60 \times 10^{-19}\,\text{C})(350\,\text{V})}{9.11 \times 10^{-31}\,\text{kg}}}$$

$$= 1.11 \times 10^7\,\text{m/s}$$

Now, using Equation 22.3, we find that

$$B = \frac{m_e v}{er} = \frac{(9.11 \times 10^{-31}\,\text{kg})(1.11 \times 10^7\,\text{m/s})}{(1.60 \times 10^{-19}\,\text{C})(0.075\,\text{m})}$$

$$= 8.4 \times 10^{-4}\,\text{T}$$

B What is the angular speed of the electrons?

Solution Using Equation 22.4, we find that

$$\omega = \frac{v}{r} = \frac{1.11 \times 10^7\,\text{m/s}}{0.075\,\text{m}} = 1.5 \times 10^8\,\text{rad/s}$$

To finalize this problem, note that the angular speed can be written as $\omega = (1.5 \times 10^8\,\text{rad/s})(1\,\text{rev}/2\pi\,\text{rad}) = 2.4 \times 10^7\,\text{rev/s}$. The electrons travel around the circle 24 million times per second! This very high speed is consistent with what we found in part A.

Physics⊗Now™ By logging into PhysicsNow at **www.pop4e.com** and going to Interactive Example 22.3, you can investigate the relationship between the radius of the circular path of the electrons and the magnetic field.

22.4 APPLICATIONS INVOLVING CHARGED PARTICLES MOVING IN A MAGNETIC FIELD

A charge moving with velocity $\vec{v}$ in the presence of an electric field $\vec{E}$ and a magnetic field $\vec{B}$ experiences both an electric force $q\vec{E}$ and a magnetic force $q\vec{v} \times \vec{B}$. The total force, called the **Lorentz force,** acting on the charge is therefore the vector sum,

$$\vec{F} = q\vec{E} + q\vec{v} \times \vec{B} \qquad [22.6]$$

In this section, we look at three applications involving particles experiencing the Lorentz force.

Velocity Selector

In many experiments involving moving charged particles, it is important to have particles that all move with essentially the same velocity. That can be achieved by applying a combination of an electric field and a magnetic field oriented as shown in Active Figure 22.11a. A uniform electric field is directed vertically downward (in the plane of the page in Active Fig. 22.11a), and a uniform magnetic field is applied perpendicular to the electric field (into the page in Active Fig. 22.11a). Particles moving through this region will experience the Lorentz force, given by Equation 22.6. For a positively charged particle, the magnetic force $q\vec{v} \times \vec{B}$ is upward and the electric force $q\vec{E}$ is downward. When the magnitudes of the two fields are chosen so that $qE = qvB$, the particle is in equilibrium (Active Fig. 22.11b) and moves in a straight horizontal line through the region of the fields. From $qE = qvB$ we find that

$$v = \frac{E}{B} \qquad [22.7]$$

Only those particles having this speed are undeflected as they move through the perpendicular electric and magnetic fields and pass through a small opening at the end of the device. The magnetic force exerted on particles moving faster than this

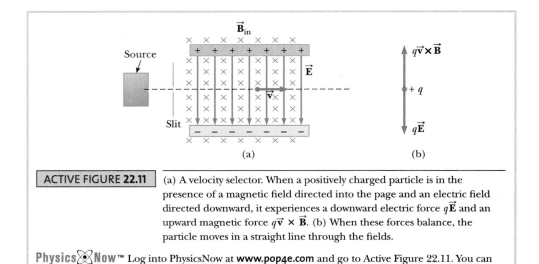

| ACTIVE FIGURE **22.11** | (a) A velocity selector. When a positively charged particle is in the presence of a magnetic field directed into the page and an electric field directed downward, it experiences a downward electric force $q\vec{E}$ and an upward magnetic force $q\vec{v} \times \vec{B}$. (b) When these forces balance, the particle moves in a straight line through the fields. |

Physics✹Now™ Log into PhysicsNow at **www.pop4e.com** and go to Active Figure 22.11. You can adjust the electric and magnetic fields to try to achieve straight line motion for the charge.

speed is stronger than the electric force, and these particles are deflected upward. Those moving slower are deflected downward.

The Mass Spectrometer

A **mass spectrometer** separates ions according to their mass-to-charge ratio. In one version, known as the *Bainbridge mass spectrometer,* a beam of ions first passes through a velocity selector and then enters a second region with no electric field and a uniform magnetic field $\vec{B}_0$ that has the same direction as the magnetic field in the selector (Active Fig. 22.12). On entering the second magnetic field, the ions move in a semicircle of radius r before striking a detector array at P. If the ions are positively charged, the beam deflects upward as in Active Figure 22.12. If the ions are negatively charged, the beam deflects downward. From Equation 22.3, we can express the ratio m/q as

$$\frac{m}{q} = \frac{rB_0}{v}$$

Using Equation 22.7, we find that

$$\frac{m}{q} = \frac{rB_0B}{E} \qquad [22.8]$$

ACTIVE FIGURE **22.12**

A mass spectrometer. Positively charged particles are sent first through a velocity selector and then into a region where the magnetic field $\vec{B}_0$ causes the particles to move in a semicircular path and strike a detector array at P.

Physics✹Now™ Log into PhysicsNow at **www.pop4e.com** and go to Active Figure 22.12 to predict where particles will strike the detector array.

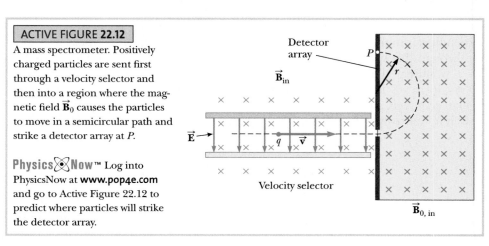

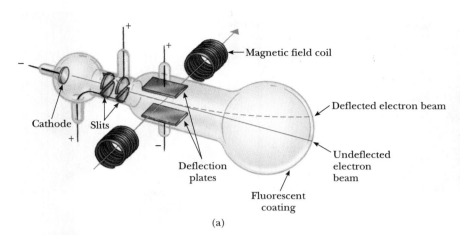

(a)

(b)

| FIGURE 22.13 | (a) Thomson's apparatus for measuring e/m_e. Electrons are accelerated from the cathode, pass through two slits, and are deflected by both an electric field and a magnetic field (directed perpendicular to the electric field). The electrons then strike a fluorescent screen. (b) J. J. Thomson (*left*) in the Cavendish Laboratory, University of Cambridge. It is interesting to note that the man on the right, Frank Baldwin Jewett, is a distant relative of John W. Jewett Jr., coauthor of this text. |

Therefore, m/q can be determined by measuring the radius of curvature and knowing the field magnitudes B, B_0, and E. In practice, one usually measures the masses of various isotopes of a given ion, with the ions all carrying the same charge q. In this way, the mass ratios can be determined even if q is unknown.

A variation of this technique was used by J. J. Thomson (1856–1940) in 1897 to measure the ratio e/m_e for electrons. Figure 22.13a shows the basic apparatus he used. Electrons are accelerated from the cathode and pass through two slits. They then drift into a region of perpendicular electric and magnetic fields. The magnitudes of the two fields are first adjusted to produce an undeflected beam. When the magnetic field is turned off, the electric field produces a measurable beam deflection that is recorded on the fluorescent screen. From the size of the deflection and the measured values of E and B, the charge-to-mass ratio can be determined. The results of this crucial experiment represent the discovery of the electron as a fundamental particle of nature.

The Cyclotron

A **cyclotron** can accelerate charged particles to very high speeds. Both electric and magnetic forces play a key role in its operation. The energetic particles produced are used to bombard atomic nuclei and thereby produce nuclear reactions of interest to researchers. A number of hospitals use cyclotron facilities to produce radioactive substances for diagnosis and treatment as well as beams of high-energy particles for treating cancer. For example, retinoblastoma, a cancer of the eye, can be treated with a series of beams of protons from a cyclotron.

 Use of cyclotrons in medicine

A schematic drawing of a cyclotron is shown in Figure 22.14a. The charges move inside two hollow metal semicircular containers, D_1 and D_2, referred to as *dees* because they are shaped like the letter D. A high-frequency alternating potential difference is applied to the dees, and a uniform magnetic field is directed perpendicular to them. A positive ion released at P near the center of the magnet moves in a semicircular path in one dee (indicated by the dashed red line in the drawing) and arrives back at the gap in a time interval $T/2$, where T is the time interval needed to make one complete trip around the two dees, given by Equation 22.5. The frequency of the applied potential difference is chosen so that the polarity of the dees is reversed during the time interval in which the ion travels around one dee. If the applied potential difference is adjusted such that D_2 is at a lower electric potential

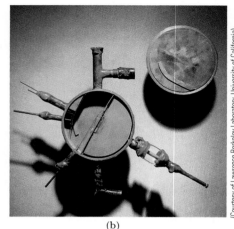

$\vec{\mathbf{B}}$

P

D_1

D_2

Alternating ΔV

Particle exits here

North pole of magnet

(a)

(b)

(Courtesy of Lawrence Berkeley Laboratory, University of California)

FIGURE 22.14 (a) A cyclotron consists of an ion source at P, two hollow sections called dees, D_1 and D_2, across which an alternating potential difference is applied, and a uniform magnetic field. (The south pole of the magnet is not shown.) The red dashed curved lines represent the path of the particles. (b) The first cyclotron, invented by E. O. Lawrence and M. S. Livingston in 1934.

than D_1 by an amount ΔV, the ion accelerates across the gap to D_2 and its kinetic energy increases by an amount $q \Delta V$. It then moves around D_2 in a semicircular path of larger radius (because its speed has increased). After a time interval $T/2$, it again arrives at the gap between the dees. By this time, the polarity across the dees has reversed again and the ion is given another "kick" across the gap. The motion continues so that for each half-circle trip, the ion gains additional kinetic energy equal to $q \Delta V$. When the radius of its path is nearly that of the dees, the energetic ion leaves the system through the exit slit. It is important to note that the operation of the cyclotron is based on T being independent of the speed of the ion and the radius of its circular path (Eq. 22.5).

We can obtain an expression for the kinetic energy of the ion when it exits from the cyclotron in terms of the radius R of the dees. From Equation 22.3 we know that $v = qBR/m$. Hence, the kinetic energy is

$$K = \tfrac{1}{2} m v^2 = \frac{q^2 B^2 R^2}{2m} \qquad [22.9]$$

When the energy of the ions in a cyclotron exceeds about 20 MeV, relativistic effects come into play. For this reason, the moving ions do not remain in phase with the applied potential difference. Some accelerators solve this problem by modifying the frequency of the applied potential difference so that it remains in phase with the moving ions.

22.5 | MAGNETIC FORCE ON A CURRENT-CARRYING CONDUCTOR

Because a magnetic force is exerted on a single charged particle when it moves through an external magnetic field, it should not surprise you to find that a current-carrying wire also experiences a magnetic force when placed in an external magnetic field because the current represents a collection of many charged particles in motion. Hence, the resultant magnetic force on the wire is due to the sum of the individual magnetic forces on the charged particles. The force on the particles is transmitted to the "bulk" of the wire through collisions with the atoms making up the wire.

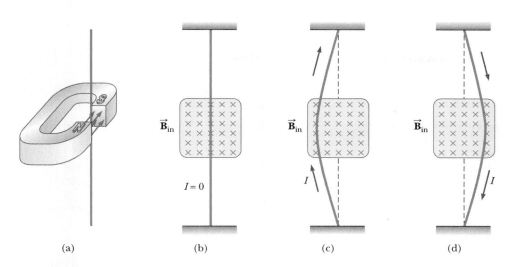

(a)   (b)   (c)   (d)

FIGURE 22.15 (a) A wire suspended vertically between the poles of a magnet. (b) The setup shown in (a) as seen looking at the south pole of the magnet so that the magnetic field (green crosses) is directed into the page. When no current is flowing in the wire, it remains vertical. (c) When the current is upward, the wire deflects to the left. (d) When the current is downward, the wire deflects to the right.

The magnetic force on a current-carrying conductor can be demonstrated by hanging a wire between the poles of a magnet as in Figure 22.15, where the magnetic field is directed into the page. The wire deflects to the left or right when a current is passed through it.

Let us quantify this discussion by considering a straight segment of wire of length ℓ and cross-sectional area A, carrying a current I in a uniform external magnetic field $\vec{\mathbf{B}}$ as in Figure 22.16. As a simplification model, we shall ignore the high-speed zigzag motion of the charges in the wire (which is valid because the net velocity associated with this motion is zero) and assume that the charges simply move with the drift velocity $\vec{\mathbf{v}}_d$. The magnetic force on a charge q moving with drift velocity $\vec{\mathbf{v}}_d$ is $q\vec{\mathbf{v}}_d \times \vec{\mathbf{B}}$. To find the total magnetic force on the wire segment, we multiply the magnetic force on one charge by the number of charges in the segment. Because the volume of the segment is $A\ell$, the number of charges in the segment is $nA\ell$, where n is the number of charges per unit volume. Hence, the total magnetic force on the wire of length ℓ is

$$\vec{\mathbf{F}}_B = (q\vec{\mathbf{v}}_d \times \vec{\mathbf{B}})nA\ell$$

This equation can be written in a more convenient form by noting that, from Equation 21.4, the current in the wire is $I = nqv_dA$. Therefore, $\vec{\mathbf{F}}_B$ can be expressed as

$$\vec{\mathbf{F}}_B = I\vec{\ell} \times \vec{\mathbf{B}} \qquad [22.10]$$

where $\vec{\ell}$ is a vector in the direction of the current I; the magnitude of $\vec{\ell}$ equals the length of the segment. Note that this expression applies only to a straight segment of wire in a uniform external magnetic field.

Now consider an arbitrarily shaped wire of uniform cross-section in an external magnetic field as in Figure 22.17. It follows from Equation 22.10 that the magnetic force on a very small segment of the wire of length ds in the presence of an external field $\vec{\mathbf{B}}$ is

$$d\vec{\mathbf{F}}_B = I\,d\vec{\mathbf{s}} \times \vec{\mathbf{B}} \qquad [22.11]$$

where $d\vec{\mathbf{s}}$ is a vector representing the length segment, with its direction the same as that of the current, and $d\vec{\mathbf{F}}_B$ is directed out of the page for the directions assumed in Figure 22.17. We can consider Equation 22.11 as an alternative definition of $\vec{\mathbf{B}}$ to Equation 22.1. That is, the field $\vec{\mathbf{B}}$ can be defined in terms of a measurable force on a current element, where the force is a maximum when $\vec{\mathbf{B}}$ is perpendicular to the element and zero when $\vec{\mathbf{B}}$ is parallel to the element.

To obtain the total magnetic force $\vec{\mathbf{F}}_B$ on a length of the wire between arbitrary points a and b, we integrate Equation 22.11 over the length of the wire between

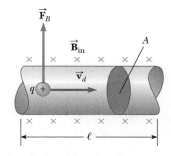

FIGURE 22.16 A section of a wire containing moving charges in a magnetic field $\vec{\mathbf{B}}$. The magnetic force on each charge is $q\vec{\mathbf{v}}_d \times \vec{\mathbf{B}}$, and the net force on a segment of length ℓ is $I\vec{\ell} \times \vec{\mathbf{B}}$.

∎ **Magnetic force on a current-carrying conductor**

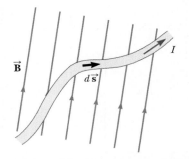

FIGURE 22.17 A wire segment of arbitrary shape carrying a current I in a magnetic field $\vec{\mathbf{B}}$ experiences a magnetic force. The force on any length element $d\vec{\mathbf{s}}$ is $I\,d\vec{\mathbf{s}} \times d\vec{\mathbf{B}}$ and is directed out of the page.

these points:

$$\vec{\mathbf{F}}_B = I \int_a^b d\vec{\mathbf{s}} \times \vec{\mathbf{B}}$$ [22.12]

When this integration is carried out, the magnitude of the magnetic field and the direction of the field relative to the vector $d\vec{\mathbf{s}}$ may vary from point to point.

QUICK QUIZ 22.3   A wire carries current in the plane of this paper toward the top of the page. The wire experiences a magnetic force toward the right edge of the page. What is the direction of the magnetic field causing this force?   **(a)** in the plane of the page and toward the left edge   **(b)** in the plane of the page and toward the bottom edge   **(c)** upward out of the page   **(d)** downward into the page

---

■ **Thinking Physics 22.3**

In a lightning stroke, negative charge rapidly moves from a cloud to the ground. In what direction is a lightning stroke deflected by the Earth's magnetic field?

Reasoning The downward flow of negative charge in a lightning stroke is equivalent to an upward-moving current. Thus, the vector $d\vec{\mathbf{s}}$ is upward, and the magnetic field vector has a northward component. According to the cross product of the length element and magnetic field vectors (Eq. 22.11), the lightning stroke would be deflected to the *west*. ■

EXAMPLE 22.4   **Force on a Semicircular Conductor**

A wire bent into the shape of a semicircle of radius R forms a closed circuit and carries a current I. The circuit lies in the xy plane, and a uniform magnetic field is present along the positive y axis as in Figure 22.18. Find the magnetic force on the straight portion of the wire and on the curved portion.

Solution The force on the straight portion of the wire has a magnitude $F_1 = I\ell B = 2IRB$ because $\ell = 2R$ and the wire is perpendicular to $\vec{\mathbf{B}}$. The direction of $\vec{\mathbf{F}}_1$ is out of the paper because $\vec{\ell} \times \vec{\mathbf{B}}$ is outward. (That is, $\vec{\ell}$ is to the right, in the direction of the current, and so by the rule of cross products, $\vec{\ell} \times \vec{\mathbf{B}}$ is outward.)

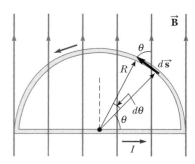

FIGURE 22.18   (Example 22.4) The net force on a closed current loop in a uniform magnetic field is zero. For the loop shown here, the force on the straight portion is $2IRB$ and out of the page, whereas the force on the curved portion is $2IRB$ and into the page.

To find the magnetic force on the curved part, we first write an expression for the magnetic force $d\vec{\mathbf{F}}_2$ on the element $d\vec{\mathbf{s}}$. If θ is the angle between $\vec{\mathbf{B}}$ and $d\vec{\mathbf{s}}$ in Figure 22.18, the magnitude of $d\vec{\mathbf{F}}_2$ is

$$dF_2 = I\left|d\vec{\mathbf{s}} \times \vec{\mathbf{B}}\right| = IB \sin \theta \, ds$$

To integrate this expression, we express ds in terms of θ. Because $s = R\theta$, $ds = R \, d\theta$, and the expression for dF_2 can be written as

$$dF_2 = IRB \sin \theta \, d\theta$$

To obtain the total magnetic force F_2 on the curved portion, we integrate this expression to account for contributions from all elements. Note that the direction of the magnetic force on every element is the same: into the paper (because $d\vec{\mathbf{s}} \times \vec{\mathbf{B}}$ is inward). Therefore, the resultant magnetic force $\vec{\mathbf{F}}_2$ on the curved wire must also be into the paper. Integrating dF_2 over the limits $\theta = 0$ to $\theta = \pi$ (i.e., the entire semicircle) gives

$$F_2 = IRB \int_0^\pi \sin \theta \, d\theta = IRB \left[-\cos \theta\right]_0^\pi$$

$$= -IRB(\cos \pi - \cos 0) = -IRB(-1 - 1) = 2IRB$$

Because $F_2 = 2IRB$ and the vector $\vec{\mathbf{F}}_2$ is directed into the paper and because the force on the straight wire has magnitude $F_1 = 2IRB$ and is out of the paper, we see that the net magnetic force on the closed loop is zero.

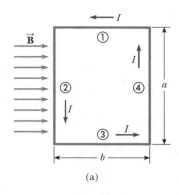

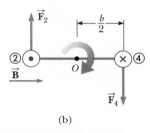

(b)

22.6 | TORQUE ON A CURRENT LOOP IN A UNIFORM MAGNETIC FIELD

In the preceding section, we showed how a magnetic force is exerted on a current-carrying conductor when the conductor is placed in an external magnetic field. Starting at this point, we shall show that a *torque* is exerted on a current loop placed in a magnetic field. The results of this analysis are of great practical value in the design of motors and generators.

Consider a rectangular loop carrying a current I in the presence of a uniform external magnetic field *in the plane of the loop* as in Figure 22.19a. The magnetic forces on sides ① and ③, of length b, are zero because these wires are parallel to the field; hence, $d\vec{\mathbf{s}} \times \vec{\mathbf{B}} = 0$ for these sides. Nonzero magnetic forces act on sides ② and ④, however, because these sides are oriented perpendicular to the field. The magnitude of these forces is

$$F_2 = F_4 = IaB$$

We see that the net force on the loop is zero. The direction of $\vec{\mathbf{F}}_2$, the magnetic force on side ②, is out of the paper, and that of $\vec{\mathbf{F}}_4$, the magnetic force on side ④, is into the paper. If we view the loop from side ③ as in Figure 22.19b, we see the forces on ② and ④ directed as shown. If we assume that the loop is pivoted so that it can rotate about an axis perpendicular to the page and passing through point O, we see that these two magnetic forces produce a net torque about this axis that rotates the loop clockwise. The magnitude of the torque, which we will call τ_{max}, is

$$\tau_{max} = F_2 \frac{b}{2} + F_4 \frac{b}{2} = (IaB) \frac{b}{2} + (IaB) \frac{b}{2} = IabB$$

where the moment arm about this axis is $b/2$ for each force. Because the area of the loop is $A = ab$, the magnitude of the torque can be expressed as

$$\tau_{max} = IAB \qquad [22.13]$$

Remember that this torque occurs only when the field $\vec{\mathbf{B}}$ is parallel to the plane of the loop. The sense of the rotation is clockwise when the loop is viewed as in Figure 22.19b. If the current were reversed, the magnetic forces would reverse their directions and the rotational tendency would be counterclockwise.

Now suppose the uniform magnetic field makes an angle θ with a line perpendicular to the plane of the loop as in Active Figure 22.20. For convenience, we shall assume that $\vec{\mathbf{B}}$ is perpendicular to sides ② and ④. (The end view of these sides is shown in Active Fig. 22.20.) In this case, the magnetic forces on sides ① and ③

FIGURE 22.19 (a) Overhead view of a rectangular current loop in a uniform magnetic field. No magnetic forces are exerted on sides ① and ③ because these sides are parallel to $\vec{\mathbf{B}}$. Forces are exerted on sides ② and ④, however. (b) Edge view of the loop sighting down ② and ④ shows that the forces $\vec{\mathbf{F}}_2$ and $\vec{\mathbf{F}}_4$ exerted on these sides create a torque that tends to rotate the loop clockwise. The purple dot in the left circle represents current in wire ② coming toward you; the purple × in the right circle represents current in wire ④ moving away from you.

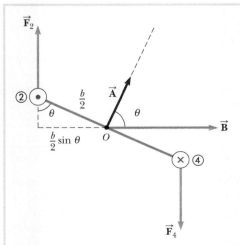

ACTIVE FIGURE 22.20

An end view of the loop in Figure 22.19b rotated through an angle with respect to the magnetic field. If $\vec{\mathbf{B}}$ is at an angle θ with respect to vector $\vec{\mathbf{A}}$, which is perpendicular to the plane of the loop, the torque is $IAB \sin \theta$.

Physics⊗Now™ Log into Physics-Now at **www.pop4e.com** and go to Active Figure 22.20. You can choose the current in the loop, the magnetic field, and the initial orientation of the loop and observe the subsequent motion.

cancel each other and produce no torque because they have the same line of action. The magnetic forces $\vec{F_2}$ and $\vec{F_4}$ acting on sides ② and ④, however, both produce a torque about an axis through the center of the loop. Referring to Active Figure 22.20, we note that the moment arm of $\vec{F_2}$ about this axis is $(b/2)\sin\theta$. Likewise, the moment arm of $\vec{F_4}$ is also $(b/2)\sin\theta$. Because $F_2 = F_4 = IaB$, the net torque τ has the magnitude

$$\tau = F_2\frac{b}{2}\sin\theta + F_4\frac{b}{2}\sin\theta$$
$$= (IaB)\left(\frac{b}{2}\sin\theta\right) + (IaB)\left(\frac{b}{2}\sin\theta\right) = IabB\sin\theta$$
$$= IAB\sin\theta$$

where $A = ab$ is the area of the loop. This result shows that the torque has its maximum value IAB (Eq. 22.13) when the field is parallel to the plane of the loop ($\theta = 90°$) and is zero when the field is perpendicular to the plane of the loop ($\theta = 0$). As we see in Active Figure 22.20, the loop tends to rotate in the direction of decreasing values of θ (i.e., so that the normal to the plane of the loop rotates toward the direction of the magnetic field). A convenient vector expression for the torque is

$$\vec{\tau} = I\vec{A} \times \vec{B} \qquad [22.14]$$

where $\vec{A}$, a vector perpendicular to the plane of the loop (Active Fig. 22.20), has a magnitude equal to the area of the loop. The sense of $\vec{A}$ is determined by the right-hand rule illustrated in Figure 22.21. When the four fingers of the right hand are curled in the direction of the current in the loop, the thumb points in the direction of $\vec{A}$. The product $I\vec{A}$ is defined to be the **magnetic dipole moment** $\vec{\mu}$ (often simply called the "magnetic moment") of the loop:

$$\vec{\mu} = I\vec{A} \qquad [22.15]$$

The SI unit of magnetic dipole moment is the ampere-meter^2 ($\text{A}\cdot\text{m}^2$). Using this definition, the torque can be expressed as

$$\vec{\tau} = \vec{\mu} \times \vec{B} \qquad [22.16]$$

Although the torque was obtained for a particular orientation of $\vec{B}$ with respect to the loop, Equation 22.16 is valid for any orientation. Furthermore, although the torque expression was derived for a rectangular loop, the result is valid for a loop of any shape. Once the torque is determined, the motion of the coil can be modeled as a rigid object under a net torque, which was studied in Chapter 10.

If a coil consists of N turns of wire, each carrying the same current and each having the same area, the total magnetic moment of the coil is the product of the number of turns and the magnetic moment for one turn, $\vec{\mu} = NI\vec{A}$. Thus, the torque on an N-turn coil is N times greater than that on a one-turn coil.

A common electric motor consists of a coil of wire mounted so that it can rotate in the field of a permanent magnet. The torque on the current-carrying coil is used to rotate a shaft that drives a mechanical device such as the power windows in your car, your household fan, or your electric hedge trimmer.

FIGURE 22.21 Right-hand rule for determining the direction of the vector $\vec{A}$. The direction of the magnetic moment $\vec{\mu}$ is the same as the direction of $\vec{A}$.

∎ Magnetic moment of a current loop

∎ Torque on a current loop

EXAMPLE 22.5 The Magnetic Moment and Torque on a Coil

A rectangular coil of dimensions 5.40 cm × 8.50 cm consists of 25 turns of wire. The coil carries a current of 15.0 mA.

A Calculate the magnitude of its magnetic moment.

Solution The magnitude of the magnetic moment of a current loop is $\mu = IA$ (Eq. 22.15). In this case, $A = (0.054\,0\text{ m})(0.085\,0\text{ m}) = 4.59 \times 10^{-3}\text{ m}^2$.
Because the coil has 25 turns and assuming that each turn has the same area A, we have

$$\mu_{\text{coil}} = NIA = (25)(15.0 \times 10^{-3}\,\text{A})(4.59 \times 10^{-3}\,\text{m}^2)$$

$$= 1.72 \times 10^{-3}\,\text{A}\cdot\text{m}^2$$

B Suppose a uniform magnetic field of magnitude 0.350 T is applied parallel to the plane of the loop. What is the magnitude of the torque acting on the loop?

Solution The torque is given by Equation 22.16, $\vec{\tau} = \vec{\mu} \times \vec{B}$. In this case, $\vec{B}$ is perpendicular to $\vec{\mu}_{\text{coil}}$, so

$$\tau = \mu_{\text{coil}}B = (1.72 \times 10^{-3}\,\text{A}\cdot\text{m}^2)(0.350\,\text{T})$$

$$= 6.02 \times 10^{-4}\,\text{N}\cdot\text{m}$$

22.7 | THE BIOT–SAVART LAW

In the previous sections, we investigated the result of placing an object in an existing magnetic field. When a moving charge is placed in the field, it experiences a magnetic force. A current-carrying wire placed in the field also experiences a magnetic force; a current loop in the field experiences a torque.

Now we shift our thinking and investigate the *source* of the magnetic field. Oersted's 1819 discovery (Section 22.1) that an electric current in a wire deflects a nearby compass needle indicates that a current acts as a source of a magnetic field. From their investigations on the force between a current-carrying conductor and a magnet in the early 19th century, Jean-Baptiste Biot and Félix Savart arrived at an expression for the magnetic field at a point in space in terms of the current that produces the field. No point currents exist comparable to point charges (because we must have a complete circuit for a current to exist). Hence, we must investigate the magnetic field due to an infinitesimally small element of current that is part of a larger current distribution. Suppose the current distribution is a wire carrying a steady current I as in Figure 22.22. The **Biot–Savart law** says that the magnetic field $d\vec{B}$ at point P created by an element of infinitesimal length ds of the wire has the following properties:

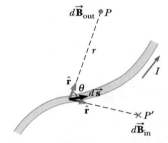

FIGURE 22.22 The magnetic field $d\vec{B}$ at a point P due to a current I through a length element $d\vec{s}$ is given by the Biot–Savart law. The field is out of the page at P and into the page at P'. (Both P and P' are in the plane of the page.)

- The vector $d\vec{B}$ is perpendicular both to $d\vec{s}$ (which is in the direction of the current) and to the unit vector $\hat{\mathbf{r}}$ directed from the element toward P.
- The magnitude of $d\vec{B}$ is inversely proportional to r^2, where r is the distance from the element to P.
- The magnitude of $d\vec{B}$ is proportional to the current I and to the length ds of the element.
- The magnitude of $d\vec{B}$ is proportional to $\sin\theta$, where θ is the angle between $d\vec{s}$ and $\hat{\mathbf{r}}$.

The **Biot–Savart law** can be summarized in the following compact form:

$$d\vec{B} = k_m \frac{I\,d\vec{s} \times \hat{\mathbf{r}}}{r^2} \qquad [22.17]$$

where k_m is a constant that in SI units is exactly $10^{-7}\,\text{T}\cdot\text{m/A}$. The constant k_m is usually written $\mu_0/4\pi$, where μ_0 is another constant, called the **permeability of free space**:

$$\frac{\mu_0}{4\pi} = k_m = 10^{-7}\,\text{T}\cdot\text{m/A} \qquad [22.18]$$

$$\mu_0 = 4\pi k_m = 4\pi \times 10^{-7}\,\text{T}\cdot\text{m/A} \qquad [22.19]$$

Hence, the Biot–Savart law, Equation 22.17, can also be written

$$d\vec{B} = \frac{\mu_0}{4\pi} \frac{I\,d\vec{s} \times \hat{\mathbf{r}}}{r^2} \qquad [22.20]$$

▦ **PITFALL PREVENTION 22.2**

THE BIOT–SAVART LAW When you are applying the Biot–Savart law, it is important to recognize that the magnetic field described in these calculations is the **field *due to* a given current-carrying conductor**. This magnetic field is not to be confused with any *external* field that may be applied to the conductor from some other source.

■ **Permeability of free space**

■ **Biot–Savart law**

It is important to note that the Biot–Savart law gives the magnetic field at a point only for a small length element of the conductor. We identify the product $I\,d\vec{s}$ as a **current element.** To find the total magnetic field $\vec{B}$ at some point due to a conductor of finite size, we must sum contributions from all current elements making up the conductor. That is, we evaluate $\vec{B}$ by integrating Equation 22.20 over the entire conductor.

There are two similarities between the Biot–Savart law of magnetism and Equation 19.7 for the electric field of a charge distribution, and there are two important differences. The current element $I\,d\mathbf{s}$ produces a magnetic field, and the charge element dq produces an electric field. Furthermore, the magnitude of the magnetic field varies as the inverse square of the distance from the current element, as does the electric field due to a charge element. The directions of the two fields are quite different, however. The electric field due to a charge element is radial; in the case of a positive point charge, $\vec{E}$ is directed away from the charge. The magnetic field due to a current element is perpendicular to both the current element and the radius vector. Hence, if the conductor lies in the plane of the page, as in Figure 22.22, $d\vec{B}$ points out of the page at the point P and into the page at P'. Another important difference is that an electric field can be a result either of a single charge or a distribution of charges, but a magnetic field can only be a result of a current distribution.

Figure 22.23 shows a convenient right-hand rule for determining the direction of the magnetic field due to a current. Note that the field lines generally encircle the current. In the case of current in a long, straight wire, the field lines form circles that are concentric with the wire and are in a plane perpendicular to the wire. If the wire is grasped in the right hand with the thumb in the direction of the current, the fingers will curl in the direction of $\vec{B}$.

Although the magnetic field due to an infinitely long, current-carrying wire can be calculated using the Biot–Savart law (Problem 22.52), in Section 22.9 we use a different method to show that the magnitude of this field at a distance r from the wire is

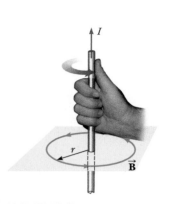

FIGURE 22.23 The right-hand rule for determining the direction of the magnetic field surrounding a long, straight wire carrying a current. Note that the magnetic field lines form circles around the wire. The magnitude of the magnetic field at a distance r from the wire is given by Equation 22.21.

▮ **Magnetic field due to a long, straight wire**

$$B = \frac{\mu_0 I}{2\pi r} \qquad [22.21]$$

QUICK QUIZ 22.4 Consider the current in the length of wire shown in Figure 22.24. Rank the points A, B, and C, in terms of magnitude of the magnetic field due to the current in the length element $d\vec{s}$ shown, from greatest to least.

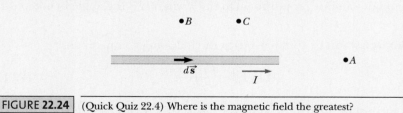

FIGURE 22.24 (Quick Quiz 22.4) Where is the magnetic field the greatest?

INTERACTIVE **EXAMPLE 22.6** **Magnetic Field on the Axis of a Circular Current Loop**

Consider a circular loop of wire of radius R located in the yz plane and carrying a steady current I as in Figure 22.25. Calculate the magnetic field at an axial point P a distance x from the center of the loop.

Solution In this situation, note that any element $d\vec{s}$ is perpendicular to $\hat{r}$. Furthermore, all elements around the loop are at the same distance r from P, where $r^2 = x^2 + R^2$. Hence, the magnitude of $d\vec{B}$ due to the element $d\vec{s}$ is

$$dB = \frac{\mu_0 I}{4\pi} \frac{|d\vec{s} \times \hat{r}|}{r^2} = \frac{\mu_0 I}{4\pi} \frac{ds}{(x^2 + R^2)} \qquad [22.22]$$

The direction of the magnetic field $d\vec{B}$ due to the element $d\vec{s}$ is perpendicular to the plane formed by $\hat{r}$ and $d\vec{s}$ as in Figure 22.25. The vector $d\vec{B}$ can be resolved into a component dB_x, along the x axis, and a component dB_y, which is perpendicular to the x axis. When the components dB_y are summed over the whole loop, the result

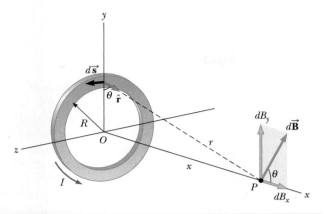

FIGURE 22.25 (Interactive Example 22.6) The geometry for calculating the magnetic field at a point P lying on the axis of a current loop. By symmetry, the total field $\vec{B}$ is along this axis.

is zero. That is, by symmetry, any element on one side of the loop sets up a component dB_y that cancels the component set up by an element diametrically opposite it.

For these reasons, the resultant field at P must be along the x axis and can be found by integrating the components $dB_x = dB \cos \theta$, where this expression is obtained from resolving the vector $d\vec{B}$ into its components as shown in Figure 22.25. That is, $\vec{B} = B_x\hat{\mathbf{i}}$, where

$$B_x = \oint dB \cos \theta = \frac{\mu_0 I}{4\pi} \oint \frac{ds \cos \theta}{x^2 + R^2}$$

and the integral must be taken over the entire loop. Because θ, x, and R are constants for all elements of the loop and because $\cos \theta = R/(x^2 + R^2)^{1/2}$, we obtain

$$B_x = \frac{\mu_0 IR}{4\pi(x^2 + R^2)^{3/2}} \oint ds = \frac{\mu_0 IR^2}{2(x^2 + R^2)^{3/2}} \quad [22.23]$$

where we have used that $\oint ds = 2\pi R$ (the circumference of the loop).

To find the magnetic field at the center of the loop, we set $x = 0$ in Equation 22.23. At this special point, we have

$$B = \frac{\mu_0 I}{2R} \qquad (\text{at } x = 0) \qquad [22.24]$$

It is also interesting to determine the behavior of the magnetic field far from the loop, that is, when x is large compared with R. In this case, we can ignore the term R^2 in the denominator of Equation 22.23 and we find that

$$B \approx \frac{\mu_0 IR^2}{2x^3} \qquad (\text{for } x \gg R) \qquad [22.25]$$

Because the magnitude of the magnetic dipole moment μ of the loop is defined as the product of the current and the area (Eq. 22.15), $\mu = I(\pi R^2)$, we can express Equation 22.25 in the form

$$B = \frac{\mu_0}{2\pi}\frac{\mu}{x^3} \qquad [22.26]$$

This result is similar in form to the expression for the electric field due to an electric dipole, $E = k_e(2qa)/y^3 = k_e p/y^3$ (Example 19.3), where p is the electric dipole moment. The pattern of the magnetic field lines for a circular loop is shown in Figure 22.26a. For clarity, the lines are drawn only for one plane that contains the axis of the loop. Note that the field-line pattern is axially symmetric and looks like the pattern around a bar magnet, shown in Figure 22.26c.

Physics⊗Now™ By logging into PhysicsNow at **www.pop4e.com** and going to Interactive Example 22.6, you can explore the field for different loop radii.

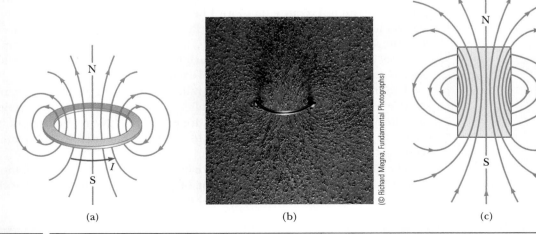

FIGURE 22.26 (Interactive Example 22.6) (a) Magnetic field lines surrounding a current loop. (b) Magnetic field lines surrounding a current loop displayed with iron filings. (c) Magnetic field lines surrounding a bar magnet. Note the similarity between this line pattern and that of a current loop.

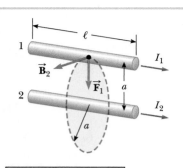

ACTIVE FIGURE 22.27

Two parallel wires that each carry a steady current exert a force on each other. The field $\vec{B}_2$ due to the current in wire 2 exerts a force of magnitude $F_1 = I_1 \ell B_2$ on wire 1. The force is attractive if the currents are parallel (as shown) and repulsive if the currents are antiparallel.

Physics⊗Now™ Log into Physics-Now at **www.pop4e.com** and go to Active Figure 22.27. You can adjust the currents in the wires and the distance between them to see the effect on the force.

▌ Magnetic force per unit length between parallel current-carrying wires

22.8 THE MAGNETIC FORCE BETWEEN TWO PARALLEL CONDUCTORS

In Section 22.5, we described the magnetic force that acts on a current-carrying conductor when the conductor is placed in an external magnetic field. Because a current in a conductor sets up its own magnetic field, it is easy to understand that two current-carrying conductors exert magnetic forces on each other. As we shall see, such forces can be used as the basis for defining the ampere and the coulomb.

Consider two infinitely long, straight, parallel wires separated by the distance a and carrying currents I_1 and I_2 in the same direction as in Active Figure 22.27. We shall adopt a simplification model in which the radii of the wires are much smaller than a so that the radius plays no role in the calculation. We can determine the force on one wire due to the magnetic field set up by the other wire. Wire 2, which carries current I_2, sets up a magnetic field $\vec{B}_2$ at the position of wire 1. The direction of $\vec{B}_2$ is perpendicular to the wire as shown in Active Figure 22.27. According to Equation 22.10, the magnetic force on a length ℓ of wire 1 is $\vec{F}_1 = I_1 \vec{\ell} \times \vec{B}_2$. Because $\vec{\ell}$ is perpendicular to $\vec{B}_2$, the magnitude of $\vec{F}_1$ is $F_1 = I_1 \ell B_2$. Because the field due to wire 2 is given by Equation 22.21, we see that

$$F_1 = I_1 \ell B_2 = I_1 \ell \left(\frac{\mu_0 I_2}{2\pi a} \right) = \frac{\ell \mu_0 I_1 I_2}{2\pi a}$$

We can rewrite this expression in terms of the force per unit length as

$$\frac{F_1}{\ell} = \frac{\mu_0 I_1 I_2}{2\pi a}$$

The direction of $\vec{F}_1$ is downward, toward wire 2, because $\vec{\ell} \times \vec{B}_2$ is downward. If one considers the field set up at wire 2 due to wire 1, the force $\vec{F}_2$ on wire 2 is found to be equal in magnitude and opposite in direction to $\vec{F}_1$. That is what one would expect because Newton's third law must be obeyed. Thus, we can drop the force subscript so that the magnetic force per unit length exerted by each long current-carrying wire on the other is

$$\frac{F}{\ell} = \frac{\mu_0 I_1 I_2}{2\pi a} \qquad [22.27]$$

This equation also applies if one of the wires is of finite length. In the discussion above, we used the equation for the magnetic field of an infinite wire carrying current I_2, but did not require that wire 1 be of infinite length.

When the currents are in opposite directions, the magnetic forces are reversed and the wires repel each other. Hence, we find that **parallel conductors carrying currents in the same direction attract each other,** whereas **parallel conductors carrying currents in opposite directions repel each other.**

The magnetic force between two parallel wires, each carrying a current, is used to define the **ampere:** If two long, parallel wires 1 m apart carry the same current and the force per unit length on each wire is 2×10^{-7} N/m, the current is defined to be 1 A. The numerical value of 2×10^{-7} N/m is obtained from Equation 22.27, with $I_1 = I_2 = 1$ A and $a = 1$ m.

The SI unit of charge, the **coulomb,** can now be defined in terms of the ampere: If a conductor carries a steady current of 1 A, the quantity of charge that flows through a cross-section of the conductor in 1 s is 1 C.

QUICK QUIZ 22.5 A loose spiral spring is hung from the ceiling and a large current is sent through it. Do the coils **(a)** move closer together, **(b)** move farther apart, or **(c)** not move at all?

22.9 │ AMPÈRE'S LAW

A simple experiment first carried out by Oersted in 1820 clearly demonstrates that a current-carrying conductor produces a magnetic field. In this experiment, several compass needles are placed in a horizontal plane near a long vertical wire as in Active Figure 22.28a. When the wire carries no current, all needles point in the same direction (that of the Earth's magnetic field), as one would expect. When the wire carries a strong, steady current, however, the needles all deflect in a direction tangent to the circle as in Active Figure 22.28b. These observations show that the direction of $\vec{B}$ is consistent with the right-hand rule described in Section 22.7. When the current is reversed, the needles in Active Figure 22.28b also reverse.

Because the needles point in the direction of $\vec{B}$, we conclude that the lines of $\vec{B}$ form circles about the wire, as discussed in Section 22.7. By symmetry, the magnitude of $\vec{B}$ is the same everywhere on a circular path that is centered on the wire and lies in a plane perpendicular to the wire. By varying the current and distance from the wire, one finds that $\vec{B}$ is proportional to the current and inversely proportional to the distance from the wire.

In Chapter 19, we investigated Gauss's law, which is a relationship between an electric charge and the electric field it produces. Gauss's law can be used to determine the electric field in highly symmetric situations. We now consider an analogous relationship in magnetism between a current and the magnetic field it produces. This relationship can be used to determine the magnetic field created by a highly symmetric current distribution.

Let us evaluate the product $\vec{B} \cdot d\vec{s}$ for a small length element $d\vec{s}$ on the circular path[1] centered on the wire in Active Figure 22.28b. Along this path, the vectors $d\vec{s}$

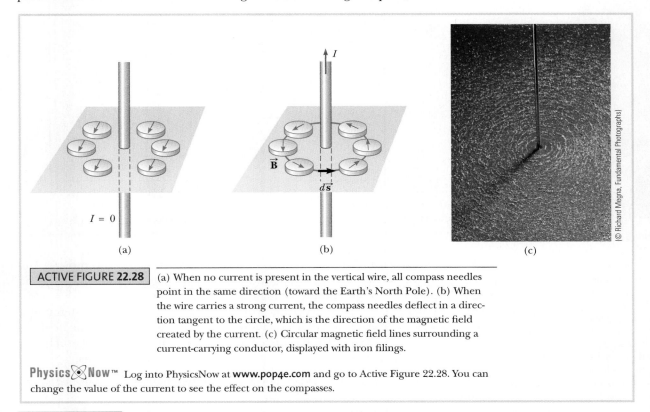

ACTIVE FIGURE 22.28 (a) When no current is present in the vertical wire, all compass needles point in the same direction (toward the Earth's North Pole). (b) When the wire carries a strong current, the compass needles deflect in a direction tangent to the circle, which is the direction of the magnetic field created by the current. (c) Circular magnetic field lines surrounding a current-carrying conductor, displayed with iron filings.

Physics⊗Now™ Log into PhysicsNow at **www.pop4e.com** and go to Active Figure 22.28. You can change the value of the current to see the effect on the compasses.

[1] You may wonder why we would choose to do this evaluation. The origin of Ampère's law is in 19th-century science, in which a "magnetic charge" (the supposed analog to an isolated electric charge) was imagined to be moved around a circular field line. The work done on the charge was related to $\vec{B} \cdot d\vec{s}$, just like the work done moving an electric charge in an electric field is related to $\vec{E} \cdot d\vec{s}$. Thus, Ampère's law, a valid and useful principle, arose from an erroneous and abandoned work calculation!

and $\vec{\mathbf{B}}$ are parallel at each point, so $\vec{\mathbf{B}} \cdot d\vec{\mathbf{s}} = B\,ds$. Furthermore, by symmetry, $\vec{\mathbf{B}}$ is constant in magnitude on this circle and is given by Equation 22.21. Therefore, the sum of the products $B\,ds$ over the closed path, which is equivalent to the line integral of $\vec{\mathbf{B}} \cdot d\vec{\mathbf{s}}$, is

$$\oint \vec{\mathbf{B}} \cdot d\vec{\mathbf{s}} = B \oint ds = \frac{\mu_0 I}{2\pi r}(2\pi r) = \mu_0 I \qquad [22.28]$$

where $\oint ds = 2\pi r$ is the circumference of the circle.

This result, known as **Ampère's law,** was calculated for the special case of a circular path surrounding a wire. It can, however, also be applied in the general case in which a steady current passes through the area surrounded by an arbitrary closed path. That is, Ampère's law says that the line integral of $\vec{\mathbf{B}} \cdot d\vec{\mathbf{s}}$ around any closed path equals $\mu_0 I$, where I is the total steady current passing through any surface bounded by the closed path:

■ Ampère's law

$$\oint \vec{\mathbf{B}} \cdot d\vec{\mathbf{s}} = \mu_0 I \qquad [22.29]$$

> **QUICK QUIZ 22.6** (a) Rank the values of $\oint \vec{\mathbf{B}} \cdot d\vec{\mathbf{s}}$ for the closed paths in Figure 22.29, from smallest to largest. (b) Rank the values of $\oint \vec{\mathbf{B}} \cdot d\vec{\mathbf{s}}$ for the closed paths in Figure 22.30, from smallest to largest.

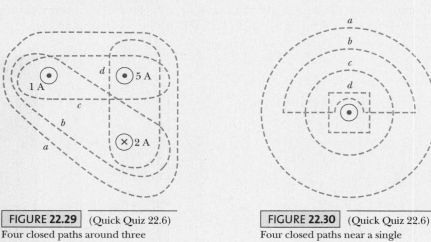

FIGURE 22.29 (Quick Quiz 22.6) Four closed paths around three current-carrying wires.

FIGURE 22.30 (Quick Quiz 22.6) Four closed paths near a single current-carrying wire.

ANDRÉ-MARIE AMPÈRE
(1775–1836)

Ampère, a Frenchman, is credited with the discovery of electromagnetism, the relationship between electric currents and magnetic fields. Ampère's genius, particularly in mathematics, became evident by the time he was 12 years old; his personal life, however, was filled with tragedy. His father, a wealthy city official, was guillotined during the French Revolution, and his wife died young, in 1803. Ampère died at the age of 61 of pneumonia. His judgment of his life is clear from the epitaph he chose for his gravestone: *Tandem Felix* (Happy at Last).

Ampère's law is valid only for steady currents. Furthermore, even though Ampère's law is *true* for all current configurations, it is only *useful* for calculating the magnetic fields of configurations with high degrees of symmetry.

In Section 19.10, we provided some conditions to be sought when defining a gaussian surface. Similarly, to apply Equation 22.29 to calculate a magnetic field, we must determine a path of integration (sometimes called an *amperian loop*) such that each portion of the path satisfies one or more of the following conditions:

1. The value of the magnetic field can be argued by symmetry to be constant over the portion of the path.
2. The dot product in Equation 22.29 can be expressed as a simple algebraic product $B\,ds$ because $\vec{\mathbf{B}}$ and $d\vec{\mathbf{s}}$ are parallel.
3. The dot product in Equation 2.29 is zero because $\vec{\mathbf{B}}$ and $d\vec{\mathbf{s}}$ are perpendicular.
4. The magnetic field can be argued to be zero at all points on the portion of the path.

The following examples illustrate some symmetric current configurations for which Ampère's law is useful.

EXAMPLE 22.7 **The Magnetic Field Created by a Long Current-Carrying Wire**

A long, straight wire of radius R carries a steady current I that is uniformly distributed through the cross-section of the wire (Fig. 22.31). Calculate the magnetic field a distance r from the center of the wire in the regions $r \geq R$ and $r < R$.

Solution As mentioned in Section 22.7, we could use the Biot–Savart law to solve this problem, but Ampère's law provides a much simpler solution. For $r \geq R$, let us choose path 1 in Figure 22.31, a circle of radius r centered on the wire. From symmetry, we see that $\overrightarrow{\mathbf{B}}$ must be constant in magnitude—condition 1—and parallel to $d\overrightarrow{\mathbf{s}}$—condition 2—at every point on this circle. Because the total current passing through the plane of the circle is I, Ampère's law applied to the circular path gives

$$\oint \overrightarrow{\mathbf{B}} \cdot d\overrightarrow{\mathbf{s}} = B \oint ds = B(2\pi r) = \mu_0 I$$

$$B = \frac{\mu_0 I}{2\pi r} \qquad \text{(for } r \geq R\text{)}$$

which is the result (Eq. 22.21) referred to in Section 22.7.

Now consider the interior of the wire, where $r < R$. We choose the circular path 2 shown in Figure 22.31.

Here the current I' passing through the plane of the circle is less than the total current I. Because the current is uniform over the cross-section of the wire, the fraction of the current enclosed by the circle of radius $r < R$ must equal the ratio of the area πr^2 enclosed by circular path 2 and the cross-sectional area πR^2 of the wire:

$$\frac{I'}{I} = \frac{\pi r^2}{\pi R^2}$$

$$I' = \frac{r^2}{R^2} I$$

Following the same procedure as for circular path 1, we apply Ampère's law to circular path 2:

$$\oint \overrightarrow{\mathbf{B}} \cdot d\overrightarrow{\mathbf{s}} = B(2\pi r) = \mu_0 I' = \mu_0 \left(\frac{r^2}{R^2} I \right)$$

$$B = \left(\frac{\mu_0 I}{2\pi R^2} \right) r \qquad \text{(for } r < R\text{)} \quad [22.30]$$

The magnitude of the magnetic field versus r for this configuration is sketched in Figure 22.32. Note that inside the wire $B \rightarrow 0$ as $r \rightarrow 0$. This result is similar in form to that of the electric field inside a uniformly charged rod.

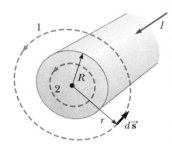

FIGURE 22.31 (Example 22.7) A long, straight wire of radius R carrying a steady current I uniformly distributed across the wire. The magnetic field at any point can be calculated from Ampère's law using a circular path of radius r, concentric with the wire.

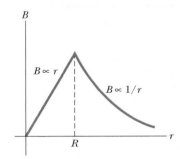

FIGURE 22.32 (Example 22.7) Magnitude of the magnetic field versus r for the wire described in Figure 22.31. The field is proportional to r inside the wire and varies as $1/r$ outside the wire.

EXAMPLE 22.8 **The Magnetic Field Created by a Toroid**

A device called a *toroid* (Fig. 22.33) is often used to create an almost uniform magnetic field in some enclosed area. The device consists of a conducting wire wrapped around a ring (a *torus*) made of a nonconduct-ing material. For a toroid having N closely spaced turns of wire and air in the torus, calculate the magnetic field in the region occupied by the torus, a distance r from the center.

Solution To calculate the field inside the toroid, we evaluate the line integral of $\vec{\mathbf{B}} \cdot d\vec{\mathbf{s}}$ over the circular amperian loop of radius r in the plane of Figure 22.33. By symmetry, we see that conditions 1 and 2 apply: the magnetic field is constant in magnitude on this circle and tangent to it, so $\vec{\mathbf{B}} \cdot d\vec{\mathbf{s}} = B\,ds$.

Furthermore, note that the closed path surrounds a circular area through which N loops of wire pass, each of which carries a current I. The right side of Equation 22.29 is therefore $\mu_0 NI$ in this case. Ampère's law

applied to the circular path gives

$$\oint \vec{\mathbf{B}} \cdot d\vec{\mathbf{s}} = B \oint ds = B(2\pi r) = \mu_0 NI$$

$$B = \frac{\mu_0 NI}{2\pi r} \qquad [22.31]$$

This result shows that B varies as $1/r$ and hence is nonuniform within the coil. If r is large compared with the cross-sectional radius a of the torus, however, the field is approximately uniform inside the coil.

For an ideal toroid in which the turns are closely spaced, the external magnetic field is close to zero. It is not exactly zero, however. In Figure 22.33, imagine the radius r of the amperian loop to be either smaller than b or larger than c. In either case, the loop encloses zero net current, so $\oint \vec{\mathbf{B}} \cdot d\vec{\mathbf{s}} = 0$. We might be tempted to claim that this expression proves that $\vec{\mathbf{B}} = 0$, but it does not. Consider the amperian loop on the right side of the toroid in Figure 22.33. The plane of this loop is perpendicular to the page and the toroid passes through the loop. As charges enter the toroid as indicated by the current directions in Figure 22.33, they work their way counterclockwise around the toroid. Thus, a current passes through the perpendicular amperian loop! This current is small, but it is not zero. As a result, the toroid acts as a current loop and produces a weak external field of the form shown in Figure 22.26a. The reason that $\oint \vec{\mathbf{B}} \cdot d\vec{\mathbf{s}} = 0$ for the amperian loops of radius $r < b$ and $r > c$ in the plane of the page is that the field lines are perpendicular to $d\vec{\mathbf{s}}$ (condition 3), *not* because $\vec{\mathbf{B}} = 0$ (condition 4).

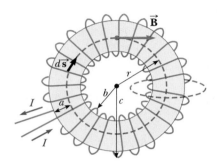

FIGURE 22.33   (Example 22.8) A toroid consisting of many turns of wire wrapped around a doughnut-shaped structure (called a torus). If the coils are closely spaced, the field in the interior of the toroid is tangent to the dashed circle and varies as $1/r$. The dimension a is the cross-sectional radius of the torus. The field outside the toroid is very small and can be described by using the amperian loop at the right side, perpendicular to the page.

22.10 THE MAGNETIC FIELD OF A SOLENOID

A solenoid is a long wire wound in the form of a helix. If the turns are closely spaced, this configuration can produce a reasonably uniform magnetic field throughout the volume enclosed by the solenoid, except close to its ends. Each of the turns can be modeled as a circular loop, and the net magnetic field is the vector sum of the fields due to all the turns.

If the turns are closely spaced and the solenoid is of finite length, the field lines are as shown in Figure 22.34a. In this case, the field lines diverge from one end and converge at the opposite end. An inspection of this field distribution exterior to the solenoid shows a similarity to the field of a bar magnet (Fig. 22.34b). Hence, one end of the solenoid behaves like the north pole of a magnet and the opposite end behaves like the south pole. As the length of the solenoid increases, the field within it becomes more and more uniform. When the solenoid's turns are closely spaced and its length is large compared with its radius, it approaches the case of an *ideal solenoid*. For an ideal solenoid, the field outside the solenoid is negligible and the field inside is uniform. We will use the ideal solenoid as a simplification model for a real solenoid.

If we consider the amperian loop perpendicular to the page in Figure 22.35, surrounding the ideal solenoid, we see that it it encloses a small current as the charges in the wire move coil by coil along the length of the solenoid. Thus, there is a

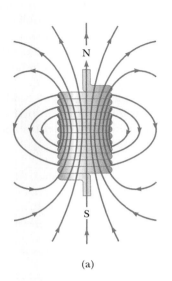

(a)

(b)

(Henry Leap and Jim Lehman)

FIGURE **22.34** (a) Magnetic field lines for a tightly wound solenoid of finite length carrying a steady current. The field in the space enclosed by the solenoid is nearly uniform and strong. Note that the field lines resemble those of a bar magnet and that the solenoid effectively has north and south poles. (b) The magnetic field pattern of a bar magnet, displayed with iron filings.

nonzero magnetic field outside the solenoid. It is a weak field, with circular field lines, like those due to a line of current as in Figure 22.23. For an ideal solenoid, it is the only field external to the solenoid. We can eliminate this field in Figure 22.35 by adding a second layer of turns of wire outside the first layer. If the first layer of turns is wrapped so that the turns progress from the bottom of Figure 22.35 to the top and the second layer has turns progressing from the top to the bottom, the net current along the axis is zero.

We can use Ampère's law to obtain an expression for the magnetic field inside an ideal solenoid. A longitudinal cross-section of part of our ideal solenoid (Fig. 22.35) carries current I. Here, $\vec{B}$ inside the ideal solenoid is uniform and parallel to the axis. Consider a rectangular path of length ℓ and width w as shown in Figure 22.35. We can apply Ampère's law to this path by evaluating the integral of $\vec{B} \cdot d\vec{s}$ over each of the four sides of the rectangle. The contribution along side 3 is zero because the magnetic field lines are perpendicular to the path in this region, which matches condition 3 in Section 22.9. The contributions from sides 2 and 4 are both zero because $\vec{B}$ is perpendicular to $d\vec{s}$ along these paths, both inside and outside the solenoid. Side 1, whose length is ℓ, gives a contribution to the integral because $\vec{B}$ along this portion of the path is constant in magnitude and parallel to $d\vec{s}$, which matches conditions 1 and 2. The integral over the closed rectangular path therefore has the value

$$\oint \vec{B} \cdot d\vec{s} = \int_{\text{side 1}} \vec{B} \cdot d\vec{s} = B \int_{\text{side 1}} ds = B\ell$$

The right side of Ampère's law involves the *total* current that passes through the surface bounded by the path of integration. In our case, the total current through the rectangular path equals the current through each turn of the solenoid multiplied by the number of turns enclosed by the path of integration. If N is the number of turns in the length ℓ, the total current through the rectangle equals NI. Ampère's law applied to this path therefore gives

$$\oint \vec{B} \cdot d\vec{s} = B\ell = \mu_0 NI$$

$$B = \mu_0 \frac{N}{\ell} I = \mu_0 nI \qquad [22.32]$$

where $n = N/\ell$ is the number of turns *per unit length* (not to be confused with N, the number of turns).

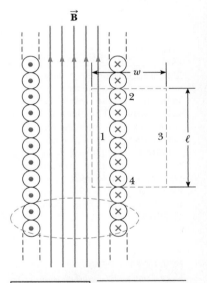

FIGURE **22.35** Cross-sectional view of an ideal solenoid, where the interior magnetic field is uniform and the exterior field is close to zero. Ampère's law applied to the circular path near the bottom whose plane is perpendicular to the page can be used to show that there is a weak field outside the solenoid. Ampère's law applied to the rectangular dashed path in the plane of the page can be used to calculate the magnitude of the interior field.

■ Magnetic field inside a long solenoid

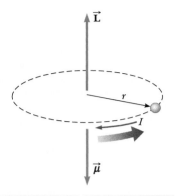

FIGURE 22.36 An electron moving in a circular orbit of radius r has an angular momentum $\vec{L}$ in one direction and a magnetic moment $\vec{\mu}$ in the opposite direction. The motion of the electron in the direction of the gray arrow results in a current in the direction shown.

▣ PITFALL PREVENTION 22.3

THE ELECTRON DOES NOT SPIN Do not be misled by the word *spin* into believing that the electron is physically spinning. The electron has an intrinsic angular momentum *as if it were spinning*, but the notion of rotation for a point particle is meaningless; remember that we described rotation of a *rigid object*, with an extent in space, in Chapter 10. Spin angular momentum is actually a relativistic effect.

TABLE 22.1

Magnetic Moments of Some Atoms and Ions

Atom or Ion	Magnet Moment per Atom or Ion (10^{-24} J/T)
H	9.27
He	0
Ne	0
Fe	2.06
Co	16.0
Ni	5.62
Gd	65.8
Dy	92.7
Co^{2+}	44.5
Ni^{2+}	29.7
Fe^{2+}	50.1
Ce^{3+}	19.8
Yb^{3+}	37.1

We also could obtain this result in a simpler manner by reconsidering the magnetic field of a toroidal coil (Example 22.8). If the radius r of the toroidal coil containing N turns is large compared with its cross-sectional radius a, a short section of the toroidal coil approximates a short section of a solenoid, with $n = N/2\pi r$. In this limit, we see that Equation 22.31 derived for the toroidal coil agrees with Equation 22.32.

Equation 22.32 is valid only for points near the center of a very long solenoid. As you might expect, the field near each end is smaller than the value given by Equation 22.32. At the very end of a long solenoid, the magnitude of the field is about one-half that of the field at the center (see Problem 22.46).

> **QUICK QUIZ 22.7** Consider a solenoid that is very long compared with the radius. Of the following choices, the most effective way to increase the magnetic field in the interior of the solenoid is to **(a)** double its length, keeping the number of turns per unit length constant, **(b)** reduce its radius by half, keeping the number of turns per unit length constant, or **(c)** overwrap the entire solenoid with an additional layer of current-carrying wire.

22.11 MAGNETISM IN MATTER

The magnetic field produced by a current in a coil of wire gives a hint about what causes certain materials to exhibit strong magnetic properties. To understand why some materials are magnetic, it is instructive to begin this discussion with the Bohr structural model of the atom, in which electrons are assumed to move in circular orbits about the much more massive nucleus. Figure 22.36 shows the angular momentum associated with the electron. In the Bohr model, each electron, with its charge of magnitude 1.6×10^{-19} C, circles the atom once in about 10^{-16} s. If we divide the electronic charge by this time interval, we find that the orbiting electron is equivalent to a current of 1.6×10^{-3} A. Each orbiting electron is therefore viewed as a tiny current loop with a corresponding magnetic moment. Because the charge of the electron is negative, the magnetic moment is directed opposite to the angular momentum as shown in Figure 22.36.

In most substances, the magnetic moment of one electron in an atom is canceled by that of another electron in the atom, orbiting in the opposite direction. The net result is that **the magnetic effect produced by the orbital motion of the electrons is either zero or very small for most materials.**

In addition to its orbital angular momentum, an electron has an **intrinsic angular momentum,** called **spin,** which also contributes to its magnetic moment. The spin of an electron is an angular momentum separate from its orbital angular momentum, just as the spin of the Earth is separate from its orbital motion about the Sun. Even if the electron is at rest, it still has an angular momentum associated with spin. We shall investigate spin more deeply in Chapter 29.

In atoms or ions containing multiple electrons, many electrons are paired up with their spins in opposite directions, an arrangement that results in a cancellation of the spin magnetic moments. An atom with an odd number of electrons, however, must have at least one "unpaired" electron and a corresponding spin magnetic moment. The net magnetic moment of the atom leads to various types of magnetic behavior. The magnetic moments of several atoms and ions are listed in Table 22.1.

Ferromagnetic Materials

Iron, cobalt, nickel, gadolinium, and dysprosium are strongly magnetic materials and are said to be **ferromagnetic.** Ferromagnetic substances, used to fabricate permanent magnets, contain atoms with spin magnetic moments that tend to align parallel to each other even in a weak external magnetic field. Once the moments are aligned, the substance remains magnetized after the external field is removed.

This permanent alignment is due to strong coupling between neighboring atoms, which can only be understood using quantum physics.

All ferromagnetic materials contain microscopic regions called **domains,** within which all magnetic moments are aligned. The domains range from about 10^{-12} to 10^{-8} m^3 in volume and contain 10^{17} to 10^{21} atoms. The boundaries between domains having different orientations are called **domain walls.** In an unmagnetized sample, the domains are randomly oriented so that the net magnetic moment is zero as in Figure 22.37a. When the sample is placed in an external magnetic field, domains with magnetic moment vectors initially oriented along the external field grow in size at the expense of other domains, which results in a magnetized sample, as in Figures 22.37b and 22.37c. When the external field is removed, the sample may retain most of its magnetism.

The extent to which a ferromagnetic substance retains its magnetism is described by its classification as being magnetically **hard** or **soft.** Soft magnetic materials, such as iron, are easily magnetized but also tend to lose their magnetism easily. When a soft magnetic material is magnetized and the external magnetic field is removed, thermal agitation produces domain motion and the material quickly returns to an unmagnetized state. In contrast, hard magnetic materials, such as cobalt and nickel, are difficult to magnetize but tend to retain their magnetism, and domain alignment persists in them after the external magnetic field is removed. Such hard magnetic materials are referred to as **permanent magnets.** Rare-earth permanent magnets, such as samarium–cobalt, are now regularly used in industry.

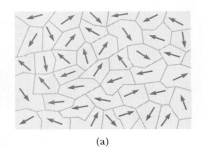

(a)

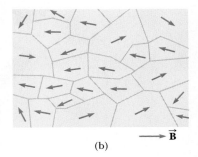

(b)

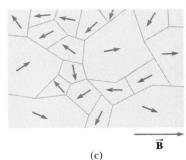

(c)

FIGURE 22.37 (a) Random orientation of atomic magnetic dipoles in the domains of an unmagnetized substance. (b) When an external field $\vec{\textbf{B}}$ is applied, the domains with components of magnetic moment in the same direction as $\vec{\textbf{B}}$ grow larger. (c) As the field is made even stronger, the domains with magnetic moment vectors not aligned with the external field become very small.

22.12 THE ATTRACTIVE MODEL FOR MAGNETIC LEVITATION

CONTEXT CONNECTION

A number of designs have been developed for magnetic levitation. In this section, we shall describe one design model called the *electromagnetic system* (EMS). This model is conceptually simple because it depends only on the attractive force between magnets and ferromagnetic materials. It has some technological complications, however. The EMS system is used in the German Transrapid design.

In an EMS system, the magnets supporting the vehicle are located below the track because the attractive force between these magnets and those in the track must lift the vehicle upward. A diagram of the German Transrapid system is shown in Figure 22.38.

The electromagnets attached to the vehicle are attracted to the steel rail, lifting the car. One disadvantage of this system is the *instability* of the vehicle caused by the variation of the magnetic force with distance. If the vehicle rises slightly, the magnet moves closer to the rail and the strength of the attractive force increases. As a result, the vehicle continues to move upward until the magnet makes contact with the rail. Conversely, if the vehicle drops slightly, the force decreases and the vehicle continues to drop. For these reasons, this system requires a proximity detector and electronic controls that adjust the magnetizing current to keep the vehicle at a constant position relative to the rail.

Figure 22.39 shows a typical method for controlling the separation between the magnets and the rails. The proximity detector is a device that uses magnetic induction (which we shall study in Chapter 23) to measure the magnet–rail separation. If the vehicle drops so that the levitation magnet moves farther from the rail, the detector causes the power supply to send more current to the magnet, pulling the vehicle back up. If the magnet rises, the decreased separation distance is detected and the power supply sends less current to the magnet so that the vehicle drops downward.

Another disadvantage of the EMS system is the relatively small separation between the levitating magnets and the track, about 10 mm. This small separation requires careful tolerance in track layout and curvature and steadfast maintenance of the track against problems with snow, ice, and temperature changes.

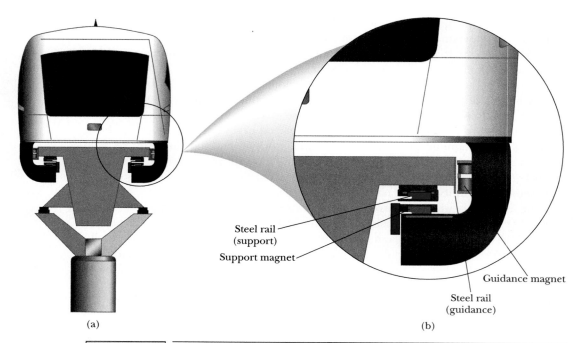

Steel rail
(support)

Support magnet

Guidance magnet

Steel rail
(guidance)

(a)   (b)

FIGURE 22.38 (a) A front view of a German Transrapid vehicle, showing it hovering above the track. (b) A close-up view of the support and guidance mechanisms. The attractive force between the support magnet and the steel rail lifts the vehicle upward. A second steel rail and the associated guidance magnet keep the vehicle laterally centered on the track. For more information, visit the Transrapid web site at www.transrapid.de/en/.

A major advantage of the EMS system is that the levitation is independent of speed so that wheels are not required; the vehicle is levitated even when stopped at a station. Wheels are still required, however, for an emergency "landing" system if a loss of power occurs.

The Transrapid system has undergone extensive testing in Germany and has achieved speeds of more than 450 km/h. As mentioned in the Context introduction,

FIGURE 22.39 The control system for maintaining a fixed separation distance between the magnets and the track. The proximity detector signals the controller if the separation distance changes. The controlled power supply changes the current in the support magnet to counteract the change in the separation distance.

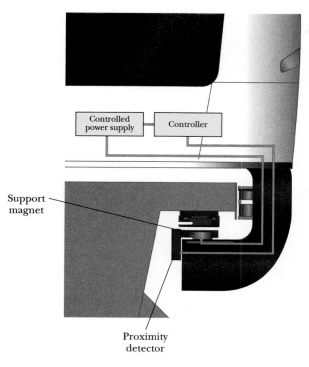

Controlled
power supply

Controller

Support
magnet

Proximity
detector

the Transrapid has entered commercial utilization in China, with a 30-km long track between Long Yang Station in Shanghai and Pudong International Airport. The station-to-station travel time is about 15 min, which is a significant reduction in time from that for a bus or a taxi. During the commissioning phase of this line, which spanned the year 2003, the vehicle achieved a speed of 501 km/h. During this phase, hundreds of thousands of visitors traveled on the line, including Chinese Premier Zhu Rongji and visiting German Chancellor Gerhard Schroeder. Scheduled commercial operations on this line began on December 29, 2003.

SUMMARY

Physics⊗Now™ Take a practice test by logging into Physics-Now at www.pop4e.com and clicking on the Pre-Test link for this chapter.

The **magnetic force** that acts on a charge q moving with velocity $\vec{v}$ in an external **magnetic field** $\vec{B}$ is

$$\vec{F}_B = q\vec{v} \times \vec{B} \qquad [22.1]$$

This force is in a direction perpendicular both to the velocity of the particle and to the magnetic field and given by the right-hand rules shown in Figure 22.4. The magnitude of the magnetic force is

$$F_B = |q|vB \sin \theta \qquad [22.2]$$

where θ is the angle between $\vec{v}$ and $\vec{B}$.

A particle with mass m and charge q moving with velocity $\vec{v}$ perpendicular to a uniform magnetic field $\vec{B}$ follows a circular path of radius

$$r = \frac{mv}{qB} \qquad [22.3]$$

If a straight conductor of length ℓ carries current I, the magnetic force on that conductor when placed in a uniform external magnetic field $\vec{B}$ is

$$\vec{F}_B = I\vec{\ell} \times \vec{B} \qquad [22.10]$$

where $\vec{\ell}$ is in the direction of the current and $|\vec{\ell}| = \ell$, the length of the conductor.

If an arbitrarily shaped wire carrying current I is placed in an external magnetic field, the magnetic force on a very small length element $d\vec{s}$ is

$$d\vec{F}_B = I\,d\vec{s} \times \vec{B} \qquad [22.11]$$

To determine the total magnetic force on the wire, one must integrate Equation 22.11 over the wire.

The **magnetic dipole moment** $\vec{\mu}$ of a loop carrying current I is

$$\vec{\mu} = I\vec{A} \qquad [22.15]$$

where $\vec{A}$ is perpendicular to the plane of the loop and $|\vec{A}|$ is equal to the area of the loop. The SI unit of $\vec{\mu}$ is the ampere-meter squared, or $A \cdot m^2$.

The torque $\vec{\tau}$ on a current loop when the loop is placed in a uniform external magnetic field $\vec{B}$ is

$$\vec{\tau} = \vec{\mu} \times \vec{B} \qquad [22.16]$$

The **Biot–Savart law** says that the magnetic field $d\vec{B}$ at a point P due to a wire element $d\vec{s}$ carrying a steady current I is

$$d\vec{B} = \frac{\mu_0}{4\pi} \frac{I\,d\vec{s} \times \hat{\mathbf{r}}}{r^2} \qquad [22.20]$$

where $\mu_0 = 4\pi \times 10^{-7}\,\text{T} \cdot \text{m/A}$ is the **permeability of free space** and r is the distance from the element to the point P. To find the total field at P due to a current distribution, one must integrate this vector expression over the entire distribution.

The magnitude of the magnetic field at a distance r from a long, straight wire carrying current I is

$$B = \frac{\mu_0 I}{2\pi r} \qquad [22.21]$$

The field lines are circles concentric with the wire.

The magnetic force per unit length between two parallel wires (at least one of which is long) separated by a distance a and carrying currents I_1 and I_2 has the magnitude

$$\frac{F}{\ell} = \frac{\mu_0 I_1 I_2}{2\pi a} \qquad [22.27]$$

The force is attractive if the currents are in the same direction and repulsive if they are in opposite directions.

Ampère's law says that the line integral of $\vec{B} \cdot d\vec{s}$ around any closed path equals $\mu_0 I$, where I is the total steady current passing through any surface bounded by the closed path:

$$\oint \vec{B} \cdot d\vec{s} = \mu_0 I \qquad [22.29]$$

Using Ampère's law, one finds that the fields inside a toroidal coil and solenoid are

$$B = \frac{\mu_0 NI}{2\pi r} \qquad \text{(toroid)} \qquad [22.31]$$

$$B = \mu_0 \frac{N}{\ell} I = \mu_0 nI \qquad \text{(solenoid)} \qquad [22.32]$$

where N is the total number of turns and n is the number of turns per unit length.

QUESTIONS

☐ = answer available in the *Student Solutions Manual and Study Guide*

1. Two charged particles are projected into a magnetic field perpendicular to their velocities. If the charges are deflected in opposite directions, what can you say about them?

2. List several similarities and differences between electric and magnetic forces.

3. The electron beam in Figure Q22.3 is projected to the right. The beam deflects downward in the presence of a magnetic field produced by a pair of current-carrying coils. (a) What is the direction of the magnetic field? (b) What would happen to the beam if the current in the coils were reversed?

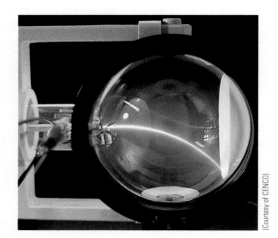

FIGURE **Q22.3** Bending of a beam of electrons in a magnetic field.

4. A current-carrying conductor experiences no magnetic force when placed in a certain manner in a uniform magnetic field. Explain.

5. Is it possible to orient a current loop in a uniform magnetic field such that the loop does not tend to rotate? Explain.

6. Explain why it is not possible to determine the charge and the mass of a charged particle separately by measuring accelerations produced by electric and magnetic forces on the particle.

7. Charged particles from outer space, called cosmic rays, strike the Earth more frequently near the poles than near the equator. Why?

8. A *bubble chamber* is a device used for observing tracks of particles that pass through the chamber, which is immersed in a magnetic field. If some of the tracks are spirals and others are straight lines, what can you say about the particles?

9. Explain why two parallel wires carrying currents in opposite directions repel each other.

10. Parallel current-carrying wires exert magnetic forces on each other. What about perpendicular wires? Imagine two such wires oriented perpendicular to each other and almost touching. Does a magnetic force exist between the wires?

11. A hollow copper tube carries a current along its length. Why is $\vec{\mathbf{B}} = 0$ inside the tube? Is $\vec{\mathbf{B}}$ nonzero outside the tube?

12. Describe the change in the magnetic field in the space enclosed by a solenoid carrying a steady current I if (a) the length of the solenoid is doubled but the number of turns remains the same and (b) the number of turns is doubled but the length remains the same.

13. A magnet attracts a piece of iron. The iron can then attract another piece of iron. On the basis of domain alignment, explain what happens in each piece of iron.

14. The "north" pole of a bar magnet is attracted toward the geographic north pole of the Earth. Yet, similar poles repel. What is the way out of this dilemma?

15. Why does hitting a magnet with a hammer cause the magnetism to be reduced?

16. Should the surface of a computer disk be made from a hard or a soft ferromagnetic substance?

17. Figure Q22.17 shows two permanent magnets, each having a hole through its center. Note that the upper magnet is levitated above the lower one. (a) How does this situation occur? (b) What purpose does the pencil serve? (c) What can you say about the poles of the magnets from this observation? (d) If the upper magnet were inverted, what do you suppose would happen?

FIGURE **Q22.17** Magnetic levitation using two ceramic magnets.

PROBLEMS

1, 2, 3 = straightforward, intermediate, challenging
☐ = full solution available in the *Student Solutions Manual and Study Guide*
Physics⊗Now™ = coached problem with hints available at www.pop4e.com
🖥 = computer useful in solving problem
▨ = paired numerical and symbolic problems
▨ = biomedical application

Section 22.2 ∎ The Magnetic Field

1. Physics⊗Now™ Determine the initial direction of the deflection of charged particles as they enter the magnetic fields as shown in Figure P22.1.

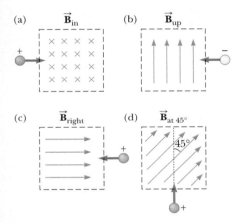

(a) $\vec{B}_{in}$ (b) $\vec{B}_{up}$

(c) $\vec{B}_{right}$ (d) $\vec{B}_{at\ 45°}$

FIGURE P22.1

2. Consider an electron near the Earth's equator. In which direction does it tend to deflect if its velocity is directed (a) downward, (b) northward, (c) westward, or (d) southeastward?

3. A proton travels with a speed of 3.00×10^6 m/s at an angle of 37.0° with the direction of a magnetic field of 0.300 T in the $+y$ direction. What are (a) the magnitude of the magnetic force on the proton and (b) its acceleration?

4. An electron is accelerated through 2 400 V from rest and then enters a uniform 1.70-T magnetic field. What are (a) the maximum and (b) the minimum values of the magnetic force this charge can experience?

5. At the equator, near the surface of the Earth, the magnetic field is approximately 50.0 μT northward and the electric field is about 100 N/C downward in fair weather. Find the gravitational, electric, and magnetic forces on an electron in this environment, assuming that the electron has an instantaneous velocity of 6.00×10^6 m/s directed to the east.

6. A proton moves with a velocity of $\vec{v} = (2\hat{i} - 4\hat{j} + \hat{k})$ m/s in a region in which the magnetic field is $\vec{B} = (\hat{i} + 2\hat{j} - 3\hat{k})$ T. What is the magnitude of the magnetic force this charge experiences?

Section 22.3 ∎ Motion of a Charged Particle in a Uniform Magnetic Field

7. **Review problem.** One electron collides elastically with a second electron initially at rest. After the collision, the radii of their trajectories are 1.00 cm and 2.40 cm. The trajectories are perpendicular to a uniform magnetic field of magnitude 0.044 0 T. Determine the energy (in keV) of the incident electron.

8. **Review problem.** An electron moves in a circular path perpendicular to a constant magnetic field of magnitude 1.00 mT. The angular momentum of the electron about the center of the circle is 4.00×10^{-25} J·s. Determine (a) the radius of the circular path and (b) the speed of the electron.

9. A cosmic-ray proton in interstellar space has an energy of 10.0 MeV and executes a circular orbit having a radius equal to that of Mercury's orbit around the Sun (5.80×10^{10} m). What is the magnetic field in that region of space?

Section 22.4 ∎ Applications Involving Charged Particles Moving in a Magnetic Field

10. A velocity selector consists of electric and magnetic fields described by the expressions $\vec{E} = E\hat{k}$ and $\vec{B} = B\hat{j}$, with $B = 15.0$ mT. Find the value of E such that a 750-eV electron moving along the positive x axis is undeflected.

11. Consider the mass spectrometer shown schematically in Active Figure 22.12. The magnitude of the electric field between the plates of the velocity selector is 2 500 V/m, and the magnetic field in both the velocity selector and the deflection chamber has a magnitude of 0.035 0 T. Calculate the radius of the path for a singly charged ion having a mass $m = 2.18 \times 10^{-26}$ kg.

12. A cyclotron designed to accelerate protons has an outer radius of 0.350 m. The protons are emitted nearly at rest from a source at the center and are accelerated through 600 V each time they cross the gap between the dees. The dees are between the poles of an electromagnet where the field is 0.800 T. (a) Find the cyclotron frequency. (b) Find the speed at which protons exit the cyclotron and (c) their maximum kinetic energy. (d) How many revolutions does a proton make in the cyclotron? (e) For what time interval does one proton accelerate?

13. The picture tube in a television uses magnetic deflection coils rather than electric deflection plates. Suppose an electron beam is accelerated through a 50.0-kV potential difference and then moves through a region of uniform magnetic field 1.00 cm wide. The screen is located 10.0 cm from the center of the coils and is 50.0 cm wide. When the field is turned off, the electron beam hits the center of the screen. What field magnitude is necessary to deflect the beam to the side of the screen? Ignore relativistic corrections.

14. The *Hall effect* finds important application in the electronics industry. It is used to find the sign and density of the carriers of electric current in semiconductor chips. The arrangement is shown in Figure P22.14. A semiconducting

block of thickness t and width d carries a current I in the x direction. A uniform magnetic field B is applied in the y direction. If the charge carriers are positive, the magnetic force deflects them in the z direction. Positive charge accumulates on the top surface of the sample and negative charge on the bottom surface, creating a downward electric field. In equilibrium, the downward electric force on the charge carriers balances the upward magnetic force and the carriers move through the sample without deflection. The *Hall voltage* $\Delta V_H = V_c - V_a$ between the top and bottom surfaces is measured, and the density of the charge carriers can be calculated from it. (a) Demonstrate that if the charge carriers are negative the Hall voltage will be negative. Hence, the Hall effect reveals the sign of the charge carriers, so the sample can be classified as p-type (with positive majority charge carriers) or n-type (with negative). (b) Determine the number of charge carriers per unit volume n in terms of I, t, B, ΔV_H, and the magnitude q of the charge carrier.

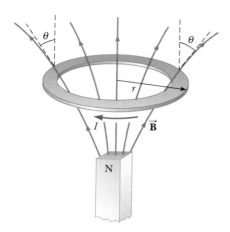

FIGURE **P22.17**

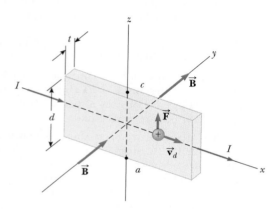

FIGURE **P22.14**

direction shown. A uniform magnetic field of magnitude $B = 0.020\ 0$ T is in the positive y direction. Determine the magnitude and direction of the magnetic force on each segment.

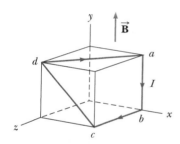

FIGURE **P22.18**

Section 22.5 ■ Magnetic Force on a Current-Carrying Conductor

15. A wire carries a steady current of 2.40 A. A straight section of the wire is 0.750 m long and lies along the x axis within a uniform magnetic field, $\vec{\mathbf{B}} = 1.60\hat{\mathbf{k}}$ T. If the current is in the $+x$ direction, what is the magnetic force on the section of wire?

16. A wire 2.80 m in length carries a current of 5.00 A in a region where a uniform magnetic field has a magnitude of 0.390 T. Calculate the magnitude of the magnetic force on the wire assuming that the angle between the magnetic field and the current is (a) 60.0°, (b) 90.0°, and (c) 120°.

17. Physics⊗Now™ *A nonuniform magnetic field exerts a net force on a magnetic dipole.* A strong magnet is placed under a horizontal conducting ring of radius r that carries current I as shown in Figure P22.17. If the magnetic field $\vec{\mathbf{B}}$ makes an angle θ with the vertical at the ring's location, what are the magnitude and direction of the resultant force on the ring?

18. In Figure P22.18, the cube is 40.0 cm on each edge. Four straight segments of wire — ab, bc, cd, and da — form a closed loop that carries a current $I = 5.00$ A, in the

Section 22.6 ■ Torque on a Current Loop in a Uniform Magnetic Field

19. A current of 17.0 mA is maintained in a single circular loop of 2.00 m circumference. A magnetic field of 0.800 T is directed parallel to the plane of the loop. (a) Calculate the magnetic moment of the loop. (b) What is the magnitude of the torque exerted by the magnetic field on the loop?

20. A current loop with magnetic dipole moment $\vec{\boldsymbol{\mu}}$ is placed in a uniform magnetic field $\vec{\mathbf{B}}$, with its moment making angle θ with the field. With the arbitrary choice of $U = 0$ for $\theta = 90°$, prove that the potential energy of the dipole-field system is $U = -\vec{\boldsymbol{\mu}} \cdot \vec{\mathbf{B}}$.

21. Physics⊗Now™ A rectangular coil consists of $N = 100$ closely wrapped turns and has dimensions $a = 0.400$ m and $b = 0.300$ m. The coil is hinged along the y axis, and its plane makes an angle $\theta = 30.0°$ with the x axis (Fig. P22.21). What is the magnitude of the torque exerted on the coil by a uniform magnetic field $B = 0.800$ T directed along the x axis when the current is $I = 1.20$ A in the direction shown? What is the expected direction of rotation of the coil?

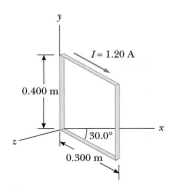

FIGURE P22.21

22. The rotor in a certain electric motor is a flat, rectangular coil with 80 turns of wire and dimensions 2.50 cm by 4.00 cm. The rotor rotates in a uniform magnetic field of 0.800 T. When the plane of the rotor is perpendicular to the direction of the magnetic field, it carries a current of 10.0 mA. In this orientation, the magnetic moment of the rotor is directed opposite the magnetic field. The rotor then turns through one-half revolution. This process is repeated to cause the rotor to turn steadily at 3 600 rev/min. (a) Find the maximum torque acting on the rotor. (b) Find the peak power output of the motor. (c) Determine the amount of work performed by the magnetic field on the rotor in every full revolution. (d) What is the average power of the motor?

Section 22.7 ■ The Biot–Savart Law

23. In Niels Bohr's 1913 model of the hydrogen atom, an electron circles the proton at a distance of 5.29×10^{-11} m with a speed of 2.19×10^6 m/s. Compute the magnitude of the magnetic field that this motion produces at the location of the proton.

24. A lightning bolt may carry a current of 1.00×10^4 A for a short time interval. What is the resulting magnetic field 100 m from the bolt? Assume that the bolt extends far above and below the point of observation.

25. Physics⊗Now™ Determine the magnetic field at a point P located a distance x from the corner of an infinitely long wire bent at a right angle as shown in Figure P22.25. The wire carries a steady current I.

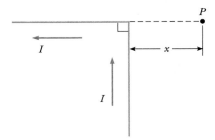

FIGURE P22.25

26. Calculate the magnitude of the magnetic field at a point 100 cm from a long, thin conductor carrying a current of 1.00 A.

27. A conductor consists of a circular loop of radius R and two straight, long sections as shown in Figure P22.27. The wire lies in the plane of the paper and carries a current I. Find an expression for the vector magnetic field at the center of the loop.

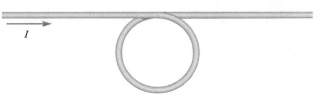

FIGURE P22.27

28. ⌨ Consider a flat, circular current loop of radius R carrying current I. Choose the x axis to be along the axis of the loop, with the origin at the center of the loop. Plot a graph of the ratio of the magnitude of the magnetic field at coordinate x to that at the origin, for $x = 0$ to $x = 5R$. It may be useful to use a programmable calculator or a computer to solve this problem.

29. Two very long, straight, parallel wires carry currents that are directed perpendicular to the page as shown in Figure P22.29. Wire 1 carries a current I_1 into the page (in the $-z$ direction) and passes through the x axis at $x = +a$. Wire 2 passes through the x axis at $x = -2a$ and carries an unknown current I_2. The total magnetic field at the origin due to the current-carrying wires has the magnitude $2\mu_0 I_1/(2\pi a)$. The current I_2 can have either of two possible values. (a) Find the value of I_2 with the smaller magnitude, stating it in terms of I_1 and giving its direction. (b) Find the other possible value of I_2.

FIGURE P22.29

30. One very long wire carries current 30.0 A to the left along the x axis. A second very long wire carries current 50.0 A to the right along the line ($y = 0.280$ m, $z = 0$). (a) Where in the plane of the two wires is the total magnetic field equal to zero? (b) A particle with a charge of -2.00 μC is moving with a velocity of $150\hat{\mathbf{i}}$ Mm/s along the line ($y = 0.100$ m, $z = 0$). Calculate the vector magnetic force acting on the particle. (c) A uniform electric field is applied to allow this particle to pass through this region undeflected. Calculate the required vector electric field.

31. A current path shaped as shown in Figure P22.31 produces a magnetic field at P, the center of the arc. If the arc subtends an angle of 30.0° and the radius of the arc is 0.600 m, what are the magnitude and direction of the field produced at P if the current is 3.00 A?

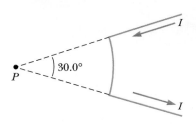

FIGURE P22.31

32. Three long, parallel conductors carry currents of I = 2.00 A. Figure P22.32 is an end view of the conductors, with each current coming out of the page. Taking a = 1.00 cm, determine the magnitude and direction of the magnetic field at points A, B, and C.

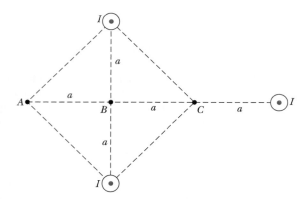

FIGURE P22.32

33.  In studies of the possibility of migrating birds using the Earth's magnetic field for navigation, birds have been fitted with coils as "caps" and "collars" as shown in Figure P22.33. (a) If the identical coils have radii of 1.20 cm and are 2.20 cm apart, with 50 turns of wire apiece, what current should they both carry to produce a magnetic field of 4.50×10^{-5} T halfway between them? (b) If the resistance of each coil is 210 Ω, what voltage should the battery supplying each coil have? (c) What power is delivered to each coil?

FIGURE P22.33

Section 22.8 ∎ The Magnetic Force Between Two Parallel Conductors

34. Two long, parallel conductors, separated by 10.0 cm, carry currents in the same direction. The first wire carries current I_1 = 5.00 A and the second carries I_2 = 8.00 A. (a) What is the magnitude of the magnetic field created by I_1 at the location of I_2? (b) What is the force per unit length exerted by I_1 on I_2? (c) What is the magnitude of the magnetic field created by I_2 at the location of I_1? (d) What is the force per length exerted by I_2 on I_1?

35. In Figure P22.35, the current in the long, straight wire is I_1 = 5.00 A and the wire lies in the plane of the rectangular loop, which carries the current I_2 = 10.0 A. The dimensions are c = 0.100 m, a = 0.150 m, and ℓ = 0.450 m. Find the magnitude and direction of the net force exerted on the loop by the magnetic field created by the wire.

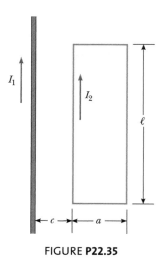

FIGURE P22.35

36. Three long wires (wire 1, wire 2, and wire 3) hang vertically. The distance between wire 1 and wire 2 is 20.0 cm. On the left, wire 1 carries an upward current of 1.50 A. To the right, wire 2 carries a downward current of 4.00 A. Wire 3 is located such that when it carries a certain current, each wire experiences no net force. Find (a) the position of wire 3 and (b) the magnitude and direction of the current in wire 3.

Section 22.9 ∎ Ampère's Law

37. Four long, parallel conductors carry equal currents of I = 5.00 A. Figure P22.37 is an end view of the conductors. The current direction is into the page at points A and B (indicated by the crosses) and out of the page at C and D (indicated by the dots). Calculate the magnitude and direction of the magnetic field at point P, located at the center of the square of edge length 0.200 m.

38. A long, straight wire lies on a horizontal table and carries a current of 1.20 μA. In a vacuum, a proton moves parallel to the wire (opposite the current) with a constant speed of 2.30×10^4 m/s at a distance d above the wire. Determine the value of d. You may ignore the magnetic field due to the Earth.

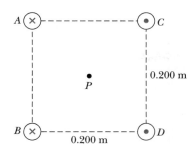

FIGURE P22.37

39. PhysicsⓍNow™ A packed bundle of 100 long, straight, insulated wires forms a cylinder of radius $R = 0.500$ cm. (a) If each wire carries 2.00 A, what are the magnitude and direction of the magnetic force per unit length acting on a wire located 0.200 cm from the center of the bundle? (b) Would a wire on the outer edge of the bundle experience a force greater or smaller than the value calculated in part (a)?

40. The magnetic field 40.0 cm away from a long, straight wire carrying current 2.00 A is 1.00 μT. (a) At what distance is it 0.100 μT? (b) At one instant, the two conductors in a long household extension cord carry equal 2.00-A currents in opposite directions. The two wires are 3.00 mm apart. Find the magnetic field 40.0 cm away from the middle of the straight cord, in the plane of the two wires. (c) At what distance is it one-tenth as large? (d) The center wire in a coaxial cable carries current 2.00 A in one direction and the sheath around it carries current 2.00 A in the opposite direction. What magnetic field does the cable create at points outside?

41. The magnetic coils of a tokamak fusion reactor are in the shape of a toroid having an inner radius of 0.700 m and an outer radius of 1.30 m. The toroid has 900 turns of large-diameter wire, each of which carries a current of 14.0 kA. Find the magnitude of the magnetic field inside the toroid along (a) the inner radius and (b) the outer radius.

42. Consider a column of electric current in a plasma (ionized gas). Filaments of current within the column are magnetically attracted to one another. They can crowd together to yield a very great current density and a very strong magnetic field in a small region. Sometimes the current can be cut off momentarily by this *pinch effect*. (In a metallic wire, a pinch effect is not important because the current-carrying electrons repel one another with electric forces.) The pinch effect can be demonstrated by making an empty aluminum can carry a large current parallel to its axis. Let R represent the radius of the can and I the upward current, uniformly distributed over its curved wall. Determine the magnetic field (a) just inside the wall and (b) just outside. (c) Determine the pressure on the wall.

43. Niobium metal becomes a superconductor when cooled below 9 K. Its superconductivity is destroyed when the surface magnetic field exceeds 0.100 T. Determine the maximum current a 2.00-mm-diameter niobium wire can carry and remain superconducting, in the absence of any external magnetic field.

Section 22.10 ■ The Magnetic Field of a Solenoid

44. A single-turn square loop of wire, 2.00 cm on each edge, carries a clockwise current of 0.200 A. The loop is inside a solenoid, with the plane of the loop perpendicular to the magnetic field of the solenoid. The solenoid has 30 turns/cm and carries a clockwise current of 15.0 A. Find the force on each side of the loop and the torque acting on the loop.

45. What current is required in the windings of a long solenoid that has 1 000 turns uniformly distributed over a length of 0.400 m to produce at the center of the solenoid a magnetic field of magnitude 1.00×10^{-4} T?

46. Consider a solenoid of length ℓ and radius R, containing N closely spaced turns and carrying a steady current I. (a) In terms of these parameters, find the magnetic field at a point along the axis as a function of distance a from the end of the solenoid. (b) Show that as ℓ becomes very long, B approaches $\mu_0 NI/2\ell$ at each end of the solenoid.

47. A solenoid 10.0 cm in diameter and 75.0 cm long is made from copper wire of diameter 0.100 cm, with very thin insulation. The wire is wound onto a cardboard tube in a single layer, with adjacent turns touching each other. To produce a field of 8.00 mT at the center of the solenoid, what power must be delivered to the solenoid?

Section 22.11 ■ Magnetism in Matter

48. In Bohr's 1913 model of the hydrogen atom, the electron is in a circular orbit of radius 5.29×10^{-11} m and its speed is 2.19×10^6 m/s. (a) What is the magnitude of the magnetic moment due to the electron's motion? (b) If the electron moves in a horizontal circle, counterclockwise as seen from above, what is the direction of this magnetic moment vector?

49. The magnetic moment of the Earth is approximately 8.00×10^{22} A·m². (a) If it were caused by the complete magnetization of a huge iron deposit, how many unpaired electrons would participate? (b) At two unpaired electrons per iron atom, how many kilograms of iron would that correspond to? (Iron has a density of 7 900 kg/m³ and approximately 8.50×10^{28} iron atoms/m³.)

Section 22.12 ■ Context Connection—The Attractive Model for Magnetic Levitation

50. The following represents a crude model for levitating a commercial transportation vehicle. Suppose the levitation is achieved by mounting small electrically charged spheres below the vehicle. The spheres pass through a magnetic field established by permanent magnets placed along the track. Let us assume that the permanent magnets produce a uniform magnetic field of 0.1 T at the location of the spheres and that an electronic control system maintains a charge of 1 μC on each sphere. The vehicle has a mass of 5×10^4 kg and travels at a speed of 400 km/h. How many charged spheres are required to support the weight of the vehicle at this speed? Your answer should suggest that this design would not be practical as a means of magnetic levitation.

51. Data for the Transrapid maglev system show that the input electric power required to operate the vehicle is on the order of 10^2 kW. (a) Assume that the Transrapid vehicle moves at 400 km/h. Approximately how much energy, in joules, is used for each mile of travel for the vehicle? (b) Calculate the energy per mile used by an automobile that achieves 20 mi/gal. The energy available from gasoline is approximately 40 MJ/kg, a typical automobile engine efficiency is 20%, and the density of gasoline is 754 kg/m^3. (c) Considering 1 passenger in the automobile and 100 on the Transrapid vehicle, the energy per mile necessary for each passenger in the Transrapid is what fraction of that for an automobile?

Additional Problems

52. Consider a thin, straight wire segment carrying a constant current I and placed along the x axis as shown in Figure P22.52. (a) Use the Biot–Savart law to show that the total magnetic field at the point P, located a distance a from the wire, is

$$B = \frac{\mu_0 I}{4\pi a} (\cos \theta_1 - \cos \theta_2)$$

(b) Assuming that the wire is infinitely long, show that the result in part (a) gives a magnetic field that agrees with that obtained by using Ampère's law in Example 22.7.

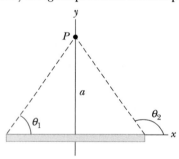

FIGURE P22.52

53. An infinite sheet of current lying in the yz plane carries a surface current of density $\vec{\mathbf{J}}_s$. The current is in the y direction, and J_s represents the current per unit length measured along the z axis. Figure P22.53 is an edge view of the sheet. Find the magnetic field near the sheet. (*Suggestion:* Use Ampère's law and evaluate the line integral for a rectangular path around the sheet, represented by the dashed line in Fig. P22.53.)

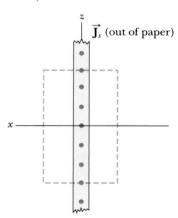

FIGURE P22.53

54. Assume that the region to the right of a certain vertical plane contains a vertical magnetic field of magnitude 1.00 mT and that the field is zero in the region to the left of the plane. An electron, originally traveling perpendicular to the boundary plane, passes into the region of the field. (a) Determine the time interval required for the electron to leave the "field-filled" region, noting that its path is a semicircle. (b) Find the kinetic energy of the electron assuming that the maximum depth of penetration into the field is 2.00 cm.

55. ▨ Heart–lung machines and artificial kidney machines employ blood pumps. A mechanical pump can mangle blood cells. Figure P22.55 represents an electromagnetic pump. The blood is confined to an electrically insulating tube, cylindrical in practice but represented as a rectangle of width w and height h. The simplicity of design makes the pump dependable. The blood is easily kept uncontaminated; the tube is simple to clean or cheap to replace. Two electrodes fit into the top and bottom of the tube. The potential difference between them establishes an electric current through the blood, with current density J over a section of length L. A perpendicular magnetic field exists in the same region. (a) Explain why this arrangement produces on the liquid a force that is directed along the length of the pipe. (b) Show that the section of liquid in the magnetic field experiences a pressure increase JLB. (c) After the blood leaves the pump, is it charged? Is it current-carrying? Is it magnetized? The same magnetic pump can be used for any fluid that conducts electricity, such as liquid sodium in a nuclear reactor.

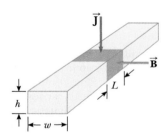

FIGURE P22.55

56. A 0.200-kg metal rod carrying a current of 10.0 A glides on two horizontal rails 0.500 m apart. What vertical magnetic field is required to keep the rod moving at a constant speed if the coefficient of kinetic friction between the rod and rails is 0.100?

57. A positive charge $q = 3.20 \times 10^{-19}$ C moves with a velocity $\vec{\mathbf{v}} = (2\hat{\mathbf{i}} + 3\hat{\mathbf{j}} - \hat{\mathbf{k}})$ m/s through a region where both a uniform magnetic field and a uniform electric field exist. (a) Calculate the total force on the moving charge (in unit-vector notation), taking $\vec{\mathbf{B}} = (2\hat{\mathbf{i}} + 4\hat{\mathbf{j}} + \hat{\mathbf{k}})$ T and $\vec{\mathbf{E}} = (4\hat{\mathbf{i}} - \hat{\mathbf{j}} - 2\hat{\mathbf{k}})$ V/m. (b) What angle does the force vector make with the positive x axis?

58. Protons having a kinetic energy of 5.00 MeV are moving in the positive x direction and enter a magnetic field $\vec{\mathbf{B}} = 0.050\,0\hat{\mathbf{k}}$ T directed out of the plane of the page and extending from $x = 0$ to $x = 1.00$ m as shown in Figure P22.58. (a) Calculate the y component of the protons'

momentum as they leave the magnetic field. (b) Find the angle α between the initial velocity vector of the proton beam and the velocity vector after the beam emerges from the field. Ignore relativistic effects and note that $1\ eV = 1.60 \times 10^{-19}\ J$.

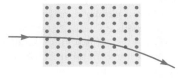

FIGURE P22.58

59. A handheld electric mixer contains an electric motor. Model the motor as a single flat, compact, circular coil carrying electric current in a region where a magnetic field is produced by an external permanent magnet. You need consider only one instant in the operation of the motor. (We will consider motors again in Chapter 23.) The coil moves because the magnetic field exerts torque on the coil as described in Section 22.6. Make order-of-magnitude estimates of the magnetic field, the torque on the coil, the current in it, its area, and the number of turns in the coil, so that they are related according to Equation 22.16. Note that the input power to the motor is electric, given by $\mathcal{P} = I\Delta V$, and the useful output power is mechanical, $\mathcal{P} = \tau\omega$.

60. A cyclotron is sometimes used for carbon dating as will be described in Chapter 30. Carbon-14 and carbon-12 ions are obtained from a sample of the material to be dated and are accelerated in the cyclotron. If the cyclotron has a magnetic field of magnitude 2.40 T, what is the difference in cyclotron frequencies for the two ions?

61. A uniform magnetic field of magnitude 0.150 T is directed along the positive x axis. A positron moving at $5.00 \times 10^6\ m/s$ enters the field along a direction that makes an angle of 85.0° with the x axis (Fig. P22.61). The motion of the particle is expected to be a helix as described in Section 22.3. Calculate (a) the pitch p and (b) the radius r of the trajectory.

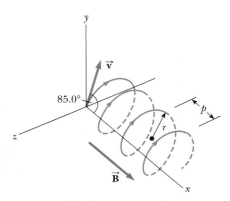

FIGURE P22.61

62. A heart surgeon monitors the flow rate of blood through an artery using an electromagnetic flowmeter (Fig. P22.62). Electrodes A and B make contact with the outer surface of the blood vessel, which has interior

diameter 3.00 mm. (a) For a magnetic field magnitude of 0.040 0 T, an emf of 160 μV appears between the electrodes. Calculate the speed of the blood. (b) Verify that electrode A is positive as shown. Does the sign of the emf depend on whether the mobile ions in the blood are predominantly positively or negatively charged? Explain.

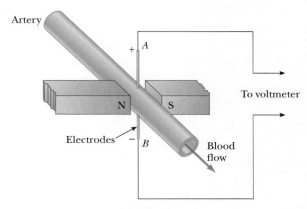

FIGURE P22.62

63. A very long, thin strip of metal of width w carries a current I along its length as shown in Figure P22.63. Find the magnetic field at the point P in the diagram. The point P is in the plane of the strip at distance b away from it.

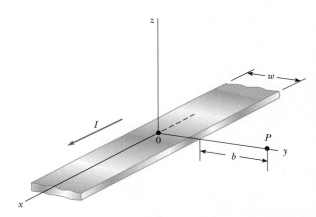

FIGURE P22.63

64. The magnitude of the Earth's magnetic field at either pole is approximately 7.00×10^{-5} T. Suppose the field fades away, before its next reversal. Scouts, sailors, and conservative politicians around the world join together in a program to replace the field. One plan is to use a current loop around the equator, without relying on magnetization of any materials inside the Earth. Determine the current that would generate such a field if this plan were carried out. (Take the radius of the Earth as $R_E = 6.37 \times 10^6$ m.)

65. A nonconducting ring of radius R is uniformly charged with a total positive charge q. The ring rotates at a constant angular speed ω about an axis through its center, perpendicular to the plane of the ring. What is the magnitude of the magnetic field on the axis of the ring a distance $R/2$ from its center?

66. Two circular coils of radius R, each with N turns, are perpendicular to a common axis. The coil centers are a distance R apart. Each coil carries a steady current I in the same direction as shown in Figure P22.66. (a) Show that the magnetic field on the axis at a distance x from the center of one coil is

$$B = \frac{N\mu_0 I R^2}{2}\left[\frac{1}{(R^2 + x^2)^{3/2}} + \frac{1}{(2R^2 + x^2 - 2Rx)^{3/2}}\right]$$

(b) Show that dB/dx and d^2B/dx^2 are both zero at the point midway between the coils. Thus, the magnetic field in the region midway between the coils is uniform. Coils in this configuration are called *Helmholtz coils*.

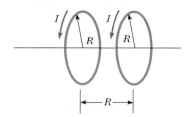

FIGURE **P22.66**

67. Two circular loops are parallel, coaxial, and almost in contact, 1.00 mm apart (Fig. P22.67). Each loop is 10.0 cm in radius. The top loop carries a clockwise current of 140 A. The bottom loop carries a counterclockwise current of 140 A. (a) Calculate the magnetic force exerted by the bottom loop on the top loop. (b) The upper loop has a mass of 0.021 0 kg. Calculate its acceleration, assuming that the only forces acting on it are the force in part (a) and the gravitational force. (*Suggestion:* Think about how one loop looks to a bug perched on the other loop.)

68. *Rail guns* have been suggested for launching projectiles into space without chemical rockets and for ground-to-air antimissile weapons of war. A tabletop model rail gun (Fig. P22.68) consists of two long, parallel, horizontal rails 3.50 cm apart, bridged by a bar BD of mass 3.00 g. The bar is originally at rest at the midpoint of the rails and is free to slide without friction. When the switch is closed, electric current is quickly established in the circuit $ABCDEA$. The rails and bar have low electric resistance, and the current is limited to a constant 24.0 A by the power supply. (a) Find the magnitude of the magnetic field 1.75 cm from a single very long, straight wire carrying current 24.0 A. (b) Find the magnitude and direction of the magnetic field at point C in the diagram, the midpoint of the bar, immediately after the switch is closed. (*Suggestion:* Consider what conclusions you can draw from the Biot–Savart law.) (c) At other points along the bar BD, the field is in the same direction as at point C but is larger in magnitude. Assume that the average effective magnetic field along BD is five times larger than the field at C. With this assumption, find the magnitude and direction of the force on the bar. (d) Find the acceleration of the bar when it is in motion. (e) Does the bar move with constant acceleration? (f) Find the velocity of the bar after it has traveled 130 cm to the end of the rails.

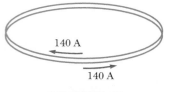

FIGURE **P22.67**

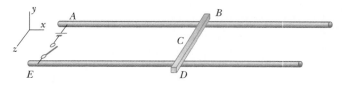

FIGURE **P22.68**

ANSWERS TO QUICK QUIZZES

22.1 (e). The right-hand rule gives the direction. Be sure to account for the negative charge on the electron.

22.2 (i), (a). The magnetic force on the particle increases in proportion to B. The result is a smaller radius, as we can see from Equation 22.3. (ii), (b). The magnetic force on the particle increases in proportion to v, but the centripetal acceleration increases according to the square of v. The result is a larger radius, as we can see from Equation 22.3.

22.3 (c). The right-hand rule is used to determine the direction of the magnetic field.

22.4 B, C, A. Point B is closest to the current element. Point C is farther away, and the field is further reduced by the $\sin\theta$ factor in the cross product $d\vec{s} \times \hat{r}$. The field at A is zero because $\theta = 0$.

22.5 (a). The coils act like wires carrying parallel currents and hence attract one another.

22.6 (a) b, d, a, c. Equation 22.29 indicates that the value of the line integral depends only on the net current through each closed path. Path b encloses 1 A, path d encloses 3 A, path a encloses 4 A, and path c encloses 6 A. (b) b, then $a = c = d$. Paths a, c, and d all give the same nonzero value $\mu_0 I$ because the size and shape of the paths do not matter. Path b does not enclose the current, and hence its line integral is zero.

22.7 (c). The magnetic field in a very long solenoid is independent of its length or radius. Overwrapping with an additional layer of wire increases the number of turns per unit length.

CHAPTER 23

Faraday's Law and Inductance

In a commercial electric power plant, large generators transform energy that is transferred out of the plant by electrical transmission. These generators use *magnetic induction* to generate a potential difference when coils of wire in the generator are rotated in a magnetic field. The source of energy to rotate the coils might be falling water, burning fossil fuels, or a nuclear reaction.

(Michael Melford/Getty Images)

Our studies in electromagnetism so far have been concerned with the electric fields due to stationary charges and the magnetic fields produced by moving charges. This chapter introduces a new type of electric field, one that is due to a changing magnetic field.

As we learned in Section 19.1, experiments conducted by Michael Faraday in England in the early 1800s and independently by Joseph Henry in the United States showed that an electric current can be induced in a circuit by a changing magnetic field. The results of those experiments led to a very basic and important law of electromagnetism known as *Faraday's law of induction*. Faraday's law explains how generators, as well as other practical devices, work.

23.1 | FARADAY'S LAW OF INDUCTION

We begin discussing the concepts in this chapter by considering a simple experiment that builds on material presented in Chapter 22. Imagine that a straight metal wire resides in a uni-

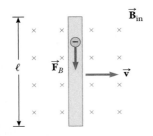

FIGURE 23.1 A straight electrical conductor of length ℓ moving with a velocity $\vec{v}$ through a uniform magnetic field $\vec{B}$ directed perpendicular to $\vec{v}$. A current is induced in the conductor due to the magnetic force on charged particles in the conductor.

form magnetic field directed into the page as in Figure 23.1. Within the wire, there are free electrons. Suppose the wire is now moved with a velocity $\vec{v}$ toward the right. Equation 22.1 tells us that a magnetic force acts on the electrons in the wire. Using the right-hand rule, the force on the electrons is downward in Figure 23.1 (remember that the electrons carry a negative charge). Because this direction is along the wire, the electrons move along the wire in response to this force. Thus, a *current* is produced in the wire as it moves through a magnetic field!

Let us consider another simple experiment that demonstrates that an electric current can be produced by a magnetic field. Consider a loop of wire connected to a sensitive ammeter, a device that measures current, as illustrated in Active Figure 23.2. If a magnet is moved toward the loop, the ammeter needle deflects in one direction as in Active Figure 23.2a. When the magnet is held stationary as in Active Figure 23.2b, the needle is not deflected. If the magnet is moved away from the loop as in Active Figure 23.2c, the ammeter needle deflects in the opposite direction from that caused by the motion of the magnet toward the ammeter. Finally, if the magnet is held stationary and the coil is moved either toward or away from it, the needle deflects. From these observations comes the conclusion that **an electric current is set up in the coil as long as relative motion occurs between the magnet and the coil.**

These results are quite remarkable when we consider that a current exists in a wire even though no batteries are connected to the wire. We call such a current an **induced current,** and it is produced by an **induced emf.**

ACTIVE FIGURE 23.2
(a) When a magnet is moved toward a loop of wire connected to a sensitive ammeter, the ammeter needle deflects as shown, indicating that a current is induced in the loop.
(b) When the magnet is held stationary, no current is induced in the loop, even when the magnet is inside the loop. (c) When the magnet is moved away from the loop, the ammeter needle deflects in the opposite direction, indicating that the induced current is opposite that shown in (a).

Physics⊗Now™ By logging into PhysicsNow at **www.pop4e.com** and going to Active Figure 23.2, you can move the magnet and observe the current in the ammeter.

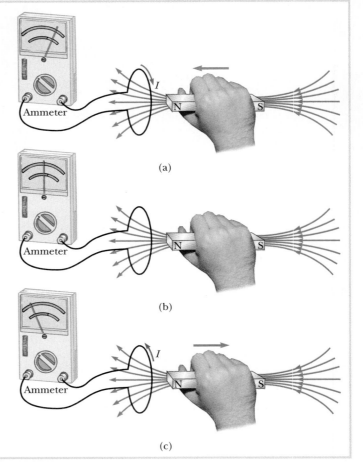

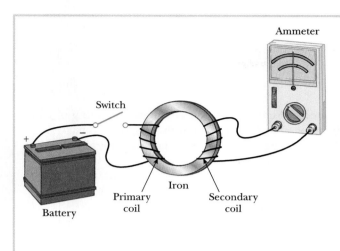

ACTIVE FIGURE 23.3

Faraday's experiment. When the switch in the primary circuit is closed, the ammeter needle in the secondary circuit deflects momentarily. The emf induced in the secondary circuit is caused by the changing magnetic field through the secondary coil.

Physics ⊗ Now™ By logging into PhysicsNow at **www.pop4e.com** and going to Active Figure 23.3, you can open and close the switch and observe the current in the ammeter.

Ammeter

Switch

Iron

Primary coil

Secondary coil

Battery

MICHAEL FARADAY (1791–1867)

Faraday, a British physicist and chemist, is often regarded as the greatest experimental scientist of the 1800s. His many contributions to the study of electricity include the invention of the electric motor, the electric generator, and the transformer as well as the discovery of electromagnetic induction and the laws of electrolysis. Greatly influenced by his religious beliefs, he refused to work on the development of poison gas for the British military.

(By kind permission of the President and Council of the Royal Society)

Another experiment, first conducted by Faraday, is illustrated in Active Figure 23.3. Part of the apparatus consists of a coil of insulated wire connected to a switch and a battery. We shall refer to this coil as the *primary coil* of wire and to the corresponding circuit as the primary circuit. The coil is wrapped around an iron ring to intensify the magnetic field produced by the current through the coil. A second coil of insulated wire at the right is also wrapped around the iron ring and is connected to a sensitive ammeter. We shall refer to this coil as the *secondary coil* and to the corresponding circuit as the secondary circuit. The secondary circuit has no battery, and the secondary coil is not electrically connected to the primary coil. The purpose of this apparatus is to detect any current that might be generated in the secondary circuit by a change in the magnetic field produced by the primary circuit.

Initially, you might guess that no current would ever be detected in the secondary circuit. Something quite surprising happens, however, when the switch in the primary circuit is opened or thrown closed. At the instant the switch is thrown closed, the ammeter needle deflects in one direction and then returns to zero. When the switch is opened, the ammeter needle deflects in the opposite direction and then again returns to zero. Finally, the ammeter reads zero when the primary circuit carries a steady current.

As a result of these observations, Faraday concluded that **an electric current can be produced by a time-varying magnetic field.** A current cannot be produced by a steady magnetic field. In the experiment shown in Active Figure 23.2, the changing magnetic field is a result of the relative motion between the magnet and the loop of wire. As long as the motion persists, the current is maintained. In the experiment shown in Active Figure 23.3, the current produced in the secondary circuit occurs for only an instant after the switch is closed while the magnetic field acting on the secondary coil builds from its zero value to its final value. In effect, the secondary circuit behaves as though a source of emf were connected to it for an instant. It is customary to say that an emf is induced in the secondary circuit by the changing magnetic field produced by the current in the primary circuit.

To quantify such observations, we define a quantity called **magnetic flux.** The flux associated with a magnetic field is defined in a similar manner to the electric flux (Section 19.8) and is proportional to the number of magnetic field lines passing through an area. Consider an element of area dA on an arbitrarily shaped open surface as in Figure 23.4. If the magnetic field at the location of this element is $\vec{B}$, the magnetic flux through the element is $\vec{B} \cdot d\vec{A}$, where $d\vec{A}$ is a vector perpendicular to the surface whose magnitude equals the area dA. Hence, the total magnetic

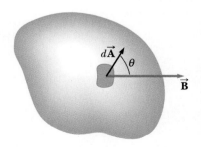

FIGURE 23.4 The magnetic flux through an area element $d\vec{A}$ is given by $\vec{B} \cdot d\vec{A} = B\, dA \cos\theta$. Note that vector $d\vec{A}$ is perpendicular to the surface.

flux Φ_B through the surface is

$$\Phi_B = \int \vec{B} \cdot d\vec{A} \qquad [23.1]$$

❚ **Magnetic flux**

The SI unit of magnetic flux is a tesla-meter squared, which is named the *weber* (Wb); $1\ \text{Wb} = 1\ \text{T} \cdot \text{m}^2$.

The two experiments illustrated in Figures 23.2 and 23.3 have one thing in common. In both cases, **an emf is induced in a circuit when the magnetic flux through the surface bounded by the circuit changes with time.** In fact, a general statement summarizes such experiments involving induced emfs:

> The emf induced in a circuit is equal to the time rate of change of magnetic flux through the circuit.

⊞ **PITFALL PREVENTION 23.1**

INDUCED EMF REQUIRES A CHANGE IN FLUX Remember that the *existence* of a magnetic flux through an area is not sufficient to create an induced emf. A *change* in the magnetic flux must occur for an emf to be induced.

This statement, known as **Faraday's law of induction,** can be written as

$$\mathcal{E} = -\frac{d\Phi_B}{dt} \qquad [23.2]$$

❚ **Faraday's law**

where Φ_B is the magnetic flux through the surface bounded by the circuit and is given by Equation 23.1. The negative sign in Equation 23.2 will be discussed in Section 23.3. If the circuit is a coil consisting of N identical and concentric loops and if the field lines pass through all loops, the induced emf is

$$\mathcal{E} = -N\frac{d\Phi_B}{dt} \qquad [23.3]$$

The emf is increased by the factor N because all the loops are in series, so the emfs in the individual loops add to give the total emf.

Suppose the magnetic field is uniform over the area A bounded by a loop lying in a plane as in Figure 23.5. In this case, the magnetic flux through the loop is

$$\Phi_B = \int \vec{B} \cdot d\vec{A} = \int B\, dA \cos\theta = B\cos\theta \int dA = BA\cos\theta$$

Hence, the induced emf is

$$\mathcal{E} = -\frac{d}{dt}(BA\cos\theta) \qquad [23.4]$$

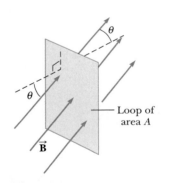

FIGURE 23.5 A conducting loop that encloses an area A in the presence of a uniform magnetic field $\vec{B}$. The angle between $\vec{B}$ and the normal to the loop is θ.

This expression shows that an emf can be induced in a circuit by changing the magnetic flux in several ways: (1) the magnitude of $\vec{B}$ can vary with time, (2) the area A of the circuit can change with time, (3) the angle θ between $\vec{B}$ and the normal to the plane can change with time, and (4) any combination of these changes can occur.

An interesting application of Faraday's law is the production of sound in an electric guitar (Fig. 23.6). The coil in this case, called the *pickup coil*, is placed near the vibrating guitar string, which is made of a metal that can be magnetized. A permanent magnet inside the coil magnetizes the portion of the string nearest the coil. When the string vibrates at some frequency, its magnetized segment produces a changing magnetic flux through the coil. The changing flux induces an emf in the coil that is fed to an amplifier. The output of the amplifier is sent to the loudspeakers, which produce the sound waves we hear.

> **QUICK QUIZ 23.1** A circular loop of wire is held in a uniform magnetic field, with the plane of the loop perpendicular to the field lines. Which of the following will *not* cause a current to be induced in the loop? **(a)** crushing the loop **(b)** rotating the loop about an axis perpendicular to the field lines **(c)** keeping the orientation of the loop fixed and moving it along the field lines **(d)** pulling the loop out of the field

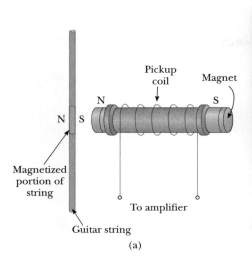

(Charles D. Winters)

FIGURE 23.6 (a) In an electric guitar, a vibrating magnetized string induces an emf in a pickup coil. (b) The pickups (the circles beneath the metallic strings) of this electric guitar detect the vibrations of the strings and send this information through an amplifier and into speakers. (A switch on the guitar allows the musician to select which set of six pickups is used.)

QUICK QUIZ 23.2 Figure 23.7 shows a graphical representation of the field magnitude versus time for a magnetic field that passes through a fixed loop and that is oriented perpendicular to the plane of the loop. The magnitude of the magnetic field at any time is uniform over the area of the loop. Rank the magnitudes of the emf generated in the loop at the five instants indicated, from largest to smallest.

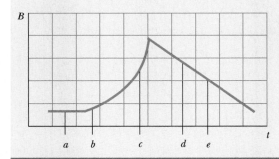

FIGURE 23.7 (Quick Quiz 23.2) The time behavior of a magnetic field through a loop.

■ **Thinking Physics 23.1**

The ground fault interrupter (GFI) is a safety device that protects users of electric power against electric shock when they touch appliances. Its essential parts are shown in Figure 23.8. How does the operation of a GFI make use of Faraday's law?

Reasoning Wire 1 leads from the wall outlet to the appliance being protected, and wire 2 leads from the appliance back to the wall outlet. An iron ring surrounds the two wires. A sensing coil wrapped around part of the iron ring activates a circuit breaker when changes in magnetic flux occur. Because the currents in the two wires are in opposite directions during normal operation of the appliance, the net magnetic field through the sensing coil due to the currents is zero. A change in magnetic flux through the sensing coil can happen, however, if one of the wires on the appliance loses its insulation and accidentally touches the metal case of the appliance, providing a direct path to ground. When such a short to ground occurs, a net magnetic flux occurs through the sensing coil that alternates in time because household current is alternating. This changing flux produces an induced voltage in the coil, which in turn triggers a circuit breaker, stopping the current before it reaches a level that might be harmful to the person using the appliance. ■

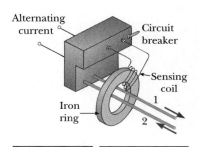

FIGURE 23.8 (Thinking Physics 23.1) Essential components of a ground fault interrupter.

EXAMPLE 23.1 One Way to Induce an emf in a Coil

A coil is wrapped with 200 turns of wire on the perimeter of a square frame with sides of 18 cm. Each turn has the same area, equal to that of the frame, and the total resistance of the coil is 2.0 Ω. A magnetic field is perpendicular to the plane of the coil and has the same magnitude at all points within the area of the coil at any time. If the field magnitude changes at a constant rate from 0 to 0.50 T in a time of 0.80 s, find the magnitude of the induced emf in the coil while the field is changing.

Solution Because the field is uniform across the area of the coil and perpendicular to the turns of wire, the magnetic flux at any time is simply the product of the magnitude of the field and the area of the turns, and Equation 23.3 becomes

$$\mathcal{E} = -N\frac{d\Phi_B}{dt} = -N\frac{d(BA)}{dt} = -NA\frac{dB}{dt}$$

Because the magnetic field changes at a constant rate, the derivative of the field with respect to time is equal to the ratio of the change in field to the time interval during which that change occurs:

$$|\mathcal{E}| = NA\frac{dB}{dt} = NA\frac{\Delta B}{\Delta t}$$

$$= (200)(0.18\text{ m})^2\frac{0.50\text{ T} - 0}{0.80\text{ s}} = \boxed{4.0\text{ V}}$$

EXAMPLE 23.2 An Exponentially Decaying B Field

A plane loop of wire of area A is placed in a region where the magnetic field is at a fixed angle θ to the normal to the plane and has the same magnitude at all points within the area of the coil at any time. The magnitude of the magnetic field varies with time according to the expression $B = B_{max}e^{-at}$. That is, at $t = 0$, the field is B_{max}, and for $t > 0$, the field decreases exponentially with time (Fig. 23.9). Find the induced emf in the loop as a function of time.

Solution Because $\vec{B}$ is uniform across the area of the coil, the magnetic flux through the loop at time $t > 0$ is

$$\Phi_B = BA\cos\theta = AB_{max}\cos\theta e^{-at}$$

Because the coefficient AB_{max} and the parameter a are constants, the induced emf from Equation 23.2 is

$$\mathcal{E} = -\frac{d\Phi_B}{dt} = -AB_{max}\cos\theta\frac{d}{dt}e^{-at}$$

$$= \boxed{aAB_{max}\cos\theta e^{-at}}$$

That is, the induced emf decays exponentially with time. Note that the maximum emf occurs at $t = 0$, where $\mathcal{E}_{max} = aAB_{max}\cos\theta$. The plot of $\mathcal{E}$ versus t is similar to the B versus t curve shown in Figure 23.9.

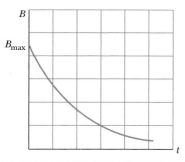

FIGURE 23.9 (Example 23.2) Exponential decrease in the magnitude of the magnetic field with time. The induced emf and induced current vary with time in the same way.

23.2 MOTIONAL emf

Examples 23.1 and 23.2 are cases in which an emf is produced in a circuit when the magnetic field changes with time. In this section, we describe **motional emf,** in which an emf is induced in a conductor moving through a magnetic field. This is the situation described in Figure 23.1 at the beginning of Section 23.1.

Consider a straight conductor of length ℓ moving with constant velocity through a uniform magnetic field directed into the page as in Figure 23.10. For simplicity, we shall assume that the conductor is moving with a velocity that is perpendicular to the field. The electrons in the conductor experience a force along the conductor with magnitude $|\vec{F}_B| = |q\vec{v} \times \vec{B}| = qvB$. According to Newton's second law, the electrons accelerate in response to this force and move along the wire. Once the electrons move to the lower end of the wire, they accumulate there, leaving a net positive charge at the upper end. As a result of this charge separation, an electric field $\vec{E}$ is produced within the conductor. The charge at the ends of the conductor builds up until the magnetic force qvB on an electron in the conductor is balanced by the electric force qE on the electron as shown in Figure 23.10. At this point, charge stops flowing. In this situation, the zero net force on an electron allows us to relate the electric field to the magnetic field:

$$\sum \vec{F} = \vec{F}_e - \vec{F}_B = 0 \quad \rightarrow \quad qE = qvB \quad \rightarrow \quad E = vB$$

Because the electric field produced in the conductor is uniform, it is related to the potential difference across the ends of the conductor according to the relation $\Delta V = E\ell$ (Section 20.2). Thus,

$$\Delta V = E\ell = B\ell v$$

where the upper end is at a higher potential than the lower end. Therefore, **a potential difference is maintained as long as the conductor is moving through the magnetic field. If the motion is reversed, the polarity of ΔV is also reversed.**

An interesting situation occurs if we now consider what happens when the moving conductor is part of a closed circuit. Consider a circuit consisting of a conducting bar of length ℓ sliding along two fixed parallel conducting rails as in Active Figure 23.11a. For simplicity, we assume that the moving bar has zero electrical resistance and that the stationary part of the circuit has a resistance R. A uniform and constant magnetic field $\vec{B}$ is applied perpendicular to the plane of the circuit.

As the bar is pulled to the right with a velocity $\vec{v}$ under the influence of an applied force $\vec{F}_{app}$, free charges in the bar experience a magnetic force along the length of the bar. Because the moving bar is part of a complete circuit, a continuous current is established in the circuit. In this case, the rate of change of magnetic flux through the loop and the accompanying induced emf across the moving bar are proportional to the change in loop area as the bar moves through the magnetic field.

Because the area of the circuit at any instant is ℓx, the magnetic flux through the circuit is

$$\Phi_B = B\ell x$$

where x is the width of the circuit, a parameter that changes with time. Using Faraday's law, we find that the induced emf is

$$\mathcal{E} = -\frac{d\Phi_B}{dt} = -\frac{d}{dt}(B\ell x) = -B\ell\frac{dx}{dt} = -B\ell v \qquad [23.5]$$

Because the resistance of the circuit is R, the magnitude of the induced current is

$$I = \frac{|\mathcal{E}|}{R} = \frac{B\ell v}{R} \qquad [23.6]$$

The equivalent circuit diagram for this example is shown in Active Figure 23.11b. The moving bar is behaving like a battery in that it is a source of emf as long as the bar continues to move.

Let us examine this situation using energy considerations in the nonisolated system model, with the system being the entire circuit. Because the circuit has no battery, you might wonder about the origin of the induced current and the energy delivered to the resistor. Note that the external force $\vec{F}_{app}$ does work on the conductor, thereby moving charges through a magnetic field, which causes the

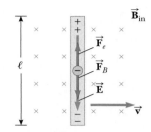

FIGURE 23.10 A straight electrical conductor of length ℓ moving with a velocity $\vec{v}$ through a uniform magnetic field $\vec{B}$ directed perpendicular to $\vec{v}$.

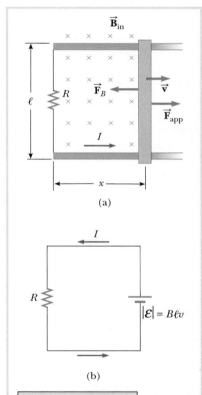

ACTIVE FIGURE 23.11

(a) A conducting bar sliding with a velocity $\vec{v}$ along two conducting rails under the action of an applied force $\vec{F}_{app}$. (b) The equivalent circuit diagram for the pictorial representation in (a).

Physics⊗Now™ By logging into PhysicsNow at **www.pop4e.com** and going to Active Figure 23.11, you can adjust the applied force, the magnetic field, and the resistance to see the effects on the motion of the bar.

charges to move along the conductor with some average drift velocity. Hence, a current is established. From the viewpoint of the continuity equation for energy (Eq. 6.20), the total work done on the system by the applied force while the bar moves with constant speed must equal the increase in internal energy in the resistor during this time interval. (This statement assumes that the energy stays in the resistor; in reality, energy leaves the resistor by heat and electromagnetic radiation.)

As the conductor of length ℓ moves through the uniform magnetic field $\vec{\mathbf{B}}$, it experiences a magnetic force $\vec{\mathbf{F}}_B$ of magnitude $I\ell B$ (Eq. 22.10), where I is the current induced due to its motion. The direction of this force is opposite the motion of the bar, or to the left in Active Figure 23.11a.

If the bar is to move with a *constant* velocity, the applied force $\vec{\mathbf{F}}_{app}$ must be equal in magnitude and opposite in direction to the magnetic force, or to the right in Active Figure 23.11a. (If the magnetic force acted in the direction of motion, it would cause the bar to accelerate once it was in motion, thereby increasing its speed. This state of affairs would represent a violation of the principle of energy conservation.) Using Equation 23.6 and that $F_{app} = F_B = I\ell B$, we find that the power delivered by the applied force is

$$\mathcal{P} = F_{app}v = (I\ell B)v = \frac{B^2\ell^2v^2}{R} = \left(\frac{B\ell v}{R}\right)^2 R = I^2 R \qquad [23.7]$$

This power is equal to the rate at which energy is delivered to the resistor, as we expect.

QUICK QUIZ 23.3 You wish to move a rectangular loop of wire into a region of uniform magnetic field at a given speed so as to induce an emf in the loop. The plane of the loop must remain perpendicular to the magnetic field lines. In which orientation should you hold the loop while you move it into the region of magnetic field so as to generate the largest emf? **(a)** with the long dimension of the loop parallel to the velocity vector **(b)** with the short dimension of the loop parallel to the velocity vector **(c)** either way because the emf is the same regardless of orientation

---

QUICK QUIZ 23.4 In Active Figure 23.11, a given applied force of magnitude F_{app} results in a constant speed v and a power input $\mathcal{P}$. Imagine that the force is increased so that the constant speed of the bar is doubled to $2v$. Under these conditions, what are the new force and the new power input? **(a)** $2F$ and $2\mathcal{P}$ **(b)** $4F$ and $2\mathcal{P}$ **(c)** $2F$ and $4\mathcal{P}$ **(d)** $4F$ and $4\mathcal{P}$

INTERACTIVE **EXAMPLE 23.3** **Motional emf Induced in a Rotating Bar**

A conducting bar of length ℓ rotates with a constant angular speed ω about a pivot at one end. A uniform magnetic field $\vec{\mathbf{B}}$ is directed perpendicular to the plane of rotation as in Figure 23.12. Find the emf induced between the ends of the bar.

Solution Consider a segment of the bar of length dr whose velocity is $\vec{\mathbf{v}}$. According to Equation 23.5, the magnitude of the emf induced in a conductor of length dr moving perpendicular to a field $\vec{\mathbf{B}}$ is

$$(1) \quad d\mathcal{E} = Bv \, dr$$

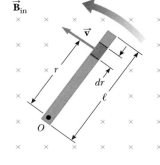

FIGURE 23.12 (Interactive Example 23.3) A conducting bar rotating about a pivot at one end in a uniform magnetic field that is perpendicular to the plane of rotation. An emf is induced between the ends of the bar.

Each segment of the bar is moving perpendicular to $\vec{\mathbf{B}}$, so an emf is generated across each segment, the value of which is given by (1). Summing the emfs induced across all elements, which are in series, gives the magnitude of the total emf between the ends of the bar. That is,

$$\mathcal{E} = \int Bv \, dr$$

To integrate this expression, note that the linear speed of an element is related to the angular speed ω through the relationship $v = r\omega$ (Eq. 10.10). Because B and ω are constants, we therefore find that

$$\mathcal{E} = B \int_0^\ell v \, dr = B\omega \int_0^\ell r \, dr = \tfrac{1}{2} B\omega\ell^2$$

Physics⊗Now™ By logging into PhysicsNow at **www.pop4e.com** and going to Interactive Example 23.3, you can explore the induced emf for different angular speeds and field magnitudes.

INTERACTIVE **EXAMPLE 23.4** **A Sliding Bar in a Magnetic Field**

The conducting bar illustrated in Figure 23.13 moves on two frictionless, parallel rails in the presence of a uniform magnetic field directed into the page. The bar has mass m and its length is ℓ. The bar is given an initial velocity $\vec{\mathbf{v}}_i$ to the right and is released at $t = 0$.

A Using Newton's laws, find the velocity of the bar as a function of time.

Solution Conceptualize this situation as follows. As the bar slides to the right in Figure 23.13, a counterclockwise current is established in the circuit consisting of the bar, the rails, and the resistor. The upward current in the bar results in a magnetic force to the left on the bar as shown in the figure. As a result, the bar will slow down, so our mathematical solution should demonstrate that. The text of the question already categorizes this problem as one using Newton's laws. To analyze the problem, we determine from Equation 22.10 that the magnetic force is $F_B = -I\ell B$, where the negative sign indicates that the retarding force is to the left. Because this force is the *only* horizontal force acting on the bar, Newton's second law applied to motion in the horizontal direction gives

$$F_x = ma = m\frac{dv}{dt} = -I\ell B$$

From Equation 23.6, we know that $I = B\ell v/R$, and so we can write this expression as

$$m\frac{dv}{dt} = -\frac{B^2\ell^2}{R}v$$

$$\frac{dv}{v} = -\left(\frac{B^2\ell^2}{mR}\right)dt$$

Integrating this equation using the initial condition that $v = v_i$ at $t = 0$, we find that

$$\int_{v_i}^{v} \frac{dv}{v} = \frac{-B^2\ell^2}{mR} \int_0^t dt$$

$$\ln\left(\frac{v}{v_i}\right) = -\left(\frac{B^2\ell^2}{mR}\right)t = -\frac{t}{\tau}$$

where the constant $\tau = mR/B^2\ell^2$. From this result, we see that the velocity can be expressed in the exponential form

$$(1) \quad v = v_i e^{-t/\tau}$$

To finalize the problem, note that this expression for v indicates that the velocity of the bar decreases with time under the action of the magnetic retarding force, as we expect from our conceptualization of the problem.

B Show that the same result is reached by using an energy approach.

Solution The wording of the text immediately categorizes this problem as one in energy conservation. Consider the sliding bar as one system possessing kinetic energy, which decreases because energy is transferring *out* of the system by electrical transmission through the rails. The resistor is another system possessing internal energy, which rises because energy is transferring *into* this system. Because energy is not leaving the combination

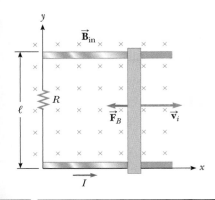

FIGURE 23.13 (Interactive Example 23.4) A conducting bar of length ℓ sliding on two fixed conducting rails is given an initial velocity $\vec{\mathbf{v}}_i$ in the positive x direction.

of two systems, the rate of energy transfer out of the bar equals the rate of energy transfer into the resistor. Therefore,

$$\mathcal{P}_{\text{resistor}} = -\mathcal{P}_{\text{bar}}$$

where the negative sign is necessary because energy is leaving the bar and $\mathcal{P}_{\text{bar}}$ is a negative number. Substituting for the electrical power delivered to the resistor and the time rate of change of kinetic energy for the bar, we have

$$I^2R = -\frac{d}{dt}\left(\tfrac{1}{2}mv^2\right)$$

Using Equation 23.6 for the current and carrying out the derivative, we find that

$$\frac{B^2\ell^2v^2}{R} = -mv\,\frac{dv}{dt}$$

Rearranging terms gives

$$\frac{dv}{v} = -\left(\frac{B^2\ell^2}{mR}\right)dt$$

To finalize this part of the problem, note that this expression is the same one that we generated in part A, so the solution for v will be the same.

Physics⊗Now™ By logging into PhysicsNow at **www.pop4e.com** and going to Interactive Example 23.4, you can study the motion of the bar after it is released.

The Alternating-Current Generator

The alternating-current (AC) generator is a device in which energy is transferred in by work and out by electrical transmission. A simplified pictorial representation of an AC generator is shown in Active Figure 23.14a. It consists of a coil of wire rotated in an external magnetic field by some external agent, which is the work input. In commercial power plants, the energy required to rotate the loop can be derived from a variety of sources. In a hydroelectric plant, for example, falling water directed against the blades of a turbine produces the rotary motion; in a coal-fired plant, the high temperature produced by burning the coal is used to convert water to steam and this steam is directed against turbine blades. As the loop rotates, the magnetic flux through it changes with time, inducing an emf and a current in a circuit connected to the coil.

Suppose the coil has N turns, all of the same area A, and suppose the coil rotates with a constant angular speed ω about an axis perpendicular to the magnetic field. If θ is the angle between the magnetic field and the direction perpendicular to the plane of the coil, the magnetic flux through the loop at any time t is given by

$$\Phi_B = BA\cos\theta = BA\cos\omega t$$

where we have used the relationship between angular position and a constant angular speed, $\theta = \omega t$. (See Eq. 10.7 and set the angular acceleration α equal to zero.)

ACTIVE FIGURE **23.14**

(a) Schematic diagram of an AC generator. An emf is induced in a loop that rotates in a magnetic field. (b) A graphical representation of the alternating emf induced in the loop as a function of time.

Physics⊗Now™ By logging into PhysicsNow at **www.pop4e.com** and going to Active Figure 23.14, you can adjust the speed of rotation and the strength of the field to see the effects on the emf generated.

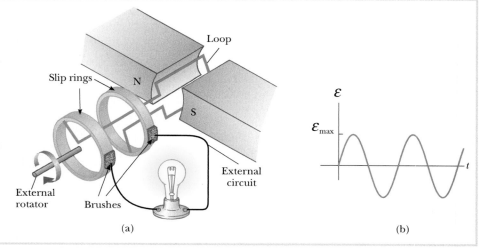

(a)

(b)

Hence, the induced emf in the coil is

$$\mathcal{E} = -N\frac{d\Phi_B}{dt} = -NAB\frac{d}{dt}(\cos \omega t) = NAB\omega \sin \omega t \qquad [23.8]$$

This result shows that the emf varies sinusoidally with time as shown in Active Figure 23.14b. From Equation 23.8, we see that the maximum emf has the value $\mathcal{E}_{max} = NAB\omega$, which occurs when $\omega t = 90°$ or $270°$. In other words, $\mathcal{E} = \mathcal{E}_{max}$ when the magnetic field is in the plane of the coil, and the time rate of change of flux is a maximum. In this position, the velocity vector for a wire in the loop is perpendicular to the magnetic field vector. Furthermore, the emf is *zero* when $\omega t = 0$ or $180°$—that is, when $\vec{\textbf{B}}$ is perpendicular to the plane of the coil—and the time rate of change of flux is zero. In this orientation, the velocity vector for a wire in the loop is parallel to the magnetic field vector.

The sinusoidally varying emf in Equation 23.8 is the source of *alternating current* delivered to customers of electrical utility companies. It is called **AC voltage** as opposed to the DC voltage from a source such as a battery.

23.3 LENZ'S LAW

Let us now address the negative sign in Faraday's law. When a change occurs in the magnetic flux, the direction of the induced emf and induced current can be found from **Lenz's law:**

> The polarity of the induced emf in a loop is such that it produces a current whose magnetic field opposes the change in magnetic flux through the loop. That is, the induced current is in a direction such that the induced magnetic field attempts to maintain the original flux through the loop.

Notice that no equation is associated with Lenz's law. The law is in words only and provides a means for determining the direction of the current in a circuit when a magnetic change occurs.

■ Thinking Physics 23.2

A transformer (Fig. 23.15) consists of a pair of coils wrapped around an iron form. When AC voltage is applied to one coil, the *primary,* the magnetic field lines cutting through the other coil, the *secondary,* induce an emf. (This arrangement is used in Faraday's experiment shown in Active Fig. 23.3.) By varying the number of turns of wire on each coil, the AC voltage in the secondary can be made larger or smaller than that in the primary. Clearly, this device cannot work with DC voltage. What's more, if DC voltage is applied, the primary coil sometimes overheats and burns. Why?

Reasoning When a current exists in the primary coil, the magnetic field lines from this current pass through the coil itself. Therefore, any change in the current causes a change in the magnetic field that in turn induces a current in the same coil. According to Lenz's law, this current is in the direction opposite the original current. The result is that when an AC voltage is applied, the opposing emf due to Lenz's law limits the current in the coil to a low value. If DC voltage is applied, no opposing emf occurs and the current can rise to a higher value. This increased current causes the temperature of the coil to rise, to the point at which the insulation on the wire sometimes burns. ■

To attain a better understanding of Lenz's law, let us return to the example of a bar moving to the right on two parallel rails in the presence of a uniform magnetic field directed into the page (Fig. 23.16a). As the bar moves to the right, the magnetic flux through the circuit increases with time because the area of the loop increases. Lenz's law says that the induced current must be in such a direction that the magnetic

⊞ **PITFALL PREVENTION 23.2**

INDUCED CURRENT OPPOSES THE CHANGE The induced current in a circuit opposes the *change* in the magnetic field, not the field itself. Therefore, in some cases the magnetic field due to the induced current is in the same direction as the changing external magnetic field. Such is the case if the external magnetic field is decreasing in magnitude, for example.

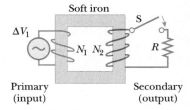

FIGURE 23.15 (Thinking Physics 23.2) An ideal transformer consists of two coils of wire wound on the same iron core. An alternating voltage ΔV_1 is applied to the primary coil, and the output voltage ΔV_2 appears across the resistance R.

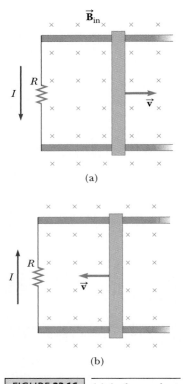

FIGURE 23.16 (a) As the conducting bar slides on the two fixed conducting rails, the flux due to the magnetic field directed inward through the area enclosed by the loop increases in time. By Lenz's law, the induced current must be counterclockwise so as to produce a counteracting magnetic field directed outward from the page. (b) When the bar moves to the left, the induced current must be clockwise. Why?

field *it* produces opposes the *change* in the magnetic flux of the external magnetic field. Because the flux is due to an external field *into* the page and is increasing, the induced current, if it is to oppose the change, must produce a magnetic field through the circuit *out* of the page. Hence, the induced current must be counterclockwise when the bar moves to the right to give a counteracting field out of the page in the region inside the loop. (Use the right-hand rule to verify this direction.) If the bar is moving to the left, as in Figure 23.16b, the magnetic flux through the loop decreases with time. Because the magnetic field is into the page, the induced current has to be clockwise to produce a magnetic field into the page inside the loop. In either case, the induced current attempts to maintain the original flux through the circuit.

Let us examine this situation from the viewpoint of energy considerations. Suppose the bar is given a slight push to the right. In the preceding analysis, we found that this motion leads to a counterclockwise current in the loop. What happens if we incorrectly assume that the current is clockwise? For a clockwise current I, the direction of the magnetic force $I\ell B$ on the sliding bar would be to the right. According to Newton's second law, this force would accelerate the rod and increase its speed, which in turn would cause the area of the loop to increase more rapidly. This increase would increase the induced current, which would increase the force, which would increase the current, and so on. In effect, the system would acquire energy with no additional energy input. This result is clearly inconsistent with all experience and with the continuity equation for energy. Thus, we are forced to conclude that the current must be counterclockwise.

Consider another situation, one in which a bar magnet is moved to the right toward a stationary loop of wire as in Figure 23.17a. As the magnet moves toward the loop, the magnetic flux through the loop increases with time. To counteract this increase in flux due to a magnetic field directed toward the right, the induced current produces a magnetic field to the left as in Figure 23.17b; hence, the induced current is in the direction shown. Therefore, the left face of the current loop is a north pole and the right face is a south pole.

If the magnet is moved to the left as in Figure 23.17c, the magnetic field through the loop, which is toward the right, decreases with time. Under these circumstances,

FIGURE 23.17 (a) When the magnet is moved toward the stationary conducting loop, a current is induced in the direction shown. (b) This induced current produces its own magnetic field that is directed to the left within the loop to counteract the increasing external flux. (c) When the magnet is moved away from the stationary conducting loop, a current is induced in the direction shown. (d) This induced current produces its own magnetic field that is directed to the right within the loop to counteract the decreasing external flux.

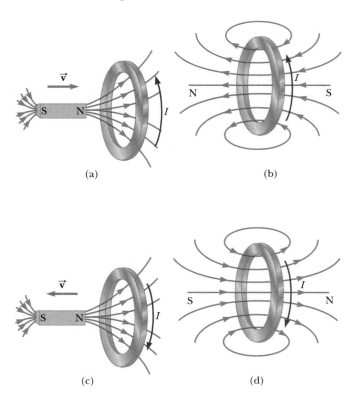

the induced current in the loop sets up a magnetic field through the loop from left to right in an effort to maintain a constant flux. Hence, the direction of the induced current in the loop is as shown in Figure 23.17d. In this case, the left face of the loop is a south pole and the right face is a north pole.

QUICK QUIZ 23.5   In equal-arm balances from the early 20th century (Fig. 23.18), it is sometimes observed that an aluminum sheet hangs from one of the arms and passes between the poles of a magnet, which causes the oscillations of the equal arm balance to decay rapidly. In the absence of such magnetic braking, the oscillation might continue for a very long time and the experimenter would have to wait to take a reading. Why do the oscillations decay? **(a)** The aluminum sheet is attracted to the magnet. **(b)** Currents in the aluminum sheet set up a magnetic field that opposes the oscillations. **(c)** Aluminum is ferromagnetic.

(Photos by John Jewett)

FIGURE 23.18   (Quick Quiz 23.5) In an old-fashioned equal-arm balance, an aluminum sheet hangs between the poles of a magnet.

EXAMPLE 23.5   **Application of Lenz's Law**

A coil of wire is placed near an electromagnet as in Figure 23.19a.

A Find the direction of the induced current in the coil at the instant the switch is closed.

Solution When the switch is closed, the situation changes from a condition in which no magnetic flux occurs through the coil to one in which flux does occur due to a magnetic field in the direction shown in Figure 23.19b. To counteract this increase in magnetic flux, the coil must set up a field from left to right in the figure, which requires a current directed as shown in Figure 23.19b.

B Find the direction of the induced current in the coil after the switch has been closed for several seconds.

Solution After the switch has been closed for several seconds, the magnetic flux through the loop does not change. Hence, the induced current is zero.

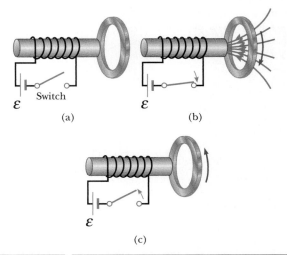

FIGURE 23.19   (Example 23.5) A current in the ring is induced when the switch is opened or closed.

[C] Find the direction of the induced current in the coil when the switch is opened.

Solution Opening the switch causes the magnetic field to change from a condition in which magnetic field lines pass through the coil from right to left to a condition of zero field. The induced current must then be as shown in Figure 23.19c so as to set up its own magnetic field from right to left.

23.4 INDUCED emfs AND ELECTRIC FIELDS

We have seen that a changing magnetic flux induces an emf and a current in a conducting loop. We can also interpret this phenomenon from another point of view. Because the normal flow of charges in a circuit is due to an electric field in the wires set up by a source such as a battery, we can interpret the changing magnetic field as creating an induced electric field. This electric field applies a force on the charges to cause them to move. With this approach, then, we see that **an electric field is created in the conductor as a result of changing magnetic flux.** In fact, the law of electromagnetic induction can be interpreted as follows: **An electric field is always generated by a changing magnetic flux,** even in free space where no charges are present. This induced electric field, however, has quite different properties from those of the electrostatic field produced by stationary charges.

Let us illustrate this point by considering a conducting loop of radius r, situated in a uniform magnetic field that is perpendicular to the plane of the loop as in Figure 23.20. If the magnetic field changes with time, Faraday's law tells us that an emf $\mathcal{E} = -d\Phi_B/dt$ is induced in the loop. The induced current thus produced implies the presence of an induced electric field $\vec{E}$ that must be tangent to the loop so as to provide an electric force on the charges around the loop. The work done by the electric field on the loop in moving a test charge q once around the loop is equal to $W = q\mathcal{E}$. Because the magnitude of the electric force on the charge is qE, the work done by the electric field can also be expressed from Equation 6.12 as $W = \int \vec{F} \cdot d\vec{r} = qE(2\pi r)$, where $2\pi r$ is the circumference of the loop. These two expressions for the work must be equal; therefore, we see that

$$q\mathcal{E} = qE(2\pi r)$$

$$E = \frac{\mathcal{E}}{2\pi r}$$

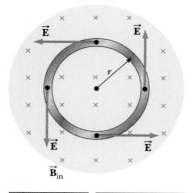

FIGURE 23.20 A conducting loop of radius r in a uniform magnetic field perpendicular to the plane of the loop. If $\vec{B}$ changes in time, an electric field is induced in a direction tangent to the loop.

Using this result along with Faraday's law and that $\Phi_B = BA = B\pi r^2$ for a circular loop, we find that the induced electric field can be expressed as

$$E = -\frac{1}{2\pi r}\frac{d\Phi_B}{dt} = -\frac{1}{2\pi r}\frac{d}{dt}(B\pi r^2) = -\frac{r}{2}\frac{dB}{dt}$$

This expression can be used to calculate the induced electric field if the time variation of the magnetic field is specified. The negative sign indicates that the induced electric field $\vec{E}$ results in a current that opposes the change in the magnetic field. It is important to understand that **this result is also valid in the absence of a conductor or charges.** That is, the same electric field is induced by the changing magnetic field in empty space.

In general, the magnitude of the emf for any closed path can be expressed as the line integral of $\vec{E} \cdot d\vec{s}$ over that path (Eq. 20.3). Hence, the general form of

Faraday's law of induction is

$$\mathcal{E} = \oint \vec{\mathbf{E}} \cdot d\vec{\mathbf{s}} = -\frac{d\Phi_B}{dt}$$

[23.9]   ∎ Faraday's law in general form

It is important to recognize that **the induced electric field $\vec{\mathbf{E}}$ that appears in Equation 23.9 is a nonconservative field that is generated by a changing magnetic field.** We call it a nonconservative field because the work done in moving a charge around a closed path (the loop in Fig. 23.20) is not zero. This type of electric field is very different from an electrostatic field.

QUICK QUIZ 23.6   In a region of space, a magnetic field is uniform over space but increases at a constant rate. This changing magnetic field induces an electric field that **(a)** increases in time, **(b)** is conservative, **(c)** is in the direction of the magnetic field, or **(d)** has a constant magnitude.

∎ Thinking Physics 23.3

In studying electric fields, we noted that electric field lines begin on positive charges and end on negative charges. Do *all* electric field lines begin and end on charges?

Reasoning The statement that electric field lines begin and end on charges is true only for *electrostatic* fields, that is, electric fields due to stationary charges. Electric field lines due to changing magnetic fields form closed loops, with no beginning and no end, and are independent of the presence of charges. ∎

EXAMPLE 23.6   Electric Field Induced by a Changing Magnetic Field in a Solenoid

A long solenoid of radius R has n turns of wire per unit length and carries a time-varying current that varies sinusoidally as $I = I_{max} \cos \omega t$, where I_{max} is the maximum current and ω is the angular frequency of the AC source (Fig. 23.21).

A   Determine the magnitude of the induced electric field outside the solenoid, a distance $r > R$ from its long central axis.

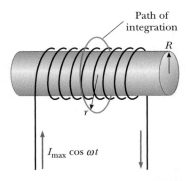

Path of integration

R

r

$I_{max} \cos \omega t$

FIGURE 23.21   (Example 23.6) A long solenoid carrying a time-varying current given by $I = I_{max} \cos \omega t$. An electric field is induced both inside and outside the solenoid.

Solution First consider an external point and take the path for our line integral to be a circle of radius r centered on the solenoid as illustrated in Figure 23.21. By symmetry, we see that the magnitude of $\vec{\mathbf{E}}$ is constant on this path and that $\vec{\mathbf{E}}$ is tangent to it. The magnetic flux through the area enclosed by the path is $\int \vec{\mathbf{B}} \cdot d\vec{\mathbf{A}} = BA = B\pi R^2$; hence, Equation 23.9 gives

$$(1) \quad \oint \vec{\mathbf{E}} \cdot d\vec{\mathbf{s}} = -\frac{d}{dt}(B\pi R^2) = -\pi R^2 \frac{dB}{dt}$$

Based on the symmetry of the situation,

$$(2) \quad \oint \vec{\mathbf{E}} \cdot d\vec{\mathbf{s}} = \oint E\,ds = E \oint ds = E(2\pi r)$$

Setting these two expressions equal, we find that

$$(3) \quad E = -\frac{R^2}{2r}\frac{dB}{dt}$$

The magnetic field inside a long solenoid is given by Equation 22.32, $B = \mu_0 n I$. When we substitute $I = I_{max} \cos \omega t$ into this equation and then substitute the result into (3), we find that

$$E = -\frac{R^2}{2r}\frac{d}{dt}(\mu_0 n I_{max}\cos\omega t)$$

$$= \frac{\mu_0 n I_{max}\omega R^2}{2r}\sin\omega t \qquad (\text{for } r > R)$$

Hence, the electric field varies sinusoidally with time, and its amplitude falls off as $1/r$ outside the solenoid. According to the Ampère-Maxwell law, which we will study in Section 24.1, the changing electric field creates an additional contribution to the magnetic field. At high frequencies, an altogether new phenomenon can occur. The electric and magnetic fields, each supporting the other, can constitute an electromagnetic wave radiated by the solenoid, as we will study in Chapter 24.

▐B▐ What is the magnitude of the induced electric field inside the solenoid, a distance r from its axis?

Solution For an interior point ($r < R$), the flux passing through the area bounded by a path of integration is given by $B\pi r^2$. Thus, the analogs to (1), (2), and (3)

become

$$(4) \quad \oint \vec{E}\cdot d\vec{s} = -\frac{d}{dt}(B\pi r^2) = \pi r^2 \frac{dB}{dt}$$

$$(5) \quad \oint \vec{E}\cdot d\vec{s} = \oint E\,ds = E\oint ds = E(2\pi r)$$

$$(6) \quad E = -\frac{r}{2}\frac{dB}{dt}$$

Substituting the expression for the magnetic field into (6) gives

$$E = -\frac{r}{2}\frac{d}{dt}(\mu_0 n I_{max}\cos\omega t)$$

$$= \frac{\mu_0 n I_{max}\omega}{2}r\sin\omega t \qquad (\text{for } r < R)$$

This expression shows that the amplitude of the electric field induced inside the solenoid by the changing magnetic field varies linearly with r and varies sinusoidally with time.

23.5 SELF-INDUCTANCE

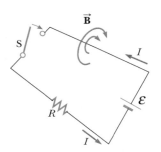

FIGURE 23.22 After the switch is closed, the current produces a magnetic flux through the area enclosed by the loop of the circuit. As the current increases toward its final value, this magnetic flux changes with time and induces an emf in the loop.

Consider an isolated circuit consisting of a switch, a resistor, and a source of emf as in Figure 23.22. The circuit diagram is represented in perspective so that we can see the orientations of some of the magnetic field lines due to the current in the circuit. When the switch is closed, the current doesn't immediately jump from zero to its maximum value $\mathcal{E}/R$; the law of electromagnetic induction (Faraday's law) describes the actual behavior. As the current increases with time, the magnetic flux through the loop of the circuit itself due to the current also increases with time. This increasing magnetic flux *from* the circuit induces an emf *in* the circuit (sometimes referred to as a *back emf*) that opposes the change in the net magnetic flux through the loop of the circuit. By Lenz's law, the induced electric field in the wires must therefore be opposite the direction of the current, and the opposing emf results in a *gradual* increase in the current. This effect is called *self-induction* because the changing magnetic flux through the circuit arises from the circuit itself. The emf set up in this case is called a **self-induced emf.**

To obtain a quantitative description of self-induction, we recall from Faraday's law that the induced emf is the negative time rate of change of the magnetic flux. The magnetic flux is proportional to the magnetic field, which in turn is proportional to the current in the circuit. Therefore, **the self-induced emf is always proportional to the time rate of change of the current.** For a closely spaced coil of N turns of fixed geometry (a toroidal coil or the ideal solenoid), we can express this proportionality as follows:

▌ Self-induced emf

$$\mathcal{E}_L = -N\frac{d\Phi_B}{dt} = -L\frac{dI}{dt} \qquad [23.10]$$

where L is a proportionality constant, called the **inductance** of the coil, that depends on the geometric features of the coil and other physical characteristics. From this expression, we see that the inductance of a coil containing N

turns is

$$L = \frac{N\Phi_B}{I} \qquad\qquad [23.11]$$

where it is assumed that the same magnetic flux passes through each turn. Later we shall use this equation to calculate the inductance of some special coil geometries.

From Equation 23.10, we can also write the inductance as the ratio

$$L = -\frac{\varepsilon_L}{dI/dt} \qquad\qquad [23.12]$$

which is usually taken to be the defining equation for the inductance of any coil, regardless of its shape, size, or material characteristics. If we compare Equation 23.10 with Equation 21.6, $R = \Delta V/I$, we see that resistance is a measure of opposition to current, whereas inductance is a measure of opposition to the *change* in current.

The SI unit of inductance is the **henry (H),** which, from Equation 23.12, is seen to be equal to 1 volt-second per ampere:

$$1\ \text{H} = 1\ \text{V}\cdot\text{s/A}$$

As we shall see, **the inductance of a coil depends on its geometry.** Because inductance calculations can be quite difficult for complicated geometries, the examples we shall explore involve simple situations for which inductances are easily evaluated.

JOSEPH HENRY (1797–1878)

Henry, an American physicist, became the first director of the Smithsonian Institution and first president of the Academy of Natural Science. He improved the design of the electromagnet and constructed one of the first motors. He also discovered the phenomenon of self-induction but failed to publish his findings. The unit of inductance, the henry, is named in his honor.

(North Wind Picture Archives)

EXAMPLE 23.7   Inductance of a Solenoid

Consider a uniformly wound solenoid having N turns and length ℓ.

A Find the inductance of the solenoid. Assume that ℓ is long compared with the radius and that the core of the solenoid is air.

Solution Because ℓ is long compared with the radius, we can model the solenoid as an ideal solenoid. In this case, the interior magnetic field is uniform and given by Equation 22.32:

$$B = \mu_0 nI = \mu_0 \frac{N}{\ell} I$$

where $n = N/\ell$ is the number of turns per unit length. The magnetic flux through each turn is

$$\Phi_B = BA = \mu_0 \frac{NA}{\ell} I$$

where A is the cross-sectional area of the solenoid. Using this expression and Equation 23.11, we find that

$$L = \frac{N\Phi_B}{I} = \frac{\mu_0 N^2 A}{\ell}$$

which shows that L depends on the geometry of the solenoid and is proportional to the square of the number of turns. Because $N = n\ell$, we can also express the result

in the form

$$L = \mu_0 \frac{(n\ell)^2}{\ell} A = \mu_0 n^2 A\ell = \mu_0 n^2 V$$

where $V = A\ell$ is the volume of the solenoid.

B Calculate the inductance of a solenoid containing 300 turns if the length of the solenoid is 25.0 cm and its cross-sectional area is $4.00\ \text{cm}^2 = 4.00 \times 10^{-4}\ \text{m}^2$.

Solution Using the expression for L from part A, we find that

$$L = \frac{\mu_0 N^2 A}{\ell}$$

$$= (4\pi \times 10^{-7}\ \text{T}\cdot\text{m/A}) \frac{(300)^2(4.00 \times 10^{-4}\ \text{m}^2)}{25.0 \times 10^{-2}\ \text{m}}$$

$$= 1.81 \times 10^{-4}\ \text{T}\cdot\text{m}^2/\text{A} = \boxed{0.181\ \text{mH}}$$

C Calculate the self-induced emf in the solenoid described in part B if the current through it is decreasing at the rate of 50.0 A/s.

Solution Using Equation 23.10 and given that $dI/dt = -50.0$ A/s, we have

$$\varepsilon_L = -L\frac{dI}{dt} = -(1.81 \times 10^{-4}\ \text{H})(-50.0\ \text{A/s})$$

$$= \boxed{9.05\ \text{mV}}$$

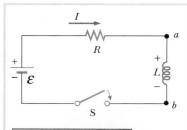

23.6 *RL* CIRCUITS

A circuit that contains a coil, such as a solenoid, has a self-inductance that prevents the current from increasing or decreasing instantaneously. A circuit element whose main purpose is to provide inductance in a circuit is called an **inductor.** The circuit symbol for an inductor is ——〰〰——. As a simplification model, we shall always assume that the self-inductance of the remainder of the circuit is negligible compared with that of any inductors in the circuit. In addition, any resistance in the inductor is assumed to be combined with other resistance in the circuit, so we model the inductor as having zero resistance.

Consider the circuit shown in Active Figure 23.23, consisting of a resistor, an inductor, a switch, and a battery. The internal resistance of the battery will be ignored as a further simplification model. Suppose the switch S is thrown closed at $t = 0$. The current begins to increase, and, due to the increasing current, the inductor produces an emf that opposes the increasing current. The back emf produced by the inductor is

$$\mathcal{E}_L = -L \frac{dI}{dt}$$

Because the current is increasing, dI/dt is positive; therefore $\mathcal{E}_L$ is negative, which corresponds to the potential drop occurring from *a* to *b* across the inductor. For this reason, point *a* is at a higher potential than point *b* as illustrated in Active Figure 23.23.

We can apply Kirchhoff's loop rule to this circuit. If we begin at the battery and travel clockwise, we have

$$\mathcal{E} - IR - L \frac{dI}{dt} = 0 \qquad [23.13]$$

where *IR* is the voltage across the resistor. The potential difference across the inductor is given a negative sign because its emf is in the opposite sense to that of the battery. We must now look for a solution to this differential equation, which is a mathematical representation of the behavior of the *RL* circuit. It is similar to Equation 21.30 for the *RC* circuit.

To obtain a mathematical solution of Equation 23.13, it is convenient to change variables by letting $x = (\mathcal{E}/R) - I$ so that $dx = -dI$. With these substitutions, Equation 23.13 can be written as

$$\frac{\mathcal{E}}{R} - I - \frac{L}{R}\frac{dI}{dt} = x + \frac{L}{R}\frac{dx}{dt} = 0$$

$$\frac{dx}{x} = -\frac{R}{L}dt$$

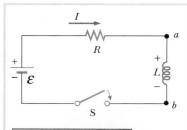

Integrating this last expression from an initial instant $t = 0$ to some later time t gives

$$\int_{x_i}^{x} \frac{dx}{x} = -\frac{R}{L}\int_0^t dt \quad \rightarrow \quad \ln\frac{x}{x_i} = -\frac{R}{L}t$$

Taking the antilog of this result gives

$$x = x_i e^{-Rt/L}$$

The value of x at $t = 0$ is expressed as $x_i = \mathcal{E}/R$ because $I = 0$ at $t = 0$. Hence, the preceding expression is equivalent to

$$\frac{\mathcal{E}}{R} - I = \frac{\mathcal{E}}{R}e^{-Rt/L}$$

$$I = \frac{\mathcal{E}}{R}(1 - e^{-Rt/L})$$

This expression represents the solution of Equation 23.13, the current as a function of time. It can also be written as

$$I(t) = \frac{\mathcal{E}}{R}(1 - e^{-t/\tau})$$ [23.14]

where τ is the **time constant** of the *RL* circuit:

$$\tau = \frac{L}{R}$$ [23.15]

It can be shown that the dimension of τ is time. Physically, τ is the time interval required for the current to reach $(1 - e^{-1}) = 0.632$ of its final value $\mathcal{E}/R$.

Active Figure 23.24 plots current versus time. Note that $I = 0$ at $t = 0$ and that the final steady-state value of the current, which occurs as $t \rightarrow \infty$, is $\mathcal{E}/R$. This result can be seen by setting dI/dt equal to zero in Equation 23.13 (in steady state, the change in the current is zero) and solving for the current. Thus, we see that the current rises very rapidly initially and then gradually approaches the maximum value $\mathcal{E}/R$ as $t \rightarrow \infty$. Notice that the final current does not involve L because the inductor has no effect on the circuit (ignoring any resistance associated with it) if the current is not changing.

Taking the first time derivative of Equation 23.14, we obtain

$$\frac{dI}{dt} = \frac{\mathcal{E}}{L}e^{-t/\tau}$$ [23.16]

From this equation, we see that the rate of change of current dI/dt is a *maximum* (equal to $\mathcal{E}/L$) at $t = 0$ and falls off exponentially to zero as $t \rightarrow \infty$ (Fig. 23.25).

Now consider the *RL* circuit arranged as shown in Active Figure 23.26. The curved lines on the switch S represent a switch that is connected either to *a* or *b* at all times. (If the switch is connected to neither *a* nor *b*, the current in the circuit suddenly stops.) Suppose the switch has been set at position *a* long enough to allow the current to reach its equilibrium value $\mathcal{E}/R$. In this situation, the circuit is described by the outer loop in Active Figure 23.26. If the switch is thrown from *a* to *b*, the circuit is now described by just the right-hand loop in Active Figure 23.26. Thus, we have a circuit with no battery ($\mathcal{E} = 0$). Applying Kirchhoff's loop rule to the right-hand loop at the instant the switch is thrown from *a* to *b*, we obtain

$$IR + L\frac{dI}{dt} = 0$$ [23.17]

It is left to Problem 23.34 to show that the solution of this differential equation is

$$I(t) = \frac{\mathcal{E}}{R}e^{-t/\tau}$$ [23.18]

where the current at $t = 0$ is $I_i = \mathcal{E}/R$ and $\tau = L/R$.

The graph of current versus time (Active Fig. 23.27) for the circuit of Active Figure 23.26 shows that the current is continuously decreasing with time, as one would expect. Furthermore, the slope dI/dt is always negative and has its maximum magnitude at $t = 0$. The negative slope signifies that $\mathcal{E}_L = -L(dI/dt)$ is now *positive*.

QUICK QUIZ 23.7 The circuit in Figure 23.28 includes a power source that provides a sinusoidal voltage. Thus, the magnetic field in the inductor is constantly changing. The inductor is a simple air-core solenoid. The switch in the circuit is closed and the lightbulb

▪ **Time constant of the *RL* circuit**

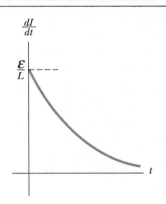

FIGURE 23.25 Plot of dI/dt versus time for the *RL* circuit shown in Active Figure 23.23. The time rate of change of current is a maximum at $t = 0$, which is the instant at which the switch is closed. The rate decreases exponentially with time as I increases toward its maximum value.

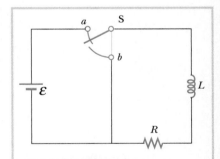

ACTIVE FIGURE 23.26
An *RL* circuit. When the switch S is in position *a*, the battery is in the circuit. When the switch is thrown to position *b*, the battery is no longer part of the circuit. The switch is designed so that it is never open, which would cause the current to stop.

Physics☒Now™ By logging into PhysicsNow at **www.pop4e.com** and going to Active Figure 23.26, you can adjust the values of *R* and *L* to see the effect on the current. A graphical display as in Active Figure 23.27 is available.

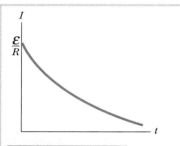

glows steadily. An iron rod is inserted into the interior of the solenoid, which increases the magnitude of the magnetic field in the solenoid. As that happens, the brightness of the lightbulb **(a)** increases, **(b)** decreases, or **(c)** is unaffected.

FIGURE 23.28 (Quick Quiz 23.7) A lightbulb is powered by an AC source with an inductor in the circuit. When the iron bar is inserted into the coil, what happens to the brightness of the lightbulb?

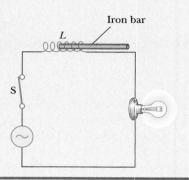

QUICK QUIZ 23.8 Two circuits like the one shown in Active Figure 23.26 are identical except for the value of *L*. In circuit A, the inductance of the inductor is L_A, and in circuit B, it is L_B. The switch has been in position *b* for both circuits for a long time. At *t* = 0, the switch is thrown to *a* in both circuits. At *t* = 10 s, the switch is thrown to *b* in both circuits. The resulting graphical representation of the current as a function of time is shown in Figure 23.29. Assuming that the time constant of each circuit is much less than 10 s, which of the following is true? (a) $L_A > L_B$. (b) $L_A < L_B$. (c) There is not enough information to determine the relative values.

FIGURE 23.29 (Quick Quiz 23.8) Current–time graphs for two circuits with different inductances.

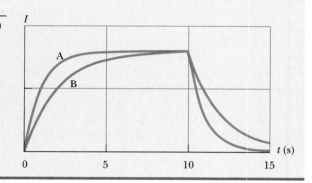

INTERACTIVE **EXAMPLE 23.8** **Time Constant of an *RL* Circuit**

Consider the *RL* circuit in Figure 23.30a.

A Find the time constant of the circuit.

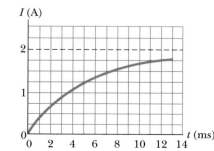

(a)

(b)

Solution The time constant is given by Equation 23.15:

$$\tau = \frac{L}{R} = \frac{30.0 \times 10^{-3}\,\text{H}}{6.00\,\Omega} = 5.00\,\text{ms}$$

FIGURE 23.30 (Interactive Example 23.8) (a) The switch in this *RL* circuit is open for *t* < 0 and then closed at *t* = 0. (b) A graph of the current versus time for the circuit in (a).

B The switch in Figure 23.30a is closed at $t = 0$. Calculate the current in the circuit at $t = 2.00$ ms.

Solution Using Equation 23.14 for the current as a function of time (with t and τ in milliseconds), we find that at $t = 2.00$ ms,

$$I = \frac{\mathcal{E}}{R}(1 - e^{-t/\tau}) = \frac{12.0 \text{ V}}{6.00 \text{ }\Omega}(1 - e^{-0.400}) = \boxed{0.659 \text{ A}}$$

A plot of Equation 23.14 for this circuit is given in Figure 23.30b.

Physics⊗Now™ By logging into PhysicsNow at **www.pop4e.com** and going to Interactive Example 23.8, you can explore the time behavior of the current in the circuit.

23.7 ENERGY STORED IN A MAGNETIC FIELD

In the preceding section, we found that the induced emf set up by an inductor prevents a battery from establishing an instantaneous current. Part of the energy supplied by the battery goes into internal energy in the resistor, and the remaining energy is stored in the inductor. If we multiply each term in Equation 23.13 by the current I and rearrange the expression, we have

$$I\mathcal{E} = I^2 R + LI\frac{dI}{dt} \qquad [23.19]$$

This expression tells us that the rate $I\mathcal{E}$ at which energy is supplied by the battery equals the sum of the rate I^2R at which energy is delivered to the resistor and the rate $LI\,(dI/dt)$ at which energy is delivered to the inductor. Thus, Equation 23.19 is simply an expression of energy conservation for the isolated system of the circuit. (Actually, energy can leave the circuit by thermal conduction into the air and by electromagnetic radiation, so the system need not be completely isolated.) If we let U_B denote the energy stored in the inductor at any time, the rate dU_B/dt at which energy is delivered to the inductor can be written as

$$\frac{dU_B}{dt} = LI\frac{dI}{dt}$$

To find the total energy stored in the inductor at any instant, we can rewrite this expression as $dU_B = LI\,dI$ and integrate:

$$U_B = \int_0^{U_B} dU_B = \int_0^I LI\,dI$$

$$U_B = \tfrac{1}{2}LI^2 \qquad [23.20]$$

■ Energy stored in an inductor

where L is constant and so has been removed from the integral. Equation 23.20 represents the energy stored in the magnetic field of the inductor when the current is I.

Equation 23.20 is similar to the equation for the energy stored in the electric field of a capacitor, $U_E = \tfrac{1}{2}C(\Delta V)^2$ (Eq. 20.29). In either case, we see that energy from a battery is required to establish a field and that energy is stored in the field. In the case of the capacitor, we can conceptually relate the energy stored in the capacitor to the electric potential energy associated with the separated charge on the plates. We have not discussed a magnetic analogy to electric potential energy, so the storage of energy in an inductor is not as easy to conceptualize.

To argue that energy is stored in an inductor, consider the circuit in Figure 23.31a, which is the same circuit as in Active Figure 23.26, with the addition of a switch S_2 across the resistor R. With switch S_1 set to position a and S_2 closed as shown, a current is established in the inductor. Now, as in Figure 23.31b, switch S_1 is thrown to position b. The current persists in this (ideally) resistance-free and battery-free circuit (the right-hand loop in Fig. 23.31b), consisting of only the inductor and a conducting path between its ends. There is no current in the resistor (because the path around it through S_2 is resistance free), so no energy is being delivered to

▦ PITFALL PREVENTION 23.3

COMPARE ENERGY IN A CAPACITOR, RESISTOR, AND INDUCTOR We have now seen three circuit elements to which we can transfer energy. Keep in mind the difference in energy transfer mechanisms. A capacitor stores a given amount of energy for a fixed charge on its plates. Further energy is delivered to the capacitor as a current in the wires connected to the capacitor delivers more charge to the plates. An inductor stores a given amount of energy if the current remains constant. Further energy is delivered to the inductor by increasing the current. A resistor acts differently because the energy is not stored as potential energy but rather is transformed to internal energy. Energy continues to be delivered to the resistor as long as it carries a current.

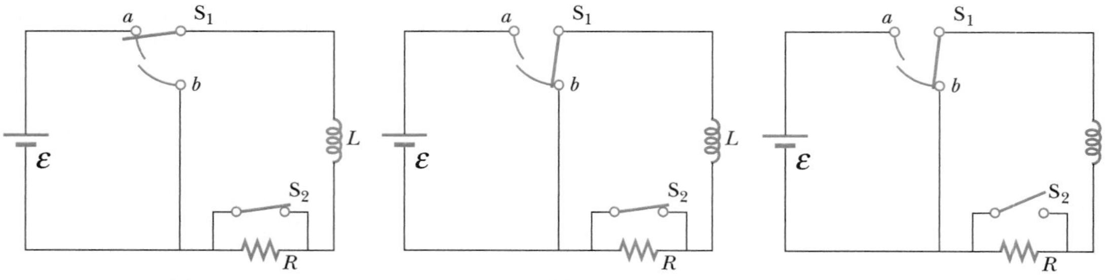

(a)   (b)   (c)

FIGURE 23.31 An *RL* circuit used for conceptualizing energy storage in an inductor. (a) With the switches as shown, the battery establishes a current through the inductor. (b) Switch S_1 is thrown to position *b*. Because the ends of the inductor are connected by a resistance-free path, the current continues to flow through the inductor. (c) Switch S_2 is opened, adding the resistor to the circuit, and energy is delivered to the resistor. This energy can only have been stored in the inductor because that is the only other element in the circuit.

it. The next step is to open switch S_2 as shown in Figure 23.31c, which puts the resistor into the circuit. There is now current in the resistor, and energy is delivered to the resistor. Where is the energy coming from? The only other element in the circuit previous to opening switch S_2 was the inductor. Energy must therefore have been stored in the inductor and is now being delivered to the resistor.

Now let us determine the energy per unit volume, or energy density, stored in a magnetic field. For simplicity, consider a solenoid whose inductance is $L = \mu_0 n^2 A\ell$ (see Example 23.7). The magnetic field of the solenoid is $B = \mu_0 nI$. Substituting the expression for L and $I = B/\mu_0 n$ into Equation 23.20 gives

$$U_B = \tfrac{1}{2}LI^2 = \tfrac{1}{2}\mu_0 n^2 A\ell \left(\frac{B}{\mu_0 n}\right)^2 = \frac{B^2}{2\mu_0}(A\ell) \qquad [23.21]$$

Because $A\ell$ is the volume of the solenoid, the energy stored per unit volume in a magnetic field—in other words, the *magnetic energy density*—is

■ **Magnetic energy density**

$$u_B = \frac{U_B}{A\ell} = \frac{B^2}{2\mu_0} \qquad [23.22]$$

Although Equation 23.22 was derived for the special case of a solenoid, **it is valid for any region of space in which a magnetic field exists.** Note that it is similar to the equation for the energy per unit volume stored in an electric field, given by $\tfrac{1}{2}\epsilon_0 E^2$ (Eq. 20.32). In both cases, the energy density is proportional to the square of the magnitude of the field.

QUICK QUIZ 23.9 You are performing an experiment that requires the highest possible energy density in the interior of a very long solenoid. Which of the following increases the energy density? (More than one choice may be correct.) **(a)** increasing the number of turns per unit length on the solenoid **(b)** increasing the cross-sectional area of the solenoid **(c)** increasing only the length of the solenoid while keeping the number of turns per unit length fixed **(d)** increasing the current in the solenoid

EXAMPLE 23.9 **What Happens to the Energy in the Inductor?**

Consider once again the *RL* circuit shown in Active Figure 23.26 in which switch S is thrown to position *b* at $t = 0$. Recall that the current in the right-hand loop decays exponentially with time according to the expression $I = I_i e^{-t/\tau}$, where $I_i = \mathcal{E}/R$ is the initial current in the circuit and $\tau = L/R$ is the time constant. Let us show explicitly that all the energy stored in

the magnetic field of the inductor is transferred to the resistor.

Solution The rate at which energy is transferred to the resistor is I^2R, where *I* is the instantaneous current. Using *I* from Equation 23.18,

$$\mathcal{P} = I^2R = (I_i e^{-Rt/L})^2 R = I_i^2 R e^{-2Rt/L}$$

To find the total energy transferred to the resistor, we integrate this expression over the limits $t = 0$ to $t = \infty$ (because it takes an infinite time for the current to reach zero):

$$(1) \quad E = \int_0^\infty \mathcal{P} \, dt = \int_0^\infty I_i^2 R e^{-2Rt/L} \, dt = I_i^2 R \int_0^\infty e^{-2Rt/L} \, dt$$

If we identify the variable $x = 2Rt/L$ so that $dx = (2R/L) \, dt$, we can rewrite (1) as,

$$E = I_i^2 R \left(\frac{L}{2R}\right) \int_0^\infty e^{-x} \, dx = \frac{I_i^2 L}{2} (-e^{-x}) \Big|_0^\infty$$

$$= \frac{I_i^2 L}{2} [0 - (-1)] = \tfrac{1}{2} I_i^2 L$$

Note that this expression is equal to the initial energy stored in the magnetic field of the inductor, given by Equation 23.20, as we set out to prove.

EXAMPLE 23.10 **The Coaxial Cable**

A long coaxial cable consists of two concentric cylindrical conductors of radii a and b and length ℓ as in Figure 23.32. The inner conductor is assumed to be a thin cylindrical shell. The conductors carry current I in opposite directions.

A Calculate the self-inductance L of this cable.

Solution To obtain L, we must know the magnetic flux through any cross-section between the two conductors. From Ampère's law (Eq. 22.29), we know that the magnetic field between the conductors is $B = \mu_0 I / 2\pi r$. The magnetic field is zero outside the conductors ($r > b$) because the net current through a circular path surrounding both wires is zero. The magnetic field is zero inside the inner conductor because it is hollow and no current flows within a radius $r < a$.

The magnetic field is perpendicular to the light blue rectangle of length ℓ and width $(b - a)$, the cross-section of interest. Dividing this rectangle into strips of width dr, such as the dark blue strip in Figure 23.32, we see that the area of each strip is $\ell \, dr$ and the flux through each strip is $B \, dA = B\ell \, dr$. Hence, the total magnetic flux through the entire cross-section is

$$\Phi_B = \int B \, dA = \int_a^b \frac{\mu_0 I}{2\pi r} \ell \, dr = \frac{\mu_0 I \ell}{2\pi} \int_a^b \frac{dr}{r}$$

$$= \frac{\mu_0 I \ell}{2\pi} \ln\left(\frac{b}{a}\right)$$

Using this result, we find that the self-inductance of the cable is

$$L = \frac{\Phi_B}{I} = \frac{\mu_0 \ell}{2\pi} \ln\left(\frac{b}{a}\right)$$

B Calculate the total energy stored in the magnetic field of the cable.

Solution Using Equation 23.20 and the results to part A gives

$$U_B = \tfrac{1}{2} L I^2 = \frac{\mu_0 \ell I^2}{4\pi} \ln\left(\frac{b}{a}\right)$$

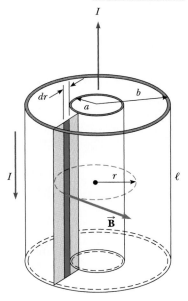

FIGURE 23.32 (Example 23.10) Section of a long coaxial cable. The inner and outer conductors carry equal currents in opposite directions.

23.8 THE REPULSIVE MODEL FOR MAGNETIC LEVITATION

CONTEXT CONNECTION

In Chapter 22, we considered a model for magnetic levitation that is based on the attractive force between a magnet and a rail made of magnetic material. The second major model for magnetically levitated vehicles is the EDS (*electrodynamic system*) model. The EDS model is used in Japan Railways's magnetic levitation system. This system uses superconducting magnets, unlike the conventional room-temperature magnets used in the German Transrapid. The result is improved energy efficiency. There is promise for even better efficiency in the future if higher-temperature superconductors are developed.

FIGURE 23.33 Schematic diagram of the levitation system for the Japanese maglev vehicle. The magnets induce currents in the coils at the side of the track so that, by Lenz's law, the repulsive force pushes the vehicle upward.

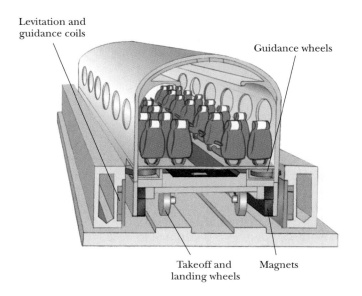

Levitation and guidance coils

Guidance wheels

Takeoff and landing wheels

Magnets

In this model, we appeal to Lenz's law. In the simplest form of the model, the vehicle carries a magnet. As the magnet passes over a metal plate that runs along the center of the track, currents are induced in the plate that tend to oppose the original change. The result is a *repulsive* force, which lifts the vehicle.

Although the idea of inducing a current in a metal plate is a valid concept, it represents a large expense in terms of the amount of metal required for a long track. Another technique is used in Japan's maglev vehicle. In this vehicle, the current is induced by magnets passing by coils located on the side of the railway channel. A schematic illustration of such a vehicle is given in Figure 23.33.

One of the disadvantages of the EMS model discussed in Chapter 22 is the instability of the attractive force, requiring feedback electronics. The EDS model, however, has a *natural* stabilizing feature. If the vehicle drops, the repulsion becomes stronger and pushes the vehicle back up. If the vehicle rises, the force decreases and the vehicle drops back down. Another advantage of the EDS system is the larger separation of about 10 cm between track and vehicle, as opposed to 10 mm in the EMS model.

A disadvantage of the EDS system is that *levitation only exists while the vehicle is moving* because it depends on Faraday's law; that is, a magnetic *change* must occur. Therefore, the vehicle must have landing wheels for stopping and starting at stations; these wheels are indicated in Figure 23.33.

Another disadvantage of the EDS system is that the induced currents result in a *drag* force as well as a lift force. The drag force requires more power for propulsion. It is larger than the lift force for small speeds, but the drag force maximizes at some speed and then begins to decrease. The lift force continues to increase as the speed increases. Therefore, it is advantageous to travel at high speeds, but the significant drag force at low speeds must be overcome every time the vehicle starts up.

The Japanese maglev project is jointly developed by the Central Japan Railway Co., the Railway Technical Research Institute, and the Japan Railway Construction, Transport, and Technology Agency. Exhaustive tests have been performed on five generations of maglev vehicles, beginning with the four-seater ML100, built in 1972 to celebrate Japan Railways's 100th anniversary. Current tests are being performed on the sixth-generation vehicle, the MLX01, a multicar train that can carry more than 100 passengers in its commercial form. A 43-km test line between Sakaigawa and Akiyama in Yamanashi Prefecture was opened in 1997. As mentioned in the Context introduction, the MLX01 holds the world speed record for magnetic levitation vehicles at 581 km/h. The Yamanashi Test Line is funded by the Japanese government, with the intention of final confirmation of maglev feasibility and commercial operation within the next few years. Once the Japanese system enters commercial operation, it will be interesting to watch the competition between it and the German Transrapid system! ▪

SUMMARY

The **magnetic flux** through a surface associated with a magnetic field $\vec{\mathbf{B}}$ is

$$\Phi_B = \int \vec{\mathbf{B}} \cdot d\vec{\mathbf{A}} \qquad [23.1]$$

where the integral is over the surface.

Faraday's law of induction states that the emf induced in a circuit is directly proportional to the time rate of change of magnetic flux through the circuit:

$$\mathcal{E} = -N \frac{d\Phi_B}{dt} \qquad [23.3]$$

where N is the number of turns and Φ_B is the magnetic flux through each turn.

When a conducting bar of length ℓ moves through a magnetic field $\vec{\mathbf{B}}$ with a velocity $\vec{\mathbf{v}}$ so that $\vec{\mathbf{v}}$ is perpendicular to $\vec{\mathbf{B}}$, the emf induced in the bar (called the **motional emf**) is

$$\mathcal{E} = -B\ell v \qquad [23.5]$$

Lenz's law states that the induced current and induced emf in a conductor are in such a direction as to oppose the change that produced them.

A general form of Faraday's law of induction is

$$\mathcal{E} = \oint \vec{\mathbf{E}} \cdot d\vec{\mathbf{s}} = -\frac{d\Phi_B}{dt} \qquad [23.9]$$

where $\vec{\mathbf{E}}$ is a nonconservative electric field produced by the changing magnetic flux.

When the current in a coil changes with time, an emf is induced in the coil according to Faraday's law. The **self-induced emf** is described by the expression

$$\mathcal{E}_L = -L \frac{dI}{dt} \qquad [23.10]$$

where L is the *inductance* of the coil. Inductance is a measure of the opposition of a device to a change in current.

The **inductance** of a coil is

$$L = \frac{N\Phi_B}{I} \qquad [23.11]$$

where Φ_B is the magnetic flux through the coil and N is the total number of turns. Inductance has the SI unit the **henry** (H), where $1\ \mathrm{H} = 1\ \mathrm{V \cdot s/A}$.

If a resistor and inductor are connected in series to a battery of emf $\mathcal{E}$ as shown in Active Figure 23.23 and a switch in the circuit is closed at $t = 0$, the current in the circuit varies with time according to the expression

$$I(t) = \frac{\mathcal{E}}{R}(1 - e^{-t/\tau}) \qquad [23.14]$$

where $\tau = L/R$ is the **time constant** of the *RL* circuit.

If the battery is removed from an *RL* circuit as in Active Figure 23.26 with the switch thrown to position *b*, the current decays exponentially with time according to the expression

$$I(t) = \frac{\mathcal{E}}{R}e^{-t/\tau} \qquad [23.18]$$

where $\mathcal{E}/R$ is the initial current in the circuit.

The energy stored in the magnetic field of an inductor carrying a current I is

$$U_B = \tfrac{1}{2}LI^2 \qquad [23.20]$$

The energy per unit volume (or energy density) at a point where the magnetic field is B is

$$u_B = \frac{B^2}{2\mu_0} \qquad [23.22]$$

QUESTIONS

☐ = answer available in the *Student Solutions Manual and Study Guide*

1. A loop of wire is placed in a uniform magnetic field. For what orientation of the loop is the magnetic flux a maximum? For what orientation is the flux zero?

2. A bar magnet is held above a loop of wire in a horizontal plane as shown in Figure Q23.2. The south end of the magnet is toward the loop of wire. The magnet is dropped toward the loop. Find the direction of the current in the resistor (a) while the magnet is falling toward the loop and (b) after the magnet has passed through the loop and is moving away from it.

3. As the bar in Figure Q23.3 moves to the right, an electric field is set up directed downward in the bar. Explain why

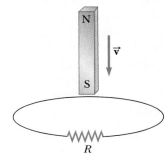

FIGURE **Q23.2**

the electric field would be upward if the bar were moving to the left.

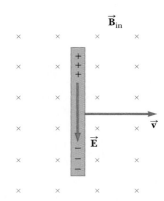

FIGURE **Q23.3** Questions 23.3 and 23.4.

4. As the bar in Figure Q23.3 moves perpendicular to the field, is an external force required to keep it moving with constant speed?

5. The bar in Figure Q23.5 moves on rails to the right with a velocity $\vec{v}$, and the uniform, constant magnetic field is directed out of the page. Why is the induced current clockwise? If the bar were moving to the left, what would be the direction of the induced current?

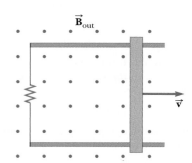

FIGURE **Q23.5** Questions 23.5 and 23.6.

6. Explain why an applied force is necessary to keep the bar in Figure Q23.5 moving with a constant speed.

7. In a hydroelectric dam, how is the energy produced that is then transferred out by electrical transmission? That is, how is the energy of motion of the water converted to energy that is transmitted by AC electricity?

8. A piece of aluminum is dropped vertically downward between the poles of an electromagnet. Does the magnetic field affect the velocity of the aluminum?

9. When the switch in Figure Q23.9a is closed, a current is set up in the coil and the metal ring springs upward (Fig. Q23.9b). Explain this behavior.

10. Assume that the battery in Figure Q23.9a is replaced by an AC source and that the switch is held closed. If it is held down, the metal ring on top of the solenoid becomes hot. Why?

11. Find the direction of the current in the resistor in Figure Q23.11 (a) at the instant the switch is closed, (b) after the switch has been closed for several minutes, and (c) at the instant the switch is opened.

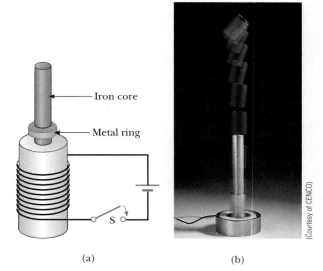

(a)   (b)

FIGURE **Q23.9** Questions 23.9 and 23.10.

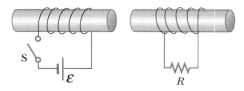

FIGURE **Q23.11**

12. An emf is induced between the wingtips of an airplane because of its motion in the Earth's magnetic field. Can this emf be used to power a light in the passenger compartment? Explain your answer.

13. Section 7.3 defined conservative and nonconservative forces. Section 20.1 stated that an electric charge creates an electric field that produces a conservative force. Argue now that induction creates an electric field that produces a nonconservative force.

14. What parameters affect the inductance of a coil? Does the inductance of a coil depend on the current in the coil?

15. Suppose the switch in Figure Q23.15 has been closed for a long time and is suddenly opened. Does the current instantaneously drop to zero? Why does a spark appear at the switch contacts at the moment the switch is opened?

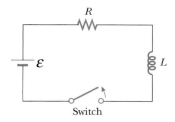

FIGURE **Q23.15**

16. Consider this thesis: "Joseph Henry, America's first professional physicist, caused the most recent basic change in the human view of the Universe when he discovered self-

induction during a school vacation at the Albany Academy about 1830. Before that time, one could think of the Universe as composed of just one thing: matter. The energy that temporarily maintains the current after a battery is removed from a coil, on the other hand, is not energy that belongs to any chunk of matter. It is energy in the massless magnetic field surrounding the coil. With Henry's discovery, Nature forced us to admit that the Universe consists of fields as well as matter." Argue for or against the statement. What in your view makes up the Universe?

17. If the current in an inductor is doubled, by what factor does the stored energy change?

18. Discuss the similarities between the energy stored in the electric field of a charged capacitor and the energy stored in the magnetic field of a current-carrying coil.

19. What is the inductance of two inductors connected in series? Does it matter if they are solenoids or toroids?

20. Can an object exert a force on itself? When a coil induces an emf in itself, does it exert a force on itself?

PROBLEMS

1, 2, 3 = straightforward, intermediate, challenging

☐ = full solution available in the *Student Solutions Manual and Study Guide*

Physics⊗Now™ = coached problem with hints available at **www.pop4e.com**

🖥 = computer useful in solving problem

▨ = paired numerical and symbolic problems

〽 = biomedical application

Section 23.1 ∎ Faraday's Law of Induction
Section 23.3 ∎ Lenz's Law

1. A flat loop of wire consisting of a single turn of cross-sectional area 8.00 cm^2 is perpendicular to a magnetic field that increases uniformly in magnitude from 0.500 T to 2.50 T in 1.00 s. What is the resulting induced current if the loop has a resistance of 2.00 Ω?

2. A 25-turn circular coil of wire has diameter 1.00 m. It is placed with its axis along the direction of the Earth's magnetic field of 50.0 μT, and then in 0.200 s it is flipped 180°. An average emf of what magnitude is generated in the coil?

3. **Physics⊗Now**™ A strong electromagnet produces a uniform magnetic field of 1.60 T over a cross-sectional area of 0.200 m^2. We place a coil having 200 turns and a total resistance of 20.0 Ω around the electromagnet. We then smoothly reduce the current in the electromagnet until it reaches zero in 20.0 ms. What is the current induced in the coil?

4. An aluminum ring of radius r_1 and resistance R is placed around the top of a long air-core solenoid with n turns per meter and smaller radius r_2 as shown in Figure P23.4. Assume that the axial component of the field produced by the solenoid over the area of the end of the solenoid is one-half as strong as at the solenoid's center. Assume that the solenoid produces negligible field outside its cross-sectional area. The current in the solenoid is increasing at a rate of $\Delta I/\Delta t$. (a) What is the induced current in the ring? (b) At the center of the ring, what is the magnetic field produced by the induced current in the ring? (c) What is the direction of this field?

5. (a) A loop of wire in the shape of a rectangle of width w and length L and a long, straight wire carrying a current

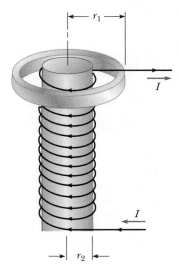

FIGURE **P23.4**

I lie on a tabletop as shown in Figure P23.5. (a) Determine the magnetic flux through the loop due to the current I. (b) Suppose the current is changing with time according to $I = a + bt$, where a and b are constants. Determine the emf that is induced in the loop if $b = 10.0$ A/s, $h = 1.00$ cm, $w = 10.0$ cm, and $L = 100$ cm. What is the direction of the induced current in the rectangle?

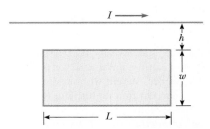

FIGURE **P23.5** Problems 23.5 and 23.59.

6. A coil of 15 turns and radius 10.0 cm surrounds a long solenoid of radius 2.00 cm and 1.00×10^3 turns/m (Fig. P23.6). The current in the solenoid changes as $I = (5.00 \text{ A}) \sin(120t)$. Find the induced emf in the 15-turn coil as a function of time.

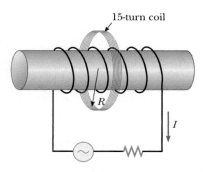

15-turn coil

R

I

FIGURE **P23.6**

7. A 30-turn circular coil of radius 4.00 cm and resistance 1.00 Ω is placed in a magnetic field directed perpendicular to the plane of the coil. The magnitude of the magnetic field varies in time according to the expression $B = 0.010\ 0t + 0.040\ 0t^2$, where t is in seconds and B is in teslas. Calculate the induced emf in the coil at $t = 5.00$ s.

8. An instrument based on induced emf has been used to measure projectile speeds up to 6 km/s. A small magnet is imbedded in the projectile as shown in Figure P23.8. The projectile passes through two coils separated by a distance d. As the projectile passes through each coil, a pulse of emf is induced in the coil. The time interval between pulses can be measured accurately with an oscilloscope, and thus the speed can be determined. (a) Sketch a graph of ΔV versus t for the arrangement shown. Consider a current that flows counterclockwise as viewed from the starting point of the projectile as positive. On your graph, indicate which pulse is from coil 1 and which is from coil 2. (b) If the pulse separation is 2.40 ms and $d = 1.50$ m, what is the projectile speed?

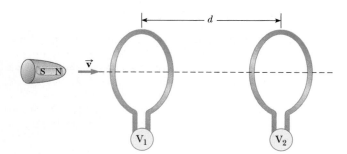

d

$\vec{v}$

S N

V_1 V_2

FIGURE **P23.8**

9. When a wire carries an AC current with a known frequency, you can use a *Rogowski coil* to determine the amplitude I_{max} of the current without disconnecting the wire to shunt the current in a meter. The Rogowski coil, shown in Figure P23.9, simply clips around the wire. It consists of a toroidal conductor wrapped around a circular return cord. The toroid has n turns per unit length and a cross-sectional area A. The current to be measured is given by $I(t) = I_{max} \sin \omega t$. (a) Show that the amplitude of the emf induced in the Rogowski coil is $\mathcal{E}_{max} = \mu_0 nA\omega I_{max}$. (b) Explain why the wire carrying the unknown current need not be at the center of the Rogowski coil and why the coil will not respond to nearby currents that it does not enclose.

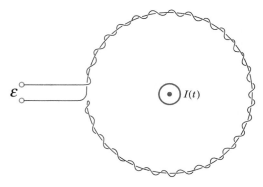

$\mathcal{E}$ $I(t)$

FIGURE **P23.9**

10. A piece of insulated wire is shaped into a figure eight as shown in Figure P23.10. The radius of the upper circle is 5.00 cm and that of the lower circle is 9.00 cm. The wire has a uniform resistance per unit length of 3.00 Ω/m. A uniform magnetic field is applied perpendicular to the plane of the two circles, in the direction shown. The magnetic field is increasing at a constant rate of 2.00 T/s. Find the magnitude and direction of the induced current in the wire.

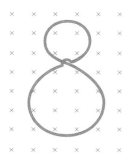

FIGURE **P23.10**

Section 23.2 ■ Motional emf
Section 23.3 ■ Lenz's Law

Note: Problem 22.62 can be assigned with this section.

11. An automobile has a vertical radio antenna 1.20 m long. The automobile travels at 65.0 km/h on a horizontal road where the Earth's magnetic field is 50.0 μT directed toward the north and downward at an angle of 65.0° below the horizontal. (a) Specify the direction that the automobile should move to generate the maximum motional emf in the antenna, with the top of the antenna positive relative to the bottom. (b) Calculate the magnitude of this induced emf.

12. Consider the arrangement shown in Figure P23.12. Assume that $R = 6.00\ \Omega$, $\ell = 1.20$ m, and a uniform 2.50-T magnetic field is directed into the page. At what speed should the bar be moved to produce a current of 0.500 A in the resistor?

13. Figure P23.12 shows a top view of a bar that can slide without friction. The resistor is 6.00 Ω, and a 2.50-T magnetic field is directed perpendicularly downward, into the paper.

Let $\ell = 1.20$ m. (a) Calculate the applied force required to move the bar to the right at a constant speed of 2.00 m/s. (b) At what rate is energy delivered to the resistor?

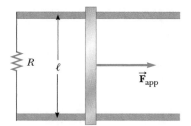

FIGURE **P23.12** Problems 23.12, 23.13, 23.14, and 23.15.

14. A conducting rod of length ℓ moves on two horizontal, frictionless rails as shown in Figure P23.12. If a constant force of 1.00 N moves the bar at 2.00 m/s through a magnetic field $\vec{\mathbf{B}}$ that is directed into the page, (a) what is the current through the 8.00-Ω resistor R? (b) What is the rate at which energy is delivered to the resistor? (c) What is the mechanical power delivered by the force $\vec{\mathbf{F}}_{app}$?

15. A metal rod of mass m slides without friction along two parallel horizontal rails, separated by a distance ℓ and connected by a resistor R, as shown in Figure P23.12. A uniform vertical magnetic field of magnitude B is applied perpendicular to the plane of the paper. The applied force shown in the figure acts only for a moment, to give the rod a speed v. In terms of m, ℓ, R, B, and v, find the distance the rod will then slide as it coasts to a stop.

16. Very large magnetic fields can be produced using a procedure called *flux compression*. A metallic cylindrical tube of radius R is placed coaxially in a long solenoid of somewhat larger radius. The space between the tube and the solenoid is filled with a highly explosive material. When the explosive is set off, it collapses the tube to a cylinder of radius $r < R$. If the collapse happens very rapidly, induced current in the tube maintains the magnetic flux nearly constant inside the tube. If the initial magnetic field in the solenoid is 2.50 T and $R/r = 12.0$, what maximum value of magnetic field can be achieved?

17. The *homopolar generator*, also called the *Faraday disk*, is a low-voltage, high-current electric generator. It consists of a rotating conducting disk with one stationary brush (a sliding electrical contact) at its axle and another at a point on its circumference as shown in Figure P23.17. A magnetic field is applied perpendicular to the plane of the disk. Assume that the field is 0.900 T, the angular speed is 3 200 rev/min, and the radius of the disk is 0.400 m. Find the emf generated between the brushes. When superconducting coils are used to produce a large magnetic field, a homopolar generator can have a power output of several megawatts. Such a generator is useful, for example, in purifying metals by electrolysis. If a voltage is applied to the output terminals of the generator, it runs in reverse as a *homopolar motor* capable of providing great torque, useful in ship propulsion.

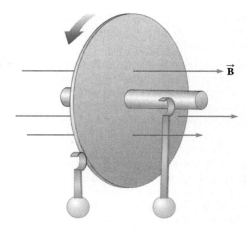

FIGURE **P23.17**

18. **Review problem.** A flexible metallic wire with linear density 3.00×10^{-3} kg/m is stretched between two fixed clamps 64.0 cm apart and held under tension 267 N. A magnet is placed near the wire as shown in Figure P23.18. Assume that the magnet produces a uniform field of 4.50 mT over a 2.00-cm length at the center of the wire and a negligible field elsewhere. The wire is set vibrating at its fundamental (lowest) frequency. The section of the wire in the magnetic field moves with a uniform amplitude of 1.50 cm. Find (a) the frequency and (b) the amplitude of the electromotive force induced between the ends of the wire.

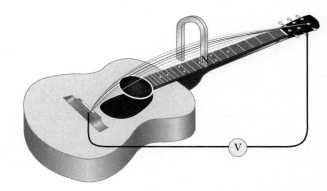

FIGURE **P23.18**

19. A helicopter (Fig. P23.19) has blades of length 3.00 m, extending out from a central hub and rotating at 2.00 rev/s.

(Ross Harrison/Getty Images)

FIGURE **P23.19**

If the vertical component of the Earth's magnetic field is 50.0 μT, what is the emf induced between the blade tip and the center hub?

20. Use Lenz's law to answer the following questions concerning the direction of induced currents. (a) What is the direction of the induced current in resistor R in Figure P23.20a when the bar magnet is moved to the left? (b) What is the direction of the current induced in the resistor R immediately after the switch S in Figure P23.20b is closed? (c) What is the direction of the induced current in R when the current I in Figure P23.20c decreases rapidly to zero? (d) A copper bar is moved to the right while its axis is maintained in a direction perpendicular to a magnetic field as shown in Figure P31.28d. If the top of the bar becomes positive relative to the bottom, what is the direction of the magnetic field?

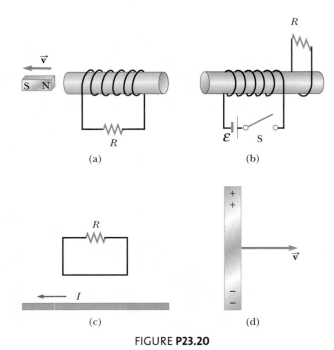

FIGURE **P23.20**

21. Physics⊗Now™ A conducting rectangular loop of mass M, resistance R, and dimensions w by ℓ falls from rest into a magnetic field $\vec{\mathbf{B}}$ as shown in Figure P23.21. During the time interval before the top edge of the loop reaches the field, the loop approaches a terminal speed v_T. (a) Show that

$$v_T = \frac{MgR}{B^2 w^2}$$

(b) Why is v_T proportional to R? (c) Why is it inversely proportional to B^2?

22. A rectangular coil with resistance R has N turns, each of length ℓ and width w as shown in Figure P23.22. The coil moves into a uniform magnetic field $\vec{\mathbf{B}}$ with constant velocity $\vec{\mathbf{v}}$. What are the magnitude and direction of the total magnetic force on the coil (a) as it enters the magnetic field, (b) as it moves within the field, and (c) as it leaves the field?

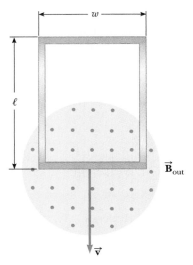

FIGURE **P23.21**

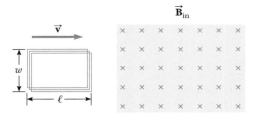

FIGURE **P23.22**

23. Physics⊗Now™ A coil of area 0.100 m² is rotating at 60.0 rev/s with the axis of rotation perpendicular to a 0.200-T magnetic field. (a) If the coil has 1 000 turns, what is the maximum emf generated in it? (b) What is the orientation of the coil with respect to the magnetic field when the maximum induced voltage occurs?

24. A long solenoid, with its axis along the x axis, consists of 200 turns per meter of wire that carries a steady current of 15.0 A. A coil is formed by wrapping 30 turns of thin wire around a circular frame that has a radius of 8.00 cm. The coil is placed inside the solenoid and mounted on an axis that is a diameter of the coil and that coincides with the y axis. The coil is then rotated with an angular speed of 4.00π rad/s. (The plane of the coil is in the yz plane at $t = 0$.) Determine the emf generated in the coil as a function of time.

Section 23.4 ▮ Induced emfs and Electric Fields

25. A magnetic field directed into the page changes with time according to $B = (0.030\,0t^2 + 1.40)$ T, where t is in seconds. The field has a circular cross-section of radius $R = 2.50$ cm (Fig. P23.25). What are the magnitude and direction of the electric field at point P_1 when $t = 3.00$ s and $r_1 = 0.020\,0$ m?

26. For the situation shown in Figure P23.25, the magnetic field changes with time according to the expression $B = (2.00t^3 - 4.00t^2 + 0.800)$ T and $r_2 = 2R = 5.00$ cm. (a) Calculate the magnitude and direction of the force

exerted on an electron located at point P_2 when $t = 2.00$ s. (b) At what time is this force equal to zero?

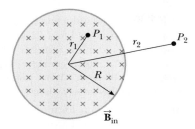

FIGURE **P23.25** Problems 23.25 and 23.26.

Section 23.5 ■ Self-Inductance

27. A coil has an inductance of 3.00 mH, and the current in it changes from 0.200 A to 1.50 A in a time interval of 0.200 s. Find the magnitude of the average induced emf in the coil during this time interval.

28. A coiled telephone cord forms a spiral with 70 turns, a diameter of 1.30 cm, and an unstretched length of 60.0 cm. Determine the self-inductance of one conductor in the unstretched cord.

29. **Physics**✕**Now**™ A 10.0-mH inductor carries a current $I = I_{max} \sin \omega t$, with $I_{max} = 5.00$ A and $\omega/2\pi = 60.0$ Hz. What is the self-induced emf as a function of time?

30. An emf of 24.0 mV is induced in a 500-turn coil at an instant when the current is 4.00 A and is changing at the rate of 10.0 A/s. What is the magnetic flux through each turn of the coil?

31. The current in a 90.0-mH inductor changes with time as $I = 1.00t^2 - 6.00t$ (in SI units). Find the magnitude of the induced emf at (a) $t = 1.00$ s and (b) $t = 4.00$ s. (c) At what time is the emf zero?

32. A toroid has a major radius R and a minor radius r, and is tightly wound with N turns of wire as shown in Figure P23.32. If $R \gg r$, the magnetic field in the region enclosed by the wire of the torus, of cross-sectional area $A = \pi r^2$, is essentially the same as the magnetic field of a solenoid that has been bent into a large circle of radius R. Modeling the field as the uniform field of a long solenoid, show that the self-inductance of such a toroid is approximately

$$L \approx \frac{\mu_0 N^2 A}{2\pi R}$$

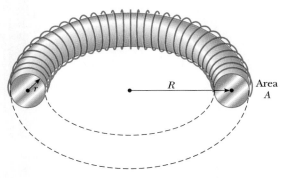

FIGURE **P23.32**

(An exact expression of the inductance of a toroid with a rectangular cross-section is derived in Problem 23.60.)

Section 23.6 ■ RL Circuits

33. A 12.0-V battery is connected into a series circuit containing a 10.0-Ω resistor and a 2.00-H inductor. In what time interval will the current reach (a) 50.0% and (b) 90.0% of its final value?

34. Show that $I = I_i e^{-t/\tau}$ is a solution of the differential equation

$$IR + L \frac{dI}{dt} = 0$$

where $\tau = L/R$ and I_i is the current at $t = 0$.

35. Consider the circuit in Figure P23.35, taking $\mathcal{E} = 6.00$ V, $L = 8.00$ mH, and $R = 4.00$ Ω. (a) What is the inductive time constant of the circuit? (b) Calculate the current in the circuit 250 μs after the switch is closed. (c) What is the value of the final steady-state current? (d) How long does it take the current to reach 80.0% of its maximum value?

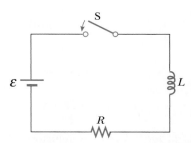

FIGURE **P23.35** Problems 23.35, 23.36, and 23.38.

36. For the RL circuit shown in Figure P23.35, let the inductance be 3.00 H, the resistance 8.00 Ω, and the battery emf 36.0 V. (a) Calculate the ratio of the potential difference across the resistor to the voltage across the inductor when the current is 2.00 A. (b) Calculate the voltage across the inductor when the current is 4.50 A.

37. A circuit consists of a coil, a switch, and a battery, all in series. The internal resistance of the battery is negligible compared with that of the coil. The switch is originally open. It is thrown closed, and after a time interval Δt, the current in the circuit reaches 80.0% of its final value. The switch remains closed for a time interval much longer than Δt. Then the battery is disconnected and the terminals of the coil are connected together to form a short circuit. (a) After an equal additional time interval Δt elapses, the current is what percentage of its maximum value? (b) At the moment $2\Delta t$ after the coil is short-circuited, the current in the coil is what percentage of its maximum value?

38. When the switch in Figure P23.35 is closed, the current takes 3.00 ms to reach 98.0% of its final value. If $R = 10.0$ Ω, what is the inductance?

39. The switch in Figure P23.39 is open for $t < 0$ and then closed at time $t = 0$. Find the current in the inductor and the current in the switch as functions of time thereafter.

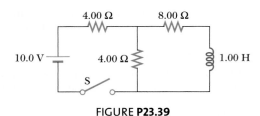

FIGURE **P23.39**

40. One application of an *RL* circuit is the generation of time-varying high voltage from a low-voltage source as shown in Figure P23.40. (a) What is the current in the circuit a long time after the switch has been in position *a*? (b) Now the switch is thrown quickly from *a* to *b*. Compute the initial voltage across each resistor and across the inductor. (c) How much time elapses before the voltage across the inductor drops to 12.0 V?

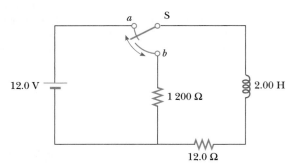

FIGURE **P23.40**

41. Physics⊗Now™ A 140-mH inductor and a 4.90-Ω resistor are connected with a switch to a 6.00-V battery as shown in Figure P23.41. (a) If the switch is thrown to the left (connecting the battery), how much time elapses before the current reaches 220 mA? (b) What is the current in the inductor 10.0 s after the switch is closed? (c) Now the switch is quickly thrown from *a* to *b*. How much time elapses before the current falls to 160 mA?

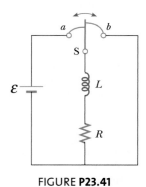

FIGURE **P23.41**

Section 23.7 ■ Energy Stored in a Magnetic Field

42. The magnetic field inside a superconducting solenoid is 4.50 T. The solenoid has an inner diameter of 6.20 cm and a length of 26.0 cm. Determine (a) the magnetic energy density in the field and (b) the energy stored in the magnetic field within the solenoid.

43. An air-core solenoid with 68 turns is 8.00 cm long and has a diameter of 1.20 cm. How much energy is stored in its magnetic field when it carries a current of 0.770 A?

44. An *RL* circuit in which the inductance is 4.00 H and the resistance is 5.00 Ω is connected to a 22.0-V battery at $t = 0$. (a) What energy is stored in the inductor when the current is 0.500 A? (b) At what rate is energy being stored in the inductor when $I = 1.00$ A? (c) What power is being delivered to the circuit by the battery when $I = 0.500$ A?

45. On a clear day at a certain location, a 100-V/m vertical electric field exists near the Earth's surface. At the same place, the Earth's magnetic field has a magnitude of 0.500×10^{-4} T. Compute the energy densities of the two fields.

Section 23.8 ■ Context Connection—The Repulsive Model for Magnetic Levitation

46. The following is a crude model for levitating a commercial transportation vehicle using Faraday's law. Assume that magnets are used to establish regions of horizontal magnetic field across the track as shown in Figure P23.46. Rectangular loops of wire are mounted on the vehicle so that the lower 20 cm of each loop passes into these regions of magnetic field. The upper portion of each loop contains a 25-Ω resistor. As the leading edge of a loop passes into the magnetic field, a current is induced in the loop as shown in the figure. The magnetic force on this current in the bottom of the loop, of length 10 cm, results in an upward force on the vehicle. (By electronic timing, a switch is opened in the loop before the loop's leading edge leaves the region of magnetic field, so a current is not induced in the opposite direction to apply a downward force on the vehicle.) The vehicle has a mass of 5×10^4 kg and travels at a speed of 400 km/h. If the vehicle has 100 loops carrying current at any moment, what is the approximate magnitude of the magnetic field required to levitate the vehicle? Assume that the magnetic force acts over the entire 10-cm length of the horizontal wire. Your answer should suggest that this design is impractical for magnetic levitation.

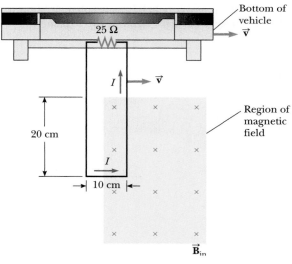

FIGURE **P23.46**

47. *The Meissner effect.* Compare this problem with Problem 20.76 on the force attracting a perfect dielectric into a strong electric field. A fundamental property of a type I superconducting material is *perfect diamagnetism*, or demonstration of the *Meissner effect,* illustrated in the photograph of the levitating magnet on page 693 and described as follows. The superconducting material has $\vec{B} = 0$ everywhere inside it. If a sample of the material is placed into an externally produced magnetic field or if it is cooled to become superconducting while it is in a magnetic field, electric currents appear on the surface of the sample. The currents have precisely the strength and orientation required to make the total magnetic field zero throughout the interior of the sample. The following problem will help you understand the magnetic force that can then act on the superconducting sample.

A vertical solenoid with a length of 120 cm and a diameter of 2.50 cm consists of 1 400 turns of copper wire carrying a counterclockwise current of 2.00 A as shown in Figure P23.47a. (a) Find the magnetic field in the vacuum inside the solenoid. (b) Find the energy density of the magnetic field. Note that the units J/m^3 of energy density are the same as the units N/m^2 of pressure. (c) Now a superconducting bar 2.20 cm in diameter is inserted partway into the solenoid. Its upper end is far outside the solenoid, where the magnetic field is negligible. The lower end of the bar is deep inside the solenoid. Identify the direction required for the current on the curved surface of the bar so that the total magnetic field is zero within the bar. The field created by the supercurrents is sketched in Figure P23.47b, and the total field is sketched in Figure P23.47c. (d) The field of the solenoid exerts a force on the current in the superconductor. Identify the direction of the force on the bar. (e) Calculate the magnitude of the force by multiplying the energy density of the solenoid field times the area of the bottom end of the superconducting bar.

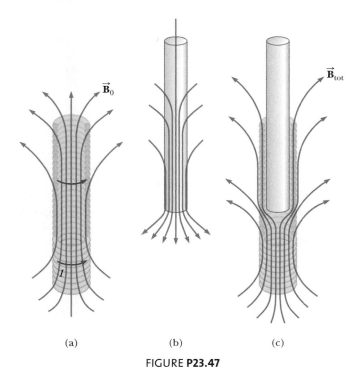

(a)   (b)   (c)

FIGURE **P23.47**

Additional Problems

48. Figure P23.48 is a graph of the induced emf versus time for a coil of N turns rotating with angular speed ω in a uniform magnetic field directed perpendicular to the axis of rotation of the coil. Copy this sketch (on a larger scale) and on the same set of axes show the graph of emf versus t (a) if the number of turns in the coil is doubled, (b) if instead the angular speed is doubled, and (c) if the angular speed is doubled while the number of turns in the coil is halved.

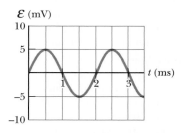

FIGURE **P23.48**

49. A steel guitar string vibrates (Figure 23.6). The component of magnetic field perpendicular to the area of a pickup coil nearby is given by

$$B = 50.0 \text{ mT} + (3.20 \text{ mT}) \sin(2\pi\,523\;t/s)$$

The circular pickup coil has 30 turns and radius 2.70 mm. Find the emf induced in the coil as a function of time.

50. ▨ Strong magnetic fields are used in such medical procedures as magnetic resonance imaging. A technician wearing a brass bracelet enclosing area $0.005\,00\text{ m}^2$ places her hand in a solenoid whose magnetic field is 5.00 T directed perpendicular to the plane of the bracelet. The electrical resistance around the circumference of the bracelet is $0.020\,0\;\Omega$. An unexpected power failure causes the field to drop to 1.50 T in a time of 20.0 ms. Find (a) the current induced in the bracelet and (b) the power delivered to the bracelet. (*Note:* As this problem implies, you should not wear any metal objects when working in regions of strong magnetic fields.)

51. Suppose you wrap wire onto the core from a roll of cellophane tape to make a coil. Describe how you can use a bar magnet to produce an induced voltage in the coil. What is the order of magnitude of the emf you generate? State the quantities you take as data and their values.

52. A bar of mass m, length d, and resistance R slides without friction in a horizontal plane, moving on parallel rails as shown in Figure P23.52. A battery that maintains a constant emf $\mathcal{E}$ is connected between the rails, and a constant

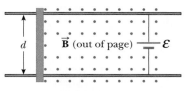

FIGURE **P23.52**

magnetic field $\vec{\mathbf{B}}$ is directed perpendicularly to the plane of the page. Assuming that the bar starts from rest, show that at time t it moves with a speed

$$v = \frac{\mathcal{E}}{Bd}(1 - e^{-B^2d^2t/mR})$$

53. **Review problem.** A particle with a mass of 2.00×10^{-16} kg and a charge of 30.0 nC starts from rest, is accelerated by a strong electric field, and is fired from a small source inside a region of uniform constant magnetic field 0.600 T. The velocity of the particle is perpendicular to the field. The circular orbit of the particle encloses a magnetic flux of 15.0 μWb. (a) Calculate the speed of the particle. (b) Calculate the potential difference through which the particle accelerated inside the source.

54. An *induction furnace* uses electromagnetic induction to produce eddy currents in a conductor, thereby raising the conductor's temperature. Commercial units operate at frequencies ranging from 60 Hz to about 1 MHz and deliver powers from a few watts to several megawatts. Induction heating can be used for warming a metal pan on a kitchen stove. It can also be used for welding in a vacuum enclosure so as to avoid oxidation and contamination of the metal. At high frequencies, induced currents occur only near the surface of the conductor—this phenomenon is the "skin effect." By creating an induced current for a short time interval at an appropriately high frequency, one can heat a sample down to a controlled depth. For example, the surface of a farm tiller can be tempered to make it hard and brittle for effective cutting while keeping the interior metal soft and ductile to resist breakage.

    To explore induction heating, consider a flat conducting disk of radius R, thickness b, and resistivity ρ. A sinusoidal magnetic field $B_{max} \cos \omega t$ is applied perpendicular to the disk. Assume that the field is uniform in space and that the frequency is so low that the skin effect is not important. Assume that the eddy currents occur in circles concentric with the disk. (a) Calculate the average power delivered to the disk. By what factor does the power change (b) when the amplitude of the field doubles, (c) when the frequency doubles, and (d) when the radius of the disk doubles?

55. The magnetic flux through a metal ring varies with time t according to $\Phi_B = 3(at^3 - bt^2)$T·m², with $a = 2.00$ s^{-3} and $b = 6.00$ s^{-2}. The resistance of the ring is 3.00 Ω. Determine the maximum current induced in the ring during the interval from $t = 0$ to $t = 2.00$ s.

56. Figure P23.56 shows a stationary conductor whose shape is similar to the letter **e**. The radius of its circular portion is

$a = 50.0$ cm. It is placed in a constant magnetic field of 0.500 T directed out of the page. A straight conducting rod, 50.0 cm long, is pivoted about point O and rotates with a constant angular speed of 2.00 rad/s. (a) Determine the induced emf in the loop POQ. Note that the area of the loop is $\theta a^2/2$. (b) If all the conducting material has a resistance per length of 5.00 Ω/m, what is the induced current in the loop POQ at the instant 0.250 s after point P passes point Q?

57. A *betatron* accelerates electrons to energies in the MeV range by means of electromagnetic induction. Electrons in a vacuum chamber are held in a circular orbit by a magnetic field perpendicular to the orbital plane. The magnetic field is gradually increased to induce an electric field around the orbit. (a) Show that the electric field is in the correct direction to make the electrons speed up. (b) Assume that the radius of the orbit remains constant. Show that the average magnetic field over the area enclosed by the orbit must be twice as large as the magnetic field at the circumference of the circle.

58. ✎ To monitor the breathing of a hospital patient, a thin belt is girded around the patient's chest. The belt is a 200-turn coil. When the patient inhales, the area encircled by the coil increases by 39.0 cm². The magnitude of the Earth's magnetic field is 50.0 μT and makes an angle of 28.0° with the plane of the coil. Assuming that a patient takes 1.80 s to inhale, find the average induced emf in the coil during this time.

59. A long, straight wire carries a current that is given by $I = I_{max} \sin(\omega t + \phi)$. The wire lies in the plane of a rectangular coil of N turns of wire as shown in Figure P23.5. The quantities I_{max}, ω, and ϕ are all constants. Determine the emf induced in the coil by the magnetic field created by the current in the straight wire. Assume that $I_{max} = 50.0$ A, $\omega = 200\pi$ s^{-1}, $N = 100$, $h = w = 5.00$ cm, and $L = 20.0$ cm.

60. The toroid in Figure P23.60 consists of N turns and has a rectangular cross-section. Its inner and outer radii are a and b, respectively. (a) Show that the inductance of the toroid is

$$L = \frac{\mu_0 N^2 h}{2\pi} \ln \frac{b}{a}$$

(b) Using this result, compute the self-inductance of a 500-turn toroid for which $a = 10.0$ cm, $b = 12.0$ cm, and $h = 1.00$ cm. (c) In Problem 23.32, an approximate expression for the inductance of a toroid with $R \gg r$ was derived. To get a feel for the accuracy of that result, use the expression in Problem 23.32 to compute the approximate inductance of the toroid described in part (b). Compare the result with the answer to part (b).

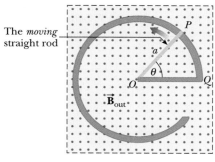

FIGURE **P23.56**

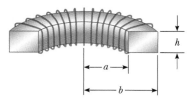

FIGURE **P23.60**

61. (a) A flat, circular coil does not really produce a uniform magnetic field in the area it encloses. Nonetheless, estimate the self-inductance of a flat, compact, circular coil, with radius R and N turns, by assuming that the field at its center is uniform over its area. (b) A circuit on a laboratory table consists of a 1.5-volt battery, a 270-Ω resistor, a switch, and three 30-cm-long patch cords connecting them. Suppose the circuit is arranged to be circular. Think of it as a flat coil with one turn. Compute the order of magnitude of its self-inductance and (c) of the time constant describing how fast the current increases when you close the switch.

62. To prevent damage from arcing in an electric motor, a discharge resistor is sometimes placed in parallel with the armature. If the motor is suddenly unplugged while running, this resistor limits the voltage that appears across the armature coils. Consider a 12.0-V DC motor with an armature that has a resistance of 7.50 Ω and an inductance of 450 mH. Assume that the magnitude of the self-induced emf in the armature coils is 10.0 V when the motor is running at normal speed. (The equivalent circuit for the armature is shown in Fig. P23.62.) Calculate the maximum resistance R that limits the voltage across the armature to 80.0 V when the motor is unplugged.

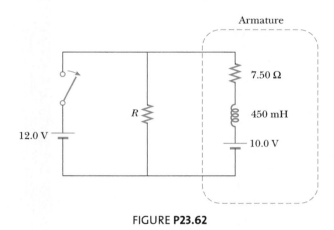

FIGURE **P23.62**

Review problems. Problems 23.63 through 23.65 apply ideas from this chapter and earlier chapters to some properties of superconductors, which were introduced in Section 21.3.

63. *The resistance of a superconductor.* In an experiment carried out by S. C. Collins between 1955 and 1958, a current was maintained in a superconducting lead ring for 2.50 yr with no observed loss. If the inductance of the ring was 3.14×10^{-8} H and the sensitivity of the experiment was 1 part in 10^9, what was the maximum resistance of the ring? (*Suggestion:* Treat this problem as a decaying current in an *RL* circuit and recall that $e^{-x} \approx 1 - x$ for small x.)

64. A novel method of storing energy has been proposed. A huge underground superconducting coil, 1.00 km in diameter, would be fabricated. It would carry a maximum current of 50.0 kA through each winding of a 150-turn Nb_3Sn solenoid. (a) If the inductance of this huge coil were 50.0 H, what would be the total energy stored? (b) What would be the compressive force per meter length acting between two adjacent windings 0.250 m apart?

65. *Superconducting power transmission.* The use of superconductors has been proposed for power transmission lines. A single coaxial cable (Fig. P23.65) could carry 1.00×10^3 MW (the output of a large power plant) at 200 kV, DC, over a distance of 1 000 km without loss. An inner wire of radius 2.00 cm, made from the superconductor Nb_3Sn, carries the current I in one direction. A surrounding superconducting cylinder, of radius 5.00 cm, would carry the return current I. In such a system, what is the magnetic field (a) at the surface of the inner conductor and (b) at the inner surface of the outer conductor? (c) How much energy would be stored in the space between the conductors in a 1 000-km superconducting line? (d) What is the pressure exerted on the outer conductor?

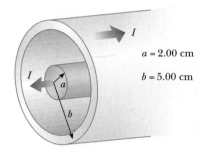

$a = 2.00$ cm

$b = 5.00$ cm

FIGURE **P23.65**

ANSWERS TO QUICK QUIZZES

23.1 (c). In all cases except this one, there is a change in the magnetic flux through the loop.

23.2 *c, d = e, b, a.* The magnitude of the emf is proportional to the rate of change of the magnetic flux. For the situation described, the rate of change of magnetic flux is proportional to the rate of change of the magnetic field. This rate of change is the slope of the graph in Figure 23.7. The magnitude of the slope is largest at *c*. Points *d* and *e* are on a straight line, so the slope is the same at each point. Point *b* represents a point of relatively small slope,

and *a* is at a point of zero slope because the curve is horizontal at that point.

23.3 (b). According to Equation 23.5, because *B* and *v* are fixed, the emf depends only on the length of the wire moving in the magnetic field. Thus, you want the long dimension moving through the magnetic field lines so that it is perpendicular to the velocity vector. In this case, the short dimension is parallel to the velocity vector.

23.4 (c). The force on the wire is of magnitude $F_{app} = F_B = I\ell B$, with I given by Equation 23.6. Thus, the force is proportional to the speed and the force doubles. Because $\mathcal{P} = F_{app}v$, the doubling of the force *and* the speed results in the power being four times as large.

23.5 (b). When the aluminum sheet moves between the poles of the magnet, circular currents called *eddy currents* are established in the aluminum. According to Lenz's law, these currents are in a direction so as to oppose the original change, which is the movement of the aluminum sheet in the magnetic field. Thus, the effect of the eddy currents is create a force opposite to the velocity. This *magnetic braking* causes the oscillations of the equal arm balance to settle down, and a reading of the mass can take place. Magnetic damping has an advantage over frictional damping in that the magnetic damping force goes exactly to zero as the speed goes to zero. On the other hand, if mechanical friction were used to damp the oscillation of the balance beam, the speed might go to zero at a final position other than zero.

23.6 (d). The constant rate of change of B will result in a constant rate of change of the magnetic flux. According to Equation 23.9, if $d\Phi_B/dt$ is constant, $\vec{\mathbf{E}}$ is constant in magnitude.

23.7 (b). When the iron rod is inserted into the solenoid, the inductance of the coil increases. As a result, more potential difference appears across the coil than before. Consequently, less potential difference appears across the lightbulb, so the bulb is dimmer.

23.8 (b). Figure 23.29 shows that circuit B has the larger time constant because in this circuit it takes longer for the current to reach its maximum value and then longer for this current to drop back down to zero after the switch is thrown to *b*. Equation 23.15 indicates that, for equal resistances R_A and R_B, the condition $\tau_B > \tau_A$ means that $L_A < L_B$.

23.9 (a), (d). Because the energy density depends on the magnitude of the magnetic field, we must increase the magnetic field to increase the energy density. For a solenoid, $B = \mu_0 nI$, where n is the number of turns per unit length. In (a), we increase n to increase the magnetic field. In (b), the change in cross-sectional area has no effect on the magnetic field. In (c), increasing the length but keeping n fixed has no effect on the magnetic field. Increasing the current in (d) increases the magnetic field in the solenoid.

Lifting, Propelling, and Braking the Vehicle

Now that we have investigated the principles of electromagnetism, let us respond to our central question for the *Magnetic Levitation Vehicles* Context:

> *How can we lift, propel, and brake a vehicle with magnetic forces?*

We have addressed two mechanisms for lifting the vehicle, one in each of the preceding chapters. Once the vehicle is suspended above the track, we must control its speed with propulsion and braking. We shall discuss these processes in this Context Conclusion.

Magnetic Propulsion

If you have a toy car made of iron, you can imagine how to propel the car with a magnet. You hold the magnet near the front of the car so that it exerts an attractive force on the car, causing it to accelerate from rest. As the car moves, you move the magnet in the same direction, not allowing the magnet and the car to touch. In essence, the car "chases" the moving magnet due to the attractive force.

You could increase the propelling force on the car by mounting a bar magnet on it, with the north pole near the front of the car and the south pole near the back. Now, you use two other bar magnets, one with its south pole in front of the car and another with its south pole near the back of the car. The magnet on the car is attracted to the front magnet and repelled by the rear magnet. In this manner, the car experiences a strong propelling force.

Such is the fundamental idea behind magnetic propulsion. Electromagnets are mounted on the magnetic levitation vehicle, and a series of propulsion coils are placed along the side of the track as shown in Figure 1. The polarity of the magnets on the vehicle remains constant. An electrical signal is passed through the coils such that each magnet on the vehicle "sees" a coil with opposite polarity ahead of it and a coil with the same polarity behind it. As a result, the vehicle experiences an attractive force from the coil ahead of it and a repulsive force from the coil behind it, both forces pushing the vehicle in the forward direction. Figure 1

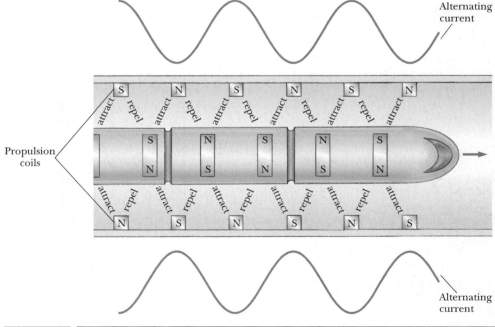

FIGURE 1 Magnetic propulsion. Magnets on the vehicle are attracted and repelled by electromagnetic poles created by a sinusoidal current passed through coils on the side of the track. As the wave of current moves along the track, the vehicle moves with it.

shows this situation at a single instant of time. As the sinusoidal wave in Figure 1 moves along the track, the vehicle "chases" it due to the magnetic forces.

Magnetic Braking

Electromagnetic transportation has the added benefit of a built-in braking mechanism. Lenz's law tells us that a magnetic change induces a current that acts to oppose the original change, which represents a natural braking mechanism. For example, if an aluminum plate is dropped between the poles of a very strong magnet, the plate drops slowly because currents established in the plate experience a magnetic force that opposes the fall.

In the case of magnetic levitation vehicles, imagine that the propulsion system is deactivated so that the vehicle begins to coast. The relative motion of magnets and coils in the train and track induces currents that slow the train down, according to Lenz's law. The propulsion system can be used in combination with this magnetic braking for complete control over the stopping process.

This principle is not new. Railroads operating in the Alps at the beginning of the 20th century included mechanisms for connecting the electric drive motor to a resistance when the train moved downhill. As the motion of the train causes the motor to turn, the motor acts as a generator. The generator produces a current in the resistance, resulting in a back emf. Because this back emf opposes the original change (the rotation of the motor), it controls the motion of the train down the hill. This same principle is now used in hybrid vehicles (see Context 1) so that the braking process feeds energy back to the battery.

A Third Levitation Model: the Inductrack

In Chapters 22 and 23, we discussed models for magnetic levitation that are under study in Germany and Japan, both of which require strong electromagnets. At Lawrence Livermore Laboratory in California, scientists are working on a magnetic levitation scheme that involves permanent magnets. The scheme is called the *Inductrack*. One attractive feature of this approach is that no energy is required to power the magnets, resulting in savings for energy costs to operate the system.

The Inductrack system uses a *Halbach array* of magnets. Figure 2 shows a one-dimensional Halbach array. Underneath the array, the magnetic field lines of adjacent magnets with poles oriented vertically combine with those with poles oriented horizontally to create a very strong magnetic field. Above the array, the magnetic field lines of vertically oriented magnets are in the opposite direction from those created by the horizontally oriented magnets, resulting in a weak field in this region.

The Halbach array, attached to the underside of the vehicle, passes over a series of coils of wire and induces currents in these coils. By Faraday's law, similar to the situation in the electrodynamic model of Section 23.8, the magnetic field resulting from the current in the coils exerts a repulsive force on the magnets, creating a levitation force on the vehicle. A levitation force of 40 metric tons per square meter can be achieved using high-field alloy magnets. A working model of the Induc-

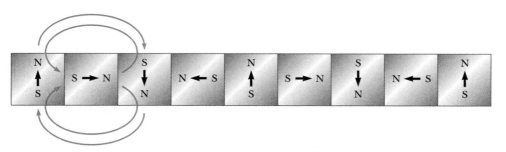

FIGURE 2 A Halbach array of magnets. A field line from the north pole of the leftmost magnet to the south pole of the third magnet is clockwise. The field line above the array from the north pole of the second magnet to the south pole of the same magnet is counterclockwise. The result is a relatively weak field above the array. Below the array, the field line from the north pole of the third magnet to the south pole of the leftmost magnet is clockwise. The field line below the array from the second magnet is also clockwise. The combination of these field lines results in a strong magnetic field below the array.

(a)

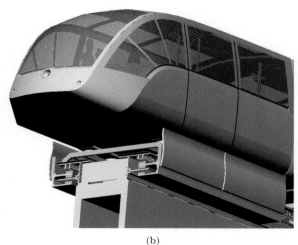

(b)

(Courtesy of Lawrence Livermore National Laboratory)

| FIGURE 3 | (a) General Atomics has built a full-scale Inductrack test vehicle, shown here on the test track in San Diego, California. (b) A drawing of the front end and magnetic components of a maglev vehicle using the Inductrack approach. |

track system successfully propelled and levitated a 22-kg vehicle over a 20-m test track. Using federal funding, General Atomics in San Diego is developing the Inductrack technology as it moves toward commercial applications. Experiments with full-scale test vehicles are currently in progress on a 120-m test track (Fig. 3a), in preparation for development of a full-scale vehicle (Fig. 3b).

What does the future of magnetic levitation transportation hold? Will the Inductrack become the system of choice, or will it be the Japanese or German system? Or will all three coexist? At this point, it is impossible to predict, and we invite you to watch the newspapers for further developments!

Problems

1. Assume that the vehicle shown in Figure 1 is moving at 400 km/h. The distance between adjacent magnets on the vehicle is 10.0 m. What is the frequency of the alternating current in the coils on the side of the track required to propel the vehicle?

2. Figure 4 represents an electromagnetic brake that uses eddy currents. An electromagnet hangs from a railroad car near one rail. To stop the car, a large current is sent through the coils of the electromagnet. The moving electromagnet induces eddy currents in the rails, whose fields oppose the change in the field of the electromagnet. The magnetic fields of the eddy currents exert force on the current in the electromagnet, thereby slowing the car. The direction of the car's motion and the direction of the current in the electromagnet are shown correctly in the picture. Determine which of the eddy currents shown on the rails is correct. Explain your answer.

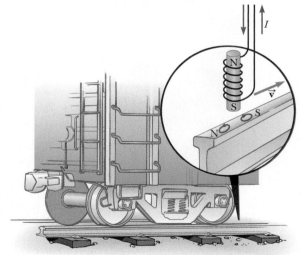

| FIGURE 4 | Magnets on a moving railroad car induce small current loops in the rail, called eddy currents. |

Lasers

The invention of the laser was popularly credited to Arthur L. Schawlow and Charles H. Townes for many years after their publication of a proposal for the laser in a 1958 issue of *Physical Review*. Schawlow and Townes received a patent for the device in 1959. In 1960, the first laser was built and operated by Theodore Maiman. This device used a ruby crystal to create the laser light, which was emitted in pulses from the end of a ruby cylinder. A flash lamp was used to excite the laser action.

In 1977, the first victory in a 30-year-long legal battle was completed in which Gordon Gould, who was a graduate student at Columbia University in the late 1950s, received a patent for inventing the laser in 1957 as well as coining the term. Believing erroneously

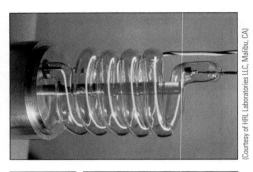

(Courtesy of HRL Laboratories LLC, Malibu, CA)

FIGURE 2 | Photograph of an early ruby laser, showing the flash lamp (glass helix) surrounding the ruby rod (red cylinder).

that he had to have a working prototype before he could file for a patent, he did not file until later in 1959 than had Schawlow and Townes. Gould's legal battles ended in 1987. By this time, Gould's technology was being widely used in industry and medicine. His victory finally resulted in his control of patent rights to perhaps 90% of the lasers used and sold in the United States.

Since the development of the first device, laser technology has experienced tremendous growth. Lasers that cover wavelengths in the infrared, visible, and ultraviolet regions are now available. Various types of lasers use solids, liquids, and gases as the active medium. Although the original laser emitted light over a very narrow range around a fixed wavelength, tunable lasers are now available, in which the wavelength can be varied.

The laser is an omnipresent technological tool in our daily life. Applications include surgical "welding" of detached retinas, precision surveying and length measurement, a potential source for inducing nuclear fusion reactions, precision cutting of metals and other materials, and telephone communication along optical fibers.

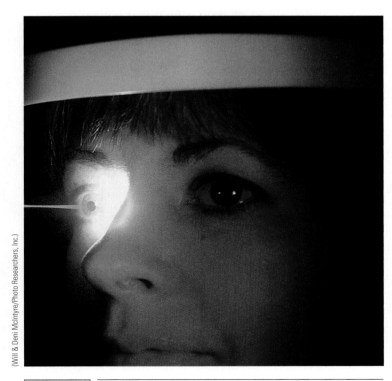

(Will & Deni McIntyre/Photo Researchers, Inc.)

FIGURE 1 | A laser is used on a human eye to perform a surgical procedure. The word *laser* is an acronym meaning light amplification by stimulated emission of radiation.

millikelvins above absolute zero and to move microscopic biological organisms around harmlessly.

These and other applications are possible because of the unique characteristics of laser light. In addition to its being almost monochromatic, laser light is also highly directional and can therefore be sharply focused to produce regions of extreme intensity.

In this Context, we shall investigate the physics of electromagnetic radiation and optics and apply the principles to an understanding of the behavior of laser light and its applications. A major focus of our

FIGURE 4 | This robotic device, one of the many technological uses of lasers in our society, carries laser scissors, which can cut up to 50 layers of fabric at a time.

FIGURE 3 | The original ruby laser emitted red light, as did many lasers developed soon afterward. Today, lasers are available in a variety of colors and various regions of the electromagnetic spectrum. In this photograph, a green laser is used to perform scientific research.

We also use lasers to read information from compact discs for use in audio entertainment and computer applications. Digital videodiscs use lasers to read video information. Lasers are used in retail stores to read price and inventory information from product labels. In the laboratory, lasers can be used to trap atoms and cool them to

FIGURE 5 | A supermarket scanner uses light from a laser to identify products being purchased. The reflections from the bar code on the package are read and entered into the computer to determine the price of the item.

study will be on the technology of optical fibers and how they are used in industry and medicine. We shall study the nature of light as we respond to our central question:

What is special about laser light, and how is it used in technological applications?

CHAPTER 24

Electromagnetic Waves

Electromagnetic waves cover a broad spectrum of wavelengths, with waves in various wavelength ranges having distinct properties. These photos of the Crab Nebula show different structure for observations made with waves of various wavelengths. The photos (clockwise starting from the upper left) were taken with x-rays, unpolarized visible light, radio waves, and visible light passing through a polarizing filter.

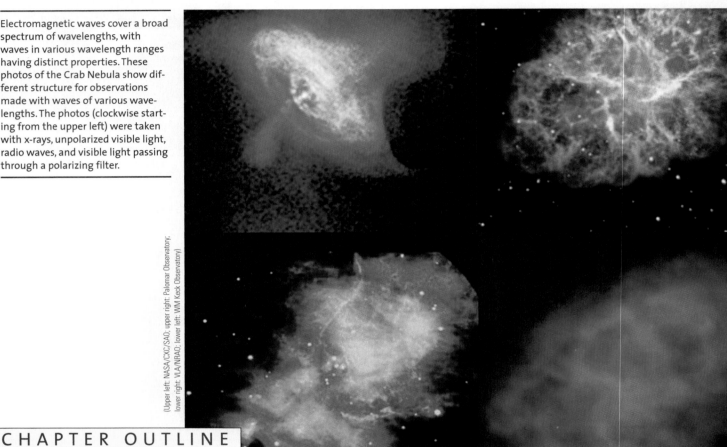

(Upper left: NASA/CXC/SAO; upper right: Palomar Observatory; lower right: VLA/NRAO; lower left: WM Keck Observatory)

CHAPTER OUTLINE

Although we are not always aware of their presence, electromagnetic waves permeate our environment. In the form of visible light, they enable us to view the world around us with our eyes. Infrared waves from the surface of the Earth warm our environment, radio-frequency waves carry our favorite radio entertainment, microwaves cook our food and are used in radar communication systems, and the list goes on and on. The waves described in Chapter 13 are mechanical waves, which require a medium through which to propagate. Electromagnetic waves, in contrast, can propagate through a vacuum. Despite this difference between mechanical and electromagnetic waves, much of the behavior in the wave models of Chapters 13 and 14 is similar for electromagnetic waves.

The purpose of this chapter is to explore the properties of electromagnetic waves. The fundamental laws of electricity and magnetism—Maxwell's equations—form the basis of all electromagnetic phenomena. One of these equations predicts that a time-varying electric field produces a magnetic field just as a time-varying magnetic field produces an electric field. From this generalization, Maxwell provided the final important link between electric and magnetic fields. The most dramatic prediction of his equations is the existence of electromagnetic waves that propagate through empty space with the speed of light. This discovery led to many practical applications, such as radio and television, and to the realization that light is one form of electromagnetic radiation.

24.1 DISPLACEMENT CURRENT AND THE GENERALIZED AMPÈRE'S LAW

We have seen that charges in motion, or currents, produce magnetic fields. When a current-carrying conductor has high symmetry, we can calculate the magnetic field using Ampère's law, given by Equation 22.29:

$$\oint \vec{\mathbf{B}} \cdot d\vec{\mathbf{s}} = \mu_0 I$$

where **the line integral is over any closed path through which the conduction current passes** and the conduction current is defined by $I = dq/dt$.

In this section, we shall use the term *conduction current* to refer to the type of current that we have already discussed, that is, current carried by charged particles in a wire. We use this term to differentiate this current from a different type of current we will introduce shortly. **Ampère's law in this form is valid only if the conduction current is continuous in space.** Maxwell recognized this limitation and modified Ampère's law to include all possible situations.

This limitation can be understood by considering a capacitor being charged as in Figure 24.1. When conduction current exists in the wires, the charge on the plates changes, but **no conduction current exists between the plates.** Consider the two surfaces S_1 (a circle, shown in blue) and S_2 (a paraboloid, in orange, passing between the plates) in Figure 24.1 bounded by the same path P. Ampère's law says that the line integral of $\vec{\mathbf{B}} \cdot d\vec{\mathbf{s}}$ around this path must equal $\mu_0 I$, where I is the conduction current through *any* surface bounded by the path P.

When the path P is considered as bounding S_1, the right-hand side of Equation 22.29 is $\mu_0 I$ because the conduction current passes through S_1 while the capacitor is charging. When the path bounds S_2, however, the right-hand side of Equation 22.29 is zero because no conduction current passes through S_2. Therefore, a contradictory situation arises because of the discontinuity of the current! Maxwell solved this problem by postulating an additional term on the right side of Equation 22.29, called the **displacement current** I_d, defined as

$$I_d \equiv \epsilon_0 \frac{d\Phi_E}{dt} \qquad \text{[24.1]}$$

Recall that Φ_E is the flux of the electric field, defined as $\Phi_E \equiv \oint \vec{\mathbf{E}} \cdot d\vec{\mathbf{A}}$ (Eq. 19.20). (The word *displacement* here does not have the same meaning as in Chapter 2; it is historically entrenched in the language of physics, however, so we continue to use it.)

Equation 24.1 is interpreted as follows. As the capacitor is being charged (or discharged), the changing electric field between the plates may be considered as equivalent to a current between the plates that acts as a continuation of the conduction current in the wire. When the expression for the displacement current given by Equation 24.1 is added to the conduction current on the right side of Ampère's law, the difficulty represented in Figure 24.1 is resolved. No matter what surface

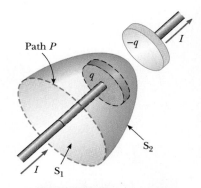

FIGURE 24.1 Two surfaces S_1 and S_2 near the plate of a capacitor are bounded by the same path P. The conduction current in the wire passes only through S_1, which leads to a contradiction in Ampère's law that is resolved only if one postulates a displacement current through S_2.

■ Displacement current

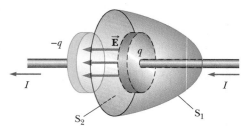

FIGURE 24.2 Because it exists only in the wires attached to the capacitor plates, the conduction current $I = dq/dt$ passes through the curved surface S_1 but not the flat surface S_2. Only the displacement current $I_d = \epsilon_0 d\Phi_E/dt$ passes through S_2. The two currents must be equal for continuity.

bounded by the path P is chosen, either conduction current or displacement current passes through it. With this new notion of displacement current, we can express the general form of Ampère's law (sometimes called the **Ampère–Maxwell law**) as[1]

∎ Ampère–Maxwell law

$$\oint \vec{\mathbf{B}} \cdot d\vec{\mathbf{s}} = \mu_0(I + I_d) = \mu_0 I + \mu_0 \epsilon_0 \frac{d\Phi_E}{dt} \qquad [24.2]$$

The meaning of this expression can be understood by referring to Figure 24.2. The electric flux through S_2 (a circle, shown in gray, between the plates) is $\Phi_E = \oint \vec{\mathbf{E}} \cdot d\vec{\mathbf{A}} = EA$, where A is the area of the capacitor plates and E is the magnitude of the uniform electric field between the plates. If q is the charge on the plates at any instant, $E = q/\epsilon_0 A$ (Section 20.7). Therefore, the electric flux through S_2 is simply

$$\Phi_E = EA = \frac{q}{\epsilon_0}$$

Hence, the displacement current I_d through S_2 is

$$I_d = \epsilon_0 \frac{d\Phi_E}{dt} = \frac{dq}{dt} \qquad [24.3]$$

That is, the displacement current through S_2 is precisely equal to the conduction current I through S_1! The central point of this formalism is that **magnetic fields are produced both by conduction currents and by changing electric fields.** This result is a remarkable example of theoretical work by Maxwell and of his major contributions in advancing the understanding of electromagnetism.

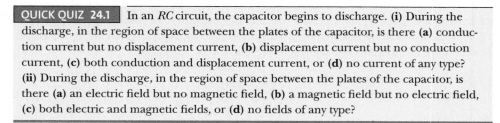

QUICK QUIZ 24.1 In an RC circuit, the capacitor begins to discharge. **(i)** During the discharge, in the region of space between the plates of the capacitor, is there **(a)** conduction current but no displacement current, **(b)** displacement current but no conduction current, **(c)** both conduction and displacement current, or **(d)** no current of any type? **(ii)** During the discharge, in the region of space between the plates of the capacitor, is there **(a)** an electric field but no magnetic field, **(b)** a magnetic field but no electric field, **(c)** both electric and magnetic fields, or **(d)** no fields of any type?

JAMES CLERK MAXWELL
(1831–1879)

Scottish theoretical physicist Maxwell developed the electromagnetic theory of light and the kinetic theory of gases, and he explained the nature of color vision and of Saturn's rings. His successful interpretation of electromagnetic fields produced the field equations that bear his name. Formidable mathematical ability combined with great insight enabled Maxwell to lead the way in the study of electromagnetism and kinetic theory. He died of cancer before he was 50.

(North Wind Picture Archives)

24.2 MAXWELL'S EQUATIONS

In this section, we gather together four equations from our studies in recent chapters that as a group can be regarded as the theoretical basis of all electric and magnetic fields. These relationships, known as Maxwell's equations after James Clerk Maxwell, are as fundamental to electromagnetic phenomena as Newton's laws are

---

[1]Strictly speaking, this expression is valid only in a vacuum. If a magnetic material is present, a magnetizing current must also be included on the right side of Equation 24.2 to make Ampère's law fully general.

to mechanical phenomena. In fact, the theory developed by Maxwell was more far reaching than even he imagined because it was shown by Albert Einstein in 1905 to be in agreement with the special theory of relativity. As we shall see, Maxwell's equations represent laws of electricity and magnetism that have already been discussed. The equations have additional important consequences, however, in that they predict the existence of electromagnetic waves (traveling patterns of electric and magnetic fields) that travel in vacuum with a speed of $c = 1/\sqrt{\epsilon_0 \mu_0} = 3.00 \times 10^8$ m/s, the speed of light. Furthermore, Maxwell's equations show that electromagnetic waves are radiated by accelerating charges, as we discussed in Chapter 17 with regard to thermal radiation.

For simplicity, we present **Maxwell's equations** as applied to free space, that is, in the absence of any dielectric or magnetic material. The four equations are

$$\oint \vec{E} \cdot d\vec{A} = \frac{q}{\epsilon_0} \qquad [24.4]$$

$$\oint \vec{B} \cdot d\vec{A} = 0 \qquad [24.5]$$

$$\oint \vec{E} \cdot d\vec{s} = -\frac{d\Phi_B}{dt} \qquad [24.6]$$

$$\oint \vec{B} \cdot d\vec{s} = \mu_0 I + \epsilon_0 \mu_0 \frac{d\Phi_E}{dt} \qquad [24.7]$$

▪ Maxwell's equations

Equation 24.4 is **Gauss's law,** which states that **the total electric flux through any closed surface equals the net charge inside that surface divided by ϵ_0** (Section 19.9). This law describes how charges create electric fields.

Equation 24.5, which can be considered **Gauss's law for magnetism, says that the net magnetic flux through a closed surface is zero.** That is, the number of magnetic field lines entering a closed volume must equal the number leaving that volume. This law implies that magnetic field lines cannot begin or end at any point. If they did, it would mean that isolated magnetic monopoles existed at those points. That isolated magnetic monopoles have not been observed in nature can be taken as a basis of Equation 24.5.

Equation 24.6 is **Faraday's law of induction** (Eq. 23.9), which describes how a changing magnetic field creates an electric field. This law states that **the line integral of the electric field around any closed path (which equals the emf) equals the rate of change of magnetic flux through any surface area bounded by that path.**

Equation 24.7 is the generalized form of Ampère's law. It describes how both an electric current and a changing electric field create a magnetic field. That is, **the line integral of the magnetic field around any closed path is determined by the net current and the rate of change of electric flux through any surface bounded by that path.**

Once the electric and magnetic fields are known at some point in space, the force those fields exert on a particle of charge q can be calculated from the expression

$$\vec{F} = q\vec{E} + q\vec{v} \times \vec{B} \qquad [24.8]$$

▪ Lorentz force

which is called the **Lorentz force** (Section 22.4). Maxwell's equations and this force law give a complete description of all classical electromagnetic interactions.

Note the interesting symmetry of Maxwell's equations. In a region of space free of charges, so that $q = 0$, Equations 24.4 and 24.5 are symmetric in that the surface integral of $\vec{E}$ or $\vec{B}$ over a closed surface equals zero. Furthermore, in a region free of conduction currents so that $I = 0$, Equations 24.6 and 24.7 are symmetric in that the line integrals of $\vec{E}$ and $\vec{B}$ around a closed path are related to the rate of change of magnetic flux and electric flux, respectively.

24.3 | ELECTROMAGNETIC WAVES

In his unified theory of electromagnetism, Maxwell showed that time-dependent electric and magnetic fields satisfy a linear wave equation. (The linear wave equation for mechanical waves is Equation 13.19.) The most significant outcome of this theory is the prediction of the existence of **electromagnetic waves.**

Maxwell's equations predict that an electromagnetic wave consists of oscillating electric and magnetic fields. The changing fields induce each other, which maintains the propagation of the wave; a changing electric field induces a magnetic field, and a changing magnetic field induces an electric field. The $\vec{E}$ and $\vec{B}$ vectors are perpendicular to each other, and to the direction of propagation, as shown in Active Figure 24.3a at one instant of time and one point in space. The direction of propagation is the direction of the vector product $\vec{E} \times \vec{B}$, which we shall explore more fully in Section 24.5. Active Figure 24.3b shows how the electric and magnetic fields vary in phase sinusoidally along the x axis in the simplest type of electromagnetic wave. We will discuss this sinusoidal behavior shortly. As time progresses, imagine the construction in Active Figure 24.3b moving to the right along the x axis. That is what happens in an electromagnetic wave, with the movement taking place at the speed of light c.

To understand the prediction of electromagnetic waves, let us focus our attention on an electromagnetic wave traveling in the x direction. For this wave, the electric field $\vec{E}$ is in the y direction and the magnetic field $\vec{B}$ is in the z direction as in Active Figure 24.3. Waves in which the electric and magnetic fields are restricted to being parallel to certain directions are said to be **linearly polarized waves.** Furthermore, let us assume that at any point in space in Active Figure 24.3, the magnitudes E and B of the fields depend on x and t only, not on the y or z coordinates.

Let us also imagine that the source of the electromagnetic waves is such that a wave radiated from *any* position in the yz plane (not just from the origin as might be suggested by Active Fig. 24.3) propagates in the x direction and that all such waves are emitted in phase. If we define a **ray** as the line along which a wave travels, all rays for these waves are parallel. This whole collection of waves is often called a **plane wave.** A surface connecting points of equal phase on all waves, which we call a **wave front,** is a geometric plane. In comparison, a point source of radiation sends waves out in all directions. A surface connecting points of equal

PITFALL PREVENTION 24.1

WHAT IS "A" WAVE? A sticky point in these types of discussions is what we mean by a *single* wave. We could define one wave as that which is emitted by a single charged particle. In practice, however, the word *wave* represents both the emission from a *single point* ("wave radiated from any position in the *yz* plane") and the collection of waves from *all points* on the source ("plane wave"). You should be able to use this term in both ways and to understand its meaning from the context.

ACTIVE FIGURE 24.3 (a) The fields in an electromagnetic wave traveling at velocity $\vec{c}$ in the positive x direction at one point on the x axis. These fields depend only on x and t.
(b) Representation of a sinusoidal electromagnetic wave moving in the positive x direction with a speed c.

Physics⊗Now™ Log into PhysicsNow at **www.pop4e.com** and go to Active Figure 24.3 to observe the wave in part (b). In addition, you can take a "snapshot" of the wave at an instant of time and investigate the electric and magnetic fields at that instant.

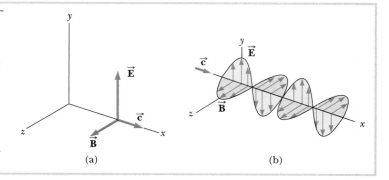

(a)   (b)

phase for this situation is a sphere, so we call the radiation from a point source a **spherical wave.**

To generate the prediction of electromagnetic waves, we start with Faraday's law, Equation 24.6:

$$\oint \vec{\mathbf{E}} \cdot d\vec{\mathbf{s}} = -\frac{d\Phi_B}{dt}$$

Let us assume that a plane electromagnetic wave is traveling in the x direction, with the electric field $\vec{\mathbf{E}}$ in the positive y direction and the magnetic field $\mathbf{B}$ in the positive z direction.

Consider a rectangle of width dx and height ℓ lying in the xy plane as in Figure 24.4. To apply Equation 24.6, we first evaluate the line integral of $\vec{\mathbf{E}} \cdot d\vec{\mathbf{s}}$ around this rectangle. The contributions from the top and bottom of the rectangle are zero because $\vec{\mathbf{E}}$ is perpendicular to $d\mathbf{s}$ for these paths. We can express the electric field on the right side of the rectangle as[2]

$$E(x + dx, t) \approx E(x, t) + \frac{dE}{dx}\bigg]_{t\,\text{constant}} dx = E(x, t) + \frac{\partial E}{\partial x}\, dx$$

whereas the field on the left side of the rectangle is simply $E(x, t)$. The line integral over this rectangle is therefore approximately

$$\oint \vec{\mathbf{E}} \cdot d\vec{\mathbf{s}} = [E(x + dx, t)]\ell - [E(x, t)]\ell \approx \ell\left(\frac{\partial E}{\partial x}\right) dx \qquad [24.9]$$

Because the magnetic field is in the z direction, the magnetic flux through the rectangle of area $\ell\, dx$ is approximately $\Phi_B = B\ell\, dx$. (This expression assumes that dx is very small compared with the wavelength of the wave so that B is uniform over the width dx.) Taking the time derivative of the magnetic flux at the location of the rectangle on the x axis gives

$$\frac{d\Phi_B}{dt} = \ell\, dx\, \frac{dB}{dt}\bigg]_{x\,\text{constant}} = \ell\, \frac{\partial B}{\partial t}\, dx \qquad [24.10]$$

Substituting Equations 24.9 and 24.10 into Equation 24.6 gives

$$\ell\left(\frac{\partial E}{\partial x}\right) dx = -\ell\, \frac{\partial B}{\partial t}\, dx$$

$$\frac{\partial E}{\partial x} = -\frac{\partial B}{\partial t} \qquad [24.11]$$

We can derive a second equation by starting with Maxwell's fourth equation in empty space (Eq. 24.7). In this case, we evaluate the line integral of $\vec{\mathbf{B}} \cdot d\vec{\mathbf{s}}$ around a rectangle lying in the xz plane and having width dx and length ℓ as in Figure 24.5. Using the sense of the integration shown and noting that the magnetic field changes from $B(x, t)$ to $B(x + dx, t)$ over the width dx, we find that

$$\oint \vec{\mathbf{B}} \cdot d\vec{\mathbf{s}} = [B(x, t)]\ell - [B(x + dx, t)]\ell = -\ell\left(\frac{\partial B}{\partial x}\right) dx \qquad [24.12]$$

The electric flux through the rectangle is $\Phi_E = E\ell\, dx$, which when differentiated with respect to time gives

$$\frac{d\Phi_E}{dt} = \ell\left(\frac{\partial E}{\partial t}\right) dx \qquad [24.13]$$

---

[2]Because dE/dx in this equation is expressed as the change in E with x at a given instant t, dE/dx is equivalent to the partial derivative $\partial E/\partial x$. Likewise, we will shortly require dB/dt, which means the change in B with time at a particular position x, and so we can replace dB/dt by $\partial B/\partial t$.

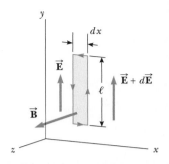

FIGURE 24.4 As a plane wave moving in the $+x$ direction passes through a rectangular path of width dx lying in the xy plane, the electric field in the y direction varies from $\vec{\mathbf{E}}$ to $\vec{\mathbf{E}} + d\vec{\mathbf{E}}$. This construction allows us to evaluate the line integral of $\vec{\mathbf{E}}$ over the perimeter of the rectangle.

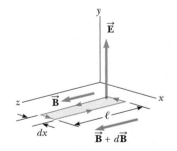

FIGURE 24.5 As a plane wave moving in the $+x$ direction passes through a rectangular path of width dx lying in the xz plane, the magnetic field in the z direction varies from $\vec{\mathbf{B}}$ to $\vec{\mathbf{B}} + d\vec{\mathbf{B}}$. This construction allows us to evaluate the line integral of $\vec{\mathbf{B}}$ over the perimeter of the rectangle.

Substituting Equations 24.12 and 24.13 into Equation 24.7 gives

$$-\ell\left(\frac{\partial B}{\partial x}\right)dx = \epsilon_0\mu_0\ell\left(\frac{\partial E}{\partial t}\right)dx$$

$$\frac{\partial B}{\partial x} = -\epsilon_0\mu_0\frac{\partial E}{\partial t} \quad [24.14]$$

Taking the derivative of Equation 24.11 with respect to x and combining it with Equation 24.14 gives

$$\frac{\partial^2 E}{\partial x^2} = -\frac{\partial}{\partial x}\left(\frac{\partial B}{\partial t}\right) = -\frac{\partial}{\partial t}\left(\frac{\partial B}{\partial x}\right) = -\frac{\partial}{\partial t}\left(-\epsilon_0\mu_0\frac{\partial E}{\partial t}\right)$$

$$\frac{\partial^2 E}{\partial x^2} = \epsilon_0\mu_0\frac{\partial^2 E}{\partial t^2} \quad [24.15]$$

■ Electric field wave equation for electromagnetic waves in free space

In the same manner, taking a derivative of Equation 24.14 with respect to x and combining it with Equation 24.11, we find that

$$\frac{\partial^2 B}{\partial x^2} = \epsilon_0\mu_0\frac{\partial^2 B}{\partial t^2} \quad [24.16]$$

■ Magnetic field wave equation for electromagnetic waves in free space

Equations 24.15 and 24.16 both have the form of a linear wave equation (Eq. 13.19). As indicated in Chapter 13, such an equation is a mathematical representation of the traveling wave model. In this discussion, Equations 24.15 and 24.16 represent traveling electromagnetic waves. In the linear wave equation, the coefficient of the time derivative is the inverse of the speed of the waves. Therefore, these electromagnetic waves travel with a speed c of

■ The speed of electromagnetic waves

$$c = \frac{1}{\sqrt{\epsilon_0\mu_0}} \quad [24.17]$$

Substituting $\epsilon_0 = 8.854\ 19 \times 10^{-12}$ C^2/N·m^2 and $\mu_0 = 4\pi \times 10^{-7}$ T·m/A in Equation 24.17, we find that $c = 2.997\ 92 \times 10^8$ m/s. Because this speed is precisely the same as the speed of light in empty space,[3] one is led to believe (correctly) that **light is an electromagnetic wave.**

The simplest wave solutions to Equations 24.15 and 24.16 are those for which the field amplitudes E and B vary with x and t according to the expressions

$$E = E_{\max}\cos(kx - \omega t) \quad [24.18]$$

$$B = B_{\max}\cos(kx - \omega t) \quad [24.19]$$

In these expressions, $E_{\max}$ and $B_{\max}$ are the maximum values of the fields, the wave number $k = 2\pi/\lambda$, where λ is the wavelength, and the angular frequency $\omega = 2\pi f$, where f is the frequency. Active Figure 24.3b represents a view at one instant of a sinusoidal electromagnetic wave moving in the positive x direction.

Because electromagnetic waves are described by the traveling wave model, we can adopt another mathematical representation from the model, first seen in Equation 13.11 for mechanical waves. It is the relationship between wave speed, wavelength, and frequency for sinusoidal waves, $v = \lambda f$, which we can write for sinusoidal electromagnetic waves as

$$c = \lambda f \quad [24.20]$$

The electric and magnetic fields of a plane electromagnetic wave are perpendicular to each other and to the direction of propagation. Therefore, **electromagnetic**

[3]Because of the redefinition of the meter in 1983, the speed of light is now a *defined* quantity with an *exact* value of $c = 2.997\ 924\ 58 \times 10^8$ m/s.

waves are transverse waves. The transverse mechanical waves studied in Chapter 13 exhibited physical displacements of the elements of the medium that were perpendicular to the direction of propagation of the wave. Electromagnetic waves do not require a medium for propagation, so there are no elements to be displaced. The transverse nature of an electromagnetic wave is represented by the direction of the field vectors with respect to the direction of propagation.

Taking partial derivatives of Equations 24.18 (with respect to x) and 24.19 (with respect to t), and substituting into Equation 24.11, we find that

$$\frac{E_{max}}{B_{max}} = c$$

Substituting from Equations 24.18 and 24.19 gives

$$\frac{E}{B} = c \qquad\qquad [24.21]$$

That is, **at every instant the ratio of the electric field to the magnetic field of an electromagnetic wave equals the speed of light.**

Finally, electromagnetic waves obey the **superposition principle** because the differential equations involving E and B are linear equations. For example, the resultant electric field magnitude of two waves coinciding in space with their $\vec{E}$ vectors parallel can be found by simply adding the individual expressions for E given by Equation 24.18.

Doppler Effect for Light

In Section 13.8, we studied the Doppler effect for sound waves, in which the apparent frequency of the sound changes due to motion of the source or the observer. Light also exhibits a Doppler effect, which is demonstrated in astronomical observations by the wavelength shift of spectral lines from receding galaxies. This movement of spectral lines is toward the red end of the spectrum. It is therefore called the *red shift* and is evidence that other galaxies are moving away from us. (See Section 31.12 for more evidence of the expanding universe.)

The equation for the Doppler effect for light is not the same equation as that for sound for the following reason. For waves requiring a medium, the speeds of the source and observer can be separately measured with respect to a third entity, the medium. In the Doppler effect for sound, these two speeds are that of the source and that of the observer relative to the air. Because light does not require a medium, no third entity exists. Therefore, we cannot identify separate speeds for the source and observer. Only their relative speed can be identified. As a result, a different equation must be used, one that contains only this single speed. This equation can be generated from the laws of relativity and is found to be

$$f' = f\sqrt{\frac{c + v}{c - v}} \qquad\qquad [24.22]$$

▪ Doppler effect for electromagnetic waves

where v is the relative speed between the source and the observer, c is the speed of light, f' is the frequency of light detected by the observer, and f is the frequency emitted by the source. For galaxies receding away from the Earth, v is entered into this equation as a negative number so that $f' < f$, which results in an apparent wavelength λ' such that $\lambda' > \lambda$. Therefore, the light should shift toward the red end of the spectrum, which is what is observed in the red shift.

INTERACTIVE **EXAMPLE 24.1** **An Electromagnetic Wave**

A sinusoidal electromagnetic wave of frequency 40.0 MHz travels in free space in the x direction as in Figure 24.6.

A Determine the wavelength and period of the wave.

Solution Because $c = \lambda f$ and we know that $f = 40.0$ MHz $= 4.00 \times 10^7$ Hz, we have

$$\lambda = \frac{c}{f} = \frac{3.00 \times 10^8 \text{ m/s}}{4.00 \times 10^7 \text{ Hz}} = \boxed{7.50 \text{ m}}$$

The period T of the wave equals the inverse of the frequency, so

$$T = \frac{1}{f} = \frac{1}{4.00 \times 10^7 \text{ Hz}} = \boxed{2.50 \times 10^{-8} \text{ s}}$$

B At some point and at some instant, the electric field has its maximum value of 750 N/C and is along the y axis. Calculate the magnitude and direction of the magnetic field at this position and time.

Solution From Equation 24.21, we see that

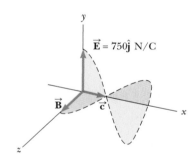

$\vec{E} = 750\hat{j}$ N/C

FIGURE 24.6 (Interactive Example 24.1) At some instant, a plane electromagnetic wave moving in the x direction has a maximum electric field of 750 N/C in the positive y direction. The corresponding magnetic field at that point has a magnitude E/c and is in the z direction.

$$B_{\text{max}} = \frac{E_{\text{max}}}{c} = \frac{750 \text{ N/C}}{3.00 \times 10^8 \text{ m/s}} = \boxed{2.50 \times 10^{-6} \text{ T}}$$

Because $\vec{E}$ and $\vec{B}$ must be perpendicular to each other and $\vec{E} \times \vec{B}$ must be in the direction of wave propagation (x in this case), we conclude that $\vec{B}$ is in the z direction.

C Write expressions for the space–time variation of the electric and magnetic field components for this wave.

Solution We can apply Equations 24.18 and 24.19 directly:

$$E = E_{\text{max}} \cos(kx - \omega t) = (750 \text{ N/C}) \cos(kx - \omega t)$$

$$B = B_{\text{max}} \cos(kx - \omega t) = (2.50 \times 10^{-6} \text{ T}) \cos(kx - \omega t)$$

where

$$\omega = 2\pi f = 2\pi(4.00 \times 10^7 \text{ Hz}) = 2.51 \times 10^8 \text{ rad/s}$$

$$k = \frac{2\pi}{\lambda} = \frac{2\pi}{7.50 \text{ m}} = 0.838 \text{ rad/m}$$

D An observer on the x axis, far to the right in Figure 24.6, moves to the left along the x axis at $0.500c$. What frequency does this observer measure for the electromagnetic wave?

Solution We use Equation 24.22 for the Doppler effect for light:

$$f' = f\sqrt{\frac{c + v}{c - v}} = 40.0 \text{ MHz}\sqrt{\frac{c + (+0.500c)}{c - (+0.500c)}}$$

$$= \boxed{69.3 \text{ MHz}}$$

We have substituted v as a positive number because the observer is moving toward the source.

Physics⊗Now™ Explore electromagnetic waves of different frequencies by logging into PhysicsNow at **www.pop4e.com** and going to Interactive Example 24.1.

24.4 HERTZ'S DISCOVERIES

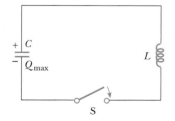

FIGURE 24.7 A simple LC circuit. The capacitor has an initial charge Q_{max}, and the switch is closed at $t = 0$.

In 1888, Heinrich Rudolf Hertz was the first to generate and detect electromagnetic waves in a laboratory setting. To appreciate the details of his experiment, let us first examine the properties of an LC circuit. In such a circuit, a charged capacitor is connected to an inductor as in Figure 24.7. When the switch is closed, both the current in the circuit and the charge on the capacitor oscillate in a manner closely related to our simple harmonic motion model in Chapter 12. If resistance is ignored, no energy is transformed to internal energy.

Let us investigate these oscillations in a way similar to our energy analysis of the simple harmonic motion model in Chapter 12. We assume that the capacitor has an initial charge of Q_{max} and that the switch is closed at $t = 0$. When the capacitor is fully charged, the total energy in the circuit is stored in the electric field of the capacitor and is equal to $Q_{max}^2/2C$. At this time, the current is zero and so no energy is stored in the inductor. As the capacitor begins to discharge, the energy stored in its electric field decreases. At the same time, the current increases and an amount of energy equal to $\frac{1}{2}LI^2$ is now stored in the magnetic field of the inductor. Therefore, energy is transferred from the electric field of the capacitor to the magnetic field of the inductor. When the capacitor is fully discharged, it stores no energy. At this time, the current reaches its maximum value and all the energy is stored in the inductor. The current continues in the same direction and begins to decrease in magnitude. While that occurs, the capacitor charges with polarity opposite to its previous polarity until the current stops and the capacitor is fully charged again. The process then repeats in the reverse direction. The energy continues to transfer between the inductor and the capacitor, corresponding to oscillations of both current and charge.

A representation of this energy transfer is shown in Active Figure 24.8. As mentioned, the behavior of the circuit is analogous to that of the oscillating block–spring system studied in Chapter 12. The potential energy $\frac{1}{2}kx^2$ stored in a stretched spring is analogous to the potential energy $Q_{max}^2/2C$ stored in the capacitor. The kinetic energy $\frac{1}{2}mv^2$ of the moving block is analogous to the magnetic energy $\frac{1}{2}LI^2$ stored in the inductor, which requires the presence of moving charges. In Active Figure 24.8a, all the energy is stored as electric potential energy in the capacitor at $t = 0$ (because $I = 0$), just like all the energy in a block–spring system is initially stored as potential energy in the spring if it is stretched and released at $t = 0$. In Active Figure 24.8b, all the energy is stored as magnetic energy $\frac{1}{2}LI_{max}^2$ in the inductor, where I_{max} is the maximum current. Active Figures 24.8c and 24.8d show subsequent quarter-cycle situations in which the energy is all electric or all magnetic. At intermediate points, part of the energy is electric and part is magnetic.

We now describe an alternative approach to the analogy between the LC circuit and the block–spring system of Chapter 12. Recall Equation 12.3, which is the differential equation describing the position of the block (modeled as a particle) in the simple harmonic motion model:

$$\frac{d^2x}{dt^2} = -\frac{k}{m}x$$

Applying Kirchhoff's loop rule to the circuit in Figure 24.7 gives

$$\frac{Q}{C} + L\frac{dI}{dt} = 0$$

Because $I = dQ/dt$, we can rewrite this equation as

$$\frac{Q}{C} = -L\frac{d}{dt}\left(\frac{dQ}{dt}\right) \quad \rightarrow \quad \frac{d^2Q}{dt^2} = -\frac{1}{LC}Q \qquad [24.23]$$

This equation has exactly the same mathematical form as Equation 12.3 for the block–spring system. Therefore, we conclude that the charge in the circuit will oscillate in a way analogous to a block on a spring.

In Chapter 12, we recognized the coefficient of x in Equation 12.3 as the square of the angular frequency (Eq. 12.4):

$$\omega^2 = \frac{k}{m}$$

Because of the identical mathematical form of the equation describing the LC circuit (Eq. 24.23), we can identify the coefficient of Q as the square of the angular

HEINRICH RUDOLF HERTZ (1857–1894)
German physicist Hertz made his greatest discovery—radio waves—in 1887. After finding that the speed of a radio wave is the same as that of light, he showed that radio waves, like light waves, could be reflected, refracted, and diffracted. Hertz died of blood poisoning at age 36. During his short life, he made many contributions to science. The hertz, equal to one complete vibration or cycle per second, is named after him.

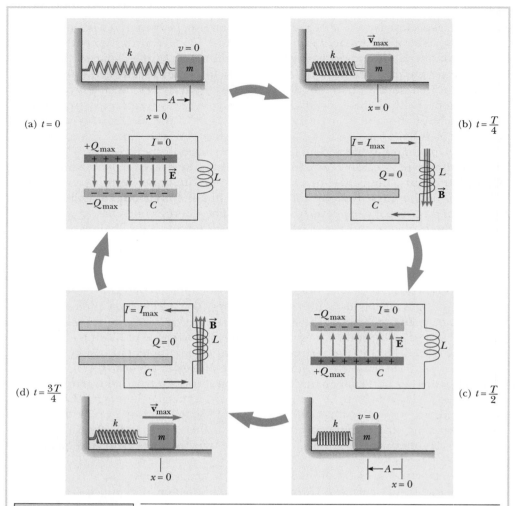

ACTIVE FIGURE 24.8 The conditions in a resistanceless LC circuit are shown at quarter-cycle intervals during its oscillation. Associated with each image of the circuit is the mechanical analog, the block–spring oscillating system. (a) At $t = 0$, the capacitor has a charge Q_{max} and there is an electric field between the plates. Because no current exists at this instant, there is no magnetic field in the inductor. In the mechanical system, the block of mass m is at its maximum displacement from equilibrium, with a speed of zero. (b) One quarter of a cycle later, the charge on the capacitor has reached zero and the current has its maximum value I_{max}, causing a magnetic field of maximum magnitude in the inductor. The block in the mechanical system is passing through $x = 0$ with maximum speed. (c) After another quarter cycle, the capacitor has charged up to its maximum value, with opposite polarity to that in (a). The mechanical system is similar to that in (a) except that the spring is at maximum compression rather than extension. (d) Circuit conditions are similar to those in (b) but with current in the opposite direction. The mechanical system is similar to that in (b) but with the direction of the velocity reversed. One quarter of a cycle later, the circuit and the mechanical system return to the conditions in (a), ready to begin a new cycle.

Physics⊗Now™ Log into PhysicsNow at **www.pop4e.com** and go to Active Figure 24.8 to adjust the values of C and L and see the effect on the oscillating circuit. The block on the spring oscillates in a mechanical analog of the electrical oscillations. A graphical display of charge and current is available, as is an energy bar graph.

frequency:

$$\omega^2 = \frac{1}{LC}$$

Therefore, the frequency of oscillation of an *LC* circuit, called the *resonance frequency*, is

$$f_0 = \frac{1}{2\pi\sqrt{LC}} \qquad [24.24]$$

The circuit Hertz used in his investigations of electromagnetic waves is shown schematically in Figure 24.9. A large coil of wire called an induction coil is connected to two metal spheres with a narrow gap between them to form a capacitor. Oscillations are initiated in the circuit by sending short voltage pulses via the coil to the spheres, initially charging one positive, the other negative. Based on the values of *L* and *C* in Hertz's circuit, the frequency of oscillation is $f \approx 100$ MHz. This circuit is called a transmitter because it produces electromagnetic waves.

Hertz placed a second circuit, the receiver, several meters from the transmitter circuit. This receiver circuit, which consisted of a single loop of wire connected to two spheres, had its own effective inductance, capacitance, and natural frequency of oscillation. Hertz found that energy was being sent from the transmitter to the receiver when the resonance frequency of the receiver was adjusted to match that of the transmitter.[4] The energy transfer was detected when the voltage across the spheres in the receiver circuit became high enough to cause sparks to appear in the air gap separating the spheres. Hertz's experiment is analogous to the mechanical phenomenon in which one tuning fork responds to acoustic vibrations from an identical vibrating fork. In the case of the tuning fork, the energy transfer from one fork to another is by means of sound, whereas the transfer mechanism is electromagnetic radiation for Hertz's apparatus.

Hertz assumed that the energy transferred from the transmitter to the receiver was carried in the form of waves, which are now known to have been electromagnetic waves. In a series of experiments, he also showed that the radiation generated by the transmitter exhibited the wave properties of interference, diffraction, reflection, refraction, and polarization. As we shall see shortly, all these properties are exhibited by light. Therefore, it became evident that the waves observed by Hertz had properties similar to those of light waves and differed only in frequency and wavelength.

Perhaps Hertz's most convincing experiment was his measurement of the speed of the waves from the transmitter. Waves of known frequency from the transmitter were reflected from a metal sheet so that a pattern of nodes and antinodes was set up, much like the standing wave pattern on a stretched string. As we saw in our discussion of standing waves (Chapter 14), the distance between nodes is $\lambda/2$, so Hertz was able to determine the wavelength λ. Using the relationship $v = f\lambda$, Hertz found that v was close to 3.00×10^8 m/s, the known speed of visible light. Therefore, Hertz's experiments provided the first evidence in support of Maxwell's theory.

■ **Resonance frequency of an *LC* circuit**

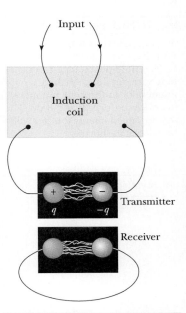

FIGURE 24.9 Schematic diagram of Hertz's apparatus for generating and detecting electromagnetic waves. The transmitter consists of two spherical electrodes connected to an induction coil, which provides short voltage surges to the spheres, setting up oscillations in the discharge. The receiver is a nearby loop containing a second spark gap.

■ Thinking Physics 24.1

In radio transmission, a radio wave serves as a carrier wave and the sound wave is superimposed on the carrier wave. In amplitude modulation (AM radio), the amplitude of the carrier wave varies according to the sound wave. (The word *modulate* means "to change.") In frequency modulation (FM radio), the frequency of the carrier wave varies according to the sound wave. The navy sometimes uses flashing

---

[4]Following Hertz's discoveries, Guglielmo Marconi succeeded in developing this phenomenon into a practical, long-range communication system, radio.

lights to send Morse code to neighboring ships, a process that is similar to radio broadcasting. Is this process AM or FM? What is the carrier frequency? What is the signal frequency? What is the broadcasting antenna? What is the receiving antenna?

Reasoning The flashing of the light according to Morse code is a drastic amplitude modulation because the amplitude is changing between a maximum value and zero. In this sense, it is similar to the on-and-off binary code used in computers and compact discs. The carrier frequency is that of the visible light, on the order of 10^{14} Hz. The signal frequency depends on the skill of the signal operator, but is on the order of a few hertz, as the light is flashed on and off. The broadcasting antenna for this modulated signal is the filament of the lightbulb in the signal source. The receiving antenna is the eye. ■

24.5 ENERGY CARRIED BY ELECTROMAGNETIC WAVES

In Section 13.6, we found that mechanical waves carry energy. Electromagnetic waves also carry energy, and as they propagate through space they can transfer energy to objects placed in their path. This notion was introduced in Chapter 6 when we discussed the transfer mechanisms in the continuity equation for energy, and it was noted again in Chapter 17 in the discussion of thermal radiation. The rate of flow of energy in an electromagnetic wave is described by a vector $\vec{S}$, called the **Poynting vector,** defined by the expression

■ Poynting vector

$$\vec{S} = \frac{1}{\mu_0} \vec{E} \times \vec{B}$$ [24.25]

The magnitude of the Poynting vector represents the rate at which energy flows through a unit surface area perpendicular to the flow and its direction is along the direction of wave propagation (Fig. 24.10). Therefore, the Poynting vector represents *power per unit area*. The SI units of the Poynting vector are $\text{J/s} \cdot \text{m}^2 = \text{W/m}^2$.

As an example, let us evaluate the magnitude of $\vec{S}$ for a plane electromagnetic wave. We have $|\vec{E} \times \vec{B}| = EB$ because $\vec{E}$ and $\vec{B}$ are perpendicular to each other. In this case,

$$S = \frac{EB}{\mu_0}$$ [24.26]

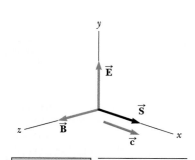

FIGURE 24.10 The Poynting vector $\vec{S}$ for an electromagnetic wave is along the direction of wave propagation.

Because $B = E/c$, we can also express the magnitude as

$$S = \frac{E^2}{\mu_0 c} = \frac{cB^2}{\mu_0}$$

These equations for S apply at any instant of time.

What is of more interest for a sinusoidal electromagnetic wave (Eqs. 24.18 and 24.19) is the time average of S over one or more cycles, which is the **intensity** I. When this average is taken, we obtain an expression involving the time average of $\cos^2(kx - \omega t)$, which equals $\frac{1}{2}$. Therefore, the average value of S (or the intensity of the wave) is

■ Intensity of electromagnetic radiation

$$I = S_{avg} = \frac{E_{max} B_{max}}{2\mu_0} = \frac{E_{max}^2}{2\mu_0 c} = \frac{cB_{max}^2}{2\mu_0}$$ [24.27]

Recall that the energy per unit volume u_E, which is the instantaneous energy density associated with an electric field (Section 20.9), is given by Equation 20.32:

$$u_E = \frac{1}{2}\epsilon_0 E^2$$ [24.28]

and that the instantaneous energy density u_B associated with a magnetic field (Section 23.7) is given by Equation 23.22:

$$u_B = \frac{B^2}{2\mu_0}$$ [24.29]

Because E and B vary with time for an electromagnetic wave, the energy densities also vary with time. Using the relationships $B = E/c$ and $c = 1/\sqrt{\epsilon_0\mu_0}$, Equation 24.29 becomes

$$u_B = \frac{(E/c)^2}{2\mu_0} = \frac{\epsilon_0\mu_0}{2\mu_0}E^2 = \tfrac{1}{2}\epsilon_0 E^2$$

Comparing this result with the expression for u_E, we see that

$$u_B = u_E$$

That is, **for an electromagnetic wave, the instantaneous energy density associated with the magnetic field equals the instantaneous energy density associated with the electric field.** Therefore, in a given volume the energy is equally shared by the two fields.

The **total instantaneous energy density** u is equal to the sum of the energy densities associated with the electric and magnetic fields:

$$u = u_E + u_B = \epsilon_0 E^2 = \frac{B^2}{\mu_0}$$

When this expression is averaged over one or more cycles of an electromagnetic wave, we again obtain a factor of $\tfrac{1}{2}$. Therefore, the total average energy per unit volume of an electromagnetic wave is

$$u_{avg} = \epsilon_0(E^2)_{avg} = \tfrac{1}{2}\epsilon_0 E_{max}^2 = \frac{B_{max}^2}{2\mu_0} \qquad [24.30]$$

Comparing this result with Equation 24.27 for the average value of S, we see that

$$I = S_{avg} = cu_{avg} \qquad [24.31]$$

In other words, **the intensity of an electromagnetic wave equals the average energy density multiplied by the speed of light.**

∎ Total instantaneous energy density of an electromagnetic wave

∎ Average energy density of an electromagnetic wave

QUICK QUIZ 24.2 An electromagnetic wave propagates in the $-y$ direction. The electric field at a point in space is momentarily oriented in the $+x$ direction. Is the magnetic field at that point momentarily oriented in the **(a)** $-x$ direction, **(b)** $+y$ direction, **(c)** $+z$ direction, or **(d)** $-z$ direction?

QUICK QUIZ 24.3 Which of the following quantities does not vary in time for plane electromagnetic waves? **(a)** magnitude of the Poynting vector **(b)** energy density u_E **(c)** energy density u_B **(d)** intensity I

EXAMPLE 24.2   **Fields Due to a Point Source**

A point source of electromagnetic radiation has an average power output of 800 W. Calculate the maximum values of the electric and magnetic fields at a point 3.50 m from the source.

Solution For waves propagating uniformly from a point source, the energy of the wave at a distance r from the source is distributed over the surface area of an imaginary sphere of radius r. Therefore, the intensity of the radiation at a point on the sphere is

$$I = \frac{\mathcal{P}_{avg}}{4\pi r^2}$$

where $\mathcal{P}_{avg}$ is the average power output of the source and $4\pi r^2$ is the area of the sphere centered on the source. Because the intensity of an electromagnetic wave is also given by Equation 24.27, we have

$$I = \frac{\mathcal{P}_{avg}}{4\pi r^2} = \frac{E_{max}^2}{2\mu_0 c}$$

Solving for E_{max} gives us

$$E_{max} = \sqrt{\frac{\mu_0 c \mathcal{P}_{avg}}{2\pi r^2}}$$

$$= \sqrt{\frac{(4\pi \times 10^{-7}\ \text{T·m/A})(3.00 \times 10^8\ \text{m/s})(800\ \text{W})}{2\pi(3.50\ \text{m})^2}}$$

$$= \boxed{62.6\ \text{V/m}}$$

We calculate the maximum value of the magnetic field using this result and Equation 24.21:

$$B_{max} = \frac{E_{max}}{c} = \frac{62.6\ \text{V/m}}{3.00 \times 10^8\ \text{m/s}} = \boxed{2.09 \times 10^{-7}\ \text{T}}$$

24.6 ▮ MOMENTUM AND RADIATION PRESSURE

Electromagnetic waves transport linear momentum as well as energy. Hence, it follows that pressure is exerted on a surface when an electromagnetic wave impinges on it. In what follows, let us assume that the electromagnetic wave strikes a surface at normal incidence and transports a total energy U to a surface in a time interval Δt. If the surface absorbs all the incident energy U in this time, Maxwell showed that the total momentum $\vec{p}$ delivered to this surface has a magnitude

> ■ Momentum delivered to a perfectly absorbing surface

$$p = \frac{U}{c} \qquad \text{(complete absorption)} \qquad [24.32]$$

The pressure exerted on the surface is defined as force per unit area F/A. Let us combine this definition with Newton's second law:

$$P = \frac{F}{A} = \frac{1}{A} \frac{dp}{dt}$$

If we now replace p, the momentum transported to the surface by radiation, from Equation 24.32, we have

$$P = \frac{1}{A} \frac{dp}{dt} = \frac{1}{A} \frac{d}{dt}\left(\frac{U}{c}\right) = \frac{1}{c} \frac{(dU/dt)}{A}$$

We recognize $(dU/dt)/A$ as the rate at which energy is arriving at the surface per unit area, which is the magnitude of the Poynting vector. Therefore, the radiation pressure P exerted on the perfectly absorbing surface is

> ■ Radiation pressure exerted on a perfect absorbing surface

$$P = \frac{S}{c} \qquad \text{(complete absorption)} \qquad [24.33]$$

An absorbing surface for which all the incident energy is absorbed (none is reflected) is called a **black body.** A more detailed discussion of a black body will be presented in Chapter 28.

If the surface is a perfect reflector, the momentum delivered in a time interval Δt for normal incidence is twice that given by Equation 24.32, or $p = 2U/c$. That is, a momentum U/c is delivered first by the incident wave and then again by the reflected wave, a situation analogous to a ball colliding elastically with a wall.[5] Finally, the radiation pressure exerted on a perfect reflecting surface for normal incidence of the wave is twice that given by Equation 24.33, or $P = 2S/c$.

Although radiation pressures are very small (about 5×10^{-6} N/m^2 for direct sunlight), they have been measured using torsion balances such as the one shown in Figure 24.11. Light is allowed to strike either a mirror or a black disk, both of which are suspended from a fine fiber. Light striking the black disk is completely absorbed, so all its momentum is transferred to the disk. Light striking the mirror (normal incidence) is totally reflected and hence the momentum transfer is twice as great as that transferred to the disk. The radiation pressure is determined by measuring the angle through which the horizontal connecting rod rotates. The apparatus must be placed in a high vacuum to eliminate the effects of air currents.

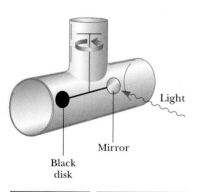

Light

Mirror

Black disk

FIGURE 24.11 An apparatus for measuring the pressure exerted by light. In practice, the system is contained in a high vacuum.

> **QUICK QUIZ 24.4** In an apparatus such as that in Figure 24.11, suppose the black disk is replaced by one with half the radius. Which of the following are different after the disk is replaced? **(a)** radiation pressure on the disk **(b)** radiation force on the disk **(c)** radiation momentum delivered to the disk in a given time interval

---

[5]For *oblique* incidence, the momentum transferred is $2U \cos\theta/c$ and the pressure is given by $P = 2S \cos^2\theta/c$, where θ is the angle between the normal to the surface and the direction of propagation.

■ Thinking Physics 24.2

A large amount of dust occurs in the interplanetary space in the Solar System. Although this dust can theoretically have a variety of sizes, from molecular size upward, very little of it is smaller than about 0.2 μm in our Solar System. Why? (*Hint:* The Solar System originally contained dust particles of all sizes.)

Reasoning Dust particles in the Solar System are subject to two forces: the gravitational force toward the Sun and the force from radiation pressure due to sunlight, which is away from the Sun. The gravitational force is proportional to the cube of the radius of a spherical dust particle because it is proportional to the particle's mass. The radiation force is proportional to the square of the radius because it depends on the circular cross-section of the particle. For large particles, the gravitational force is larger than the force from radiation pressure. For small particles, less than about 0.2 μm, the larger force from radiation pressure sweeps these particles out of the Solar System. ■

EXAMPLE 24.3 Solar Energy

The Sun delivers about 1 000 W/m^2 of energy to the Earth's surface.

A Calculate the total power incident on a roof of dimensions 8.00 m $\times$ 20.0 m.

Solution The Poynting vector has an average magnitude $I = S_{avg} = 1\,000$ W/m^2, which represents the power per unit area. Assuming that the radiation is incident normal to the roof, we can find the power for the whole roof:

$$\mathcal{P} = IA = (1\,000 \text{ W/m}^2)(8.00 \times 20.0 \text{ m}^2)$$

$$= 1.60 \times 10^5 \text{ W}$$

If solar energy could all be converted to electric energy, it would provide more than enough power for the average home. Solar energy is not easily harnessed, however, and the prospects for large-scale conversion are not as bright as they may appear from this simple calculation. For example, the conversion efficiency from solar to electric energy is typically 10% for photovoltaic cells. Solar energy has other practical problems that must also be considered, such as overcast days, geographic location, and energy storage.

B Determine the radiation pressure and radiation force on the roof, assuming that the roof covering is a perfect absorber.

Solution Using Equation 24.33 with $I = 1\,000$ W/m^2, we find that the average radiation pressure is

$$P = \frac{I}{c} = \frac{1\,000 \text{ W/m}^2}{3.00 \times 10^8 \text{ m/s}} = 3.33 \times 10^{-6} \text{ N/m}^2$$

Because pressure equals force per unit area, this value of P corresponds to a radiation force of

$$F = PA = (3.33 \times 10^{-6} \text{ N/m}^2)(160 \text{ m}^2)$$

$$= 5.33 \times 10^{-4} \text{ N}$$

INTERACTIVE EXAMPLE 24.4 Pressure from a Laser Pointer

Many people giving presentations use a laser pointer to direct the attention of their audience. If a 3.0-mW pointer creates a spot that is 2.0 mm in diameter, determine the radiation pressure on a screen that reflects 70% of the light striking it. The power of 3.0 mW is a time-averaged power.

Solution In conceptualizing this problem, we certainly do not expect the pressure to be very large. We categorize this problem as one in which we calculate the radiation pressure by using something like Equation 24.33, but which is complicated by the 70% reflection. To analyze the problem, we begin by determining the Poynting vector of the beam. We divide the time-averaged power delivered via the electromagnetic wave by the cross-sectional area of the beam. Thus,

$$I = \frac{\mathcal{P}}{A} = \frac{\mathcal{P}}{\pi r^2} = \frac{3.0 \times 10^{-3} \text{ W}}{\pi \left(\dfrac{2.0 \times 10^{-3} \text{ m}}{2} \right)^2}$$

$$= 9.6 \times 10^2 \text{ W/m}^2$$

Now we can determine the radiation pressure from the laser beam. A completely reflected beam would apply an average pressure of $P_{avg} = 2S_{avg}/c$. We can model the actual reflection as follows. Imagine that the surface absorbs the beam, resulting in pressure

$P_{avg} = S_{avg}/c$. Then the surface emits the beam, resulting in additional pressure $P_{avg} = S_{avg}/c$. If the surface emits only a fraction f of the beam (so that f is the amount of the incident beam reflected), the pressure due to the emitted beam is $P_{avg} = fS_{avg}/c$. Therefore, the total pressure on the surface due to absorption and re-emission (reflection) is

$$P_{avg} = \frac{S_{avg}}{c} + f\frac{S_{avg}}{c} = (1 + f)\frac{S_{avg}}{c}$$

For a beam that is 70% reflected, the pressure is

$$P = (1 + 0.70)\frac{9.6 \times 10^2 \text{ W/m}^2}{3.0 \times 10^8 \text{ m/s}} = \boxed{5.4 \times 10^{-6} \text{ N/m}^2}$$

To finalize the problem, consider first the magnitude of the Poynting vector. It is about the same as the intensity of sunlight at the Earth's surface. (Therefore, it is not safe to shine the beam of a laser pointer into a person's eyes; that may be more dangerous than looking directly at the Sun.) To finalize further, note that the pressure has an extremely small value, as expected. (Recall from Section 15.1 that atmospheric pressure is approximately 10^5 N/m².)

Physics⊗Now™ Log into PhysicsNow at **www.pop4e.com** and go to Interactive Example 24.4 to investigate the pressure on the screen for various laser and screen parameters.

Space Sailing

When imagining a trip to another planet, we normally think of traditional rocket engines that convert chemical energy in fuel carried on the spacecraft to kinetic energy of the spacecraft. An interesting alternative to this approach is that of **space sailing**. A space-sailing craft includes a very large sail that reflects light. The motion of the spacecraft depends on pressure from light, that is, the force exerted on the sail by the reflection of light from the Sun. Calculations performed (before U.S. government budget cutbacks shelved early space-sailing projects) showed that sailing craft could travel to and from the planets in times similar to those for traditional rockets, but for less cost.

Calculations show that the radiation force from the Sun on a practical sailcraft with large sails could be equal to or slightly larger than the gravitational force on the sailcraft. If these two forces are equal, the sailcraft can be modeled as a particle in equilibrium because the inward gravitational force of the Sun balances the outward force exerted by the light from the Sun. If the sailcraft has an initial velocity in some direction away from the Sun, it would move in a straight line under the action of these two forces, with no necessity for fuel. A traditional spacecraft with its rocket engines turned off, on the other hand, would slow down as a result of the gravitational force on it due to the Sun. Both the force on the sail and the gravitational force from the Sun fall off as the inverse square of the Sun–sailcraft separation. Therefore, in theory, the straight-line motion of the sailcraft would continue forever with no fuel requirement.

By using just the motion imparted to a sailcraft by the Sun, the craft could reach Alpha Centauri in about 10 000 years. This time interval can be reduced to 30 to 100 years using a *beamed power system*. In this concept, light from the Sun is gathered by a transformation device in orbit around the Earth and is converted to a laser beam or microwave beam aimed at the sailcraft. The force from this intense beam of radiation increases the acceleration of the craft, and the transit time is significantly reduced. Calculations indicate that the sailcraft could achieve design speeds of up to 20% of the speed of light using this technique.

24.7 │ THE SPECTRUM OF ELECTROMAGNETIC WAVES

Electromagnetic waves travel through vacuum with speed c, frequency f, and wavelength λ. The various types of electromagnetic waves, all produced by accelerating charges, are shown in Figure 24.12. Note the wide range of frequencies and wavelengths. Let us briefly describe the wave types shown in Figure 24.12.

Radio waves are the result of charges accelerating, for example, through conducting wires in a radio antenna. They are generated by such electronic devices as LC oscillators and are used in radio and television communication systems.

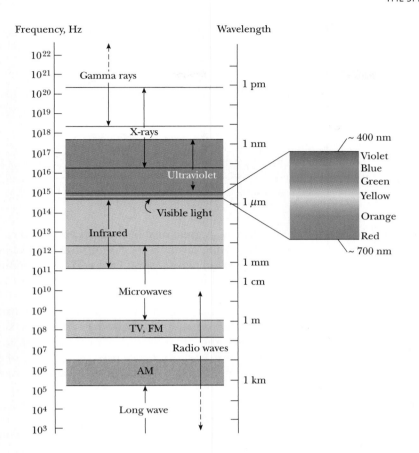

Frequency, Hz   Wavelength

FIGURE 24.12 The electromagnetic spectrum. Note the overlap between adjacent wave types. The expanded view to the right shows details of the visible spectrum.

(Ron Chapple/Getty Images)

Wearing sunglasses that do not block ultraviolet (UV) light is worse for your eyes than wearing no sunglasses. The lenses of any sunglasses absorb some visible light, thus causing the wearer's pupils to dilate. If the glasses do not also block UV light, more damage may be done to the eye's lens because of the dilated pupils. If you wear no sunglasses at all, your pupils are contracted, you squint, and much less UV light enters your eyes. High-quality sunglasses block nearly all the eye-damaging UV light. ∎

Microwaves (short-wavelength radio waves) have wavelengths ranging between about 1 mm and 30 cm and are also generated by electronic devices. Because of their short wavelengths, they are well suited for radar systems used in aircraft navigation and for studying the atomic and molecular properties of matter. Microwave ovens are a domestic application of these waves.

Infrared waves have wavelengths ranging from about 1 mm to the longest wavelength of visible light, 7×10^{-7} m. These waves, produced by objects at room temperature and by molecules, are readily absorbed by most materials. Infrared radiation has many practical and scientific applications, including physical therapy, infrared photography, and vibrational spectroscopy. Your remote control for your TV, VCR, or DVD player likely uses an infrared beam to communicate with the video device.

Visible light, the most familiar form of electromagnetic waves, is that part of the spectrum the human eye can detect. Light is produced by hot objects like lightbulb filaments and by the rearrangement of electrons in atoms and molecules. The wavelengths of visible light are classified by color, ranging from violet ($\lambda \approx 4 \times 10^{-7}$ m) to red ($\lambda \approx 7 \times 10^{-7}$ m). The eye's sensitivity is a function of wavelength and is a maximum at a wavelength of about 5.5×10^{-7} m (yellow–green). Table 24.1 provides approximate correspondences between the wavelength of visible light and the color assigned to it by humans. Light is the basis of the science of optics and optical instruments, to be discussed in Chapters 25 through 27.

Ultraviolet light covers wavelengths ranging from about 4×10^{-7} m (400 nm) down to 6×10^{-10} m (0.6 nm). The Sun is an important source of ultraviolet waves, which are the main cause of suntans and sunburns. Atoms in the stratosphere absorb most of the ultraviolet waves from the Sun (which is fortunate because ultraviolet waves in large quantities have harmful effects on humans). One important constituent of the stratosphere is ozone (O_3), which results from reactions of oxygen with ultraviolet radiation. This ozone shield converts lethal high-energy ultraviolet

▦ PITFALL PREVENTION 24.3

HEAT RAYS Infrared rays are often called "heat rays." This terminology is a misnomer. Although infrared radiation is used to raise or maintain temperature, as in the case of keeping food warm with "heat lamps" at a fast-food restaurant, all wavelengths of electromagnetic radiation carry energy that can cause the temperature of a system to increase. As an example, consider using your microwave oven to bake a potato, whose temperature increases because of microwaves.

TABLE 24.1	Approximate Correspondence Between Wavelengths of Visible Light and Color
Wavelength Range (nm)	**Color Description**
400–430	Violet
430–485	Blue
485–560	Green
560–575	Yellow
575–625	Orange
625–700	Red

Note: The wavelength ranges here are approximate. Different people will describe colors differently.

radiation to harmless infrared radiation. A great deal of concern has arisen concerning the depletion of the protective ozone layer by the use of a class of chemicals called chlorofluorocarbons (e.g., Freon) in aerosol spray cans and as refrigerants.

X-rays are electromagnetic waves with wavelengths in the range of about 10^{-8} m (10 nm) down to 10^{-13} m (10^{-4} nm). The most common source of x-rays is the acceleration of high-energy electrons bombarding a metal target. X-rays are used as a diagnostic tool in medicine and as a treatment for certain forms of cancer. Because x-rays damage or destroy living tissues and organisms, care must be taken to avoid unnecessary exposure and overexposure. X-rays are also used in the study of crystal structure; x-ray wavelengths are comparable to the atomic separation distances (≈ 0.1 nm) in solids.

Gamma rays are electromagnetic waves emitted by radioactive nuclei and during certain nuclear reactions. They have wavelengths ranging from about 10^{-10} m to less than 10^{-14} m. Gamma rays are highly penetrating and produce serious damage when absorbed by living tissues. Consequently, those working near such dangerous radiation must be protected with heavily absorbing materials, such as layers of lead.

QUICK QUIZ 24.5 In many kitchens, a microwave oven is used to cook food. The frequency of the microwaves is on the order of 10^{10} Hz. The wavelengths of these microwaves are on the order of **(a)** kilometers, **(b)** meters, **(c)** centimeters, or **(d)** micrometers.

QUICK QUIZ 24.6 A radio wave of frequency on the order of 10^5 Hz is used to carry a sound wave with a frequency on the order of 10^3 Hz. The wavelength of this radio wave is on the order of **(a)** kilometers, **(b)** meters, **(c)** centimeters, or **(d)** micrometers.

■ **Thinking Physics 24.3**

The center of sensitivity of our eyes is close to the same frequency as the center of the wavelength distribution of light from the Sun. Is that an amazing coincidence?

Reasoning It is not a coincidence; rather, it is the result of biological evolution. Humans have evolved so as to be most visually sensitive to the wavelengths that are strongest from the Sun. It is an interesting conjecture to imagine aliens from another planet, with a Sun with a different temperature, arriving at Earth. Their eyes would have the center of sensitivity at different wavelengths than ours. How would their vision of the Earth compare with ours? ■

 Center of eyesight sensitivity

24.8 POLARIZATION

As we learned in Section 24.3, the electric and magnetic vectors associated with an electromagnetic wave are perpendicular to each other and also to the direction of wave propagation as shown in Active Figure 24.3. The phenomenon of polarization described in this section is a property that specifies the directions of the electric and magnetic fields associated with an electromagnetic wave.

An ordinary beam of light consists of a large number of waves emitted by the atoms of the light source. Each atom produces a wave with its own orientation of the electric field $\vec{\mathbf{E}}$, corresponding to the direction of vibration in the atom. The direction of polarization of the electromagnetic wave is defined to be the direction in which $\vec{\mathbf{E}}$ is vibrating. Because all directions of vibration are possible in a group of atoms emitting a beam of light, however, the resultant beam is a superposition of waves produced by the individual atomic sources. The result is an **unpolarized** light wave, represented schematically in Figure 24.13a. The direction of wave propagation in this figure is perpendicular to the page. The figure suggests that *all* directions of the electric field vector lying in a plane perpendicular to the direction of propagation are equally probable.

A wave is said to be **linearly polarized** if the orientation of $\vec{\mathbf{E}}$ is the same for all individual waves *at all times* at a particular point as suggested in Figure 24.13b. (Sometimes such a wave is described as **plane polarized.**) The wave described in Active Figure 24.3 is an example of a wave linearly polarized along the y axis. As the field propagates in the x direction, $\vec{\mathbf{E}}$ is always along the y axis. The plane formed by $\vec{\mathbf{E}}$ and the direction of propagation is called the **plane of polarization** of the wave. In Active Figure 24.3, the plane of polarization is the xy plane. It is possible to obtain a linearly polarized wave from an unpolarized wave by removing from the unpolarized wave all components of electric field vectors except those that lie in a single plane.

The most common technique for polarizing light is to send it through a material that passes only components of electric field vectors that are parallel to a characteristic direction of the material called the **polarizing direction.** In 1938, E. H. Land discovered such a material, which he called **Polaroid,** that polarizes light through selective absorption by oriented molecules. This material is fabricated in thin sheets of long-chain hydrocarbons, which are stretched during manufacture so that the molecules align. After a sheet is dipped into a solution containing iodine, the molecules become good electric conductors. The conduction, however, takes place primarily along the hydrocarbon chains because the valence electrons of the molecules can move easily only along the chains (valence electrons are "free" electrons that can readily move through the conductor). As a result, the molecules readily *absorb* light whose electric field vector is parallel to their length and *transmit* light whose electric field vector is perpendicular to their length. It is common to refer to the direction perpendicular to the molecular chains as the **transmission axis.** An ideal polarizer passes the components of electric vectors that are parallel to the transmission axis. Components perpendicular to the transmission axis are absorbed. If light passes through several polarizers, whatever is transmitted has the plane of polarization parallel to the polarizing direction of the last polarizer through which it passed.

Let us now obtain an expression for the intensity of light that passes through a polarizing material. In Active Figure 24.14, an unpolarized light beam is incident

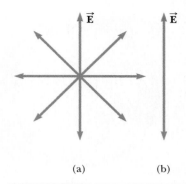

FIGURE 24.13 (a) An unpolarized light beam viewed along the direction of propagation (perpendicular to the page). The time-varying electric field vector can be in any direction in the plane of the page with equal probability. (b) A linearly polarized light beam with the time-varying electric field vector in the vertical direction.

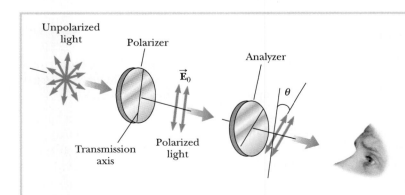

ACTIVE FIGURE 24.14

Two polarizing sheets whose transmission axes make an angle θ with each other. Only a fraction of the polarized light incident on the analyzer is transmitted through it.

Physics⊗Now™ Log into PhysicsNow at **www.pop4e.com** and go to Active Figure 24.14 to rotate the analyzer and see the effect on the transmitted light.

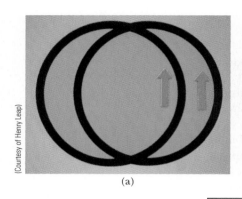

(a)

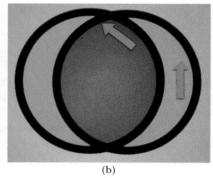

(b)

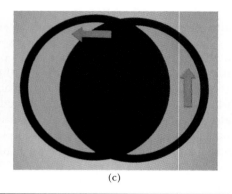

(c)

(Courtesy of Henry Leap)

FIGURE 24.15 The intensity of light transmitted through two polarizers depends on the relative orientation of their transmission axes. (a) The transmitted light has maximum intensity when the transmission axes are aligned with each other. (b) The transmitted light intensity diminishes when the transmission axes are at an angle of 45° with each other. (c) The transmitted light intensity is a minimum when the transmission axes are perpendicular to each other.

on the first polarizing sheet, called the **polarizer,** where the transmission axis is as indicated. The light that passes through this sheet is polarized vertically, and the transmitted electric field vector is $\vec{E}_0$. A second polarizing sheet, called the **analyzer,** intercepts this beam with its transmission axis at an angle of θ to the axis of the polarizer. The component of $\vec{E}_0$ that is perpendicular to the axis of the analyzer is completely absorbed, and the component parallel to that axis is $E_0 \cos \theta$. We know from Equation 24.27 that the transmitted intensity varies as the *square* of the transmitted amplitude, so we conclude that the intensity of the transmitted (polarized) light varies as

■ Malus's law

$$I = I_0 \cos^2 \theta \qquad [24.34]$$

where I_0 is the intensity of the polarized wave incident on the analyzer. This expression, known as **Malus's law,** applies to any two polarizing materials whose transmission axes are at an angle of θ to each other. From this expression, note that the transmitted intensity is a maximum when the transmission axes are parallel ($\theta = 0$ or 180°) and zero (complete absorption by the analyzer) when the transmission axes are perpendicular to each other. This variation in transmitted intensity through a pair of polarizing sheets is illustrated in Figure 24.15. Because the average value of $\cos^2 \theta$ is $\frac{1}{2}$, the intensity of initially unpolarized light is reduced by a factor of one half as the light passes through a single ideal polarizer.

QUICK QUIZ 24.7 A polarizer for microwaves can be made as a grid of parallel metal wires about a centimeter apart. Is the electric field vector for microwaves transmitted through this polarizer **(a)** parallel or **(b)** perpendicular to the metal wires?

24.9 | THE SPECIAL PROPERTIES OF LASER LIGHT

CONTEXT CONNECTION

In this chapter and the next three, we shall explore the nature of laser light and a variety of applications of lasers in our technological society. The primary properties of laser light that make it useful in these applications are the following:

• The light is coherent. The individual rays of light in a laser beam maintain a fixed phase relationship with one another, resulting in no destructive interference.
• The light is monochromatic. Laser light has a very small range of wavelengths.
• The light has a small angle of divergence. The beam spreads out very little, even over large distances.

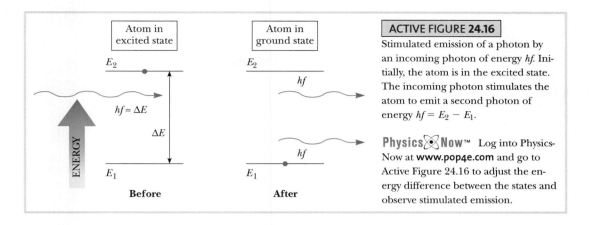

ACTIVE FIGURE 24.16
Stimulated emission of a photon by an incoming photon of energy hf. Initially, the atom is in the excited state. The incoming photon stimulates the atom to emit a second photon of energy $hf = E_2 - E_1$.

Physics⊗Now™ Log into Physics-Now at **www.pop4e.com** and go to Active Figure 24.16 to adjust the energy difference between the states and observe stimulated emission.

To understand the origin of these properties, let us combine our knowledge of atomic energy levels from Chapter 11 with some special requirements for the atoms that emit laser light.

As we found in Chapter 11, the energies of an atom are quantized. We used a semigraphical representation called an *energy level diagram* in that chapter to help us understand the quantized energies in an atom. The production of laser light depends heavily on the properties of these energy levels in the atoms, the source of the laser light.

The word *laser* is an acronym for **l**ight **a**mplification by **s**timulated **e**mission of **r**adiation. The full name indicates one of the requirements for laser light, that the process of **stimulated emission** must occur to achieve laser action.

Suppose an atom is in the excited state E_2 as in Active Figure 24.16 and a photon with energy $hf = E_2 - E_1$ is incident on it. The incoming photon can stimulate the excited atom to return to the ground state and thereby emit a second photon having the same energy hf and traveling in the same direction. Note that the incident photon is not absorbed, so after the stimulated emission, two identical photons exist: the incident photon and the emitted photon. The emitted photon is in phase with the incident photon. These photons can stimulate other atoms to emit photons in a chain of similar processes. The many photons produced in this fashion are the source of the intense, coherent light in a laser.

For the stimulated emission to result in laser light, we must have a buildup of photons in the system. The following three conditions must be satisfied to achieve this buildup:

- The system must be in a state of **population inversion.** More atoms must be in an excited state than in the ground state. Atoms in the ground state can absorb photons, raising them to the excited state. The population inversion assures that we have more emission of photons from excited atoms than absorption by atoms in the ground state.
- The excited state of the system must be a *metastable state,* which means that its lifetime must be long compared with the usually short lifetime of excited states, which is typically 10^{-8} s. In this case, stimulated emission is likely to occur before spontaneous emission. The energy of a metastable state is indicated with an asterisk, E^*.
- The emitted photons must be confined in the system long enough to enable them to stimulate further emission from other excited atoms, which is achieved by using reflecting mirrors at the ends of the system. One end is made totally reflecting, and the other is slightly transparent to allow the laser beam to escape (Fig. 24.17).

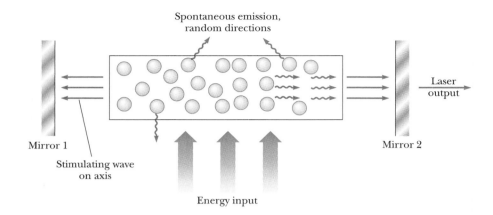

Spontaneous emission, random directions

Mirror 1

Stimulating wave on axis

Energy input

Laser output

Mirror 2

A schematic of a laser design. The tube contains atoms, which represent the active medium. An external source of energy (optical, electric, etc.) is needed to "pump" the atoms to excited energy states. The parallel end mirrors confine the photons to the tube. Mirror 2 is slightly transparent so that laser light leaves the tube through this mirror.

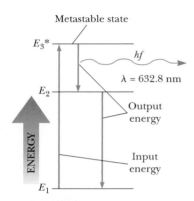

Metastable state

E_3*

hf

$\lambda = 632.8$ nm

E_2

Output energy

Input energy

ENERGY

E_1

FIGURE 24.18 Energy level diagram for a neon atom in a helium–neon laser. The atom emits 632.8-nm photons through stimulated emission in the transition $E_3* \rightarrow E_2$, which is the source of coherent light in the laser.

(Courtesy of Mark Helfer/National Institute of Standards and Technology)

FIGURE 24.19 A staff member of the National Institute of Standards and Technology views a sample of trapped sodium atoms (the small yellow dot in the center of the vacuum chamber) cooled to a temperature of less than 1 mK.

One device that exhibits stimulated emission of radiation is the helium–neon gas laser. Figure 24.18 is an energy level diagram for the neon atom in this system. The mixture of helium and neon is confined to a glass tube that is sealed at the ends by mirrors. A voltage applied across the tube causes electrons to sweep through the tube, colliding with the atoms of the gases and raising them into excited states. Neon atoms are excited to state E_3* through this process and also as a result of collisions with excited helium atoms. Stimulated emission occurs as the neon atoms make a transition to state E_2 and neighboring excited atoms are stimulated. The result is the production of coherent light at a wavelength of 632.8 nm.

An exciting area of research and technological applications began in the 1990s with the development of *laser trapping* of atoms (Fig. 24.19). One scheme, called *optical molasses* and developed by Steven Chu of Stanford University and his colleagues, involves focusing six laser beams onto a small region in which atoms are to be trapped. Each pair of lasers is along one of the x, y, and z axes and emits light in opposite directions (Fig. 24.20). The frequency of the laser light is tuned to be just below the absorption frequency of the subject atom. Imagine that an atom has been placed into the trap region and moves along the positive x axis toward the laser that is emitting light toward it (the right-hand laser on the x axis in Fig. 24.20). Because the atom is moving, the light from the laser appears Doppler shifted upward in frequency in the reference frame of the atom. This shift creates a match between the Doppler-shifted laser frequency and the absorption frequency of the atom, and the atom absorbs photons.[6] The momentum carried by these photons results in the atom being pushed back to the center of the trap. By incorporating six lasers, the atoms are pushed back into the trap regardless of which way they move along any axis.

In 1986, Chu developed *optical tweezers* in which a single tightly focused laser beam can be used to trap and manipulate small particles. In combination with microscopes, optical tweezers have opened up many new possibilities for biologists. Optical tweezers have been used to manipulate live bacteria without damage, move chromosomes within a cell nucleus, and measure the elastic properties of a single DNA molecule. Chu shared the 1997 Nobel Prize in Physics with Claude Cohen-Tannoudji (Collège de France) and William Phillips (National Institute of Standards and Technology) for the development of the techniques of optical trapping.

An extension of laser trapping, *laser cooling*, is due to the reduction of the normal high speeds of the atoms when they are restricted to the region of the trap. As a result, the temperature of the collection of atoms can be reduced to a few

[6]The laser light traveling in the same direction as the atom (from the left-hand laser on the x axis in Fig. 24.20) is Doppler shifted further downward in frequency, so no absorption occurs. Therefore, the atom is not pushed out of the trap by the diametrically opposed laser.

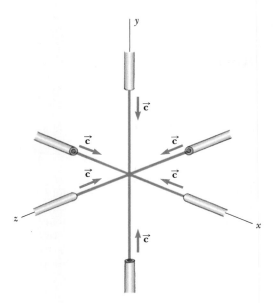

FIGURE 24.20 An optical trap for atoms is formed at the intersection point of six counterpropagating laser beams along mutually perpendicular axes. The frequency of the laser light is tuned to be just below that for absorption by the trapped atoms. If an atom moves away from the trap, it absorbs the Doppler-shifted laser light and the momentum of the light pushes the atom back into the trap.

nanokelvins. This laser cooling allows scientists to study the behavior of atoms at extremely low temperatures.

In the 1920s, Satyendra Nath Bose (1894–1974) was studying photons and investigating collections of identical photons, which can all be in the same quantum state. Einstein followed up on the work of Bose and predicted that a collection of atoms could all be in the same quantum state if the temperature were low enough. The proposed collection of atoms is called a *Bose–Einstein condensate*. In 1995, using laser cooling supplemented with evaporative cooling, the first Bose–Einstein condensate was created in the laboratory by Eric Cornell and Carl Wieman, who won the 2001 Nobel Prize in Physics for their work. Many laboratories are now creating Bose–Einstein condensates and studying their properties and possible applications. One interesting result was reported by a Harvard University group led by Lene Vestergaard Hau in 2001. She and her colleagues announced that they were able to bring a light pulse to a complete stop by using a Bose–Einstein condensate.[7]

We have explored general properties of laser light in this chapter. In the Context Connection of Chapter 25, we shall explore the technology of optical fibers, in which lasers are used in a variety of applications. ▮

SUMMARY

Physics⊗Now™ Take a practice test by logging into Physics-Now at **www.pop4e.com** and clicking on the Pre-Test link for this chapter.

Displacement current I_d is defined as

$$I_d \equiv \epsilon_0 \frac{d\Phi_E}{dt} \qquad [24.1]$$

and represents an effective current through a region of space in which an electric field is changing in time.

When used with the Lorentz force law ($\vec{F} = q\vec{E} + q\vec{v} \times \vec{B}$), **Maxwell's equations** describe *all* electromagnetic phenomena:

$$\oint \vec{E} \cdot d\vec{A} = \frac{q}{\epsilon_0} \qquad [24.4]$$

$$\oint \vec{B} \cdot d\vec{A} = 0 \qquad [24.5]$$

$$\oint \vec{E} \cdot d\vec{s} = -\frac{d\Phi_B}{dt} \qquad [24.6]$$

$$\oint \vec{B} \cdot d\vec{s} = \mu_0 I + \epsilon_0 \mu_0 \frac{d\Phi_E}{dt} \qquad [24.7]$$

Electromagnetic waves, which are predicted by Maxwell's equations, have the following properties:

[7]C. Liu, Z. Dutton, C. H. Behroozi, and L. V. Hau, "Observation of coherent optical information storage in an atomic medium using halted light pulses," *Nature*, 409, 490–493, January 25, 2001.

- The electric and magnetic fields satisfy the following wave equations, which can be obtained from Maxwell's third and fourth equations:

$$\frac{\partial^2 E}{\partial x^2} = \epsilon_0 \mu_0 \frac{\partial^2 E}{\partial t^2} \qquad [24.15]$$

$$\frac{\partial^2 B}{\partial x^2} = \epsilon_0 \mu_0 \frac{\partial^2 B}{\partial t^2} \qquad [24.16]$$

- Electromagnetic waves travel through a vacuum with the speed of light $c = 3.00 \times 10^8$ m/s, where

$$c = \frac{1}{\sqrt{\epsilon_0 \mu_0}} \qquad [24.17]$$

- The electric and magnetic fields of an electromagnetic wave are perpendicular to each other and perpendicular to the direction of wave propagation; hence, electromagnetic waves are transverse waves. The electric and magnetic fields of a sinusoidal plane electromagnetic wave propagating in the positive x direction can be written

$$E = E_{\max} \cos(kx - \omega t) \qquad [24.18]$$

$$B = B_{\max} \cos(kx - \omega t) \qquad [24.19]$$

where ω is the angular frequency of the wave and k is the angular wave number. These equations represent special solutions to the wave equations for $\vec{\mathbf{E}}$ and $\vec{\mathbf{B}}$.

- The instantaneous magnitudes of $\vec{\mathbf{E}}$ and $\vec{\mathbf{B}}$ in an electromagnetic wave are related by the expression

$$\frac{E}{B} = c \qquad [24.21]$$

- Electromagnetic waves carry energy. The rate of flow of energy crossing a unit area is described by the **Poynting vector** $\vec{\mathbf{S}}$, where

$$\vec{\mathbf{S}} = \frac{1}{\mu_0} \vec{\mathbf{E}} \times \vec{\mathbf{B}} \qquad [24.25]$$

The average value of the Poynting vector for a plane electromagnetic wave has the magnitude

$$I = S_{\text{avg}} = \frac{E_{\max} B_{\max}}{2\mu_0} = \frac{E_{\max}^2}{2\mu_0 c} = \frac{c B_{\max}^2}{2\mu_0} \qquad [24.27]$$

The average power per unit area (intensity) of a sinusoidal plane electromagnetic wave equals the average value of the Poynting vector taken over one or more cycles.

- Electromagnetic waves carry momentum and hence can exert pressure on surfaces. If an electromagnetic wave whose intensity is I is completely absorbed by a surface on which it is normally incident, the radiation pressure on that surface is

$$P = \frac{S}{c} \qquad \text{(complete absorption)} \qquad [24.33]$$

If the surface totally reflects a normally incident wave, the pressure is doubled.

The **electromagnetic spectrum** includes waves covering a broad range of frequencies and wavelengths.

When polarized light of intensity I_0 is incident on a polarizing film, the light transmitted through the film has an intensity equal to $I_0 \cos^2 \theta$, where θ is the angle between the transmission axis of the polarizing film and the electric field vector of the incident light.

QUESTIONS

☐ = answer available in the *Student Solutions Manual and Study Guide*

1. Radio station announcers often advertise "instant news." If they mean that you can hear the news the instant they speak it, is their claim true? About how long would it take for a message to travel across this country by radio waves, assuming that the waves could be detected at this range?

2. When light (or other electromagnetic radiation) travels across a given region, what is it that oscillates? What is it that is transported?

3. What is the fundamental source of electromagnetic radiation?

4. Does a wire connected to the terminals of a battery emit electromagnetic waves? Explain.

5. If you charge a comb by running it through your hair and then hold the comb next to a bar magnet, do the electric and magnetic fields produced constitute an electromagnetic wave?

6. List as many similarities and differences between sound waves and light waves as you can.

7. In the *LC* circuit shown in Figure 24.7, the charge on the capacitor is sometimes zero, but at such instants the current in the circuit is not zero. How is that possible?

8. Describe the physical significance of the Poynting vector.

9. Before the advent of cable television and satellite dishes, city dwellers often used "rabbit ears" atop their sets (Fig. Q24.9). Certain orientations of the receiving antenna on a television set give better reception than others. Furthermore, the best orientation varies from station to station. Explain.

10. Often when you touch the indoor antenna on a radio or television receiver, the reception instantly improves. Why?

11. What does a radio wave do to the charges in the receiving antenna to provide a signal for your car radio?

12. An empty plastic or glass dish being removed from a microwave oven is cool to the touch. How can that be possible? (Assume that your electric bill has been paid.)

FIGURE **Q24.9** Question 24.9 and Problem 24.57.

13. Suppose a creature from another planet had eyes that were sensitive to infrared radiation. Describe what the alien would see if it looked around the room you are now in. In particular, what would be bright and what would be dim?

14. Why should an infrared photograph of a person look different from a photograph taken with visible light?

15. ▨ A welder must wear protective glasses and clothing to prevent eye damage and sunburn. What does this practice imply about the nature of the light produced by the welding?

16. A home microwave oven uses electromagnetic waves with a wavelength of about 12.2 cm. Some 2.4-GHz cordless telephones suffer noisy interference when a microwave oven is used nearby. Locate the waves used by both devices on the electromagnetic spectrum. Do you expect them to interfere with each other?

17. Why is stimulated emission so important in the operation of a laser?

18. For a given incident energy of an electromagnetic wave, why is the radiation pressure on a perfectly reflecting surface twice as great as that on a perfect absorbing surface?

PROBLEMS

1, 2, 3	= straightforward, intermediate, challenging
▢	= full solution available in the *Student Solutions Manual and Study Guide*
Physics⊗Now™	= coached problem with hints available at **www.pop4e.com**
🖥	= computer useful in solving problem
▬	= paired numerical and symbolic problems
▨	= biomedical application

Section 24.1 ▪ Displacement Current and the Generalized Ampère's Law

1. Consider the situation shown in Figure P24.1. An electric field of 300 V/m is confined to a circular area 10.0 cm in

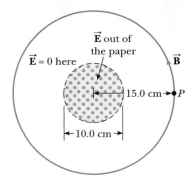

FIGURE **P24.1**

diameter and directed outward perpendicular to the plane of the figure. If the field is increasing at a rate of 20.0 V/m·s, what are the direction and magnitude of the magnetic field at the point P, 15.0 cm from the center of the circle?

Section 24.2 ▪ Maxwell's Equations

2. A very long, thin rod carries electric charge with the linear density 35.0 nC/m. It lies along the x axis and moves in the x direction at a speed of 15.0 Mm/s. (a) Find the electric field the rod creates at the point (0, 20.0 cm, 0). (b) Find the magnetic field it creates at the same point. (c) Find the force exerted on an electron at this point, moving with a velocity of $(240\hat{\mathbf{i}})$ Mm/s.

3. A proton moves through a uniform electric field $\vec{\mathbf{E}} = 50\hat{\mathbf{j}}$ V/m and a uniform magnetic field $\vec{\mathbf{B}} = (0.200\hat{\mathbf{i}} + 0.300\hat{\mathbf{j}} + 0.400\hat{\mathbf{k}})$ T. Determine the acceleration of the proton when it has a velocity $\vec{\mathbf{v}} = 200\hat{\mathbf{i}}$ m/s.

Section 24.3 ▪ Electromagnetic Waves

Note: Assume that the medium is vacuum unless specified otherwise.

4. (a) The distance to the North Star, Polaris, is approximately 6.44×10^{18} m. If Polaris were to burn out today, in what year would we see it disappear? (b) How long does it take for sunlight to reach the Earth? (c) How long does it take for a microwave radar signal to travel from the Earth

to the Moon and back? (d) How long does it take for a radio wave to travel once around the Earth in a great circle, close to the planet's surface? (e) How long does it take for light to reach you from a lightning stroke 10.0 km away?

5. The speed of an electromagnetic wave traveling in a transparent nonmagnetic substance is $v = 1/\sqrt{\kappa\mu_0\epsilon_0}$, where κ is the dielectric constant of the substance. Determine the speed of light in water, which has a dielectric constant at optical frequencies of 1.78.

6. An electromagnetic wave in vacuum has an electric field amplitude of 220 V/m. Calculate the amplitude of the corresponding magnetic field.

7. **Physics⊗Now™** Figure 24.3 shows a plane electromagnetic sinusoidal wave propagating in the x direction. Suppose the wavelength is 50.0 m and the electric field vibrates in the xy plane with an amplitude of 22.0 V/m. Calculate (a) the frequency of the wave and (b) the magnitude and direction of $\vec{B}$ when the electric field has its maximum value in the negative y direction. (c) Write an expression for $\vec{B}$ with the correct unit vector, with numerical values for B_{max}, k, and ω, and with its magnitude in the form

$$B = B_{max}\cos(kx - \omega t)$$

8. In SI units, the electric field in an electromagnetic wave is described by

$$E_y = 100\sin(1.00 \times 10^7 x - \omega t)$$

Find (a) the amplitude of the corresponding magnetic field oscillations, (b) the wavelength λ, and (c) the frequency f.

9. Verify by substitution that the following equations are solutions to Equations 24.15 and 24.16, respectively:

$$E = E_{max}\cos(kx - \omega t)$$
$$B = B_{max}\cos(kx - \omega t)$$

10. **Review problem.** A standing wave interference pattern is set up by radio waves between two metal sheets 2.00 m apart. That is the shortest distance between the plates that will produce a standing wave pattern. What is the fundamental frequency?

11. A microwave oven is powered by an electron tube called a magnetron, which generates electromagnetic waves of frequency 2.45 GHz. The microwaves enter the oven and are reflected by the walls. The standing wave pattern produced in the oven can cook food unevenly, with hot spots in the food at antinodes and cool spots at nodes, so a turntable is often used to rotate the food and distribute the energy. If a microwave oven intended for use with a turntable is instead used with a cooking dish in a fixed position, the antinodes can appear as burn marks on foods such as carrot strips or cheese. The separation distance between the burns is measured to be 6 cm ± 5%. From these data, calculate the speed of the microwaves.

12. **Review problem.** An alien civilization occupies a brown dwarf, nearly stationary relative to the Sun, several lightyears away. The extraterrestrials have come to love original broadcasts of *I Love Lucy*, on our television channel 2, at carrier frequency 57.0 MHz. Their line of sight to us is in the plane of the Earth's orbit. Find the difference between the highest and lowest frequencies they receive due to the Earth's orbital motion around the Sun.

13. Police radar detects the speed of a car (Fig. P24.13) as follows. Microwaves of a precisely known frequency are broadcast toward the car. The moving car reflects the microwaves with a Doppler shift. The reflected waves are received and combined with an attenuated version of the transmitted wave. Beats occur between the two microwave signals. The beat frequency is measured. (a) For an electromagnetic wave reflected back to its source from a mirror approaching at speed v, show that the reflected wave has frequency

$$f = f_{source}\frac{c + v}{c - v}$$

where f_{source} is the source frequency. (b) When v is much less than c, the beat frequency is much smaller than the transmitted frequency. In this case, use the approximation $f + f_{source} \approx 2f_{source}$ and show that the beat frequency can be written as $f_{beat} = 2v/\lambda$. (c) What beat frequency is measured for a car speed of 30.0 m/s if the microwaves have frequency 10.0 GHz? (d) If the beat frequency measurement is accurate to ± 5 Hz, how accurate is the speed measurement?

(Trent Steffler/David R. Frazier Photo Library)

FIGURE **P24.13**

14. *The red shift.* A light source recedes from an observer with a speed v_{source} that is small compared with c. (a) Show that the fractional shift in the measured wavelength is given by the approximate expression

$$\frac{\Delta\lambda}{\lambda} \approx \frac{v_{source}}{c}$$

This phenomenon is known as the red shift because the visible light is shifted toward the red. (b) Spectroscopic measurements of light at $\lambda = 397$ nm coming from a galaxy in Ursa Major reveal a red shift of 20.0 nm. What is the recessional speed of the galaxy?

15. A physicist drives through a stop light. When he is pulled over, he tells the police officer that the Doppler shift made the red light of wavelength 650 nm appear green to him, with a wavelength of 520 nm. The police officer writes out a traffic citation for speeding. How fast was the physicist traveling, according to his own testimony?

16. A Doppler weather radar station broadcasts a pulse of radio waves at frequency 2.85 GHz. From a relatively small batch of raindrops at bearing 38.6° east of north, the station receives a reflected pulse after 180 μs with a frequency shifted upward by 254 Hz. From a similar batch of raindrops at bearing 39.6° east of north, the station receives a reflected pulse after the same time delay, with a frequency shifted downward by 254 Hz. These pulses have the highest and lowest frequencies the station receives. (a) Calculate the radial velocity components of both batches of raindrops. (b) Assume that these raindrops are swirling in a uniformly rotating vortex. Find the angular speed of their rotation.

Section 24.4 ∎ Hertz's Discoveries

17. A fixed inductance $L = 1.05$ μH is used in series with a variable capacitor in the tuning section of a radiotelephone on a ship. What capacitance tunes the circuit to the signal from a transmitter broadcasting at 6.30 MHz?

18. Calculate the inductance of an LC circuit that oscillates at 120 Hz when the capacitance is 8.00 μF.

19. The switch in Figure P24.19 is connected to point a for a long time. After the switch is thrown to point b, what are (a) the frequency of oscillation of the LC circuit, (b) the maximum charge that appears on the capacitor, (c) the maximum current in the inductor, and (d) the total energy the circuit possesses at $t = 3.00$ s?

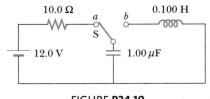

FIGURE P24.19

Section 24.5 ∎ Energy Carried by Electromagnetic Waves

20. How much electromagnetic energy per cubic meter is contained in sunlight if the intensity of sunlight at the Earth's surface under a fairly clear sky is 1 000 W/m²?

21. What is the average magnitude of the Poynting vector 5.00 miles from a radio transmitter broadcasting isotropically (equally in all directions) with an average power of 250 kW?

22. An AM radio station broadcasts isotropically (equally in all directions) with an average power of 4.00 kW. A dipole receiving antenna 65.0 cm long is at a location 4.00 miles from the transmitter. Compute the amplitude of the emf that is induced by this signal between the ends of the receiving antenna.

23. Physics⊗Now™ A community plans to build a facility to convert solar radiation to electrical power. The community requires 1.00 MW of power, and the system to be installed has an efficiency of 30.0% (that is, 30.0% of the solar energy incident on the surface is converted to useful energy that can power the community). What must be the effective area of a perfectly absorbing surface used in such an installation if sunlight has a constant intensity of 1 000 W/m²?

24. One of the weapons considered for the "Star Wars" antimissile system is a laser that could destroy ballistic missiles. When a high-power laser is used in the Earth's atmosphere, the electric field can ionize the air, turning it into a conducting plasma that reflects the laser light. In dry air at 0°C and 1 atm, electric breakdown occurs for fields with amplitudes above about 3.00 MV/m. (a) What laser beam intensity will produce such a field? (b) At this maximum intensity, what power can be delivered in a cylindrical beam of diameter 5.00 mm?

25. Physics⊗Now™ The filament of an incandescent lamp has a 150-Ω resistance and carries a direct current of 1.00 A. The filament is 8.00 cm long and 0.900 mm in radius. (a) Calculate the Poynting vector at the surface of the filament, associated with the static electric field producing the current and the current's static magnetic field. (b) Find the magnitude of the static electric and magnetic fields at the surface of the filament.

26. In a region of free space, the electric field at an instant of time is $\vec{\mathbf{E}} = (80.0\hat{\mathbf{i}} + 32.0\hat{\mathbf{j}} - 64.0\hat{\mathbf{k}})$ N/C and the magnetic field is $\vec{\mathbf{B}} = (0.200\hat{\mathbf{i}} + 0.0800\hat{\mathbf{j}} + 0.290\hat{\mathbf{k}})$ μT. (a) Show that the two fields are perpendicular to each other. (b) Determine the Poynting vector for these fields.

27. At what distance from a 100-W electromagnetic wave point source does $E_{max} = 15.0$ V/m?

28. Consider a bright star in our night sky. Assume that its power output is 4.00×10^{28} W, about 100 times that of the Sun, and that its distance is 20.0 ly. (a) Find the intensity of the starlight at the Earth. (b) Find the power of the starlight that the Earth intercepts.

Section 24.6 ∎ Momentum and Radiation Pressure

29. A 15.0-mW helium-neon laser ($\lambda = 632.8$ nm) emits a beam of circular cross section with a diameter of 2.00 mm. (a) Find the maximum electric field in the beam. (b) What total energy is contained in a 1.00-m length of the beam? (c) Find the momentum carried by a 1.00-m length of the beam.

30. A possible means of space flight is to place a perfectly reflecting aluminized sheet into orbit around the Earth and then use the light from the Sun to push this "solar sail." Suppose a sail of area 6.00×10^5 m² and mass 6 000 kg is placed in orbit facing the Sun. (a) What force is exerted on the sail? (b) What is the sail's acceleration? (c) How long does it take the sail to reach the Moon, 3.84×10^8 m away? Ignore all gravitational effects, assume that the acceleration calculated in part (b) remains constant, and assume a solar intensity of 1 370 W/m².

Section 24.7 ∎ The Spectrum of Electromagnetic Waves

31. *This just in!* An important news announcement is transmitted by radio waves to people sitting next to their radios 100 km from the station and by sound waves to people sitting across the newsroom 3.00 m from the newscaster. Who receives the news first? Explain. Take the speed of sound in air to be 343 m/s.

32. Classify waves with frequencies of 2 Hz, 2 kHz, 2 MHz, 2 GHz, 2 THz, 2 PHz, 2 EHz, 2 ZHz, and 2 YHz on the electromagnetic spectrum. Classify waves with wavelengths of 2 km, 2 m, 2 mm, 2 μm, 2 nm, 2 pm, 2 fm, and 2 am.

33. ▨ The human eye is most sensitive to light having a wavelength of 5.50×10^{-7} m, which is in the green–yellow region of the visible electromagnetic spectrum. What is the frequency of this light?

34. Compute an order-of-magnitude estimate for the frequency of an electromagnetic wave with wavelength equal to (a) your height and (b) the thickness of this sheet of paper. How is each wave classified on the electromagnetic spectrum?

35. What are the wavelengths of electromagnetic waves in free space that have frequencies of (a) 5.00×10^{19} Hz and (b) 4.00×10^{9} Hz?

36. ▨ A diathermy machine, used in physiotherapy, generates electromagnetic radiation that gives the effect of "deep heat" when absorbed in tissue. One assigned frequency for diathermy is 27.33 MHz. What is the wavelength of this radiation?

37. **Review problem.** Accelerating charges radiate electromagnetic waves. Calculate the wavelength of radiation produced by a proton in a cyclotron with a radius of 0.500 m and magnetic field of 0.350 T.

38. Twelve VHF television channels (Channels 2 through 13) lie in the range of frequencies between 54.0 MHz and 216 MHz. Each channel is assigned a width of 6.0 MHz, with the two ranges 72.0–76.0 MHz and 88.0–174 MHz reserved for non-TV purposes. (Channel 2, for example, lies between 54.0 and 60.0 MHz.) Calculate the broadcast wavelength range for (a) Channel 4, (b) Channel 6, and (c) Channel 8.

39. Suppose you are located 180 m from a radio transmitter. (a) How many wavelengths are you from the transmitter if the station calls itself 1 150 AM? (The AM band frequencies are in kilohertz.) (b) What if this station is 98.1 FM? (The FM band frequencies are in megahertz.)

40. A radar pulse returns to the transmitter-receiver after a total travel time of 4.00×10^{-4} s. How far away is the object that reflected the wave?

Section 24.8 ∎ Polarization

41. Plane-polarized light is incident on a single polarizing disk with the direction of $\vec{E}_0$ parallel to the direction of the transmission axis. Through what angle should the disk be rotated so that the intensity in the transmitted beam is reduced by a factor of (a) 3.00, (b) 5.00, and (c) 10.0?

42. Unpolarized light passes through two Polaroid sheets. The axis of the first is vertical and that of the second is at 30.0° to the vertical. What fraction of the incident light is transmitted?

43. In Figure P24.43, suppose the transmission axes of the left and right polarizing disks are perpendicular to each other.

In addition, let the center disk be rotated on the common axis with an angular speed ω. Show that if unpolarized light is incident on the left disk with an intensity I_{max}, the intensity of the beam emerging from the right disk is

$$I = \tfrac{1}{16} I_{max}(1 - \cos 4\omega t)$$

Hence, the intensity of the emerging beam is modulated at a rate that is four times the rate of rotation of the center disk. [*Suggestion:* Use the trigonometric identities $\cos^2 \theta = (1 + \cos 2\theta)/2$ and $\sin^2 \theta = (1 - \cos 2\theta)/2$, and recall that $\theta = \omega t$.]

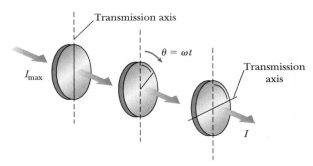

FIGURE P24.43

44. Two handheld radio transceivers with dipole antennas are separated by a large fixed distance. If the transmitting antenna is vertical, what fraction of the maximum received power will appear in the receiving antenna when it is inclined from the vertical by (a) 15.0°, (b) 45.0°, and (c) 90.0°?

45. Two polarizing sheets are placed together with their transmission axes crossed so that no light is transmitted. A third sheet is inserted between them with its transmission axis at an angle of 45.0° with respect to each of the other axes. Find the fraction of incident unpolarized light intensity transmitted by the three-sheet combination. (Assume each polarizing sheet is ideal.)

46. You want to rotate the plane of polarization of a polarized light beam by 45.0° with a maximum intensity reduction of 10.0%. (a) How many sheets of perfect polarizers do you need to achieve your goal? (b) What is the angle between adjacent polarizers?

Section 24.9 ∎ Context Connection—The Special Properties of Laser Light

47. Figure P24.47 shows portions of the energy level diagrams of the helium and neon atoms in a helium–neon laser. An

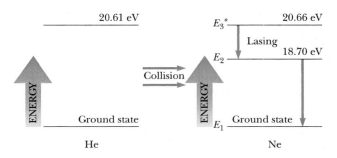

FIGURE P24.47

electrical discharge excites the He atom from its ground state to its excited state of 20.61 eV. The excited He atom collides with a Ne atom in its ground state and excites this atom to the state at 20.66 eV. Lasing action takes place for electron transitions from E_3* to E_2 in the Ne atoms. From the data in the figure, show that the wavelength of the red He−Ne laser light is approximately 633 nm.

48. High-power lasers in factories are used to cut through cloth and metal (Fig. P24.48). One such laser has a beam diameter of 1.00 mm and generates an electric field having an amplitude of 0.700 MV/m at the target. Find (a) the amplitude of the magnetic field produced, (b) the intensity of the laser, and (c) the power delivered by the laser.

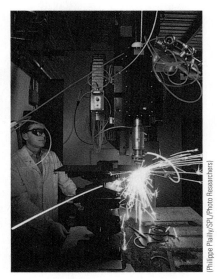

(Philippe Plailly/SPL/Photo Researchers)

FIGURE P24.48 A laser cutting device mounted on a robot arm is being used to cut through a metallic plate.

49. A neodymium−yttrium−aluminum garnet laser used in eye surgery emits a 3.00-mJ pulse in 1.00 ns, focused to a spot 30.0 μm in diameter on the retina. (a) Find (in SI units) the power per unit area at the retina. (This quantity is called the *irradiance* in the optics industry.) (b) What energy is delivered to an area of molecular size, taken as a circular area 0.600 nm in diameter?

50. The carbon dioxide laser is one of the most powerful developed. The energy difference between the two laser levels is 0.117 eV. Determine the frequency and wavelength of the radiation emitted by this laser. In what portion of the electromagnetic spectrum is this radiation?

51. Physics⊗Now™ A ruby laser delivers a 10.0-ns pulse of 1.00 MW average power. If the photons have a wavelength of 694.3 nm, how many are contained in the pulse?

52. A pulsed ruby laser emits light at 694.3 nm. For a 14.0-ps pulse containing 3.00 J of energy, find (a) the physical length of the pulse as it travels through space and (b) the number of photons in it. (c) Assuming that the beam has a circular cross-section of 0.600 cm diameter, find the number of photons per cubic millimeter.

53. **Review problem.** Figure 24.17 represents the light bouncing between two mirrors in a laser cavity as two traveling waves. These traveling waves moving in opposite directions constitute a standing wave. If the reflecting surfaces are metallic films, the electric field has nodes at both ends. The electromagnetic standing wave is analogous to the standing string wave represented in Figure 14.9. (a) Assume that a helium−neon laser has precisely flat and parallel mirrors 35.124 103 cm apart. Assume that the active medium can efficiently amplify only light with wavelengths between 632.808 40 nm and 632.809 80 nm. Find the number of components that constitute the laser light, and the wavelength of each component, precise to eight digits. (b) Find the root-mean-square speed for a neon atom at 120°C. (c) Show that at this temperature the Doppler effect for light emission by moving neon atoms should realistically make the bandwidth of the light amplifier larger than the 0.001 40 nm assumed in part (a).

54. The number N of atoms in a particular state is called the population of that state. This number depends on the energy of that state and the temperature. In thermal equilibrium, the population of atoms in a state of energy E_n is given by a Boltzmann distribution expression

$$N = N_g e^{-(E_n - E_g)/k_B T}$$

where T is the absolute temperature and N_g is the population of the ground state, of energy E_g. For simplicity, we assume that each energy level has only one quantum state associated with it. (a) Before the power is switched on, the neon atoms in a laser are in thermal equilibrium at 27.0°C. Find the equilibrium ratio of the populations of the states E_3* and E_2 shown in Figure 24.18. Lasers operate by a clever artificial production of a "population inversion" between the upper and lower atomic energy states involved in the lasing transition. Thus, more atoms are in the upper excited state than in the lower one. Consider the helium−neon laser transition at 632.8 nm. Assume that 2% more atoms occur in the upper state than in the lower. (b) To demonstrate how unnatural such a situation is, find the temperature for which the Boltzmann distribution describes a 2.00% population inversion. (c) Why does such a situation not occur naturally?

Additional Problems

55. Assume that the intensity of solar radiation incident on the cloudtops of the Earth is 1 370 W/m². (a) Calculate the total power radiated by the Sun, taking the average Earth−Sun separation to be 1.496×10^{11} m. (b) Determine the maximum values of the electric and magnetic fields in the sunlight at the Earth's location.

56. The intensity of solar radiation at the top of the Earth's atmosphere is 1 370 W/m². Assuming that 60% of the incoming solar energy reaches the Earth's surface and assuming that you absorb 50% of the incident energy, make an order-of-magnitude estimate of the amount of solar energy you absorb in a 60-min sunbath.

57. Physics⊗Now™ **Review problem.** In the absence of cable input or a satellite dish, a TV set can use a dipole-receiving antenna for VHF channels and a loop antenna for UHF channels (Fig. Q24.9). The UHF antenna produces an emf from the changing magnetic flux through the loop. The TV station broadcasts a signal with a frequency f, and the signal has an electric-field amplitude E_{max} and a magnetic-field amplitude B_{max} at the location of the receiving antenna. (a) Using Faraday's law, derive an expression for the amplitude of the emf that appears in a single-turn circular loop antenna with a radius r, which is small compared with the wavelength of the wave. (b) If the electric field in the signal points vertically, what orientation of the loop gives the best reception?

58. One goal of the Russian space program is to illuminate dark northern cities with sunlight reflected to the Earth from a 200-m diameter mirrored surface in orbit. Several smaller prototypes have already been constructed and put into orbit. (a) Assume that sunlight with intensity $1\,370\ \text{W/m}^2$ falls on the mirror nearly perpendicularly and that the atmosphere of the Earth allows 74.6% of the energy of sunlight to pass though it in clear weather. What is the power received by a city when the space mirror is reflecting light to it? (b) The plan is for the reflected sunlight to cover a circle of diameter 8.00 km. What is the intensity of light (the average magnitude of the Poynting vector) received by the city? (c) This intensity is what percentage of the vertical component of sunlight at St. Petersburg in January, when the sun reaches an angle of 7.00° above the horizon at noon?

59. A dish antenna having a diameter of 20.0 m receives (at normal incidence) a radio signal from a distant source as shown in Figure P24.59. The radio signal is a continuous sinusoidal wave with amplitude $E_{max} = 0.200\ \mu\text{V/m}$. Assume that the antenna absorbs all the radiation that falls on the dish. (a) What is the amplitude of the magnetic field in this wave? (b) What is the intensity of the radiation received by this antenna? (c) What is the power received by the antenna? (d) What force do the radio waves exert on the antenna?

FIGURE **P24.59**

60. ▨ A handheld cellular telephone operates in the 860- to 900-MHz band and has a power output of 0.600 W from an antenna 10.0 cm long (Fig. P24.60). (a) Find the average magnitude of the Poynting vector 4.00 cm from the antenna, at the location of a typical person's head. Assume that the antenna emits energy with cylindrical wave fronts. (The actual radiation from antennas follows a more complicated pattern.) (b) The ANSI/IEEE C95.1-1991 maximum exposure standard is $0.57\ \text{mW/cm}^2$ for persons living near cellular telephone base stations, who would be continuously exposed to the radiation. Compare the answer to part (a) with this standard.

FIGURE **P24.60**

61. In 1965, Arno Penzias and Robert Wilson discovered the cosmic microwave radiation left over from the Big Bang expansion of the Universe. Suppose the energy density of this background radiation is $4.00 \times 10^{-14}\ \text{J/m}^3$. Determine the corresponding electric field amplitude.

62. A linearly polarized microwave of wavelength 1.50 cm is directed along the positive x axis. The electric field vector has a maximum value of 175 V/m and vibrates in the xy plane. (a) Assume that the magnetic field component of the wave can be written as $B = B_{max} \sin(kx - \omega t)$ and give values for B_{max}, k, and ω. Also determine in which plane the magnetic field vector vibrates. (b) Calculate the average magnitude of the Poynting vector for this wave. (c) What radiation pressure would this wave exert if it were directed at normal incidence onto a perfectly reflecting sheet? (d) What acceleration would be imparted to a 500-g sheet (perfectly reflecting and at normal incidence) with dimensions of 1.00 m × 0.750 m?

63. **Review problem.** A 1.00-m-diameter mirror focuses the Sun's rays onto an absorbing plate 2.00 cm in radius, which holds a can containing 1.00 L of water at 20.0°C. (a) If the solar intensity is $1.00\ \text{kW/m}^2$, what is the intensity on the absorbing plate? (b) What are the maximum magnitudes of the fields $\vec{\mathbf{E}}$ and $\vec{\mathbf{B}}$? (c) If 40.0% of the energy is absorbed, how long does it take to bring the water to its boiling point?

64. A microwave source produces pulses of 20.0-GHz radiation, with each pulse lasting 1.00 ns. A parabolic reflector with a face area of radius 6.00 cm is used to focus the microwaves into a parallel beam of radiation as shown in Figure P24.64. The average power during each pulse is 25.0 kW. (a) What is the wavelength of these microwaves? (b) What is the total energy contained in each pulse?

(c) Compute the average energy density inside each pulse. (d) Determine the amplitude of the electric and magnetic fields in these microwaves. (e) Assuming that this pulsed beam strikes an absorbing surface, compute the force exerted on the surface during the 1.00-ns duration of each pulse.

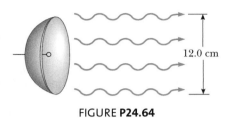

12.0 cm

FIGURE **P24.64**

65. The electromagnetic power radiated by a nonrelativistic moving point charge q having an acceleration a is

$$\mathcal{P} = \frac{q^2 a^2}{6\pi\epsilon_0 c^3}$$

where ϵ_0 is the permittivity of free space and c is the speed of light in vacuum. (a) Show that the right side of this equation has units of watts. (b) An electron is placed in a constant electric field of magnitude 100 N/C. Determine the acceleration of the electron and the electromagnetic power radiated by this electron. (c) If a proton is placed in a cyclotron with a radius of 0.500 m and a magnetic field of magnitude 0.350 T, what electromagnetic power does this proton radiate?

> **Review problems.** Section 17.10 discussed electromagnetic radiation as a mode of energy transfer. Problems 66 through 68 use ideas introduced both there and in this chapter.

66. Eliza is a black cat with four black kittens: Penelope, Rosalita, Sasha, and Timothy. Eliza's mass is 5.50 kg, and each kitten has mass 0.800 kg. One cool night, all five sleep snuggled together on a mat, with their bodies forming one hemisphere. (a) Assuming that the purring heap has uniform density 990 kg/m^3, find the radius of the hemisphere. (b) Find the area of its curved surface. (c) Assume that the surface temperature is uniformly 31.0°C and the emissivity is 0.970. Find the intensity of radiation emitted by the cats at their curved surface and (d) the radiated power from this surface. (e) You may think of the emitted electromagnetic wave as having a single predominant frequency (of 31.2 THz). Find the amplitude of the electric field just outside the surface of the cozy pile and (f) the amplitude of the magnetic field. (g) Are the sleeping cats charged? Are they current-carrying? Are they magnetic? Are they a radiation source? Do they glow in the dark? Give an explanation for your answers so that they do not seem contradictory. (h) The next night, the kittens all sleep alone, curling up into separate hemispheres like their mother. Find the total radiated power of the family. (For simplic-

ity, we ignore throughout the cats' absorption of radiation from the environment.)

67. (a) An elderly couple has a solar water heater installed on the roof of their house (Fig. P24.67). The heater consists of a flat closed box with extraordinarily good thermal insulation. Its interior is painted black, and its front face is made of insulating glass. Assume that its emissivity for visible light is 0.900 and its emissivity for infrared light is 0.700. Assume that light from the noon Sun is incident perpendicular to the glass with an intensity of 1 000 W/m^2 and that no water enters or leaves the box. Find the steady-state temperature of the interior of the box. (b) The homeowners build an identical box with no water tubes. It lies flat on the ground in front of the house. They use it as a cold frame where they plant seeds in early spring. Assuming that the same noon Sun is at an elevation angle of 50.0°, find the steady-state temperature of the interior of this box when its ventilation slots are tightly closed.

FIGURE **P24.67**

68. The study of Creation suggests a Creator with an inordinate fondness for beetles and for small red stars. A small red star radiates electromagnetic waves with power 6.00×10^{23} W, which is only 0.159% of the luminosity of the Sun. Consider a spherical planet in a circular orbit around this star. Assume that the emissivity of the planet is equal for infrared and for visible light. Assume that the planet has a uniform surface temperature. Identify the projected area over which the planet absorbs starlight and the radiating area of the planet. If beetles thrive at a temperature of 310 K, what should be the radius of the planet's orbit?

69. An astronaut, stranded in space 10.0 m from her spacecraft and at rest relative to it, has a mass (including equipment) of 110 kg. Because she has a 100-W light source that forms a directed beam, she considers using the beam as a photon rocket to propel herself continuously toward the spacecraft. (a) Calculate the time interval required for her to reach the spacecraft by this method. (b) Assume, instead, that she throws the light source in the direction away from the spacecraft. The mass of the light source is 3.00 kg and, after being thrown, it moves at 12.0 m/s relative to the recoiling astronaut. After what time interval will the astronaut reach the spacecraft?

ANSWERS TO QUICK QUIZZES

24.1 (i), (b). There can be no conduction current because there is no conductor between the plates. There is a time-varying electric field because of the decreasing charge on the plates, and the time-varying electric flux represents a displacement current. (ii), (c). There is a time-varying electric field because of the decreasing charge on the plates. This time-varying electric field produces a magnetic field.

24.2 (c). The $\vec{\mathbf{B}}$ field must be in the $+z$ direction so that the Poynting vector is directed along the $-y$ direction.

24.3 (d). The first three choices are instantaneous values and vary in time. The intensity is an average value over a full cycle.

24.4 (b), (c). The radiation pressure (a) does not change because pressure is force per unit area. In (b), the smaller disk absorbs less radiation, resulting in a smaller force. For the same reason, the momentum in (c) is reduced.

24.5 (c). The order of magnitude of the wavelengths can be found either from the equation $c = \lambda f$ or from Figure 24.12.

24.6 (a). The order of magnitude of the wavelengths can be found either from the equation $c = \lambda f$ or from Figure 24.12.

24.7 (b). Electric field vectors parallel to the metal wires cause electrons in the metal to oscillate along the wires. Therefore, the energy from the waves with these electric field vectors is transferred to the metal by accelerating these electrons and is eventually transformed to internal energy through the resistance of the metal. Waves with electric field vectors perpendicular to the metal wires are not able to accelerate electrons and pass through.

CHAPTER 25

Reflection and Refraction of Light

(Patrick J. Endres/Visuals Unlimited)

This photograph of a rainbow shows a distinct secondary rainbow with the colors reversed. The appearance of the rainbow depends on three optical phenomena discussed in this chapter: reflection, refraction, and dispersion.

CHAPTER OUTLINE

The preceding chapter serves as a bridge between electromagnetism and the area of physics called *optics*. Now that we have established the wave nature of electromagnetic radiation, we shall study the behavior of visible light and apply what we learn to all electromagnetic radiation. Our emphasis in this chapter will be on the behavior of light as it encounters an interface between two media.

So far, we have focused on the wave nature of light and discussed it in terms of our wave simplification model. As we learn more about the behavior of light, however, we shall return to our particle simplification model, especially as we incorporate the notions of quantum physics, beginning in Chapter 28. As we discuss in Section 25.1, a long historical debate took place between proponents of wave and particle models for light.

25.1 | THE NATURE OF LIGHT

We encounter light every day, as soon as we open our eyes in the morning. This everyday experience involves a phenomenon that is actually quite complicated. Since the beginning of this book, we have discussed both the particle model and the wave model as simplification models to help us gain understanding of physical phenomena. Both of these models have been applied to the behavior of light. Until the beginning of the 19th century, most scientists thought that light was a stream of particles emitted by a light source. According to this model, the light particles stimulated the sense of sight on entering the eye. The chief architect of this particle model of light was Isaac Newton. The model provided a simple explanation of some known experimental facts concerning the nature of light—namely, the laws of reflection and refraction—to be discussed in this chapter.

Most scientists accepted the particle model of light. During Newton's lifetime, however, another model was proposed—a model that views light as having wave-like properties. In 1678, a Dutch physicist and astronomer, Christiaan Huygens, showed that a wave model of light can also explain the laws of reflection and refraction. The wave model did not receive immediate acceptance for several reasons. All the waves known at the time (sound, water, and so on) traveled through a medium, but light from the Sun could travel to Earth through empty space. Even though experimental evidence for the wave nature of light was discovered by Francesco Grimaldi (1618–1663) around 1660, most scientists rejected the wave model for more than a century and adhered to Newton's particle model due, for the most part, to Newton's great reputation as a scientist.

The first clear and convincing demonstration of the wave nature of light was provided in 1801 by Englishman Thomas Young (1773–1829), who showed that under appropriate conditions, light exhibits interference behavior. That is, light waves emitted by a single source and traveling along two different paths can arrive at some point, combine, and cancel each other by destructive interference. Such behavior could not be explained at that time by a particle model, because scientists could not imagine how two or more particles could come together and cancel one another. Additional developments during the 19th century led to the general acceptance of the wave model of light.

A critical development concerning the understanding of light was the work of James Clerk Maxwell, who in 1865 mathematically predicted that light is a form of high-frequency electromagnetic wave. As discussed in Chapter 24, Hertz in 1887 provided experimental confirmation of Maxwell's theory by producing and detecting other electromagnetic waves. Furthermore, Hertz and other investigators showed that these waves exhibited reflection, refraction, and all the other characteristic properties of waves.

Although the electromagnetic wave model seemed to be well established and could explain most known properties of light, some experiments could not be explained by the assumption that light was a wave. The most striking of these was the *photoelectric effect,* discovered by Hertz, in which electrons are ejected from a metal when its surface is exposed to light. We shall explore this experiment in detail in Chapter 28.

In view of these developments, light must be regarded as having a dual nature. **In some cases, light acts like a wave, and in others, it acts like a particle.** The classical electromagnetic wave model provides an adequate explanation of light propagation and interference, whereas the photoelectric effect and other experiments involving the interaction of light with matter are best explained by assuming that light is a particle. Light is light, to be sure. The question "Is light a wave or a particle?" is inappropriate; in some experiments, we measure its wave properties; in other experiments, we measure its particle properties. This curious dual nature of light may be unsettling at this point, but it will be clarified when we introduce the notion of a *quantum particle.* The photon, a particle of light, is our first example of a quantum particle, which we shall explore more fully in Chapter 28. Until then, we focus our attention on the properties of light that can be satisfactorily explained with the wave model.

25.2 THE RAY MODEL IN GEOMETRIC OPTICS

In the beginning of our study of optics, we shall use a simplification model called the **ray model** or the **ray approximation.** A **ray** is a straight line drawn along the direction of propagation of a single wave, showing the path of the wave as it travels through space. The ray approximation involves geometric models based on these straight lines. Phenomena explained with the ray approximation do not depend explicitly on the wave nature of light, other than its propagation along a straight line.

A set of light waves can be represented by wave fronts (defined in Section 24.3) as illustrated in the pictorial representation in Figure 25.1 for a plane wave, which was introduced in Section 24.3. The definition of a wave front requires that the rays are perpendicular to the wave front at every location in space.

If a plane wave meets a barrier containing an opening whose size is large relative to the wavelength as in Active Figure 25.2a, the individual waves emerging from the opening continue to move in a straight line (apart from some small edge effects); hence, the ray approximation continues to be valid. If the size of the opening is on the order of the wavelength as in Active Figure 25.2b, the waves (and, consequently, the rays we draw) spread out from the opening in all directions. We say that the incoming plane wave undergoes *diffraction* as it passes through the opening. If the opening is small relative to the wavelength, the diffraction is so strong that the opening can be approximated as a point source of waves (Active Fig. 25.2c). Thus, diffraction is more pronounced as the ratio d/λ approaches zero.

Suppose the opening is a circle of diameter d. The ray approximation assumes that $\lambda \ll d$ so that we do not concern ourselves with diffraction effects, which depend on the full wave nature of light. We shall delay studying diffraction until Chapter 27. The ray approximation is used in the current chapter and in Chapter 26. The material in these chapters is often called *geometric optics*. The ray

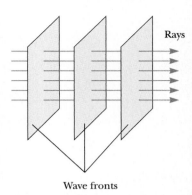

FIGURE 25.1 A plane wave propagating to the right. Note that the rays, which always point in the direction of wave motion, are straight lines perpendicular to the wave fronts.

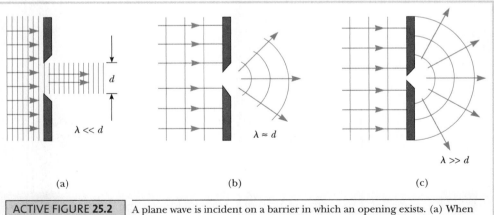

(a)　　　　　(b)　　　　　(c)

ACTIVE FIGURE 25.2 A plane wave is incident on a barrier in which an opening exists. (a) When the wavelength of the light is much smaller than the size of the opening, almost no observable diffraction takes place and the ray approximation remains valid. (b) When the wavelength of the light is comparable to the size of the opening, diffraction becomes significant. (c) When the wavelength of the light is much larger than the size of the opening, the opening behaves as a point source emitting spherical waves.

Physics⊗Now™ Log into PhysicsNow at **www.pop4e.com** and go to Active Figure 25.2 to adjust the size of the opening and observe the effect on the waves passing through.

approximation is very good for the study of mirrors, lenses, prisms, and associated optical instruments, such as telescopes, cameras, and eyeglasses.

25.3 | THE WAVE UNDER REFLECTION

In Chapter 13, we introduced a one-dimensional version of the model of a wave under reflection by considering waves on strings. When such a wave meets a discontinuity between strings representing different wave speeds, some of the energy is reflected and some of the energy is transmitted. In that discussion, the waves are constrained to move along the one-dimensional string. In this discussion of optics, we are not subject to that restriction. Light waves can move in three dimensions.

Figure 25.3 shows several rays of light incident on a surface. Unless the surface is perfectly absorbing, some portion of the light is reflected from the surface. (The transmitted portion will be discussed in Section 25.4.) If the surface is very smooth, the reflected rays are parallel as indicated in Figure 25.3a. Reflection of light from such a smooth surface is called **specular reflection.** If the reflecting surface is rough as in Figure 25.3b, it reflects the rays in various directions. Reflection from a rough surface is known as **diffuse reflection.** A surface behaves as a smooth surface as long as the surface variations are small compared with the wavelength of the incident light. For example, light passes through the small holes in a microwave oven door, allowing you to see the interior because the holes are large relative to the wavelengths of visible light. The large-wavelength microwaves, however, reflect from the door as if it were a solid piece of metal.

Figures 25.3c and 25.3d are photographs of specular reflection and diffuse reflection using laser light, made visible by dust in the air, which scatters the light toward the camera. The reflected laser beam is clearly visible in Figure 25.3c. In Figure 25.3d, the diffuse reflection has caused the incident beam to be reflected in many directions so that no clear outgoing beam is visible.

Specular reflection is necessary for the formation of clear images from reflecting surfaces, a topic we shall investigate in Chapter 26. Figure 25.4 shows an image resulting from specular reflection from a smooth water surface. If the water surface were rough, diffuse reflection would occur and the reflected image would not be visible.

Both types of reflection can occur from a road surface that you observe when you drive at night. On a dry night, light from oncoming vehicles is scattered off the

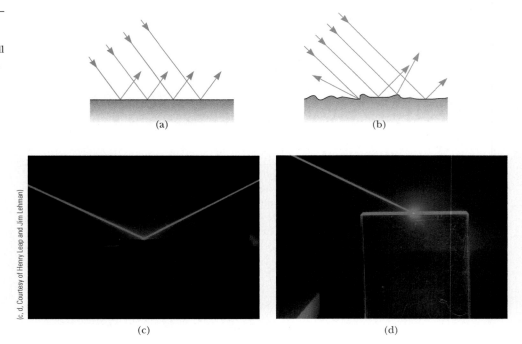

FIGURE 25.3 Schematic representation of (a) specular reflection, in which the reflected rays are all parallel, and (b) diffuse reflection, in which the reflected rays travel in scattered directions. (c) and (d) Photographs of specular and diffuse reflection using laser light.

(c, d. Courtesy of Henry Leap and Jim Lehman)

(a)

(b)

(c)

(d)

(David Parker/Photo Researchers, Inc.)

FIGURE 25.4 This photograph, taken in Salamanca, Spain, shows the reflection of the New Cathedral in the Tormes River. Because the water is so calm, the reflection is specular.

road in different directions (diffuse reflection) and the road is quite visible. On a rainy night, the small irregularities in the road surface are filled with water. Because the water surface is smooth, the light undergoes specular reflection and the glare from reflected light makes the road less visible.

Let us now develop the mathematical representation for the wave under reflection model. Consider a light ray that travels in air and is incident at an angle on a flat, smooth surface as in Active Figure 25.5. The incident and reflected rays make angles of θ_1 and θ_1', respectively, with a line drawn normal to the surface at the point where the incident ray strikes the surface. Experiments show that the incident ray, the normal to the surface, and the reflected ray all lie in the same plane and that **the angle of reflection equals the angle of incidence:**

$$\theta_1' = \theta_1 \qquad [25.1]$$

Equation 25.1 is called the **law of reflection.** By convention, the angles of incidence and reflection are measured from the normal to the surface rather than from the surface itself.

In diffuse reflection, the law of reflection is obeyed *with respect to the local normal.* Because of the roughness of the surface, the local normal varies significantly from one location to another. In this book, we shall concern ourselves only with specular reflection and shall use the term *reflection* to mean specular reflection.

As you might guess from Equation 25.1 and the figures we have seen so far, geometric models are used extensively in the study of optics. As we represent physical situations with geometric constructions, the mathematics of triangles and the principles of trigonometry will find many applications.

The path of a light ray is reversible. For example, the ray in Active Figure 25.5 travels from the upper left, reflects from the mirror, and then moves toward a point at the upper right. If the ray originated at the same point at the upper right, it would follow the same path in reverse to reach the same point at the upper left. This reversible property will be useful when we set up geometric constructions for finding the paths of light rays.

A practical application of the law of reflection is the digital projection of movies, television shows, and computer presentations. A digital projector makes use of an optical semiconductor chip called a *digital micromirror device.* This device contains an

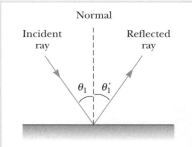

ACTIVE FIGURE 25.5

According to the law of reflection, $\theta_1 = \theta_1'$. The incident ray, the reflected ray, and the normal all lie in the same plane.

Physics⊗Now™ Log into Physics-Now at **www.pop4e.com** and go to Active Figure 25.5 to vary the incident angle and see the effect on the reflected ray.

▦ **PITFALL PREVENTION 25.1**

SUBSCRIPT NOTATION We use the subscript 1 to refer to parameters for the light in the initial medium. When light travels from one medium to another, we use the subscript 2 for the parameters associated with the light in the new medium. In the current discussion, the light stays in the same medium, so we only have to use subscripts 1.

(a)

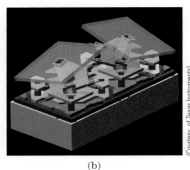

(b)

(Courtesy of Texas Instruments)

FIGURE 25.6 (a) An array of mirrors on the surface of a digital micromirror device. Each mirror has an area of about 16 μm². To provide a sense of scale, the leg of an ant appears in the photograph. (b) A close-up view of two single micromirrors. The mirror on the left is "on," and the one on the right is "off."

array of more than one million tiny mirrors (Fig. 25.6a) that can be individually tilted by means of signals to an address electrode underneath the edge of the mirror. Each mirror corresponds to a pixel in the projected image. When the pixel corresponding to a given mirror is to be bright, the mirror is in the "on" position and is oriented so as to reflect light from a source illuminating the array to the screen (Fig. 25.6b). When the pixel for this mirror is to be dark, the mirror is "off" and is tilted so that the light is reflected away from the screen. The brightness of the pixel is determined by the total time interval during which the mirror is in the "on" position during the display of one image.

Digital movie projectors use three micromirror devices, one for each of the primary colors red, blue, and green, so that movies can be displayed with up to 35 trillion colors. Because there is no physical storage mechanism for the movie, a digital movie does not degrade with time as does film. Furthermore, because the movie is entirely in the form of computer software, it can be delivered to theaters by means of satellites, optical discs, or optical fiber networks.

Several movies have been projected digitally to audiences and polls show that 85 percent of the viewers describe the image quality as "excellent." The first all-digital movie, from cinematography to postproduction to projection, was *Star Wars Episode II: Attack of the Clones* in 2002.

QUICK QUIZ 25.1 In the movies, you sometimes see an actor looking in a mirror and you can see his face in the mirror. During the filming of this scene, what does the actor see in the mirror? **(a)** his face **(b)** your face **(c)** the director's face **(d)** the movie camera **(e)** impossible to determine

▌ Thinking Physics 25.1

When looking through a glass window to the outdoors at night, you sometimes see a *double* image of yourself. Why?

Reasoning Reflection occurs whenever light encounters an interface between two optical media. For the glass in the window, two such interfaces exist. The first is the inner surface of the glass and the second is the outer surface. Each interface results in an image. ▪

INTERACTIVE | **EXAMPLE 25.1** | **The Double-Reflected Light Ray**

Two mirrors make an angle of 120° with each other as in Figure 25.7. A ray is incident on mirror M₁ at an angle of 65° to the normal. Find the direction of the ray after it is reflected from mirror M₂.

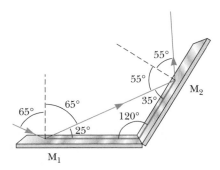

FIGURE 25.7 (Interactive Example 25.1) Mirrors M₁ and M₂ make an angle of 120° with each other.

Solution From the law of reflection, we know that the first reflected ray also makes an angle of 65° with the normal. Thus, this ray makes an angle of 90° − 65°, or 25°, with the horizontal. We identify the geometric model triangle as the triangle made by the first reflected ray and the two mirrors in Figure 25.7. The first reflected ray makes an angle of 35° with M₂ (because the sum of the interior angles of any triangle is 180°). Thus, this ray makes an angle of 55° with the normal to M₂. Hence, from the law of reflection, the second reflected ray makes an angle of 55° with the normal to M₂.

Physics⊗Now™ Log into PhysicsNow at **www.pop4e.com** and go to Interactive Example 25.1 to investigate this reflection situation for various mirror angles.

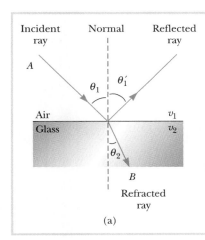

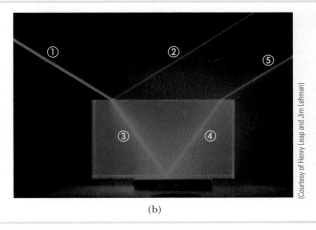

(a) (b)

(Courtesy of Henry Leap and Jim Lehman)

ACTIVE FIGURE 25.8

(a) A light ray obliquely incident on an air–glass interface. The refracted ray is deviated toward the normal because $v_2 < v_1$. All rays and the normal lie in the same plane. (b) (Quick Quiz 25.2) Of light rays ② through ⑤, which are reflected and which are refracted?

Physics ⊗ Now™ Log into Physics-Now at **www.pop4e.com** and go to Active Figure 25.8 to vary the incident angle and see the effect on the reflected and refracted rays.

25.4 THE WAVE UNDER REFRACTION

Referring again to our discussion of string waves in Chapter 13, we discussed that some of the energy of a wave incident on a discontinuity in the string is transmitted through the discontinuity. As a light wave moves through three dimensions, understanding the transmitted light wave involves new principles that we now discuss.

When a ray of light traveling through a transparent medium is obliquely incident on a boundary leading into another transparent medium as in Active Figure 25.8a, part of the ray is reflected but part is transmitted into the second medium. The ray that enters the second medium experiences a change in direction at the boundary and is said to undergo **refraction. The incident ray, the reflected ray, and the refracted ray all lie in the same plane.** The **angle of refraction** θ_2 in Active Figure 25.8a depends on the properties of the two media and on the angle of incidence through the relationship

$$\frac{\sin \theta_2}{\sin \theta_1} = \frac{v_2}{v_1} = \text{constant} \qquad [25.2]$$

where v_1 is the speed of light in medium 1 and v_2 is the speed of light in medium 2. Equation 25.2 is a mathematical representation of the wave under refraction model, although we find a more commonly used form in Equation 25.7.

The path of a light ray through a refracting surface is reversible, as was the case for reflection. For example, the ray in Active Figure 25.8a travels from point A to point B. If the ray originated at B, it would follow the same path in reverse to reach point A. In the latter case, however, the reflected ray would be in the glass.

> **QUICK QUIZ 25.2** If beam ① is the incoming beam in Active Figure 25.8b, which of the other four red lines are reflected beams and which are refracted beams?

Equation 25.2 shows that when light moves from a material in which its speed is high to a material in which its speed is lower, the angle of refraction θ_2 is less than the angle of incidence. The refracted ray therefore deviates toward the normal as shown in Active Figure 25.9a. If the ray moves from a material in which it travels slowly to a material in which it travels more rapidly, θ_2 is greater than θ_1, so the ray deviates away from the normal as shown in Active Figure 25.9b.

The behavior of light as it passes from air into another substance and then re-emerges into air is often a source of confusion to students. Why is this behavior so different from other occurrences in our daily lives? When light travels in air, its speed is $c = 3.0 \times 10^8$ m/s; on entry into a block of glass, its speed is reduced to approximately 2.0×10^8 m/s. When the light re-emerges into air, its speed increases to its

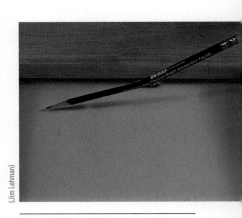

(Jim Lehman)

The pencil partially immersed in water appears bent because light from the lower part of the pencil is refracted as it travels across the boundary between water and air. ■

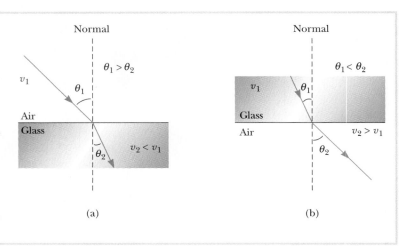

ACTIVE FIGURE 25.9

(a) When the light ray moves from air into glass, its path deviates toward the normal. (b) When the ray moves from glass into air, its path deviates away from the normal.

Physics⊗Now™ Log into Physics-Now at **www.pop4e.com** and go to Active Figure 25.9 to see light passing through three layers of material. You can vary the incident angle and see the effect on the refracted rays for a variety of values of the index of refraction of the three materials.

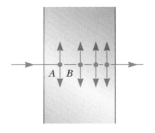

FIGURE 25.10 Light passing from one atom to another in a medium. The dots are atoms, and the vertical arrows represent their oscillations.

▦ PITFALL PREVENTION 25.2

n IS NOT AN INTEGER HERE We have seen *n* used in Chapter 11 to indicate the quantum number of a Bohr orbit and in Chapter 14 to indicate the standing wave mode on a string or in an air column. In those cases, *n* was an integer. The index of refraction *n* is *not* an integer.

■ Index of refraction

original value 3.0×10^8 m/s. This process is very different from what happens, for example, when a bullet is fired through a block of wood. In that case, the speed of the bullet is reduced as it moves through the wood because some of its original energy is used to tear apart the fibers of the wood. When the bullet enters the air again, it emerges at a speed lower than that with which it entered the block of wood.

To see why light behaves as it does, consider Figure 25.10, which represents a beam of light entering a piece of glass from the left. Once inside the glass, the light may encounter an atom, represented by point *A* in the figure. Let us assume that light is absorbed by the atom, causing it to oscillate (a detail represented by the double-headed arrows in the drawing). The oscillating atom then radiates (emits) the beam of light toward an atom at point *B*, where the light is again absorbed. The details of these absorptions and emissions are best explained in terms of quantum physics, a subject we shall study in Chapter 28. For now, think of the process as one in which the light passes from one atom to another through the glass. (The situation is somewhat analogous to a relay race in which a baton is passed between runners on the same team.) Although light travels from one atom to another through the empty space between the atoms with a speed of $c = 3.0 \times 10^8$ m/s, the absorptions and emissions of light by the atoms require time to occur. Therefore, the *average* speed of light through the glass is lower than *c*. Once the light emerges into the air, the absorptions and emissions cease and the light's average speed returns to its original value.[1] Thus, whether the light is inside the material or outside, it always travels through vacuum with the same speed.

Light passing from one medium to another is refracted because the average speed of light is different in the two media. In fact, **light travels at its maximum speed in vacuum.** It is convenient to define the **index of refraction** *n* of a medium to be the ratio

$$n \equiv \frac{\text{speed of light in vacuum}}{\text{average speed of light in the medium}} = \frac{c}{v} \qquad [25.3]$$

From this definition, we see that the index of refraction is a dimensionless number greater than or equal to unity because *v* in a medium is less than *c*. Furthermore, *n* is equal to unity for vacuum. The indices of refraction for various substances are listed in Table 25.1.

---

[1]As an analogy, consider a subway entering a city at a constant speed *v* and then stopping at several stations in the downtown region of the city. Although the subway may achieve the instantaneous speed *v* between stations, the *average* speed across the city is less than *v*. Once the subway leaves the city and makes no stops, it moves again at a constant speed *v*. The analogy, as is the case with many analogies, is not perfect because the subway requires time to accelerate to the speed *v* between stations, whereas light achieves speed *c* immediately as it travels between atoms.

TABLE 25.1	Indices of Refraction for Various Substances		
Substance	**Index of Refraction**	**Substance**	**Index of Refraction**
Solids at 20° C		**Liquids at 20° C**	
Cubic zirconia	2.20	Benzene	1.501
Diamond (C)	2.419	Carbon disulfide	1.628
Fluorite (CaF_2)	1.434	Carbon tetrachloride	1.461
Fused quartz (SiO_2)	1.458	Corn syrup	2.21
Gallium phosphide	3.50	Ethyl alcohol	1.361
Glass, crown	1.52	Glycerin	1.473
Glass, flint	1.66	Water	1.333
Ice (H_2O)	1.309	**Gases at 0°C, 1 atm**	
Polystyrene	1.49	Air	1.000 293
Sodium chloride (NaCl)	1.544	Carbon dioxide	1.000 45

Note: All values are for light having a wavelength of 589 nm in vacuum.

As a wave travels from one medium to another, its frequency does not change. Let us first consider this notion for waves passing from a light string to a heavier string. If the frequencies of the incident and transmitted waves on the two strings at the junction point were different, the strings could not remain tied together because the joined ends of the two pieces of string would not move up and down in unison!

For a light wave passing from one medium to another, the frequency also remains constant. To see why, consider Figure 25.11. Wave fronts pass an observer at point A in medium 1 with a certain frequency and are incident on the boundary between medium 1 and medium 2. The frequency at which the wave fronts pass an observer at point B in medium 2 must equal the frequency at which they arrive at point A. If that were not the case, the wave fronts would either pile up at the boundary or be destroyed or created at the boundary. Because this situation does not occur, the frequency must be a constant as a light ray passes from one medium into another.

Therefore, because the relation $v = f\lambda$ (Eq. 13.11) must be valid in both media and because $f_1 = f_2 = f$, we see that

$$v_1 = f\lambda_1 \quad \text{and} \quad v_2 = f\lambda_2$$

Because $v_1 \neq v_2$, it follows that $\lambda_1 \neq \lambda_2$. A relationship between index of refraction and wavelength can be obtained by dividing these two equations and making use of the definition of the index of refraction given by Equation 25.3:

$$\frac{\lambda_1}{\lambda_2} = \frac{v_1}{v_2} = \frac{c/n_1}{c/n_2} = \frac{n_2}{n_1} \qquad [25.4]$$

which gives

$$\lambda_1 n_1 = \lambda_2 n_2 \qquad [25.5]$$

It follows from Equation 25.5 that the index of refraction of any medium can be expressed as the ratio

$$n = \frac{\lambda_0}{\lambda_n} \qquad [25.6]$$

where λ_0 is the wavelength of light in vacuum and λ_n is the wavelength in the medium whose index of refraction is n.

We are now in a position to express Equation 25.2 in an alternative form. If we combine Equation 25.3 and Equation 25.2, we find that

$$n_1 \sin \theta_1 = n_2 \sin \theta_2 \qquad [25.7]$$

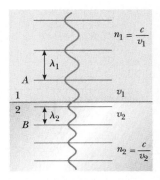

FIGURE 25.11 As a wave front moves from medium 1 to medium 2, its wavelength changes but its frequency remains constant.

▦ **PITFALL PREVENTION 25.3**

AN INVERSE RELATIONSHIP The index of refraction is *inversely* proportional to the wave speed. As the wave speed v decreases, the index of refraction n increases. Thus, the higher the index of refraction of a material, the more it *slows down* light from its speed in vacuum. The more the light slows down, the more θ_2 differs from θ_1 in Equation 25.7.

■ **Law of refraction (Snell's law)**

This equation is the **law of refraction** and is the mathematical representation of the wave under refraction model. The experimental discovery of this relationship is usually credited to Willebrord Snell (1591–1626) and is therefore known as **Snell's law.**[2] Equation 25.7 is the conventional form of the law of refraction used in optics, expressed in terms of n values rather than speeds as in Equation 25.2.

> **QUICK QUIZ 25.3** Light passes from a material with index of refraction 1.3 into one with index of refraction 1.2. Compared with the incident ray, what happens to the refracted ray? **(a)** It bends toward the normal. **(b)** It is undeflected. **(c)** It bends away from the normal.

> **QUICK QUIZ 25.4** As light from the Sun enters the atmosphere, it refracts due to the small difference between the speeds of light in air and in vacuum. The *optical* length of the day is defined as the time interval between the instant when the top of the Sun is just visibly observed above the horizon to the instant at which the top of the Sun just disappears below the horizon. The *geometric* length of the day is defined as the time interval between the instant when a geometric straight line drawn from the observer to the top of the Sun just clears the horizon to the instant at which this line just dips below the horizon. Which is longer, **(a)** the optical length of a day or **(b)** the geometric length of a day?

▮ Thinking Physics 25.2

Why do face masks make vision clearer under water? A face mask includes a flat piece of glass; the mask does not have lenses like those in eyeglasses.

Underwater vision

Reasoning The refraction necessary for focused viewing in the eye occurs at the air–cornea interface. The lens of the eye only performs some fine-tuning of this image, allowing for accommodation for objects at various distances. When the eye is opened underwater, the interface is water–cornea rather than air–cornea. Thus, the light from the scene is not focused on the retina and the scene is blurry. The face mask simply provides a layer of air in front of the eyes so that the air–cornea interface is re-established and the refraction is correct to focus the light on the retina. ▮

EXAMPLE 25.2 | **Refraction in a Material**

A beam of light of wavelength 550 nm traveling in air is incident on a slab of transparent material. The incident beam makes an angle of 40.0° with the normal, and the refracted beam makes an angle of 26.0° with the normal.

A Find the index of refraction of the material.

Solution We conceptualize the problem by looking again at Active Figure 25.9. Because the refracted angle is smaller than the incident angle, the situation is described by Active Figure 25.9a. The statement of the problem tells us to categorize this problem as one involving the model of a wave under refraction. To analyze the problem, we note that the index of refrac-

tion of air can be approximated as $n_1 = 1.00$. Snell's law of refraction (see Eq. 25.7) with these data gives

$$n_1 \sin \theta_1 = n_2 \sin \theta_2$$
$$n_2 = n_1 \frac{\sin \theta_1}{\sin \theta_2} = (1.00) \frac{\sin 40.0°}{\sin 26.0°}$$
$$= \frac{0.643}{0.438} = 1.47$$

B Find the speed of light in the material.

Solution The speed of light in the material can be easily obtained from Equation 25.3:

---

[2]The same law was deduced from the particle theory of light in 1637 by René Descartes (1596–1650) and hence is known as *Descartes's law* in France.

$$v = \frac{c}{n} = \frac{3.00 \times 10^8 \text{ m/s}}{1.47} = \boxed{2.04 \times 10^8 \text{ m/s}}$$

[C] What is the wavelength of the light in the material?

Solution We use Equation 25.6 to calculate the wavelength in the material, noting that we are given the wavelength in vacuum to be $\lambda_0 = 550$ nm:

$$\lambda_n = \frac{\lambda_0}{n} = \frac{550 \text{ nm}}{1.47} = \boxed{374 \text{ nm}}$$

To finalize the problem, note that the wavelength in the material in part C is shorter than that in vacuum. That is consistent with the concept of the wave slowing down in the material, as evidenced by the speed calculated in part B; the wave doesn't travel as far during one period of its oscillation.

INTERACTIVE **EXAMPLE 25.3** **Light Passing Through a Slab**

A light beam passes from medium 1 to medium 2, with the latter being a thick slab of material whose index of refraction is n_2 (Fig. 25.12).

[A] Show that the emerging beam is parallel to the incident beam.

Solution First, let us apply Snell's law to the upper surface:

$$(1) \quad \sin \theta_2 = \frac{n_1}{n_2} \sin \theta_1$$

Applying Snell's law to the lower surface gives

$$(2) \quad \sin \theta_3 = \frac{n_2}{n_1} \sin \theta_2$$

Substituting (1) into (2) gives

$$\sin \theta_3 = \frac{n_2}{n_1} \left(\frac{n_1}{n_2} \sin \theta_1 \right) = \sin \theta_1$$

Thus, $\theta_3 = \theta_1$, and so the layer does not alter the direction of the beam. It does, however, produce a lateral displacement d of the beam as shown in Figure 25.12.

[B] What if the thickness t of the slab is doubled? Does the lateral displacement d also double?

Solution Consider the magnification of the area of the light path within the slab in Figure 25.12b. The distance a is the hypotenuse of two right triangles. From the gold triangle, we see that

$$a = \frac{t}{\cos \theta_2}$$

and from the blue triangle, we see that

$$d = a \sin \gamma = a \sin(\theta_1 - \theta_2)$$

Combining these equations, we have

$$d = \frac{t}{\cos \theta_2} \sin(\theta_1 - \theta_2)$$

For a given incident angle θ_1, the refracted angle θ_2 is determined solely by the index of refraction, so the lateral displacement d is proportional to t. If the thickness doubles, so does the lateral displacement.

Physics⊗Now™ By logging into PhysicsNow at **www.pop4e.com** and going to Interactive Example 25.3 you can explore refraction through slabs of various thicknesses.

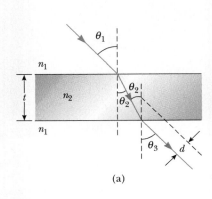

(a)

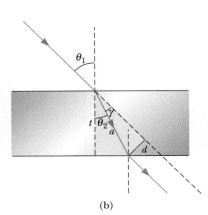

(b)

FIGURE 25.12 (Interactive Example 25.3) When light passes through a flat slab of material, the emerging beam is parallel to the incident beam and therefore $\theta_1 = \theta_3$. The dashed line parallel to the ray coming out the bottom of the slab represents the path the light would take if the slab were not there. (b) A magnification of the area of the light path inside the slab.

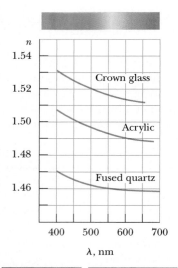

FIGURE 25.13 Variation of index of refraction with vacuum wavelength for three materials.

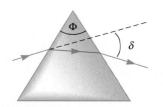

FIGURE 25.14 A prism refracts single-wavelength light and deviates the light through an angle δ. The apex angle Φ is the angle between the sides of the prism through which the light enters and leaves.

⊞ PITFALL PREVENTION 25.4

A RAINBOW OF MANY LIGHT RAYS Pictorial representations such as Active Figure 25.16 are subject to misinterpretation. The figure shows one ray of light entering the raindrop and undergoing reflection and refraction, exiting the raindrop in a range of 40° to 42° from the entering ray. This figure might be interpreted incorrectly as meaning that *all* light entering the raindrop exits in this small range of angles. In reality, light exits the raindrop over a much larger range of angles, from 0° to 42°. A careful analysis of the reflection and refraction from the spherical raindrop shows that the range of 40° to 42° is where the *highest intensity light* exits the raindrop.

25.5 DISPERSION AND PRISMS

In the preceding section, we developed Snell's law, which incorporates the index of refraction of a material. In Table 25.1, we presented index of refraction values for a number of materials. If we make careful measurements, however, we find that the value of the index of refraction in anything but vacuum depends on the wavelength of light. The dependence of the index of refraction on wavelength, which results from the dependence of the wave speed on wavelength, is called **dispersion.** Figure 25.13 is a graphical representation of this variation in index of refraction with wavelength. Because n is a function of wavelength, Snell's law indicates that **the angle of refraction when light enters a material depends on the wavelength of the light.** As we see from Figure 25.13, the index of refraction for a material generally decreases with increasing wavelength in the visible range. Thus, violet light ($\lambda \approx 400$ nm) refracts more than red light ($\lambda \approx 650$ nm) when passing from air into a material.

To understand the effects of dispersion on light, consider what happens when light strikes a prism as in Figure 25.14. The apex angle Φ of the prism is defined as shown in the figure. A ray of light of a single wavelength that is incident on the prism from the left emerges in a direction deviated from its original direction of travel by an angle of deviation δ that depends on the apex angle and the index of refraction of the prism material. Now suppose a beam of white light (a combination of all visible wavelengths) is incident on a prism. Because of dispersion, the different colors refract through different angles of deviation, and the rays that emerge from the second face of the prism spread out in a series of colors known as a **visible spectrum** as shown in Figure 25.15. These colors, in order of decreasing wavelength, are red, orange, yellow, green, blue, and violet.[3] Violet light deviates the most, red light deviates the least, and the remaining colors in the visible spectrum fall between these extremes.

The dispersion of light into a spectrum is demonstrated most vividly in nature through the formation of a rainbow, often seen by an observer positioned between the Sun and a rain shower. To understand how a rainbow is formed, consider Active Figure 25.16. A ray of light passing overhead strikes a spherical drop of water in the

FIGURE 25.15 White light enters a glass prism at the upper left. A reflected beam of light comes out of the prism just below the incoming beam. The beam moving toward the lower right shows distinct colors. Different colors are refracted at different angles because the index of refraction of the glass depends on wavelength. Violet light deviates the most; red light deviates the least.

---

[3]In Newton's time, the colors we now call teal and blue were called blue and indigo. Your "blue jeans" are dyed with indigo. A mnemonic device for remembering the colors of the spectrum is the acronym ROYGBIV, from the first letters of the colors: red, orange, yellow, green, blue, indigo, violet. Some individuals think of this acronym as the name of a person, Roy G. Biv!

atmosphere and is refracted and reflected as follows. It is first refracted at the front surface of the drop, with the violet light deviating the most and the red light the least. At the back surface of the drop, the light is reflected and returns to the front surface, where it again undergoes refraction as it moves from water into air.

Because light enters the front surface of the raindrop at all locations, there is a range of exit angles for the light leaving the raindrop after reflecting from the back surface. A careful analysis of the spherical shape of the water drop, however, shows that the exit angle of highest light intensity is 42° for the red light and 40° for the violet light. Thus, the light from the raindrop seen by the observer is brightest for these angles, and the observer sees a rainbow. Figure 25.17 shows the geometry for the observer. The colors of the rainbow are seen in a range of 40° to 42° from the antisolar direction, which is exactly 180° from the Sun. If red light is seen coming from a raindrop high in the sky, the violet light from this drop passes over the observer's head and is not seen. Thus, the portion of the rainbow in the vicinity of this drop is red. The violet portion of the rainbow seen by an observer is supplied by drops lower in the sky, which send violet light to the observer's eyes and red light below the eyes.

The opening photograph for this chapter shows a *double rainbow*. The secondary rainbow is fainter than the primary rainbow, and its colors are reversed. The secondary rainbow arises from light that makes two reflections from the interior surface before exiting the raindrop. In the laboratory, rainbows have been observed in which the light makes more than 30 reflections before exiting the water drop. Because each reflection involves some loss of light due to refraction out of the water drop, the intensity of these higher-order rainbows is very small.

QUICK QUIZ 25.5 In dispersive materials, the angle of refraction for a light ray depends on the wavelength of the light. True or false: The angle of reflection from the surface of the material depends on the wavelength.

25.6 | HUYGENS'S PRINCIPLE

In this section, we introduce a geometric construction proposed by Huygens in 1678. Huygens assumed that light consists of waves rather than a stream of particles. He had no knowledge of the electromagnetic character of light. Nevertheless, his geometric model is adequate for understanding many practical aspects of the propagation of light.

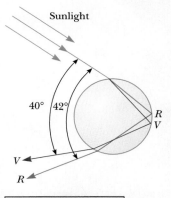

ACTIVE FIGURE 25.16

Path of sunlight through a spherical raindrop. Light following this path contributes to the visible rainbow.

Physics⊗Now™ Log into PhysicsNow at **www.pop4e.com** and go to Active Figure 25.16 to vary the point at which the sunlight enters the raindrop and verify that the angles shown are the maximum angles.

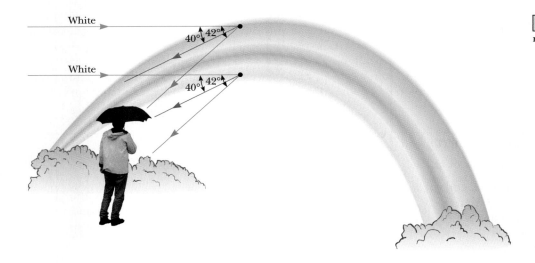

FIGURE 25.17 The formation of a rainbow.

CHRISTIAAN HUYGENS (1629–1695)

Huygens, a Dutch physicist and astronomer, is best known for his contributions to the fields of optics and dynamics. To Huygens, light was a type of vibratory motion, spreading out and producing the sensation of sight when impinging on the eye.

(Courtesy of Rijksmuseum voor de Geschiedenis der Natuurwetenschappen. Courtesy AIP Niels Bohr Library)

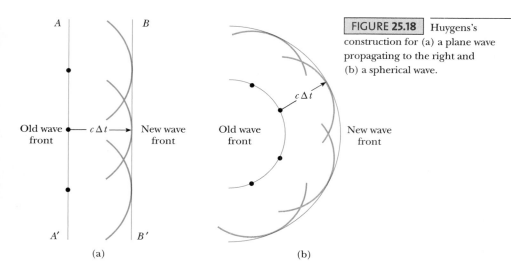

FIGURE 25.18 Huygens's construction for (a) a plane wave propagating to the right and (b) a spherical wave.

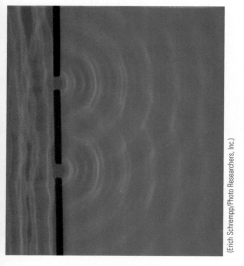

(Erich Schrempp/Photo Researchers, Inc.)

FIGURE 25.19 Water waves in a ripple tank demonstrate Huygens wavelets. A plane wave is incident on a barrier with two small openings. The openings act as sources of circular wavelets.

Huygens's principle is a geometric model that allows us to determine the position of a wave front from a knowledge of an earlier wave front. In Huygens's construction, all points on a given wave front are taken as point sources for the production of spherical secondary waves, called *wavelets,* that propagate outward with speeds characteristic of waves in that medium. After some time interval has elapsed, the new position of the wave front is the surface tangent to the wavelets.

Figure 25.18 illustrates two simple examples of a Huygens's principle construction. First, consider a plane wave moving through free space as in Figure 25.18a. At $t = 0$, the wave front is indicated by the plane labeled AA'. Each point on this wave front is a point source for a wavelet. Showing three of these points, we draw arcs of circles, each of radius $c\,\Delta t$, where c is the speed of light in free space and Δt is the time interval during which the wave propagates. The surface drawn tangent to the wavelets is the plane BB', which is parallel to AA'. This plane is the wave front at the end of the time interval Δt. In a similar manner, Figure 25.18b shows Huygens's construction for an outgoing spherical wave.

A convincing demonstration of the existence of Huygens wavelets is obtained with water waves in a shallow tank (called a ripple tank) as in Figure 25.19. Plane waves produced to the left of the slits emerge to the right of the slits as two-dimensional circular waves propagating outward. In the plane wave, each point on the wave front acts as a source of circular waves on the two-dimensional water surface. At a later time, the tangent of the circular wave fronts remains a straight line. As the wave front encounters the barrier, however, waves at all points on the wave front, except those that encounter the openings, are reflected. For very small openings, we can model this situation as if only one source of Huygens wavelets exists at each of the two openings. As a result, the Huygens wavelets from those single sources are seen as the outgoing circular waves in the right portion of Figure 25.19. This is a dramatic example of diffraction that was mentioned in the opening section of this chapter, a phenomenon we shall study in more detail in Chapter 27.

EXAMPLE 25.4 **Deriving the Laws of Reflection and Refraction**

Use Huygens's principle to derive the law of reflection.

Solution To derive the law of reflection, consider the rays shown in Figure 25.20a. The line AB represents a wave front of the incident light just as ray 1 strikes the surface. At this instant, the wave at A sends out a Huygens wavelet (the circular arc centered on A)

toward D. At the same time, the wave at B emits a Huygens wavelet (the circular arc centered on B) toward C. Figure 25.20a shows these wavelets after a time interval Δt, after which ray 2 strikes the surface. Because both rays 1 and 2 move with the same speed, we must have $AD = BC = c\,\Delta t$.

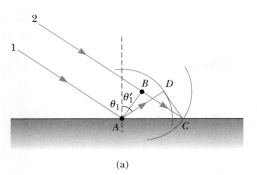

(a)

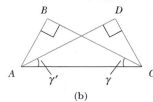

FIGURE **25.20** (Example 25.4)
(a) Huygens's construction for proving the law of reflection. At the instant ray 1 strikes the surface, it sends out a Huygens wavelet from A and ray 2 sends out a Huygens wavelet from B. We choose a radius of the wavelet to be $c\,\Delta t$, where Δt is the time interval for ray 2 to travel from B to C.
(b) Triangle ADC is congruent with triangle ABC.

The remainder of our analysis depends on geometry, as summarized in Figure 25.20b, in which we isolate the triangles ABC and ADC. Note that these two triangles are congruent because they have the same hypotenuse AC and because $AD = BC$. From Figure 25.20b, we have

$$\cos \gamma = \frac{BC}{AC} \quad \text{and} \quad \cos \gamma' = \frac{AD}{AC}$$

where, comparing Figures 25.20a and 25.20b, we see that $\gamma = 90° - \theta_1$ and $\gamma' = 90° - \theta_1'$. Because $AD = BC$,

$$\cos \gamma = \cos \gamma'$$

Therefore,

$$\gamma = \gamma'$$

$$90° - \theta_1 = 90° - \theta_1'$$

and

$$\theta_1 = \theta_1'$$

which is the law of reflection.

B Use Huygens's principle to derive the law of refraction.

Solution For the law of refraction, consider the geometric construction shown in Figure 25.21. We focus our attention on the instant ray 1 strikes the surface and the subsequent time interval until ray 2 strikes the surface. During this time interval, the wave at A sends out a Huygens wavelet (the arc centered on A) toward D. In the same time interval, the wave at B sends out a Huygens wavelet (the arc centered on B) toward C. Because these two wavelets travel through different media, the radii of the wavelets are different. The radius of the wavelet from A is $AD = v_2\,\Delta t$, where v_2 is the wave

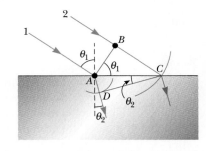

FIGURE **25.21** (Example 25.4) Huygens's construction for proving Snell's law of refraction. At the instant ray 1 strikes the surface, it sends out a Huygens wavelet from A and ray 2 sends out a Huygens wavelet from B. The two wavelets have different radii because they travel in different media.

speed in the second medium. The radius of the wavelet from B is $BC = v_1\,\Delta t$, where v_1 is the wave speed in the original medium.

From triangles ABC and ADC, we find that

$$\sin \theta_1 = \frac{BC}{AC} = \frac{v_1\,\Delta t}{AC} \quad \text{and} \quad \sin \theta_2 = \frac{AD}{AC} = \frac{v_2\,\Delta t}{AC}$$

If we divide the first equation by the second, we obtain

$$\frac{\sin \theta_1}{\sin \theta_2} = \frac{v_1}{v_2}$$

From Equation 25.3, however, we know that $v_1 = c/n_1$ and $v_2 = c/n_2$. Therefore,

$$\frac{\sin \theta_1}{\sin \theta_2} = \frac{c/n_1}{c/n_2} = \frac{n_2}{n_1}$$

$$n_1 \sin \theta_1 = n_2 \sin \theta_2$$

which is Snell's law of refraction.

25.7 TOTAL INTERNAL REFLECTION

An interesting effect called **total internal reflection** can occur when light travels from a medium with a high index of refraction to one with a lower index of refraction. Consider a light ray traveling in medium 1 and meeting the boundary between media 1 and 2, where $n_1 > n_2$ (Active Fig. 25.22a). Various possible directions of the ray are indicated by rays 1 through 5. The refracted rays are bent away

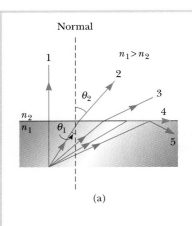

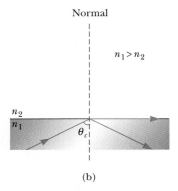

ACTIVE FIGURE 25.22

(a) Rays travel from a medium of index of refraction n_1 into a medium of index of refraction n_2, where $n_1 > n_2$. As the angle of incidence increases, the angle of refraction θ_2 increases until θ_2 is 90° (ray 4). For even larger angles of incidence, total internal reflection occurs (ray 5). (b) The angle of incidence producing an angle of refraction equal to 90° is the critical angle θ_c.

Physics⊗Now™ Log into Physics-Now at **www.pop4e.com** and go to Active Figure 25.22 to vary the incident angle and see the effect on the refracted ray and the distribution of incident energy between the reflected and refracted rays.

from the normal because $n_1 > n_2$. (Remember that when light refracts at the interface between the two media, it is also partially reflected. For simplicity, we ignore these reflected rays here, except for ray 5.) At some particular angle of incidence θ_c, called the **critical angle,** the refracted light ray moves parallel to the boundary so that $\theta_2 = 90°$ (Active Fig. 25.22b). For angles of incidence greater than θ_c, no ray is refracted and the incident ray is entirely reflected at the boundary, as is ray 5 in Active Figure 25.22a. This ray is reflected at the boundary as though it had struck a perfectly reflecting surface. It obeys the law of reflection; that is, the angle of incidence equals the angle of reflection.

We can use Snell's law to find the critical angle. When $\theta_1 = \theta_c$, $\theta_2 = 90°$, and Snell's law (Eq. 25.7) gives

$$n_1 \sin \theta_c = n_2 \sin 90° = n_2$$

$$\sin \theta_c = \frac{n_2}{n_1} \qquad \text{(for } n_1 > n_2\text{)} \qquad [25.8]$$

This equation can be used only when n_1 is greater than n_2. That is, **total internal reflection occurs only when light travels from a medium of high index of refraction to a medium of lower index of refraction.** That is why the word *internal* is in the name. The light must initially be *inside* a material of higher index of refraction than the medium outside the material. If n_1 were less than n_2, Equation 25.8 would give $\sin \theta_c > 1$, which is meaningless because the sine of an angle can never be greater than unity.

The critical angle for total internal reflection is small when n_1 is considerably larger than n_2. Examples of this situation are diamond ($n = 2.42$ and $\theta_c = 24°$) and crown glass ($n = 1.52$ and $\theta_c = 41°$), where the angles given correspond to light refracting from the material into air. Total internal reflection combined with proper faceting causes diamonds and crystal glass to sparkle when observed in light.

QUICK QUIZ 25.6 **(i)** In Figure 25.23, five light rays enter a glass prism from the left. How many of these rays undergo total internal reflection at the slanted surface of the prism? **(a)** 1 **(b)** 2 **(c)** 3 **(d)** 4 **(e)** 5 **(ii)** Suppose the prism in Figure 25.23 can be rotated in the plane of the paper. For *all five* rays to experience total internal reflection from the slanted surface, should the prism be rotated **(a)** clockwise or **(b)** counterclockwise?

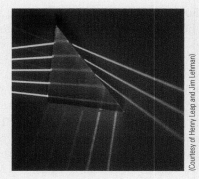

FIGURE 25.23 (Quick Quiz 25.6) Five nonparallel rays of light enter a glass prism from the left.

(Courtesy of Henry Leap and Jim Lehman)

QUICK QUIZ 25.7 A beam of white light is incident on a crown glass–air interface as shown in Active Figure 25.22. The incoming beam is rotated clockwise, so the incident angle θ increases. Because of dispersion in the glass, some colors of light experience total internal reflection (ray 4 in Active Fig. 25.22a) before other colors, so the beam refracting out of the glass is no longer white. What is the last color to refract out of the upper surface? **(a)** violet **(b)** green **(c)** red **(d)** impossible to determine

EXAMPLE 25.5 | A View from the Fish's Eye

A Find the critical angle for a water–air boundary if the index of refraction of water is 1.33.

Solution Applying Equation 25.8, we find the critical angle to be

$$\sin \theta_c = \frac{n_2}{n_1} = \frac{1}{1.33} = 0.752$$

$$\theta_c = \boxed{48.8°}$$

B What if a fish in a still pond looks upward toward the water's surface at different angles relative to the surface as in Figure 25.24? What does it see?

Solution Examine Active Figure 25.22a. Because the path of a light ray is reversible, light traveling from medium 2 into medium 1 in Active Figure 25.22a follows the paths shown, but in the *opposite* direction. A fish looking upward toward the water surface as in Figure 25.24 can see out of the water if it looks toward the surface at an angle less than the critical angle. Thus, for example, when the fish's line of vision makes an angle of 40° with the normal to the surface, light from above the water reaches the fish's eye. At 48.8°, the critical angle for water, the light has to skim along the water's surface before being refracted to the fish's eye; at this angle, the fish can in principle see the whole shore of the pond. At angles greater than the critical angle, the light reaching the fish comes by means of internal reflection at the surface. Thus, at 60°, the fish sees a reflection of the bottom of the pond.

FIGURE 25.24 (Example 25.5) A fish looks upward toward the surface of the water.

25.8 | OPTICAL FIBERS

CONTEXT CONNECTION

An interesting application of total internal reflection is the use of glass or transparent plastic rods to "pipe" light from one place to another. In the communication industry, digital pulses of laser light move along these light pipes, carrying information at an extremely high rate. In this Context Connection, we investigate the physics of this technological advance.

Figure 25.25 shows light traveling within a narrow transparent rod. The light is limited to traveling within the rod, even around gentle curves, as the result of successive total internal reflections. Such a light pipe can be flexible if thin fibers—called **optical fibers**—are used rather than thick rods. If a bundle of parallel optical fibers is used to construct an optical transmission line, images can be transferred from one point to another as we shall discuss in the Context Connection of Chapter 26. Typical diameters for optical fibers are measured in tens of micrometers.

A typical optical fiber consists of a transparent core surrounded by a *cladding,* a material that has a lower index of refraction than the core. The combination may be surrounded by a plastic *jacket* to prevent mechanical damage. Figure 25.26 shows a cutaway view of this construction. Because the index of refraction of the cladding is less than that of the core, light traveling in the core experiences total internal reflection if it arrives at the interface between the core and the cladding at an angle of incidence that exceeds the critical angle. In this case, light "bounces" along the core of the optical fiber, losing very little of its intensity as it travels.

Figure 25.27 shows a cross-sectional view from the side of a simple type of optical fiber known as a *multimode, stepped index fiber.* The term *stepped index* refers to the

FIGURE 25.25 Light travels in a curved transparent rod by multiple internal reflections.

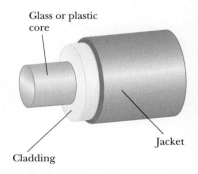

Glass or plastic core

Jacket

Cladding

FIGURE 25.26 The construction of an optical fiber. Light travels in the core, which is surrounded by a cladding and a protective jacket.

Strands of glass or plastic optical fibers are used to carry voice, video, and data signals in telecommunication networks. Typical fibers have diameters of 60 μm. ▪

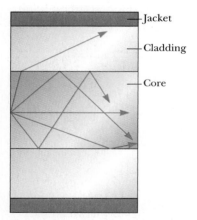

FIGURE 25.27 A multimode, stepped index optical fiber. Light rays entering over a wide range of angles pass through the core. Those making large angles with the axis take longer to travel the length of the fiber than those making small angles.

discontinuity in index of refraction between the core and the cladding, and *multimode* means that light entering the fiber at many angles is transmitted. This type of fiber is acceptable for transmitting signals over a short distance but not long distances because a digital pulse spreads with distance. Let us imagine that we input a perfectly rectangular pulse of laser light to the core of the optical fiber. Active Figure 25.28a shows the idealized time behavior of the laser light intensity for the input pulse. The laser light intensity rises instantaneously to its highest value, stays constant for the duration of the pulse, and then instantaneously drops to zero. The light from the pulse entering along the axis in Figure 25.27 travels the shortest distance and arrives at the other end first. The other light paths represent longer distance of travel because of the angled bounces. As a result, the light from the pulse arrives at the other end over a longer period and the pulse is spread out as in Active Figure 25.28b. If a series of pulses represents zeroes and ones for a binary signal, this spreading could cause the pulses to overlap or might reduce the peak intensity below the detection threshold; either situation would result in obliteration of the information.

One way to improve optical transmission in such a situation is to use a *multimode, graded index fiber.* This fiber has a core whose index of refraction is smaller at larger radii from the center as suggested by the shading in Figure 25.29. With a graded index core, off-axis rays of light experience continuous refraction and curve gradually away from the edges and back toward the center as shown by the light path in Figure 25.29. Such curving reduces the transit time through the fiber for off-axis rays and also reduces the spreading out of the pulse. The transit time is reduced for two reasons. First, the path length is reduced, and second, much of the time the wave travels in the lower index of refraction region, where the speed of light is higher than at the center.

The spreading effect in Active Figure 25.28 can be further reduced and almost eliminated by designing the fiber with two changes from the multimode, stepped index fiber in Figure 25.27. The core is made very small so that all paths within it are more nearly the same length, and the difference in index of refraction between core and cladding is made relatively small so that off-axis rays enter the cladding and are absorbed. These changes are suggested in Active Figure 25.30. This kind of fiber is called a *single-mode, stepped index fiber.* It can carry information at high bit rates because the pulses are minimally spread out.

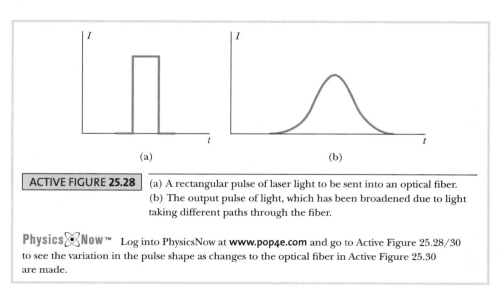

ACTIVE FIGURE 25.28 (a) A rectangular pulse of laser light to be sent into an optical fiber. (b) The output pulse of light, which has been broadened due to light taking different paths through the fiber.

Physics Now™ Log into PhysicsNow at **www.pop4e.com** and go to Active Figure 25.28/30 to see the variation in the pulse shape as changes to the optical fiber in Active Figure 25.30 are made.

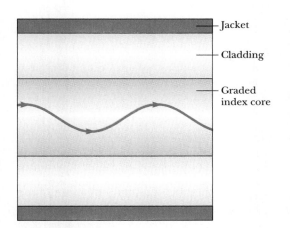

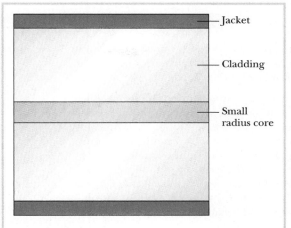

FIGURE 25.29 A multimode, graded index optical fiber. Because the index of refraction of the core varies radially, off-axis light rays follow curved paths through the core.

ACTIVE FIGURE 25.30 A single-mode, stepped index optical fiber. The small radius of the core and the small difference between the indices of refraction of the core and cladding reduce the broadening of light pulses.

Physics⊗Now™ Log into PhysicsNow at www.pop4e.com and go to Active Figure 25.28/30 to make changes to the optical fiber and see the variation in the pulse shape in Active Figure 25.28.

In reality, the material of the core is not perfectly transparent. Some absorption and scattering occurs as the light travels down the fiber. Absorption transforms energy being transferred by electromagnetic radiation into increased internal energy in the fiber. Scattering causes light to strike the core–cladding interface at angles less than the critical angle for total internal reflection, resulting in some loss in the cladding or jacket. Even with these problems, optical fibers can transmit about 95% of the input energy over a kilometer. The problems are minimized by using as long a wavelength as possible for which the core material is transparent. The scattering and absorption centers then appear as small as possible to the waves and minimize the probability of interaction. Much of optical fiber communication occurs with light from infrared lasers, having wavelengths of about 1 300 nm.

The field of developing applications for optical fibers is called **fiber optics.** One common application is the use of optical fibers in telecommunications because the fibers can carry a much higher volume of telephone calls, or other forms of communication, than electric wires. Optical fibers are also used in "smart buildings." In this application, sensors are located at various points within a building and an optical fiber carries laser light to the sensor, which reflects it back to a control system. If any distortion occurs in the building due to earthquake or other causes, the intensity of the reflected light from the sensor changes and the control system locates the point of distortion by identifying the particular sensor involved.

A single optical fiber can carry a digital signal, as we already described. If it is desired for optical fibers to carry an image of a scene, it is necessary to use a bundle of optical fibers. A popular use of such bundles is in the use of *fiberscopes* in medicine. In the Context Connection of Chapter 26, we shall investigate these devices. ■

SUMMARY

Physics⊗Now™ Take a practice test by logging into Physics-Now at **www.pop4e.com** and clicking on the Pre-Test link for this chapter

In geometric optics, we use the **ray approximation** in which we assume that a wave travels through a medium in straight lines in the direction of the rays of that wave. We ignore diffraction effects, which is a good approximation as long as the wavelength is short compared with the size of any openings.

The **law of reflection** states that part of a wave incident on a surface reflects from the surface so that the angle of reflection θ_1' equals the angle of incidence θ_1.

The **index of refraction** n of a material is defined as

$$n \equiv \frac{c}{v} \qquad [25.3]$$

where c is the speed of light in a vacuum and v is the speed of light in the material.

Part of a light wave striking an interface between two media is transmitted into the second medium and undergoes a change in the direction of propagation. The **law of refraction, or Snell's law,** states that

$$n_1 \sin \theta_1 = n_2 \sin \theta_2 \qquad [25.7]$$

In general, n varies with wavelength, which is called **dispersion.** **Huygens's principle** states that all points on a wave front can be taken as point sources for the production of secondary wavelets. At some later time, the new position of the wave front is the surface tangent to these secondary wavelets.

Total internal reflection can occur when light travels from a medium of high index of refraction to one of lower index of refraction. The **critical angle** of incidence θ_c for which total internal reflection occurs at an interface is

$$\sin \theta_c = \frac{n_2}{n_1} \qquad (\text{for } n_1 > n_2) \qquad [25.8]$$

QUESTIONS

☐ = answer available in the *Student Solutions Manual and Study Guide*

1. Light of wavelength λ is incident on a slit of width d. Under what conditions is the ray approximation valid? Under what circumstances does the slit produce enough diffraction to make the ray approximation invalid?

2. The display windows of some department stores are slanted slightly inward at the bottom to decrease the glare from streetlights or the Sun, which would make it difficult for shoppers to see the display inside. Sketch a light ray reflecting from such a window to show how this design works.

3. The rectangular aquarium sketched in Figure Q25.3 contains only one goldfish. When the fish is near a corner of the tank and is viewed along a direction that make an equal angle with two adjacent faces, the observer sees two fish mirroring each other, as shown. Explain this observation.

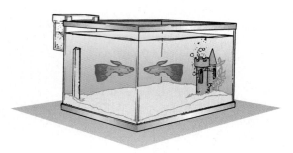

FIGURE **Q25.3**

4. Sound waves have much in common with light waves, including the properties of reflection and refraction. Give examples of these phenomena for sound waves.

5. As light travels from one medium to another, does the wavelength of the light change? Does the frequency change? Does the speed change? Explain.

6. A laser beam passing through a nonhomogeneous sugar solution follows a curved path. Explain.

7. Explain why a diamond sparkles more than a glass crystal of the same shape and size.

8. Why does a diamond show flashes of color when observed under white light?

9. Explain why a diamond loses most of its sparkle when it is submerged in carbon disulfide and why an imitation diamond of cubic zirconia loses all its sparkle in corn syrup.

10. Describe an experiment in which total internal reflection is used to determine the index of refraction of a medium.

11. When two colors of light (X and Y) are sent through a glass prism, X is bent more than Y. Which color travels more slowly in the prism?

12. Is it possible to have total internal reflection for light incident from air on water? Explain.

13. Total internal reflection is applied in the periscope of a submarine to let the user "see around corners." In this device, two prisms are arranged as shown in Figure Q25.13 so that an incident beam of light follows the path shown. Parallel tilted silvered mirrors could be used, but glass prisms with no silvered surfaces give higher light throughput. Propose a reason for the higher efficiency.

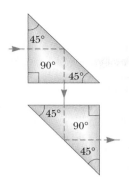

FIGURE **Q25.13**

14. At one restaurant, a worker uses colored chalk to write the daily specials on a blackboard illuminated with a spotlight. At another restaurant, a worker writes with colored grease pencils on a flat, smooth sheet of transparent acrylic plastic with index of refraction 1.55. The plastic panel hangs in front of a piece of black felt. Small, bright electric lights are installed all along the edges of the plastic sheet, inside an opaque channel. Figure Q25.14 shows a cutaway view. Explain why viewers at both restaurants see the letters shining against a black background. Explain why the sign at the second restaurant may use less energy from the electric company. What would be a good choice for the index of refraction of the material in the grease pencils?

FIGURE **Q25.14**

15. How is it possible that a complete circle of a rainbow can sometimes be seen from an airplane? With a stepladder, a lawn sprinkler, and a sunny day, how can you show the complete circle to children?

16. Under what conditions is a mirage formed? On a hot day, what are we seeing when we observe "water on the road"?

PROBLEMS

1, 2, 3 = straightforward, intermediate, challenging	
☐ = full solution available in the *Student Solutions Manual and Study Guide*	
Physics⊗Now™ = coached problem with hints available at **www.pop4e.com**	
💻 = computer useful in solving problem	
▨ = paired numerical and symbolic problems	
🗟 = biomedical application	

Section 25.2 ■ The Ray Model in Geometric Optics
Section 25.3 ■ The Wave Under Reflection
Section 25.4 ■ The Wave Under Refraction

Note: You may look up indices of refraction in Table 25.1.

1. The two mirrors illustrated in Figure P25.1 meet at a right angle. The beam of light in the vertical plane P strikes mirror 1 as shown. (a) Determine the distance the reflected light beam travels before striking mirror 2. (b) In what direction does the light beam travel after being reflected from mirror 2?

2. Two flat, rectangular mirrors, both perpendicular to a horizontal sheet of paper, are set edge to edge with their re-

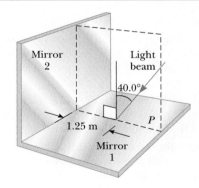

FIGURE **P25.1**

flecting surfaces perpendicular to each other. (a) A light ray in the plane of the paper strikes one of the mirrors at an arbitrary angle of incidence θ_1. Prove that the final direction of the ray, after reflection from both mirrors, is opposite to its initial direction. In a clothing store, such a pair of mirrors shows you an image of yourself as others see you, with no apparent right–left reversal. (b) Now assume that the paper is replaced with a third flat mirror, touching edges with the other two and perpendicular to both. The set of three mirrors is called a *corner-cube reflector*. A ray of light is incident from any direction within the octant of space bounded by the reflecting surfaces. Argue that the ray will reflect once from each mirror and that its final direction will be opposite to its original direction. The *Apollo 11* astronauts placed a panel of corner cube reflectors on the Moon. Analysis of timing data taken with the panel reveals that the radius of the Moon's orbit is increasing at the rate of 3.8 cm/yr as it loses kinetic energy because of tidal friction.

3. How many times will the incident beam shown in Figure P25.3 be reflected by each of the parallel mirrors?

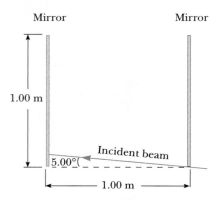

FIGURE **P25.3**

4. A narrow beam of sodium yellow light, with wavelength 589 nm in vacuum, is incident from air onto a smooth water surface at an angle of incidence of 35.0°. Determine the angle of refraction and the wavelength of the light in water.

5. *Compare this problem with Problem 25.4.* A plane sound wave in air at 20°C, with wavelength 589 mm, is incident on a smooth surface of water at 25°C, at an angle of incidence of 3.50°. Determine the angle of refraction for the sound wave and the wavelength of the sound in water.

6. The wavelength of red helium–neon laser light in air is 632.8 nm. (a) What is its frequency? (b) What is its wavelength in glass that has an index of refraction of 1.50? (c) What is its speed in the glass?

7. An underwater scuba diver sees the Sun at an apparent angle of 45.0° above the horizon. What is the actual elevation angle of the Sun above the horizon?

8. A ray of light is incident on a flat surface of a block of crown glass that is surrounded by water. The angle of refraction is 19.6°. Find the angle of reflection.

9. A laser beam with vacuum wavelength 632.8 nm is incident from air onto a block of glass as shown in Active Figure 25.8b. The line of sight of the photograph is perpendicular to the plane in which the light moves. Find the (a) speed, (b) frequency, and (c) wavelength of the light in the glass. The glass is not necessarily either of the types listed in Table 25.1. (*Suggestion:* Use a protractor.)

10. A laser beam is incident at an angle of 30.0° from the vertical onto a solution of corn syrup in water. The beam is refracted to 19.24° from the vertical. (a) What is the index of refraction of the corn syrup solution? Assume that the light is red, with vacuum wavelength 632.8 nm. Find its (b) wavelength, (c) frequency, and (d) speed in the solution.

11. Find the speed of light in (a) flint glass, (b) water, and (c) cubic zirconia.

12. A light ray initially in water enters a transparent substance at an angle of incidence of 37.0°, and the transmitted ray is refracted at an angle of 25.0°. Calculate the speed of light in the transparent substance.

13. Physics⊗Now™ A ray of light strikes a flat block of glass ($n = 1.50$) of thickness 2.00 cm at an angle of 30.0° with the normal. Trace the light beam through the glass and find the angles of incidence and refraction at each surface.

14. An opaque cylindrical tank with an open top has a diameter of 3.00 m and is completely filled with water. When the afternoon Sun reaches an angle of 28.0° above the horizon, sunlight ceases to illuminate any part of the bottom of the tank. How deep is the tank?

15. Unpolarized light in vacuum is incident onto a sheet of glass with index of refraction n. The reflected and refracted rays are perpendicular to each other. Find the angle of incidence. This angle is called *Brewster's angle* or the *polarizing angle*. In this situation, the reflected light is linearly polarized, with its electric field restricted to be perpendicular to the plane containing the rays and the normal.

16. A narrow beam of ultrasonic waves reflects off the liver tumor in Figure P25.16. The speed of the wave is 10.0% less in the liver than in the surrounding medium. Determine the depth of the tumor.

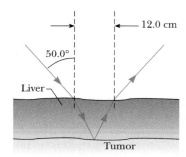

FIGURE **P25.16**

17. When the light illustrated in Figure P25.17 passes through the glass block, it is shifted laterally by the distance d. Taking $n = 1.50$, find the value of d.

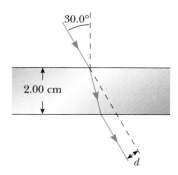

FIGURE **P25.17** Problems 25.17 and 25.18.

18. Find the time interval required for the light to pass through the glass block described in Problem 25.17.

19. The light beam shown in Figure P25.19 makes an angle of 20.0° with the normal line NN' in the linseed oil. Determine the angles θ and θ'. (*Note:* The index of refraction of linseed oil is 1.48.)

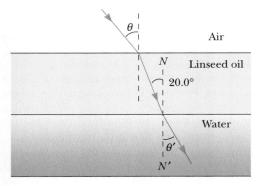

FIGURE **P25.19**

20. A digital video disc records information in a spiral track about 1 μm wide. The track consists of a series of pits in the information layer (see Fig. P25.20a) that scatter light from a laser beam sharply focused on them. The laser shines in through transparent plastic of thickness $t = 1.20$ mm and index of refraction 1.55. Assume that the width of the laser beam at the information layer must be

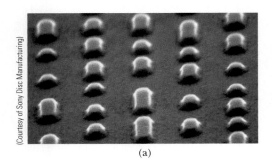

(a)

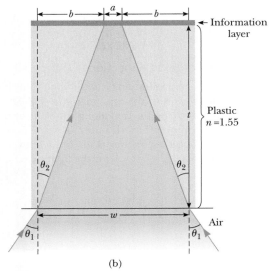

(b)

FIGURE **P25.20** (a) A micrograph of a DVD surface showing pits along each track. (b) Cross-section of a cone-shaped laser beam used to read a DVD.

$a = 1.00$ μm to read from just one track and not from its neighbors (Fig. P25.20b). Assume that the width of the beam as it enters the transparent plastic from below is $w = 0.700$ mm. A lens makes the beam converge into a cone with an apex angle $2\theta_1$ before it enters the disk. Find the incidence angle θ_1 of the light at the edge of the conical beam. Note that this design is relatively immune to small dust particles degrading the video quality. Particles on the plastic surface would have to be as large as 0.7 mm to obscure the beam.

21. When you look through a window, by what time interval is the light you see delayed by having to go through glass instead of air? Make an order-of-magnitude estimate on the basis of data you specify. By how many wavelengths is it delayed?

22. The reflecting surfaces of two intersecting flat mirrors are at an angle θ ($0° < \theta < 90°$) as shown in Figure P25.22. For a light ray that strikes the horizontal mirror, show that the emerging ray will intersect the incident ray at an angle $\beta = 180° - 2\theta$.

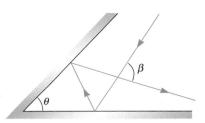

FIGURE **P25.22**

Section 25.5 ■ Dispersion and Prisms

23. A narrow white light beam is incident on a block of fused quartz at an angle of 30.0°. Find the angular width of the light beam inside the quartz.

24. A ray of light strikes the midpoint of one face of an equiangular glass prism ($n = 1.50$) at an angle of incidence of 30.0°. Trace the path of the light ray through the glass and find the angles of incidence and refraction at each surface.

25. A triangular glass prism with apex angle $\Phi = 60.0°$ has an index of refraction $n = 1.50$ (Fig. P25.25). What is the smallest angle of incidence θ_1 for which a light ray can emerge from the other side?

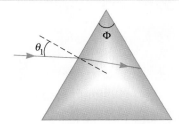

FIGURE **P25.25** Problems 25.25 and 25.26.

26. A triangular glass prism with apex angle Φ has index of refraction n. (See Fig. P25.25.) What is the smallest angle of incidence θ_1 for which a light ray can emerge from the other side?

27. Physics ⊗ Now™ The index of refraction for violet light in silica flint glass is 1.66 and that for red light is 1.62. What is the angular dispersion of visible light passing through a prism of apex angle 60.0° if the angle of incidence is 50.0°? (See Fig. P25.27.)

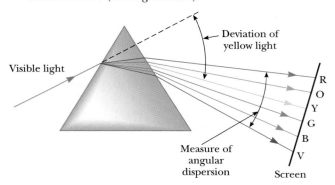

Deviation of yellow light

Visible light

Measure of angular dispersion

R
O
Y
G
B
V

Screen

FIGURE **P25.27**

Section 25.6 ■ Huygens's Principle

28. The speed of a water wave is described by $v = \sqrt{gd}$, where d is the water depth, assumed to be small compared to the wavelength. Because their speed changes, water waves refract when moving into a region of different depth. Sketch a map of an ocean beach on the eastern side of a landmass. Show contour lines of constant depth under water, assuming reasonably uniform slope. (a) Suppose waves approach the coast from a storm far away to the north–northeast. Demonstrate that the waves will move nearly perpendicular to the shoreline when they reach the beach. (b) Sketch a map of a coastline with alternating bays and headlands as suggested in Figure P25.28. Again make a reasonable guess about the shape of contour lines of constant depth. Suppose waves approach the coast, carrying energy with uniform density along originally straight wavefronts. Show that the energy reaching the coast is concentrated at the headlands and has lower intensity in the bays.

(Ray Atkeson/Image Archive)

FIGURE **P25.28**

Section 25.7 ■ Total Internal Reflection

29. For 589-nm light, calculate the critical angle for the following materials surrounded by air: (a) diamond, (b) flint glass, and (c) ice.

30. A room contains air in which the speed of sound is 343 m/s. The walls of the room are made of concrete, in which the speed of sound is 1 850 m/s. (a) Find the critical angle for total internal reflection of sound at the concrete–air boundary. (b) In which medium must the sound be traveling to undergo total internal reflection? (c) "A bare concrete wall is a highly efficient mirror for sound." Give evidence for or against this statement.

31. Consider a common mirage formed by super-heated air just above a roadway. A truck driver whose eyes are 2.00 m above the road, where $n = 1.000\ 3$, looks forward. She perceives the illusion of a patch of water ahead on the road, where her line of sight makes an angle of 1.20° below the horizontal. Find the index of refraction of the air just above the road surface. (*Suggestion:* Treat this problem as one about total internal reflection.)

32. In about 1965, engineers at the Toro Company invented a gasoline gauge for small engines, diagrammed in Figure P25.32. The gauge has no moving parts. It consists of a flat slab of transparent plastic fitting vertically into a slot in the cap on the gas tank. None of the plastic has a reflective coating. The plastic projects from the horizontal top down nearly to the bottom of the opaque tank. Its lower edge is cut with facets making angles of 45° with the horizontal. A lawn mower operator looks down from above and sees a boundary between bright and dark on the gauge. The location of the boundary, across the width of the plastic, indicates the quantity of gasoline in the tank. Explain how the gauge works. Explain the design requirements, if any, for the index of refraction of the plastic.

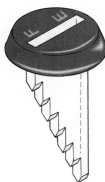

FIGURE **P25.32**

Section 25.8 ■ Context Connection — Optical Fibers

33. Determine the maximum angle θ for which the light rays incident on the end of the pipe in Figure P25.33 are subject to total internal reflection along the walls of the pipe. Assume that the pipe has an index of refraction of 1.36 and that the outside medium is air. Your answer defines the size of the *cone of acceptance* for the light pipe.

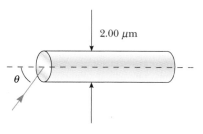

2.00 μm

θ

FIGURE **P25.33**

34. A glass fiber ($n = 1.50$) is submerged in water ($n = 1.33$). What is the critical angle for light to stay inside the optical fiber?

35. Physics⊗Now™ A laser beam strikes one end of a slab of material as shown in Figure P25.35. The index of refraction of the slab is 1.48. Determine the number of internal reflections of the beam before it emerges from the opposite end of the slab.

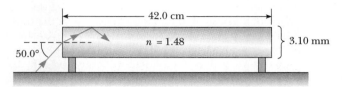

FIGURE **P25.35**

36. An optical fiber has index of refraction n and diameter d. It is surrounded by air. Light is sent into the fiber along its axis as shown in Figure P25.36. (a) Find the smallest outside radius R permitted for a bend in the fiber if no light is to escape. (b) Does the result for part (a) predict reasonable behavior as d approaches zero? As n increases? As n approaches 1? (c) Evaluate R assuming the fiber diameter is 100 μm and its index of refraction is 1.40.

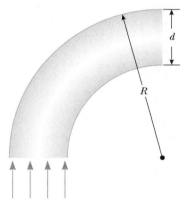

FIGURE **P25.36**

Additional Problems

37. Three sheets of plastic have unknown indices of refraction. Sheet 1 is placed on top of sheet 2, and a laser beam is directed onto the sheets from above so that it strikes the interface at an angle of 26.5° with the normal. The refracted beam in sheet 2 makes an angle of 31.7° with the normal. The experiment is repeated with sheet 3 on top of sheet 2, and, with the same angle of incidence, the refracted beam makes an angle of 36.7° with the normal. If the experiment is repeated again with sheet 1 on top of sheet 3, what is the expected angle of refraction in sheet 3? Assume the same angle of incidence.

38. Figure P25.38 shows a desk ornament globe containing a photograph. The flat photograph is in air, inside a vertical slot located behind a water-filled compartment having the shape of one half of a cylinder. Suppose you are looking at the center of the photograph and then rotate the globe about a vertical axis. You find that the center of the photograph disappears when you rotate the globe beyond a certain maximum angle (Fig. P25.38b). Account for this phenomenon and calculate the maximum angle. Briefly describe what you see when you turn the globe beyond this angle.

FIGURE **P25.38**

39. A light ray enters the atmosphere of a planet where it descends vertically to the surface a distance h below. The index of refraction where the light enters the atmosphere is 1.000, and it increases linearly to the surface where it has the value n. (a) How long does it take the ray to traverse this path? (b) Compare this time interval to that required in the absence of an atmosphere.

40. 💻 (a) Consider a horizontal interface between air above and glass of index 1.55 below. Draw a light ray incident from the air at angle of incidence 30.0°. Determine the angles of the reflected and refracted rays and show them on the diagram. (b) Now suppose the light ray is incident from the glass at angle of incidence 30.0°. Determine the angles of the reflected and refracted rays and show all three rays on a new diagram. (c) For rays incident from the air onto the air–glass surface, determine and tabulate the angles of reflection and refraction for all the angles of incidence at 10.0° intervals from 0° to 90.0°. (d) Do the same for light rays coming up to the interface through the glass.

41. Physics⊗Now™ A small light fixture is on the bottom of a swimming pool, 1.00 m below the surface. The light emerging from the water forms a circle on the still water surface. What is the diameter of this circle?

42. One technique for measuring the angle of a prism is shown in Figure P25.42. A parallel beam of light is directed on the angle so that parts of the beam reflect from opposite sides. Show that the angular separation of the two reflected beams is given by $B = 2A$.

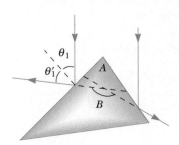

FIGURE **P25.42**

43. The walls of a prison cell are perpendicular to the four cardinal compass directions. On the first day of spring, light from the rising Sun enters a rectangular window in the eastern wall. The light traverses 2.37 m horizontally to shine perpendicularly on the wall opposite the window. A young prisoner observes the patch of light moving across this western wall and for the first time forms his own understanding of the rotation of the Earth. (a) With what speed does the illuminated rectangle move? (b) The prisoner holds a small, square mirror flat against the wall at one corner of the rectangle of light. The mirror reflects light back to a spot on the eastern wall close beside the window. How fast does the smaller square of light move across that wall? (c) Seen from a latitude of 40.0° north, the rising Sun moves through the sky along a line making a 50.0° angle with the southeastern horizon. In what direction does the rectangular patch of light on the western wall of the prisoner's cell move? (d) In what direction does the smaller square of light on the eastern wall move?

44. Figure P25.44 shows a top view of a square enclosure. The inner surfaces are plane mirrors. A ray of light enters a small hole in the center of one mirror. (a) At what angle θ must the ray enter so as to exit through the hole after being reflected once by each of the other three mirrors? (b) Are there other values of θ for which the ray can exit after multiple reflections? If so, make a sketch of one of the ray's paths.

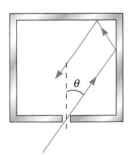

FIGURE **P25.44**

45. A hiker stands on an isolated mountain peak near sunset and observes a rainbow caused by water droplets in the air 8.00 km away. The valley is 2.00 km below the mountain peak and entirely flat. What fraction of the complete circular arc of the rainbow is visible to the hiker? (See Fig. 25.17.)

46. A 4.00-m-long pole stands vertically in a lake having a depth of 2.00 m. The Sun is 40.0° above the horizontal. Determine the length of the pole's shadow on the bottom of the lake. Take the index of refraction for water to be 1.33.

47. When light is incident normally on the interface between two transparent optical media, the intensity of the reflected light is given by the expression

$$S_1' = \left(\frac{n_2 - n_1}{n_2 + n_1} \right)^2 S_1$$

In this equation, S_1 represents the average magnitude of the Poynting vector in the incident light (the incident intensity), S_1' is the reflected intensity, and n_1 and n_2 are the refractive indices of the two media. (a) What fraction of the incident intensity is reflected for 589-nm light normally incident on an interface between air and crown glass? (b) Does it matter in part (a) whether the light is in the air or in the glass as it strikes the interface?

48. Refer to Problem 25.47 for its description of the reflected intensity of light normally incident on an interface between two transparent media. (a) For light normally incident on an interface between vacuum and a transparent medium of index n, show that the intensity S_2 of the transmitted light is given by $S_2/S_1 = 4n/(n + 1)^2$. (b) Light travels perpendicularly through a diamond slab, surrounded by air, with parallel surfaces of entry and exit. Apply the transmission fraction in part (a) to find the approximate overall transmission through the slab of diamond, as a percentage. Ignore light reflected back and forth within the slab.

49. This problem builds upon the results of Problems 25.47 and 25.48. Light travels perpendicularly through a diamond slab, surrounded by air, with parallel surfaces of entry and exit. The intensity of the transmitted light is what fraction of the incident intensity? Include the effects of light reflected back and forth inside the slab.

50. Builders use a leveling instrument with the beam from a fixed helium–neon laser reflecting in a horizontal plane from a small, flat mirror mounted on an accurately vertical rotating shaft. The light is sufficiently bright and the rotation rate is sufficiently high that the reflected light appears as a horizontal line wherever it falls on a wall. (a) Assume that the mirror is at the center of a circular grain elevator of radius R. The mirror spins with constant angular speed ω_m. Find the speed of the spot of laser light on the wall. (b) Assume that the spinning mirror is at a perpendicular distance d from point O on a flat vertical wall. When the spot of laser light on the wall is at distance x from point O, what is its speed?

51. The light beam in Figure P25.51 strikes surface 2 at the critical angle. Determine the angle of incidence θ_1.

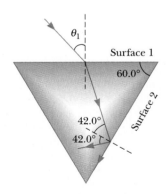

FIGURE **P25.51**

52. Refer to Quick Quiz 25.4. By how much does the duration of an optical day exceed that of a geometric day? Model the Earth's atmosphere as uniform, with index of refraction 1.000 293, a sharply defined upper surface, and depth 8 614 m. Assume that the observer is at the Earth's equator

so that the apparent path of the rising and setting Sun is perpendicular to the horizon.

53. **Physics ⊗Now™** A light ray of wavelength 589 nm is incident at an angle θ on the top surface of a block of polystyrene as shown in Figure P25.53. (a) Find the maximum value of θ for which the refracted ray undergoes total internal reflection at the left vertical face of the block. Repeat the calculation for cases in which the polystyrene block is immersed in (b) water and (c) carbon disulfide.

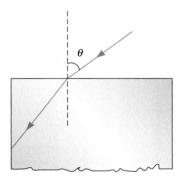

FIGURE **P25.53**

54. A ray of light passes from air into water. For its deviation angle $\delta = |\theta_1 - \theta_2|$ to be 10.0°, what must be its angle of incidence?

55. A shallow glass dish is 4.00 cm wide at the bottom as shown in Figure P25.55. When an observer's eye is placed as shown, the observer sees the edge of the bottom of the empty dish. When this dish is filled with water, the observer sees the center of the bottom of the dish. Find the height of the dish.

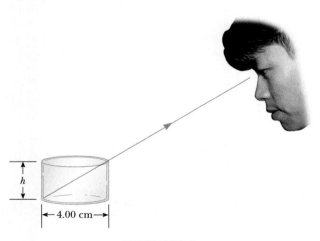

FIGURE **P25.55**

56. A material having an index of refraction n is surrounded by a vacuum and is in the shape of a quarter circle of radius R (Fig. P25.56). A light ray parallel to the base of the material is incident from the left at a distance L above the base and emerges from the material at the angle θ. Determine an expression for θ.

57. A transparent cylinder of radius $R = 2.00$ m has a mirrored surface on its right half as shown in Figure P25.57. A

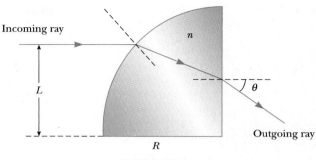

FIGURE **P25.56**

light ray traveling in air is incident on the left side of the cylinder. The incident light ray and exiting light ray are parallel, and $d = 2.00$ m. Determine the index of refraction of the material.

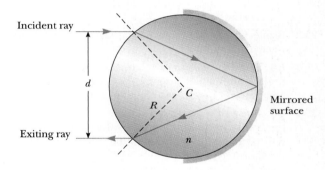

FIGURE **P25.57**

58. 🖥 Students allow a narrow beam of laser light to strike a water surface. They arrange to measure the angle of refraction for selected angles of incidence and record the data shown in the accompanying table. Use the data to verify Snell's law of refraction by plotting the sine of the angle of incidence versus the sine of the angle of refraction. Use the resulting plot to deduce the index of refraction of water.

Angle of Incidence (degrees)	Angle of Refraction (degrees)
10.0	7.5
20.0	15.1
30.0	22.3
40.0	28.7
50.0	35.2
60.0	40.3
70.0	45.3
80.0	47.7

59. A light ray enters a rectangular block of plastic at an angle $\theta_1 = 45.0°$ and emerges at an angle $\theta_2 = 76.0°$ as shown in Figure P25.59. (a) Determine the index of refraction of the plastic. (b) If the light ray enters the plastic at a point $L = 50.0$ cm from the bottom edge, how long does it take the light ray to travel through the plastic?

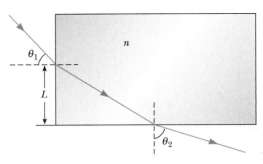

FIGURE **P25.59**

60. **Review problem.** A mirror is often "silvered" with aluminum. By adjusting the thickness of the metallic film, one can make a sheet of glass into a mirror that reflects anything between say 3% and 98% of the incident light, transmitting the rest. Prove that it is impossible to construct a "one-way mirror" that would reflect 90% of the electromagnetic waves incident from one side and reflect 10% of those incident from the other side. (*Suggestion:* Use Clausius's statement of the second law of thermodynamics.)

ANSWERS TO QUICK QUIZZES

25.1 (d). The light rays from the actor's face must reflect from the mirror and into the camera. If these light rays are reversed, light from the camera reflects from the mirror into the actor's eyes.

25.2 Beams ② and ④ are reflected; beams ③ and ⑤ are refracted.

25.3 (c). Because the light is entering a material in which the index of refraction is lower, the speed of light is higher and the light bends away from the normal.

25.4 (a). Due to the refraction of light by air, light rays from the Sun deviate slightly downward toward the surface of the Earth as the light enters the atmosphere. Thus, in the morning, light rays from the upper edge of the Sun arrive at your eyes before the geometric line from your eyes to the top of the Sun clears the horizon. In the evening, light rays from the top of the Sun continue to arrive at your eyes even after the geometric line from your eyes to the top of the Sun dips below the horizon.

25.5 False. There is no dependence of the angle of reflection on wavelength because the light does not enter deeply into the material during reflection; rather, it reflects from the surface. Thus, the properties of the material do not affect the angle of reflection.

25.6 (i), (b). The two bright rays exiting the bottom of the prism on the right in Figure 25.23 result from total internal reflection at the right face of the prism. Note that there is no refracted light exiting the slanted side for these rays. The light from the other three rays is divided into reflected and refracted parts. (ii), (b). Counterclockwise rotation of the prism will cause the rays to strike the slanted side of the prism at a larger angle. When all five rays strike at an angle larger than the critical angle, they will all undergo total internal reflection.

25.7 (c). When the outgoing beam approaches the direction parallel to the straight side, the incident angle is approaching the critical angle for total internal reflection. The index of refraction for light at the violet end of the visible spectrum is larger than that at the red end. Thus, as the outgoing beam approaches the straight side, the violet light experiences total internal reflection first, followed by the other colors. The red light is the last to experience total internal reflection.

CHAPTER 26

Image Formation by Mirrors and Lenses

(© Don Hammond/CORBIS)

The light rays coming from the leaves in the background of this scene did not form a focused image on the film of the camera that took this photograph. Consequently, the background appears very blurry. Light rays passing though the raindrop, however, have been altered so as to form a focused image of the background leaves on the film. In this chapter, we investigate the formation of images as light rays reflect from mirrors and refract through lenses.

This chapter is concerned with the images formed when light interacts with flat and curved surfaces. We find that images of an object can be formed by reflection or by refraction and that mirrors and lenses work because of these phenomena.

Images formed by reflection and refraction are used in a variety of everyday devices, such as the rearview mirror in your car, a shaving or makeup mirror, a camera, your eyeglasses, and a magnifying glass. In addition, more scientific devices, such as telescopes and microscopes, take advantage of the image formation principles discussed in this chapter.

We shall make extensive use of geometric models developed from the principles of reflection and refraction. Such constructions allow us to develop mathematical representations for the image locations of various types of mirrors and lenses.

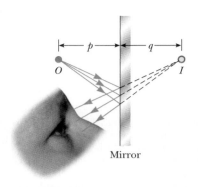

FIGURE 26.1 An image formed by reflection from a flat mirror. The image point I is located behind the mirror at a distance q, which is equal to the object distance p.

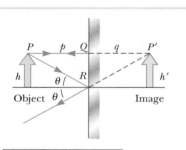

ACTIVE FIGURE 26.2

Geometric construction used to locate the image of an object placed in front of a flat mirror. Because the triangles PQR and $P'QR$ are congruent, $p = |q|$ and $h = h'$.

Physics⊗Now™ Log into Physics-Now at **www.pop4e.com** and go to Active Figure 26.2 to move the object and see the effect on the image.

⊞ PITFALL PREVENTION 26.1

MAGNIFICATION DOES NOT NECESSA-RILY IMPLY ENLARGEMENT For optical elements other than flat mirrors, the magnification defined in Equation 26.1 can result in a number with a magnitude larger *or* smaller than 1. Thus, despite the cultural usage of the word *magnification* to mean *enlargement,* the image could be smaller than the object. We shall see examples of such a situation in this chapter.

26.1 IMAGES FORMED BY FLAT MIRRORS

We begin by considering the simplest possible mirror, the flat mirror. Consider a point source of light[1] placed at O in Figure 26.1, a distance p in front of a flat mirror. The distance p is called the **object distance.** Light rays leave the source and are reflected from the mirror. Upon reflection, the rays continue to diverge (spread apart). The dashed lines in Figure 26.1 are extensions of the diverging rays back to a point of intersection at I. The diverging rays appear to the viewer to come from the point I behind the mirror. Point I is called the **image** of the object at O. Regardless of the system under study, we always locate images by extending diverging rays back to a point at which they intersect.[2] **Images are located either at a point from which rays of light *actually* diverge or at a point from which they *appear* to diverge.** Because the rays in Figure 26.1 appear to originate at I, which is a distance q behind the mirror, that is the location of the image. The distance q is called the **image distance.**

Images are classified as **real** or **virtual. A real image is formed when light rays pass through and diverge from the image point; a virtual image is formed when the light rays do not pass through the image point but only appear to diverge from that point.** The image formed by the mirror in Figure 26.1 is virtual. The image of an object seen in a flat mirror is *always* virtual. Real images can be displayed on a screen (as at a movie), but virtual images cannot be displayed on a screen. We shall see an example of a real image in Section 26.2.

Active Figure 26.2 is an example of a specialized pictorial representation, called a **ray diagram,** that is very useful in studies of mirrors and lenses. In a ray diagram, a small number of the myriad rays leaving a point source are drawn, and the location of the image is found by applying the laws of reflection (and refraction, in the case of refracting surfaces and lenses) to these rays. A carefully drawn ray diagram allows us to build a geometric model so that geometry and trigonometry can be used to solve a problem mathematically.

We can use the simple geometry in Active Figure 26.2 to examine the properties of the images of extended objects formed by flat mirrors. Let us locate the image of the tip of the blue arrow. To find out where the image is formed, it is necessary to follow at least two rays of light as they reflect from the mirror. One of those rays starts at P, follows the horizontal path PQ to the mirror, and reflects back on itself. The second ray follows the oblique path PR and reflects at the same angle according to the law of reflection. We can extend the two reflected rays back to the point from which they appear to diverge, point P'. A continuation of this process for points other than P on the object would result in an image (drawn as a yellow arrow) to the right of the mirror. These rays and the extensions of the rays allow us to build a geometric model for the image formation based on triangles PQR and $P'QR$. Because these two triangles are identical, $PQ = P'Q$, or $p = |q|$. (We use the absolute value notation because, as we shall see shortly, a sign convention is associated with the values of p and q.) Hence, we conclude that **the image formed by an object placed in front of a flat mirror is as far behind the mirror as the object is in front of the mirror.**

Our geometric model also shows that the object height h equals the image height h'. We define the **lateral magnification** (or simply the **magnification**) M of an

---

[1]We imagine the object to be a point source of light. It could actually *be* a point source, such as a very small lightbulb, but more often is a single point on some extended object that is illuminated from the exterior by a light source. Thus, the reflected light leaves the point on the object as if the point were a source of light.

[2]Your eyes and brain interpret diverging light rays as originating at the point from which the rays diverge. Your eye–brain system can detect the rays only *as they enter your eye* and has no access to information about what experiences the rays underwent before reaching your eyes. Thus, even though the light rays did not *actually originate* at point I, they enter the eye *as if they had,* and I is the point at which your brain locates the object.

image as follows:

$$M \equiv \frac{\text{image height}}{\text{object height}} = \frac{h'}{h}$$ [26.1]

▪ **Magnification of an image**

which is a general definition of the magnification for any type of image formed by a mirror or lens. Because $h' = h$ in this case, $M = 1$ for a flat mirror. We also note that the image is **upright** because the image arrow points in the same direction as the object arrow. An upright image is indicated mathematically by a positive value of the magnification. (Later we discuss situations in which *inverted* images, with negative magnifications, are formed.)

Finally, note that a flat mirror produces an image having an *apparent* left–right reversal. This reversal can be seen by standing in front of a mirror and raising your right hand. The image you see raises its left hand. Likewise, your hair appears to be parted on the opposite side, and a mole on your right cheek appears to be on your left cheek.

This reversal is not *actually* a left–right reversal. Imagine, for example, lying on your left side on the floor, with your body parallel to the mirror surface. Now, your head is on the left and your feet are on the right as you face the mirror. If you shake your feet, the image does not shake its head! If you raise your right hand, however, the image raises its left hand. Thus, it again appears like a left–right reversal, but in an up–down direction!

The apparent left–right reversal is actually a *front–back* reversal caused by the light rays going forward toward the mirror and then reflecting back from it. Figure 26.3 shows a person's right hand and its image in a flat mirror. Notice that no left–right reversal takes place; rather, the thumbs on both the real hand and the image are on the left side. It is the front–back reversal that makes the image of the right hand appear similar to the real left hand at the left side of the photograph.

An interesting experience with front–back reversal is to stand in front of a mirror while holding an overhead transparency in front of you so that you can read the writing on the transparency. You are also able to read the writing on the image of the transparency. You might have had a similar experience if you have a transparent decal with words on it on the rear window of your car. If the decal is placed so that it can be read from outside the car, you can also read it when looking into your rearview mirror from the front seat.

(George Sample)

FIGURE **26.3**   The image in the mirror of a person's right hand is reversed front to back, which makes the image in the mirror appear to be a left hand. Notice that the thumb is on the left side of both real hands and on the left side of the image. That the thumb is not on the right side of the image indicates that the reversal is not left–right.

QUICK QUIZ **26.1**   In the overhead view of Figure 26.4, the image of the stone seen by observer 1 is at *C*. At which of the five points *A*, *B*, *C*, *D*, or *E* does observer 2 see the image?

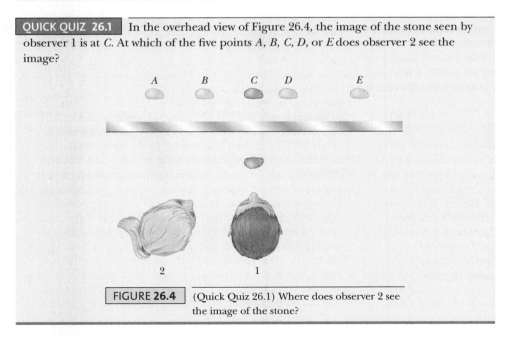

FIGURE **26.4**   (Quick Quiz 26.1) Where does observer 2 see the image of the stone?

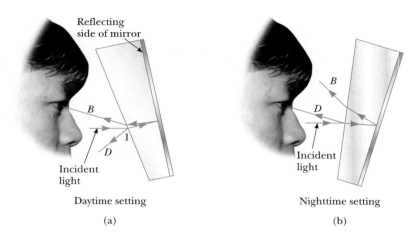

FIGURE **26.5** | (Thinking Physics
26.1) (a) Daytime and (b) nighttime
settings of a rearview mirror in an automobile.

Daytime setting

(a)

Nighttime setting

(b)

▪ Thinking Physics 26.1

Most rearview mirrors on cars have a day setting and a night setting. The night setting greatly diminishes the intensity of the image so that lights from trailing vehicles do not blind the driver. How does such a mirror work?

Reasoning Figure 26.5 represents a cross-sectional view of the mirror for the two
settings. The mirror is a wedge of glass with a reflecting surface on the back side.
When the mirror is in the day setting, as in Figure 26.5a, the light from an object
behind the car strikes the mirror at point 1. Most of the light enters the wedge, is
refracted, and reflects from the back surface to return to the front surface, where it
is refracted again as it re-enters the air as ray *B* (for *bright*). In addition, a small portion of the light is reflected at the front surface as indicated by ray *D* (for *dim*). This
dim reflected light is responsible for the image observed when the mirror is in the
night setting, as in Figure 26.5b. In this case, the wedge is rotated so that the path
followed by the bright light (ray *B*) does not lead to the eye. Instead, the dim light
reflected from the front surface travels to the eye, and the brightness of trailing
headlights does not become a hazard. ▪

QUICK QUIZ 26.2 You are standing about 2 m away from a mirror. The mirror has water
spots on its surface. True or false: It is possible for you to see the water spots and your
image both in focus at the same time.

EXAMPLE **26.1** | **Multiple Images Formed by Two Mirrors**

Two flat mirrors are perpendicular to each other as
in Figure 26.6, and an object is placed at point *O*. In
this situation, multiple images are formed. Locate the
positions of these images.

Solution The image of the object is at I_1 in
mirror 1 and at I_2 in mirror 2. In addition, a third
image is formed at I_3, which is the image of I_1 in
mirror 2 or, equivalently, the image of I_2 in
mirror 1. That is, the image at I_1 (or I_2) serves
as the object for I_3. Note that to form this image
at I_3, the rays reflect twice after leaving the object
at *O*.

FIGURE **26.6** | (Example 26.1)
When an object is placed in front
of two mutually perpendicular
mirrors as shown, three images are
formed.

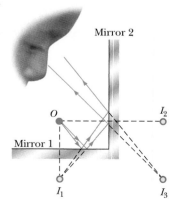

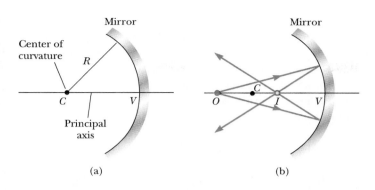

(a)   (b)

FIGURE 26.7 (a) A concave mirror of radius R. The center of curvature C is located on the principal axis. (b) A point source of light placed at O in front of a concave spherical mirror of radius R, where O is any point on the principal axis farther than R from the mirror surface, forms a real image at I. If the rays diverge from O at small angles, they all reflect through the same image point.

26.2 IMAGES FORMED BY SPHERICAL MIRRORS

In Section 26.1, we investigated images formed by a flat reflecting surface. In this section, we will explore images formed by curved mirrors, either from a concave surface of the mirror or a convex surface.

Concave Mirrors

A **spherical mirror,** as its name implies, has the shape of a segment of a sphere. Figure 26.7a shows the cross-section of a spherical mirror with its reflecting surface represented by the solid curved line. Such a mirror in which light is reflected from the inner, concave surface is called a **concave mirror.** The mirror's radius of curvature is R, and its center of curvature is at point C. Point V is the center of the spherical segment, and a line drawn from C to V is called the **principal axis** of the mirror.

Now consider a point source of light placed at point O in Figure 26.7b, on the principal axis and outside point C. Two diverging rays that originate at O are shown. After reflecting from the mirror, these rays converge and meet at I, the image point. They then continue to diverge from I as if a source of light existed there. Therefore, if your eyes detect the rays diverging from point I, you would claim that a light source is located at that point.

This example is the second one we have seen of rays diverging from an image point. Because the light rays pass through the image point in this case, unlike the situation in Active Figure 26.2, the image in Figure 26.7b is a real image.

In what follows, we shall adopt a simplification model that assumes that all rays diverging from an object make small angles with the principal axis. Such rays, called **paraxial rays,** always reflect through the image point as in Figure 26.7b. Rays that make large angles with the principal axis as in Figure 26.8 converge at other points on the principal axis, producing a blurred image.

We can use a geometric model based on the ray diagram in Figure 26.9 to calculate the image distance q if we know the object distance p and radius of curvature R. By convention, these distances are measured from point V. Figure 26.9 shows two of the many light rays leaving the tip of the object. One ray passes through the center of curvature C of the mirror, hitting the mirror perpendicular to the mirror surface and

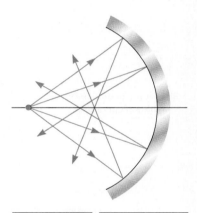

FIGURE 26.8 Rays diverging from an object at large angles from the principal axis reflect from a spherical concave mirror to intersect the principal axis at different points, resulting in a blurred image.

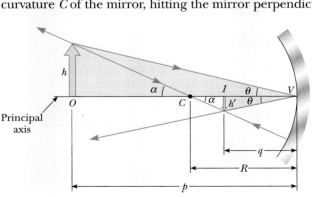

FIGURE 26.9 The image formed by a spherical concave mirror when the object O lies outside the center of curvature C. This geometric construction is used to derive Equation 26.4.

reflecting back on itself. The second ray strikes the mirror at the center point V and reflects as shown, obeying the law of reflection. The image of the tip of the arrow is at the point at which these two reflected rays intersect. Using these rays, we identify the gold and blue model right triangles in Figure 26.9. From the gold triangle, we see that $\tan\theta = h/p$, whereas the blue triangle gives $\tan\theta = -h'/q$. The negative sign signifies that the image is inverted, so h' is a negative number. Therefore, from Equation 26.1 and these results, we find that the magnification of the image is

$$M = \frac{h'}{h} = \frac{-q\tan\theta}{p\tan\theta} = -\frac{q}{p} \qquad [26.2]$$

We can identify two additional right triangles in the figure, with a common point at C and with angle α. These triangles tell us that

$$\tan\alpha = \frac{h}{p - R} \qquad \text{and} \qquad \tan\alpha = -\frac{h'}{R - q}$$

from which we find that

$$\frac{h'}{h} = -\frac{R - q}{p - R} \qquad [26.3]$$

If we compare Equations 26.2 and 26.3, we see that

$$\frac{R - q}{p - R} = \frac{q}{p}$$

Algebra reduces this expression to

> ∎ Mirror equation in terms of the radius of curvature

$$\frac{1}{p} + \frac{1}{q} = \frac{2}{R} \qquad [26.4]$$

which is called the **mirror equation.** It is applicable only to the paraxial ray simplification model.

If the object is very far from the mirror — that is, if the object distance p is large compared with R, so that p can be said to approach infinity — $1/p \rightarrow 0$, and we see from Equation 26.4 that $q \approx R/2$. In other words, **when the object is very far from the mirror, the image point is halfway between the center of curvature and the center of the mirror** as in Figure 26.10a. The rays are essentially parallel in this figure because only those few rays traveling parallel to the axis from the distant object encounter the mirror. Rays not parallel to the axis miss the mirror. Figure 26.10b shows an experimental setup of this situation, demonstrating the crossing of the light rays at a single point. The point at which the parallel rays intersect after reflecting from the mirror is called the **focal point** of the mirror. The focal point is a

FIGURE 26.10 (a) Light rays from a distant object ($p \approx \infty$) reflect from a concave mirror through the focal point F. In this case, the image distance $q \approx R/2 = f$, where f is the focal length of the mirror. (b) Reflection of parallel rays from a concave mirror.

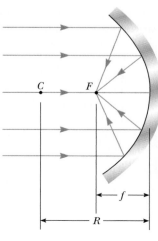

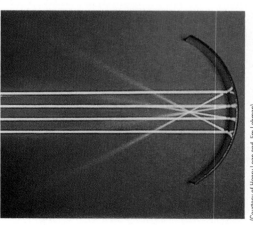

(Courtesy of Henry Leap and Jim Lehman)

(a)   (b)

distance f from the mirror, called the **focal length.** The focal length is a parameter associated with the mirror and is given by

$$f = \frac{R}{2} \qquad [26.5]$$

■ Focal length of a mirror

The mirror equation can therefore be expressed in terms of the focal length:

$$\frac{1}{p} + \frac{1}{q} = \frac{1}{f} \qquad [26.6]$$

■ Mirror equation in terms of focal length

This equation is the commonly used mirror equation, in terms of the focal length of the mirror rather than its radius of curvature, as in Equation 26.4. We shall see how to use this equation in examples that follow shortly.

Convex Mirrors

Figure 26.11 shows the formation of an image by a **convex mirror,** a mirror that is silvered so that light is reflected from the outer, convex surface. Convex mirrors are sometimes called **diverging mirrors** because the rays from any point on an object diverge after reflection as though they were coming from some point behind the mirror. The image in Figure 26.11 is virtual rather than real because it lies behind the mirror at the point from which the reflected rays appear to diverge. In general, as shown in the figure, the image formed by a convex mirror is always upright, virtual, and smaller than the object.

We can set up a geometric model for a convex mirror using the ray diagram in Figure 26.11. The equations developed for concave mirrors can also be used with convex mirrors if we adhere to a particular sign convention. Let us refer to the region in which light rays move as the *front side* of the mirror and the other side, where virtual images are formed, as the *back side.* For example, in Figures 26.9 and 26.11, the side to the left of the mirror is the front side and that to the right of the mirror is the back side. Table 26.1 summarizes the sign conventions for all the necessary quantities. Notice in particular that we handle a convex mirror by assigning it a negative focal length. With this convention, the mirror equation for a convex mirror is the same as that for a concave mirror, Equation 26.6.

One entry in Table 26.1 that may appear strange is a "virtual object." A virtual object will only occur in some situations when combining two or more optical elements as we shall see in Section 26.4.

Constructing Ray Diagrams for Mirrors

We have been using the specialized pictorial representations called ray diagrams to help us locate images for flat and curved mirrors. Let us now formalize the procedure for drawing accurate ray diagrams. To construct such a diagram, we must know the position of the object and the locations of the focal point and center of

(Courtesy of Thomson Consumer Electronics).

PITFALL PREVENTION 26.2

THE *FOCAL* **POINT IS NOT THE** *FOCUS* **POINT** The focal point *is usually not* the point at which the light rays focus to form an image. The focal point is determined solely by the curvature of the mirror; it does not depend on the location of the object at all. In general, an image forms at a point different from the focal point of a mirror (or a lens). The *only* exception is when the object is located infinitely far away from the mirror.

A satellite-dish antenna is a concave reflector for television signals from a satellite in orbit around the Earth. The signals are carried by microwaves that, because the satellite is so far away, are parallel when they arrive at the dish. These waves reflect from the dish and are focused on the receiver at the focal point of the dish. ■

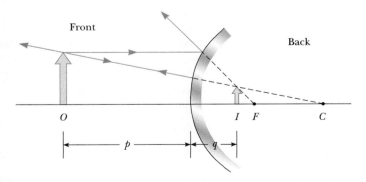

FIGURE 26.11 Formation of an image by a spherical convex mirror. The image formed by the real object is virtual and upright.

TABLE 26.1	Sign Conventions for Mirrors	
Quantity	Positive when . . .	Negative when . . .
Object location (p)	object is in front of mirror (real object).	object is in back of mirror (virtual object).
Image location (q)	image is in front of mirror (real image).	image is in back of mirror (virtual image).
Image height (h')	image is upright.	image is inverted.
Focal length (f) and radius (R)	mirror is concave.	mirror is convex.
Magnification (M)	image is upright.	image is inverted.

curvature of the mirror. We will construct three rays in the examples shown in Active Figure 26.12. Only two rays are necessary to locate the image, but we will include a third as a check. In each part of the figure, the right-hand portion shows a photograph of the situation described by the ray diagram in the left-hand portion. All three rays start from the same object point; in these examples, the top of the arrow is chosen as the starting point. For the concave mirrors in Active Figure 26.12a and 26.12b, the rays are drawn as follows:

- Ray 1 is drawn parallel to the principal axis and is reflected back through the focal point F. (This ray would be a light path followed by light from an object infinitely far from the mirror.)
- Ray 2 is drawn through the focal point (or as if coming from the focal point if $p < f$ as in Active Fig. 26.12b). It is reflected parallel to the principal axis. (This ray would be a light path followed by light from an object at the focal point and is the reverse of a ray approaching the mirror from an object infinitely far away.)
- Ray 3 is drawn through the center of curvature C and is reflected back on itself. (This ray follows the law of reflection for light incident along the normal to the surface.)

The image point obtained in this fashion must always agree with the value of q calculated from the mirror equation. With concave mirrors, note what happens as the object is moved closer to the mirror from infinity. The real, inverted image in Active Figure 26.12a moves to the left as the object approaches the mirror. When the object is at the center of curvature, the object and image are at the same distance from the mirror and are the same size. When the object is at the focal point, the image is infinitely far to the left. (Check these last three sentences with the mirror equation!)

When the object lies between the focal point and the mirror surface as in Active Figure 26.12b, the image is virtual, upright, and located on the back side of the mirror. The image is also larger than the object in this case. This situation illustrates the principle behind a shaving mirror or a makeup mirror. Your face is located closer to the concave mirror than the focal point, so you see an enlarged, upright image of your face, to assist you with shaving or applying makeup. If you have such a mirror, look into it and move your face farther from the mirror. Your head will pass through a point at which the image is indistinct and then the image will reappear with your face upside down as you continue to move farther away. The region where the image is indistinct is where your head passes through the focal point and the image is infinitely far away.

Notice that the image of the camera in Active Figures 26.12a and 26.12b is upside down. Regardless of the position of the candle, the camera remains farther away from the mirror than the focal point, so its image is inverted.

For a convex mirror as shown in Active Figure 26.12c, the rays are drawn as follows:

- Ray 1 is drawn parallel to the principal axis and is reflected as if coming from the focal point F.
- Ray 2 is drawn heading toward the focal point on the back side of the mirror. It is reflected parallel to the principal axis.
- Ray 3 is drawn heading toward the center of curvature C on the back side of the mirror and is reflected back on itself.

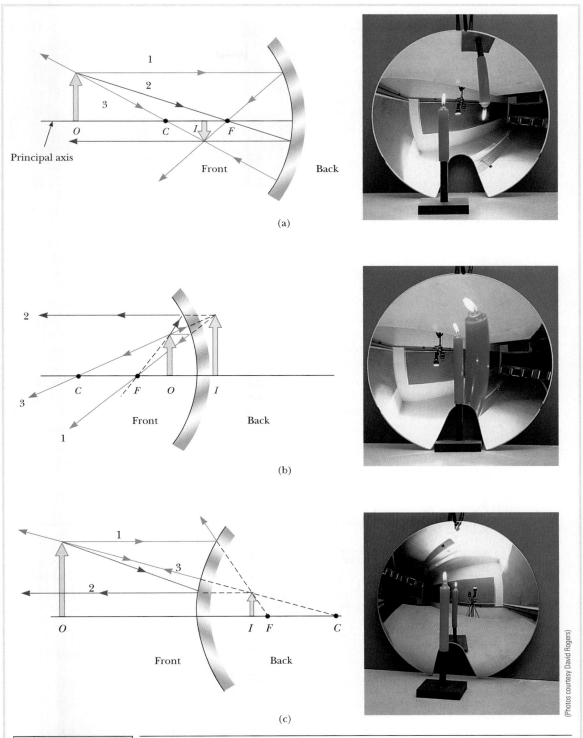

ACTIVE FIGURE 26.12 | Ray diagrams for spherical mirrors, along with corresponding photographs of the images of a candle as the object. (a) When the object is located so that the focal point lies between the object and a concave mirror surface, the image is real and inverted. (b) When the object is located between the focal point and a concave mirror surface, the image is virtual, upright, and enlarged. (c) When the object is in front of a spherical convex mirror, the image is virtual, upright, and reduced in size.

(Photos courtesy David Rogers)

Physics⊗Now™ Log into PhysicsNow at **www.pop4e.com** and go to Active Figure 26.12 to move the objects and change the focal lengths of the mirrors to see the effect on the images.

FIGURE **26.13** An approaching truck is seen in a convex mirror on the right side of an automobile. Because the image is reduced in size, the truck appears to be farther away than it actually is. Notice also that the image of the truck is in focus but that the frame of the mirror is not, which demonstrates that the image is not at the same location as the mirror surface.

(© Bo Zaunders/CORBIS)

The image of a real object in a convex mirror is always virtual and upright. Notice that the images of both the candle and the camera in Active Figure 26.12c are upright. As the object distance increases, the virtual image becomes smaller and approaches the focal point as p approaches infinity. You should construct other diagrams to verify how the image position varies with object position.

Convex mirrors are often used as security devices in large stores, where they are hung at a high position on the wall. The large field of view of the store is made smaller by the convex mirror so that store personnel can observe possible shoplifting activity in several aisles at once. Mirrors on the passenger side of automobiles are also often made with a convex surface. This type of mirror allows a wider field of view behind the automobile to be available to the driver (Fig. 26.13) than is the case with a flat mirror. These mirrors introduce a perceptual distortion, however, in that they cause cars behind the viewer to appear smaller and therefore farther away. That is why these mirrors carry the inscription, "Objects in this mirror are closer than they appear."

QUICK QUIZ 26.3 You wish to reflect sunlight from a mirror onto some paper under a pile of wood to start a fire. Which would be the best choice for the type of mirror? **(a)** flat **(b)** concave **(c)** convex

QUICK QUIZ 26.4 Consider the image in the mirror in Figure 26.14. Based on the appearance of this image, what conclusion would you make? **(a)** The mirror is concave and the image is real. **(b)** The mirror is concave and the image is virtual. **(c)** The mirror is convex and the image is real. **(d)** The mirror is convex and the image is virtual.

FIGURE **26.14** (Quick Quiz 26.4) What type of mirror is this one?

(NASA)

INTERACTIVE   EXAMPLE 26.2   **The Image Formed by a Concave Mirror**

A concave spherical mirror has a focal length of 10.0 cm.

A Find the location of the image for an object distance of 25.0 cm and describe the image.

Solution For an object distance of 25.0 cm, we find the image distance using the mirror equation:

$$\frac{1}{p} + \frac{1}{q} = \frac{1}{f}$$

$$\frac{1}{25.0 \text{ cm}} + \frac{1}{q} = \frac{1}{10.0 \text{ cm}}$$

$$q = \boxed{16.7 \text{ cm}}$$

The magnification is given by Equation 26.2:

$$M = -\frac{q}{p} = -\frac{16.7 \text{ cm}}{25.0 \text{ cm}} = -0.668$$

The magnitude of M less than unity tells us that the image is smaller than the object. The negative sign for M tells us that the image is inverted. Finally, because q is positive, the image is located on the front side of the mirror and is real. This situation is pictured in Active Figure 26.12a.

B Find the location of the image for an object distance of 10.0 cm and describe the image.

Solution When the object distance is 10.0 cm, the object is located at the focal point. Substituting the values $p = 10.0$ cm and $f = 10.0$ cm into the mirror equation, we find that

$$\frac{1}{10.0 \text{ cm}} + \frac{1}{q} = \frac{1}{10.0 \text{ cm}}$$

$$q = \boxed{\infty}$$

Thus, we see that light rays originating from an object located at the focal point of a mirror are reflected so that the image is formed at an infinite distance from the mirror; that is, the rays travel parallel to one another after reflection.

C Find the location of the image for an object distance of 5.00 cm and describe the image.

Solution When the object is at the position $p = 5.00$ cm, it lies between the focal point and the mirror surface. In this case, the mirror equation gives

$$\frac{1}{5.00 \text{ cm}} + \frac{1}{q} = \frac{1}{10.0 \text{ cm}}$$

$$q = \boxed{-10.0 \text{ cm}}$$

The negative value for q tells us the image is virtual and located on the back side of the mirror. The magnification is

$$M = -\frac{q}{p} = -\left(\frac{-10.0 \text{ cm}}{5.00 \text{ cm}}\right) = 2.00$$

From this value, we see that the image is larger than the object by a factor of 2.00. The positive sign for M indicates that the image is upright (see Active Fig. 26.12b).

Note the characteristics of the images formed by a concave spherical mirror. When the object is farther from the mirror than the focal point, the image is inverted and real; with the object at the focal point, the image is formed at infinity; with the object between the focal point and mirror surface, the image is upright and virtual.

Physics⊗Now™ Investigate the image formed for various object positions and mirror focal lengths by logging into PhysicsNow at **www.pop4e.com** and going to Interactive Example 26.2.

INTERACTIVE   EXAMPLE 26.3   **The Image Formed by a Convex Mirror**

An object 3.00 cm high is placed 20.0 cm from a convex mirror having a focal length of 8.00 cm.

A Find the position of the final image.

Solution Because the mirror is convex, its focal length is negative. To find the image position, we use the mirror equation:

$$\frac{1}{p} + \frac{1}{q} = \frac{1}{f} = \frac{1}{-8.00 \text{ cm}}$$

$$\frac{1}{q} = -\frac{1}{8.00 \text{ cm}} - \frac{1}{20.0 \text{ cm}}$$

$$q = \boxed{-5.71 \text{ cm}}$$

The negative value of q indicates that the image is virtual, or behind the mirror, as in Active Figure 26.12c.

B Find the height of the image.

Solution The magnification is

$$M = -\frac{q}{p} = -\left(\frac{-5.71 \text{ cm}}{20.0 \text{ cm}}\right) = 0.286$$

The image is upright because M is positive. Its height is

$$h' = Mh = (0.286)(3.00 \text{ cm}) = \boxed{0.858 \text{ cm}}$$

Physics⊗Now™ Investigate the image formed for various object positions and mirror focal lengths by logging into PhysicsNow at **www.pop4e.com** and going to Interactive Example 26.3.

26.3 IMAGES FORMED BY REFRACTION

In this section, we describe how images are formed by the refraction of rays at the surface of a transparent material. We shall apply the law of refraction and use the simplification model in which we consider only paraxial rays.

Consider two transparent media with indices of refraction n_1 and n_2, where the boundary between the two media is a spherical surface with radius of curvature R (Fig. 26.15). We shall assume that the object at point O is in the medium with index of refraction n_1. As we shall see, all paraxial rays are refracted at the spherical surface and converge to a single point I, the image point.

Let us proceed by considering the geometric construction in Figure 26.16, which shows a single ray leaving point O and passing through point I. Snell's law applied to this refracted ray gives

$$n_1 \sin \theta_1 = n_2 \sin \theta_2$$

Because the angles θ_1 and θ_2 are small for paraxial rays, we can use the approximation $\sin \theta \approx \theta$ (angles in radians). Therefore, Snell's law becomes

$$n_1 \theta_1 = n_2 \theta_2$$

Now we make use of geometric model triangles and recall that an exterior angle of any triangle equals the sum of the two opposite interior angles. Applying this rule to the triangles OPC and PIC in Figure 26.16 gives

$$\theta_1 = \alpha + \beta$$

$$\beta = \theta_2 + \gamma$$

If we combine the last three equations and eliminate θ_1 and θ_2, we find that

$$n_1 \alpha + n_2 \gamma = (n_2 - n_1)\beta \qquad [26.7]$$

In the small angle approximation, $\tan \theta \approx \theta$, and so from Figure 26.16 we can write the approximate relations

$$\tan \alpha \approx \alpha \approx \frac{d}{p} \qquad \tan \beta \approx \beta \approx \frac{d}{R} \qquad \tan \gamma \approx \gamma \approx \frac{d}{q}$$

where d is the distance shown in Figure 26.16. We substitute these equations into Equation 26.7 and divide through by d to give

$$\frac{n_1}{p} + \frac{n_2}{q} = \frac{n_2 - n_1}{R} \qquad [26.8]$$

❚ Images formed by a refracting surface

Because this expression does not involve any angles, all paraxial rays leaving an object at distance p from the refracting surface will be focused at the same distance q from the surface on the back side.

By setting up a geometric construction with an object and a refracting surface, we can show that the magnification of an image due to a refracting surface is

FIGURE 26.15 An image formed by refraction at a spherical surface. Rays making small angles with the principal axis diverge from a point object at O and are refracted through the image point I.

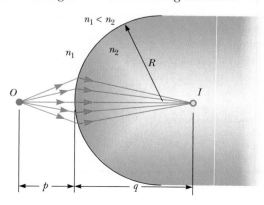

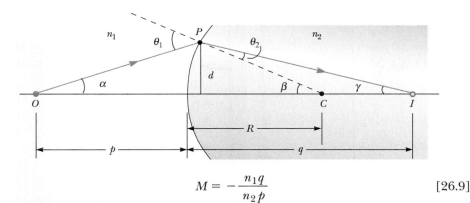

FIGURE 26.16 Geometry used to derive Equation 26.8, assuming that $n_1 < n_2$.

$$M = -\frac{n_1 q}{n_2 p} \qquad [26.9]$$

▪ **Magnification of an image formed by a refracting surface**

As with mirrors, we must use a sign convention if we are to apply Equations 26.8 and 26.9 to a variety of circumstances. Note that real images are formed on the side of the surface that is *opposite* the side from which the light comes. That is in contrast to mirrors, for which real images are formed on the side where the light originates. Therefore, **the sign conventions for spherical refracting surfaces are similar to the conventions for mirrors, recognizing the change in sides of the surface for real and virtual images.** For example, in Figure 26.16, p, q, and R are all positive.

The sign conventions for spherical refracting surfaces are summarized in Table 26.2. The same conventions will be used for thin lenses discussed in the next section. As with mirrors, we assume that the front of the refracting surface is the side from which the light approaches the surface.

Flat Refracting Surfaces

If the refracting surface is flat, R approaches infinity and Equation 26.8 reduces to

$$\frac{n_1}{p} = -\frac{n_2}{q}$$

or

$$q = -\frac{n_2}{n_1} p \qquad [26.10]$$

From Equation 26.10, we see that the sign of q is opposite that of p. Thus, **the image formed by a flat refracting surface is on the same side of the surface as the object.** This situation is illustrated in Active Figure 26.17 for the case in which n_1 is greater than n_2, where a virtual image is formed between the object and the surface. Note that the refracted ray bends *away* from the normal in this case because $n_1 > n_2$.

The value of q given by Equation 26.10 is always smaller in magnitude than p when $n_1 > n_2$. This fact indicates that the image of an object located within a material with higher index of refraction than that of the material from which it is viewed is always closer to the flat refracting surface than the object. Thus, transparent bodies of water such as streams and swimming pools always appear shallower than they are because the image of the bottom of the body of water is closer to the surface than the bottom is in reality.

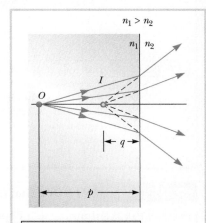

ACTIVE FIGURE 26.17

The image formed by a flat refracting surface is virtual; that is, it forms on the same side of the refracting surface as the object. All rays are assumed to be paraxial.

Physics⊗Now™ Log into PhysicsNow at **www.pop4e.com** and go to Active Figure 26.17 to move the object and see the effect on the location of the image.

TABLE **26.2**	Sign Conventions for Refracting Surfaces	
Quantity	**Positive when . . .**	**Negative when . . .**
Object location (p)	object is in front of surface (real object).	object is in back of surface (virtual object).
Image location (q)	image is in back of surface (real image).	image is in front of surface (virtual image).
Image height (h')	image is upright.	image is inverted.
Radius (R)	center of curvature is in back of surface.	center of curvature is in front of surface.

EXAMPLE 26.4 Gaze into the Crystal Ball

A set of coins is embedded in a spherical plastic paperweight having a radius of 3.0 cm. The index of refraction of the plastic is $n_1 = 1.50$. One coin is located 2.0 cm from the edge of the sphere (Fig. 26.18).

A Find the position of the coin's image.

Solution Because $n_1 > n_2$, where $n_2 = 1.00$ is the index of refraction for air, the rays originating from the coin are refracted away from the normal at the surface

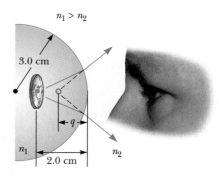

$n_1 > n_2$

3.0 cm

n_1

q

n_2

2.0 cm

FIGURE 26.18 (Example 26.4) Light rays from a coin embedded in a plastic sphere form a virtual image between the surface of the object and the sphere surface. Because the object is inside the sphere, the front of the refracting surface is the *interior* of the sphere.

and diverge outward. Hence, the image is formed inside the paperweight and is virtual. Applying Equation 26.8, we have

$$\frac{n_1}{p} + \frac{n_2}{q} = \frac{n_2 - n_1}{R}$$

$$\frac{1.50}{2.0 \text{ cm}} + \frac{1.00}{q} = \frac{1.00 - 1.50}{-3.0 \text{ cm}}$$

where the radius of curvature is indicated as negative because the center of curvature is in front of the concave surface (see Table 26.2). Solving for q gives

$$q = \boxed{-1.7 \text{ cm}}$$

The negative sign indicates that the image is in the same medium as the object (the side of the incident light), in agreement with our ray diagram. Because the light rays do not pass through the image point, the image is virtual. The coin appears to be closer to the paperweight surface than it actually is.

B What is the magnification of the image?

Solution Using Equation 26.9, we have

$$M = -\frac{n_1 q}{n_2 p} = -\frac{(1.50)(-1.7 \text{ cm})}{(1.00)(2.0 \text{ cm})} = \boxed{1.28}$$

Thus, the image is 28% larger than the actual object.

EXAMPLE 26.5 The One That Got Away

A small fish is swimming at a depth d below the surface of a pond (Fig. 26.19).

A What is the apparent depth of the fish as viewed from directly overhead?

Solution In this example, the refracting surface is flat, so R is infinite. Therefore, we can use Equation 26.10 to

FIGURE 26.19 (Example 26.5) (a) The apparent depth q of the fish is less than the true depth d. All rays are assumed to be paraxial. (b) Your face appears to the fish to be higher above the surface than it is.

determine the location of the image. Using that $n_1 = 1.33$ for water and $p = d$ gives

$$q = -\frac{n_2}{n_1} p = -\frac{1.00}{1.33} d = \boxed{-0.752d}$$

Again, because q is negative, the image is virtual as indicated in Figure 26.19a. The apparent depth is approximately three-fourths the actual depth.

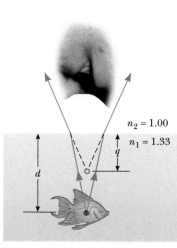

$n_2 = 1.00$
$n_1 = 1.33$
d
q

(a)

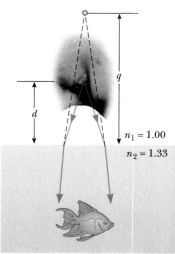

$n_1 = 1.00$
$n_2 = 1.33$
d
q

(b)

B If your face is a distance d above the water surface, at what apparent distance above the surface does the fish see your face?

Solution The light rays from your face are shown in Figure 26.19b. Because the rays refract toward the normal, your face will appear higher above the surface than it actually is. Using Equation 26.10,

$$q = -\frac{n_2}{n_1}p = -\frac{1.33}{1.00}d = -1.33d$$

The negative sign indicates that the image is in the medium from which the light originated, which is the air above the water.

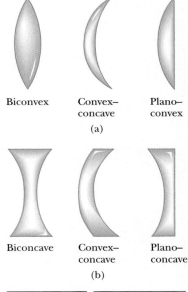

Biconvex Convex–concave Plano–convex

(a)

Biconcave Convex–concave Plano–concave

(b)

FIGURE 26.20 Cross sectional shapes of various lenses. (a) Converging lenses have a positive focal length and are thickest at the middle. (b) Diverging lenses have a negative focal length and are thickest at the edges.

26.4 THIN LENSES

A typical **thin lens** consists of a piece of glass or plastic, ground so that its two surfaces are either segments of spheres or planes. Lenses are commonly used in optical instruments such as cameras, telescopes, and microscopes to form images by refraction.

Figure 26.20 shows some representative shapes of lenses. These lenses have been placed in two groups. Those in Figure 26.20a are thicker at the center than at the rim, and those in Figure 26.20b are thinner at the center than at the rim. The lenses in the first group are examples of **converging lenses,** and those in the second group are called **diverging lenses.** The reason for these names will become apparent shortly.

As with mirrors, it is convenient to define a point called the **focal point** for a lens. For example, in Figure 26.21a, a group of rays parallel to the principal axis passes through the focal point after being converged by the lens. The distance from the focal point to the lens is again called the **focal length** f. **The focal length is the image distance that corresponds to an infinite object distance.**

To avoid the complications arising from the thickness of the lens, we adopt a simplification model called the **thin lens approximation, in which the thickness of the lens is assumed to be negligible.** As a result, it makes no difference whether we take the focal length to be the distance from the focal point to the surface of the lens or from the focal point to the center of the lens because the difference in

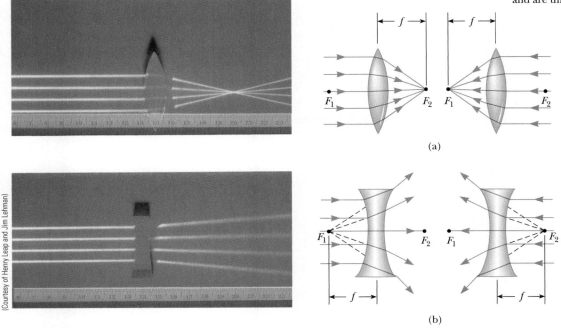

(a)

(b)

FIGURE 26.21 (*Left*) Effects of a converging lens (*top*) and a diverging lens (*bottom*) on parallel rays. (*Right*) Light rays passing through (a) a converging lens and (b) a diverging lens. The focal length is the same for light rays passing through a given lens in either direction. Both focal points F_1 and F_2 are the same distance from the lens.

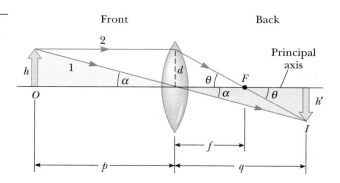

FIGURE **26.22** A geometric construction for developing the thin lens equation.

these two lengths is assumed to be negligible. (We will draw lenses in the diagrams with a thickness so that they can be seen.) A thin lens has one focal length and *two* focal points as illustrated in Figure 26.21, corresponding to parallel light rays traveling from the left or right.

Rays parallel to the axis diverge after passing through a lens of the shape shown in Figure 26.21b. In this case, the focal point is defined as the point from which the diverging rays appear to originate, as in Figure 26.21b. Figures 26.21a and 26.21b indicate why the names *converging* and *diverging* are applied to these lenses in Figure 26.20.

Consider now the ray diagram in Figure 26.22. Ray 1 passes through the center of the lens. Ray 2 is parallel to the principal axis of the lens (the horizontal axis passing through the center of the lens), and as a result it passes through the focal point *F* after refraction. The point at which these two rays intersect is the image point.

The tangent of the angle α can be found by using the blue and gold geometric model triangles in Figure 26.22:

$$\tan \alpha = \frac{h}{p} \quad \text{and} \quad \tan \alpha = -\frac{h'}{q}$$

from which

$$M = \frac{h'}{h} = -\frac{q}{p} \tag{26.11}$$

Thus, the equation for magnification of an image by a lens is the same as the equation for magnification due to a mirror (Eq. 26.2). We also note from Figure 26.22 that

$$\tan \theta = \frac{d}{f} \quad \text{and} \quad \tan \theta = -\frac{h'}{q - f}$$

The height *d*, however, is the same as *h*. Therefore,

$$\frac{h}{f} = -\frac{h'}{q - f}$$

$$\frac{h'}{h} = -\frac{q - f}{f}$$

Using this expression in combination with Equation 26.11 gives us

$$\frac{q}{p} = \frac{q - f}{f}$$

which reduces to

■ Thin lens equation

$$\frac{1}{p} + \frac{1}{q} = \frac{1}{f} \tag{26.12}$$

TABLE **26.3**	Sign Conventions for Thin Lenses	
Quantity	Positive when . . .	Negative when . . .
Object location (p)	object is in front of lens (real object).	object is in back of lens (virtual object).
Image location (q)	image is in back of lens (real image).	image is in front of lens (virtual image).
Image height (h')	image is upright.	image is inverted.
R_1 and R_2	center of curvature is in back of lens.	center of curvature is in front of lens.
Focal length (f)	a converging lens.	a diverging lens.

This equation, called the **thin lens equation** (which is identical to the mirror equation, Eq. 26.6), can be used with either converging or diverging lenses if we adhere to a set of sign conventions. Figure 26.23 is useful for obtaining the signs of p and q. (As with mirrors, we call the side from which the light approaches the *front* of the lens.) The complete sign conventions for lenses are provided in Table 26.3. Note that **a converging lens has a positive focal length** under this convention and **a diverging lens has a negative focal length.** Hence, the names *positive* and *negative* are often given to these lenses.

The focal length for a lens in air is related to the curvatures of its surfaces and to the index of refraction n of the lens material by

$$\frac{1}{f} = (n - 1)\left(\frac{1}{R_1} - \frac{1}{R_2}\right) \qquad [26.13]$$

where R_1 is the radius of curvature of the front surface and R_2 is the radius of curvature of the back surface. Equation 26.13 enables us to calculate the focal length from the known properties of the lens. It is called the **lens makers' equation.** Table 26.3 includes the sign conventions for determining the signs of the radii R_1 and R_2.

Ray Diagrams for Thin Lenses

Our specialized pictorial representations called ray diagrams are very convenient for locating the image of a thin lens or system of lenses. They should also help clarify the sign conventions we have already discussed. Active Figure 26.24 illustrates this method for three single-lens situations. To locate the image of a converging lens (Active Figs. 26.24a and 26.24b), the following three rays are drawn from the top of the object:

• Ray 1 is drawn parallel to the principal axis. After being refracted by the lens, this ray passes through the focal point on the back side of the lens.
• Ray 2 is drawn through the center of the lens and continues in a straight line.
• Ray 3 is drawn through the focal point on the front side of the lens (or as if coming from the focal point if $p < f$, as in Active Fig. 26.24b) and emerges from the lens parallel to the principal axis.

To locate the image of a diverging lens (Active Fig. 26.24c), the following three rays are drawn from the top of the object:

• Ray 1 is drawn parallel to the principal axis. After being refracted by the lens, this ray emerges directed away from the focal point on the front side of the lens.
• Ray 2 is drawn through the center of the lens and continues in a straight line.
• Ray 3 is drawn in the direction toward the focal point on the back side of the lens and emerges from the lens parallel to the principal axis.

In these ray diagrams, the point of intersection of *any two* of the rays can be used to locate the image. The third ray serves as a check of construction.

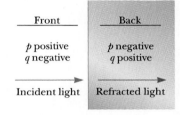

Front	Back
p positive q negative	p negative q positive
Incident light	Refracted light

FIGURE 26.23 A diagram for obtaining the signs of p and q for a thin lens or a refracting surface.

■ **Lens makers' equation**

PITFALL PREVENTION 26.4

LENS HAVE TWO FOCAL POINTS BUT ONE FOCAL LENGTH A lens has a focal point on each side, front and back. There is, however, only one focal length for a thin lens. Each of the two focal points is located the same distance from the lens (Fig. 26.21), as can be seen mathematically by interchanging R_1 and R_2 in Equation 26.13 (and changing the signs of the radii because back and front have been interchanged). As a result, the lens forms an image of an object at the same point if it is turned around. In practice, that might not happen because real lenses are not infinitesimally thin.

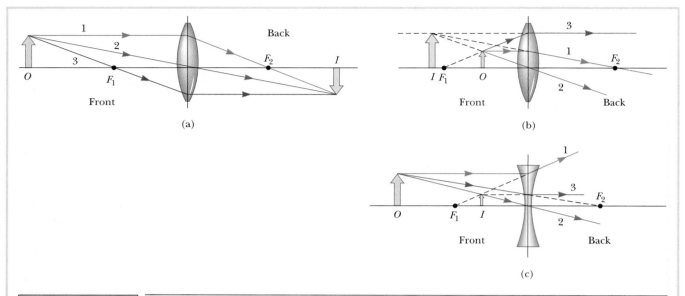

ACTIVE FIGURE 26.24 Ray diagrams for locating the image formed by a thin lens. (a) When the object is in front of and outside the focal point F_1 of a converging lens, the image is real, inverted, and on the back side of the lens. (b) When the object is between F_1 and a converging lens, the image is virtual, upright, larger than the object and on the front side of the lens. (c) When an object is anywhere in front of a diverging lens, the image is virtual, upright, smaller than the object and is on the front side of the lens.

Physics⊗Now™ Log into PhysicsNow at **www.pop4e.com** and go to Active Figure 26.24 to move the objects and change the focal lengths of the lenses to see the effect on the images.

For the converging lens in Active Figure 26.24a where the object is *outside* the front focal point ($p > f$), the image is real and inverted and is located on the back side of the lens. This diagram would be representative of a movie projector, for which the film is the object, the lens is in the projector, and the image is projected on a large screen for the audience to watch. The film is placed in the projector with the scene upside down so that the inverted image is right side up for the audience.

When the object is *inside* the front focal point ($p < f$) as in Active Figure 26.24b, the image is virtual and upright. When used in this way, the lens is acting as a magnifying glass, providing an enlarged upright image for closer study of an object. The object might be a stamp, a fingerprint, or a printed page for someone with failing eyesight.

For the diverging lens of Active Figure 26.24c, the image is virtual and upright for all object locations. A diverging lens is used in a security peephole in a door to give a wide-angle view. Nearsighted individuals use diverging eyeglass lenses or contact lenses. Another use is for a panoramic lens for a camera (although a sophisticated camera "lens" is actually a combination of several lenses). A diverging lens in this application creates a small image of a wide field of view.

QUICK QUIZ 26.5 What is the focal length of a pane of window glass? **(a)** zero **(b)** infinity **(c)** the thickness of the glass **(d)** impossible to determine

QUICK QUIZ 26.6 If you cover the top half of the lens in Active Figure 26.24a with a piece of paper, which of the following happens to the appearance of the image of the object? **(a)** The bottom half disappears. **(b)** The top half disappears. **(c)** The entire image is visible but dimmer. **(d)** There is no change. **(e)** The entire image disappears.

■ Thinking Physics 26.2

Diving masks often have lenses built into the glass for divers who do not have perfect vision. This kind of mask allows the individual to dive without the necessity for glasses because the lenses in the faceplate perform the necessary refraction to provide clear vision. Normal glasses have lenses that are curved on both the front and rear surfaces. The lenses in a diving mask faceplate often only have curved surfaces on the *inside* of the glass. Why is this design desirable?

Reasoning The main reason for curving only the inner surface of the lenses in the diving mask faceplate is so that the diver can see clearly when looking at objects straight ahead while underwater *and* in the air. Consider light rays approaching the mask along a normal to the plane of the faceplate. If curved surfaces were on both the front and the back of the diving lens on the faceplate, refraction would occur at each surface. The lens could be designed so that these two refractions would give clear vision while the diver is in air. When the diver is underwater, however, the refraction between the water and the glass at the first interface is now different because the index of refraction of water is different from that of air. Thus, the vision would not be clear underwater.

By making the outer surface of the lens flat, light is not refracted at normal incidence to the faceplate at the outer surface *in either air or water;* all the refraction occurs at the inner glass–air surface. Thus, the same refractive correction exists in water and in air, and the diver can see clearly in both environments. ■

EXAMPLE 26.6 | The Lens Makers' Equation

The biconvex lens of Figure 26.25 has an index of refraction of 1.50. The radius of curvature of the front surface is 10 cm and that of the back surface is 15 cm. Find the focal length of the lens.

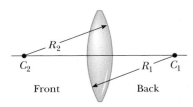

FIGURE 26.25 | (Example 26.6) This lens has two curved surfaces with radii of curvature R_1 and R_2.

Solution From the sign conventions in Table 26.3 we find that $R_1 = +10$ cm and $R_2 = -15$ cm. Thus, using the lens makers' equation, we have

$$\frac{1}{f} = (n - 1)\left(\frac{1}{R_1} - \frac{1}{R_2}\right)$$

$$= (1.50 - 1)\left(\frac{1}{10 \text{ cm}} - \frac{1}{-15 \text{ cm}}\right)$$

$$f = \boxed{12 \text{ cm}}$$

INTERACTIVE | EXAMPLE 26.7 | The Image Formed by a Converging Lens

A A converging lens of focal length 10.0 cm forms an image of an object placed 30.0 cm from the lens. Construct a ray diagram, find the image distance, and describe the image.

Solution First we construct a ray diagram as shown in Figure 26.26a. The diagram shows that we should expect a real, inverted, smaller image to be formed on the back side of the lens. The thin lens equation, Equation 26.12, can be used to find the image distance:

$$\frac{1}{p} + \frac{1}{q} = \frac{1}{f}$$

$$\frac{1}{30.0 \text{ cm}} + \frac{1}{q} = \frac{1}{10.0 \text{ cm}}$$

$$q = \boxed{15.0 \text{ cm}}$$

The positive sign for the image distance tells us that the image is indeed real and on the back side of the lens. The magnification of the image is

$$M = -\frac{q}{p} = -\frac{15.0 \text{ cm}}{30.0 \text{ cm}} = \boxed{-0.500}$$

Thus, the image is reduced in size by one half, and the negative sign for M tells us that the image is inverted.

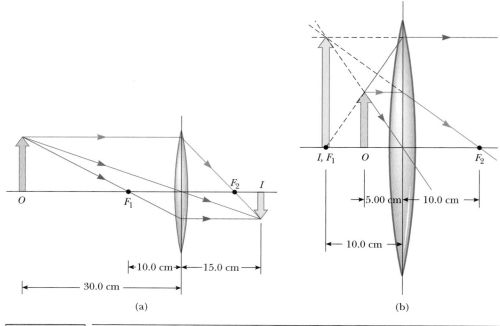

FIGURE 26.26 (Interactive Example 26.7) An image is formed by a converging lens. (a) The object is farther from the lens than the focal point. (b) The object is closer to the lens than the focal point.

B The object is now placed 10.0 cm from the lens. Construct a ray diagram, find the image distance, and describe the image.

Solution No calculation is necessary for this case because we know that when the object is placed at the focal point, the image is formed at infinity. That is verified by substituting $p = 10.0$ cm into the lens equation.

C Finally, the object is placed 5.00 cm from the lens. Construct a ray diagram, find the image distance, and describe the image.

Solution We now move inside the focal point. The ray diagram in Figure 26.26b shows that in this case the lens acts as a magnifying glass; that is, the image is magnified, upright, on the same side of the lens as the object, and virtual. Because the object distance is 5.00 cm, the thin lens equation gives us

$$\frac{1}{5.00 \text{ cm}} + \frac{1}{q} = \frac{1}{10.0 \text{ cm}}$$

$$q = \boxed{-10.0 \text{ cm}}$$

and the magnification of the image is

$$M = -\frac{q}{p} = -\left(\frac{-10.0 \text{ cm}}{5.00 \text{ cm}}\right) = \boxed{2.00}$$

The negative image distance tells us that the image is virtual and formed on the side of the lens from which the light is incident, the front side. The image is enlarged, and the positive sign for M tells us that the image is upright.

Physics☣Now™ Investigate the image formed for various object positions and lens focal lengths by logging into PhysicsNow at **www.pop4e.com** and going to Interactive Example 26.7.

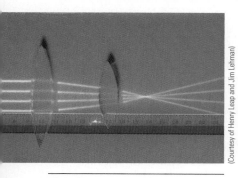

Light from a distant object brought into focus by two converging lenses. ▮

Combinations of Thin Lenses

If two thin lenses are used to form an image, the system can be treated in the following manner. The position of the image of the first lens is calculated as though the second lens were not present. The light then approaches the second lens *as if* it had originally come from the image formed by the first lens. Hence, the image of the first lens is treated as the object of the second lens. The image of the second lens is the final image of the system. If the image of the first lens lies on the back side of the second lens, the image is treated as a *virtual object* for the second lens (i.e., p is negative). The same procedure can be extended to a system of three or more lenses. The overall magnification of a system of thin lenses equals the *product* of the magnifications of the separate lenses.

INTERACTIVE EXAMPLE **26.8**   **Where Is the Final Image?**

Two thin converging lenses of focal lengths 10.0 cm and 20.0 cm are separated by 20.0 cm as in Figure 26.27a. An object is placed 30.0 cm to the left of the first lens. Find the position and magnification of the final image.

Solution Conceptualize by imagining light rays passing through the first lens and forming a real image (because $p > f$) in the absence of the second lens. Figure 26.27b shows these light rays forming the inverted image I_1. Once the light rays converge to the image point, they do not stop. They continue through the image point and interact with the second lens. The rays leaving the image point behave in the same way as the rays leaving an object. Thus, the image of the first lens serves as the object of the

second lens. We categorize this problem as one in which we apply the thin lens equation to the two lenses, but in stepwise fashion. To analyze the problem, we first draw a ray diagram (Fig. 26.27b) showing where the image from the first lens falls and how it acts as the object for the second lens. The location of the image formed by lens 1 is found from the thin lens equation:

$$\frac{1}{p_1} + \frac{1}{q_1} = \frac{1}{f}$$

$$\frac{1}{30.0 \text{ cm}} + \frac{1}{q_1} = \frac{1}{10.0 \text{ cm}}$$

$$q_1 = 15.0 \text{ cm}$$

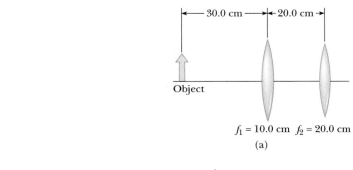

f_1 = 10.0 cm f_2 = 20.0 cm

(a)

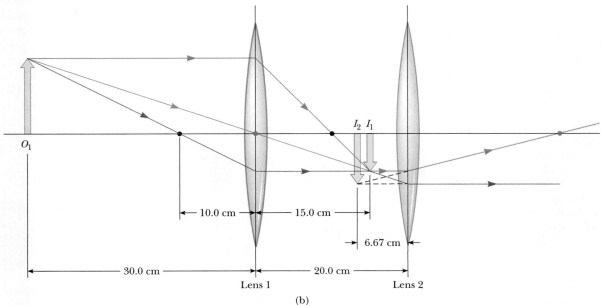

(b)

FIGURE **26.27** (Interactive Example 26.8) (a) A combination of two converging lenses. (b) The ray diagram showing the location of the final image due to the combination of lenses. The black dots are the focal points of lens 1, and the red dots are the focal points of lens 2.

where q_1 is measured from the first lens. The magnification of this image is

$$M_1 = -\frac{q_1}{p_1} = -\frac{15.0 \text{ cm}}{30.0 \text{ cm}} = -0.500$$

The image formed by this lens acts as the object for the second lens. The object distance for the second lens is 20.0 cm − 15.0 cm = 5.00 cm from the second lens. We again apply the thin lens equation to find the location of the final image:

$$\frac{1}{5.00 \text{ cm}} + \frac{1}{q_2} = \frac{1}{20.0 \text{ cm}}$$

$$q_2 = -6.67 \text{ cm}$$

Therefore, the final image lies 6.67 cm to the left of the second lens. The magnification of the second image is

$$M_2 = -\frac{q_2}{p_2} = -\frac{(-6.67 \text{ cm})}{5.00 \text{ cm}} = +1.33$$

The total magnification M of the image due to the two lenses is the product

$$M = M_1 M_2 = (-0.500)(1.33) = -0.667$$

To finalize the problem, note that the negative sign on the overall magnification indicates that the final image is inverted with respect to the initial object. That the absolute value of the magnification is less than 1 tells us that the final image is smaller than the object. That q_2 is negative tells us that the final image is on the front, or left, side of lens 2. All these conclusions are consistent with the ray diagram in Figure 26.27b.

Physics⊗Now™ Investigate the image formed by a combination of lenses by logging into PhysicsNow at **www.pop4e.com** and going to Interactive Example 26.8.

26.5 MEDICAL FIBERSCOPES

 Electromagnetic radiation in medicine

 Medical uses of the fiberscope

Electromagnetic radiation has played a role in the transfer of information in medicine for decades. Of particular interest is the ability to gain information about the relatively inaccessible regions inside the body without using invasive procedures such as surgery. An early advance in this area was the use of x-rays to create shadowy images of bones and other internal structures. In this section, we consider advances that have been made in image formation using optical fibers in medical instruments. These advances have in turn opened up new uses for lasers in medicine.

The first use of optical fibers in medicine appeared with the invention of the *fiberscope* in 1957. Figure 26.28 indicates the construction of a fiberscope, which consists of two bundles of optical fibers. The *illuminating bundle* is an *incoherent* bundle, meaning that no effort is made to match the relative positions of the fibers at the two ends. This matching is not necessary because the sole purpose of this bundle is to deliver light to illuminate the scene. A lens (called the *objective lens*) is used at the internal end of the fiberscope to create a real image of the illuminated scene on the ends of the *viewing bundle* of fibers. The light from the image is transmitted along the fibers to the viewing end. An eyepiece lens is used at this end to magnify the image appearing on the ends of the fibers in the viewing bundle.

The viewing bundle is coherent, so the fibers have the same relative relationships at both ends of the bundle. If one end of an individual fiber is at the very top

FIGURE 26.28 The construction of a fiberscope for viewing the interior of the body. The objective lens forms a real image of the scene on the end of a bundle of optical fibers. This image is carried to the other end of the bundle, where an eyepiece lens is used to magnify the image for the physician.

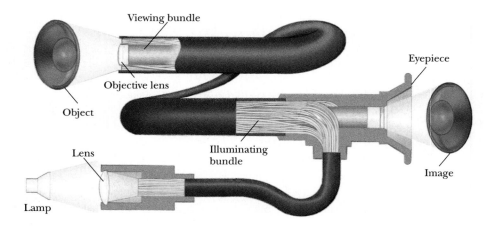

of the eyepiece end of the bundle, the other end of the fiber must be at the very top of the interior end of the bundle. This alignment is necessary because each fiber in the viewing bundle collects light from a particular part of the real image of the scene formed by the objective lens on the ends of the fibers. That part of the scene's image must appear in the correct place with all the parts at the other end for the image to make sense!

The diameter of such a fiberscope can be as small as 1 mm and still provide excellent optical imaging of the scene to be viewed. Therefore, the fiberscope can be inserted through very small surgical openings in the skin and threaded through narrow areas such as arteries. Fiber densities are currently about 10 000 fibers for a 1-mm-diameter scope. Resolution is as high as 70 μm.

As another example, a fiberscope can be passed through the esophagus and into the stomach to enable a physician to look for ulcers. The resulting image can be viewed directly by the physician through the eyepiece lens, but most often it is displayed on a television monitor, captured on film, or digitized for computer storage and display.

Endoscopes are fiberscopes with additional channels besides those for the illuminating and viewing fibers. These channels may be used for

withdrawing fluids
introducing fluids
vacuum suction
wire manipulators
scalpels for cutting tissue
needles for injections
lasers for surgical applications

Because these additional channels require more room, endoscopes range from 2 to 15 mm in diameter. Despite this larger size, however, endoscopes can be used to perform surgery within the body using incisions that are much smaller than those in traditional surgery.

Lasers are used with endoscopes in a variety of medical diagnostic and treatment procedures. As a diagnostic example, the dependence on wavelength of the amount of reflection from a surface allows a fiberscope to be used to make a direct measurement of the blood's oxygen content. Using two laser sources, red light and infrared light are both sent into the blood through optical fibers. Hemoglobin reflects a known fraction of infrared light, regardless of the oxygen carried. Thus, the measurement of the infrared reflection gives a total hemoglobin count. Red light is reflected much more by hemoglobin carrying oxygen than by hemoglobin that does not. Therefore, the amount of red laser light reflected allows a measurement of the ability of the patient's blood to carry oxygen.

Lasers are used to treat medical conditions such as *hydrocephalus,* which occurs in about 0.1% of births. This condition involves an increase in intracranial pressure due to an overproduction of cerebrospinal fluid (CSF), an obstruction of the flow of CSF, or insufficient absorption of CSF. In addition to congenital hydrocephalus, the condition can be acquired later in life due to trauma to the head, brain tumors, or other factors.

The older treatment method for obstructive hydrocephalus involved placing a shunt (tube) between ventricular chambers in the brain to allow passage of CSF. A new alternative is *laser-assisted ventriculostomy,* in which a new pathway for CSF is made with an infrared laser beam and an endoscope having a spherical end as shown in Figure 26.29. As the laser beam strikes the spherical end, refraction at the spherical surface causes light waves to spread out in all directions as if the end of the endoscope were a point source of radiation. The result is a rapid decrease in intensity with distance from the sphere, avoiding damage to vital structures in the brain that are close to the area in which a new passageway is to be made. The surface of the spherical end is coated with an infrared radiation-absorbing material,

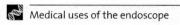 Medical uses of the endoscope

 Use of lasers in treating hydrocephalus

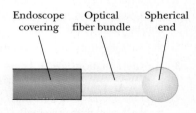

Endoscope covering   Optical fiber bundle   Spherical end

FIGURE 26.29 An endoscope probe used to open new passageways for cerebrospinal fluid in the treatment of hydrocephalus. Laser light raises the temperature of the sphere and radiates from the sphere to provide energy to tissues for cutting the new passageway.

and the absorbed laser energy raises the temperature of the sphere. As the sphere is placed in contact with the location of the desired passageway, the combination of the high temperature and laser radiation leaving the sphere burns a new passageway for the CSF. This treatment requires much less recovery time as well as significantly less postoperative care than that associated with the placement of shunts.

In Chapter 27, we shall investigate another application of lasers — the technology of *holography* — that has grown tremendously in recent years. In holography, three-dimensional images of objects are recorded on film. ■

SUMMARY

Physics⊗Now™ Take a practice test by logging into PhysicsNow at **www.pop4e.com** and clicking on the Pre-Test link for this chapter.

An **image** of an object is a point from which light either diverges or seems to diverge after interacting with a mirror or lens. If light passes through the image point, the image is a **real image.** If light only appears to diverge from the image point, the image is a **virtual image.**

In the **paraxial ray** simplification model, the object distance p and image distance q for a spherical mirror of radius R are related by the **mirror equation**

$$\frac{1}{p} + \frac{1}{q} = \frac{2}{R} = \frac{1}{f} \qquad [26.4, 26.6]$$

where $f = R/2$ is the **focal length** of the mirror.

The **magnification** M of a mirror or lens is defined as the ratio of the image height h' to the object height h:

$$M = \frac{h'}{h} = -\frac{q}{p} \qquad [26.2, 26.11]$$

An image can be formed by refraction from a spherical surface of radius R. The object and image distances for refraction

from such a surface are related by

$$\frac{n_1}{p} + \frac{n_2}{q} = \frac{n_2 - n_1}{R} \qquad [26.8]$$

where the light is incident from the medium of index of refraction n_1 and is refracted in the medium whose index of refraction is n_2.

For a thin lens, and in the paraxial ray approximation, the object and image distances are related by the **thin lens equation:**

$$\frac{1}{p} + \frac{1}{q} = \frac{1}{f} \qquad [26.12]$$

The **focal length** f of a thin lens in air is related to the curvature of its surfaces and to the index of refraction n of the lens material by

$$\frac{1}{f} = (n - 1)\left(\frac{1}{R_1} - \frac{1}{R_2}\right) \qquad [26.13]$$

Converging lenses have positive focal lengths, and **diverging lenses** have negative focal lengths.

QUESTIONS

□ = answer available in the *Student Solutions Manual and Study Guide*

1. Consider a concave spherical mirror with a real object. Is the image always inverted? Is the image always real? Give conditions for your answers.

2. Repeat Question 26.1 for a convex spherical mirror.

3. Do the equations $1/p + 1/q = 1/f$ or $M = -q/p$ apply to the image formed by a flat mirror? Explain your answer.

4. Why does a clear stream, such as a creek, always appear to be shallower than it actually is? By how much is its depth apparently reduced?

5. Consider the image formed by a thin converging lens. Under what conditions is the image (a) inverted, (b) upright, (c) real, (d) virtual, (e) larger than the object, and (f) smaller than the object?

6. Repeat Question 26.5 for a thin diverging lens.

7. Use the lens makers' equation to verify the sign of the focal length of each of the lenses in Figure 26.20.

8. If a solid cylinder of glass or clear plastic is placed above the words LEAD OXIDE and viewed from above as shown in Figure Q26.8, the LEAD appears inverted but the OXIDE does not. Explain.

FIGURE **Q26.8**

9. Consider a spherical concave mirror with the object located to the left of the mirror beyond the focal point. Using ray diagrams, show that the image moves to the left as the object approaches the focal point.

10. Explain why a fish in a spherical goldfish bowl appears larger than it really is.

11. Why do some emergency vehicles have the symbol ƎƆИA⅃UꓭMA written on the front?

12. ◩ Lenses used in eyeglasses, whether converging or diverging, are always designed so that the middle of the lens curves away from the eye, like the center lenses of Figure 26.20a and 26.20b. Why?

13. In Active Figure 26.24a, assume that the blue object arrow is replaced by one that is much taller than the lens. How many rays from the object will strike the lens? How many principal rays can be drawn in a ray diagram?

14. In a Jules Verne novel, a piece of ice is shaped to form a magnifying lens to focus sunlight to start a fire. Is that possible?

15. Explain this statement: "The focal point of a lens is the location of the image of a point object at infinity." Discuss the notion of infinity in real terms as it applies to object distances. Based on this statement, can you think of a "quick and dirty" method for determining the focal length of a converging lens?

16. Discuss the proper position of a photographic slide relative to the lens in a slide projector. What type of lens must the slide projector have?

17. A solar furnace can be constructed by using a concave mirror to reflect and focus sunlight into a furnace enclosure. What factors in the design of the reflecting mirror would guarantee very high temperatures?

18. Figure Q26.18 shows a lithograph by M. C. Escher titled *Hand with Reflection Sphere (Self-Portrait in Spherical Mirror)*. Escher had this to say about the work:

> The picture shows a spherical mirror, resting on a left hand. But as a print is the reverse of the original drawing on stone, it was my right hand that you see depicted. (Be-

ing left-handed, I needed my left hand to make the drawing.) Such a globe reflection collects almost one's whole surroundings in one disk-shaped image. The whole room, four walls, the floor, and the ceiling, everything, albeit distorted, is compressed into that one small circle. Your own head, or more exactly the point between your eyes, is the absolute center. No matter how you turn or twist yourself, you can't get out of that central point. You are immovably the focus, the unshakable core, of your world.

Comment on the accuracy of Escher's description.

FIGURE **Q26.18**

19. You can make a corner reflector by placing three flat mirrors in the corner of a room where the ceiling meets the walls. Show that no matter where you are in the room, you can see yourself reflected in the mirrors, upside down.

PROBLEMS

1, 2, 3 = straightforward, intermediate, challenging

☐ = full solution available in the *Student Solutions Manual and Study Guide*

Physics⊗Now™ = coached problem with hints available at **www.pop4e.com**

🖥 = computer useful in solving problem

▬ = paired numerical and symbolic problems

◩ = biomedical application

Section 26.1 ▪ Images Formed by Flat Mirrors

1. Does your bathroom mirror show you older or younger than you actually are? Compute an order-of-magnitude estimate for the age difference, based on data you specify.

2. In a church choir loft, two parallel walls are 5.30 m apart. The singers stand against the north wall. The organist faces the south wall, sitting 0.800 m away from it. To enable her to see the choir, a flat mirror 0.600 m wide is mounted on the south wall, straight in front of her. What width of the north wall can she see? (*Suggestion:* Draw a top-view diagram to justify your answer.)

3. Determine the minimum height of a vertical flat mirror in which a person 5′10″ in height can see his or her full image. (A ray diagram would be helpful.)

4. Two flat mirrors have their reflecting surfaces facing each other, with the edge of one mirror in contact with an edge of the other, so that the angle between the mirrors is α. When an object is placed between the mirrors, a number of images are formed. In general, if the angle α is such that $n\alpha = 360°$, where n is an integer, the number of images formed is $n - 1$. Graphically, find all the image positions for the case $n = 6$ when a point object is between the mirrors (but not on the angle bisector).

5. A person walks into a room with two flat mirrors on opposite walls, which produce multiple images. When the person is 5.00 ft from the mirror on the left wall and 10.0 ft from the mirror on the right wall, find the distance from the person to the first three images seen in the mirror on the left.

6. A periscope (Fig. P26.6) is useful for viewing objects that cannot be seen directly. It finds use in submarines and in watching golf matches or parades from behind a crowd of people. Suppose the object is a distance p_1 from the upper mirror and the two flat mirrors are separated by a distance h. (a) What is the distance of the final image from the lower mirror? (b) Is the final image real or virtual? (c) Is it upright or inverted? (d) What is its magnification? (e) Does it appear to be left–right reversed?

FIGURE **P26.6**

Section 26.2 ▪ Images Formed by Spherical Mirrors

7. A concave spherical mirror has a radius of curvature of 20.0 cm. Find the location of the image for object distances of (a) 40.0 cm, (b) 20.0 cm, and (c) 10.0 cm. For each case, state whether the image is real or virtual and upright or inverted. Find the magnification in each case.

8. At an intersection of hospital hallways, a convex mirror is mounted high on a wall to help people avoid collisions. The mirror has a radius of curvature of 0.550 m. Locate and describe the image of a patient 10.0 m from the mirror. Determine the magnification.

9. Physics⊗Now™ A spherical convex mirror (Fig. P26.9) has a radius of curvature with a magnitude of 40.0 cm. Determine the position of the virtual image and the magnification for object distances of (a) 30.0 cm and (b) 60.0 cm. (c) Are the images upright or inverted?

10. A large church has a niche in one wall. On the floor plan it appears as a semicircular indentation of radius 2.50 m. A worshiper stands on the center line of the niche, 2.00 m out from its deepest point, and whispers a prayer. Where is the sound concentrated after reflection from the back wall of the niche?

11. A concave mirror has a radius of curvature of 60.0 cm. Calculate the image position and magnification of an

FIGURE **P26.9** Convex mirrors, often used for security in department stores, provide wide-angle viewing.

object placed in front of the mirror at distances of (a) 90.0 cm and (b) 20.0 cm. (c) Draw ray diagrams to obtain the image characteristics in each case.

12. A dentist uses a mirror to examine a tooth. The tooth is 1.00 cm in front of the mirror, and the image is formed 10.0 cm behind the mirror. Determine (a) the mirror's radius of curvature and (b) the magnification of the image.

13. A certain Christmas tree ornament is a silver sphere having a diameter of 8.50 cm. Determine an object location for which the size of the reflected image is three-fourths the size of the object. Use a principal-ray diagram to arrive at a description of the image.

14. (a) A concave mirror forms an inverted image four times larger than the object. Find the focal length of the mirror, assuming that the distance between object and image is 0.600 m. (b) A convex mirror forms a virtual image half the size of the object. Assuming that the distance between image and object is 20.0 cm, determine the radius of curvature of the mirror.

15. To fit a contact lens to a patient's eye, a *keratometer* can be used to measure the curvature of the front surface of the eye, the cornea. This instrument places an illuminated object of known size at a known distance p from the cornea. The cornea reflects some light from the object, forming an image of the object. The magnification M of the image is measured by using a small viewing telescope that allows comparison of the image formed by the cornea with a second calibrated image projected into the field of view by a prism arrangement. Determine the radius of curvature of the cornea for the case $p = 30.0$ cm and $M = 0.013\ 0$.

16. An object 10.0 cm tall is placed at the zero mark of a meter stick. A spherical mirror located at some point on the meter stick creates an image of the object that is upright, 4.00 cm tall, and located at the 42.0-cm mark of the meter stick. (a) Is the mirror convex or concave? (b) Where is the mirror? (c) What is the mirror's focal length?

17. A spherical mirror is to be used to form, on a screen located 5.00 m from the object, an image five times the size of the object. (a) Describe the type of mirror required. (b) Where should the mirror be positioned relative to the object?

18. A dedicated sports car enthusiast polishes the inside and outside surfaces of a hubcap that is a section of a sphere. When she looks into one side of the hubcap, she sees an image of her face 30.0 cm in back of the hubcap. She then flips the hubcap over and sees another image of her face 10.0 cm in back of the hubcap. (a) How far is her face from the hubcap? (b) What is the radius of curvature of the hubcap?

19. You unconsciously estimate the distance to an object from the angle it subtends in your field of view. This angle θ in radians is related to the linear height of the object h and to the distance d by $\theta = h/d$. Assume that you are driving a car and that another car, 1.50 m high, is 24.0 m behind you. (a) Suppose your car has a flat passenger-side rearview mirror, 1.55 m from your eyes. How far from your eyes is the image of the car following you? (b) What angle does the image subtend in your field of view? (c) Suppose instead your car has a convex rearview mirror with a radius of curvature of magnitude 2.00 m (Fig. 26.13 and Fig. P26.19). How far from your eyes is the image of the car behind you? (d) What angle does the image subtend at your eyes? (e) Based on its angular size, how far away does the following car appear to be?

THE FAR SIDE BY GARY LARSON

OBJECTS IN MIRROR ARE CLOSER THAN THEY APPEAR

FIGURE P26.19

20. Review problem. A ball is dropped at $t = 0$ from rest 3.00 m directly above the vertex of a concave mirror that has a radius of curvature of 1.00 m and lies in a horizontal plane. (a) Describe the motion of the ball's image in the mirror. (b) At what time do the ball and its image coincide?

Section 26.3 ∎ Images Formed by Refraction

21. A cubical block of ice 50.0 cm on a side is placed on a level floor over a speck of dust. Find the location of the image

of the speck as viewed from above. The index of refraction of ice is 1.309.

22. A flint glass plate ($n = 1.66$) rests on the bottom of an aquarium tank. The plate is 8.00 cm thick (vertical dimension) and is covered with a layer of water ($n = 1.33$) 12.0 cm deep. Calculate the apparent thickness of the plate as viewed from straight above the water.

23. A glass sphere ($n = 1.50$) with a radius of 15.0 cm has a tiny air bubble 5.00 cm above its center. The sphere is viewed looking down along the extended radius containing the bubble. What is the apparent depth of the bubble below the surface of the sphere?

24. A simple model of the human eye ignores its lens entirely. Most of what the eye does to light happens at the outer surface of the transparent cornea. Assume that this surface has a radius of curvature of 6.00 mm and that the eyeball contains just one fluid with a refractive index of 1.40. Prove that a very distant object will be imaged on the retina, 21.0 mm behind the cornea. Describe the image.

25. One end of a long glass rod ($n = 1.50$) is formed into a convex surface with a radius of curvature of 6.00 cm. An object is located in air along the axis of the rod. Find the image positions corresponding to object distances of (a) 20.0 cm, (b) 10.0 cm, and (c) 3.00 cm from the end of the rod.

26. A goldfish is swimming at 2.00 cm/s toward the front wall of a rectangular aquarium. What is the apparent speed of the fish measured by an observer looking in from outside the front wall of the tank? The index of refraction of water is 1.33.

Section 26.4 ∎ Thin Lenses

27. Physics⊗Now™ The left face of a biconvex lens has a radius of curvature of magnitude 12.0 cm, and the right face has a radius of curvature of magnitude 18.0 cm. The index of refraction of the glass is 1.44. (a) Calculate the focal length of the lens. (b) Calculate the focal length the lens has after is turned around to interchange the radii of curvature of the two faces.

28. A contact lens is made of plastic with an index of refraction of 1.50. The lens has an outer radius of curvature of +2.00 cm and an inner radius of curvature of +2.50 cm. What is the focal length of the lens?

29. A thin lens has a focal length of 25.0 cm. Locate and describe the image when the object is placed (a) 26.0 cm and (b) 24.0 cm in front of the lens.

30. A converging lens has a focal length of 20.0 cm. Locate the image for object distances of (a) 40.0 cm, (b) 20.0 cm, and (c) 10.0 cm. For each case, state whether the image is real or virtual and upright or inverted. Find the magnification in each case.

31. Physics⊗Now™ The nickel's image in Figure P26.31 has twice the diameter of the nickel and is 2.84 cm from the lens. Determine the focal length of the lens.

32. An object located 32.0 cm in front of a lens forms an image on a screen 8.00 cm behind the lens. (a) Find the focal length of the lens. (b) Determine the magnification. (c) Is the lens converging or diverging?

FIGURE **P26.31**

33. Suppose an object has thickness dp so that it extends from object distance p to $p + dp$. Prove that the thickness dq of its image is given by $(-q^2/p^2)\,dp$. Then the longitudinal magnification is $dq/dp = -M^2$, where M is the lateral magnification.

34. The projection lens in a certain slide projector is a single thin lens. A slide 24.0 mm high is to be projected so that its image fills a screen 1.80 m high. The slide-to-screen distance is 3.00 m. (a) Determine the focal length of the projection lens. (b) How far from the slide should the lens of the projector be placed so as to form the image on the screen?

35. An object is located 20.0 cm to the left of a diverging lens having a focal length $f = -32.0$ cm. Determine (a) the location and (b) the magnification of the image. (c) Construct a ray diagram for this arrangement.

36. The use of a lens in a certain situation is described by the equation

$$\frac{1}{p} + \frac{1}{-3.50p} = \frac{1}{7.50 \text{ cm}}$$

Determine (a) the object distance and (b) the image distance. (c) Use a ray diagram to obtain a description of the image. (d) Identify a practical device described by the given equation and write the statement of a problem for which the equation appears in the solution.

37. An antelope is at a distance of 20.0 m from a converging lens of focal length 30.0 cm. The lens forms an image of the animal. If the antelope runs away from the lens at a speed of 5.00 m/s, how fast does the image move? Does the image move toward or away from the lens?

38. Figure P26.38 shows a thin glass ($n = 1.50$) converging lens for which the radii of curvature are $R_1 = 15.0$ cm and

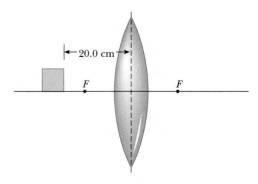

FIGURE **P26.38**

$R_2 = -12.0$ cm. To the left of the lens is a cube having a face area of 100 cm². The base of the cube is on the axis of the lens, and the right face is 20.0 cm to the left of the lens. (a) Determine the focal length of the lens. (b) Draw the image of the square face formed by the lens. What type of geometric figure is it? (c) Determine the area of the image.

39. An object is at a distance d to the left of a flat screen. A converging lens with focal length $f < d/4$ is placed between object and screen. (a) Show that two lens positions exist that form an image on the screen and determine how far these positions are from the object. (b) How do the two images differ from each other?

40. Figure P26.40 diagrams a cross-section of a camera. It has a single lens of focal length 65.0 mm, which is to form an image on the film at the back of the camera. Suppose the position of the lens has been adjusted to focus the image of a distant object. How far and in what direction must the lens be moved to form a sharp image of an object that is 2.00 m away?

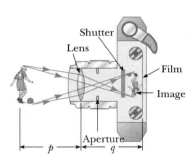

FIGURE **P26.40**

Section 26.5 ▪ Context Connection—Medical Fiberscopes

41. You are designing an endoscope for use inside an air-filled body cavity. A lens at the end of the endoscope will form an image covering the end of a bundle of optical fibers. This image will then be carried by the optical fibers to an eyepiece lens at the outside end of the fiberscope. The radius of the bundle is 1.00 mm. The scene within the body that is to appear within the image fills a circle of radius 6.00 cm. The lens will be located 5.00 cm from the tissues you wish to observe. (a) How far should the lens be located from the end of an optical fiber bundle? (b) What is the focal length of the lens required?

42. Consider the endoscope probe used for treating hydrocephalus and shown in Figure 26.29. The spherical end, with refractive index 1.50, is attached to an optical fiber bundle of radius 1.00 mm, which is smaller than the radius of the sphere. The center of the spherical end is on the central axis of the bundle. Consider laser light that travels precisely parallel to the central axis of the bundle and then refracts out from the surface of the sphere into air. (a) In Figure 26.29, does light that refracts out of the sphere and travels toward the upper right come from the top half of the sphere or from the bottom half of the sphere? (b) If laser light that travels along the edge of the optical fiber bundle refracts out of the sphere tangent to

the surface of the sphere, what is the radius of the sphere? (c) Find the angle of deviation of the ray considered in part (b), that is, the angle by which its direction changes as it leaves the sphere. (d) Show that the ray considered in part (b) has a greater angle of deviation than any other ray. Show that the light from all parts of the optical fiber bundle does not refract out of the sphere with spherical symmetry, but rather fills a cone around the forward direction. Find the angular diameter of the cone. (e) In reality, however, laser light can diverge from the sphere with approximate spherical symmetry. What considerations that we have not addressed will lead to this approximate spherical symmetry in practice?

Additional Problems

43. The distance between an object and its upright image is d. If the magnification is M, what is the focal length of the lens being used to form the image?

44. The lens and mirror in Figure P26.44 have focal lengths of $+80.0$ cm and -50.0 cm, respectively. An object is placed 1.00 m to the left of the lens as shown. Locate the final image, formed by light that has gone through the lens twice. State whether the image is upright or inverted, and determine the overall magnification.

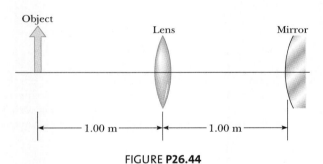

FIGURE P26.44

45. A real object is located at the zero end of a meter stick. A large concave mirror at the 100-cm end of the meter stick forms an image of the object at the 70.0-cm position. A small convex mirror placed at the 20.0-cm position forms a final image at the 10.0-cm point. What is the radius of curvature of the convex mirror?

46. Derive the lens makers' equation as follows. Consider an object in vacuum at $p_1 = \infty$ from a first refracting surface of radius of curvature R_1. Locate its image. Use this image as the object for the second refracting surface, which has nearly the same location as the first because the lens is thin. Locate the final image, proving it is at the image distance q_2 given by

$$\frac{1}{q_2} = (n-1)\left(\frac{1}{R_1} - \frac{1}{R_2}\right)$$

47. A *zoom lens* system is a combination of lenses that produces a variable magnification while maintaining fixed object and image positions. The magnification is varied by moving one or more lenses along the axis. Although multiple lenses are used in practice to obtain high-quality images, the effect of zooming in on an object can be demonstrated with a simple two-lens system. An object, two converging lenses, and a screen are mounted on an optical bench. The first lens, which is to the right of the object, has a focal length of 5.00 cm, and the second lens, which is to the right of the first lens, has a focal length of 10.0 cm. The screen is to the right of the second lens. Initially, an object is situated at a distance of 7.50 cm to the left of the first lens, and the image formed on the screen has a magnification of $+1.00$. (a) Find the distance between the object and the screen. (b) Both lenses are now moved along their common axis, while the object and the screen maintain fixed positions, until the image formed on the screen has a magnification of $+3.00$. Find the displacement of each lens from its initial position in part (a). Can the lenses be displaced in more than one way?

48. The object in Figure P26.48 is midway between the lens and the mirror. The mirror's radius of curvature is 20.0 cm, and the lens has a focal length of -16.7 cm. Considering only the light that leaves the object and travels first toward the mirror, locate the final image formed by this system. Is this image real or virtual? Is it upright or inverted? What is the overall magnification?

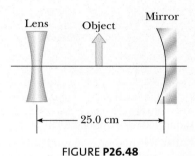

FIGURE P26.48

49. **Physics⊗Now™** A parallel beam of light enters a glass hemisphere perpendicular to the flat face as shown in Figure P26.49. The magnitude of the radius is 6.00 cm, and the index of refraction is 1.560. Determine the point at which the beam is focused. (Assume paraxial rays.)

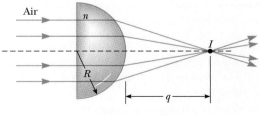

FIGURE P26.49

50. **Review problem.** A spherical lightbulb of diameter 3.20 cm radiates light equally in all directions, with power 4.50 W. (a) Find the light intensity at the surface of the lightbulb. (b) Find the light intensity 7.20 m away from the center of the lightbulb. (c) At this 7.20-m distance, a lens is set up with its axis pointing toward the lightbulb. The lens has a circular face with a diameter 15.0 cm and has a focal

length of 35.0 cm. Find the diameter of the image of the bulb. (d) Find the light intensity at the image.

51. An object is placed 12.0 cm to the left of a diverging lens of focal length − 6.00 cm. A converging lens of focal length 12.0 cm is placed a distance d to the right of the diverging lens. Find the distance d so that the final image is at infinity. Draw a ray diagram for this case.

52. An observer to the right of the mirror–lens combination shown in Figure P26.52 sees two real images that are the same size and in the same location. One image is upright and the other is inverted. Both images are 1.50 times larger than the object. The lens has a focal length of 10.0 cm. The lens and mirror are separated by 40.0 cm. Determine the focal length of the mirror. Do not assume that the figure is drawn to scale.

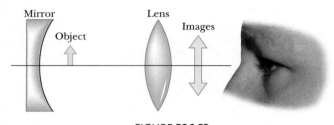

FIGURE **P26.52**

53. **Physics⊗Now**™ The disk of the Sun subtends an angle of 0.533° at the Earth. What are the position and diameter of the solar image formed by a concave spherical mirror with a radius of curvature of 3.00 m?

54. Assume that the intensity of sunlight is 1.00 kW/m² at a particular location. A highly reflecting concave mirror is to be pointed toward the Sun to produce a power of at least 350 W at the image. (a) Find the required radius R_a of the circular face area of the mirror. (b) Now suppose the light intensity is to be at least 120 kW/m² at the image. Find the required relationship between R_a and the radius of curvature R of the mirror. The disk of the Sun subtends an angle of 0.533° at the Earth.

55. In a darkened room, a burning candle is placed 1.50 m from a white wall. A lens is placed between candle and wall at a location that causes a larger, inverted image to form on the wall. When the lens is moved 90.0 cm toward the wall, another image of the candle is formed. Find (a) the two object distances that produce the specified images and (b) the focal length of the lens. (c) Characterize the second image.

56. In many applications, it is necessary to expand or to decrease the diameter of a beam of parallel rays of light. This change can be made by using a converging lens and a diverging lens in combination. Suppose you have a converging lens of focal length 21.0 cm and a diverging lens of focal length −12.0 cm. How can you arrange these lenses to increase the diameter of a beam of parallel rays? By what factor will the diameter increase?

57. The lens makers' equation applies to a lens immersed in a liquid if n in the equation is replaced by n_2/n_1. Here n_2 refers to the refractive index of the lens material and n_1 is that of the medium surrounding the lens. (a) A certain lens has focal length 79.0 cm in air and refractive index 1.55. Find its focal length in water. (b) A certain mirror has focal length 79.0 cm in air. Find its focal length in water.

58. Figure P26.58 shows a thin converging lens for which the radii of curvature are $R_1 = 9.00$ cm and $R_2 = − 11.0$ cm. The lens is in front of a concave spherical mirror with the radius of curvature $|R| = 8.00$ cm. (a) Assume that its focal points F_1 and F_2 are 5.00 cm from the center of the lens. Determine its index of refraction. (b) The lens and mirror are 20.0 cm apart, and an object is placed 8.00 cm to the left of the lens. Determine the position of the final image and its magnification as seen by the eye in the figure. (c) Is the final image inverted or upright? Explain.

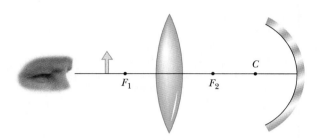

FIGURE **P26.58**

59. A floating strawberry illusion is achieved with two parabolic mirrors, each having a focal length 7.50 cm, facing each other so that their centers are 7.50 cm apart (Fig. P26.59). If a strawberry is placed on the lower mirror, an image of

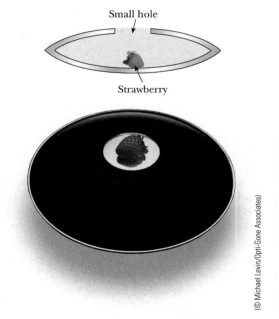

FIGURE **P26.59**

the strawberry is formed at the small opening at the center of the top mirror. Show that the final image is formed at that location and describe its characteristics. (*Note:* A very startling effect is to shine a flashlight beam on this image. Even at a glancing angle, the incoming light beam is seemingly reflected from the image! Do you understand why?)

60. An object 2.00 cm high is placed 40.0 cm to the left of a converging lens having a focal length of 30.0 cm. A diverg-

ing lens with a focal length of − 20.0 cm is placed 110 cm to the right of the converging lens. (a) Determine the position and magnification of the final image. (b) Is the image upright or inverted? (c) Repeat parts (a) and (b) for the case where the second lens is a converging lens having a focal length of + 20.0 cm.

ANSWERS TO QUICK QUIZZES

26.1 At *C*. A ray traced from the stone to the mirror and then to observer 2 looks like this illustration:

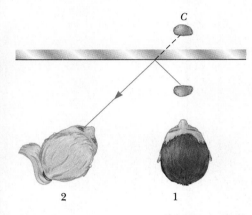

26.2 False. The water spots are 2 m away from you and your image is 4 m away. You cannot focus your eyes on both at the same time.

26.3 (b). A concave mirror will focus the light from a large area of the mirror onto a small area of the paper, resulting in a very high power input to the paper.

26.4 (b). A convex mirror always forms an image with a magnification less than one, so the mirror must be concave. In a concave mirror, only virtual images are upright. This particular photograph is of the Hubble Space Telescope primary mirror.

26.5 (b). Because the flat surfaces of the pane have infinite radii of curvature, Equation 26.13 indicates that the focal length is also infinite. Parallel rays striking the pane focus at infinity, which means that they remain parallel after passing through the glass.

26.6 (c). The entire image is visible but has half the intensity. Each point on the object is a source of rays that travel in all directions. Thus, light from all parts of the object goes through all parts of the lens and forms an image. If you block part of the lens, you are blocking some of the rays, but the remaining ones still come from all parts of the object.

CHAPTER 27

Wave Optics

Interference in soap bubbles. The colors are due to interference between light rays reflected from the front and back surfaces of the thin film of soap making up the bubble. The color depends on the thickness of the film, ranging from black where the film is thinnest to red where it is thickest.

(Dr. Jeremy Burgess/SPL/Photo Researchers, Inc.)

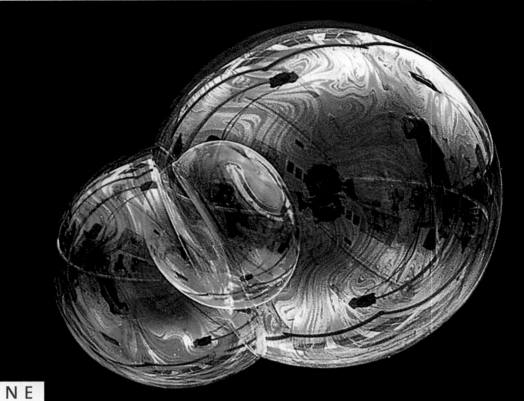

CHAPTER OUTLINE

In Chapters 25 and 26, we used the ray approximation to examine what happens when light reflects from a surface or refracts into a new medium. We used the general term *geometric optics* for these discussions. This chapter is concerned with **wave optics,** a subject that addresses the optical phenomena of interference and diffraction. These phenomena cannot be adequately explained with the ray approximation. We must address the wave nature of light to be able to understand these phenomena.

We introduced the concept of wave interference in Chapter 14 for one-dimensional waves. This phenomenon depends on the principle of superposition, which tells us that when two or more traveling mechanical waves combine at a given point, the resultant displacement of the elements of the medium at that point is the sum of the displacements due to the individual waves.

We shall see the full richness of the waves in interference model in this chapter as we apply it to light. We used one-dimensional waves on strings to introduce interference in Figures 14.1 and 14.2. As we discuss the interference of light waves, two major changes from this previous discussion must be noted. First, we shall no longer focus on one-dimensional waves, so we must build geometric models to analyze the situation in two or three dimensions. Second, we shall study electromagnetic waves rather than mechanical waves. Therefore, the principle of superposition needs to be cast in terms of addition of field vectors rather than displacements of the elements of the medium.

27.1 CONDITIONS FOR INTERFERENCE

In our discussion of wave interference for mechanical waves in Chapter 14, we found that two waves can add together constructively or destructively. In constructive interference between waves, the amplitude of the resultant wave is greater than that of either individual wave, whereas in destructive interference, the resultant amplitude is less than that of either individual wave. Electromagnetic waves also undergo interference. Fundamentally, all interference associated with electromagnetic waves arises as a result of combining the electric and magnetic fields that constitute the individual waves.

In Figure 14.4, we described a device that allows interference to be observed for sound waves. Interference effects in visible electromagnetic waves are not easy to observe because of their short wavelengths (from about 4×10^{-7} to 7×10^{-7} m). Two sources producing two waves of identical wavelengths are needed to create interference. To produce a stable interference pattern, however, the individual waves must maintain a constant phase relationship with one another; they must be **coherent.** As an example, the sound waves emitted by two side-by-side loudspeakers driven by a single amplifier can produce interference because the two loudspeakers respond to the amplifier in the same way at the same time.

If two separate light sources are placed side by side, no interference effects are observed because the light waves from one source are emitted independently of the other source; hence, the emissions from the two sources do not maintain a constant phase relationship with each other over the time of observation. An ordinary light source undergoes random changes in time intervals less than a nanosecond. Therefore, the conditions for constructive interference, destructive interference, or some intermediate state are maintained only for such short time intervals. The result is that no interference effects are observed because the eye cannot follow such rapid changes. Such light sources are said to be **incoherent.**

27.2 YOUNG'S DOUBLE-SLIT EXPERIMENT

A common method for producing two coherent light sources is to use a monochromatic source to illuminate a barrier containing two small openings (usually in the shape of slits). The light emerging from the two slits is coherent because a single source produces the original light beam and the two slits serve only to separate the original beam into two parts (which, after all, is what was done to the sound signal from the side-by-side loudspeakers at the end of the preceding section). Any random change in the light emitted by the source occurs in both beams at the same time, and, as a result, interference effects can be observed when the light from the two slits arrives at a viewing screen.

If the light traveled only in its original direction after passing through the slits as shown in Figure 27.1a, the waves would not overlap and no interference pattern would be seen. Instead, as we have discussed in our treatment of Huygens's principle (Section 25.6), the waves spread out from the slits as shown in Figure 27.1b. In other words, the light deviates from a straight-line path and enters the region that would otherwise be shadowed. As noted in Section 25.2, this divergence of light from its initial line of travel is called **diffraction.**

Interference in light waves from two sources was first demonstrated by Thomas Young in 1801. A schematic diagram of the apparatus that Young used is shown in

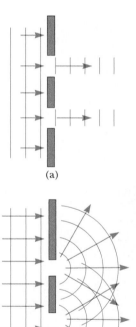

(a)

(b)

FIGURE 27.1 (a) If light waves did not spread out after passing through the slits, no interference would occur. (b) The light waves from the two slits overlap as they spread out, filling what we expect to be shadowed regions with light and producing interference fringes on a screen placed to the right of the slits.

ACTIVE FIGURE 27.2

(a) Schematic diagram of Young's double-slit experiment. Slits S_1 and S_2 behave as coherent sources of light waves that produce an interference pattern on the viewing screen (drawing not to scale).
(b) An enlargement of the center of a fringe pattern formed on the viewing screen could look like this photograph.

Physics⊗Now™ Log into PhysicsNow at **www.pop4e.com** and go to Active Figure 27.2 to adjust the slit separation and the wavelength of the light to see the effect on the interference pattern.

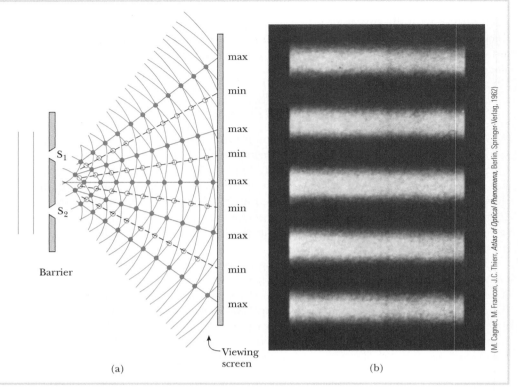

(a)

(b)

Active Figure 27.2a. Plane light waves arrive at a barrier that contains two parallel slits S_1 and S_2. These two slits serve as a pair of coherent light sources because waves emerging from them originate from the same wave front and therefore maintain a constant phase relationship. The light from S_1 and S_2 produces on a viewing screen a visible pattern of bright and dark parallel bands called **fringes** (Active Fig. 27.2b). When the light from S_1 and that from S_2 both arrive at a point on the screen such that constructive interference occurs at that location, a bright fringe appears. When the light from the two slits combines destructively at any location on the screen, a dark fringe results.

Figure 27.3 is a schematic diagram that allows us to generate a mathematical representation by modeling the interference as if waves combine at the viewing screen.[1]

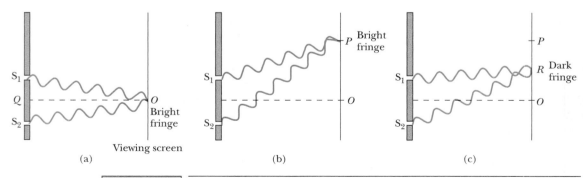

(a)

(b)

(c)

FIGURE 27.3 (a) Constructive interference occurs at point *O* when the waves combine.
(b) Constructive interference also occurs at point *P*. (c) Destructive interference occurs at *R* because the wave from the upper slit falls half a wavelength behind the wave from the lower slit. (All figures not to scale.)

---

[1]The interference occurs everywhere between the slits and the screen, not only at the screen. See Thinking Physics 27.1. The model we have proposed will give us a valid result.

In Figure 27.3a, two waves leave the two slits in phase and strike the screen at the central point O. Because these waves travel equal distances, they arrive in phase at O. As a result, constructive interference occurs at this location and a bright fringe is observed. In Figure 27.3b, the two light waves again start in phase, but the lower wave has to travel one wavelength farther to reach point P on the screen. Because the lower wave falls behind the upper one by exactly one wavelength, they still arrive in phase at P. Hence, a second bright fringe appears at this location. Now consider point R located between O and P in Figure 27.3c. At this location, the lower wave has fallen half a wavelength behind the upper wave when they arrive at the screen. Hence, the trough from the lower wave overlaps the crest from the upper wave, giving rise to destructive interference at R. For this reason, one observes a dark fringe at this location.

Young's double-slit experiment is the prototype for many interference effects. Interference of waves occurs relatively commonly in technological applications, so this phenomenon represents an important analysis model to understand. In the next section, we develop the mathematical representation for interference of light.

27.3 | LIGHT WAVES IN INTERFERENCE

We can obtain a quantitative description of Young's experiment with the help of a geometric model constructed from Figure 27.4a. The viewing screen is located a perpendicular distance L from the slits S_1 and S_2, which are separated by a distance d. Consider point P on the screen. Angle θ is measured from a line perpendicular to the screen from the midpoint between the slits and a line from the midpoint to point P. We identify r_1 and r_2 as the distances the waves travel from slit to screen. Let us assume that the source is monochromatic. Under these conditions, the waves emerging from S_1 and S_2 have the same wavelength and amplitude and are in phase. The light intensity on the screen at P is the result of the superposition of the light coming from both slits. Note from the geometric model triangle in gold in Figure 27.4a that a wave from the lower slit travels farther than a wave from the upper slit by an amount δ. This distance is called the **path difference.**

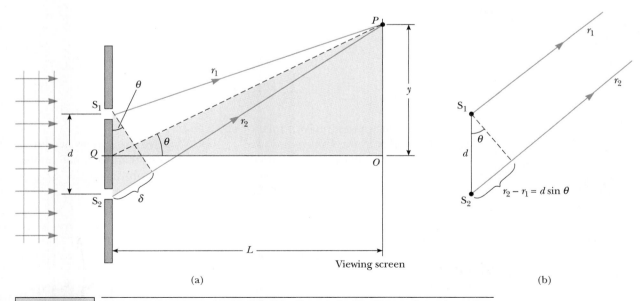

FIGURE 27.4 (a) Geometric construction for describing Young's double-slit experiment (not to scale). (b) When we assume that r_1 is parallel to r_2, the path difference between the two rays is $\delta = r_2 - r_1 = d \sin \theta$. For this approximation to be valid, it is essential that $L \gg d$.

If L is much greater than d, the two paths are very close to being parallel. We shall adopt a simplification model in which the two paths are exactly parallel. In this case, from Figure 27.4b, we see that

■ Path difference

$$\delta = r_2 - r_1 = d \sin \theta \qquad [27.1]$$

In Figure 27.4a, the condition $L \gg d$ is not satisfied because the figure is not to scale; in Figure 27.4b, the rays leave the slits as if the condition is satisfied. As noted earlier, the value of this path difference determines whether the two waves are in phase or out of phase when they arrive at P. If the path difference is either zero or some integral multiple of the wavelength, the two waves are in phase at P and **constructive interference** results. The condition for bright fringes at P is therefore

■ Conditions for constructive interference for two slits

$$\delta = d \sin \theta_{\text{bright}} = m\lambda \qquad (m = 0, \pm 1, \pm 2, \ldots) \qquad [27.2]$$

The number m is an integer called the **order number.** The central bright fringe at $\theta_{\text{bright}} = 0$ is associated with the order number $m = 0$ and is called the **zeroth-order maximum.** The first maximum on either side, for which $m = \pm 1$, is called the **first-order maximum,** and so forth.

Similarly, when the path difference is an odd multiple of $\lambda/2$, the two waves arriving at P are 180° out of phase and give rise to **destructive interference.** Therefore, the condition for dark fringes at P is

■ Conditions for destructive interference for two slits

$$\delta = d \sin \theta_{\text{dark}} = (m + \tfrac{1}{2})\lambda \qquad (m = 0, \pm 1, \pm 2, \ldots) \qquad [27.3]$$

These equations provide the *angular* positions of the fringes. It is also useful to obtain expressions for the *linear* positions measured along the screen from O to P. From the geometric model triangle OPQ in Figure 27.4a, we see that

$$\tan \theta = \frac{y}{L} \qquad [27.4]$$

Using this result, we can see that the linear positions of bright and dark fringes are given by

$$y_{\text{bright}} = L \tan \theta_{\text{bright}} \qquad [27.5]$$

$$y_{\text{dark}} = L \tan \theta_{\text{dark}} \qquad [27.6]$$

where θ_{bright} and θ_{dark} are given by Equations 27.2 and 27.3.

When the angles to the fringes are small, the positions of the fringes are linear near the center of the pattern. To verify this statement, note that, for small angles, $\tan \theta \approx \sin \theta$ and Equation 27.5 gives the positions of the bright fringes as $y_{\text{bright}} = L \sin \theta_{\text{bright}}$. Incorporating Equation 27.2, we find that

$$y_{\text{bright}} = L\left(\frac{m\lambda}{d}\right) \qquad \text{(small angles)}$$

and we see that y_{bright} is linear in the order number m, so the fringes are equally spaced.

As we shall demonstrate in Interactive Example 27.1, Young's double-slit experiment provides a method for measuring the wavelength of light. In fact, Young used this technique to make the first measurement of the wavelength of light. Young's experiment gave the wave model of light a great deal of credibility. Today we still use the phenomenon of interference to describe many observations of wave-like behavior.

Which of the following will cause the fringes in a two-slit interference pattern to move farther apart?   (a) decreasing the wavelength of the light   (b) decreasing the screen distance L (c) decreasing the slit spacing d (d) immersing the entire apparatus in water

■ Thinking Physics 27.1

Consider a double-slit experiment in which a laser beam is passed through a pair of very closely spaced slits and a clear interference pattern is displayed on a distant screen. Now suppose you place smoke particles between the double slit and the screen. With the presence of the smoke particles, will you see the effects of the interference in the space between the slits and the screen, or will you only see the effects on the screen?

Reasoning You see the effects in the area filled with smoke. Bright beams of light are directed toward the bright areas on the screen, and dark regions are directed toward the dark areas on the screen. The geometrical construction shown in Figure 27.4a is important for developing the mathematical description of interference. It is subject to misinterpretation, however, because it might suggest that the interference can only occur at the position of the screen. A better diagram for this situation is Active Figure 27.2a, which shows *paths* of destructive and constructive interference all the way from the slits to the screen. These paths are made visible by the smoke. ■

INTERACTIVE EXAMPLE 27.1   Measuring the Wavelength of Laser Light

A laser is used to illuminate a double slit. The distance between the two slits is 0.030 mm. A viewing screen is separated from the double slit by 1.2 m. The second-order bright fringe ($m = 2$) is 5.1 cm from the center line.

A Determine the wavelength of the laser light.

Solution Because the distance between the screen and the slits is much larger than the slit separation, Equation 27.2 is a valid mathematical representation of this situation. Incorporating Equation 27.5, with $m = 2$, $y_2 = 5.1 \times 10^{-2}$ m, $L = 1.2$ m, and $d = 3.0 \times 10^{-5}$ m, we have

$$\lambda = \frac{d \sin \theta_{\text{bright}}}{m} = \frac{d \sin \left(\tan^{-1} \dfrac{y_{\text{bright}}}{L} \right)}{m}$$

$$= \frac{(3.0 \times 10^{-5} \text{ m}) \sin \left(\tan^{-1} \dfrac{5.1 \times 10^{-2} \text{ m}}{1.2 \text{ m}} \right)}{2}$$

$$= 6.4 \times 10^{-7} \text{ m} = \boxed{6.4 \times 10^{2} \text{ nm}}$$

B Calculate the distance between adjacent bright fringes near the center of the interference pattern.

Solution The position of the $m = 2$ fringe, 5.1 cm, is much smaller than the screen distance, 1.2 m. Therefore, the angular positions of the fringes near the center of the pattern are small. Consequently, these fringes are equally spaced, so the distance between fringes can be found by dividing the distance between the $m = 0$ and $m = 2$ fringes by 2:

$$\Delta y = \frac{y_2 - y_0}{2} = \frac{5.1 \text{ cm} - 0}{2} = \boxed{2.6 \text{ cm}}$$

Physics⊗Now™ Investigate the double-slit interference pattern by logging into PhysicsNow at **www.pop4e.com** and going to Interactive Example 27.1.

FIGURE **27.5** Light intensity versus $d \sin \theta$ for the double-slit interference pattern when the screen is far from the two slits ($L \gg d$).

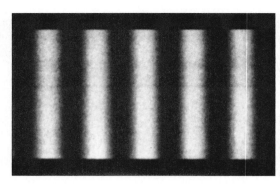

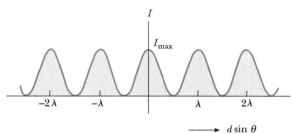

Intensity Distribution of the Double-Slit Interference Pattern

We shall now discuss briefly the distribution of light intensity I (the energy delivered by the light per unit area per unit time) associated with the double-slit interference pattern. Again, suppose the two slits represent coherent sources of sinusoidal waves. In this case, the two waves have the same angular frequency ω and a constant phase difference ϕ. Although the waves have equal phase at the slits, their phase difference ϕ at P depends on the path difference $\delta = r_2 - r_1 = d \sin \theta$. Because a path difference of λ corresponds to a phase difference of 2π rad, we can establish the equality of the ratios:

$$\frac{\delta}{\phi} = \frac{\lambda}{2\pi}$$

■ **Phase difference**

$$\phi = \frac{2\pi}{\lambda} \delta = \frac{2\pi}{\lambda} d \sin \theta \qquad [27.7]$$

This equation tells us how the phase difference ϕ depends on the angle θ.

Although we shall not prove it here, a careful analysis of the electric fields arriving at the screen from the two very narrow slits shows that the **time-averaged light intensity** at a given angle θ is

$$I_{\text{avg}} = I_{\text{max}} \cos^2 \left(\frac{\pi d \sin \theta}{\lambda} \right) \qquad [27.8]$$

where I_{max} is the intensity at point O in Figure 27.4a, directly behind the midpoint between the slits. Intensity versus $d \sin \theta$ is plotted in Figure 27.5.

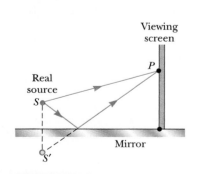

FIGURE **27.6** Lloyd's mirror. An interference pattern is produced on a screen at point P as a result of the combination of the direct ray (blue) and the reflected ray (brown). The reflected ray undergoes a phase change of 180°.

27.4 CHANGE OF PHASE DUE TO REFLECTION

Young's method of producing two coherent light sources involves illuminating a pair of slits with a single source. Another simple arrangement for producing an interference pattern with a single light source is known as *Lloyd's mirror.* A light source is placed at point S close to a mirror as illustrated in Figure 27.6. Waves can reach the point P either by the direct path SP or by the indirect path involving reflection

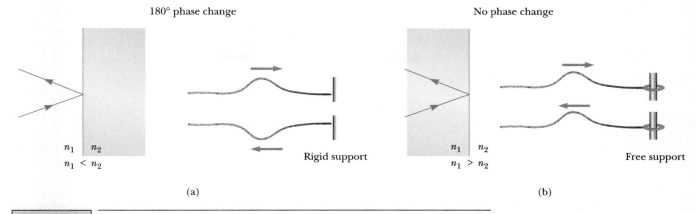

180° phase change No phase change

n_1 n_2
$n_1 < n_2$ Rigid support

n_1 n_2
$n_1 > n_2$ Free support

(a) (b)

FIGURE 27.7 (a) For $n_1 < n_2$, a light ray traveling in medium 1 and reflected from the surface of medium 2 undergoes a 180° phase change. The same thing happens with a reflected pulse traveling along a string fixed at one end. (b) For $n_1 > n_2$, a light ray traveling in medium 1 undergoes no phase change when reflected from the surface of medium 2. The same is true of a reflected wave pulse on a string whose supported end is free to move.

from the mirror. The reflected ray strikes the screen as if it originated from a source at S' located below the mirror.

At points far from the source, one would expect an interference pattern due to waves from S and S', just as is observed for two real coherent sources at these points. An interference pattern is indeed observed. The positions of the dark and bright fringes, however, are *reversed* relative to the pattern of two real coherent sources (Young's experiment) because the coherent sources at S and S' differ in phase by 180°. This 180° phase change is produced on reflection. In general, an electromagnetic wave undergoes a phase change of 180° on reflection from a medium of higher index of refraction than the one in which it is traveling.

It is useful to draw an analogy between reflected light waves and the reflections of a transverse wave on a stretched string when the wave meets a boundary (Section 13.5) as in Figure 27.7. The reflected pulse on a string undergoes a phase change of 180° when it is reflected from a rigid end, and no phase change when it is reflected from a free end, as illustrated in Figures 13.12 and 13.13. If the boundary is between two strings, the transmitted wave exhibits no phase change. Similarly, an electromagnetic wave undergoes a 180° phase change when reflected from the boundary of a medium of higher index of refraction than the one in which it is traveling. There is no phase change for the reflected ray when the wave is incident on a boundary leading to a medium of lower index of refraction. In either case, the transmitted wave exhibits no phase change.

27.5 INTERFERENCE IN THIN FILMS

Interference effects can be observed in many situations in which one beam of light is split and then recombined. A common occurrence is the appearance of colored bands in a film of oil on water or in a soap bubble illuminated with white light. The colors in these situations result from the interference of waves reflected from the opposite surfaces of the film.

Consider a film of uniform thickness t and index of refraction n as in Figure 27.8. We adopt a simplification model in which the light ray is incident on the film from above and nearly normal to the surface of the film. Two rays are reflected from the film, one from the upper surface and one from the lower surface after the refracted ray has traveled through the film. Because the film is thin and has parallel sides, the reflected rays are parallel. Hence, rays reflected from the top surface can interfere with rays reflected from the bottom surface. To determine whether the reflected rays interfere constructively or destructively, we first note the following facts:

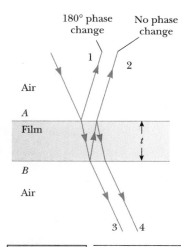

FIGURE 27.8 Interference in light reflected from a thin film is due to a combination of rays 1 and 2 reflected from the upper and lower surfaces of the film. Rays 3 and 4 lead to interference effects for light transmitted through the film.

■ **Condition for constructive interference in thin films**

■ **Condition for destructive interference in thin films**

• An electromagnetic wave traveling from a medium of index of refraction n_1 toward a medium of index of refraction n_2 undergoes a 180° phase change on reflection when $n_2 > n_1$. No phase change occurs in the reflected wave if $n_2 < n_1$.

• The wavelength λ_n of light in a medium whose index of refraction n is

$$\lambda_n = \frac{\lambda}{n} \qquad [27.9]$$

where λ is the wavelength of light in free space.

Let us apply these rules to the film of Figure 27.8. According to the first rule, ray 1, which is reflected from the upper surface (A), undergoes a phase change of 180° with respect to the incident wave. Ray 2, which is reflected from the lower surface (B), undergoes no phase change with respect to the incident wave. Therefore, ignoring the path difference for now, outgoing ray 1 is 180° out of phase with respect to ray 2, a phase difference that is equivalent to a path difference of $\lambda_n/2$. We must also consider, however, that ray 2 travels an extra distance approximately equal to $2t$ before the waves recombine. The *total* phase difference arises from a combination of the path difference and the 180° phase change on reflection. For example, if $2t = \lambda_n/2$, rays 1 and 2 will recombine in phase and constructive interference will result. In general, the condition for constructive interference is

$$2t = (m + \tfrac{1}{2})\lambda_n \qquad (m = 0, 1, 2, \ldots) \qquad [27.10]$$

This condition takes into account two factors: (a) the difference in optical path length for the two rays (the term $m\lambda_n$) and (b) the 180° phase change on reflection (the term $\lambda_n/2$). Because $\lambda_n = \lambda/n$, we can write Equation 27.10 in the form

$$2nt = (m + \tfrac{1}{2})\lambda \qquad (m = 0, 1, 2, \ldots) \qquad [27.11]$$

If the extra distance $2t$ traveled by ray 2 corresponds to a multiple of λ_n, the two waves will combine out of phase and destructive interference results. The general equation for destructive interference is

$$2nt = m\lambda \qquad (m = 0, 1, 2, \ldots) \qquad [27.12]$$

The preceding conditions for constructive and destructive interference are valid when the medium above the top surface of the film is the same as the medium below the bottom surface. The surrounding medium may have a refractive index less than or greater than that of the film. In either case, the rays reflected from the two surfaces will be out of phase by 180°. The conditions are also valid if different media are above and below the film and if both have n less than or larger than that of the film.

If the film is placed between two different media, one with $n < n_{\text{film}}$ and the other with $n > n_{\text{film}}$, the conditions for constructive and destructive interference are reversed. In this case, either a phase change of 180° takes place for both ray 1 reflecting from surface A and ray 2 reflecting from surface B, or no phase change occurs for either ray; hence, the net change in relative phase due to the reflections is zero.

Rays 3 and 4 in Figure 27.8 lead to interference effects in the light transmitted through the thin film. The analysis of these effects is similar to that of the reflected light.

QUICK QUIZ 27.2 In a laboratory accident, you spill two liquids onto water, neither of which mixes with the water. They both form thin films on the water surface. When the films become very thin as they spread, you observe that one film becomes bright and the other dark in reflected light. The film that appears dark (a) has an index of refraction higher than that of water, (b) has an index of refraction lower than that of water, (c) has an index of refraction equal to that of water, or (d) has an index of refraction lower than that of the bright film.

One microscope slide is placed on top of another with their left edges in contact and a human hair under the right edge of the upper slide. As a result, a wedge of air exists between the slides. An interference pattern results when monochromatic light is incident on the wedge. At the left edges of the slides, what kind of fringe is there? **(a)** a dark fringe **(b)** a bright fringe **(c)** impossible to determine

PROBLEM-SOLVING STRATEGY Thin-Film Interference

The following suggestions should be kept in mind while working thin-film interference problems:

1. Conceptualize Think about what is going on physically in the problem. Identify the light source and the location of the observer.

2. Categorize Confirm that you should use the techniques for thin film interference by identifying the thin film causing the interference.

3. Analyze The type of interference that occurs is determined by the phase relationship between the portion of the wave reflected at the upper surface of the film and the portion reflected at the lower surface. Phase differences between the two portions of the wave have two causes: (a) differences in the distances traveled by the two portions and (b) phase changes occurring on reflection. *Both* causes must be considered when determining which type of interference occurs. If the media above and below the film both have index of refraction larger than that of the film or if both indices are smaller, use Equation 27.11 for constructive interference and Equation 27.12 for destructive interference. If the film is located between two different media, one with $n < n_{film}$ and the other with $n > n_{film}$, reverse these two equations for constructive and destructive interference.

4. Finalize Inspect your final results to see if they make sense physically and are of an appropriate size.

EXAMPLE 27.2 Interference in a Soap Film

Calculate the minimum thickness of a soap film ($n = 1.33$) that results in constructive interference in reflected light if the film is illuminated with light whose wavelength in free space is 600 nm.

Solution The minimum film thickness for constructive interference in the reflected light corresponds to $m = 0$ in Equation 27.11, which gives $2nt = \lambda/2$, or

$$t = \frac{\lambda}{4n} = \frac{600 \text{ nm}}{4(1.33)} = \boxed{113 \text{ nm}}$$

INTERACTIVE EXAMPLE 27.3 Nonreflecting Coatings for Solar Cells

Semiconductors such as silicon are used to fabricate solar cells, devices that absorb energy by electromagnetic radiation (e.g., sunlight), resulting in a potential difference so that the cell can transfer energy to a device by electrical transmission. Solar cells are often coated with a transparent thin film, such as silicon monoxide (SiO, $n = 1.45$), to minimize reflective losses from the surface. Suppose a silicon solar cell ($n = 3.5$) is coated with a thin film of silicon monoxide for this purpose (Fig. 27.9). Determine the minimum film thickness that produces the least reflection at a wavelength of 550 nm, which is the center of the visible spectrum.

Solution The reflected light is a minimum when rays 1 and 2 in Figure 27.9 meet the condition of destructive interference. Note that both rays undergo a 180° phase change on reflection in this case, one from the upper surface and one from the lower surface. Hence, the net change in phase due to reflection is zero, and the condition for a reflection minimum requires a path difference of $\lambda_n/2$; thus, $2t = \lambda/2n$. Therefore, the required thickness is

$$t = \frac{\lambda}{4n} = \frac{550 \text{ nm}}{4(1.45)} = \boxed{94.8 \text{ nm}}$$

Typically, such antireflecting coatings reduce the reflective loss from 30% (with no coating) to 10% (with coating), thereby increasing the cell's efficiency because more light is available to provide energy to the cell. In reality, the coating is never perfectly

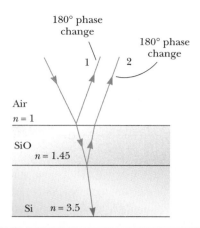

FIGURE **27.9** (Interactive Example 27.3) Reflective losses from a silicon solar cell are minimized by coating it with a thin film of silicon monoxide.

FIGURE **27.10** (Interactive Example 27.3) This camera lens has several coatings (of different thicknesses) that minimize reflection of light waves having wavelengths near the center of the visible spectrum. As a result, the little light that is reflected by the lens has a greater proportion of the far ends of the spectrum and appears purple.

nonreflecting for all light because the required thickness is wavelength dependent and the incident light covers a wide range of wavelengths.

Glass lenses used in cameras and other optical instruments are usually coated with a transparent thin film, such as magnesium fluoride (MgF_2), to reduce or eliminate unwanted reflection. The result is the enhancement of the transmission of light through the lenses. Figure 27.10 shows such a camera lens. Notice that the light reflecting from the lens is tinged purple.

The coating on the lens is designed with a thickness such that light near the center of the visible spectrum experiences little reflection. Light near the ends of the spectrum is reflected from the coating. The combination of red and violet light from the ends of the spectrum provides the purple tinge.

Physics⊗Now™ Investigate the interference for various film properties by logging into PhysicsNow at **www.pop4e.com** and going to Interactive Example 27.3.

EXAMPLE 27.4 **Interference in a Wedge-Shaped Film**

A thin, wedge-shaped film of refractive index n is illuminated with monochromatic light of wavelength λ as illustrated in Figure 27.11a. Describe the interference pattern observed for this case.

Solution The interference pattern is that of a thin film of variable thickness surrounded by air. Hence, the pattern is a series of alternating bright and dark parallel bands. A dark band corresponding to destructive interference appears at point O (where the path length difference is zero) because the ray reflected from the first surface undergoes a 180° phase change but the one reflected from the second surface does not. According to Equation 27.12, other dark bands appear when $2nt = m\lambda$, so that $t_1 = \lambda/2n$, $t_2 = \lambda/n$, $t_3 = 3\lambda/2n$, and so on. Similarly, bright bands are observed when the thickness satisfies the condition $2nt = (m + \frac{1}{2})\lambda$, corresponding to thicknesses of $\lambda/4n$, $3\lambda/4n$, $5\lambda/4n$, and so on. If white light is used, bands of different colors are observed at different points, corresponding to the different wavelengths of light. This situation is shown in the soap film in Figure 27.11b.

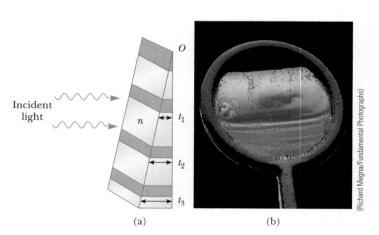

(a) (b)

FIGURE **27.11** (Example 27.4) (a) Interference bands in reflected light can be observed by illuminating a wedge-shaped film with monochromatic light. The darker areas correspond to regions at which rays cancel due to destructive interference. (b) Interference in a vertical film of variable thickness. The top of the film appears darkest where the film is thinnest.

27.6 | DIFFRACTION PATTERNS

In Sections 25.2 and 27.2, we discussed briefly the phenomenon of **diffraction,** and now we shall investigate this phenomenon more fully for light waves. In general, diffraction occurs when waves pass through small openings, around obstacles, or by sharp edges.

We might expect that the light passing through one such small opening would simply result in a broad region of light on a screen due to the spreading of the light as it passes through the opening. We find something more interesting, however. A **diffraction pattern** consisting of light and dark areas is observed, somewhat similar to the interference patterns discussed earlier. For example, when a narrow slit is placed between a distant light source (or a laser beam) and a screen, the light produces a diffraction pattern like that in Figure 27.12. The pattern consists of a broad, intense central band (called the **central maximum**), flanked by a series of narrower, less intense additional bands (called **side maxima**) and a series of dark bands (or **minima**).

Figure 27.13 shows the shadow of a penny, which displays bright and dark rings of a diffraction pattern. The bright spot at the center (called the *Arago bright spot* after its discoverer, Dominique Arago) can be explained using the wave theory of light. Waves that diffract from all points on the edge of the penny travel the same distance to the midpoint on the screen. Thus, the midpoint is a region of constructive interference and a bright spot appears. In contrast, from the viewpoint of geometric optics, the center of the pattern would be completely screened by the penny, and so an approach that does not include the wave nature of light would not predict a central bright spot.

Let us consider a common situation, that of light passing through a narrow opening modeled as a slit and projected onto a screen. As a simplification model, we assume that the observing screen is far from the slit so that the rays reaching the screen are approximately parallel. This situation can also be achieved experimentally by using a converging lens to focus the parallel rays on a nearby screen. In this model, the pattern on the screen is called a **Fraunhofer diffraction pattern.**[2]

Active Figure 27.14a shows light entering a single slit from the left and diffracting as it propagates toward a screen. Active Figure 27.14b is a photograph of a

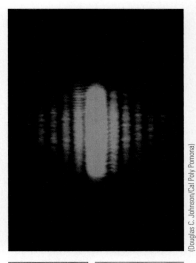

FIGURE 27.12 The diffraction pattern that appears on a screen when light passes through a narrow vertical slit. The pattern consists of a broad central band and a series of less intense and narrower side bands.

FIGURE 27.13 Diffraction pattern of a penny, taken with the penny midway between screen and source.

▦ **PITFALL PREVENTION 27.1**

DIFFRACTION VERSUS DIFFRACTION PATTERN The word *diffraction* refers to the general behavior of waves spreading out as they pass through a slit. We used diffraction in explaining the existence of an interference pattern. A *diffraction pattern* is actually a misnomer, but it is deeply entrenched in the language of physics. We describe here the diffraction pattern seen on a screen when a single slit is illuminated. In reality, it is another interference pattern. The interference is between parts of the incident light illuminating different regions of the slit.

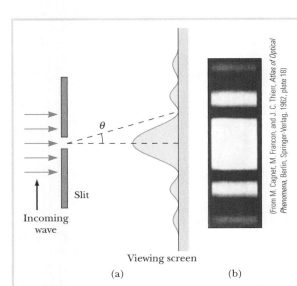

ACTIVE FIGURE 27.14

(a) Fraunhofer diffraction pattern of a single slit. The pattern consists of a central bright region flanked by much weaker maxima alternating with dark bands. (Drawing not to scale.)
(b) Photograph of a single-slit Fraunhofer diffraction pattern.

Physics⊗Now™ Log into Physics-Now at **www.pop4e.com** and go to Active Figure 27.14 to adjust the slit width and the wavelength of the light to see the effect on the diffraction pattern.

[2]If the screen were brought close to the slit (and no lens is used), the pattern is a *Fresnel* diffraction pattern. The Fresnel pattern is more difficult to analyze, so we shall restrict our discussion to Fraunhofer diffraction.

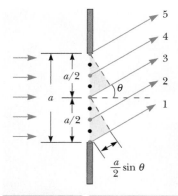

FIGURE 27.15 Diffraction of light by a narrow slit of width a. Each portion of the slit acts as a point source of waves. The path difference between rays 1 and 3, rays 2 and 4, or rays 3 and 5 is $(a/2) \sin \theta$. (Drawing not to scale.)

single-slit Fraunhofer diffraction pattern. A bright fringe is observed along the axis at $\theta = 0$, with alternating dark and bright fringes on each side of the central bright fringe.

Until now, we assumed that slits act as point sources of light. In this section, we shall determine how their finite widths are the basis for understanding the nature of the Fraunhofer diffraction pattern produced by a single slit. We can deduce some important features of this problem by examining waves coming from various portions of the slit as shown in the geometric model of Figure 27.15. According to Huygens's principle, **each portion of the slit acts as a source of waves. Hence, light from one portion of the slit can interfere with light from another portion,** and the resultant intensity on the screen depends on the direction θ.

To analyze the diffraction pattern, it is convenient to divide the slit into two halves as in Figure 27.15. All the waves that originate at the slit are in phase. Consider waves 1 and 3, which originate at the bottom and center of the slit, respectively. To reach the same point on the viewing screen, wave 1 travels farther than wave 3 by an amount equal to the path difference $(a/2) \sin \theta$, where a is the width of the slit. Similarly, the path difference between waves 3 and 5 is also $(a/2) \sin \theta$. If the path difference between two waves is exactly one half of a wavelength (corresponding to a phase difference of 180°), the two waves cancel each other and destructive interference results. That is true, in fact, for any two waves that originate at points separated by half the slit width because the phase difference between two such points is 180°. Therefore, waves from the upper half of the slit interfere *destructively* with waves from the lower half of the slit when

$$\frac{a}{2} \sin \theta = \frac{\lambda}{2}$$

or when

$$\sin \theta = \frac{\lambda}{a}$$

■ **Condition for destructive inter-**
ference in a diffraction pattern

If we divide the slit into four parts rather than two and use similar reasoning, we find that the screen is also dark when

$$\sin \theta = \frac{2\lambda}{a}$$

Likewise, we can divide the slit into six parts and show that darkness occurs on the screen when

$$\sin \theta = \frac{3\lambda}{a}$$

Therefore, the general condition for destructive interference is

$$\sin \theta_{\text{dark}} = m \frac{\lambda}{a} \qquad (m = \pm 1, \pm 2, \pm 3, \ldots) \qquad [27.13]$$

Equation 27.13 gives the values of θ for which the diffraction pattern has zero intensity, that is, a dark fringe is formed. Equation 27.13, however, tells us nothing about the variation in intensity along the screen. The general features of the intensity distribution are shown in Figure 27.16: a broad central bright fringe flanked by much weaker, alternating bright fringes. The various dark fringes (points of zero intensity) occur at the values of θ that satisfy Equation 27.13. The position of the points of constructive interference lie approximately halfway between the dark fringes. Note that the central bright fringe is twice as wide as the weaker maxima.

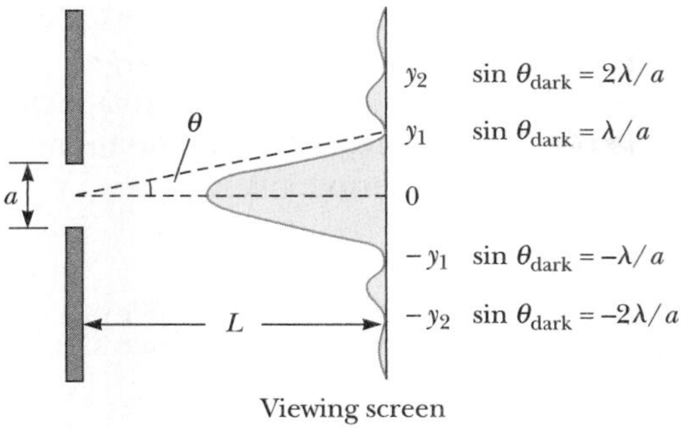

FIGURE 27.16 Light intensity distribution for the Fraunhofer diffraction pattern from a single slit of width a. The positions of two minima on each side of the central maximum are labeled. (Drawing not to scale.)

$y_2 \quad \sin \theta_{dark} = 2\lambda/a$

$y_1 \quad \sin \theta_{dark} = \lambda/a$

0

$-y_1 \quad \sin \theta_{dark} = -\lambda/a$

$-y_2 \quad \sin \theta_{dark} = -2\lambda/a$

Viewing screen

QUICK QUIZ 27.4 **(i)** Suppose the slit width in Figure 27.16 is made half as wide. The central bright fringe **(a)** becomes wider, **(b)** remains the same, or **(c)** becomes narrower. **(ii)** From the same choices, what happens to the central bright fringe when the wavelength of the light is made half as great?

■ Thinking Physics 27.2

If a classroom door is open slightly, you can hear sounds coming from the hallway. Yet you cannot see what is happening in the hallway. What accounts for the difference?

Reasoning The space between the slightly open door and the wall is acting as a single slit for waves. Sound waves have wavelengths larger than the slit width, so sound is effectively diffracted by the opening and spread throughout the room. The sound is then reflected from walls, floor, and ceiling, further distributing the sound throughout the room. Light wavelengths are much smaller than the slit width, so virtually no diffraction for the light occurs. You must have a direct line of sight to detect the light waves. ■

INTERACTIVE **EXAMPLE 27.5** **Where Are the Dark Fringes?**

Light of wavelength 580 nm is incident on a slit of width 0.300 mm. The observing screen is 2.00 m from the slit.

A Find the positions of the first dark fringes and the width of the central bright fringe.

Solution The problem statement cues us to conceptualize a single-slit diffraction pattern similar to that in Figure 27.16. We categorize it as a straightforward application of our discussion of single-slit diffraction patterns. To analyze the problem, note that the two dark fringes that flank the central bright fringe correspond to $m = \pm 1$ in Equation 27.13. Hence, we find that

$$\sin \theta_{dark} = \pm \frac{\lambda}{a} = \pm \frac{5.80 \times 10^{-7} \text{ m}}{0.300 \times 10^{-3} \text{ m}}$$

$$= \pm 1.933 \times 10^{-3}$$

From the triangle in Figure 27.16, note that $\tan \theta_{dark} = y_1/L$. Because θ_{dark} is very small, we can use the approximation $\sin \theta_{dark} \approx \tan \theta_{dark}$; thus, $\sin \theta_{dark} \approx y_1/L$.

Therefore, the positions of the first minima measured from the central axis are given by

$$y_1 \approx L \sin \theta_{dark} = (2.00 \text{ m})(\pm 1.933 \times 10^{-3})$$

$$= \pm 3.87 \times 10^{-3} \text{ m}$$

The positive and negative signs correspond to the dark fringes on either side of the central bright fringe. Hence, the width of the central bright fringe is equal to $2|y_1| = 7.74 \times 10^{-3} \text{ m} = $ **7.74 mm**. To finalize this problem, note that this value is much greater than the width of the slit. We finalize further by exploring what happens if we change the slit width in part B.

B What if the slit width is increased by an order of magnitude to 3.00 mm? What happens to the diffraction pattern?

Solution Based on Equation 27.13, we expect that the angles at which the dark bands appear will decrease as a increases. Thus, the diffraction pattern narrows. For $a = 3.00$ mm, the sines of the angles θ_{dark} for the $m = \pm 1$ dark fringes are

$$\sin \theta_{\text{dark}} = \pm \frac{\lambda}{a} = \pm \frac{5.80 \times 10^{-7}\,\text{m}}{3.00 \times 10^{-3}\,\text{m}}$$
$$= \pm 1.933 \times 10^{-4}$$

The positions of the first minima measured from the central axis are given by

$$y_1 \approx L \sin \theta_{\text{dark}} = (2.00\,\text{m})(\pm 1.933 \times 10^{-4})$$
$$= \pm 3.87 \times 10^{-4}\,\text{m}$$

and the width of the central bright fringe is equal to $2|y_1| = 7.74 \times 10^{-4}\,\text{m} = 0.774\,\text{mm}$. Notice that this result is *smaller* than the width of the slit.

In general, for large values of a, the various maxima and minima are so closely spaced that only a large, central bright area resembling the geometric image of the slit is observed. This behavior is very important in the performance of optical instruments such as telescopes.

Physics⊗Now™ Investigate the single-slit diffraction pattern by logging into PhysicsNow at **www.pop4e.com** and going to Interactive Example 27.5.

27.7 | RESOLUTION OF SINGLE-SLIT AND CIRCULAR APERTURES

Imagine you are driving in the middle of a dark desert at night, along a road that is perfectly straight and flat for many kilometers. You see another vehicle coming toward you from a distance. When the vehicle is far away, you might be unable to determine whether it is an automobile with two headlights or a motorcycle with one. As it approaches you, at some point you will be able to distinguish the two headlights and determine that it is an automobile. Once you are able to see two separate headlights, you describe the light sources as being **resolved.**

The ability of optical systems to distinguish between closely spaced objects is limited because of the wave nature of light. To understand this limitation, consider Figure 27.17, which shows two light sources far from a narrow slit. The sources can be considered as two point sources S_1 and S_2 that are incoherent. For example, they could be two distant stars observed through the aperture of a telescope tube. If no diffraction occurred, one would observe two distinct bright spots (or images) on the screen at the right in the figure. Because of diffraction, however, each source is imaged as a bright central region flanked by weaker bright and dark bands. What is observed on the screen is the sum of two diffraction patterns: one from S_1 and the other from S_2.

If the two sources are far enough apart to ensure that their central maxima do not overlap as in Figure 27.17a, their images can be distinguished and are said to be resolved. If the sources are close together, however, as in Figure 27.17b, the two

FIGURE 27.17 Two point sources far from a narrow slit each produce a diffraction pattern. (a) The angle subtended by the sources at the slit is large enough for the diffraction patterns to be distinguishable. (b) The angle subtended by the sources is so small that their diffraction patterns overlap and the images are not well resolved. (Note that the angles are greatly exaggerated. The drawings are not to scale.)

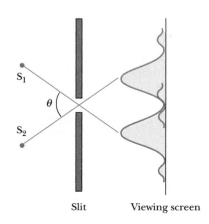

Slit   Viewing screen

(a)

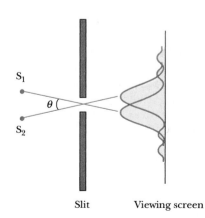

Slit   Viewing screen

(b)

central maxima may overlap and the sources are not resolved. To decide when two sources are resolved, the following condition is often used:

When the central maximum of the diffraction pattern of one source falls on the first minimum of the diffraction pattern of another source, the sources are said to be just resolved. This limiting condition of resolution is known as **Rayleigh's criterion.**

■ Rayleigh's criterion

Figure 27.18 shows the diffraction patterns from circular apertures for three situations. When the objects are far apart, they are well resolved (Fig. 27.18a). They are just resolved when their angular separation satisfies Rayleigh's criterion (Fig. 27.18b). Finally, the sources are not resolved in Figure 27.18c.

From Rayleigh's criterion, we can determine the minimum angular separation θ_{min} subtended by the sources at a slit such that the sources are just resolved. In Section 27.4, we found that the first minimum in a single-slit diffraction pattern occurs at the angle that satisfies the relationship

$$\sin \theta = \frac{\lambda}{a}$$

where a is the width of the slit. According to Rayleigh's criterion, this expression gives the smallest angular separation for which the two sources are resolved. Because $\lambda \ll a$ in most situations, $\sin \theta$ is small and we can use the approximation $\sin \theta \approx \theta$. Therefore, the limiting angle of resolution for a slit of width a is

$$\theta_{min} = \frac{\lambda}{a} \qquad [27.14]$$

■ Limiting angle of resolution for a slit

where θ_{min} is expressed in radians. Hence, the angle subtended by the two sources at the slit must be *greater* than λ/a if the sources are to be resolved.

Many optical systems use circular apertures rather than slits. The diffraction pattern of a circular aperture, as seen in Figure 27.18, consists of a central circular

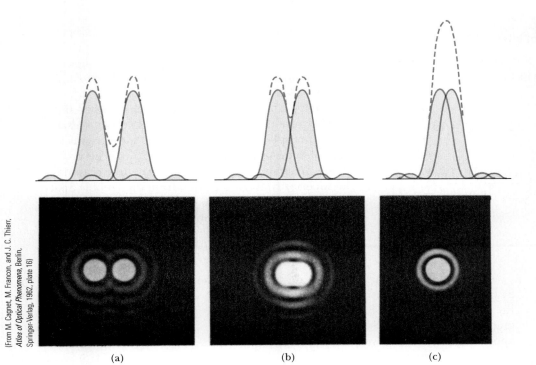

(a)   (b)   (c)

FIGURE 27.18 Individual diffraction patterns of two point sources (solid curves) and the resultant pattern (dashed curves) for various angular separations of the sources. In each case, the dashed curve is the sum of the two solid curves. (a) The sources are far apart, and the images are well resolved. (b) The sources are closer together such that the patterns satisfy Rayleigh's criterion, and the images are just resolved. (c) The sources are so close together that their images are not resolved.

bright disk surrounded by progressively fainter rings. Analysis shows that the limiting angle of resolution of the circular aperture is

$$\theta_{min} = 1.22\frac{\lambda}{D} \qquad [27.15]$$

where D is the diameter of the aperture. Note that Equation 27.15 is similar to Equation 27.14 except for the factor of 1.22, which arises from a mathematical analysis of diffraction from a circular aperture. This equation is related to the difficulty we had seeing the two headlights at the beginning of this section. When observing with the eye, D in Equation 27.15 is the diameter of the pupil. The diffraction pattern formed when light passes through the pupil causes the difficulty in resolving the headlights.

Another example of the effect of diffraction on resolution for circular apertures is the astronomical telescope. The end of the tube through which the light passes is circular, so the ability of the telescope to resolve light from closely spaced stars is limited by the diameter of this opening.

QUICK QUIZ 27.5 Suppose you are observing a binary star with a telescope and are having difficulty resolving the two stars. You decide to use a colored filter to maximize the resolution. (A filter of a given color transmits only that color of light.) What color filter should you choose? (a) blue (b) green (c) yellow (d) red

■ Thinking Physics 27.3

Cats' eyes have pupils that can be modeled as vertical slits. At night, are cats more successful in resolving headlights on a distant car or vertically separated lights on the mast of a distant boat?

Reasoning The effective slit width in the vertical direction of the cat's eye is larger than that in the horizontal direction. Thus, the eye has more resolving power for lights separated in the vertical direction and would be more effective at resolving the mast lights on the boat. ■

EXAMPLE 27.6 Resolution of a Telescope

The Keck telescope at Mauna Kea, Hawaii, has an effective diameter of 10 m. What is its limiting angle of resolution for 600-nm light?

Solution Because $D = 10$ m and $\lambda = 6.00 \times 10^{-7}$ m, Equation 27.15 gives

$$\theta_{min} = 1.22\frac{\lambda}{D} = 1.22\left(\frac{6.00 \times 10^{-7}\,m}{10\,m}\right)$$
$$= 7.3 \times 10^{-8}\,rad \approx 0.015\,s\,of\,arc$$

Any two stars that subtend an angle greater than or equal to this value are resolved (if atmospheric conditions are ideal).

The Keck telescope can never reach its diffraction limit because the limiting angle of resolution is always set by atmospheric blurring at optical wavelengths. This seeing limit is usually about 1 s of arc and is never smaller than about 0.1 s of arc. (That is one reason for the superiority of photographs from the Hubble Space Telescope, which views celestial objects from an orbital position above the atmosphere.)

As an example of the effects of atmospheric turbulence discussed in Example 27.6, consider telescopic images of Pluto and its moon Charon. Figure 27.19a shows the image taken in 1978 that represents the discovery of Charon. In this photograph from an Earth-based telescope, atmospheric turbulence results in Charon appearing only as a bump on the edge of Pluto. In comparison, Figure 27.19b shows a photograph taken with the Hubble Space Telescope in 1994. Without the problems of atmospheric turbulence, Pluto and its moon are clearly resolved.

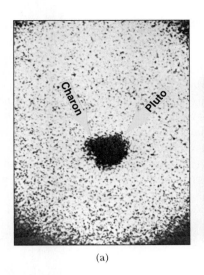

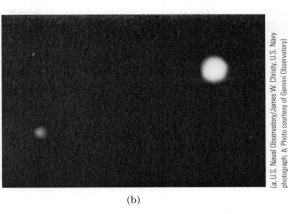

(a)   (b)

(a. U.S. Naval Observatory/James W. Christy, U.S. Navy photograph; b. Photo courtesy of Gemini Observatory)

27.8 | THE DIFFRACTION GRATING

The **diffraction grating,** a useful device for analyzing light sources, consists of a large number of equally spaced parallel slits. A grating can be made by cutting parallel, equally spaced grooves on a glass or metal plate with a precision ruling machine. In a *transmission grating,* the spaces between lines are transparent to the light and hence act as separate slits. In a *reflection grating,* the spaces between lines are highly reflective. Gratings with many lines very close to one another can have very small slit spacings. For example, a grating ruled with 5 000 lines/cm has a slit spacing of $d = (1/5\,000)$ cm $= 2 \times 10^{-4}$ cm.

Figure 27.20 shows a pictorial representation of a section of a flat diffraction grating. A plane wave is incident from the left, normal to the plane of the grating. The pattern observed on the screen at the right in Figure 27.20 is the result of the

PITFALL PREVENTION 27.3

A DIFFRACTION GRATING IS AN INTERFERENCE GRATING As with the term *diffraction pattern, diffraction grating* is a misnomer but is deeply entrenched. The diffraction grating depends on diffraction in the same way as the double slit, spreading the light so that light from different slits can interfere. It would be more correct to call it an *interference grating.* It is unlikely, however, that you will hear anything other than *diffraction grating* for this device.

Incoming plane wave of light

P | First-order maximum ($m = 1$)

Central or zeroth-order maximum ($m = 0$)

First-order maximum ($m = -1$)

P |

Diffraction grating

θ

d

θ

$\delta = d \sin \theta$

FIGURE 27.20 Side view of a diffraction grating. The slit separation is d and the path difference between adjacent slits is $d \sin \theta$.

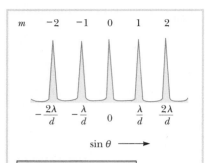

ACTIVE FIGURE 27.21

Intensity versus sin θ for a diffraction grating. The zeroth-, first-, and second-order maxima are shown.

Physics⊗Now™ Log into Physics-Now at **www.pop4e.com** and go to Active Figure 27.21 to choose the number of slits to be illuminated to see the effect on the interference pattern.

combined effects of interference and diffraction. Each slit produces diffraction, and the diffracted beams interfere with one another to produce the final pattern. Each slit acts as a source of waves, and all waves start at the slits in phase. For some arbitrary direction θ measured from the horizontal, however, the waves must travel different path lengths before reaching a particular point on the screen. From Figure 27.20, note that the path difference between waves from any two adjacent slits is equal to $d \sin \theta$. (We assume once again that the distance L to the screen is much larger than d.) If this path difference equals one wavelength or some integral multiple of a wavelength, waves from all slits will be in phase at the screen and a bright line will be observed. When the light is incident normally on the plane of the grating, the condition for *maxima* in the interference pattern at the angle θ is therefore[3]

$$d \sin \theta_{\text{bright}} = m\lambda \qquad (m = 0, 1, 2, 3, \ldots) \qquad [27.16]$$

This expression can be used to calculate the wavelength from a knowledge of the grating spacing d and the angle of deviation θ. If the incident radiation contains several wavelengths, the mth-order maximum for each wavelength occurs at an angle determined from Equation 27.16. All wavelengths are mixed together at $\theta = 0$, corresponding to $m = 0$.

The intensity distribution for a diffraction grating is shown in Active Figure 27.21. If the source contains various wavelengths, a spectrum of lines at different positions for different order numbers will be observed. Note the sharpness of the principal maxima and the broad range of dark areas, which are in contrast to the broad, bright fringes characteristic of the two-slit interference pattern (see Fig. 27.5).

A simple arrangement for measuring the wavelength of light is shown in Active Figure 27.22. This arrangement is called a *diffraction grating spectrometer*. The light to be analyzed passes through a slit,[4] and a parallel beam of light exits from the collimator perpendicular to the grating. The diffracted light leaves the grating and

ACTIVE FIGURE 27.22

Diagram of a diffraction grating spectrometer. The collimated beam incident on the grating is spread into its various wavelength components with constructive interference for a particular wavelength occurring at the angles θ_{bright} that satisfy the equation $d \sin \theta_{\text{bright}} = m\lambda$, where $m = 0, 1, 2, \ldots$.

Physics⊗Now™ Log into Physics-Now at **www.pop4e.com** and go to Active Figure 27.22 to use the spectrometer to observe constructive interference for various wavelengths.

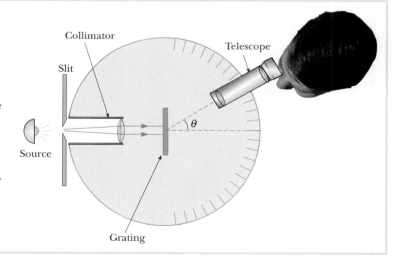

[3]Notice that this equation is identical to Equation 27.2. This equation can be used for a number of slits from two to any number N. The intensity distribution will change with the number of slits, but the locations of the maxima are the same.

[4]A long, narrow slit enables us to observe *line* spectra in the light coming from atomic and molecular systems, as discussed in Chapter 11.

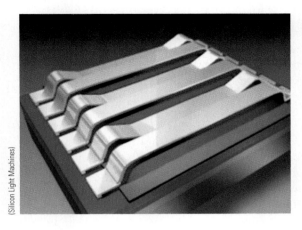

FIGURE 27.23 A small portion of a grating light valve. The alternating reflective ribbons at different levels act as a diffraction grating, offering very high speed control of the direction of light toward a digital display device.

exhibits constructive interference at angles that satisfy Equation 27.16. A telescope is used to view the image of the slit. The wavelength can be determined by measuring the precise angles at which the images of the slit appear for the various orders.

The spectrometer is a useful tool in *atomic spectroscopy*, in which the light from an atom is analyzed to find the wavelength components. These wavelength components can be used to identify the atom as discussed in Section 11.5. We will investigate atomic spectra further in Chapter 29.

Another application of diffraction gratings is in the recently developed *grating light valve* (GLV), which may compete in the near future in video projection with the digital micromirror devices (DMD) discussed in Section 25.3. The grating light valve consists of a silicon microchip fitted with an array of parallel silicon nitride ribbons coated with a thin layer of aluminum (Fig. 27.23). Each ribbon is about 20 μm long and about 5 μm wide and is separated from the silicon substrate by an air gap on the order of 100 nm. With no voltage applied, all ribbons are at the same level. In this situation, the array of ribbons acts as a flat surface, specularly reflecting incident light.

When a voltage is applied between a ribbon and the electrode on the silicon substrate, an electric force pulls the ribbon downward, closer to the substrate. Alternate ribbons can be pulled down, while those in between remain in the higher configuration. As a result, the array of ribbons acts as a diffraction grating, such that the constructive interference for a particular wavelength of light can be directed toward a screen or other optical display system. By using three such devices, one each for red, blue, and green light, full color display is possible.

The GLV tends to be simpler to fabricate and higher in resolution than comparable DMD devices. On the other hand, DMD devices have already made an entry into the market. It will be interesting to watch this technology competition in future years.

QUICK QUIZ 27.6 Ultraviolet light of wavelength 350 nm is incident on a diffraction grating with slit spacing d and forms an interference pattern on a screen a distance L away. The angular positions θ_{bright} of the interference maxima are large. The locations of the bright fringes are marked on the screen. Now red light of wavelength 700 nm is used with a diffraction grating to form another diffraction pattern on the screen. The bright fringes of this pattern will be located at the marks on the screen if (a) the screen is moved to a distance $2L$ from the grating, (b) the screen is moved to a distance $L/2$ from the grating, (c) the grating is replaced with one of slit spacing $2d$, (d) the grating is replaced with one of slit spacing $d/2$, or (e) nothing is changed

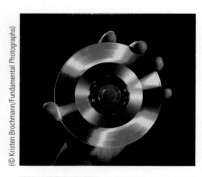

FIGURE 27.24 (Thinking Physics 27.4) A compact disc observed under white light. The colors observed in the reflected light and their intensities depend on the orientation of the disc relative to the eye and relative to the light source.

■ Thinking Physics 27.4

White light reflected from the surface of a compact disc has a multicolored appearance as shown in Figure 27.24. Furthermore, the observation depends on the orientation of the disc relative to the eye and the position of the light source. Explain how that works.

Reasoning The surface of a compact disc has a spiral track with a spacing of approximately 1 μm that acts as a reflection grating. The light scattered by these closely spaced tracks interferes constructively in directions that depend on the wavelength and on the direction of the incident light. Any one section of the disc serves as a diffraction grating for white light, sending beams of constructive interference for different colors in different directions. The different colors you see when viewing one section of the disc change as the light source, the disc, or you move to change the angle of incidence or the viewing angle. ■

INTERACTIVE **EXAMPLE 27.7** **The Orders of a Diffraction Grating**

Monochromatic light from a helium–neon laser ($\lambda = 632.8$ nm) is incident normally on a diffraction grating containing 6 000 lines/cm. Find the angles at which the first-order, second-order, and third-order maxima can be observed.

Solution First, we calculate the slit separation, which is equal to the inverse of the number of lines per cm:

$$d = (1/6\,000) \text{ cm} = 1.667 \times 10^{-4} \text{ cm} = 1\,667 \text{ nm}$$

For the first-order maximum ($m = 1$), we find that

$$\sin \theta_1 = \frac{\lambda}{d} = \frac{632.8 \text{ nm}}{1\,667 \text{ nm}} = 0.379\,6$$

$$\theta_1 = \boxed{22.31°}$$

For $m = 2$, we find that

$$\sin \theta_2 = \frac{2\lambda}{d} = \frac{2(632.8 \text{ nm})}{1\,667 \text{ nm}} = 0.759\,2$$

$$\theta_2 = \boxed{49.39°}$$

For $m = 3$, we find that $\sin \theta_3 = 1.139$. Because $\sin \theta$ cannot exceed unity, this result does not represent a realistic solution. Hence, only zeroth-, first-, and second-order maxima are observed for this situation.

Physics⊗Now™ Investigate the interference pattern from a diffraction grating by logging into PhysicsNow at **www.pop4e.com** and going to Interactive Example 27.7.

27.9 | DIFFRACTION OF X-RAYS BY CRYSTALS

In principle, the wavelength of any electromagnetic wave can be determined if a grating of the proper spacing (on the order of λ) is available. **X-rays,** discovered in 1895 by Wilhelm Roentgen (1845–1923), are electromagnetic waves with very short wavelengths (on the order of 10^{-10} m = 0.1 nm). In 1913, Max von Laue (1879–1960) suggested that the regular array of atoms in a crystal, whose spacing is known to be about 10^{-10} m, could act as a three-dimensional diffraction grating for x-rays. Subsequent experiments confirmed his prediction. The observed diffraction patterns are complicated because of the three-dimensional nature of the crystal. Nevertheless, x-ray diffraction is an invaluable technique for elucidating crystalline structures and for understanding the structure of matter.

Figure 27.25 is one experimental arrangement for observing x-ray diffraction from a crystal. A collimated beam of x-rays with a continuous range of wavelengths is incident on a crystal. The diffracted beams are very intense in certain directions, corresponding to constructive interference from waves reflected from layers of atoms in the crystal. The diffracted beams, which can be detected by a photographic film,

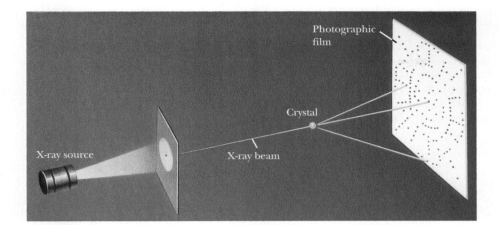

FIGURE 27.25 Schematic diagram of the technique used to observe the diffraction of x-rays by a crystal. The array of spots formed on the film is called a Laue pattern.

form an array of spots known as a *Laue pattern,* as in Figure 27.26a. One can deduce the crystalline structure by analyzing the positions and intensities of the various spots in the pattern. Figure 27.26b shows a Laue pattern from a crystalline enzyme, using a wide range of wavelengths so that a swirling pattern results.

Laue pattern of a crystalline enzyme

The arrangement of atoms in a crystal of NaCl is shown in Figure 27.27. The red spheres represent Na^+ ions, and the blue spheres represent Cl^- ions. Each unit cell (the geometric shape that repeats through the crystal) contains four Na^+ and four Cl^- ions. The unit cell is a cube whose edge length is a.

The ions in a crystal lie in various planes as shown in Figure 27.28. Suppose an incident x-ray beam makes an angle θ with one of the planes as in Figure 27.28. (Note that the angle θ is traditionally measured from the reflecting surface rather than from the normal, as in the case of the law of reflection in Chapter 25.) The beam can be reflected from both the upper plane and the lower one; the geometric construction in Figure 27.28, however, shows that the beam reflected from the lower surface travels farther than the beam reflected from the upper surface. The path difference between the two beams is $2d \sin \theta$, where d is the distance between the planes. The two beams reinforce each other (constructive interference) when this path difference equals some integral multiple of the wavelength λ. The same is

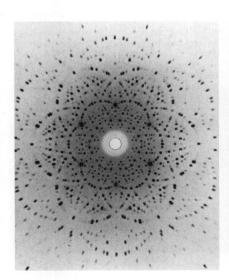

(a)

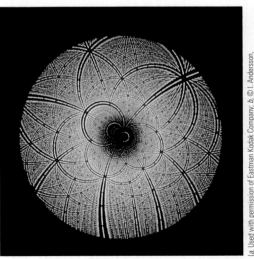

(b)

FIGURE 27.26 (a) A Laue pattern of a single crystal of the mineral beryl (beryllium aluminum silicate). (b) A Laue pattern of the enzyme Rubisco, produced with a wide-band x-ray spectrum. This enzyme is present in plants and takes part in the process of photosynthesis. The Laue pattern is used to determine the crystal structure of Rubisco.

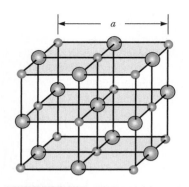

FIGURE 27.27 Crystalline structure of sodium chloride (NaCl). The blue spheres represent Cl⁻ ions, and the red spheres represent Na⁺ ions.

FIGURE 27.28 A two-dimensional description of the reflection of an x-ray beam from two parallel crystalline planes separated by a distance d. The beam reflected from the lower plane travels farther than the one reflected from the upper plane by a distance equal to 2d sin θ.

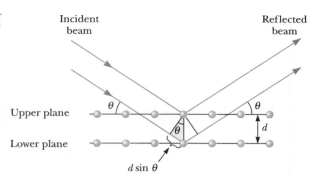

true of reflection from the entire family of parallel planes. Hence, the condition for constructive interference (maxima in the reflected wave) is

$$2d \sin \theta = m\lambda \qquad (m = 1, 2, 3, \ldots) \qquad [27.17]$$

This condition is known as **Bragg's law** after W. Lawrence Bragg (1890–1971), who first derived the relationship. If the wavelength and diffraction angle are measured, Equation 27.17 can be used to calculate the spacing between atomic planes.

27.10 HOLOGRAPHY

CONTEXT CONNECTION

One interesting application of the laser is **holography,** the production of three-dimensional images of objects. The physics of holography was developed by Dennis Gabor (1900–1979) in 1948, for which he was awarded the 1971 Nobel Prize in Physics. The requirement of coherent light for holography, however, delayed the realization of holographic images from Gabor's work until the development of lasers in the 1960s. Figure 27.29 shows a hologram and the three-dimensional character of its image.

Figure 27.30 shows how a hologram is made. Light from the laser is split into two parts by a half-silvered mirror at B. One part of the beam reflects off the object to be photographed and strikes an ordinary photographic film. The other half of the beam is diverged by lens L_2, reflects from mirrors M_1 and M_2, and finally strikes the film. The two beams overlap to form an extremely complicated interference pattern on the film. Such an interference pattern can be produced only if the phase relationship of the two waves is constant throughout the exposure of the film. This condition is met by illuminating the scene with light coming through a pinhole or with coherent laser radiation. The hologram records not only the

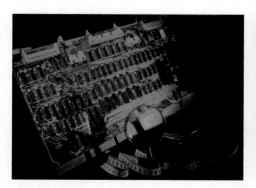
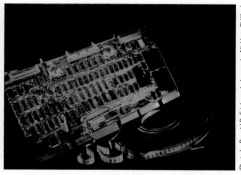

(Photo by Ronald R. Erickson; hologram by Nicklaus Phillips)

FIGURE 27.29 In this hologram, a circuit board is shown from two different views. Notice the difference in the appearance of the measuring tape and the view through the magnifying lens.

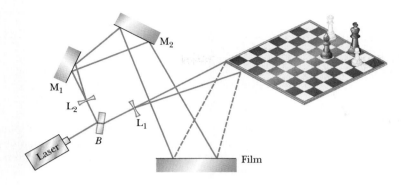

FIGURE 27.30 Experimental arrangement for producing a hologram.

intensity of the light scattered from the object (as in a conventional photograph), but also the phase difference between the reference beam and the beam scattered from the object. This phase difference results in an interference pattern that produces an image with full three-dimensional perspective.

In a normal photographic image, a lens is used to focus the image so that each point on the object corresponds to a single point on the film. Notice that no lens is used in Figure 27.30 to focus the light onto the film. Thus, light from each point on the object reaches *all* points on the film. As a result, each region of the photographic film on which the hologram is recorded contains information about all illuminated points on the object, which leads to a remarkable result: If a small section of the hologram is cut from the film, the complete image can be formed from this small piece!

A hologram is best viewed by allowing coherent light to pass through the developed film as one looks back along the direction from which the beam comes. The interference pattern on the film acts as a diffraction grating. Figure 27.31 shows two rays of light striking the film and passing through. For each ray, the $m = 0$ and $m = \pm 1$ rays in the diffraction pattern are shown emerging from the right side of the film. Notice that the $m = +1$ rays converge to form a real image of the scene, which is not the image that is normally viewed. By extending the light rays corresponding to $m = -1$ back behind the film, we see that there is a virtual image located there, with light coming from it in exactly the same way that light came from the actual object when the film was exposed. This image is the one we see by looking through the holographic film.

Holograms are finding a number of applications in displays and in precision measurements. You may have a hologram on your credit card. This special type of hologram is called a *rainbow hologram,* designed to be viewed in reflected white light.

Holograms represent a means of storing visual information using lasers. In the Context Conclusion, we will investigate means of using lasers to store digital information that can be converted into sound waves or video displays.

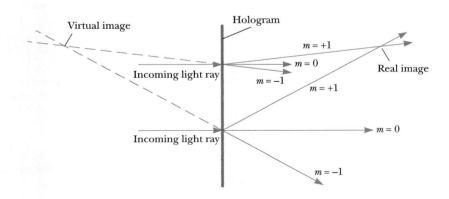

SUMMARY

Physics⊗Now™ Take a practice test by logging into Physics-Now at **www.pop4e.com** and clicking on the Pre-Test link for this chapter.

Interference of light waves is the result of the linear superposition of two or more waves at a given point. A sustained interference pattern is observed if (1) the sources have identical wavelengths and (2) the sources are coherent.

In Young's double-slit experiment, two slits separated by a distance d are illuminated by a monochromatic light source. An interference pattern consisting of bright and dark fringes is observed on a screen that is a distance of $L \gg d$ from the slits. The condition for **constructive interference** is

$$\delta = d \sin \theta_{\text{bright}} = m\lambda \qquad (m = 0, \pm 1, \pm 2, \ldots) \qquad [27.2]$$

The number m is called the **order number** of the fringe.

The condition for **destructive interference** is

$$\delta = d \sin \theta_{\text{dark}} = (m + \tfrac{1}{2})\lambda \qquad (m = 0, \pm 1, \pm 2, \ldots) \qquad [27.3]$$

The **time-averaged light intensity** of the double-slit interference pattern is

$$I_{\text{avg}} = I_{\text{max}} \cos^2 \left(\frac{\pi d \sin \theta}{\lambda} \right) \qquad [27.8]$$

where I_{max} is the maximum intensity on the screen.

An electromagnetic wave traveling from a medium with an index of refraction n_1 toward a medium with index of refraction n_2 undergoes a 180° phase change on reflection when $n_2 > n_1$. No phase change occurs in the reflected wave if $n_2 < n_1$.

The condition for constructive interference in a film of thickness t and refractive index n with the same medium on both sides of the film is given by

$$2nt = (m + \tfrac{1}{2})\lambda \qquad (m = 0, 1, 2, \ldots) \qquad [27.11]$$

Similarly, the condition for destructive interference is

$$2nt = m\lambda \qquad (m = 0, 1, 2, \ldots) \qquad [27.12]$$

Diffraction is the spreading of light from a straight-line path when the light passes through an aperture or around obstacles. A **diffraction pattern** can be analyzed as the interference of a large number of coherent Huygens sources spread across the aperture.

The diffraction pattern produced by a single slit of width a on a distant screen consists of a central, bright maximum and alternating bright and dark regions of much lower intensities. The angles θ at which the diffraction pattern has *zero* intensity are given by

$$\sin \theta_{\text{dark}} = m \frac{\lambda}{a} \qquad (m = \pm 1, \pm 2, \pm 3, \ldots) \qquad [27.13]$$

Rayleigh's criterion, which is a limiting condition of resolution, says that two images formed by an aperture are just distinguishable if the central maximum of the diffraction pattern for one image falls on the first minimum of the other image. The limiting angle of resolution for a slit of width a is given by $\theta_{\text{min}} = \lambda / a$, and the limiting angle of resolution for a circular aperture of diameter D is given by $\theta_{\text{min}} = 1.22\lambda / D$.

A **diffraction grating** consists of a large number of equally spaced, identical slits. The condition for intensity maxima in the interference pattern of a diffraction grating for normal incidence is

$$d \sin \theta_{\text{bright}} = m\lambda \qquad (m = 0, 1, 2, 3, \ldots) \qquad [27.16]$$

where d is the spacing between adjacent slits and m is the order number of the diffraction maximum.

QUESTIONS

☐ = answer available in the *Student Solutions Manual and Study Guide*

1. What is the necessary condition on the path length difference between two waves that interfere (a) constructively and (b) destructively?

2. Explain why two flashlights held close together do not produce an interference pattern on a distant screen.

3. In Young's double-slit experiment, why do we use monochromatic light? If white light is used, how would the pattern change?

4. If Young's double-slit experiment were performed under water, how would the observed interference pattern be affected?

5. A simple way to observe an interference pattern is to look at a distant light source through a stretched handkerchief or an opened umbrella. Explain how that works.

6. A certain oil film on water appears brightest at the outer regions, where it is thinnest. From this information, what can you say about the index of refraction of oil relative to that of water?

7. As a soap bubble evaporates, it appears black just before it breaks. Explain this phenomenon in terms of the phase changes that occur on reflection from the two surfaces of the soap film.

8. If we are to observe interference in a thin film, why must the film not be very thick (with thickness only on the order of a few wavelengths)?

9. Suppose reflected white light is used to observe a thin transparent coating on glass as the coating material is gradually deposited by evaporation in a vacuum. Describe color changes that might occur during the process of building up the thickness of the coating.

10. Holding your hand at arm's length, you can readily block sunlight from your eyes. Why can you not block sound from reaching your ears this way?

11. Why can you hear around corners, but not see around corners?

12. ▨ When you receive a chest x-ray at a hospital, the rays pass through a series of parallel ribs in your chest. Do the ribs act as a diffraction grating for x-rays?

13. Describe the change in width of the central maximum of the single-slit diffraction pattern as the width of the slit is made narrower.

FIGURE **Q27.14**

14. John William Strutt, Lord Rayleigh (1842–1919), is known as the last person to understand all of physics and all of mathematics. He invented an improved foghorn. To warn ships of a coastline, a foghorn should radiate sound in a wide horizontal sheet over the ocean's surface. It should not waste energy by broadcasting sound upward. It should not emit sound downward because the water in front of the foghorn would reflect that sound upward. Rayleigh's foghorn trumpet is shown in Figure Q27.14. Is it installed in the correct orientation? Decide whether the long dimension of the rectangular opening should be horizontal or vertical, and argue for your decision.

15. A laser produces a beam a few millimeters wide, with uniform intensity across its width. A hair is stretched vertically across the front of the laser to cross the beam. How is the diffraction pattern it produces on a distant screen related to that of a vertical slit equal in width to the hair? How could you determine the width of the hair from measurements of its diffraction pattern?

16. A radio station serves listeners in a city to the northeast of its broadcast site. It broadcasts from three adjacent towers on a mountain ridge, along a line running east and west. Show that by introducing time delays among the signals the individual towers radiate, the station can maximize net intensity in the direction toward the city (and in the opposite direction) and minimize the signal transmitted in other directions. The towers together are said to form a *phased array*.

PROBLEMS

1, 2, 3 = straightforward, intermediate, challenging

☐ = full solution available in the *Student Solutions Manual and Study Guide*

Physics⊗Now™ = coached problem with hints available at **www.pop4e.com**

🖥 = computer useful in solving problem

▬ = paired numerical and symbolic problems

▨ = biomedical application

Section 27.1 ▪ Conditions for Interference
Section 27.2 ▪ Young's Double-Slit Experiment
Section 27.3 ▪ Light Waves in Interference

Note: Problems 14.8, 14.10, and 14.11 in Chapter 14 can be assigned with this section.

1. A Young's interference experiment is performed with monochromatic light. The separation between the slits is 0.500 mm, and the interference pattern on a screen 3.30 m away shows the first side maximum 3.40 mm from the center of the pattern. What is the wavelength?

2. In a location where the speed of sound is 354 m/s, a 2 000-Hz sound wave impinges on two slits 30.0 cm apart.

(a) At what angle is the first maximum located? (b) If the sound wave is replaced by 3.00-cm microwaves, what slit separation gives the same angle for the first maximum? (c) If the slit separation is 1.00 μm, what frequency of light gives the same first maximum angle?

3. Two radio antennas separated by 300 m as shown in Figure P27.3 simultaneously broadcast identical signals at the same wavelength. A radio in a car traveling due north

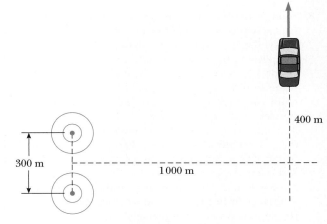

FIGURE **P27.3**

receives the signals. (a) If the car is at the position of the second maximum, what is the wavelength of the signals? (b) How much farther must the car travel to encounter the next minimum in reception?

4. The two speakers of a boom box are 35.0 cm apart. A single oscillator makes the speakers vibrate in phase at a frequency of 2.00 kHz. At what angles, measured from the perpendicular bisector of the line joining the speakers, would a distant observer hear maximum sound intensity? Minimum sound intensity? (Take the speed of sound as 340 m/s.)

5. Physics⊗Now™ Young's double-slit experiment is performed with 589-nm light and a distance of 2.00 m between the slits and the screen. The tenth interference minimum is observed 7.26 mm from the central maximum. Determine the spacing of the slits.

6. A riverside warehouse has two open doors as shown in Figure P27.6. Its walls are lined with sound-absorbing material. A boat on the river sounds its horn. To person A the sound is loud and clear. To person B the sound is barely audible. The principal wavelength of the sound waves is 3.00 m. Assuming that person B is at the position of the first minimum, determine the distance between the doors, center to center.

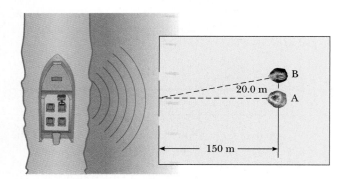

FIGURE **P27.6**

7. Two slits are separated by 0.320 mm. A beam of 500-nm light strikes the slits, producing an interference pattern. Determine the number of maxima observed in the angular range $-30.0° < \theta < 30.0°$.

8. Young's double-slit experiment underlies the *instrument landing system* used to guide aircraft to safe landings when the visibility is poor. Although real systems are more complicated than the example described here, they operate on the same principles. A pilot is trying to align her plane with a runway, as suggested in Figure P27.8a. Two radio antennas A_1 and A_2 are positioned adjacent to the runway, separated by 40.0 m. The antennas broadcast unmodulated coherent radio waves at 30.0 MHz. (a) Find the wavelength of the waves. The pilot "locks onto" the strong signal radiated along an interference maximum and steers the plane to keep the received signal strong. If she has found the central maximum, the plane will have just the right heading to land when it reaches the runway. (b) Suppose instead the plane is flying along the first side maximum (Fig. P27.8b). How far to the side of the runway

centerline will the plane be when it is 2.00 km from the antennas? (c) It is possible to tell the pilot that she is on the wrong maximum by sending out two signals from each antenna and equipping the aircraft with a two-channel receiver. The ratio of the two frequencies must not be the ratio of small integers (such as 3/4). Explain how this two-frequency system would work and why it would not necessarily work if the frequencies were related by an integer ratio.

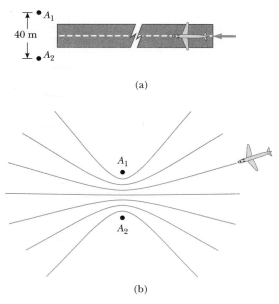

(a)

(b)

FIGURE **P27.8**

9. In Figure 27.4, let $L = 1.20$ m and $d = 0.120$ mm and assume that the slit system is illuminated with monochromatic 500-nm light. Calculate the phase difference between the two wave fronts arriving at P when (a) $\theta = 0.500°$ and (b) $y = 5.00$ mm. (c) What is the value of θ for which the phase difference is 0.333 rad? (d) What is the value of θ for which the path difference is $\lambda/4$?

10. Coherent light rays of wavelength λ strike a pair of slits separated by distance d at an angle θ_1 as shown in Figure P27.10. Assume that an interference maximum is formed at an angle θ_2 a great distance from the slits. Show that $d(\sin \theta_2 - \sin \theta_1) = m\lambda$, where m is an integer.

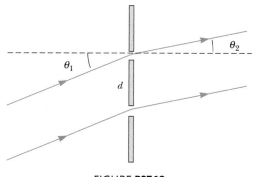

FIGURE **P27.10**

11. In Figure 27.4, let $L = 120$ cm and $d = 0.250$ cm. The slits are illuminated with coherent 600-nm light. Calculate the distance y above the central maximum for which the average intensity on the screen is 75.0% of the maximum.

12. The intensity on the screen at a certain point in a double-slit interference pattern is 64.0% of the maximum value. (a) What minimum phase difference (in radians) between sources produces this result? (b) Express this phase difference as a path difference for 486.1-nm light.

13. Two slits are separated by 0.180 mm. An interference pattern is formed on a screen 80.0 cm away by 656.3-nm light. Calculate the fraction of the maximum intensity 0.600 cm above the central maximum.

Section 27.4 ■ Change of Phase Due to Reflection
Section 27.5 ■ Interference in Thin Films

14. A soap bubble ($n = 1.33$) is floating in air. If the thickness of the bubble wall is 115 nm, what is the wavelength of the light that is most strongly reflected?

15. An oil film ($n = 1.45$) floating on water is illuminated by white light at normal incidence. The film is 280 nm thick. Find (a) the color of the light in the visible spectrum most strongly reflected and (b) the color of the light in the spectrum most strongly transmitted. Explain your reasoning.

16. A possible means for making an airplane invisible to radar is to coat the plane with an antireflective polymer. If radar waves have a wavelength of 3.00 cm and the index of refraction of the polymer is $n = 1.50$, how thick would you make the coating?

17. A material having an index of refraction of 1.30 is used as an antireflective coating on a piece of glass ($n = 1.50$). What should be the minimum thickness of this film to minimize reflection of 500-nm light?

18. Astronomers observe the chromosphere of the Sun with a filter that passes the red hydrogen spectral line of wavelength 656.3 nm, called the H_α line. The filter consists of a transparent dielectric of thickness d held between two partially aluminized glass plates. The filter is held at a constant temperature. (a) Find the minimum value of d that produces maximum transmission of perpendicular H_α light if the dielectric has index of refraction 1.378. (b) If the temperature of the filter increases above the normal value, what happens to the transmitted wavelength? (Its index of refraction does not change significantly.) (c) The dielectric will also pass what near-visible wavelength? One of the glass plates is colored red to absorb this light.

19. Physics✸Now™ An air wedge is formed between two glass plates separated at one edge by a very fine wire as shown in Figure P27.19. When the wedge is illuminated from above by 600-nm light and viewed from above, 30 dark fringes are observed. Calculate the radius of the wire.

FIGURE P27.19

Section 27.6 ■ Diffraction Patterns

20. Helium–neon laser light ($\lambda = 632.8$ nm) is sent through a 0.300-mm-wide single slit. What is the width of the central maximum on a screen 1.00 m from the slit?

21. Physics✸Now™ A screen is placed 50.0 cm from a single slit, which is illuminated with 690-nm light. If the distance between the first and third minima in the diffraction pattern is 3.00 mm, what is the width of the slit?

22. A beam of monochromatic green light is diffracted by a slit of width 0.550 mm. The diffraction pattern forms on a wall 2.06 m beyond the slit. The distance between the positions of zero intensity on both sides of the central bright fringe is 4.10 mm. Calculate the wavelength of the light.

23. Coherent microwaves of wavelength 5.00 cm enter a long, narrow window in a building otherwise essentially opaque to the microwaves. If the window is 36.0 cm wide, what is the distance from the central maximum to the first-order minimum along a wall 6.50 m from the window?

24. Sound with a frequency 650 Hz from a distant source passes through a doorway 1.10 m wide in a sound-absorbing wall. Find the number and approximate directions of the diffraction-maximum beams radiated into the space beyond.

25. A beam of laser light of wavelength 632.8 nm has a circular cross-section 2.00 mm in diameter. A rectangular aperture is to be placed in the center of the beam so that when the light falls perpendicularly on a wall 4.50 m away, the central maximum fills a rectangle 110 mm wide and 6.00 mm high. The dimensions are measured between the minima bracketing the central maximum. Find the required width and height of the aperture.

Section 27.7 ■ Resolution of Single-Slit and Circular Apertures

26. The pupil of a cat's eye narrows to a vertical slit of width 0.500 mm in daylight. What is the angular resolution for horizontally separated mice? Assume that the average wavelength of the light is 500 nm.

27. Physics✸Now™ A helium–neon laser emits light that has a wavelength of 632.8 nm. The circular aperture through which the beam emerges has a diameter of 0.500 cm. Estimate the diameter of the beam 10.0 km from the laser.

28. Narrow, parallel, glowing gas-filled tubes in a variety of colors form block letters to spell out the name of a nightclub. Adjacent tubes are all 2.80 cm apart. The tubes forming one letter are filled with neon and radiate predominantly red light with a wavelength of 640 nm. For another letter, the tubes emit predominantly violet light at 440 nm. The pupil of a dark-adapted viewer's eye is 5.20 mm in diameter. If she is in a certain range of distances away, the viewer can resolve the separate tubes of one color but not the other. Which color is easier to resolve? The viewer's distance must be in what range for her to resolve the tubes of only one of these two colors?

29. The Impressionist painter Georges Seurat created paintings with an enormous number of dots of pure pigment, each of which was approximately 2.00 mm in diameter.

The idea was to have colors such as red and green next to each other to form a scintillating canvas (Fig. P27.29). Outside what distance would one be unable to discern individual dots on the canvas? (Assume that $\lambda = 500$ nm and that the pupil diameter is 4.00 mm.)

FIGURE **P27.29** *Sunday Afternoon on the Isle of La Grande Jatte,* by Georges Seurat.

30. A spy satellite can consist essentially of a large-diameter concave mirror forming an image on a digital-camera detector and sending the picture to a ground receiver by radio waves. In effect, it is an astronomical telescope in orbit, looking down instead of up. Can a spy satellite read a license plate? Can it read the date on a dime? Argue for your answers by making an order-of-magnitude calculation, specifying the data you estimate.

31. A circular radar antenna on a Coast Guard ship has a diameter of 2.10 m and radiates at a frequency of 15.0 GHz. Two small boats are located 9.00 km away from the ship. How close together could the boats be and still be detected as two objects?

Section 27.8 ∎ The Diffraction Grating

Note: In the following problems, assume that the light is incident normally on the gratings.

32. Light from an argon laser strikes a diffraction grating that has 5 310 grooves per centimeter. The central and first-order principal maxima are separated by 0.488 m on a wall 1.72 m from the grating. Determine the wavelength of the laser light.

33. **Physics⊗Now™** The hydrogen spectrum has a red line at 656 nm and a blue line at 434 nm. What are the angular separations between two spectral lines obtained with a diffraction grating that has 4 500 grooves/cm?

34. A helium–neon laser ($\lambda = 632.8$ nm) is used to calibrate a diffraction grating. If the first-order maximum occurs at 20.5°, what is the spacing between adjacent grooves in the grating?

35. A grating with 250 grooves/mm is used with an incandescent light source. Assume that the visible spectrum ranges in wavelength from 400 to 700 nm. In how many orders can one see (a) the entire visible spectrum and (b) the short-wavelength region?

36. Show that whenever white light is passed through a diffraction grating of any spacing size, the violet end of the continuous visible spectrum in third order always overlaps with red light at the other end of the second-order spectrum.

37. A refrigerator shelf is an array of parallel wires with uniform spacing of 1.30 cm between centers. In air at 20°C, ultrasound with a frequency of 37.2 kHz from a distant source falls perpendicularly on the shelf. Find the number of diffracted beams leaving the other side of the shelf. Find the direction of each beam.

Section 27.9 ∎ Diffraction of X-Rays by Crystals

38. Potassium iodide (KI) has the same crystalline structure as NaCl, with atomic planes separated by 0.353 nm. A monochromatic x-ray beam shows a first-order diffraction maximum when the grazing angle is 7.60°. Calculate the x-ray wavelength.

39. If the interplanar spacing of NaCl is 0.281 nm, what is the predicted angle at which 0.140-nm x-rays are diffracted in a first-order maximum?

40. In water of uniform depth, a wide pier is supported on pilings in several parallel rows 2.80 m apart. Ocean waves of uniform wavelength roll in, moving in a direction that makes an angle of 80.0° with the rows of posts. Find the three longest wavelengths of waves that will be strongly reflected by the pilings.

Section 27.10 ∎ Context Connection—Holography

41. A wide beam of laser light with a wavelength of 632.8 nm is directed through several narrow parallel slits, separated by 1.20 mm, and falls on a sheet of photographic film 1.40 m away. The exposure time is chosen so that the film stays unexposed everywhere except at the central region of each bright fringe. (a) Find the distance between these interference maxima. The film is printed as a transparency; it is opaque everywhere except at the exposed lines. Next, the same beam of laser light is directed through the transparency and is allowed to fall on a screen 1.40 m beyond. (b) Argue that several narrow parallel bright regions, separated by 1.20 mm, will appear on the screen as real images of the original slits. If at last the screen is removed, light will diverge from the images of the original slits with the same reconstructed wave fronts as the original slits produced. (*Suggestion:* You may find it useful to draw a diagram similar to Fig. 27.20. A similar train of thought, at a soccer game, led Dennis Gabor to the invention of holography.)

42. A helium–neon laser can produce a green laser beam instead of red. Refer to Figure 24.18, which omits some energy levels between E_2 and E_1. After a population inversion is established, neon atoms make a variety of downward transitions in falling from the state labeled E_3^* down eventually to level E_1. The atoms emit both red light with a wavelength of 632.8 nm and green light with a wavelength of 543 nm in a competing transition. Assume that the atoms are in a cavity between mirrors designed to reflect the green light with high efficiency but to allow the red light to leave the cavity immediately. Then stimulated emission can lead to the buildup of a collimated beam of green

light between the mirrors, having a greater intensity than does the red light. A small fraction of the green light can be permitted to escape by transmission through one mirror to constitute the radiated laser beam. The mirrors forming the resonant cavity are not made of shiny metal, but of layered dielectrics, say silicon dioxide and titanium dioxide. (a) How thick a layer of silicon dioxide, between layers of titanium dioxide, would minimize reflection of the red light? (b) What should be the thickness of a similar but separate layer of silicon dioxide to maximize reflection of the green light?

Additional Problems

43. **Review problem.** This problem extends the result of Problem 14.11. Figure P27.43 shows two adjacent vibrating balls dipping into a tank of water. At distant points they produce an interference pattern as diagrammed in Figure 27.2. Let λ represent the wavelength of the ripples. Show that the two sources produce a standing wave along the line segment, of length d, between them. In terms of λ and d, find the number of nodes and the number of antinodes in the standing wave. Find the number of zones of constructive and of destructive interference in the interference pattern far away from the sources. Each line of destructive interference springs from a node in the standing wave, and each line of constructive interference springs from an antinode.

FIGURE **P27.43**

44. Raise your hand and hold it flat. Think of the space between your index finger and your middle finger as one slit, and think of the space between middle finger and ring finger as a second slit. (a) Consider the interference resulting from sending coherent visible light perpendicularly through this pair of openings. Compute an order-of-magnitude estimate for the angle between adjacent zones of constructive interference. (b) To make the angles in the interference pattern easy to measure with a plastic protractor, you should use an electromagnetic wave with frequency of what order of magnitude? How is this wave classified on the electromagnetic spectrum?

45. **Review problem.** A flat piece of glass is held stationary and horizontal above the flat top end of a 10.0-cm-long vertical metal rod that has its lower end rigidly fixed. The thin film of air between the rod and glass is observed to be bright by

reflected light when it is illuminated by light of wavelength 500 nm. As the temperature is slowly increased by 25.0°C, the film changes from bright to dark and back to bright 200 times. What is the coefficient of linear expansion of the metal?

46. Laser light with a wavelength of 632.8 nm is directed through one slit or two slits and allowed to fall on a screen 2.60 m beyond. Figure P27.46 shows the pattern on the screen, nearly actual size, with a centimeter rule below it. Did the light pass through one slit or two slits? If one, find its width. If two, find the distance between their centers.

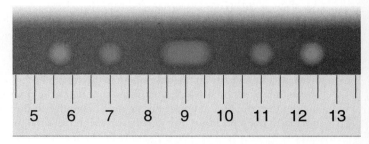

FIGURE **P27.46**

47. Interference effects are produced at point P on a screen as a result of direct rays from a 500-nm source and reflected rays from the mirror as shown in Figure P27.47. Assume that the source is 100 m to the left of the screen and 1.00 cm above the mirror. Find the distance y to the first dark band above the mirror.

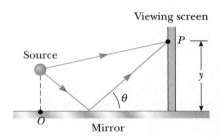

FIGURE **P27.47**

48. The waves from a radio station can reach a home receiver by two paths. One is a straight-line path from transmitter to home, a distance of 30.0 km. The second path is by reflection from the ionosphere (a layer of ionized air molecules high in the atmosphere). Assume that this reflection takes place at a point midway between receiver and transmitter and that the wavelength broadcast by the radio station is 350 m. Find the minimum height of the ionospheric layer that produces destructive interference between the direct and reflected beams. (Assume that no phase change occurs on reflection.)

49. ▨ Many cells are transparent and colorless. Structures of great interest in biology and medicine can be practically invisible to ordinary microscopy. An *interference microscope* reveals a difference in refractive index as a shift in interference fringes to indicate the size and shape of cell structures. The idea is exemplified in the following problem.

An air wedge is formed between two glass plates in contact along one edge and slightly separated at the opposite edge. When the plates are illuminated with monochromatic light from above, the reflected light has 85 dark fringes. Calculate the number of dark fringes that appear if water ($n = 1.33$) replaces the air between the plates.

50. (a) Both sides of a uniform film that has index of refraction n and thickness d are in contact with air. For normal incidence of light, an intensity minimum is observed in the reflected light at λ_2 and an intensity maximum is observed at λ_1, where $\lambda_1 > \lambda_2$. Assuming that no intensity minima are observed between λ_1 and λ_2, show that the integer m in Equations 27.11 and 27.12 is given by $m = \lambda_1 / 2(\lambda_1 - \lambda_2)$. (b) Determine the thickness of the film, assuming that $n = 1.40$, $\lambda_1 = 500$ nm, and $\lambda_2 = 370$ nm.

51. The condition for constructive interference by reflection from a thin film in air as developed in Section 27.5 assumes nearly normal incidence. Show that if the light is incident on the film at a nonzero angle ϕ_1 (relative to the normal), the condition for constructive interference is $2nt \cos \theta_2 = (m + \frac{1}{2})\lambda$, where θ_2 is the angle of refraction.

52. A soap film ($n = 1.33$) is contained within a rectangular wire frame. The frame is held vertically so that the film drains downward and forms a wedge with flat faces. The thickness of the film at the top is essentially zero. The film is viewed in reflected white light with near-normal incidence, and the first violet ($\lambda = 420$ nm) interference band is observed 3.00 cm from the top edge of the film. (a) Locate the first red ($\lambda = 680$ nm) interference band. (b) Determine the film thickness at the positions of the violet and red bands. (c) What is the wedge angle of the film?

53. Light from a helium–neon laser ($\lambda = 632.8$ nm) is incident on a single slit. What is the maximum width of the slit for which no diffraction minima are observed?

54. Figure P27.54 shows a megaphone in use. Construct a theoretical description of how a megaphone works. You may assume that the sound of your voice radiates just through the opening of your mouth. Most of the information in speech is carried not in a signal at the fundamental frequency, but in noises and in harmonics, with frequencies of a few thousand hertz. Does your theory allow any prediction that is simple to test?

FIGURE **P27.54**

55. **Review problem.** A beam of 541-nm light is incident on a diffraction grating that has 400 grooves/mm. (a) Determine the angle of the second-order ray. (b) If the entire apparatus is immersed in water, what is the new second-order angle of diffraction? (c) Show that the two diffracted rays of parts (a) and (b) are related through the law of refraction.

56. The *Very Large Array* (VLA) is a set of 27 radio telescope dishes in Caton and Socorro counties, New Mexico (Fig P27.56). The antennas can be moved apart on railroad tracks, and their combined signals give the resolving power of a synthetic aperture 36.0 km in diameter. (a) If the detectors are tuned to a frequency of 1.40 GHz, what is the angular resolution of the VLA? (b) Clouds of hydrogen radiate at this frequency. What must be the separation distance of two clouds at the center of the galaxy, 26 000 lightyears away, if they are to be resolved? (c) As the telescope looks up, a circling hawk looks down. Find the angular resolution of the hawk's eye. Assume that that the hawk is most sensitive to green light having wavelength 500 nm and that it has a pupil of diameter 12.0 mm. (d) A mouse is on the ground 30.0 m below. By what distance must the mouse's whiskers be separated if the hawk can resolve them?

FIGURE **P27.56** A rancher in New Mexico rides past one of the 27 radio telescopes that make up the Very Large Array (VLA).

57. Light of wavelength 500 nm is incident normally on a diffraction grating. If the third-order maximum of the diffraction pattern is observed at 32.0°, (a) what is the number of rulings per centimeter for the grating? (b) Determine the total number of primary maxima that can be observed in this situation.

58. Iridescent peacock feathers are shown in Figure P27.58a. The surface of one microscopic barbule is composed of transparent keratin that supports rods of dark brown melanin in a regular lattice, represented in Figure P27.58b. (Your fingernails are made of keratin, and melanin is the dark pigment giving color to human skin.) In a portion of the feather that can appear turquoise, assume that the melanin rods are uniformly separated by 0.25 μm, with air between them. (a) Explain how this

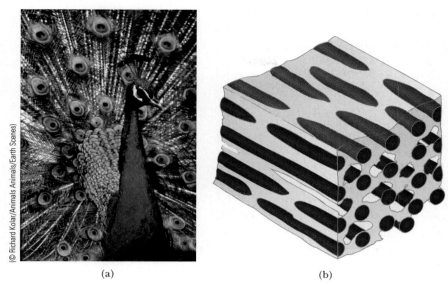

FIGURE **P27.58** (a) Iridescence in peacock feathers. (b) Microscopic section of a feather showing dark melanin rods in a pale keratin matrix.

structure can appear blue–green when it contains no blue or green pigment. (b) Explain how it can also appear violet if light falls on it in a different direction. (c) Explain how it can present different colors to your two eyes at the same time, a characteristic of iridescence. (d) A compact disc can appear to be any color of the rainbow. Explain why this portion of the feather cannot appear yellow or red. (e) What could be different about the array of melanin rods in a portion of the feather that does appear to be red?

59. A beam of bright red light of wavelength 654 nm passes through a diffraction grating. Enclosing the space beyond the grating is a large screen forming one half of a cylinder centered on the grating, with its axis parallel to the slits in the grating. Fifteen bright spots appear on the screen. Find the maximum and minimum possible values for the slit separation in the diffraction grating.

60. A *pinhole camera* has a small circular aperture of diameter D. Light from distant objects passes through the aperture into an otherwise dark box, falling on a screen located a distance L away. If D is too large, the display on the screen will be fuzzy because a bright point in the field of view will send light onto a circle of diameter slightly larger than D. On the other hand, if D is too small, diffraction will blur the display on the screen. The screen shows a reasonably sharp image if the diameter of the central disk of the diffraction pattern, specified by Equation 27.15, is equal to D at the screen. (a) Show that for monochromatic light with plane wave fronts and $L \gg D$, the condition for a sharp view is fulfilled if $D^2 = 2.44 \lambda L$. (b) Find the optimum pinhole diameter for 500-nm light projected onto a screen 15.0 cm away.

61. Two wavelengths λ and $\lambda + \Delta\lambda$ (with $\Delta\lambda \ll \lambda$) are incident on a diffraction grating. Show that the angular separation between the spectral lines in the mth-order spectrum is

$$\Delta\theta = \frac{\Delta\lambda}{\sqrt{(d/m)^2 - \lambda^2}}$$

where d is the slit spacing and m is the order number.

ANSWERS TO QUICK QUIZZES

27.1 (c). Equation 27.2 shows that decreasing λ will decrease the angle θ_{bright} and bring the fringes closer together. Equation 27.5 shows that decreasing L decreases y_{bright} and brings the fringes closer together. Immersing the apparatus in water decreases the wavelength so that the fringes move closer together.

27.2 (a). One of the materials has a higher index of refraction than water, the other lower. For the material with a higher index of refraction, there is a 180° phase shift for the light reflected from the upper surface but no such phase change from the lower surface because the index of refraction for water on the other side is lower than that of the film. Thus, the two reflections are out of phase and interfere destructively.

27.3 (a). At the left edge, the air wedge has zero thickness and the only contribution to the interference is the 180°

phase shift as the light reflects from the upper surface of the glass slide.

27.4 (i), (a). Equation 27.13 shows that a decrease in a results in an increase in the angles at which the dark fringes appear. (ii), (c). Equation 27.13 shows that a decrease in λ results in a decrease in the angles at which the dark fringes appear.

27.5 (a). We would like to reduce the minimum angular separation for two objects below the angle subtended by the two stars in the binary system. We can do that by reducing the wavelength of the light, which in essence makes the aperture larger, relative to the light wavelength, increasing the resolving power. Thus, we should choose a blue filter.

27.6 (c). With the doubled wavelength, the pattern will be wider. Choices (a) and (d) make the pattern even wider. From Equation 27.16, we see that choice (b) causes $\sin \theta_{bright}$ to be twice as large. Because we cannot use the small angle approximation, however, a doubling of $\sin \theta_{bright}$ is not the same as a doubling of θ_{bright}, which would translate to a doubling of the position of a maximum along the screen. If we only consider small-angle maxima, choice (b) would work, but it does not work in the large-angle case.

Using Lasers to Record and Read Digital Information

We have now investigated the principles of optics and can respond to our central question for the *Lasers* Context:

> **What is special about laser light and how is it used in technological applications?**

In the Context Connections in Chapters 24 to 27, we discussed two primary technological applications of lasers: optical fibers and holography. In this Context Conclusion, we will choose one more from the vast number of possibilities, the storage and retrieval of information on compact discs (as well as CD-ROMs and digital video, or versatile, discs, DVDs).

The storage of information in a small volume of space is a goal toward which humans have worked for several decades. In the early days of computing, information was stored on punched cards. This method seems humorous in today's world, especially because the area taken up by laying the cards representing a page of text out on a table was larger than the original page of text.

The magnetic disc recording and storage technique introduced in the 1950s allowed a reduction in space over that taken up by the original data. The beginning of optical storage occurred in the 1970s with the introduction of videodiscs. These plastic discs included encoded pits representing the analog information associated with a video signal. A laser, focused by lenses to a spot about 1 micrometer (μm) in diameter, is used to read the data. When the laser light reflects off the flat area of the disc, the light is reflected back into the system and is detected. When the light encounters a pit, some of it is scattered. The light reflected from the bottom of the pit interferes destructively with that reflected from the surface, and very little of the incident light finds its way back to the detection system.

The next step in the optical recording story involves the digital revolution, exemplified by the introduction of the compact disc, or CD. The reading of the disc is similar to that of the videodisc, but the information is stored in a *digital* format. Musical CDs were rapidly accepted by the public with much more enthusiasm than videodiscs. Shortly after the introduction of CDs, plans were announced to market an optical disc for storage of information for computers, the CD-ROM.

Digital Recording

In digital recording, information is converted to binary code (ones and zeros), similar to the dots and dashes of Morse code. First, the waveform of the sound is *sampled,* typically at the rate of 44 100 times per second. Figure 1 illustrates this process. The sampling frequency is much higher than the upper range of hearing, about 20 000 Hz, so all audible frequencies of sound are sampled at this rate. During each sampling, the pressure of the wave is measured and converted to a voltage. Thus, there are 44 100 numbers associated with each second of the sound being sampled.

These measurements are then converted to *binary numbers,* which are numbers expressed to base 2 rather than base 10. Table 1 shows some sample binary numbers.

FIGURE 1 Sound is digitized by sampling the sound waveform at periodic intervals. During each interval, a number is recorded for the average voltage during the interval. The sampling rate shown here is much slower than the actual sampling rate of 44 100 per second.

TABLE 1	Sample Binary Numbers	
Number in Base 10	**Number in Binary**	**Sum**
1	0000000000000001	1
2	0000000000000010	2 + 0
3	0000000000000011	2 + 1
10	0000000000001010	8 + 0 + 2 + 0
37	0000000000100101	32 + 0 + 0 + 4 + 0 + 1
275	0000000100010011	256 + 0 + 0 + 0 + 16 + 0 + 0 + 2 + 1

Generally, voltage measurements are recorded in 16-bit "words," where each bit is a one or a zero. Thus, the number of different voltage levels that can be assigned codes is $2^{16} = 65\ 536$. The number of bits in 1 second of sound is $16 \times 44\ 100 = 705\ 600$. These strings of ones and zeros, in 16-bit words, are recorded on the surface of a CD.

Figure 2 shows a magnification of the surface of a CD. There are two types of areas that are detected by the laser playback system: *lands* and *pits*. The lands are untouched regions of the disc surface that are highly reflective. The pits are areas that have been burned into the surface by a recording laser. The playback system, described below, converts the pits and lands into binary ones and zeros.

The binary numbers read from the CD are converted back to voltages, and the waveform is reconstructed as shown in Figure 3. Because the sampling rate is so high—44 100 voltage readings each second—the step-wise nature of the reconstructed waveform is not evident in the sound.

The advantage of digital recording is in the high fidelity of the sound. With analog recording, any small imperfection in the record surface or the recording equipment can cause a distortion of the waveform. If all peaks of a maximum in a waveform are clipped off so as to be only 90% as high, for example, there will be a major effect on the spectrum of the sound in an analog recording. With digital recording, however, it takes a major imperfection to turn a one into a zero. If an imperfection causes the magnitude of a one to be 90% of the original value, it still registers as a one and there is no distortion. Another advantage of digital recording is that the information is extracted optically, so there is no mechanical wear on the disc.

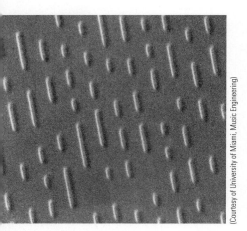

FIGURE 2 The surface of a compact disc, showing the pits. Transitions between pits and lands correspond to ones. Regions without transitions correspond to zeros.

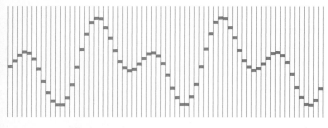

FIGURE 3 The reconstruction of the sound wave sampled in Figure 1. Notice that the reconstruction is step-wise, rather than the continuous waveform in Figure 1.

Digital Playback

Figure 4 shows the detection system of a CD player. The optical components are mounted on a track (not shown in the figure) that rolls radially so that the system can access all regions of the disc. The laser is located near the bottom of the figure, directing its light upward. The light is collimated by a lens into a parallel beam and passes through a beam splitter. The beam splitter serves no purpose for light on the way up, but it is important for the return light. The laser beam is then focused to a very small spot on the disc by the objective lens.

If the light encounters a pit in the disc, the light is scattered and very little light returns along the original path. If the light encounters a flat region of the disc at which a pit has not been recorded, the light reflects back along its original path. The reflected light moves downward in the diagram, arriving at the beam splitter so that it is partially reflected to the right. Lenses focus the beam, which is then detected by the photocell.

The playback system samples the reflected light 705 600 times per second. When the laser moves from a pit to a land or from a land to a pit, the reflected light changes during the sampling and the bit is recorded as a one. If there is no change during the sampling, the bit is recorded as a zero. The electronic circuitry in the CD player converts the series of zeros and ones back into an audible signal. This technology can also be used to store video information on a disc, leading to the rapid growth of DVD in the later years of the 20th century.

Problems

1. Compact disc (CD) and digital video disc (DVD) players use interference to generate a strong signal from a tiny bump. The depth of a pit is chosen to be one quarter of the wavelength of the laser light used to read the disc. Then light reflected from the pit and light reflected from the adjoining land differ in path length traveled by one-half wavelength, to interfere destructively at the detector. As the disc rotates, the light intensity drops significantly whenever light is reflected from near a pit edge. The space between the leading and trailing edges of a pit determines the time interval between the fluctuations. The series of time intervals is decoded into a series of zeros and ones that carries the stored information. Assume that infrared light with a wavelength of 780 nm in vacuum is used in a CD player. The disc is coated with plastic having a refractive index of 1.50. What should be the depth of each pit? A DVD player uses light of a shorter wavelength, and the pit dimensions are correspondingly smaller, one factor that results in greater storage capacity on a DVD compared with a CD.

2. The laser in a CD player must precisely follow the spiral track, along which the distance between one loop of the spiral and the next is only about 1.25 μm. A feedback mechanism lets the player know if the laser drifts off the track so that the player can steer it back again. Figure 5 shows how a diffraction grating is used to provide information to keep the beam on track. The laser light passes through a diffraction grating just before it reaches the disc. The strong central maximum of the diffraction pattern is used to read the information in the track of pits. The two first-order side maxima are used for steering. The grating is designed so that the first-order maxima fall on the flat surfaces on both sides of the information track. Both side beams are reflected into their own detectors. As long as both beams are reflecting from smooth, nonpitted surfaces they are detected with constant high intensity. If the main beam wanders off the track, however, one of the side beams will begin to strike pits on the information track and the reflected light will diminish. This change is used with an electronic circuit to guide the beam back to the desired location. Assume that the laser light has a wavelength of 780 nm and that the diffraction grating is positioned 6.90 μm from the disc. Assume that the first-order beams are to fall on the disc 0.400 μm on either side of the information track. What should be the number of grooves per millimeter in the grating?

3. The speed with which the surface of a compact disc passes the laser is 1.3 m/s. What is the average length of the audio track on a CD associated with each bit of the audio information?

4. Consider the photograph of the compact disc surface in Figure 2. Audio data undergoes complicated processing to reduce a variety of errors in reading the data. Therefore, an audio "word" is not laid out linearly on the disc. Suppose data

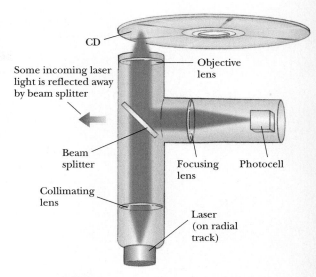

FIGURE 4 The detection system of a compact disc player. The laser (bottom) sends a beam of light upward. Laser light reflected back from the disc and then reflected to the right by the beam splitter enters a photocell. The digital information entering the photocell as pulses of light is converted to audio information.

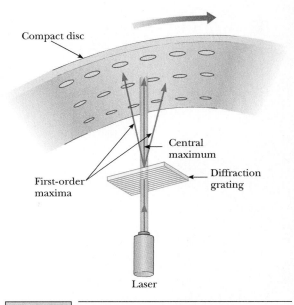

FIGURE 5 A tracking system in a CD player.

has been read from the disc, the error coding has been removed, and the resulting audio word is

$$1\ 0\ 1\ 1\ 1\ 0\ 1\ 1\ 1\ 0\ 1\ 1\ 1\ 0\ 1\ 1$$

What is the decimal number represented by this 16-bit word?

5. Lasers are also used in the recording process for a *magnetooptical disc*. To record a pit, its location on the ferromagnetic layer of the disc must be raised above a minimum temperature called the Curie temperature. Imagine that the surface moves past the laser at a speed on the order of 1 m/s and that the pit is modeled as a cylinder 1 μm deep with a radius of 1 μm. The ferromagnetic material has the following properties: its Curie temperature is 600 K, its specific heat is 300 J/kg·°C, and its density is 2×10^3 kg/m^3. What is the order of magnitude of the intensity of the laser beam necessary to raise the pit above the Curie temperature?

CONTEXT 9

The Cosmic Connection

In this final Context, we investigate the principles included in the area of physics commonly called *modern physics.* Modern physics encompasses the revolution in physics that commenced at the beginning of the 20th century. We began our discussion of modern physics in Chapter 9 in our study of relativity. Other aspects of modern physics—including atomic spectra and the Bohr model in Chapter 11, quantization of angular momentum and energy in Chapter 11, black holes in Chapter 11, black bodies in Chapter 24, and the discussion of the photon in Chapter 24—have appeared at various locations throughout the book.

In this book, we stress the importance of models in understanding physical phenomena. At the turn of the 20th century, classical physics was well established and provided many principles on which models for phenomena could be built. Many experimental observations, however, could not be brought into agreement with theory using classical models. Attempts to apply the laws of classical physics to atomic systems were consistently unsuccessful in making accurate predictions of the behavior of matter on the atomic scale. Various phenomena such as blackbody radiation,

the photoelectric effect, and the emission of sharp spectral lines by atoms in a gas discharge could not be understood within the framework of classical physics. Between 1900 and 1930, however, new models collectively called *quantum physics* or *quantum mechanics* were highly successful in explaining the behavior of atoms, molecules, and nuclei. Like relativity, quantum physics requires a modification of our ideas concerning the physical world. Quantum mechanics does not, however, directly contradict or invalidate classical mechanics. As with relativity, the equations of quantum physics reduce to classical equations in the appropriate realm, that is, when the quantum equations are used to describe macroscopic systems.

An extensive study of quantum physics is certainly beyond the scope of this book and therefore this Context is simply an introduction to its underlying ideas. One of the true successes of quantum physics is the connection it makes between microscopic phenomena and the structure and evolution of the Universe. Ironically, recent developments in physics that probe smaller and smaller scales allow us to advance our understanding of the larger and larger systems that are familiar to us. This connection

(Comstock Royalty Free/Getty)

FIGURE 1 A person works on a personal digital assistant. The appearance of information on the display is due to the behavior of microscopic electrons in the circuitry of the microprocessor.

(a)

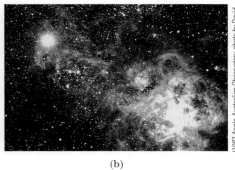

(b)

(1987 Anglo-Australian Observatory, photo by David Malin)

FIGURE 2 Supernova 1987A. (a) The region of the Tarantula Nebula (lower right) of the Large Magellanic Cloud before the supernova. (b) The supernova appears at the upper left on February 24, 1987. An understanding of this cosmic explosion is found in the interactions between the microscopic particles within the nucleus.

(NASA, ESA, and The Hubble Heritage Team)

FIGURE 3 An image taken by the Hubble Space Telescope in January 2004 of galaxy AM 0644-741, called a "ring galaxy." Such a galaxy is formed from a collision with a second galaxy, called the intruder. The intruder punches through the center of the target galaxy, leaving a yellow nucleus in the case of AM 0644-741. The surrounding ring is expanding, similar to a ripple expanding outward from a disturbance in a pond. In the chaos in the ring, gas clouds collide and collapse gravitationally into new stars of large mass and high temperature, emitting light that is strong in the blue part of the visible spectrum. Several other galaxies are also visible in this photograph. Across the entire sky, it is estimated that the Hubble Space Telescope can detect 100 billion galaxies. It is also estimated that this is a very small fraction of all the galaxies in the visible part of the Universe. To develop a theory of the origin of this tremendously large system, we need to understand quarks, the most fundamental theorized particles.

between the small and the large is the theme of this Context.

Let us consider some examples of macroscopic systems and their connection to the behavior of microscopic particles. Consider your experiences with common electronic devices that are used today to view information on a liquid crystal display: handheld calculators, personal digital assistants (PDAs), cell phones, and video monitors. The events you observe—the appearance of numbers, to-do lists, or photographs on an LCD display—are macroscopic, but what controls these macroscopic events? They are controlled by a microprocessor within the electronic device. The operation of the microprocessor depends on the behavior of electrons within the solid-state material in an integrated circuit chip. The design and manufacture of the macroscopic electronic device are not possible without an understanding of the behavior of the electrons.

As a second example, a supernova explosion is clearly a macroscopic event; it is a star with a radius on the order of billions of meters undergoing a violent event. We have been able to advance our understanding of such events by studying the atomic nucleus, which is on the order of 10^{-15} m in size.

If we imagine an even larger system than a star—the entire Universe—we can advance our understanding of its origin by thinking about particles even smaller than the nucleus. Consider the constituents of protons and neutrons, called *quarks*. Models based on quarks provide further understanding of a theory of the origin of the Universe called the *Big Bang*. In this Context, we shall study both quarks and the Big Bang.

It seems that the larger the system we wish to investigate, the smaller are the particles whose behavior we must understand! We shall explore this relationship and study the principles of quantum physics as we respond to our central question:

How can we connect the physics of microscopic particles to the physics of the Universe?

CHAPTER 28

Quantum Physics

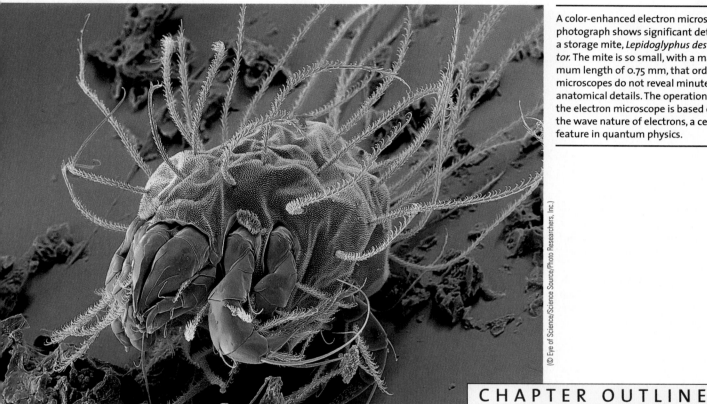

A color-enhanced electron microscope photograph shows significant detail of a storage mite, *Lepidoglyphus destructor*. The mite is so small, with a maximum length of 0.75 mm, that ordinary microscopes do not reveal minute anatomical details. The operation of the electron microscope is based on the wave nature of electrons, a central feature in quantum physics.

(© Eye of Science/Science Source/Photo Researchers, Inc.)

In the earlier chapters of this book, we focused on the physics of particles. The particle model was a simplification model that allowed us to ignore the unnecessary details of an object when studying its behavior. We later combined particles into additional simplification models of systems and rigid objects. In Chapter 13, we introduced the wave as yet another simplification model and found that we could understand the motion of vibrating strings and the intricacies of sound by studying simple waves. In Chapters 24 to 27, we found that the wave model for light helped us understand many phenomena associated with optics.

It is hoped that you now have confidence in your abilities to analyze problems in the very different worlds of particles and waves. Your confidence may have been shaken somewhat by the discussion at the beginning of Chapter 25 in which we indicated that light has both wave-like and particle-like behaviors.

In this chapter, we return to this dual nature of light and study it in more detail. This study leads to two final analysis models: the quantum particle and the quantum particle under boundary conditions. A careful analysis of these two models shows that particles and waves are not as unrelated as you might expect.

EXPECT TO BE CHALLENGED If the discussions of quantum physics in this chapter seem strange and confusing to you, it's because your whole life experience has taken place in the macroscopic world, where quantum effects are not evident.

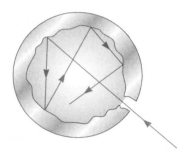

FIGURE 28.1 The opening to the cavity inside a hollow object is a good approximation of a black body. Light entering the small opening strikes the interior walls, where some is absorbed and some is reflected at a random angle. The cavity walls re-radiate at wavelengths corresponding to their temperature. Some of the energy from these standing waves can leave through the opening.

■ Stefan's law

■ Wien's displacement law

(Corbis)

The glow emanating from the spaces between these hot charcoal briquettes is, to a close approximation, black-body radiation. The color of the light depends on the temperature of the briquettes. ■

28.1 BLACKBODY RADIATION AND PLANCK'S THEORY

As we discussed in Chapter 17, an object at any temperature emits energy referred to as **thermal radiation.** The characteristics of this radiation depend on the temperature and properties of the surface of the object. If the surface is at room temperature, the wavelengths of the thermal radiation are primarily in the infrared region and hence are not observed by the eye. As the temperature of the surface increases, the object eventually begins to glow red. At sufficiently high temperatures, the object appears to be white, as in the glow of the hot tungsten filament of a lightbulb. A careful study of thermal radiation shows that it consists of a continuous distribution of wavelengths from all portions of the electromagnetic spectrum.

From a classical viewpoint, thermal radiation originates from accelerated charged particles near the surface of the object. The thermally agitated charges can have a distribution of accelerations, which accounts for the continuous spectrum of radiation emitted by the object. By the end of the 19th century, it had become apparent that this classical explanation of thermal radiation was inadequate. The basic problem was in understanding the observed distribution of wavelengths in the radiation emitted by an ideal object called a black body. As mentioned in Chapter 24, a **black body** is an ideal system that absorbs all radiation incident on it. A good approximation of a black body is a small hole leading to the inside of a hollow object as shown in Figure 28.1. The nature of the radiation emitted from the hole depends only on the temperature of the cavity walls.

The wavelength distribution of radiation from cavities was studied extensively in the late 19th century. Experimental data for the distribution of energy in **blackbody radiation** at three temperatures are shown in Active Figure 28.2. The distribution of radiated energy varies with wavelength and temperature. Two regular features of the distribution were noted in these experiments.

1. **The total power of emitted radiation increases with temperature.** We discussed this feature briefly in Chapter 17, where we introduced **Stefan's law,** Equation 17.36, for the power emitted from a surface of area A and temperature T:

    $$\mathcal{P} = \sigma A e T^4$$

    For a black body, the emissivity is $e = 1$ exactly.

2. **The peak of the wavelength distribution shifts to shorter wavelengths as the temperature increases.** This shift was found experimentally to obey the following relationship, called **Wien's displacement law:**

    $$\lambda_{\max} T = 2.898 \times 10^{-3} \text{ m} \cdot \text{K} \qquad [28.1]$$

    where $\lambda_{\max}$ is the wavelength at which the curve peaks and T is the absolute temperature of the surface emitting the radiation.

ACTIVE FIGURE 28.2 Intensity of blackbody radiation versus wavelength at three temperatures. Note that the amount of radiation emitted (the area under a curve) increases with increasing temperature. The visible range of wavelengths is between 0.4 μm and 0.7 μm. Therefore, the 4 000-K curve has a peak that is near the visible range and represents an object that would glow with a yellowish-white appearance. At about 6 000 K, the peak is in the center of the visible wavelengths and the object appears white.

Physics⊗Now™ By logging into PhysicsNow at **www.pop4e.com** and going to Active Figure 28.2, you can adjust the temperature of the black body and study the radiation emitted from it.

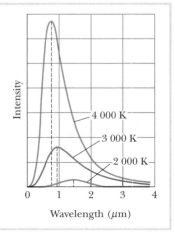

A successful theoretical model for blackbody radiation must predict the shape of the curve in Active Figure 28.2, the temperature dependence expressed in Stefan's law, and the shift of the peak with temperature described by Wien's displacement law. Early attempts to use classical ideas to explain the shapes of the curves in Active Figure 28.2 failed. Figure 28.3 shows an experimental plot of the blackbody radiation spectrum (red curve) together with the curve predicted by classical theory (blue curve). At long wavelengths, classical theory is in good agreement with the experimental data. At short wavelengths, however, major disagreement exists between classical theory and experiment. This disagreement is often called the **ultraviolet catastrophe.** (This "catastrophe"—infinite energy—occurs as the wavelength approaches zero; the word "ultraviolet" was applied because ultraviolet wavelengths are short.)

In 1900, Max Planck developed a structural model for blackbody radiation that leads to a theoretical equation for the wavelength distribution that is in complete agreement with experimental results at all wavelengths. In his model, which represented the dawn of **quantum physics,** Planck imagined that oscillators exist at the surface of the black body, related to the charges within the molecules. He made two bold and controversial assumptions concerning the nature of these oscillators:

- The energy of the oscillator is quantized; that is, it can have only certain *discrete* amounts of energy E_n given by

$$E_n = nhf \qquad \text{[28.2]}$$

where n is a positive integer called a **quantum number,**[1] f is the frequency of oscillation of the oscillator, and h is **Planck's constant,** first introduced in Chapter 11. Because the energy of each oscillator can have only discrete values given by Equation 28.2, we say that the energy is **quantized.** Each discrete energy value corresponds to a different **quantum state,** represented by the quantum number n. When the oscillator is in the $n = 1$ quantum state, its energy is hf; when it is in the $n = 2$ quantum state, its energy is $2hf$; and so on.

- The oscillators emit or absorb energy in discrete units. They emit or absorb these energy units by making a transition from one quantum state to another, similar to the transitions discussed in the Bohr model in Chapter 11. The entire energy difference between the initial and final states in the transition is emitted as a single quantum of radiation. If the transition is from one state to an adjacent state—say, from the $n = 3$ state to the $n = 2$ state—Equation 28.2 shows that the amount of energy radiated by the oscillator is

$$E = hf \qquad \text{[28.3]}$$

An oscillator radiates or absorbs energy only when it changes quantum states. If it remains in one quantum state, no energy is absorbed or emitted. Figure 28.4 shows the quantized energy levels and allowed transitions proposed by Planck.

These assumptions may not sound bold to you because we have seen them in the Bohr model of the hydrogen atom in Chapter 11. It is important to keep in mind, however, that the Bohr model was not introduced until 1913, whereas Planck made his assumptions in 1900. The key point in Planck's theory is the radical assumption of quantized energy states. This development marked the birth of the quantum theory. Using these assumptions, Planck was able to generate a theoretical expression for the wavelength distribution that agreed remarkably well with the experimental curves in Active Figure 28.2. When Planck presented his theory, most scientists (including Planck!) did not consider the quantum concept realistic. It was believed to be a mathematical trick that happened to predict the correct results. Hence, Planck and others continued to search for what they believed to be a more rational explanation of blackbody radiation. Subsequent developments, however,

---

[1]We first introduced the notion of a quantum number for microscopic systems in Section 11.5, in which we incorporated it into the Bohr model of the hydrogen atom. We put it in bold again here because it is an important notion for the remaining chapters in this book.

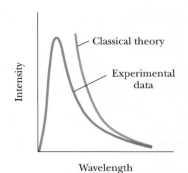

FIGURE 28.3 Comparison of the experimental results with the curve predicted by classical theory for the distribution of blackbody radiation.

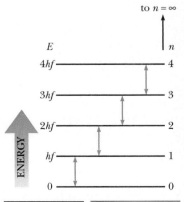

MAX PLANCK (1858–1947)

Planck introduced the concept of a "quantum of action" (Planck's constant, h) in an attempt to explain the spectral distribution of blackbody radiation, which laid the foundations for quantum theory. In 1918, he was awarded the Nobel Prize in Physics for this discovery of the quantized nature of energy.

FIGURE 28.4 Allowed energy levels for an oscillator with a natural frequency f. Allowed transitions are indicated by the double-headed arrows.

The ear thermometer

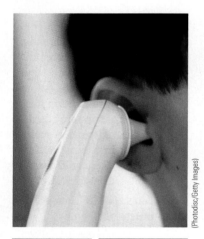

FIGURE **28.5** An ear thermometer measures a patient's temperature by detecting the intensity of infrared radiation leaving the eardrum.

(Photodisc/Getty Images)

showed that a theory based on the quantum concept (rather than on classical concepts) was required to explain a number of other phenomena at the atomic level.

We don't see quantum effects on an everyday basis because the energy change in a macroscopic system due to a transition between adjacent states is such a small fraction of the total energy of the system that we could never expect to detect the change. (See Example 28.2 for a numerical example.) Therefore, even though changes in the energy of a macroscopic system are indeed quantized and proceed by small quantum jumps, our senses perceive the decrease as continuous. **Quantum effects become important and measurable only on the submicroscopic level of atoms and molecules.** Furthermore, quantum results must blend smoothly with classical results when the quantum number becomes large. This statement is known as the **correspondence principle.**

You may have had your body temperature measured at the doctor's office by an *ear thermometer,* which can read your temperature in a matter of seconds (Fig. 28.5). This type of thermometer measures the amount of infrared radiation emitted by the eardrum in a fraction of a second. It then converts the amount of radiation into a temperature reading. This thermometer is very sensitive because temperature is raised to the fourth power in Stefan's law. Problem 28.1 allows you to explore the sensitivity of this device.

QUICK QUIZ 28.1 Figure 28.6 shows two stars in the constellation Orion. Betelgeuse appears to glow red, whereas Rigel looks blue in color. Which star has a higher surface temperature? **(a)** Betelgeuse **(b)** Rigel **(c)** both have the same surface temperature **(d)** impossible to determine

(John Chumack/Photo Researchers, Inc.)

FIGURE **28.6** (Quick Quiz 28.1) Which star is hotter?

∎ Thinking Physics 28.1

You are observing a yellow candle flame, and your laboratory partner claims that the light from the flame is atomic in origin. You disagree, claiming that the candle flame is hot, so the radiation must be thermal in origin. Before this disagreement leads to fisticuffs, how could you determine who is correct?

Reasoning A simple determination could be made by observing the light from the candle flame through a diffraction grating spectrometer, which was discussed in Section 27.8. If the spectrum of the light is continuous, it is thermal in origin. If the spectrum shows discrete lines, it is atomic in origin. The results of the experiment show that the light is primarily thermal in origin and originates in the hot particles of soot in the candle flame. ∎

EXAMPLE 28.1 Thermal Radiation from the Human Body

The temperature of your skin is approximately 35°C.

A What is the peak wavelength of the radiation it emits?

Solution From Wien's displacement law (Eq. 28.1), we have

$$\lambda_{\max} T = 2.898 \times 10^{-3} \text{ m} \cdot \text{K}$$

Solving for $\lambda_{\max}$ and noting that 35°C corresponds to an absolute temperature of 308 K, we have

$$\lambda_{\max} = \frac{2.898 \times 10^{-3} \text{ m} \cdot \text{K}}{308 \text{ K}} = \boxed{9.41 \ \mu\text{m}}$$

This radiation is in the infrared region of the spectrum.

B What total power is emitted by your skin, assuming that it emits like a black body?

Solution We need to make an estimate of the surface area of your skin. If we model your body as a rectangular box of height 2 m, width 0.3 m, and depth 0.2 m, the total surface area is

$$A = 2(2 \text{ m})(0.3 \text{ m}) + 2(2 \text{ m})(0.2 \text{ m}) + 2(0.2 \text{ m})(0.3 \text{ m})$$
$$\approx 2 \text{ m}^2$$

Therefore, from Stefan's law, we have

$$\mathcal{P} = \sigma A e T^4 \approx (5.7 \times 10^{-8} \text{ W/m}^2 \cdot \text{K}^4)(2 \text{ m}^2)(1)(308 \text{ K})^4$$
$$\approx \boxed{10^3 \text{ W}}$$

C Based on your answer to part B, why don't you glow as brightly as several lightbulbs?

Solution The answer to part B indicates that your skin is radiating energy at approximately the rate as that which enters ten 100-W lightbulbs by electrical transmission. You are not visibly glowing, however, because most of this radiation is in the infrared range, as we found in part A, and our eyes are not sensitive to infrared radiation.

EXAMPLE 28.2 The Quantized Oscillator

A 2.0-kg block is attached to a massless spring of force constant $k = 25$ N/m. The spring is stretched 0.40 m from its equilibrium position and released.

A Find the total energy and frequency of oscillation according to classical calculations.

Solution Because of our study of oscillating blocks in Chapter 12, this problem is easy to conceptualize. The phrase "according to classical calculations" tells us that we should categorize this part of the problem as a classical analysis of the oscillator. To analyze the problem, we know that the total energy of a simple harmonic oscillator having an amplitude A is $\frac{1}{2}kA^2$ (Eq. 12.21). Therefore,

$$E = \tfrac{1}{2}kA^2 = \tfrac{1}{2}(25 \text{ N/m})(0.40 \text{ m})^2 = \boxed{2.0 \text{ J}}$$

The frequency of oscillation is, from Equation 12.14,

$$f = \frac{1}{2\pi}\sqrt{\frac{k}{m}} = \frac{1}{2\pi}\sqrt{\frac{25 \text{ N/m}}{2.0 \text{ kg}}} = \boxed{0.56 \text{ Hz}}$$

B Assuming that the energy is quantized, find the quantum number n for the system.

Solution This part of the problem is categorized as a quantum analysis of the oscillator. To analyze the problem, we note that the energy of the oscillator is quantized according to Equation 28.2. Therefore,

$$E_n = nhf = n(6.63 \times 10^{-34} \text{ J} \cdot \text{s})(0.56 \text{ Hz}) = 2.0 \text{ J}$$

Solving for n,

$$n = \frac{2.0 \text{ J}}{(6.63 \times 10^{-34} \text{ J} \cdot \text{s})(0.56 \text{ Hz})} = \boxed{5.4 \times 10^{33}}$$

C How much energy is carried away when the oscillator makes a transition to the next lowest quantum state?

Solution The energy difference between adjacent quantum states is $\Delta E = hf$. Therefore, the energy carried away is

$$E = hf = (6.63 \times 10^{-34} \text{ J} \cdot \text{s})(0.56 \text{ Hz})$$
$$= \boxed{3.7 \times 10^{-34} \text{ J}}$$

To finalize the problem, note that the energy carried away in part C due to a transition between adjacent states is a small fraction of the total energy of the oscillator (about one part in ten million billion billion billion, or $1:10^{34}$!). Consequently, we do not see the quantized nature of the oscillator for such a large quantum number as we found in part B, in agreement with the correspondence principle.

28.2 THE PHOTOELECTRIC EFFECT

Blackbody radiation was historically the first phenomenon to be explained with a quantum model. In the latter part of the 19th century, at the same time as data were being taken on thermal radiation, experiments showed that light incident on certain metallic surfaces causes electrons to be emitted from the surfaces. As mentioned in Section 25.1, this phenomenon, first discovered by Hertz, is known as the **photoelectric effect.** The emitted electrons are called **photoelectrons.**[2]

Active Figure 28.7 is a schematic diagram of a photoelectric effect apparatus. An evacuated glass or quartz tube contains a metal plate E connected to the negative terminal of a battery. Another metal plate C is maintained at a positive potential by the battery. When the tube is kept in the dark, the ammeter reads zero, indicating that there is no current in the circuit. When light of the appropriate wavelength shines on plate E, however, a current is detected by the ammeter, indicating a flow of charges across the gap between E and C. This current arises from electrons emitted from the negative plate E (the emitter) and collected at the positive plate C (the collector).

Active Figure 28.8, a graphical representation of the results of a photoelectric experiment, plots the photoelectric current versus the potential difference ΔV between E and C for two light intensities. For large positive values of ΔV, the current reaches a maximum value. In addition, the current increases as the incident light intensity increases, as you might expect. Finally, when ΔV is negative—that is, when the battery polarity is reversed to make E positive and C negative—the current drops because many of the photoelectrons emitted from E are repelled by the negative collecting plate C. Only those electrons ejected from the metal with a kinetic energy greater than $e|\Delta V|$ will reach C, where e is the magnitude of the charge on the electron. When the magnitude of ΔV is equal to ΔV_s, the **stopping potential,** no electrons reach C and the current is zero.

Let us consider the combination of the electric field between the plates and an electron ejected from plate E with the maximum kinetic energy to be an isolated system. Suppose this electron stops just as it reaches plate C. Applying the isolated

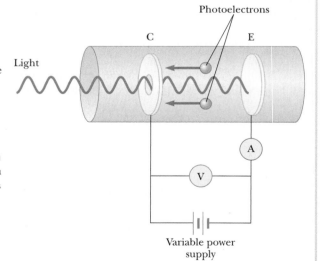

ACTIVE FIGURE 28.7

A circuit diagram for studying the photoelectric effect. When light strikes the plate E (the emitter), photoelectrons are ejected from the plate. Electrons moving from plate E to plate C (the collector) constitute a current in the circuit.

Physics⊗Now™ By logging into PhysicsNow at **www.pop4e.com** and going to Active Figure 28.7, you can observe the motion of electrons for various frequencies and voltages.

[2]Photoelectrons are not different from other electrons. They are given this name solely because of their ejection from the metal by photons in the photoelectric effect.

system model, the total energy of the system must be conserved:

$$E_f = E_i \quad \rightarrow \quad K_f + U_f = K_i + U_i$$

where the initial configuration of the system refers to the instant that the electron leaves the metal with the maximum possible kinetic energy K_{max} and the final configuration is when the electron stops just before touching plate C. If we define the electric potential energy of the system in the initial configuration to be zero, we have

$$0 + (-e)(-\Delta V_s) = K_{max} + 0$$

$$K_{max} = e \Delta V_s \qquad [28.4]$$

This equation allows us to measure K_{max} experimentally by measuring the voltage at which the current drops to zero.

The following are several features of the photoelectric effect in which the predictions made by a classical approach are compared, using the wave model for light, with the experimental results. Notice the strong contrast between the predictions and the results.

1. Dependence of photoelectron kinetic energy on light intensity

    Classical prediction: Electrons should absorb energy continuously from the electromagnetic waves. A more intense light should transfer energy into the metal faster, and the electrons should be ejected with more kinetic energy.

    Experimental result: The maximum kinetic energy of the photoelectrons is *independent* of light intensity. This result is shown in Active Figure 28.8 by both curves falling to zero at the *same* negative voltage.

2. Time interval between incidence of light and ejection of photoelectrons

    Classical prediction: For very weak light, a measurable time interval should pass between the incidence of the light and the ejection of an electron. This time interval is required for the electron to absorb the incident radiation before it acquires enough energy to escape from the metal.

    Experimental result: Electrons are emitted from the surface almost *instantaneously* (less than 10^{-9} s after the surface is illuminated), even at very low light intensities.

3. Dependence of ejection of electrons on light frequency

    Classical prediction: Electrons should be ejected at any frequency of the incident light, as long as the intensity is high enough, because energy is being transferred to the metal regardless of the frequency.

    Experimental result: No electrons are emitted if the incident light frequency falls below some **cutoff frequency** f_c, which is characteristic of the material being illuminated. No electrons are ejected below this cutoff frequency *regardless* of how intense the light is.

4. Dependence of photoelectron kinetic energy on light frequency

    Classical prediction: No relationship should exist between the frequency of the light and the electron kinetic energy. The kinetic energy should be related to the intensity of the light.

    Experimental result: The maximum kinetic energy of the photoelectrons increases with increasing light frequency.

Notice that *all four* predictions of the classical model are incorrect. A successful explanation of the photoelectric effect was given by Einstein in 1905, the same year he published his special theory of relativity. As part of a general paper on electromagnetic radiation, for which he received the Nobel Prize in Physics in 1921, Einstein extended Planck's concept of quantization to electromagnetic waves. He assumed that light (or any other electromagnetic wave) of frequency f can be considered to be a stream of quanta, regardless of the source of the radiation. Today we call these quanta **photons**. Each photon has an energy E given by Equation 28.3, $E = hf$, and moves in a vacuum at the speed of light c, where is $c = 3.00 \times 10^8$ m/s.

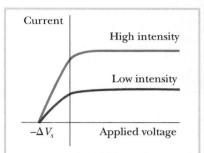

ACTIVE FIGURE 28.8

Photoelectric current versus applied potential difference for two light intensities. The current increases with intensity but reaches a saturation level for large values of ΔV. At voltages equal to or more negative than $-\Delta V_s$, where ΔV_s is the stopping potential, the current is zero.

Physics⊗Now™ By logging into PhysicsNow at **www.pop4e.com** and going to Active Figure 28.8, you can sweep through the voltage range and observe the current curve for different intensities of radiation.

QUICK QUIZ 28.2 While standing outdoors on a dark night, you are subjected to the following four types of electromagnetic radiation: yellow light from a sodium street lamp, radio waves from a nearby AM radio station, radio waves from a nearby FM radio station, and microwaves from a nearby antenna of a communications system. Rank these types of waves in terms of increasing photon energy, lowest first.

In Einstein's model, a photon of the incident light gives *all* its energy hf to a *single* electron in the metal. Therefore, the absorption of energy by the electrons is not a continuous process as envisioned in the wave model, but rather a discontinuous process in which energy is delivered to the electrons in bundles. The energy transfer is accomplished via a one-photon/one-electron event.

Electrons ejected from the surface of the metal possess the maximum kinetic energy K_{max}. According to Einstein, the maximum kinetic energy for these liberated electrons is

■ **Photoelectric effect equation**

$$K_{max} = hf - \phi \qquad [28.5]$$

where ϕ is called the **work function** of the metal. **The work function represents the minimum energy with which an electron is bound in the metal** and is on the order of a few electron volts. Table 28.1 lists selected values.

Equation 28.5 is a statement of the continuity equation for energy, Equation 6.20, from Chapter 6:

$$\Delta E_{system} = \sum T$$

We imagine the system to consist of an electron that is to be ejected and the remainder of the metal, and then apply the nonisolated system model for energy. Energy is transferred into the system by electromagnetic radiation, the photon. The system has two types of energy: the potential energy of the metal–electron system and the kinetic energy of the electron. Therefore, we can write the continuity equation as

$$\Delta K + \Delta U = T_{ER} \qquad [28.6]$$

The energy transfer is that of the photon, $T_{ER} = hf$. During the process, the kinetic energy of the electron increases from zero to its final value, which we assume to be the maximum possible value K_{max}. The potential energy of the system increases because the electron is pulled away from the metal to which it is attracted. We define the potential energy of the system when the electron is outside the metal as zero. The potential energy of the system when the electron is in the metal is $U = -\phi$, where ϕ is the work function. Therefore, the increase in potential energy when the electron is removed from the metal is the work function ϕ. Substituting these energies into Equation 28.6, we have

$$K_{max} + \phi = hf$$

which is the same as Equation 28.5. If the electron makes collisions with other electrons or metal ions as it is being ejected, some of the incoming energy is transferred to the metal and the electron is ejected with less kinetic energy than K_{max}.

With the photon model of light, one can explain the observed features of the photoelectric effect that cannot be understood using classical concepts:

1. Dependence of photoelectron kinetic energy on light intensity

That K_{max} is independent of the light intensity can be understood with the following argument. The maximum kinetic energy of any one electron, which equals $hf - \phi$, depends only on the light frequency and the work function, not on the light intensity. If the light intensity is doubled, the number of photons

TABLE 28.1

Work Functions of Selected Metals

Metal	ϕ (eV)
Na	2.46
Al	4.08
Cu	4.70
Zn	4.31
Ag	4.73
Pt	6.35
Pb	4.14
Fe	4.50

arriving per unit time interval is doubled, which doubles the rate at which photoelectrons are emitted. The maximum possible kinetic energy of any one emitted electron, however, is unchanged.

2. Time interval between incidence of light and ejection of photoelectrons

That the electrons are emitted almost instantaneously is consistent with the photon model of light, in which the incident energy appears in small packets and the interaction between photons and electrons is one to one. Therefore, for very weak incident light, very few photons may arrive per unit time interval, but each one has sufficient energy to eject an electron immediately.

3. Dependence of ejection of electrons on light frequency

That the effect is not observed below a certain cutoff frequency follows because the photon must have energy greater than the work function ϕ to eject an electron. If the energy of an incoming photon does not satisfy this requirement, an electron cannot be ejected from the surface, regardless of light intensity.

4. Dependence of photoelectron kinetic energy on light frequency

That K_{max} increases with increasing frequency is easily understood with Equation 28.5.

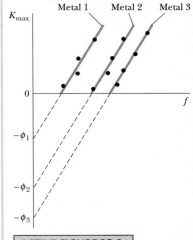

ACTIVE FIGURE 28.9

A plot of results for K_{max} of photoelectrons versus frequency of incident light in a typical photoelectric effect experiment. Photons with frequency less than the cutoff frequency for a given metal do not have sufficient energy to eject an electron from the metal.

Physics⊗Now™ By logging into PhysicsNow at **www.pop4e.com** and going to Active Figure 28.9, you can sweep through the frequency range and observe the curve for different target metals.

Einstein's theoretical result (Eq. 28.5) predicts a linear relationship between the maximum electron kinetic energy K_{max} and the light frequency f. Experimental observation of such a linear relationship would be a final confirmation of Einstein's theory. Indeed, such a linear relationship is observed as sketched in Active Figure 28.9. The slope of the curves for all metals is Planck's constant h. The absolute value of the intercept on the vertical axis is the work function ϕ, which varies from one metal to another. The intercept on the horizontal axis is the cutoff frequency, which is related to the work function through the relation $f_c = \phi/h$. This cutoff frequency corresponds to a **cutoff wavelength** of

$$\lambda_c = \frac{c}{f_c} = \frac{c}{\phi/h} = \frac{hc}{\phi} \qquad [28.7]$$

where c is the speed of light. Light with wavelength *greater* than λ_c incident on a material with a work function of ϕ does not result in the emission of photoelectrons.

The combination hc occurs often when relating the energy of a photon to its wavelength. A common shortcut to use in solving problems is to express this combination in useful units according to the numerical value

$$hc = 1\ 240 \text{ eV} \cdot \text{nm}$$

One of the first practical uses of the photoelectric effect was as a detector in a light meter of a camera. Light reflected from the object to be photographed strikes a photoelectric surface in the meter, causing it to emit photoelectrons that then pass through a sensitive ammeter. The magnitude of the current in the ammeter depends on the light intensity.

The phototube, another early application of the photoelectric effect, acts much like a switch in an electric circuit. It produces a current in the circuit when light of sufficiently high frequency falls on a metal plate in the phototube, but produces no current in the dark. Phototubes were used in burglar alarms and in the detection of the soundtrack on motion picture film. Modern semiconductor devices have now replaced older devices based on the photoelectric effect.

The photoelectric effect is used today in the operation of photomultiplier tubes. Figure 28.10 shows the structure of such a device. A photon striking the photocathode ejects an electron by means of the photoelectric effect. This electron is accelerated across the potential difference between the photocathode and the first *dynode,* shown as being at +200 V relative to the photocathode in Figure 28.10. This high-energy electron strikes the dynode and ejects several more electrons. This process is repeated through a series of dynodes at ever higher potentials until an electrical pulse is produced as millions of electrons strike the last dynode. Thus, the tube is

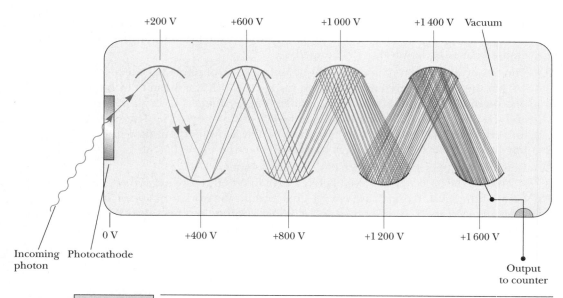

+200 V   +600 V   +1 000 V   +1 400 V   Vacuum

0 V   +400 V   +800 V   +1 200 V   +1 600 V

Incoming Photocathode
photon

Output
to counter

FIGURE 28.10 The multiplication of electrons in a photomultiplier tube.

called a *multiplier* because one photon at the input has resulted in millions of electrons at the output.

The photomultiplier tube is used in nuclear detectors to detect the presence of gamma rays emitted from radioactive nuclei, which we will study in Chapter 30. It is also used in astronomy in a technique called *photoelectric photometry*. In this technique, the light collected by a telescope from a single star is allowed to fall on a photomultiplier tube for a time interval. The tube measures the total light energy during the time interval, which can then be converted to a luminosity of the star.

The photomultiplier tube is being replaced in many astronomical observations with a *charge-coupled device* (CCD), which is the same device that is used in a digital camera. In this device, an array of pixels are formed on the silicon surface of an integrated circuit. When the surface is exposed to light from an astronomical scene through a telescope or a terrestrial scene through a digital camera, electrons generated by the photoelectric effect are caught in "traps" beneath the surface. The number of electrons is related to the intensity of the light striking the surface. A signal processor measures the number of electrons associated with each pixel and converts this information into a digital code that a computer can use to reconstruct and display the scene.

The *electron bombardment CCD camera* allows higher sensitivity than a conventional CCD. In this device, electrons ejected from a photocathode by the photoelectric effect are accelerated through a high voltage before striking a CCD array. The higher energy of the electrons results in a very sensitive detector of low-intensity radiation.

The explanation of the photoelectric effect with a quantum model, combined with Planck's quantum model for blackbody radiation, laid a strong foundation for further investigation into quantum physics. In the next section, we present a third experimental result that provides further strong evidence of the quantum nature of light.

QUICK QUIZ 28.3 Consider one of the curves in Active Figure 28.8. Suppose the intensity of the incident light is held fixed but its frequency is increased. The stopping potential in Active Figure 28.8 **(a)** remains fixed, **(b)** moves to the right, or **(c)** moves to the left.

Suppose classical physicists had come up with the idea of predicting the appearance of a plot of K_{max} versus f as in Active Figure 28.9. What would their expected plot look like, based on the wave model for light?

INTERACTIVE | EXAMPLE 28.3 | **The Photoelectric Effect for Sodium**

A sodium surface is illuminated with light of wavelength 300 nm. The work function for sodium metal is 2.46 eV.

A Find the maximum kinetic energy of the ejected photoelectrons.

Solution The energy of photons in the illuminating light beam is

$$E = hf = \frac{hc}{\lambda} = \frac{1\ 240\ \text{eV}\cdot\text{nm}}{300\ \text{nm}} = 4.13\ \text{eV}$$

Using Equation 28.5 gives

$$K_{max} = hf - \phi = 4.13\ \text{eV} - 2.46\ \text{eV} = \boxed{1.67\ \text{eV}}$$

B Find the cutoff wavelength for sodium.

Solution The cutoff wavelength can be calculated from Equation 28.7:

$$\lambda_c = \frac{hc}{\phi} = \frac{1\ 240\ \text{eV}\cdot\text{nm}}{2.46\ \text{eV}} = \boxed{504\ \text{nm}}$$

This wavelength is in the yellow–green region of the visible spectrum.

Physics ⊗ Now™ Investigate the photoelectric effect for different materials and different wavelengths of light by logging into PhysicsNow at **www.pop4e.com** and going to Interactive Example 28.3.

28.3 THE COMPTON EFFECT

In 1919, Einstein proposed that a photon of energy E carries a momentum equal to $E/c = hf/c$. In 1923, Arthur Holly Compton carried Einstein's idea of photon momentum further with the **Compton effect.**

Prior to 1922, Compton and his coworkers had accumulated evidence that showed that the classical wave theory of light failed to explain the scattering of x-rays from electrons. According to classical theory, incident electromagnetic waves of frequency f_0 should have two effects: (1) the electrons should accelerate in the direction of propagation of the x-ray by radiation pressure (see Section 24.6), and (2) the oscillating electric field should set the electrons into oscillation at the apparent frequency of the radiation as detected by the moving electron. The apparent frequency detected by the electron differs from f_0 due to the Doppler effect (see Section 24.3) because the electron absorbs as a moving particle. The electron then re-radiates as a moving particle, exhibiting another Doppler shift in the frequency of emitted radiation.

Because different electrons move at different speeds, depending on the amount of energy absorbed from the electromagnetic waves, the scattered wave frequency at a given angle should show a distribution of Doppler-shifted values. Contrary to this prediction, Compton's experiment showed that, at a given angle, only *one* frequency of radiation was observed that was different from that of the incident radiation. Compton and his coworkers realized that the scattering of x-ray photons from electrons could be explained by treating photons as point-like particles with energy hf and momentum hf/c and by assuming that the energy and momentum of the isolated system of the photon and the electron are conserved in a collision. By doing so, Compton was adopting a particle model for something that was well known as a wave, as had Einstein in his explanation of the photoelectric effect. Figure 28.11 shows the quantum picture of the exchange of momentum and energy between an individual x-ray photon and an electron. In the classical model, the electron is

(Courtesy of AIP Niels Bohr Library)

ARTHUR HOLLY COMPTON
(1892–1962)

Compton measured and explained the effect named for him at the University of Chicago in 1923 and shared the 1927 Nobel Prize in Physics. He went on to demonstrate that cosmic rays are charged particles and to direct research on producing plutonium for nuclear weapons.

FIGURE 28.11 The quantum model for x-ray scattering from an electron. The collision of the photon with the electron displays the particle-like nature of the photon.

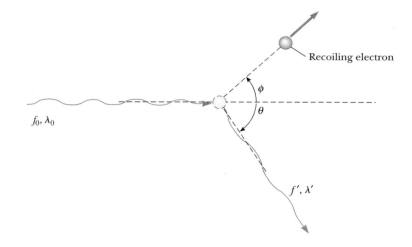

pushed along the direction of propagation of the incident x-ray by radiation pressure. In the quantum model in Figure 28.11, the electron is scattered through an angle ϕ with respect to this direction as if it were a billiard-ball type collision.

Figure 28.12 is a schematic diagram of the apparatus used by Compton. In his original experiment, Compton measured how scattered x-ray intensity depends on wavelength at various scattering angles. The incident beam consisted of monochromatic x-rays of wavelength $\lambda_0 = 0.071$ nm. The experimental plots of intensity versus wavelength obtained by Compton for four scattering angles are shown in Figure 28.13. They show two peaks, one at λ_0 and the other at a longer wavelength λ'. The peak at λ_0 is caused by x-rays scattered from electrons that are tightly bound to the target atoms, and the shifted peak at λ' is caused by x-rays scattered from free electrons in the target. In his analysis, Compton predicted that the shifted peak should depend on scattering angle θ as

■ Compton shift equation

$$\lambda' - \lambda_0 = \frac{h}{m_e c} (1 - \cos \theta) \qquad [28.8]$$

In this expression, known as the **Compton shift equation,** m_e is the mass of the electron; $h/m_e c$ is called the **Compton wavelength** λ_C for the electron and has the value

■ Compton wavelength

$$\lambda_C = \frac{h}{m_e c} = 0.002\,43 \text{ nm} \qquad [28.9]$$

FIGURE 28.12 Schematic diagram of Compton's apparatus. Photons are scattered through 90° from a carbon target. The wavelength is measured with a rotating crystal spectrometer using Bragg's law (Section 27.9).

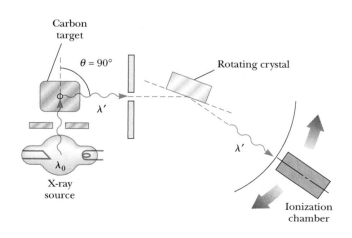

Compton's measurements were in excellent agreement with the predictions of Equation 28.8. They were the first experimental results to convince most physicists of the fundamental validity of the quantum theory!

The Compton effect should be kept in mind by x-ray technicians working in hospitals and radiology laboratories. X-rays directed into the patient's body are Compton scattered by electrons in the body in all directions. Equation 28.8 shows that the scattered wavelength is still well within the x-ray region so that these scattered x-rays can damage human tissue. In general, technicians operate the x-ray machine from behind an absorbing wall to avoid exposure to the scattered x-rays. Furthermore, when dental x-rays are taken, a lead apron is placed over the patient to reduce the absorption of scattered x-rays by other parts of the patient's body.

■ **Thinking Physics 28.2**

The Compton effect involves a change in wavelength as photons are scattered through different angles. Suppose we illuminate a piece of material with a beam of light and then view the material from different angles relative to the beam of light. Will we see a *color change* corresponding to the change in wavelength of the scattered light?

Reasoning Visible light scattered by the material undergoes a change in wavelength, but the change is far too small to detect as a color change. The largest possible change in wavelength, at 180° scattering, is twice the Compton wavelength, about 0.005 nm, which represents a change of less than 0.001% of the wavelength of red light. The Compton effect is only detectable for wavelengths that are very short to begin with, so the Compton wavelength is an appreciable fraction of the incident wavelength. As a result, the usual radiation for observing the Compton effect is in the x-ray range of the electromagnetic spectrum. ∎

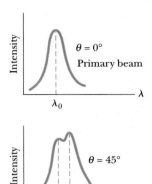
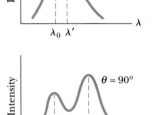
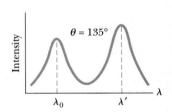

FIGURE 28.13 Scattered x-ray intensity versus wavelength for Compton scattering at $\theta = 0°$, 45°, 90°, and 135°.

INTERACTIVE | EXAMPLE 28.4 | **Compton Scattering at 45°**

X-rays of wavelength $\lambda_0 = 0.200\,000$ nm are scattered from a block of material. The scattered x-rays are observed at an angle of 45.0° to the incident beam. Calculate the wavelength of the x-rays scattered at this angle.

Solution The shift in wavelength of the scattered x-rays is given by Equation 28.8:

$$\Delta\lambda = \frac{h}{m_e c}(1 - \cos\theta)$$

$$= \frac{6.626 \times 10^{-34}\,\text{J}\cdot\text{s}}{(9.11 \times 10^{-31}\,\text{kg})(3.00 \times 10^8\,\text{m/s})}(1 - \cos 45°)$$

$$= 7.10 \times 10^{-13}\,\text{m} = 0.000\,710\,\text{nm}$$

Hence, the wavelength of the scattered x-rays at this angle is

$$\lambda' = \Delta\lambda + \lambda_0 = \boxed{0.200\,710\,\text{nm}}$$

Physics⊗Now™ Study Compton scattering for different angles by logging into PhysicsNow at **www.pop4e.com** and going to Interactive Example 28.4.

28.4 PHOTONS AND ELECTROMAGNETIC WAVES

The agreement between experimental measurements and theoretical predictions based on quantum models for phenomena such as the photoelectric effect and the Compton effect offers clear evidence that when light and matter interact, the light behaves as if it were composed of particles with energy hf and momentum hf/c. An obvious question at this point is, "How can light be considered a photon when it exhibits wave-like properties?" We describe light in terms of photons having energy and momentum, which are parameters of the particle model. Remember, however, that light and other electromagnetic waves exhibit interference and diffraction effects, which are consistent only with the wave model.

Which model is correct? Is light a wave or a particle? The answer depends on the phenomenon being observed. Some experiments can be explained better, or solely, with the photon model, whereas others are best described, or can only be described, with a wave model. The end result is that **we must accept both models and admit that the true nature of light is not describable in terms of any single classical picture.** Hence, **light has a dual nature in that it exhibits both wave and particle characteristics.** You should recognize, however, that the same beam of light that can eject photoelectrons from a metal can also be diffracted by a grating. In other words, the **particle model and the wave model of light complement each other.**

The success of the particle model of light in explaining the photoelectric effect and the Compton effect raises many other questions. Because a photon is a particle, what is the meaning of its "frequency" and "wavelength," and which determines its energy and momentum? Is light in some sense simultaneously a wave and a particle? Although photons have no rest energy, can some simple expression describe the effective mass of a "moving" photon? If a "moving" photon has mass, do photons experience gravitational attraction? What is the spatial extent of a photon, and how does an electron absorb or scatter one photon? Some of these questions can be answered, but others demand a view of atomic processes that is too pictorial and literal. Furthermore, many of these questions stem from classical analogies such as colliding billiard balls and water waves breaking on a shore. Quantum mechanics gives light a more fluid and flexible nature by treating the particle model and wave model of light as both necessary and complementary. Neither model can be used exclusively to describe all properties of light. A complete understanding of the observed behavior of light can be attained only if the two models are combined in a complementary manner. Before discussing this combination in more detail, we now turn our attention from electromagnetic waves to the behavior of entities that we have called particles.

28.5 THE WAVE PROPERTIES OF PARTICLES

We feel quite comfortable in adopting a particle model for matter because we have studied such concepts as conservation of energy and momentum for particles as well as extended objects. It might therefore be even more difficult to accept that *matter* also has a dual nature!

In 1923, in his doctoral dissertation, Louis Victor de Broglie postulated that **because photons have wave and particle characteristics, perhaps all forms of matter have wave as well as particle properties.** This postulate was a highly revolutionary idea with no experimental confirmation at that time. According to de Broglie, an electron in motion exhibits both wave and particle characteristics. De Broglie explained the source of this assertion in his 1929 Nobel Prize acceptance speech:

> On the one hand the quantum theory of light cannot be considered satisfactory since it defines the energy of a light corpuscle by the equation $E = hf$ containing the frequency f. Now a purely corpuscular theory contains nothing that enables us to define a frequency; for this reason alone, therefore, we are compelled, in the case of light, to introduce the idea of a corpuscle and that of periodicity simultaneously. On the other hand, determination of the stable motion of electrons in the atom introduces integers, and up to this point the only phenomena involving integers in physics were those of interference and of normal modes of vibration. This fact suggested to me the idea that electrons too could not be considered simply as corpuscles, but that periodicity must be assigned to them also.

LOUIS DE BROGLIE (1892–1987)
A French physicist, de Broglie was awarded the Nobel Prize in Physics in 1929 for his prediction of the wave nature of electrons.

(AIP Niels Bohr Library)

In Chapter 9, we found that the relationship between energy and momentum for a photon is $p = E/c$. We also know from Equation 28.3 that the energy of a photon is $E = hf = hc/\lambda$. Therefore, the momentum of a photon can be expressed as

$$p = \frac{E}{c} = \frac{hf}{c} = \frac{hc}{c\lambda} = \frac{h}{\lambda}$$

From this equation, we see that the photon wavelength can be specified by its momentum: $\lambda = h/p$. De Broglie suggested that material particles of momentum p should also have wave properties and a corresponding wavelength. Because the magnitude of the momentum of a nonrelativistic particle of mass m and speed v is $p = mv$, the **de Broglie wavelength** of that particle is[3]

$$\lambda = \frac{h}{p} = \frac{h}{mv} \qquad [28.10]$$

■ De Broglie wavelength of a particle

Furthermore, in analogy with photons, de Broglie postulated that particles obey the Einstein relation $E = hf$, so the frequency of a particle is

$$f = \frac{E}{h} \qquad [28.11]$$

■ Frequency of a particle

The dual nature of matter is apparent in these last two equations because each contains both particle concepts (p and E) and wave concepts (λ and f). That these relationships are established experimentally for photons makes the de Broglie hypothesis that much easier to accept.

The Davisson–Germer Experiment

De Broglie's proposal that any kind of particle exhibits both wave and particle properties was first regarded as pure speculation. If particles such as electrons had wavelike properties, under the correct conditions they should exhibit diffraction effects. In 1927, three years after de Broglie published his work, C. J. Davisson and L. H. Germer of the United States succeeded in measuring the wavelength of electrons. Their important discovery provided the first experimental confirmation of the wave nature of particles proposed by de Broglie.

Interestingly, the intent of the initial Davisson–Germer experiment was not to confirm the de Broglie hypothesis. In fact, the discovery was made by accident (as is often the case). The experiment involved the scattering of low-energy electrons (≈ 54 eV) projected toward a nickel target in a vacuum. During one experiment, the nickel surface was badly oxidized because of an accidental break in the vacuum system. After the nickel target was heated in a flowing stream of hydrogen to remove the oxide coating, electrons scattered by it exhibited intensity maxima and minima at specific angles. The experimenters finally realized that the nickel had formed large crystal regions on heating and that the regularly spaced planes of atoms in the crystalline regions served as a diffraction grating (Section 27.8) for electrons.

Shortly thereafter, Davisson and Germer performed more extensive diffraction measurements on electrons scattered from single-crystal targets. Their results showed conclusively the wave nature of electrons and confirmed the de Broglie relation $p = h/\lambda$. A year later in 1928, G. P. Thomson of Scotland observed electron diffraction patterns by passing electrons through very thin gold foils. Diffraction patterns have since been observed for helium atoms, hydrogen atoms, and neutrons. Hence, the wave nature of particles has been established in a variety of ways.

PITFALL PREVENTION 28.3

WHAT'S WAVING? If particles have wave properties, what's waving? You are familiar with waves on strings, which are very concrete. Sound waves are more abstract, but you are likely comfortable with them. Electromagnetic waves are even more abstract, but at least they can be described in terms of physical variables, electric and magnetic fields. Waves associated with particles are very abstract and cannot be associated with a physical variable. Later in this chapter, we will describe the wave associated with a particle in terms of probability.

---

[3] The de Broglie wavelength for a particle moving at any speed v, including relativistic speeds, is $\lambda = h/\gamma mv$, where $\gamma = (1 - v^2/c^2)^{-1/2}$.

EXAMPLE 28.5 The Wavelength of an Electron

Calculate the de Broglie wavelength for an electron ($m_e = 9.11 \times 10^{-31}$ kg) moving with a speed of 1.00×10^7 m/s.

Solution Equation 28.10 gives

$$\lambda = \frac{h}{m_e v}$$

$$= \frac{6.626 \times 10^{-34}\,\text{J}\cdot\text{s}}{(9.11 \times 10^{-31}\,\text{kg})(1.00 \times 10^7\,\text{m/s})}$$

$$= 7.27 \times 10^{-11}\,\text{m}$$

This wavelength corresponds to that of typical x-rays in the electromagnetic spectrum. Furthermore, note that the calculated wavelength is on the order of the spacing of atoms in a crystalline substance such as sodium chloride.

EXAMPLE 28.6 The Wavelength of a Rock

A rock of mass 50.0 g is thrown with a speed of 40.0 m/s. What is its de Broglie wavelength?

Solution From Equation 28.10, we have

$$\lambda = \frac{h}{mv} = \frac{6.626 \times 10^{-34}\,\text{J}\cdot\text{s}}{(50.0 \times 10^{-3}\,\text{kg})(40.0\,\text{m/s})}$$

$$= 3.31 \times 10^{-34}\,\text{m}$$

This wavelength is much smaller than any aperture through which the rock could possibly pass. Thus, we could not observe diffraction effects, and as a result the wave properties of large-scale objects cannot be observed.

EXAMPLE 28.7 An Accelerated Charge

A particle of charge q and mass m is accelerated from rest through a potential difference ΔV. Assuming that the particle moves with a nonrelativistic speed, find its de Broglie wavelength.

Solution We apply the isolated system model for the particle and the electric field associated with the potential difference. The total energy of the system must be conserved:

$$K_f + U_f = K_i + U_i$$

where the initial configuration of the system refers to the instant the particle begins to move from rest and the final configuration is when the particle reaches its final speed after accelerating through the potential difference ΔV. If we define the electric potential energy of the system in the initial configuration to be zero, we have

$$\tfrac{1}{2}mv^2 + q(-\Delta V) = 0 + 0$$

where the negative sign indicates that a positive charge accelerates in the direction of decreasing potential. Because $p = mv$, we can express this equation in the form

$$\frac{p^2}{2m} = q\,\Delta V \qquad \text{or} \qquad p = \sqrt{2mq\,\Delta V}$$

Substituting this expression for p in the de Broglie relation $\lambda = h/p$ gives

$$\lambda = \frac{h}{\sqrt{2mq\,\Delta V}}$$

The Electron Microscope

A practical device that relies on the wave characteristics of electrons is the **electron microscope.** A *transmission* electron microscope, used for viewing flat, thin samples, is shown in Figure 28.14. In many respects, it is similar to an optical microscope, but the electron microscope has a much greater resolving power because it can accelerate electrons to very high kinetic energies, giving them very short wavelengths. No microscope can resolve details that are significantly smaller than the wavelength of the waves used to illuminate the object. Typically, the wavelengths of electrons are about 100 times shorter than those of the visible light used in optical microscopes. As a result, an electron microscope with ideal lenses would be able to distinguish details about 100 times smaller than those distinguished by an optical microscope. (Electromagnetic radiation of the same wavelength as the electrons in an electron microscope is in the x-ray region of the spectrum.)

The electron beam in an electron microscope is controlled by electrostatic or magnetic deflection, which acts on the electrons to focus the beam and form an image. Rather than examining the image through an eyepiece as in an optical microscope, the viewer looks at an image formed on a monitor or other type of display screen. The photograph at the beginning of this chapter shows the amazing detail available with an electron microscope.

The electron microscope

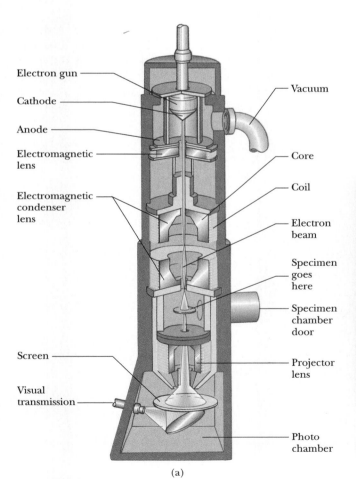

Electron gun
Cathode
Anode
Electromagnetic lens
Electromagnetic condenser lens
Screen
Visual transmission

Vacuum
Core
Coil
Electron beam
Specimen goes here
Specimen chamber door
Projector lens
Photo chamber

(a)

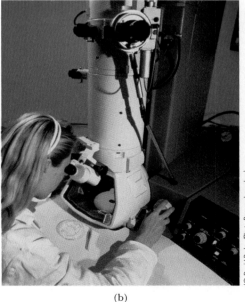

(© David Parker/Photo Researchers, Inc.)

(b)

FIGURE 28.14 (a) Diagram of a transmission electron microscope for viewing a thinly sectioned sample. The "lenses" that control the electron beam are magnetic deflection coils. (b) An electron microscope in use.

28.6 THE QUANTUM PARTICLE

The discussions presented in previous sections may be quite disturbing because we considered the particle and wave models to be distinct in earlier chapters. The notion that both light and material particles have both particle and wave properties does not fit with this distinction. We have experimental evidence, however, that this dual nature is just what we must accept. This acceptance leads to a new simplification model, the **quantum particle model.** In this model, entities have both particle and wave characteristics, and we must choose one appropriate behavior—particle or wave—to understand a particular phenomenon.

In this section, we shall investigate this model, which might bring you more comfort with this idea. As we shall demonstrate, we can construct from waves an entity that exhibits properties of a particle.

Let us first review the characteristics of ideal particles and waves. An ideal particle has zero size. As mentioned in Section 13.2, an ideal wave has a single frequency and is infinitely long. Therefore, an essential identifying feature of a particle that differentiates it from a wave is that it is *localized* in space. Let us show that we can build a localized entity from infinitely long waves. Imagine drawing one wave along the x axis, with one of its crests located at x = 0, as in Figure 28.15a. Now, draw a second wave, of the same amplitude but a different frequency, with one of its crests also at x = 0. The result of the superposition of these two waves is a *beat* because the waves are alternately in phase and out of phase. (Beats were discussed in Section 14.6.) Figure 28.15b shows the results of superposing these two waves.

Notice that we have already introduced some localization by doing so. A single wave has the same amplitude everywhere in space; no point in space is any different from any other point. By adding a second wave, however, something is different between the in-phase and the out-of-phase points.

FIGURE 28.15 (a) An idealized wave of an exact single frequency is the same throughout space and time. (b) If two ideal waves with slightly different frequencies are combined, beats result (Section 14.6). The regions of space at which there is constructive interference are different from those at which there is destructive interference.

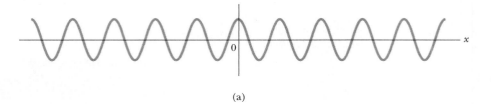

(a)

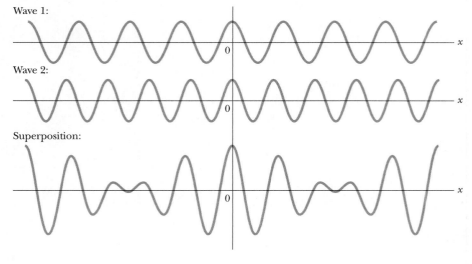

(b)

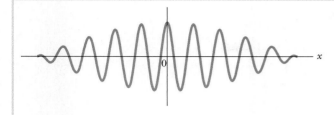

ACTIVE FIGURE 28.16 If a large number of waves are combined, the result is a wave packet, which represents a particle.

Physics⊗Now™ Choose the number of waves to add together and observe the resulting wave packet by logging into PhysicsNow at **www.pop4e.com** and going to Active Figure 28.16.

Now imagine that more and more waves are added to our original two, each new wave having a new frequency. Each new wave is added so that one of its crests is at $x = 0$. The result at $x = 0$ is that all the waves add constructively. When we consider a large number of waves, the probability of a positive value of a wave function at any point x is equal to the probability of a negative value and destructive interference occurs *everywhere* except near $x = 0$, where we superposed all the crests. The result is shown in Active Figure 28.16. The small region of constructive interference is called a **wave packet.** This wave packet is a localized region of space that is different from all other regions, because the result of the superposition of the waves everywhere else is zero. We can identify the wave packet as a particle because it has the localized nature of what we have come to recognize as a particle!

The localized nature of this entity is the *only* characteristic of a particle that was generated with this process. We have not addressed how the wave packet might achieve such particle characteristics as mass, electric charge, spin, and so on. Therefore, you may not be completely convinced that we have built a particle. As further evidence that the wave packet can represent the particle, let us show that the wave packet has another characteristic of a particle.

Let us return to our combination of only two waves so as to make the mathematical representation simple. Consider two waves with equal amplitudes but different frequencies f_1 and f_2. We can represent the waves mathematically as

$$y_1 = A \cos(k_1 x - \omega_1 t) \qquad \text{and} \qquad y_2 = A \cos(k_2 x - \omega_2 t)$$

where, as in Chapter 13, $\omega = 2\pi f$ and $k = 2\pi/\lambda$. Using the superposition principle, we add the waves:

$$y = y_1 + y_2 = A \cos(k_1 x - \omega_1 t) + A \cos(k_2 x - \omega_2 t)$$

It is convenient to write this expression in a form that uses the trigonometric identity

$$\cos a + \cos b = 2 \cos\left(\frac{a - b}{2}\right) \cos\left(\frac{a + b}{2}\right)$$

Letting $a = k_1 x - \omega_1 t$ and $b = k_2 x - \omega_2 t$, we find that

$$y = 2A \cos\left[\frac{(k_1 x - \omega_1 t) - (k_2 x - \omega_2 t)}{2}\right] \cos\left[\frac{(k_1 x - \omega_1 t) + (k_2 x - \omega_2 t)}{2}\right]$$

$$= \left[2A \cos\left(\frac{\Delta k}{2} x - \frac{\Delta \omega}{2} t\right)\right] \cos\left(\frac{k_1 + k_2}{2} x - \frac{\omega_1 + \omega_2}{2} t\right) \qquad [28.12]$$

The second cosine factor represents a wave with a wave number and frequency equal to the averages of the values for the individual waves.

The factor in brackets represents the envelope of the wave as shown in Active Figure 28.17. Notice that this factor also has the mathematical form of a wave. **This envelope of the combination can travel through space with a different speed than the individual waves.** As an extreme example of this possibility, imagine combining two identical waves moving in opposite directions. The two waves move with the

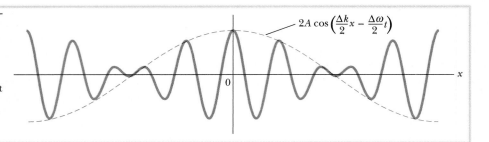

same speed, but the envelope has a speed of *zero* because we have built a standing wave, which we studied in Section 14.3.

For an individual wave, the speed is given by Equation 13.10:

■ Phase speed for a wave

$$v_{\text{phase}} = \frac{\omega}{k}$$

It is called the **phase speed** because it is the rate of advance of a crest on a single wave, which is a point of fixed phase. This equation can be interpreted as the following: the phase speed of a wave is the ratio of the coefficient of the time variable t to the coefficient of the space variable x in the equation for the wave, $y = A \cos(kx - \omega t)$.

The factor in brackets in Equation 28.12 is of the form of a wave, so it moves with a speed given by this same ratio:

$$v_g = \frac{\text{coefficient of time variable } t}{\text{coefficient of space variable } x} = \frac{(\Delta\omega/2)}{(\Delta k/2)} = \frac{\Delta\omega}{\Delta k}$$

The subscript g on the speed indicates that it is commonly called the **group speed,** or the speed of the wave packet (the *group* of waves) that we have built. We have generated this expression for a simple addition of two waves. For a superposition of a very large number of waves to form a wave packet, this ratio becomes a derivative:

■ Group speed for a wave packet

$$v_g = \frac{d\omega}{dk} \qquad [28.13]$$

Let us multiply the numerator and the denominator by $\hbar$, where $\hbar = h/2\pi$:

$$v_g = \frac{\hbar \, d\omega}{\hbar \, dk} = \frac{d(\hbar\omega)}{d(\hbar k)} \qquad [28.14]$$

We look at the terms in the parentheses in the numerator and denominator in this equation separately. For the numerator

$$\hbar\omega = \frac{h}{2\pi} (2\pi f) = hf = E$$

For the denominator,

$$\hbar k = \frac{h}{2\pi} \left(\frac{2\pi}{\lambda} \right) = \frac{h}{\lambda} = p$$

Therefore, Equation 28.14 can be written as

$$v_g = \frac{d(\hbar\omega)}{d(\hbar k)} = \frac{dE}{dp} \qquad [28.15]$$

Because we are exploring the possibility that the envelope of the combined waves represents the particle, consider a free particle moving with a speed u that is small compared with that of light. The energy of the particle is its kinetic energy:

$$E = \tfrac{1}{2}mu^2 = \frac{p^2}{2m}$$

Differentiating this equation with respect to p, where $p = mu$, gives

$$v_g = \frac{dE}{dp} = \frac{d}{dp}\left(\frac{p^2}{2m}\right) = \frac{1}{2m}(2p) = u \qquad [28.16]$$

Therefore, the group speed of the wave packet is identical to the speed of the particle that it is modeled to represent! Thus, we have further confidence that the wave packet is a reasonable way to build a particle.

QUICK QUIZ **28.7** As an analogy to wave packets, consider an "automobile packet" that occurs near the scene of an accident on a freeway. The phase speed is analogous to the speed of individual automobiles as they move through the backup caused by the accident. The group speed can be identified as the speed of the leading edge of the packet of cars. For the automobile packet, is the group speed **(a)** the same as the phase speed, **(b)** less than the phase speed, or **(c)** greater than the phase speed?

28.7 THE DOUBLE-SLIT EXPERIMENT REVISITED

One way to crystallize our ideas about the electron's wave–particle duality is to consider a hypothetical experiment in which electrons are fired at a double slit. Consider a parallel beam of monoenergetic electrons that is incident on a double slit as in Figure 28.18. We shall assume that the slit widths are small compared with the electron wavelength, so we need not worry about diffraction maxima and minima as discussed for light in Section 27.6. An electron detector is positioned far from the slits at a distance much greater than the separation distance d of the slits. If the detector collects electrons for a long enough time interval, one finds a typical wave interference pattern for the counts per minute, or probability of arrival of

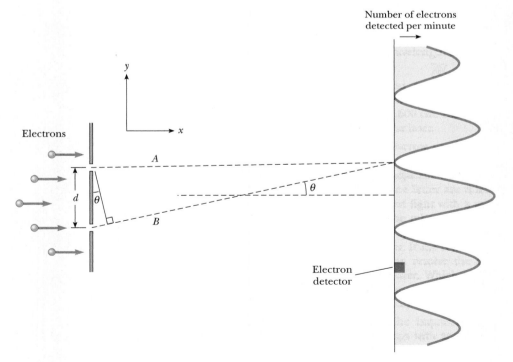

FIGURE **28.18** Electron interference. The slit separation d is much greater than the individual slit widths and much less than the distance between the slit and the detector. The electron detector is movable along the y direction in the drawing and so can detect electrons diffracted at different values of θ. The detector acts like the "viewing screen" of Young's double-slit experiment with light discussed in Chapter 27.

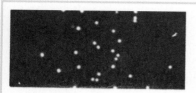

(a) After 28 electrons

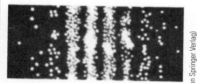

(b) After 1000 electrons

(c) After 10000 electrons

(d) Two-slit electron pattern

(a–d, From C. Jönsson, *Zeitschrift für Physik* 161:454, 1961; used with permission Springer Verlag)

ACTIVE FIGURE 28.19

(a, b, c) Computer-simulated interference patterns for a beam of electrons incident on a double slit. (d) Photograph of a double-slit interference pattern produced by electrons.

Physics⊗Now™ By logging into PhysicsNow at **www.pop4e.com** and going to Active Figure 28.19, you can watch the interference pattern develop over time and see how it is destroyed by the action of keeping track of which slit an electron goes through.

electrons. Such an interference pattern would not be expected if the electrons behaved as classical particles. It is clear that electrons are interfering, which is a distinct wave-like behavior.

If the experiment is carried out at lower electron beam intensities, the interference pattern is still observed if the time interval of the measurement is sufficiently long as illustrated by the computer-simulated patterns in Active Figure 28.19. Note that the interference pattern becomes clearer as the number of electrons reaching the screen increases.

If one imagines a single electron in the beam producing in-phase "wavelets" as it reaches one of the slits, the waves in interference model (Section 27.3) can be used to find the angular separation θ between the central probability maximum and its neighboring minimum. The minimum occurs when the path length difference between A and B is half a wavelength, or when

$$d \sin \theta = \frac{\lambda}{2}$$

Because an electron's wavelength is given by $\lambda = h/p_x$, we see that for small θ,

$$\sin \theta \approx \theta = \frac{h}{2p_x d}$$

Thus, the dual nature of the electron is clearly shown in this experiment. **The electrons are detected as particles at a localized spot at some instant of time, but the probability of arrival at that spot is determined by finding the intensity of two interfering waves.**

Let us now look at this experiment from another point of view. If one slit is covered during the experiment, a symmetric curve peaked around the center of the open slit is observed; it is the central maximum of the single-slit diffraction pattern. Plots of the counts per minute (probability of arrival of electrons) with the lower or upper slit closed are shown as blue curves in the central part of Figure 28.20.

If another experiment is now performed with slit 2 of Figure 28.20 blocked half of the time and then slit 1 blocked during the remaining time, the accumulated pattern of counts per minute shown by the blue curve on the right side of the

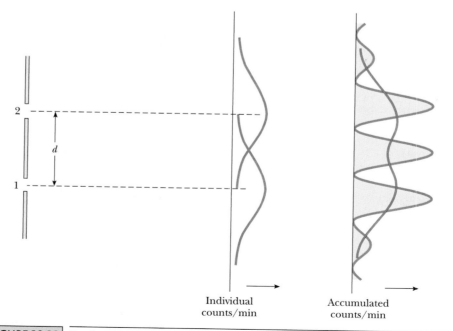

Individual counts/min

Accumulated counts/min

FIGURE 28.20 Results of the two-slit electron diffraction experiment with each slit closed half the time (blue). The result with both slits open is shown in brown.

figure is completely different from the case with both slits open (brown curve). A maximum probability of arrival of an electron at $\theta = 0$ no longer exists. In fact, **the interference pattern has been lost, and the accumulated result is simply the sum of the individual results.** When only one slit is open at a time, we know that the electron has the same localizability and indivisibility at the slits as we measure at the detector because the electron clearly goes through slit 1 or slit 2. Therefore, the total must be analyzed as the sum of those electrons that come through slit 1 and those that come through slit 2.

When both slits are open, it is tempting to assume that the electron goes through either slit 1 or slit 2 and that the counts per minute are again given by the combination of the single-slit distributions. We know, however, that the experimental results indicated by the brown interference pattern in Figure 28.20 contradict this assumption. Hence, our assumption that the electron is localized and goes through only one slit when both slits are open must be wrong (a painful conclusion!).

To interpret these results, we are forced to conclude that **an electron interacts with both slits simultaneously.** If we attempt to determine experimentally which slit the electron goes through, the act of measuring destroys the interference pattern. It is impossible to determine which slit the electron goes through. In effect, **we can say only that the electron passes through both slits!** The same arguments apply to photons.

If we restrict ourselves to a pure particle model, it is an uncomfortable notion that the electron can be present at both slits at once. From the quantum particle model, however, the particle can be considered to be built from waves that exist throughout space. Therefore, the wave components of the electron are present at both slits at the same time, and this model leads to a more comfortable interpretation of this experiment.

28.8 THE UNCERTAINTY PRINCIPLE

Whenever one measures the position or velocity of a particle at any instant, experimental uncertainties are built into the measurements. According to classical mechanics, there is no fundamental barrier to an ultimate refinement of the apparatus or experimental procedures. In other words, it is possible, in principle, to make such measurements with arbitrarily small uncertainty. Quantum theory predicts, however, that **it is fundamentally impossible to make simultaneous measurements of a particle's position and momentum with infinite accuracy.**

In 1927, Werner Heisenberg introduced this notion, which is now known as the **Heisenberg uncertainty principle:**

WERNER HEISENBERG (1901–1976)

A German theoretical physicist, Heisenberg made many significant contributions to physics, including his famous uncertainty principle, for which he received the Nobel Prize in Physics in 1932; the development of an abstract model of quantum mechanics called matrix mechanics; the prediction of two forms of molecular hydrogen; and theoretical models of the nucleus.

(Courtesy of the University of Hamburg)

If a measurement of the position of a particle is made with uncertainty Δx and a simultaneous measurement of its momentum is made with uncertainty Δp_x, the product of the two uncertainties can never be smaller than $\hbar/2$:

$$\Delta x \, \Delta p_x \geq \frac{\hbar}{2} \qquad [28.17]$$

■ Uncertainty principle for momentum and position

That is, **it is physically impossible to simultaneously measure the exact position and exact momentum of a particle.** Heisenberg was careful to point out that the inescapable uncertainties Δx and Δp_x do not arise from imperfections in practical measuring instruments. Furthermore, they do not arise due to any perturbation of the system that we might cause in the measuring process. Rather, **the uncertainties arise from the quantum structure of matter.**

To understand the uncertainty principle, consider a particle for which we know the wavelength *exactly*. According to the de Broglie relation $\lambda = h/p$, we would know the momentum to infinite accuracy, so $\Delta p_x = 0$.

In reality, as we have mentioned, a single-wavelength wave would exist throughout space. Any region along this wave is the same as any other region (see Fig. 28.15a). If we were to ask, "Where is the particle that this wave represents?" no special location in space along the wave could be identified with the particle because all points along the wave are the same. Therefore, we have *infinite* uncertainty in the position of the particle and we know nothing about where it is. Perfect knowledge of the momentum has cost us all information about the position.

In comparison, now consider a particle with some uncertainty in momentum so that a range of values of momentum are possible. According to the de Broglie relation, the result is a range of wavelengths. Therefore, the particle is not represented by a single wavelength, but a combination of wavelengths within this range. This combination forms a wave packet as we discussed in Section 28.6 and illustrated in Active Figure 28.16. Now, if we are asked to determine the location of the particle, we can only say that it is somewhere in the region defined by the wave packet because a distinct difference exists between this region and the rest of space. Therefore, by losing some information about the momentum of the particle, we have gained information about its position.

If we were to lose all information about the momentum, we would be adding together waves of all possible wavelengths. The result would be a wave packet of zero length. Therefore, if we know nothing about the momentum, we know exactly where the particle is.

The mathematical form of the uncertainty principle argues that the product of the uncertainties in position and momentum will always be larger than some minimum value. This value can be calculated from the types of arguments discussed earlier, which result in the value of $\hbar/2$ in Equation 28.17.

Another form of the uncertainty principle can be generated by reconsidering Active Figure 28.16. Imagine that the horizontal axis is time rather than spatial position x. We can then make the same arguments that we made about knowledge of wavelength and position in the time domain. The corresponding variables would be frequency and time. Because frequency is related to the energy of the particle by $E = hf$, the uncertainty principle in this form is

■ Uncertainty principle for energy and time

$$\Delta E \, \Delta t \geq \frac{\hbar}{2} \qquad\qquad [28.18]$$

This form of the uncertainty principle suggests that energy conservation can appear to be violated by an amount ΔE as long as it is only for a short time interval Δt consistent with Equation 28.18. We shall use this notion to estimate the rest energies of particles in Chapter 31.

EXAMPLE 28.8 | **Locating an Electron**

The speed of an electron is measured to be 5.00×10^3 m/s ± 0.003%. Within what limits could one determine the position of this electron along the direction of its velocity vector?

Solution The momentum of the electron is

$$p = m_e v = (9.11 \times 10^{-31} \text{ kg})(5.00 \times 10^3 \text{ m/s})$$
$$= 4.56 \times 10^{-27} \text{ kg·m/s}$$

Because the uncertainty is 0.003% of this value, we

have

$$\Delta p = 0.000\,03p = 1.37 \times 10^{-31} \text{ kg·m/s}$$

The minimum uncertainty in position can now be calculated by using this value of Δp and Equation 28.17:

$$\Delta x \geq \frac{\hbar}{2\,\Delta p} = \frac{1.05 \times 10^{-34} \text{ J·s}}{2(1.37 \times 10^{-31} \text{ kg·m/s})}$$
$$= 0.384 \times 10^{-3} \text{ m} = \boxed{0.384 \text{ mm}}$$

28.9 AN INTERPRETATION OF QUANTUM MECHANICS

We have been introduced to some new and strange ideas so far in this chapter. In an effort to understand the concepts of quantum physics better, let us investigate another bridge between particles and waves. We first think about electromagnetic radiation from the particle point of view. The probability per unit volume of finding a photon in a given region of space at an instant of time is proportional to the number of photons per unit volume at that time:

$$\frac{\text{probability}}{V} \propto \frac{N}{V}$$

The number of photons per unit volume is proportional to the intensity of the radiation:

$$\frac{N}{V} \propto I$$

Now, we form the bridge to the wave model by recalling that the intensity of electromagnetic radiation is proportional to the square of the electric field amplitude for the electromagnetic wave (Section 24.5):

$$I \propto E^2$$

Equating the beginning and the end of this string of proportionalities, we have

$$\frac{\text{probability}}{V} \propto E^2 \qquad [28.19]$$

Therefore, for electromagnetic radiation, the probability per unit volume of finding a particle associated with this radiation (the photon) is proportional to the square of the amplitude of the wave associated with the particle.

Recognizing the wave–particle duality of both electromagnetic radiation and matter, we should suspect a parallel proportionality for a material particle. That is, the probability per unit volume of finding the particle is proportional to the square of the amplitude of a wave representing the particle. In Section 28.5 we learned that there is a de Broglie wave associated with every particle. The amplitude of the de Broglie wave associated with a particle is not a measurable quantity (because the wave function representing a particle is generally a complex function, as we discuss below). In contrast, the electric field is a measurable quantity for an electromagnetic wave. The matter analog to Equation 28.19 relates the square of the wave's amplitude to the probability per unit volume of finding the particle. As a result, we call the amplitude of the wave associated with the particle the **probability amplitude,** or the **wave function,** and give it the symbol Ψ. In general, the complete wave function Ψ for a system depends on the positions of all the particles in the system and on time; therefore, it can be written $\Psi(\vec{r}_1, \vec{r}_2, \vec{r}_3, \ldots, \vec{r}_j, \ldots, t)$, where $\vec{r}_j$ is the position vector of the jth particle in the system. For many systems of interest, including all those in this text, the wave function Ψ is mathematically separable in space and time and can be written as a product of a space function ψ for one particle of the system and a complex time function:[4]

$$\Psi(\vec{r}_1, \vec{r}_2, \vec{r}_3, \ldots, \vec{r}_j, \ldots, t) = \psi(\vec{r}_j)\, e^{-i\omega t} \qquad [28.20]$$

where $\omega \,(= 2\pi f)$ is the angular frequency of the wave function and $i = \sqrt{-1}$.

∎ Space- and time-dependent wave function Ψ

---

[4]The standard form of a complex number is $a + ib$. The notation $e^{i\theta}$ is equivalent to the standard form as follows:

$$e^{i\theta} = \cos\theta + i\sin\theta$$

Therefore, the notation $e^{-i\omega t}$ in Equation 28.20 is equivalent to $\cos(-\omega t) + i\sin(-\omega t) = \cos\omega t - i\sin\omega t$.

THE WAVE FUNCTION BELONGS TO A SYSTEM The common language in quantum mechanics is to associate a wave function with a particle. The wave function, however, is determined by the particle and its interaction with its environment, so it more rightfully belongs to a system. In many cases, the particle is the only part of the system that experiences a change, which is why the common language has developed. You will see examples in the future in which it is more proper to think of the system wave function rather than the particle wave function.

For any system in which the potential energy is time-independent and depends only on the positions of particles within the system, the important information about the system is contained within the space part of the wave function. The time part is simply the factor $e^{-i\omega t}$. Therefore, the understanding of ψ is the critical aspect of a given problem.

The wave function ψ is often complex-valued. The quantity $|\psi|^2 = \psi^*\psi$, where ψ^* is the complex conjugate[5] of ψ, is always real and positive and is proportional to the probability per unit volume of finding a particle at a given point at some instant. The wave function contains within it all the information that can be known about the particle.

This probability interpretation of the wave function was first suggested by Max Born (1882–1970) in 1928. In 1926, Erwin Schrödinger (1887–1961) proposed a wave equation that describes the manner in which the wave function changes in space and time. The *Schrödinger wave equation,* which we shall examine in Section 28.12, represents a key element in the theory of quantum mechanics.

In Section 28.5, we found that the de Broglie equation relates the momentum of a particle to its wavelength through the relation $p = h/\lambda$. If an ideal free particle has a precisely known momentum p_x, its wave function is a sinusoidal wave of wavelength $\lambda = h/p_x$ and the particle has equal probability of being at any point along the x axis. The wave function for such a free particle moving along the x axis can be written as

■ **Wave function for a free particle**

$$\psi(x) = Ae^{ikx} \qquad [28.21]$$

where $k = 2\pi/\lambda$ is the angular wave number and A is a constant amplitude.[6]

Although we cannot measure ψ, we can measure the quantity $|\psi|^2$, the absolute square of ψ, which can be interpreted as follows. If ψ represents a single particle, $|\psi|^2$—called the **probability density**—is the relative probability per unit volume that the particle will be found at any given point in the volume. This interpretation can also be stated in the following manner. If dV is a small volume element surrounding some point, the probability of finding the particle in that volume element is $|\psi|^2\,dV$. In this section, we deal only with one-dimensional systems, where the particle must be located along the x axis, and we therefore replace dV with dx. In this case, the probability $P(x)\,dx$ that the particle will be found in the infinitesimal interval dx around the point x is

$$P(x)\,dx = |\psi|^2\,dx \qquad [28.22]$$

Because the particle must be somewhere along the x axis, the sum of the probabilities over all values of x must be 1:

■ **Normalization condition on ψ**

$$\int_{-\infty}^{\infty} |\psi|^2\,dx = 1 \qquad [28.23]$$

Any wave function satisfying Equation 28.23 is said to be **normalized.** Normalization is simply a statement that the particle exists at some point at all times.

Although it is not possible to specify the position of a particle with complete certainty, it is possible through $|\psi|^2$ to specify the probability of observing it in a small

---

[5]For a complex number $z = a + ib$, the complex conjugate is found by changing i to $-i$: $z^* = a - ib$. The product of a complex number and its complex conjugate is always real and positive: $z^*z = (a - ib)(a + ib) = a^2 - (ib)^2 = a^2 - (i)^2b^2 = a^2 + b^2$.

[6]For the free particle, the full wave function, based on Equation 28.20, is

$$\Psi(x, t) = Ae^{ikx}e^{-i\omega t} = Ae^{i(kx - \omega t)} = A[\cos(kx - \omega t) + i\sin(kx - \omega t)]$$

The real part of this wave function has the same form as the waves that we added together to form wave packets in Section 28.6.

region surrounding a given point. **The probability of finding the particle in the arbitrarily sized interval $a \leq x \leq b$ is**

$$P_{ab} = \int_a^b |\psi|^2 \, dx \qquad [28.24]$$

The probability P_{ab} is the area under the curve of $|\psi|^2$ versus x between the points $x = a$ and $x = b$ as in Figure 28.21.

Experimentally, the probability is finite of finding a particle in an interval near some point at some instant. The value of that probability must lie between the limits 0 and 1. For example, if the probability is 0.3, there is a 30% chance of finding the particle in the interval.

The wave function ψ satisfies a wave equation, just as the electric field associated with an electromagnetic wave satisfies a wave equation that follows from Maxwell's equations. The wave equation satisfied by ψ is the Schrödinger equation (Section 28.12), and ψ can be computed from it. Although ψ is not a measurable quantity, all the measurable quantities of a particle, such as its energy and momentum, can be derived from a knowledge of ψ. For example, once the wave function for a particle is known, it is possible to calculate the average position at which you would find the particle after many measurements. This average position is called the **expectation value** of x and is defined by the equation

$$\langle x \rangle \equiv \int_{-\infty}^{\infty} \psi^* x \psi \, dx \qquad [28.25]$$

where brackets $\langle \ \rangle$ are used to denote expectation values. Furthermore, one can find the expectation value of any function $f(x)$ associated with the particle by using the following equation:

$$\langle f(x) \rangle \equiv \int_{-\infty}^{\infty} \psi^* f(x) \psi \, dx \qquad [28.26]$$

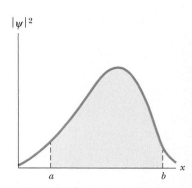

$|\psi|^2$

FIGURE 28.21 The probability of a particle being in the interval $a \leq x \leq b$ is the area under the probability density curve from a to b.

■ **Expectation value for position x**

28.10 A PARTICLE IN A BOX

In this section, we shall apply some of the ideas we have developed to a sample problem. Let us choose a simple problem: a particle confined to a one-dimensional region of space, called the *particle in a box* (even though the "box" is one-dimensional!). From a classical viewpoint, if a particle is confined to bouncing back and forth along the x axis between two impenetrable walls as in the pictorial representation in Figure 28.22a, its motion is easy to describe. If the speed of the particle is v, the magnitude of its momentum mv remains constant, as does its kinetic energy. Classical physics places no restrictions on the values of a particle's momentum and energy. The quantum mechanics approach to this problem is quite different and requires that we find the appropriate wave function consistent with the conditions of the situation.[7]

Because the walls are impenetrable, the probability of finding the particle outside the box is zero, so the wave function $\psi(x)$ must be zero for $x < 0$ and for $x > L$, where L is the distance between the two walls. A mathematical condition for any wave function is that it must be continuous in space.[8] Therefore, if ψ is zero outside the walls, it must also be zero *at* the walls; that is, $\psi(0) = 0$ and $\psi(L) = 0$. Only those wave functions that satisfy this condition are allowed.

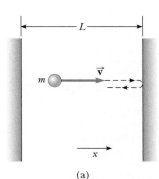

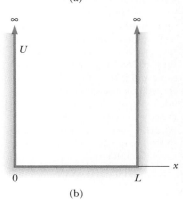

(a)

(b)

FIGURE 28.22 (a) A particle of mass m and velocity $\vec{v}$, confined to bouncing between two impenetrable walls separated by a distance L. (b) The potential energy function for the system.

---

[7] Before continuing, you might want to review Sections 14.3 and 14.4 on standing mechanical waves.

[8] If the wave function is not continuous at a point, the derivative of the wave function at that point is infinite. This issue leads to problems in the Schrödinger equation, for which the wave function is a solution and which is discussed in Section 28.12.

Figure 28.22b shows a graphical representation of the particle in a box problem, which graphs the potential energy of the particle–environment system as a function of the position of the particle. When the particle is inside the box, the potential energy of the system does not depend on the particle's location and we can choose its value to be zero. Outside the box, we have to ensure that the wave function is zero. We can do so by defining the potential energy of the system as infinitely large if the particle were outside the box. Because kinetic energy is necessarily positive, the only way a particle could be outside the box is if the system has an infinite amount of energy.

The wave function for a particle in the box can be expressed as a real sinusoidal function:[9]

$$\psi(x) = A \sin\left(\frac{2\pi x}{\lambda}\right) \tag{28.27}$$

This wave function must satisfy the boundary conditions at the walls. The boundary condition at $x = 0$ is satisfied already because the sine function is zero when $x = 0$. For the boundary condition at $x = L$, we have

$$\psi(L) = 0 = A \sin\left(\frac{2\pi L}{\lambda}\right)$$

which can only be true if

$$\frac{2\pi L}{\lambda} = n\pi \quad \rightarrow \quad \lambda = \frac{2L}{n} \tag{28.28}$$

where $n = 1, 2, 3, \ldots$. Therefore, only certain wavelengths for the particle are allowed! Each of the allowed wavelengths corresponds to a quantum state for the system, and n is the quantum number. Expressing the wave function in terms of the quantum number n, we have

$$\psi(x) = A \sin\left(\frac{2\pi x}{\lambda}\right) = A \sin\left(\frac{2\pi x}{2L/n}\right) = A \sin\left(\frac{n\pi x}{L}\right) \tag{28.29}$$

Active Figures 28.23a and 28.23b are graphical representations of ψ versus x and $|\psi|^2$ versus x for $n = 1, 2$, and 3 for the particle in a box. Note that although ψ can be positive or negative, $|\psi|^2$ is always positive. Because $|\psi|^2$ represents a probability density, a negative value for $|\psi|^2$ is meaningless.

Further inspection of Active Figure 28.23b shows that $|\psi|^2$ is zero at the boundaries, satisfying our boundary condition. In addition, $|\psi|^2$ is zero at other points, depending on the value of n. For $n = 2$, $|\psi|^2 = 0$ at $x = L/2$; for $n = 3$, $|\psi|^2 = 0$ at $x = L/3$ and $x = 2L/3$. The number of zero points increases by one each time the quantum number increases by one.

Because the wavelengths of the particle are restricted by the condition $\lambda = 2L/n$, the magnitude of the momentum of the particle is also restricted to specific values that we can find from the expression for the de Broglie wavelength, Equation 28.10:

$$p = \frac{h}{\lambda} = \frac{h}{2L/n} = \frac{nh}{2L}$$

From this expression, we find that the allowed values of the energy, which is simply the kinetic energy of the particle, are

$$E_n = \tfrac{1}{2}mv^2 = \frac{p^2}{2m} = \frac{(nh/2L)^2}{2m}$$
$$= \left(\frac{h^2}{8mL^2}\right)n^2 \quad n = 1, 2, 3, \ldots \tag{28.30}$$

■ Allowed wave functions for a particle in a box

PITFALL PREVENTION 28.6

REMINDER: ENERGY BELONGS TO A SYSTEM We describe Equation 28.30 as representing the energy of the particle; it is commonly used language for the particle in a box problem. In reality, we are analyzing the energy of the *system* of the particle and whatever environment is establishing the impenetrable walls. In the case of a particle in a box, the only nonzero type of energy is kinetic and it belongs to the particle. In general, energies that we calculate using quantum physics are associated with a system of interacting particles, such as the electron and proton in the hydrogen atom studied in Chapter 11.

■ Allowed energies for a particle in a box

---
[9] We show that this function is the correct one explicitly in Section 28.12.

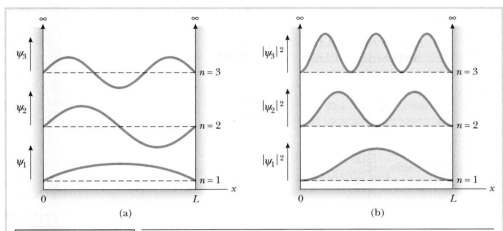

ACTIVE FIGURE **28.23** | The first three allowed states for a particle confined to a one-dimensional box. The states are shown superimposed on the potential energy function of Figure 28.22b. (a) The wave functions ψ for $n = 1$, 2, and 3. (b) The probability densities $|\psi|^2$ for $n = 1$, 2, and 3. The wave functions and probability densities are plotted vertically from separate axes that are offset vertically for clarity. The positions of these axes on the potential energy function suggest the relative energies of the states, but the positions are not shown to scale.

Physics⊗Now™ By logging into PhysicsNow at **www.pop4e.com** and going to Active Figure 28.23, you can measure the probability of a particle being between two points for the three quantum states in the figure.

As we see from this expression, **the energy of the particle is quantized,** similar to our quantization of energy in the hydrogen atom in Chapter 11. The lowest allowed energy corresponds to $n = 1$, for which $E_1 = h^2/8mL^2$. Because $E_n = n^2E_1$, the excited states corresponding to $n = 2$, 3, 4, . . . have energies given by $4E_1$, $9E_1$, $16E_1$, ...

Active Figure 28.24 is an energy level diagram[10] describing the energy values of the allowed states. Note that the state $n = 0$, for which E would be equal to zero, is not allowed. Thus, according to quantum mechanics, the particle can never be at rest. The least energy it can have, corresponding to $n = 1$, is called the **zero-point energy.** This result is clearly contradictory to the classical viewpoint, in which $E = 0$ is an acceptable state, as are all positive values of E.

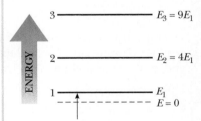

ACTIVE FIGURE **28.24**

Energy level diagram for a particle confined to a one-dimensional box of length L. The lowest allowed energy is $E_1 = h^2/8mL^2$.

Physics⊗Now™ Adjust the length of the box and the mass of the particle to see the effect on the energy levels by logging into PhysicsNow at **www.pop4e.com** and going to Active Figure 28.24.

QUICK QUIZ **28.8** Redraw Active Figure 28.23b, the probability of finding a particle at a particular location in a box, on the basis of expectations from classical physics rather than quantum physics.

QUICK QUIZ **28.9** A particle is in a box of length L. Suddenly, the length of the box is increased to $2L$. What happens to the energy levels shown in Active Figure 28.24? **(a)** Nothing happens; they are unaffected. **(b)** They move farther apart. **(c)** They move closer together.

---

[10]We introduced the energy level diagram as a specialized semigraphical representation in Chapter 11.

INTERACTIVE EXAMPLE 28.9   A Bound Electron

An electron is confined between two impenetrable walls 0.200 nm apart. Determine the allowed energies of the particle for the quantum states described by $n = 1, 2$, and 3.

Solution We apply Equation 28.30, using the value $m_e = 9.11 \times 10^{-31}$ kg for the electron. For the state described by $n = 1$, we have

$$E_1 = \frac{h^2}{8m_e L^2} = \frac{(6.63 \times 10^{-34}\,\text{J}\cdot\text{s})^2}{8(9.11 \times 10^{-31}\,\text{kg})(2.00 \times 10^{-10}\,\text{m})^2}$$

$$= 1.51 \times 10^{-18}\,\text{J} = \boxed{9.42\ \text{eV}}$$

For $n = 2$ and $n = 3$, we find that $E_2 = 4E_1 = \boxed{37.7\ \text{eV}}$ and $E_3 = 9E_1 = \boxed{84.8\ \text{eV}}$.

Physics⊗Now™ Investigate the energy levels of various particles trapped in a box by logging into PhysicsNow at **www.pop4e.com** and going to Interactive Example 28.9.

EXAMPLE 28.10   Energy Quantization for a Macroscopic Object

A 1.00-mg object is confined between two rigid walls separated by 1.00 cm.

A Calculate its minimum speed.

Solution The minimum speed corresponds to the state for which $n = 1$. Using Equation 28.30 with $n = 1$ gives the zero-point energy:

$$E_1 = \frac{h^2}{8mL^2} = \frac{(6.63 \times 10^{-34}\,\text{J}\cdot\text{s})^2}{8(1.00 \times 10^{-6}\,\text{kg})(1.00 \times 10^{-2}\,\text{m})^2}$$

$$= 5.49 \times 10^{-58}\,\text{J}$$

Because $E = K = \frac{1}{2}mv^2$, we can find v as follows:

$$\tfrac{1}{2}mv^2 = 5.49 \times 10^{-58}\,\text{J}$$

$$v = \left[\frac{2(5.49 \times 10^{-58}\,\text{J})}{1.00 \times 10^{-6}\,\text{kg}}\right]^{1/2} = \boxed{3.31 \times 10^{-26}\ \text{m/s}}$$

This speed is so small that the object appears to be at rest, which is what one would expect for the zero-point speed of a macroscopic object.

B If the speed of the object is 3.00×10^{-2} m/s, find the corresponding value of n.

Solution The kinetic energy of the object is

$$K = \tfrac{1}{2}mv^2 = \tfrac{1}{2}(1.00 \times 10^{-6}\,\text{kg})(3.00 \times 10^{-2}\,\text{m/s})^2$$

$$= 4.50 \times 10^{-10}\,\text{J}$$

Because $E_n = n^2E_1$ and $E_1 = 5.49 \times 10^{-58}$ J, we find that

$$K = E_n = n^2E_1 = 4.50 \times 10^{-10}\,\text{J}$$

$$n = \left(\frac{4.50 \times 10^{-10}\,\text{J}}{E_1}\right)^{1/2} = \left(\frac{4.50 \times 10^{-10}\,\text{J}}{5.49 \times 10^{-58}\,\text{J}}\right)^{1/2}$$

$$= \boxed{9.05 \times 10^{23}}$$

This value of n is so large that we would never be able to distinguish the quantized nature of the energy levels. That is, the difference in energy between the two states $n_1 = 9.05 \times 10^{23}$ and $n_2 = (9.05 \times 10^{23}) + 1$ is too small to be detected experimentally. Like Example 28.2, this example illustrates the working of the correspondence principle; that is, as m or L become large, the quantum description must agree with the classical result.

28.11 THE QUANTUM PARTICLE UNDER BOUNDARY CONDITIONS

The particle in a box discussed in Section 28.10 is an example of how all quantum problems can be addressed. To begin, consider Equation 28.28 and compare it with Equation 14.6. The allowed wavelengths for the particle in a box are identical to the allowed wavelengths for mechanical waves on a string fixed at both ends. In both the string wave and the particle wave, we apply **boundary conditions** to determine the allowed states of the system. For the string fixed at both ends, the boundary condition is that the displacement of the string at the boundaries is zero. For the particle in a box, the probability amplitude at the boundaries is zero. In both cases, the result is quantized wavelengths. In the case of the vibrating string, wavelength is related to the frequency, so we have a set of harmonics, or quantized frequencies, given by Equation 14.8. In the case of the particle in a box, we also have quantized frequencies. We can go further in this case, however, because the frequency is related to the energy through $E = hf$, and we generate a set of quantized *energies*.

The quantization of energy for a quantum particle is therefore no more surprising than the quantization of frequencies for the vibrating guitar string. The essential feature of the analysis model of the quantum particle under boundary conditions is the recognition that **an interaction of a particle with its environment represents one or more boundary conditions and, if the interaction restricts the particle to a finite region of space, results in quantization of the energy of the system.** Because particles have wave-like characteristics, the allowed quantum states of a system are those in which the boundary conditions on the wave function representing the system are satisfied.

The only quantization of energy we have seen before this chapter is that of the hydrogen atom in Chapter 11. In that case, the electric force between the proton and the electron creates a constraint that requires the electron and the proton to stay near each other (assuming that we have not supplied enough energy to ionize the atom). This constraint results in boundary conditions that limit the energies of the atom to those corresponding to specific allowed wave functions.

In general, boundary conditions are related to the coordinates describing the problem. For the particle in a box, we required a zero value of the wave function at two values of x. In the case of the hydrogen atom, the problem is best presented in *spherical coordinates*. These coordinates are an extension of the polar coordinates introduced in Chapter 1 and consist of a radial coordinate r and two angular coordinates. Boundary conditions on the wave function related to r are that the radial part of the wave function must approach zero as $r \to \infty$ (so that the wave function can be normalized) and remain finite as $r \to 0$. A boundary condition on the wave function related to an angular coordinate is that adding 2π to the angle must return the wave function to the same value because an addition of 2π results in the same angular position. The generation of the wave function and application of the boundary conditions for the hydrogen atom are beyond the scope of this book. We shall, however, examine the behavior of some of the wave functions in Section 29.3.

28.12 THE SCHRÖDINGER EQUATION

In Section 24.3, we discussed a wave equation for electromagnetic radiation. The waves associated with particles also satisfy a wave equation. We might guess that the wave equation for material particles is different from that associated with photons because material particles have a nonzero rest energy. The appropriate wave equation was developed by Schrödinger in 1926. In analyzing the behavior of a quantum system, the approach is to determine a solution to this equation and then apply the appropriate boundary conditions to the solution. The solution yields the allowed wave functions and energy levels of the system under consideration. Proper manipulation of the wave function then enables one to calculate all measurable features of the system.

The Schrödinger equation as it applies to a particle of mass m confined to moving along the x axis and interacting with its environment through a potential energy function $U(x)$ is

$$-\frac{\hbar^2}{2m}\frac{d^2\psi}{dx^2} + U\psi = E\psi \qquad [28.31]$$

where E is the total energy of the system (particle and environment). Because this equation is independent of time, it is commonly referred to as the **time-independent**

ERWIN SCHRÖDINGER (1887–1961)

An Austrian theoretical physicist, Schrödinger is best known as the creator of quantum mechanics. He also produced important papers in the fields of statistical mechanics, color vision, and general relativity. Schrödinger did much to hasten the universal acceptance of quantum theory by demonstrating the mathematical equivalence between his wave mechanics and the more abstract matrix mechanics developed by Heisenberg.

■ Time-independent Schrödinger equation

Schrödinger equation. (We shall not discuss the time-dependent Schrödinger equation, whose solution is Ψ, Eq. 28.20, in this text.)

This equation is consistent with the energy version of the isolated system model. The system is the particle and its environment. Problem 28.44 shows, both for a free particle and a particle in a box, that the first term in the Schrödinger equation reduces to the kinetic energy of the particle multiplied by the wave function. Therefore, Equation 28.31 tells us that the total energy is the sum of the kinetic energy and the potential energy and that the total energy is a constant: $K + U = E =$ constant.

In principle, if the potential energy $U(x)$ for the system is known, one can solve Equation 28.31 and obtain the wave functions and energies for the allowed states of the system. Because U may vary with position, it may be necessary to solve the equation separately for various regions. In the process, the wave functions for the different regions must join smoothly at the boundaries and we require that $\psi(x)$ be *continuous*. Furthermore, so that $\psi(x)$ obeys the normalization condition, we require that $\psi(x)$ approach zero as x approaches $\pm \infty$. Finally, $\psi(x)$ must be *single-valued* and $d\psi/dx$ must also be continuous[11] for finite values of $U(x)$.

The task of solving the Schrödinger equation may be very difficult, depending on the form of the potential energy function. As it turns out, the Schrödinger equation has been extremely successful in explaining the behavior of atomic and nuclear systems, whereas classical physics has failed to do so. Furthermore, when quantum mechanics is applied to macroscopic objects, the results agree with classical physics, as required by the correspondence principle.

The Particle in a Box via the Schrödinger Equation

To see how the Schrödinger equation is applied to a problem, let us return to our particle in a one-dimensional box of width L (see Fig. 28.22) and analyze it with the Schrödinger equation. In association with Figure 28.22b, we discussed the potential energy diagram that describes the problem. A potential energy diagram such as this one is a useful representation for understanding and solving problems with the Schrödinger equation.

Because of the shape of the curve in Figure 28.22b, the particle in a box is sometimes said to be in a **square well,**[12] where a **well** is an upward-facing region of the curve in a potential energy diagram. (A downward-facing region is called a *barrier,* which we shall investigate in Section 28.13.)

In the region $0 < x < L$, where $U = 0$, we can express the Schrödinger equation in the form

$$\frac{d^2\psi}{dx^2} = -\frac{2mE}{\hbar^2}\,\psi = -k^2\psi \qquad [28.32]$$

where

$$k = \frac{\sqrt{2mE}}{\hbar} \qquad [28.33]$$

The solution to Equation 28.32 is a function whose second derivative is the negative of the same function multiplied by a constant k^2. We recognize both the sine and cosine functions as satisfying this requirement. Therefore, the most general solution

---

[11]If $d\psi/dx$ were not continuous, we would not be able to evaluate $d^2\psi/dx^2$ in Equation 28.31 at the point of discontinuity.

[12]It is called a square well even if it has a rectangular shape in a potential energy diagram.

to the equation is a linear combination of both solutions:

$$\psi(x) = A \sin kx + B \cos kx$$

where A and B are constants determined by the boundary conditions.

Our first boundary condition is that $\psi(0) = 0$:

$$\psi(0) = A \sin 0 + B \cos 0 = 0 + B = 0$$

Therefore, our solution reduces to

$$\psi(x) = A \sin kx$$

The second boundary condition, $\psi(L) = 0$, when applied to the reduced solution, gives

$$\psi(L) = A \sin kL = 0$$

which is satisfied only if kL is an integral multiple of π, that is, if $kL = n\pi$, where n is an integer. Because $k = \sqrt{2mE}/\hbar$, we have

$$kL = \frac{\sqrt{2mE}}{\hbar} L = n\pi$$

For each integer choice for n, this equation determines a quantized energy E_n. Solving for the allowed energies E_n gives

$$E_n = \left(\frac{h^2}{8mL^2} \right) n^2 \qquad [28.34]$$

which are identical to the allowed energies in Equation 28.30.

Substituting the values of k in the wave function, the allowed wave functions $\psi_n(x)$ are given by

$$\psi_n(x) = A \sin \left(\frac{n\pi x}{L} \right) \qquad [28.35]$$

This wave function agrees with Equation 28.29.

Normalizing this relationship shows that $A = \sqrt{(2/L)}$. (See Problem 28.46.) Therefore, the normalized wave function is

$$\psi(x) = \sqrt{\frac{2}{L}} \sin \left(\frac{n\pi x}{L} \right) \qquad [28.36]$$

The notion of trapping particles in potential wells is used in the burgeoning field of **nanotechnology,** which refers to the design and application of devices having dimensions ranging from 1 to 100 nm. The fabrication of these devices often involves manipulating single atoms or small groups of atoms to form structures such as the quantum corral in Figure 28.25.

One area of nanotechnology of interest to researchers is the **quantum dot.** The quantum dot, a small region that is grown in a silicon crystal, acts as a potential well. This region can trap electrons into states with quantized energies. The wave functions for a particle in a quantum dot look similar to those in Active Figure 28.23a if L is on the order of nanometers. The storage of binary information using quantum dots is an active field of research. A simple binary scheme would involve associating a one with a quantum dot containing an electron and a zero with an empty dot. Other schemes involve cells of multiple dots such that arrangements of electrons among the dots correspond to ones and zeros. Several research laboratories are studying the properties and potential applications of quantum dots. Information should be forthcoming from these laboratories at a steady rate in the next few years.

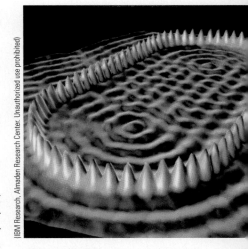

(IBM Research, Almaden Research Center. Unauthorized use prohibited)

FIGURE 28.25 This photograph is a demonstration of a quantum corral consisting of a ring of 48 iron atoms located on a copper surface. The diameter of the ring is 143 nm, and the photograph was obtained using a low-temperature scanning tunneling microscope (STM) as mentioned in Section 28.13. Corrals and other structures are able to confine surface electron waves. The study of such structures will play an important role in determining the future of small electronic devices.

EXAMPLE **28.11** The Expectation Values for the Particle in a Box

A particle of mass m is confined to a one-dimensional box between $x = 0$ and $x = L$. Find the expectation value of the position x of the particle for a state with quantum number n.

Solution Using Equation 28.25 and the wave function in Equation 28.36, we can set up the expectation value for x:

$$\langle x \rangle = \int_{-\infty}^{\infty} \psi^* x \psi \, dx = \int_0^L x \left[\sqrt{\frac{2}{L}} \sin \left(\frac{n\pi x}{L} \right) \right]^2 dx$$

$$= \frac{2}{L} \int_0^L x \sin^2 \left(\frac{n\pi x}{L} \right) dx$$

where we have reduced the limits on the integral to 0 to L because the value of the wave function is zero

elsewhere. Evaluating the integral by consulting an integral table or by mathematical integration[13] gives

$$\langle x \rangle = \frac{2}{L} \left[\frac{x^2}{4} - \frac{x \sin \left(2 \dfrac{n\pi x}{L} \right)}{4 \dfrac{n\pi}{L}} - \frac{\cos \left(2 \dfrac{n\pi x}{L} \right)}{8 \left(\dfrac{n\pi}{L} \right)^2} \right]_0^L$$

$$= \frac{2}{L} \left(\frac{L^2}{4} \right) = \boxed{\frac{L}{2}}$$

Notice that the expectation value is right at the center of the box, which we would expect from the symmetry of the square of the wave function about the center (see Active Fig. 28.23b). Because the squares of all wave functions are symmetric about the midpoint, the expectation value does not depend on n.

28.13 TUNNELING THROUGH A POTENTIAL ENERGY BARRIER

Consider the potential energy function shown in Figure 28.26, in which the potential energy of the system is zero everywhere except for a region of width L where the potential energy has a constant value of U. This type of potential energy function is called a **square barrier,** and U is called the **barrier height.** A very interesting and peculiar phenomenon occurs when a moving particle encounters such a barrier of finite height and width. Consider a particle of energy $E < U$ that is incident on the barrier from the left (see Fig. 28.26). Classically, the particle is reflected by the barrier. If the particle were to exist in region II, its kinetic energy would be negative, which is not allowed classically. Therefore, region II, and in turn region III, are both classically *forbidden* to the particle incident from the left. According to quantum mechanics, however, **all regions are accessible to the particle, regardless of its energy.** (Although all regions are accessible, the probability of the particle being in a region that is classically forbidden is very low.) According to the uncertainty principle, the particle can be within the barrier as long as the time interval during which it is in the barrier is short and consistent with Equation 28.18. If the barrier is

FIGURE 28.26 Wave function ψ for a particle incident from the left on a barrier of height U and width L. The wave function is sinusoidal in regions I and III but exponentially decaying in region II. The wave function is plotted vertically from an axis positioned at the energy of the particle.

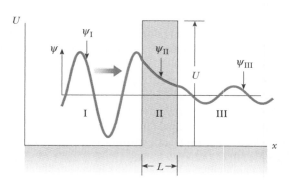

---

[13]To integrate this function, first replace $\sin^2(\pi x/L)$ with $\frac{1}{2}(1 - \cos 2\pi x/L)$ (Table B.3 in Appendix B). That step will allow $\langle x \rangle$ to be expressed as two integrals. The second integral can then be evaluated by partial integration (Section B.7 in Appendix B).

relatively narrow, this short time interval can allow the particle to move across the barrier. Therefore, it is possible for us to understand the passing of the particle through the barrier with the help of the uncertainty principle.

Let us approach this situation using a mathematical representation. The Schrödinger equation has valid solutions in all three regions I, II, and III. The solutions in regions I and III are sinusoidal as in Equation 28.21. In region II, the solution is exponential. Applying the boundary conditions that the wave functions in the three regions must join smoothly at the boundaries, we find that a full solution can be found such as that represented by the curve in Figure 28.26. Therefore, Schrödinger's equation and the boundary conditions are satisfied, which tells us mathematically that such a process can theoretically occur according to the quantum theory.

Because the probability of locating the particle is proportional to $|\psi|^2$, we conclude that the chance of finding the particle beyond the barrier in region III is nonzero. This result is in complete disagreement with classical physics. The movement of the particle to the far side of the barrier is called **tunneling** or **barrier penetration.**

The probability of tunneling can be described with a **transmission coefficient** T and a **reflection coefficient** R. **The transmission coefficient represents the probability that the particle penetrates to the other side of the barrier, and the reflection coefficient is the probability that the particle is reflected by the barrier.** Because the incident particle is either reflected or transmitted, we require that $T + R = 1$. An approximate expression for the transmission coefficient, obtained when $T \ll 1$ (a very wide barrier or a very high barrier, that is, $U \gg E$), is

$$T \approx e^{-2CL} \qquad [28.37]$$

where

$$C = \frac{\sqrt{2m(U - E)}}{\hbar} \qquad [28.38]$$

According to quantum physics, Equation 28.37 tells us that T can be nonzero, which is in contrast to the classical point of view that requires that $T = 0$. That we experimentally observe the phenomenon of tunneling provides further confidence in the principles of quantum physics.

Figure 28.26 shows the wave function of a particle tunneling through a barrier in one dimension. A similar wave function having spherical symmetry describes the barrier penetration of a particle leaving a radioactive nucleus, which we will study in Chapter 30. The wave function exists both inside and outside the nucleus, and its amplitude is constant in time. In this way, the wave function correctly describes the small but constant probability that the nucleus will decay. The moment of decay cannot be predicted. In general, quantum mechanics implies that the future is indeterminate. (This feature is in contrast to classical mechanics, from which the trajectory of an object can be calculated to arbitrarily high precision from precise knowledge of its initial position and velocity and of the forces exerted on it.) We must conclude that the fundamental laws of nature are probabilistic.

A radiation detector can be used to show that a nucleus decays by radiating a particle at a particular moment and in a particular direction. To point out the contrast between this experimental result and the wave function describing it, Schrödinger imagined a box containing a cat, a radioactive sample, a radiation counter, and a vial of poison. When a nucleus in the sample decays, the counter triggers the administration of lethal poison to the cat. Quantum mechanics correctly predicts the probability of finding the cat dead when the box is opened. Before the box is opened, does the animal have a wave function describing it as a fractionally dead cat, with some chance of being alive?

This question is currently under investigation, never with actual cats, but sometimes with interference experiments building upon the experiment described in

PITFALL PREVENTION 28.8

"HEIGHT" ON AN ENERGY DIAGRAM
The word *height* (as in *barrier height*) refers to an energy in discussions of barriers in potential energy diagrams. For example, we might say the height of the barrier is 10 eV. On the other hand, the barrier *width* refers to our traditional usage of such a word. It is an actual physical length measurement between the two locations of the vertical sides of the barrier.

Section 28.7. Does the act of measurement change the system from a probabilistic to a definite state? When a particle emitted by a radioactive nucleus is detected at one particular location, does the wave function describing the particle drop instantaneously to zero everywhere else in the Universe? (Einstein called such a state change a "spooky action at a distance.") Is there a fundamental difference between a quantum system and a macroscopic system? The answers to these questions are basically unknown.

QUICK QUIZ 28.10 Which of the following changes would increase the probability of transmission of a particle through a potential barrier? (You may choose more than one answer.)   **(a)** decreasing the width of the barrier   **(b)** increasing the width of the barrier   **(c)** decreasing the height of the barrier   **(d)** increasing the height of the barrier   **(e)** decreasing the kinetic energy of the incident particle   **(f)** increasing the kinetic energy of the incident particle

---

INTERACTIVE EXAMPLE 28.12 Transmission Coefficient for an Electron

A 30-eV electron is incident on a square barrier of height 40 eV.

A What is the probability that the electron will tunnel through if the barrier width is 1.0 nm?

Solution Let us assume that the probability of transmission is low so that we can use the approximation in Equation 28.37. For the given barrier height and electron energy, the quantity $U - E$ has the value

$$U - E = (40 \text{ eV} - 30 \text{ eV}) = 10 \text{ eV} = 1.6 \times 10^{-18} \text{ J}$$

Using Equation 28.38, the quantity $2CL$ is

$$2CL = 2\frac{\sqrt{2(9.11 \times 10^{-31} \text{kg})(1.6 \times 10^{-18} \text{J})}}{1.054 \times 10^{-34} \text{J} \cdot \text{s}} (1.0 \times 10^{-9} \text{m})$$

$$= 32.4$$

Therefore, the probability of tunneling through the barrier is

$$T \approx e^{-2CL} = e^{-32.4} = \boxed{8.5 \times 10^{-15}}$$

That is, the electron has only about 1 chance in 10^{14} to tunnel through the 1.0-nm-wide barrier.

B What is the probability that the electron will tunnel through if the barrier width is 0.10 nm?

Solution For $L = 0.10$ nm, we find $2CL = 3.24$, and

$$T \approx e^{-2CL} = e^{-3.24} = \boxed{0.039}$$

This result shows that the electron has a relatively high probability, about 4%, compared with 10^{-12}% in part A, of penetrating the 0.10-nm barrier. Notice an important behavior that leads to effective practical applications for tunneling: that reducing the width of the barrier by only one order of magnitude increases the probability of tunneling by about 12 orders of magnitude!

Physics⊗Now™ Investigate the tunneling of particles through barriers by logging into PhysicsNow at **www.pop4e.com** and going to Interactive Example 28.12.

Applications of Tunneling

As we have seen, tunneling is a quantum phenomenon, a result of the wave nature of matter. Many applications may be understood only on the basis of tunneling.

- **Alpha decay.** One form of radioactive decay is the emission of alpha particles (the nuclei of helium atoms) by unstable, heavy nuclei (Chapter 30). For an alpha particle to escape from the nucleus, it must penetrate a barrier whose height is several times larger than the energy of the nucleus–alpha particle system. The barrier is due to a combination of the attractive nuclear force (discussed in Chapter 30) and the Coulomb repulsion (discussed in detail in Chapter 19) between the alpha particle and the rest of the nucleus. Occasionally, an alpha particle tunnels through the barrier, which explains the basic mechanism for this type of decay and the large variations in the mean lifetimes of various radioactive nuclei.

- **Nuclear fusion.** The basic reaction that powers the Sun and, indirectly, almost everything else in the solar system is fusion, which we will study in Chapter 30. In one step of the process that occurs at the core of the Sun, protons must approach each other to within such a small distance that they fuse to form a deuterium nucleus. According to classical physics, these protons cannot overcome and penetrate the barrier caused by their mutual electrical repulsion. Quantum-mechanically, however, the protons are able to tunnel through the barrier and fuse together.

- **Scanning tunneling microscope.** The scanning tunneling microscope, or STM, is a remarkable device that uses tunneling to create images of surfaces with resolution comparable to the size of a single atom. A small probe with a very fine tip is made to scan very close to the surface of a specimen. A tunneling current is maintained between the probe and specimen; the current (which is related to the probability of tunneling) is very sensitive to the barrier height (which is related to the separation between the tip and specimen) as seen in Interactive Example 28.12. Maintaining a constant tunneling current produces a feedback signal that is used to raise and lower the probe as the surface is scanned. Because the vertical motion of the probe follows the contour of the specimen's surface, an image of the surface is obtained. The image of the quantum corral shown in Figure 28.25 is made with a scanning tunneling microscope.

28.14 THE COSMIC TEMPERATURE

CONTEXT CONNECTION

Now that we have introduced the concepts of quantum physics for microscopic particles and systems, let us see how we can connect these concepts to processes occurring on a cosmic scale. For our first such connection, consider the Universe as a system. It is widely believed that the Universe began with a cataclysmic explosion called the **Big Bang,** first mentioned in Chapter 5. Because of this explosion, all the material in the Universe is moving apart. This expansion causes a Doppler shift in radiation left over from the Big Bang such that the wavelength of the radiation lengthens. In the 1940s, Ralph Alpher, George Gamow, and Robert Hermann developed a structural model of the Universe in which they predicted that the thermal radiation from the Big Bang should still be present and that it should now have a wavelength distribution consistent with a black body with a temperature of a few kelvins.

In 1965, Arno Penzias and Robert Wilson of Bell Telephone Laboratories were measuring radiation from the Milky Way galaxy using a special 20-ft antenna as a radio telescope. They noticed a consistent background "noise" of radiation in the signals from the antenna. Despite their great efforts to test alternative hypotheses for the origin of the noise in terms of interference from the Sun, an unknown source in the Milky Way, structural problems in the antenna, and even the presence of pigeon droppings in the antenna, none of the hypotheses was sufficient to explain the noise.

What Penzias and Wilson were detecting was the thermal radiation from the Big Bang. That it was detected by their system regardless of the direction of the antenna was consistent with the radiation being spread throughout the Universe, as the Big Bang model predicts. A measurement of the intensity of this radiation suggested that the temperature associated with the radiation was about 3 K, consistent with Alpher, Gamow, and Hermann's prediction from the 1940s. Although the measured intensity was consistent with their prediction, the measurement was taken at only a single wavelength. Full agreement with the model of the Universe as a black body would come only if measurements at many wavelengths demonstrated a distribution in wavelengths consistent with Active Figure 28.2.

In the years following Penzias and Wilson's discovery, other researchers made measurements at different wavelengths. In 1989, the COBE (*CO*smic *B*ackground *E*xplorer) satellite was launched by NASA and added critical measurements at wavelengths below 0.1 cm. The results of these measurements are shown in

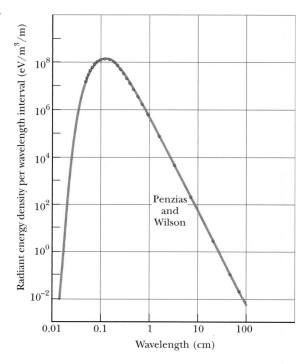

FIGURE 28.27 | Theoretical black-body wavelength distribution (brown curve) and measured data points (blue) for radiation from the Big Bang. Most of the data were collected from the Cosmic Background Explorer (COBE) satellite. The datum of Penzias and Wilson is indicated.

Figure 28.27. The series of measurements taken since 1965 are consistent with thermal radiation associated with a temperature of 2.7 K. The whole story of the cosmic temperature is a remarkable example of science at work: building a model, making a prediction, taking measurements, and testing the measurements against the predictions.

The first chapter of our *Cosmic Connection* Context describes the first example of this connection. By studying the thermal radiation from microscopic vibrating objects, we learn something about the origin of our Universe. In Chapter 29, we shall see more examples of this fascinating connection.

SUMMARY

Physics⊗Now™ Take a practice test by logging into Physics-Now at **www.pop4e.com** and clicking on the Pre-Test link for this chapter.

The characteristics of **blackbody radiation** cannot be explained by classical concepts. Planck introduced the first model of **quantum physics** when he argued that the atomic oscillators responsible for this radiation exist only in discrete **quantum states.**

In the **photoelectric effect,** electrons are ejected from a metallic surface when light is incident on that surface. Einstein provided a successful explanation of this effect by extending Planck's quantum theory to the electromagnetic field. In this model, light is viewed as a stream of particles called **photons,** each with energy $E = hf$, where f is the frequency and h is **Planck's constant.** The maximum kinetic energy of the ejected photoelectron is given by

$$K_{\max} = hf - \phi \qquad [28.5]$$

where ϕ is the **work function** of the metal.

X-rays striking a target are scattered at various angles by electrons in the target. A shift in wavelength is observed for the scattered x-rays, and the phenomenon is known as the **Compton effect.** Classical physics does not correctly explain the experimental results of this effect. If the x-ray is treated as a photon, conservation of energy and momentum applied to the isolated system of the photon and the electron yields for the Compton shift the expression

$$\lambda' - \lambda_0 = \frac{h}{m_e c} (1 - \cos \theta) \qquad [28.8]$$

where m_e is the mass of the electron, c is the speed of light, and θ is the scattering angle.

Every object of mass m and momentum p has wave-like properties, with a **de Broglie wavelength** given by the relation

$$\lambda = \frac{h}{p} = \frac{h}{mv} \qquad [28.10]$$

The wave–particle duality is the basis of the **quantum particle model.** It can be interpreted by imagining a particle to be made up of a combination of a large number of waves. These waves interfere constructively in a small region of space called a **wave packet.**

The **uncertainty principle** states that if a measurement of position is made with uncertainty Δx and a *simultaneous* measurement of momentum is made with uncertainty Δp_x, the product of the two uncertainties can never be less than $\hbar/2$:

$$\Delta x \, \Delta p_x \geq \frac{\hbar}{2} \qquad [28.17]$$

The uncertainty principle is a natural outgrowth of the wave packet model.

Particles are represented by a **wave function** $\psi(x, y, z)$. The **probability density** that a particle will be found at a point is $|\psi|^2$. If the particle is confined to moving along the x axis, the probability that it will be located in an interval dx is given by $|\psi|^2 \, dx$. Furthermore, the wave function must be **normalized:**

$$\int_{-\infty}^{\infty} |\psi|^2 \, dx = 1 \qquad [28.23]$$

The measured position x of the particle, averaged over many trials, is called the **expectation value** of x and is defined by

$$\langle x \rangle \equiv \int_{-\infty}^{\infty} \psi^* x \psi \, dx \qquad [28.25]$$

If a particle of mass m is confined to moving in a one-dimensional box of width L whose walls are perfectly rigid, the allowed wave functions for the particle are

$$\psi(x) = A \sin\left(\frac{n\pi x}{L}\right) \qquad [28.29]$$

where n is an integer quantum number starting at 1. The particle has a well-defined wavelength λ whose values are such that the width L of the box is equal to an integral number of half wavelengths, that is, $L = n\lambda/2$. The energies of a particle in a box are quantized and are given by

$$E_n = \left(\frac{h^2}{8mL^2}\right) n^2 \qquad n = 1, 2, 3, \ldots \qquad [28.30]$$

Quantum systems generally involve a particle under some constraints imposed by the environment, which is the basis of the quantum particle under **boundary conditions** model. In this model, the wave function for a system is found and application of boundary conditions on the system allows a determination of the allowed energies and unknown constants in the wave function.

The wave function must satisfy the Schrödinger equation. The **time-independent Schrödinger equation** for a particle confined to moving along the x axis is

$$-\frac{\hbar^2}{2m} \frac{d^2\psi}{dx^2} + U\psi = E\psi \qquad [28.31]$$

where E is the total energy of the system and U is the potential energy of the system.

When a particle of energy E meets a barrier of height U, where $E < U$, the particle has a finite probability of penetrating the barrier. This process, called **tunneling,** is the basic mechanism that explains the operation of the scanning tunneling microscope and the phenomenon of alpha decay in some radioactive nuclei.

QUESTIONS

◻ = answer available in the *Student Solutions Manual and Study Guide*

1. What assumptions did Planck make in dealing with the problem of blackbody radiation? Discuss the consequences of these assumptions.

2. ◻ Which is more likely to cause sunburn because individual molecules in skin cells absorb more energy: (a) infrared light, (b) visible light, or (c) ultraviolet light?

3. ◻ If the photoelectric effect is observed for one metal, can you conclude that the effect will also be observed for another metal under the same conditions? Explain.

4. How does the Compton effect differ from the photoelectric effect?

5. ◻ Why does the existence of a cutoff frequency in the photoelectric effect favor a particle theory for light over a wave theory?

6. Suppose a photograph were made of a person's face using only a few photons. Would the result be simply a very faint image of the face? Explain your answer.

7. ◻ An x-ray photon is scattered by an electron. What happens to the frequency of the scattered photon relative to that of the incident photon?

8. Is light a wave or a particle? Support your answer by citing specific experimental evidence.

9. Is an electron a wave or a particle? Support your answer by citing some experimental results.

10. Why was the demonstration of electron diffraction by Davisson and Germer an important experiment?

11. ◻ If matter has a wave nature, why is this wave-like characteristic not observable in our daily experiences?

12. An electron and a proton are accelerated from rest through the same potential difference. Which particle has the longer wavelength?

13. In describing the passage of electrons through a slit and arriving at a screen, physicist Richard Feynman said that "electrons arrive in lumps, like particles, but the probability of arrival of these lumps is determined as the intensity of the waves would be. It is in this sense that the electron behaves sometimes like a particle and sometimes like a wave." Elaborate on this point in your own words. For a further discussion of this point, see R. Feynman, *The Character of Physical Law* (Cambridge, MA: MIT Press, 1980), Chapter 6.

14. *Blacker than black, brighter than white.* (a) Take a large, closed, empty cardboard box. Cut a slot a few millimeters wide in one side. Use black pens, markers, and black material to make some stripes next to the slot as shown in Figure Q28.14a. Inspect them with care and choose which is blackest (the figure does not show enough contrast to

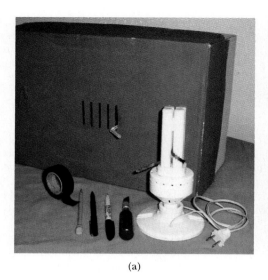

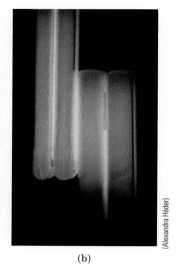

(a)

(b)

(Alexandra Héder)

FIGURE **Q28.14**

reveal which it is). Explain why it is blackest. (b) Locate an intricately shaped compact fluorescent light fixture. Look at it through dark glasses and describe where it appears brightest. Explain why it is brightest there. Figure Q28.14b shows two such light fixtures held near each other. [*Suggestion:* Gustav Kirchhoff, professor at Heidelberg and master of the obvious, gave the same answer to part (a) as you likely will. His answer to part (b) would begin as follows. When electromagnetic radiation falls on its surface, an object reflects some fraction r of the energy and absorbs the rest. Whether the fraction reflected is 0.8 or 0.001, the fraction absorbed is $a = 1 - r$. Suppose the object and its surroundings are at the same temperature. The energy the

object absorbs joins its fund of internal energy, but the second law of thermodynamics implies that the absorbed energy cannot raise the object's temperature. It does not produce a temperature increase because the object's energy budget has one more term: energy radiated. . . . You still have to make the observations and answer parts (a) and (b), but you can incorporate some of Kirchhoff's ideas into your answer if you wish.]

15. For a particle in a box, the probability density at certain points is zero as seen in Active Figure 28.23b. Does that imply that the particle cannot move across these points? Explain.

PROBLEMS

1, **2**, **3** = straightforward, intermediate, challenging
☐ = full solution available in the *Student Solutions Manual and Study Guide*
Physics⊗Now™ = coached problem with hints available at www.pop4e.com
🖥 = computer useful in solving problem
▬ = paired numerical and symbolic problems
🔬 = biomedical application

Section 28.1 ■ Blackbody Radiation and Planck's Theory

1. 🔬 With young children and the elderly, use of a traditional fever thermometer has risks of bacterial contamination and tissue perforation. The radiation thermometer shown in Figure 28.5 works fast and avoids most risks. The instrument measures the power of infrared radiation from the ear canal. This cavity is accurately described as a black body and is close to the hypothalamus, the body's temperature control center. Take normal body temperature as 37.0°C. If the body temperature of a feverish patient is

38.3°C, what is the percentage increase in radiated power from his ear canal?

2. The radius of our Sun is 6.96×10^8 m, and its total power output is 3.85×10^{26} W. (a) Assuming that the Sun's surface emits as a black body, calculate its surface temperature. (b) Using the result of part (a), find λ_{max} for the Sun.

3. 🔬 Figure P28.3 shows the spectrum of light emitted by a firefly. Determine the temperature of a black body that

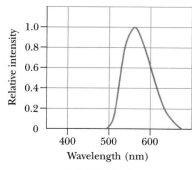

FIGURE **P28.3**

would emit radiation peaked at the same wavelength. Based on your result, would you say that firefly radiation is blackbody radiation?

4. Calculate the energy, in electron volts, of a photon whose frequency is (a) 620 THz, (b) 3.10 GHz, and (c) 46.0 MHz. (d) Determine the corresponding wavelengths for these photons and state the classification of each on the electromagnetic spectrum.

5. An FM radio transmitter has a power output of 150 kW and operates at a frequency of 99.7 MHz. How many photons per second does the transmitter emit?

6. The average threshold of dark-adapted (scotopic) vision is 4.00×10^{-11} W/m^2 at a central wavelength of 500 nm. If light having this intensity and wavelength enters the eye and the pupil is open to its maximum diameter of 8.50 mm, how many photons per second enter the eye?

7. A simple pendulum has a length of 1.00 m and a mass of 1.00 kg. The amplitude of oscillations of the pendulum is 3.00 cm. Estimate the quantum number for the pendulum.

8. **Review problem.** This problem is about how strongly matter is coupled to radiation, the subject with which quantum mechanics began. For a very simple model, consider a solid iron sphere 2.00 cm in radius. Assume that its temperature is always uniform throughout its volume. (a) Find the mass of the sphere. (b) Assume that it is at 20°C and has emissivity 0.860. Find the power with which it is radiating electromagnetic waves. (c) If it were alone in the Universe, at what rate would its temperature be changing? (d) Assume that Wien's law describes the sphere. Find the wavelength λ_{max} of electromagnetic radiation it emits most strongly. Although it emits a spectrum of waves having all different wavelengths, model its whole power output as carried by photons of wavelength λ_{max}. Find (e) the energy of one photon and (f) the number of photons it emits each second. The answer to part (f) gives an indication of how fast the object is emitting and also absorbing photons when it is in thermal equilibrium with its surroundings at 20°C.

Section 28.2 ∎ The Photoelectric Effect

9. Molybdenum has a work function of 4.20 eV. (a) Find the cutoff wavelength and cutoff frequency for the photoelectric effect. (b) What is the stopping potential if the incident light has a wavelength of 180 nm?

10. Electrons are ejected from a metallic surface with speeds ranging up to 4.60×10^5 m/s when light with a wavelength of 625 nm is used. (a) What is the work function of the surface? (b) What is the cutoff frequency for this surface?

11. Two light sources are used in a photoelectric experiment to determine the work function for a particular metal surface. When green light from a mercury lamp ($\lambda = 546.1$ nm) is used, a stopping potential of 0.376 V reduces the photocurrent to zero. (a) Based on this measurement, what is the work function for this metal? (b) What stopping potential would be observed when using the yellow light from a helium discharge tube ($\lambda = 587.5$ nm)?

12. From the scattering of sunlight, J. J. Thomson calculated the classical radius of the electron as having a value of 2.82×10^{-15} m. Sunlight with an intensity of 500 W/m^2 falls on a disk with this radius. Calculate the time interval required to accumulate 1.00 eV of energy. Assume that light is a classical wave and that the light striking the disk is completely absorbed. How does your result compare with the observation that photoelectrons are emitted promptly (within 10^{-9} s)?

13. **Review problem.** An isolated copper sphere of radius 5.00 cm, initially uncharged, is illuminated by ultraviolet light of wavelength 200 nm. What charge will the photoelectric effect induce on the sphere? The work function for copper is 4.70 eV.

Section 28.3 ∎ The Compton Effect

14. Calculate the energy and momentum of a photon of wavelength 700 nm.

15. X-rays having an energy of 300 keV undergo Compton scattering from a target. The scattered rays are detected at 37.0° relative to the incident rays. Find (a) the Compton shift at this angle, (b) the energy of the scattered x-ray, and (c) the energy of the recoiling electron.

16. A 0.110-nm photon collides with a stationary electron. After the collision, the electron moves forward and the photon recoils backward. Find the momentum and the kinetic energy of the electron.

17. Physics⊗Now™ A 0.001 60-nm photon scatters from a free electron. For what (photon) scattering angle does the recoiling electron have kinetic energy equal to the energy of the scattered photon?

18. After a 0.800-nm x-ray photon scatters from a free electron, the electron recoils at 1.40×10^6 m/s. (a) What was the Compton shift in the photon's wavelength? (b) Through what angle was the photon scattered?

Section 28.4 ∎ Photons and Electromagnetic Waves

19. An electromagnetic wave is called *ionizing radiation* if its photon energy is larger than about 10.0 eV so that a single photon has enough energy to break apart an atom. With reference to Figure 24.12, identify what regions of the electromagnetic spectrum fit this definition of ionizing radiation and what do not.

Section 28.5 ∎ The Wave Properties of Particles

20. Calculate the de Broglie wavelength for a proton moving with a speed of 1.00×10^6 m/s.

21. (a) An electron has kinetic energy 3.00 eV. Find its wavelength. (b) A photon has energy 3.00 eV. Find its wavelength.

22. In the Davisson–Germer experiment, 54.0-eV electrons were diffracted from a nickel lattice. If the first maximum in the diffraction pattern was observed at $\phi = 50.0°$ (Fig. P28.22), what was the lattice spacing a between the vertical

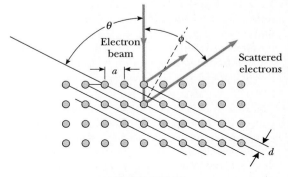

FIGURE P28.22

rows of atoms in the figure? (It is not the same as the spacing between the horizontal rows of atoms.)

23. Physics⊗Now™ The nucleus of an atom is on the order of 10^{-14} m in diameter. For an electron to be confined to a nucleus, its de Broglie wavelength would have to be on this order of magnitude or smaller. (a) What would be the kinetic energy of an electron confined to this region? (b) Make also an order-of-magnitude estimate of the electric potential energy of a system of an electron inside an atomic nucleus. Would you expect to find an electron in a nucleus? Explain.

24. After learning about de Broglie's hypothesis that particles of momentum p have wave characteristics with wavelength $\lambda = h/p$, an 80.0-kg student has grown concerned about being diffracted when passing through a 75.0-cm-wide doorway. Assume that significant diffraction occurs when the width of the diffraction aperture is less than 10.0 times the wavelength of the wave being diffracted. (a) Determine the maximum speed at which the student can pass through the doorway so as to be significantly diffracted. (b) With that speed, how long will it take the student to pass through the doorway if it is in a wall 15.0 cm thick? Compare your result to the currently accepted age of the Universe, which is 4×10^{17} s. (c) Should this student worry about being diffracted?

25. The resolving power of a microscope depends on the wavelength used. If one wished to "see" an atom, a resolution of approximately 1.00×10^{-11} m would be required. (a) If electrons are used (in an electron microscope), what minimum kinetic energy is required for the electrons? (b) If photons are used, what minimum photon energy is needed to obtain the required resolution?

Section 28.6 ■ The Quantum Particle

26. Consider a freely moving quantum particle with mass m and speed u. Its energy is $E = K = \frac{1}{2}mu^2$. Determine the phase speed of the quantum wave representing the particle and show that it is different from the speed at which the particle transports mass and energy.

27. For a free relativistic quantum particle moving with speed v, the total energy is $E = hf = \hbar\omega = \sqrt{p^2c^2 + m^2c^4}$ and the momentum is $p = h/\lambda = \hbar k = \gamma mv$. For the quantum wave representing the particle, the group speed is $v_g = d\omega/dk$. Prove that the group speed of the wave is the same as the speed of the particle.

Section 28.7 ■ The Double-Slit Experiment Revisited

28. A modified oscilloscope is used to perform an electron interference experiment. Electrons are incident on a pair of narrow slits 0.060 0 μm apart. The bright bands in the interference pattern are separated by 0.400 mm on a screen 20.0 cm from the slits. Determine the potential difference through which the electrons were accelerated to give this pattern.

29. Neutrons traveling at 0.400 m/s are directed through a pair of slits having a 1.00-mm separation. An array of detectors is placed 10.0 m from the slits. (a) What is the de Broglie wavelength of the neutrons? (b) How far off axis is the first zero-intensity point on the detector array? (c) When

a neutron reaches a detector, can we say which slit the neutron passed through? Explain.

30. In a certain vacuum tube, electrons evaporate from a hot cathode at a slow, steady rate and accelerate from rest through a potential difference of 45.0 V. Then they travel 28.0 cm as they pass through an array of slits and fall on a screen to produce an interference pattern. If the beam current is below a certain value, only one electron at a time will be in flight in the tube. What is this value? In this situation, the interference pattern still appears, showing that each individual electron can interfere with itself.

Section 28.8 ■ The Uncertainty Principle

31. An electron ($m_e = 9.11 \times 10^{-31}$ kg) and a bullet ($m = 0.020\ 0$ kg) each have a velocity with a magnitude of 500 m/s, accurate to within 0.010 0%. Within what limits could we determine the position of the objects along the direction of the velocity?

32. Suppose Fuzzy, a quantum-mechanical duck, lives in a world in which $h = 2\pi$ J·s. Fuzzy has a mass of 2.00 kg and is initially known to be within a pond 1.00 m wide. (a) What is the minimum uncertainty in the component of the duck's velocity parallel to the width of the pond? (b) Assuming that this uncertainty in speed prevails for 5.00 s, determine the uncertainty in the duck's position after this time interval.

33. An air rifle is used to shoot 1.00-g particles at 100 m/s through a hole of diameter 2.00 mm. How far from the rifle must an observer be to see the beam spread by 1.00 cm because of the uncertainty principle? Compare this answer with the diameter of the visible Universe (2×10^{26} m).

34. A π^0 meson is an unstable particle produced in high-energy particle collisions. Its rest energy is about 135 MeV, and it exists for an average lifetime of only 8.70×10^{-17} s before decaying into two gamma rays. Using the uncertainty principle, estimate the fractional uncertainty $\Delta m/m$ in its mass determination.

35. A woman on a ladder drops small pellets toward a point target on the floor. (a) Show that, according to the uncertainty principle, the average miss distance must be at least

$$\Delta x_f = \left(\frac{2\hbar}{m}\right)^{1/2}\left(\frac{2H}{g}\right)^{1/4}$$

where H is the initial height of each pellet above the floor and m is the mass of each pellet. Assume that the spread in impact points is given by $\Delta x_f = \Delta x_i + (\Delta v_x)t$. (b) If $H = 2.00$ m and $m = 0.500$ g, what is Δx_f?

Section 28.9 ■ An Interpretation of Quantum Mechanics

36. The wave function for a particle is

$$\psi(x) = \sqrt{\frac{a}{\pi(x^2 + a^2)}}$$

for $a > 0$ and $-\infty < x < +\infty$. Determine the probability that the particle is located somewhere between $x = -a$ and $x = +a$.

37. A free electron has a wave function

$$\psi(x) = Ae^{i(5.00 \times 10^{10}x)}$$

where x is in meters. Find (a) its de Broglie wavelength, (b) its momentum, and (c) its kinetic energy in electron volts.

Section 28.10 ∎ A Particle in a Box

38. An electron that has an energy of approximately 6 eV moves between rigid walls 1.00 nm apart. Find (a) the quantum number n for the energy state that the electron occupies and (b) the precise energy of the electron.

39. Physics⚛Now™ An electron is contained in a one-dimensional box of length 0.100 nm. (a) Draw an energy level diagram for the electron for levels up to $n = 4$. (b) Find the wavelengths of all photons that can be emitted by the electron in making downward transitions that could eventually carry it from the $n = 4$ state to the $n = 1$ state.

40. The nuclear potential energy that binds protons and neutrons in a nucleus is often approximated by a square well. Imagine a proton confined in an infinitely high square well of length 10.0 fm, a typical nuclear diameter. Calculate the wavelength and energy associated with the photon emitted when the proton moves from the $n = 2$ state to the ground state. In what region of the electromagnetic spectrum does this wavelength belong?

41. A photon with wavelength λ is absorbed by an electron confined to a box. As a result, the electron moves from state $n = 1$ to $n = 4$. (a) Find the length of the box. (b) What is the wavelength of the photon emitted in the transition of that electron from the state $n = 4$ to the state $n = 2$?

Section 28.11 ∎ The Quantum Particle Under Boundary Conditions
Section 28.12 ∎ The Schrödinger Equation

42. The wave function of a particle is given by

$$\psi(x) = A\cos(kx) + B\sin(kx)$$

where A, B, and k are constants. Show that ψ is a solution of the Schrödinger equation (Eq. 28.31), assuming the particle is free ($U = 0$), and find the corresponding energy E of the particle.

43. Show that the wave function $\psi = Ae^{i(kx - \omega t)}$ is a solution to the Schrödinger equation (Eq. 28.31) where $k = 2\pi/\lambda$ and $U = 0$.

44. Prove that the first term in the Schrödinger equation, $-(\hbar^2/2m)(d^2\psi/dx^2)$, reduces to the kinetic energy of the particle multiplied by the wave function (a) for a freely moving particle, with the wave function given by Equation 28.21, and (b) for a particle in a box, with the wave function given by Equation 28.36.

45. A particle in an infinitely deep square well has a wave function given by

$$\psi_2(x) = \sqrt{\frac{2}{L}}\sin\left(\frac{2\pi x}{L}\right)$$

for $0 \le x \le L$ and zero otherwise. (a) Determine the expectation value of x. (b) Determine the probability of finding the particle near $L/2$ by calculating the probability that the particle lies in the range $0.490L \le x \le 0.510L$. (c) Determine the probability of finding the particle near $L/4$ by

calculating the probability that the particle lies in the range $0.240L \le x \le 0.260L$. (d) Argue that the result of part (a) does not contradict the results of parts (b) and (c).

46. The wave function for a particle confined to moving in a one-dimensional box is

$$\psi(x) = A\sin\left(\frac{n\pi x}{L}\right)$$

Use the normalization condition on ψ to show that

$$A = \sqrt{\frac{2}{L}}$$

(*Suggestion:* Because the box length is L, the wave function is zero for $x < 0$ and for $x > L$, so the normalization condition, Equation 28.23, reduces to $\int_0^L |\psi|^2\,dx = 1$.)

47. The wave function of an electron is

$$\psi(x) = \sqrt{\frac{2}{L}}\sin\left(\frac{2\pi x}{L}\right)$$

Calculate the probability of finding the electron between $x = 0$ and $x = L/4$.

48. A particle of mass m moves in a potential well of length $2L$. The potential energy is infinite for $x < -L$ and for $x > +L$. Inside the region $-L < x < L$, the potential energy is given by

$$U(x) = \frac{-\hbar^2 x^2}{mL^2(L^2 - x^2)}$$

In addition, the particle is in a stationary state that is described by the wave function $\psi(x) = A(1 - x^2/L^2)$ for $-L < x < +L$ and by $\psi(x) = 0$ elsewhere. (a) Determine the energy of the particle in terms of $\hbar$, m, and L. (*Suggestion:* Use the Schrödinger equation, Eq. 28.31.) (b) Show that $A = (15/16L)^{1/2}$. (c) Determine the probability that the particle is located between $x = -L/3$ and $x = +L/3$.

Section 28.13 ∎ Tunneling Through a Potential Energy Barrier

49. An electron with kinetic energy $E = 5.00$ eV is incident on a barrier with thickness $L = 0.200$ nm and height $U = 10.0$ eV (Fig. P28.49). What is the probability that the electron (a) will tunnel through the barrier and (b) will be reflected?

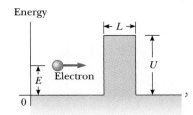

FIGURE P28.49 Problems 28.49 and 28.50.

50. An electron having total energy $E = 4.50$ eV approaches a rectangular energy barrier with $U = 5.00$ eV and $L = 950$ pm as shown in Figure P28.49. Classically, the electron cannot pass through the barrier because $E < U$. Quantum-mechanically, however, the probability of tunneling is not zero. Calculate this probability, which is the transmission coefficient.

51. An electron has a kinetic energy of 12.0 eV. The electron is incident upon a rectangular barrier of height 20.0 eV and thickness 1.00 nm. By what factor would the electron's probability of tunneling through the barrier increase if the electron absorbs all the energy of a photon of green light (with wavelength 546 nm) just as it reaches the barrier?

Section 28.14 ■ Context Connection — The Cosmic Temperature

Problems 24.14 and 24.59 in Chapter 24 can be assigned with this section.

52. **Review problem.** A star moving away from the Earth at $0.280c$ emits radiation that we measure to be most intense at the wavelength 500 nm. Determine the surface temperature of this star.

53. The cosmic background radiation is blackbody radiation from a source at a temperature of 2.73 K. (a) Determine the wavelength at which this radiation has its maximum intensity. (b) In what part of the electromagnetic spectrum is the peak of the distribution?

54. Find the intensity of the cosmic background radiation, emitted by the fireball of the Big Bang at a temperature of 2.73 K.

Additional Problems

55. **Review problem.** Design an incandescent lamp filament. Specify the length and radius a tungsten wire can have to radiate electromagnetic waves with power 75.0 W when its ends are connected across a 120-V power supply. Assume that its constant operating temperature is 2 900 K and that its emissivity is 0.450. Assume that it takes in energy only by electrical transmission and loses energy only by electromagnetic radiation. From Table 21.1, you may take the resistivity of tungsten at 2 900 K as $5.6 \times 10^{-8} \, \Omega \cdot m \times [1 + (4.5 \times 10^{-3}/°C)(2\,607\,°C)] = 7.13 \times 10^{-7} \, \Omega \cdot m$.

56. Figure P28.56 shows the stopping potential versus the incident photon frequency for the photoelectric effect for sodium. Use the graph to find (a) the work function, (b) the ratio h/e, and (c) the cutoff wavelength. The data are taken from R. A. Millikan, *Physical Review* 7:362 (1916).

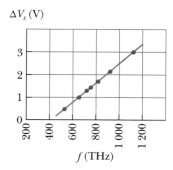

ΔV_s (V)

FIGURE P28.56

57. **Physics⊗Now™** The following table shows data obtained in a photoelectric experiment. (a) Using these data, make a graph similar to Active Figure 28.9 that plots as a straight line. From the graph, determine (b) an experimental value for Planck's constant (in joule-seconds) and (c) the work function (in electron volts) for the surface. (Two significant figures for each answer are sufficient.)

Wavelength (nm)	Maximum Kinetic Energy of Photoelectrons (eV)
588	0.67
505	0.98
445	1.35
399	1.63

58. **Review problem.** Photons of wavelength λ are incident on a metal. The most energetic electrons ejected from the metal are bent into a circular arc of radius R by a magnetic field having a magnitude B. What is the work function of the metal?

59. Johnny Jumper's favorite trick is to step out of his 16th-story window and fall 50.0 m into a pool. A news reporter takes a picture of 75.0-kg Johnny just before he makes a splash, using an exposure time of 5.00 ms. Find (a) Johnny's de Broglie wavelength at this moment, (b) the uncertainty of his kinetic energy measurement during such a period of time, and (c) the percent error caused by such an uncertainty.

60. A particle of mass 2.00×10^{-28} kg is confined to a one-dimensional box of length 1.00×10^{-10} m. For $n = 1$, what are (a) the particle's wavelength, (b) its momentum, and (c) its ground-state energy?

61. **Physics⊗Now™** An electron is represented by the time-independent wave function

$$\psi(x) = \begin{cases} Ae^{-\alpha x} & \text{for } x > 0 \\ Ae^{+\alpha x} & \text{for } x < 0 \end{cases}$$

(a) Sketch the wave function as a function of x. (b) Sketch the probability density representing the likelihood that the electron is found between x and $x + dx$. (c) Only an infinite value of potential energy could produce the discontinuity in the derivative of the wave function at $x = 0$. Aside from this feature, argue that $\psi(x)$ can be a physically reasonable wave function. (d) Normalize the wave function. (e) Determine the probability of finding the electron somewhere in the range

$$x_1 = -\frac{1}{2\alpha} \quad \text{to} \quad x_2 = \frac{1}{2\alpha}$$

62. Particles incident from the left are confronted with a step in potential energy shown in Figure P28.62. Located at $x = 0$, the step has a height U. The particles have energy $E > U$. Classically, we would expect all the particles to continue on, although with reduced speed. According to quantum mechanics, a fraction of the particles are reflected at the barrier. (a) Prove that the reflection coefficient R for this case is

$$R = \frac{(k_1 - k_2)^2}{(k_1 + k_2)^2}$$

where $k_1 = 2\pi/\lambda_1$ and $k_2 = 2\pi/\lambda_2$ are the wave numbers for the incident and transmitted particles. Proceed as follows. Show that the wave function $\psi_1 = Ae^{ik_1x} + Be^{-ik_1x}$ satisfies the Schrödinger equation in region 1, for $x < 0$. Here Ae^{ik_1x} represents the incident beam and Be^{-ik_1x} represents the reflected particles. Show that $\psi_2 = Ce^{ik_2x}$ satisfies the Schrödinger equation in region 2, for $x > 0$. Impose the boundary conditions $\psi_1 = \psi_2$ and $d\psi_1/dx = d\psi_2/dx$ at $x = 0$ to find the relationship between B and A. Then evaluate $R = B^2/A^2$. (b) A particle that has kinetic energy $E = 7.00$ eV is incident from a region where the potential energy is zero onto one in which $U = 5.00$ eV. Find its probability of being reflected and its probability of being transmitted.

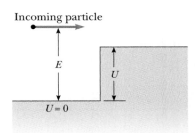

FIGURE P28.62

63. For a particle described by a wave function $\psi(x)$, the expectation value of a physical quantity $f(x)$ associated with

the particle is defined by

$$\langle f(x) \rangle \equiv \int_{-\infty}^{\infty} \psi^* f(x) \psi \, dx$$

For a particle in a one-dimensional box extending from $x = 0$ to $x = L$, show that

$$\langle x^2 \rangle = \frac{L^2}{3} - \frac{L^2}{2n^2\pi^2}$$

64. A particle of mass m is placed in a one-dimensional box of length L. Assume that the box is so small that the particle's motion is *relativistic*, so $K = p^2/2m$ is not valid. (a) Derive an expression for the kinetic energy levels of the particle. (b) Assume that the particle is an electron in a box of length $L = 1.00 \times 10^{-12}$ m. Find its lowest possible kinetic energy. By what percent is the nonrelativistic equation in error? (*Suggestion:* See Eq. 9.18.)

65. Imagine that a particle has a wave function

$$\psi(x) = \begin{cases} \sqrt{\dfrac{2}{a}}\, e^{-x/a} & \text{for } x > 0 \\ 0 & \text{for } x < 0 \end{cases}$$

(a) Find and sketch the probability density. (b) Find the probability that the particle will be at any point where $x < 0$. (c) Show that ψ is normalized, and then find the probability that the particle will be found between $x = 0$ and $x = a$.

ANSWERS TO QUICK QUIZZES

28.1 (b). A very hot star has a peak in the blackbody intensity distribution curve at wavelengths shorter than the visible. As a result, more blue light is emitted than red light.

28.2 AM radio, FM radio, microwaves, sodium light. The order of photon energy is the same as the order of frequency. See Figure 24.12 for a pictorial representation of electromagnetic radiation in order of frequency.

28.3 (c). When the frequency is increased, the photons each carry more energy, so a stopping potential larger in magnitude is required for the current to fall to zero.

28.4 Classical physics predicts that light of sufficient intensity causes emission of photoelectrons, independent of frequency and without a cutoff frequency. Also, the greater the intensity, the larger the maximum kinetic energy of the electrons, with some time delay in emission at low

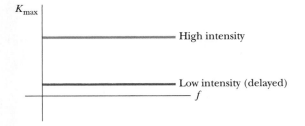

intensities. Therefore, the classical expectation (which did not match experiment) yields a graph that looks like the one at the bottom of the left column.

28.5 (c). According to Equation 28.10, two particles with the same de Broglie wavelength have the same momentum $p = mv$. If the electron and proton have the same momentum, they cannot have the same speed (a) because of the difference in their masses. For the same reason, remembering that $K = p^2/2m$, they cannot have the same kinetic energy (b). Because the particles have different kinetic energies, Equation 28.11 tells us that the particles do not have the same frequency (d).

28.6 (b). The Compton wavelength (Eq. 28.9) is a combination of constants and has no relation to the motion of the electron. The de Broglie wavelength (Eq. 28.10) is associated with the motion of the electron through its momentum.

28.7 (b). The group speed is zero because the leading edge of the packet remains fixed at the location of the accident.

28.8 Classically, we expect the particle to bounce back and forth between the two walls at constant speed. Therefore, we are as likely to find it on the left side of the box as in the middle, on the right side, or anywhere else inside the box. Our graph of probability density versus x would therefore be a horizontal line, with a total area under the line of unity, as shown on the next page.

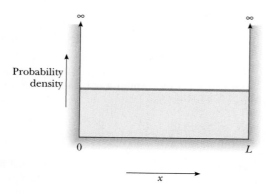

28.9 (c). According to Equation 28.30, if the length L is increased, all quantized energies become smaller. Therefore, the energy levels move closer together. As L becomes macroscopic, the energy levels are so close together that we do not observe the quantized behavior.

28.10 (a), (c), (f). Decreasing the barrier height and increasing the particle energy both reduce the value of C in Equation 28.38, increasing the transmission coefficient in Equation 28.37. Decreasing the width L of the barrier increases the transmission coefficient in Equation 28.37.

CHAPTER 29

Atomic Physics

This fireworks display shows several different colors. The colors are determined by the types of atoms in the material burning in the explosion. Bright white light often comes from oxidizing magnesium or aluminum. Red light often comes from strontium and yellow from sodium. Blue light is more difficult to achieve, but can be obtained by burning a mixture of copper powder, copper chloride, and hexachloroethane. The emission of light from atoms is an important clue that allows us to learn about the structure of the atom.

(© Jeff Hunter/Image Bank/Getty Images)

In Chapter 28, we introduced some of the basic concepts and techniques used in quantum physics along with their applications to various simple systems. This chapter describes the application of quantum physics to more sophisticated structural models of atoms than we have seen previously.

We studied the hydrogen atom in Chapter 11 using Bohr's semiclassical approach. In this chapter, we shall analyze the hydrogen atom with a full quantum model. Although the hydrogen atom is the simplest atomic system, it is an especially important system to understand, for several reasons:

- Much of what we learn about the hydrogen atom, with its single electron, can be extended to such single-electron ions as He^+ and Li^{2+}.
- The hydrogen atom is an ideal system for performing precise tests of theory against experiment and for improving our overall understanding of atomic structure.

- The quantum numbers used to characterize the allowed states of hydrogen can be used to qualitatively describe the allowed states of more complex atoms. This characterization enables us to understand the periodic table of the elements, which is one of the greatest triumphs of quantum physics.
- The basic ideas about atomic structure must be well understood before we attempt to deal with the complexities of molecular structures and the electronic structures of solids.

29.1 EARLY STRUCTURAL MODELS OF THE ATOM

The structural model of the atom in Newton's day described the atom as a tiny, hard, indestructible sphere, a particle model that ignored any internal structure of the atom. Although this model was a good basis for the kinetic theory of gases (Chapter 16), new structural models had to be devised when later experiments revealed the electrical nature of atoms. J. J. Thomson suggested a structural model that describes the atom as a continuous volume of positive charge with electrons embedded throughout it (Fig. 29.1).

In 1911, Ernest Rutherford and his students Hans Geiger and Ernst Marsden performed a critical experiment that showed that Thomson's model could not be correct. In this experiment, a beam of positively charged alpha particles was projected into a thin metal foil as in Figure 29.2a. Most of the particles passed through the foil as if it were empty space, which is consistent with the Thomson model. Some of the results of the experiment, however, were astounding. Many alpha particles were deflected from their original direction of travel through large angles. Some particles were even deflected backward, reversing their direction of travel. When Geiger informed Rutherford of these results, Rutherford wrote, "It was quite the most incredible event that has ever happened to me in my life. It was almost as incredible as if you fired a 15-inch [artillery] shell at a piece of tissue paper and it came back and hit you."

Such large deflections were not expected on the basis of Thomson's model. According to this model, a positively charged alpha particle would never come close enough to a sufficiently large concentration of positive charge to cause any large-angle deflections. Rutherford explained his astounding results with a new

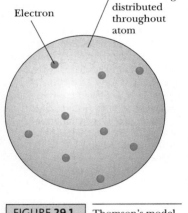

FIGURE **29.1** Thomson's model of the atom: negatively charged electrons in a volume of continuous positive charge.

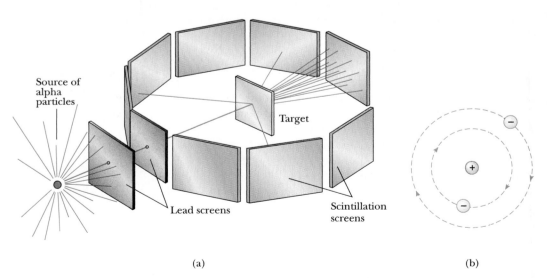

(a)   (b)

FIGURE **29.2** (a) Rutherford's technique for observing the scattering of alpha particles from a thin foil target. The source is a naturally occurring radioactive substance, such as radium. (b) Rutherford's planetary model of the atom.

structural model: he assumed that the positive charge was concentrated in a region that was small relative to the size of the atom. He called this concentration of positive charge the **nucleus** of the atom. Any electrons belonging to the atom were assumed to be outside the nucleus. To explain why these electrons were not pulled into the nucleus by the attractive electric force, Rutherford imagined that the electrons move in orbits about the nucleus in the same manner as the planets orbit the Sun, as in Figure 29.2b.

There are two basic difficulties with Rutherford's planetary structural model. As we saw in Chapter 11, an atom emits discrete characteristic frequencies of electromagnetic radiation and no others; the Rutherford model is unable to explain this phenomenon. A second difficulty is that Rutherford's electrons experience a centripetal acceleration. According to Maxwell's equations in electromagnetism, charges orbiting with frequency f experience centripetal acceleration and therefore should radiate electromagnetic waves of frequency f. Unfortunately, this classical model leads to disaster when applied to the atom. As the electron radiates energy from the electron–proton system, the radius of the orbit of the electron steadily decreases and its frequency of revolution increases. Energy is continuously transferred out of the system by electromagnetic radiation. As a result, the energy of the system decreases, resulting in the decay of the orbit of the electron. This decrease in total energy leads to an increase in the kinetic energy of the electron,[1] an ever-increasing frequency of emitted radiation, and a rapid collapse of the atom as the electron plunges into the nucleus (Fig. 29.3).

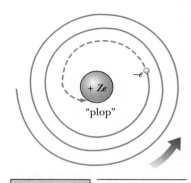

FIGURE 29.3 The classical model of the nuclear atom. Because the accelerating electron radiates energy, the orbit decays until the electron falls into the nucleus.

The stage was set for Bohr! To circumvent the erroneous predictions of the Rutherford model—electrons falling into the nucleus and a continuous emission spectrum from elements—Bohr postulated that classical radiation theory does not hold for atomic-sized systems. He overcame the problem of an atom that continuously loses energy by applying Planck's ideas of quantized energy levels to orbiting atomic electrons. Therefore, as described in Section 11.5, Bohr postulated that electrons in atoms are generally confined to stable, nonradiating orbits called stationary states. Furthermore, he applied Einstein's concept of the photon to arrive at an expression for the frequency of radiation emitted when the atom makes a transition from one stationary state to another.

One of the first indications that the Bohr theory needed modification arose when improved spectroscopic techniques were used to examine the spectral lines of hydrogen. It was found that many of the lines in the Balmer and other series were not single lines at all. Instead, each was a group of closely spaced lines. An additional difficulty arose when it was observed that, in some situations, some single spectral lines were split into three closely spaced lines when the atoms were placed in a strong magnetic field. The Bohr model cannot explain this phenomenon.

Efforts to explain these difficulties with the Bohr model led to improvements in the structural model of the atom. One of the changes introduced was the concept that the electron has an intrinsic angular momentum called *spin*, which we introduced in Chapter 22 in terms of the contribution of spin to the magnetic properties of materials. We shall discuss spin in more detail in this chapter.

29.2 │ THE HYDROGEN ATOM REVISITED

A quantum treatment of the hydrogen atom requires a solution to the Schrödinger equation (Eq. 28.31), with U being the electric potential energy of the electron–proton system. The full mathematical solution of the Schrödinger equation as applied to the hydrogen atom gives a complete and beautiful description of

---

[1]As an orbital system that interacts via an inverse square force law loses energy, the kinetic energy of the orbiting object increases but the potential energy of the system decreases by a larger amount; thus, the change in the total energy of the system is negative.

the atom's properties. The mathematical procedures that make up the solution are beyond the scope of this text, however, and so the details shall be omitted. The solutions for some states of hydrogen will be discussed, together with the quantum numbers used to characterize allowed stationary states. We also discuss the physical significance of the quantum numbers.

Let us outline the steps we take in developing a quantum structural model for the hydrogen atom. We apply the quantum particle under boundary conditions model by solving the Schrödinger equation and then applying boundary conditions to the solution to determine the allowed wave functions and energies of the atom. For the particle in a one-dimensional box in Section 28.10, we found that the imposition of boundary conditions generated a single quantum number. For the three-dimensional system of the hydrogen atom, the application of boundary conditions in each dimension introduces a quantum number, so the model will generate three quantum numbers. We also find the need for a fourth quantum number, representing the spin, that cannot be extracted from the Schrödinger equation.

To set up the Schrödinger equation, we must first specify the potential energy function for the system. For the hydrogen atom, this function is

$$U(r) = -k_e \frac{e^2}{r} \qquad [29.1]$$

where k_e is the Coulomb constant and r is the radial distance between the proton (situated at $r = 0$) and the electron.

The formal procedure for solving the problem of the hydrogen atom is to substitute $U(r)$ into the Schrödinger equation and find appropriate solutions to the equation. We did that for the particle in a box in Section 28.12. The current problem is more complicated, however, because it is three dimensional and because U is not constant. In addition, U depends on the radial coordinate r rather than a Cartesian coordinate x, y, or z. As a result, we must use spherical coordinates. We shall not attempt to carry out these solutions because they are quite complicated. Rather, we shall simply describe their properties and some of their implications with regard to atomic structure.

When the boundary conditions are applied to the solutions of the Schrödinger equation, we find that the energies of the allowed states for the hydrogen atom are

▪ Allowed energies for the hydrogen atom

$$E_n = -\left(\frac{k_e e^2}{2a_0}\right)\frac{1}{n^2} = -\frac{13.606 \text{ eV}}{n^2} \qquad n = 1, 2, 3, \ldots \qquad [29.2]$$

where a_0 is the Bohr radius. This result is in precise agreement with the Bohr model and with observed spectral lines, which is a triumph for both the Bohr approach and the quantum approach! Note that the allowed energies in our model depend only on the quantum number n, called the **principal quantum number.**

The imposition of boundary conditions also leads to two new quantum numbers that do not appear in the Bohr model. The quantum number ℓ is called the **orbital quantum number,** and m_ℓ is called the **orbital magnetic quantum number.** Although n is related to the energy of the atom, the quantum numbers ℓ and m_ℓ are related to the angular momentum of the atom as described in Section 29.4. From the solution to the Schrödinger equation, we find the following allowed values for these three quantum numbers:

▪ n is an integer that can range from 1 to ∞.

For a particular value of n,

▪ ℓ is an integer that can range from 0 to $n - 1$.

For a particular value of ℓ,

▪ m_ℓ is an integer that can range from $-\ell$ to ℓ.

PITFALL PREVENTION 29.1

ENERGY DEPENDS ON n ONLY FOR HYDROGEN The statement after Equation 29.2 that the energy depends only on the quantum number n is a simplification model. The energy levels for all atoms depend primarily on n, but also depend to a lesser degree on other quantum numbers, especially for heavier atoms.

TABLE 29.1	Three Quantum Numbers for the Hydrogen Atom		
Quantum Number	Name	Allowed Values	Number of Allowed States
n	Principal quantum number	1, 2, 3, . . .	Any number
ℓ	Orbital quantum number	0, 1, 2, . . . , $n - 1$	n
m_ℓ	Orbital magnetic quantum number	$-\ell, -\ell + 1, \ldots,$ 0, . . . , $\ell - 1, \ell$	$2\ell + 1$

Table 29.1 summarizes the rules for determining the allowed values of ℓ and m_ℓ for a given value of n.

For historical reasons, all states with the same principal quantum number are said to form a **shell.** Shells are identified by the letters K, L, M, . . . , which designate the states for which n = 1, 2, 3, ... Likewise, all states with given values of n and ℓ are said to form a **subshell.** Based on early practices in spectroscopy, the letters[2] s, p, d, f, g, h, . . . are used to designate the subshells for which ℓ = 0, 1, 2, 3, 4, 5, ... For example, the subshell designated by $3p$ has the quantum numbers n = 3 and ℓ = 1; the $2s$ subshell has the quantum numbers n = 2 and ℓ = 0. These notations are summarized in Table 29.2.

States with quantum numbers that violate the rules given in Table 29.1 cannot exist because they do not satisfy the boundary conditions on the wave function of the system. For instance, a $2d$ state, which would have n = 2 and ℓ = 2, cannot exist; the highest allowed value of ℓ is $n - 1$, or 1 in this case. Therefore, for n = 2, $2s$ and $2p$ are allowed states but $2d$, $2f$, . . . are not. For n = 3, the allowed subshells are $3s$, $3p$, and $3d$.

TABLE 29.2			
Atomic Shell and Subshell Notations			
n	Shell Symbol	ℓ	Subshell Symbol
1	K	0	s
2	L	1	p
3	M	2	d
4	N	3	f
5	O	4	g
6	P	5	h
.		.	
.		.	
.		.	

QUICK QUIZ 29.1 How many possible subshells are there for the n = 4 level of hydrogen? **(a)** 5 **(b)** 4 **(c)** 3 **(d)** 2 **(e)** 1

QUICK QUIZ 29.2 When the principal quantum number is n = 5, how many different values of **(a)** ℓ and **(b)** m_ℓ are possible?

EXAMPLE 29.1 The n = 2 Level of Hydrogen

For a hydrogen atom, determine the number of allowed states corresponding to the principal quantum number n = 2 and calculate the energies of these states.

Solution When n = 2, ℓ can be 0 or 1. For ℓ = 0, m_ℓ can only be 0; for ℓ = 1, m_ℓ can be −1, 0, or 1. Hence, we have one allowed state designated as the $2s$ state associated with the quantum numbers n = 2, ℓ = 0, and m_ℓ = 0, and three states designated as $2p$ states for

which the quantum numbers are n = 2, ℓ = 1, m_ℓ = −1; n = 2, ℓ = 1, m_ℓ = 0; and n = 2, ℓ = 1, m_ℓ = 1, for a total of four states.

Because all these states have the same principal quantum number, they also have the same energy, which can be calculated with Equation 29.2, with n = 2:

$$E_2 = -\frac{13.606 \text{ eV}}{2^2} = -3.401 \text{ eV}$$

29.3 THE WAVE FUNCTIONS FOR HYDROGEN

The potential energy of the hydrogen atom depends only on the radial distance r between nucleus and electron. We therefore expect that some of the allowed states for this atom can be represented by wave functions that depend only on r, which

---

[2] These seemingly strange letter designations come from descriptions of spectral lines in the early history of spectroscopy: s—sharp; p—principal; d—diffuse; f—fine. After s, p, d, and f, the subsequent letters follow alphabetically from f.

indeed is the case. (Other wave functions depend on r and on the angular coordinates.) The simplest wave function for the hydrogen atom describes the $1s$ state and is designated $\psi_{1s}(r)$:

$$\psi_{1s}(r) = \frac{1}{\sqrt{\pi a_0{}^3}} \, e^{-r/a_0} \qquad [29.3]$$

∎ Wave function for hydrogen in its ground state

where a_0 is the Bohr radius and the wave function as given is normalized. This wave function satisfies the boundary conditions mentioned in Section 28.11; that is, ψ_{1s} approaches zero as $r \to \infty$ and remains finite as $r \to 0$. Because ψ_{1s} depends only on r, it is spherically symmetric. In fact, **all s states have spherical symmetry.**

Recall that the probability of finding the electron in any region is equal to an integral of the probability density $|\psi|^2$ over the region, if ψ is normalized. The probability density for the $1s$ state is

$$|\psi_{1s}|^2 = \left(\frac{1}{\pi a_0{}^3}\right) e^{-2r/a_0} \qquad [29.4]$$

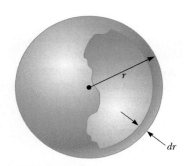

FIGURE 29.4 A spherical shell of radius r and thickness dr has a volume equal to $4\pi r^2 \, dr$.

The probability of finding the electron in a volume element dV is $|\psi|^2 \, dV$. It is convenient to define the **radial probability density function** $P(r)$ as the probability per unit radial distance of finding the electron in a spherical shell of radius r and thickness dr. The volume of such a shell equals its surface area $4\pi r^2$ multiplied by the shell thickness dr (Fig. 29.4), so that

$$P(r) \, dr = |\psi|^2 \, dV = |\psi|^2 4\pi r^2 \, dr \qquad [29.5]$$

$$P(r) = 4\pi r^2 |\psi|^2 \qquad [29.6]$$

Substituting Equation 29.4 into Equation 29.6 gives the radial probability density function for the hydrogen atom in its ground state:

∎ Radial probability density for the $1s$ state of hydrogen

$$P_{1s}(r) = \left(\frac{4r^2}{a_0{}^3}\right) e^{-2r/a_0} \qquad [29.7]$$

A graphical representation of the function $P_{1s}(r)$ versus r is presented in Figure 29.5a. The peak of the curve corresponds to the most probable value of r for this particular state. The spherical symmetry of the distribution function is shown in Figure 29.5b.

In Example 29.2, we show that the most probable value of r for the ground state of hydrogen equals the Bohr radius a_0. It turns out that the average value of r for the ground state of hydrogen is $\frac{3}{2}a_0$, which is 50% larger than the most probable value of r. (See Problem 29.45.) The reason that the average value is larger than the most probable value lies in the asymmetry in the radial distribution function shown in Figure 29.5a. According to quantum mechanics, the atom has no sharply defined

FIGURE 29.5 (a) The probability density of finding the electron as a function of distance from the nucleus for the hydrogen atom in the $1s$ (ground) state. Note that the probability has its maximum value when r equals the Bohr radius a_0. (See Example 29.2.) (b) The cross-section in the xy plane of the spherical electronic charge distribution for the hydrogen atom in its $1s$ state.

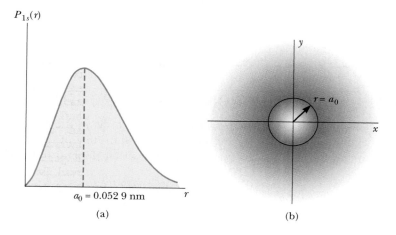

boundary. The probability distribution in Figure 29.5a suggests that the charge of the electron is extended throughout a diffuse region of space, commonly referred to as an **electron cloud.** This electron cloud model is quite different from the Bohr model, which places the electron at a fixed distance from the nucleus. Figure 29.5b shows the probability density of the electron in a hydrogen atom in the $1s$ state as a function of position in the xy plane. The darkest portion of the distribution appears at $r = a_0$, corresponding to the most probable value of r for the electron.

For an atom in a quantum state that is a solution to the Schrödinger equation, the electron cloud structure remains the same, on the average, over time. Therefore, *the atom does not radiate when it is in one particular quantum state.* This fact removes the problem that plagued the Rutherford model, in which the atom continuously radiates until the electron spirals into the nucleus. Because no change occurs in the charge structure in the electron cloud, the atom does not radiate. Radiation occurs only when a transition is made, so the structure of the electron cloud changes in time.

The next simplest wave function for the hydrogen atom is the one corresponding to the $2s$ state ($n = 2$, $\ell = 0$). The normalized wave function for this state is

$$\psi_{2s}(r) = \frac{1}{4\sqrt{2\pi}} \left(\frac{1}{a_0} \right)^{3/2} \left[2 - \frac{r}{a_0} \right] e^{-r/2a_0} \qquad [29.8]$$

▮ **Wave function for hydrogen in the 2s state**

Like the ψ_{1s} function, ψ_{2s} depends only on r and is spherically symmetric. The energy corresponding to this state is $E_2 = -(13.6\ \text{eV}/4) = -3.4\ \text{eV}$. This energy level represents the first excited state of hydrogen.

A plot of the radial probability density function for this state in comparison to the $1s$ state is shown in Active Figure 29.6. The plot for the $2s$ state has two peaks. In this case, the most probable value corresponds to that value of r that corresponds to the highest value of P_{2s}, which is at $r \approx 5a_0$. An electron in the $2s$ state would be much farther from the nucleus (on the average) than an electron in the $1s$ state.

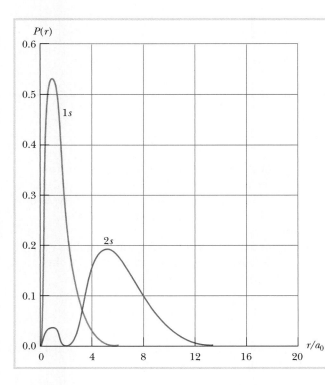

ACTIVE FIGURE 29.6

The radial probability density function versus r/a_0 for the $1s$ and $2s$ states of the hydrogen atom.

Physics⊗Now™ By logging into PhysicsNow at **www.pop4e.com** and going to Active Figure 29.6, you can choose values of r/a_0 and find the probability that the electron is located between two values.

EXAMPLE 29.2 | **The Ground State of Hydrogen**

Calculate the most probable value of r for a hydrogen atom in its ground state.

Solution We conceptualize a hydrogen atom as having a single electron and proton. Because the statement of the problem asks for the "most probable value of r," we categorize this problem as one in which we use the quantum approach. (In the Bohr atom, the electron moves in an orbit with an *exact* value of r.) Therefore, our conceptualization should include the electron cloud image of the electron rather than the well-defined orbits of the Bohr model. To analyze the problem, we note that the most probable value of r corresponds to the peak of the plot of $P_{1s}(r)$ versus r. Because the slope of the curve at this point is zero, we can evaluate the most probable value of r by setting $dP_{1s}/dr = 0$ and solving for r. Using Equation 29.7, we find that

$$\frac{dP_{1s}(r)}{dr} = \frac{d}{dr}\left[\left(\frac{4r^2}{a_0^3}\right)e^{-2r/a_0}\right] = 0$$

Carrying out the derivative operation and simplifying the expression, we have

$$e^{-2r/a_0}\frac{d}{dr}(r^2) + r^2\frac{d}{dr}(e^{-2r/a_0}) = 0$$

$$2re^{-2r/a_0} + r^2\left(-\frac{2}{a_0}\right)e^{-2r/a_0} = 0$$

$$(1) \quad 2r\left[1 - \left(\frac{r}{a_0}\right)\right]e^{-2r/a_0} = 0$$

This expression is satisfied if

$$1 - \left(\frac{r}{a_0}\right) = 0 \quad \rightarrow \quad r = \boxed{a_0}$$

To finalize the problem, notice that although the quantum model differs from the Bohr model in that the electron has a finite probability of being at *any* distance from the nucleus, the most probable distance is the same as the orbital radius in the Bohr model! Note also that (1) is satisfied at $r = 0$ and as $r \rightarrow \infty$. These are points of *minimum* probability, which is equal to zero, as seen in Figure 29.5a.

EXAMPLE 29.3 | **Probabilities for the Electron in Hydrogen**

Calculate the probability that the electron in the ground state of hydrogen will be found outside the Bohr radius.

Solution The probability is found by integrating the radial probability density $P_{1s}(r)$ for this state from the Bohr radius a_0 to ∞. Using Equation 29.7, we have

$$P = \int_{a_0}^{\infty} P_{1s}(r)\, dr = \frac{4}{a_0^3}\int_{a_0}^{\infty} r^2 e^{-2r/a_0}\, dr$$

We can put the integral in dimensionless form by changing variables from r to $z = 2r/a_0$. Noting that $z = 2$ when $r = a_0$ and that $dr = (a_0/2)\, dz$, we find that

$$P = \frac{1}{2}\int_{2}^{\infty} z^2 e^{-z}\, dz = -\frac{1}{2}(z^2 + 2z + 2)e^{-z}\Big|_{2}^{\infty}$$

$$P = 5e^{-2} = 0.677 \quad \text{or} \quad \boxed{67.7\%}$$

EXAMPLE 29.4 | **The Quantized Solar System**

Consider the Schrödinger equation for the Earth and the Sun as a system of two particles interacting via the gravitational force. What is the quantum number of the system with the Earth in its present orbit?

Solution The potential energy function for the system is

$$U(r) = -G\frac{M_E M_S}{r}$$

where M_E is the mass of the Earth and M_S is the mass of the Sun. Comparing this expression with Equation 29.1 for the hydrogen atom, $U(r) = -k_e e^2/r$, we see that it has the same mathematical form and that the

constant $GM_E M_S$ plays the role of $k_e e^2$. Therefore, the solutions to the Schrödinger equation for the Earth–Sun system will be the same as those of the hydrogen atom with the appropriate change in the constants.

If we make the substitution for the constants in Equation 29.2, we find the allowed energies of the quantized states of the Earth–Sun system:

$$E_n = -\left(\frac{GM_E M_S}{2a_0}\right)\frac{1}{n^2} \qquad n = 1, 2, 3, \ldots$$

From Equation 11.23, we can find the Bohr radius for the Earth–Sun system:

$$a_0 = \frac{\hbar^2}{M_E(GM_EM_S)} = \frac{\hbar^2}{GM_E^2M_S}$$

$$= \frac{(1.055 \times 10^{-34}\,\text{J}\cdot\text{s})^2}{(6.67 \times 10^{-11}\,\text{N}\cdot\text{m}^2/\text{kg}^2)(5.98 \times 10^{24}\,\text{kg})^2(1.99 \times 10^{30}\,\text{kg})}$$

$$= 2.22 \times 10^{-104}\,\text{m}$$

Therefore, evaluating the allowed energies of the system, we have

$$E_n = -\left(\frac{GM_EM_S}{2a_0}\right)\frac{1}{n^2}$$

$$= -\frac{(6.67 \times 10^{-11}\,\text{N}\cdot\text{m}^2/\text{kg}^2)(5.98 \times 10^{24}\,\text{kg})(1.99 \times 10^{30}\,\text{kg})}{2(2.22 \times 10^{-104}\,\text{m})n^2}$$

$$= -\frac{1.79 \times 10^{148}\,\text{J}}{n^2} \qquad n = 1, 2, 3, \ldots$$

We now evaluate the energy of the Earth–Sun system from Equation 11.10, assuming a circular orbit:

$$E_n = -\frac{GM_EM_S}{2r}$$

$$= -\frac{(6.67 \times 10^{-11}\,\text{N}\cdot\text{m}^2/\text{kg}^2)(5.98 \times 10^{24}\,\text{kg})(1.99 \times 10^{30}\,\text{kg})}{2(1.50 \times 10^{11}\,\text{m})}$$

$$= -2.65 \times 10^{33}\,\text{J}$$

Finally, we find the quantum number associated with this state:

$$E_n = -\frac{1.79 \times 10^{148}\,\text{J}}{n^2}$$

$$n = \sqrt{\frac{-1.79 \times 10^{148}\,\text{J}}{E_n}} = \sqrt{\frac{-1.79 \times 10^{148}\,\text{J}}{-2.65 \times 10^{33}\,\text{J}}}$$

$$= 2.60 \times 10^{57}$$

This result is a tremendously large quantum number. Therefore, according to the correspondence principle, classical mechanics describes the Earth's motion as well as quantum mechanics does. The energies of quantum states for adjacent values of n are so close together that we do not see the quantized nature of the energy. For example, if the Earth were to move into the next higher quantum state, calculations show that it would be farther from the Sun by a distance on the order of 10^{-80} m. Even on a nuclear scale of 10^{-15} m, that value is undetectable.

29.4 PHYSICAL INTERPRETATION OF THE QUANTUM NUMBERS

As discussed in Section 29.2, the energy of a particular state in our model depends on the principal quantum number. Now let us see what the other three quantum numbers contribute to the physical nature of our quantum structural model of the atom.

The Orbital Quantum Number ℓ

If a particle moves in a circle of radius r, the magnitude of its angular momentum relative to the center of the circle is $L = mvr$. The direction of $\vec{L}$ is perpendicular to the plane of the circle, and the sense of $\vec{L}$ is given by a right-hand rule.[3] According to classical physics, L can have any value. The Bohr model of hydrogen, however, postulates that the angular momentum is restricted to integer multiples of $\hbar$; that is, $mvr = n\hbar$. This model must be modified because it predicts (incorrectly) that the ground state of hydrogen ($n = 1$) has one unit of angular momentum. Our quantum model shows that the lowest value of the orbital quantum number, which is related to the orbital momentum, is $\ell = 0$, which corresponds to zero angular momentum.

According to the quantum model, an atom in a state whose principal quantum number is n can take on the following *discrete* values for the magnitude of the **orbital angular momentum** vector:[4]

---

[3]See Sections 10.8 and 10.9 for a review of this material on angular momentum.

[4]Equation 29.9 on the next page is a direct result of the mathematical solution of the Schrödinger equation and the application of angular boundary conditions. This development, however, is beyond the scope of this text and will not be presented.

■ Allowed values of L

$$|\vec{L}| = L = \sqrt{\ell(\ell + 1)}\,\hbar \qquad \ell = 0, 1, 2, \ldots, n-1 \qquad\qquad [29.9]$$

That L can be zero in this model points out the difficulties inherent in any attempt to describe results based on quantum mechanics in terms of a purely particle-like model. We cannot think in terms of electrons traveling in well-defined orbits of circular shape or any other shape, for that matter. It is more consistent with the probability notions of quantum physics to imagine the electron smeared out in space in an electron cloud, with the "density" of the cloud highest where the probability is highest. In the quantum mechanical interpretation, the electron cloud for the $L = 0$ state is spherically symmetric and has no fundamental axis of rotation.

EXAMPLE 29.5 **Calculating L for a p State**

Calculate the magnitude of the orbital angular momentum for a p state of hydrogen.

Solution Because we know that $\hbar = 1.055 \times 10^{-34}$ J·s, we can use Equation 29.9 to calculate L. With $\ell = 1$ for a p state, we have

$$L = \sqrt{\ell(\ell + 1)}\,\hbar = \sqrt{2}\hbar = \boxed{1.49 \times 10^{-34}\,\text{J·s}}$$

This value is extremely small relative to that of the orbital angular momentum of a macroscopic system,

such as the Earth orbiting the Sun, which is about 2.7×10^{40} J·s. The quantum number that describes L for macroscopic systems, such as the Earth and the Sun, is so large that the separation between adjacent states cannot be measured. We do not see quantized angular momentum for macroscopic systems. Once again, the correspondence principle is upheld.

The Magnetic Orbital Quantum Number m_ℓ

We have seen in the preceding discussion that the magnitude of the orbital angular momentum is quantized. Because angular momentum is a vector, its direction must also be specified. An orbiting electron can be considered an effective current loop with a corresponding magnetic moment. Such a moment placed in a magnetic field $\vec{B}$ will interact with the field.

Suppose a weak magnetic field is applied to an atom and we define the direction of the field as the z axis. According to quantum mechanics, we find a startling result in that the *direction* of the angular momentum vector relative to the z axis is quantized! Once a z axis is specified, the angular momentum vector can only point in certain directions with respect to this axis. That the direction of $\vec{L}$ is quantized is often referred to as **space quantization** because we are quantizing a *direction* rather than a *magnitude*.

The quantization of the direction of $\vec{L}$ is described by giving the allowed z components of the vector. The magnetic orbital quantum number m_ℓ specifies the allowed values of L_z according to the expression

■ Allowed values of L_z

$$L_z = m_\ell \hbar \qquad\qquad [29.10]$$

Let us look at the possible orientations of $\vec{L}$ for a given value of ℓ. Recall that m_ℓ can have values ranging from $-\ell$ to ℓ. If $\ell = 0$, then $L = 0$ and there is no vector for which to consider a direction. If $\ell = 1$, then the possible values of m_ℓ are -1, 0, and 1, so L_z may be $-\hbar$, 0, or $\hbar$. If $\ell = 2$, m_ℓ can be -2, -1, 0, 1, or 2, corresponding to L_z values of $-2\hbar$, $-\hbar$, 0, $\hbar$, or $2\hbar$, and so on.

A useful specialized pictorial representation for understanding space quantization is commonly called a **vector model**. A vector model for $\ell = 2$ is shown in Figure 29.7a. Note that $\vec{L}$ **can never be aligned parallel or antiparallel to the z axis** because L_z must be smaller than the magnitude of the angular momentum $\vec{L}$. The vector $\vec{L}$ can be *perpendicular* to the z axis, which is the case if $m_\ell = 0$. From a

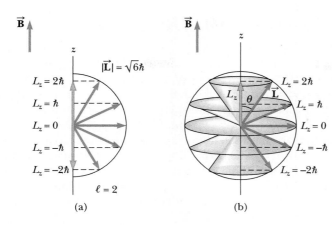

(a)   (b)

FIGURE 29.7 A vector model for $\ell = 2$. (a) The allowed projections of the orbital angular momentum $\vec{L}$ relative to a magnetic field that defines the z direction. (b) The orbital angular momentum vector $\vec{L}$ lies on the surface of a cone.

three-dimensional viewpoint, $\vec{L}$ can lie on the surfaces of cones that make angles θ with the z axis as shown in Figure 29.7b. From the figure, we see that θ is also quantized and that its values are specified through a relation based on a geometric model triangle with the $\vec{L}$ vector as the hypotenuse and the z component as one leg of the triangle:

$$\cos\theta = \frac{L_z}{|\vec{L}|} = \frac{m_\ell}{\sqrt{\ell(\ell + 1)}} \qquad [29.11]$$

Note that m_ℓ is never greater than ℓ, so m_ℓ is always smaller than $\sqrt{\ell(\ell + 1)}$ and therefore θ can never be zero, consistent with our restriction on $\vec{L}$ not being parallel to the z axis.

Because of the uncertainty principle, $\vec{L}$ does not point in a specific direction but rather lies somewhere on a cone as mentioned above. If $\vec{L}$ had a definite direction, all three components L_x, L_y, and L_z would be exactly specified. For the moment, let us assume this case to be true and let us suppose the electron moves in the xy plane, so the uncertainty $\Delta z = 0$. Because the electron moves in the xy plane, $p_z = 0$. Thus, p_z is *precisely* known, so $\Delta p_z = 0$. The product of these two uncertainties is $\Delta z \, \Delta p_z = 0$, but that is in violation of the uncertainty principle, which requires that $\Delta z \, \Delta p_z \geq \hbar/2$. In reality, only the magnitude of $\vec{L}$ and one component (which is traditionally chosen as L_z) can have definite values at the same time. In other words, quantum mechanics allows us to specify L and L_z but not L_x and L_y. Because the direction of $\vec{L}$ is constantly changing, the average values of L_x and L_y are zero and L_z maintains a fixed value $m_\ell \hbar$.

QUICK QUIZ 29.3 Sketch a vector model (shown in Fig. 29.7 for $\ell = 2$) for $\ell = 1$.

INTERACTIVE **EXAMPLE 29.6**   **Space Quantization for Hydrogen**

For the hydrogen atom in the $\ell = 3$ state, calculate the magnitude of $\vec{L}$ and the allowed values of L_z and θ.

Solution We use Equation 29.9 with $\ell = 3$:

$$L = |\vec{L}| = \sqrt{\ell(\ell + 1)}\,\hbar = \sqrt{3(3 + 1)}\,\hbar = \boxed{2\sqrt{3}\,\hbar}$$

The allowed values of L_z are $L_z = m_\ell \hbar$ with $m_\ell = -3, -2, -1, 0, 1, 2,$ and 3:

$$L_z = \boxed{-3\hbar, -2\hbar, -\hbar, 0, \hbar, 2\hbar, 3\hbar}$$

Finally, we use Equation 29.11 to calculate the allowed values of θ. Because $L = 2\sqrt{3}\hbar$, we have

$$\cos\theta = \frac{m_\ell}{2\sqrt{3}}$$

Substitution of the allowed values of m_ℓ gives

$$\cos\theta = \pm 0.866, \pm 0.577, \pm 0.289, 0$$

$$\theta = \boxed{30.0°, 54.8°, 73.2°, 90.0°, 107°, 125°, 150°}$$

Physics✕**Now**™ Log into PhysicsNow at **www.pop4e.com** and go to Interactive Example 29.6 to practice evaluating the angular momentum for various quantum states of the hydrogen atom.

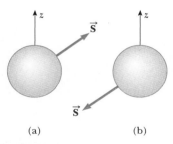

FIGURE 29.8 The spin of an electron can be either (a) up or (b) down relative to a specified z axis. The spin can never be aligned with the axis.

The Spin Magnetic Quantum Number m_s

The three quantum numbers n, ℓ, and m_ℓ discussed so far are generated by applying boundary conditions to solutions of the Schrödinger equation, and we can assign a physical interpretation to each of the quantum numbers. Let us now consider **electron spin,** which does *not* come from the Schrödinger equation.

Example 29.1 was presented to give you practice in manipulating quantum numbers, but, as we shall see in this section, there are *eight* electron states for $n = 2$ rather than the four we found. These extra states can be explained by requiring a fourth quantum number for each state, the **spin magnetic quantum number** m_s.

Evidence of the need for this new quantum number came about because of an unusual feature in the spectra of certain gases such as sodium vapor. Close examination of one of the prominent lines of sodium shows that it is, in fact, two very closely spaced lines called a doublet. The wavelengths of these lines occur in the yellow region at 589.0 nm and 589.6 nm. In 1925, when this doublet was first noticed, atomic models could not explain it. To resolve this dilemma, Samuel Goudsmit and George Uhlenbeck, following a suggestion by the Austrian physicist Wolfgang Pauli, proposed a new quantum number, called the spin quantum number. The origin of this fourth quantum number was shown by Arnold Sommerfeld and Paul Dirac to lie in the relativistic properties of the electron, which requires four quantum numbers to describe it in four-dimensional space-time.

To describe the spin quantum number, it is convenient (but incorrect!) to think of the electron as spinning on its axis as it orbits the nucleus in a planetary model, just as the Earth spins on its axis as it orbits the Sun. The direction in which the spin angular momentum vector can point is quantized; it can have only two directions as shown in Figure 29.8. If the direction of spin is as shown in Figure 29.8a, the electron is said to have "spin up." If the direction of spin is as shown in Figure 29.8b, the electron is said to have "spin down." In the presence of a magnetic field, the energy of the system (the electron and the magnetic field) is slightly different for the two spin directions, and this energy difference accounts for the sodium doublet. The quantum numbers associated with electron spin are $m_s = \frac{1}{2}$ for the spin-up state and $m_s = -\frac{1}{2}$ for the spin-down state. As we shall see in Example 29.7, this added quantum number doubles the number of allowed states specified by the quantum numbers n, ℓ, and m_ℓ.

In 1921, Otto Stern and Walther Gerlach performed an experiment (Fig. 29.9) that detected the effects of the force on a magnetic moment in a nonuniform magnetic field. The experiment demonstrated that the angular momentum of an atom is quantized. In their experiment, a beam of neutral silver atoms was sent through a

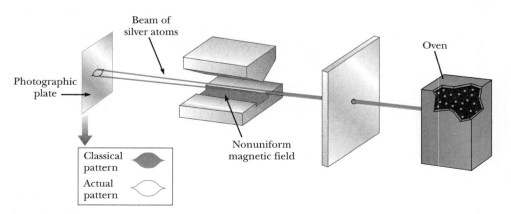

FIGURE 29.9 The apparatus used by Stern and Gerlach to verify space quantization. A beam of neutral silver atoms is split into two components by a nonuniform magnetic field as shown by the actual pattern in the box.

nonuniform magnetic field. In such a situation, the atoms experience a force (in the vertical direction in Fig. 29.9) due to their magnetic moments in this field. Classically, we would expect the beam to be spread out into a continuous distribution on the photographic plate in Figure 29.9 because all possible directions of the atomic magnetic moments are allowed. Stern and Gerlach found, however, that the beam split into two *discrete* components. The experiment was repeated using other atoms, and in each case the beam split into two or more discrete components.

These results are clearly inconsistent with the prediction of a classical model. According to a quantum model, however, the direction of the total angular momentum of the atom, and hence the direction of its magnetic moment, is quantized. Therefore, the deflected beam has an integral number of discrete components, and the number of components determines the number of possible values of μ_z. Because the Stern–Gerlach experiment showed discrete beams, space quantization was at least qualitatively verified.

For the moment, let us assume that the angular momentum of the atom is due to the orbital angular momentum.[5] Because μ_z is proportional to m_ℓ, the number of possible values of μ_z is $2\ell + 1$. Furthermore, because ℓ is an integer, the number of values of μ_z is always odd. This prediction was not consistent with the observations of Stern and Gerlach, who observed two components, an even number, in the deflected beam of silver atoms. Therefore, although the Stern–Gerlach experiment demonstrated space quantization, the number of components was not consistent with the quantum model developed at that time.

In 1927, T. E. Phipps and J. B. Taylor repeated the Stern–Gerlach experiment using a beam of hydrogen atoms. This experiment is important because it deals with an atom with a single electron in its ground state, for which the quantum model makes reliable predictions. At room temperature, almost all hydrogen atoms are in the ground state. Recall that $\ell = 0$ for hydrogen in its ground state, and so $m_\ell = 0$. Hence, from the orbital angular momentum approach, one would not expect the beam to be deflected by the field at all because μ_z would be zero. The beam in the Phipps–Taylor experiment, however, was again split into two components. On the basis of this result, one can conclude only one thing: that there is some contribution to the angular momentum of the atom and its magnetic moment other than the orbital angular momentum.

As we learned earlier, Goudsmit and Uhlenbeck had proposed that the electron has an intrinsic angular momentum, spin, apart from its orbital angular momentum. In other words, the total angular momentum of the electron in a particular electronic state contains both an orbital contribution $\vec{\mathbf{L}}$ and a spin contribution $\vec{\mathbf{S}}$. A quantum number s exists for spin that is analogous to ℓ for orbital angular momentum. The value of s for an electron, however, is *always* $s = \frac{1}{2}$, unlike ℓ, which varies for different states of the atom.

Like $\vec{\mathbf{L}}$, the **spin angular momentum** vector $\vec{\mathbf{S}}$ must obey the rules of the quantum model. In analogy with Equation 29.9, the **magnitude of the spin angular momentum $\vec{\mathbf{S}}$** for the electron is

$$S = \sqrt{s(s + 1)}\hbar = \frac{\sqrt{3}}{2}\hbar \qquad [29.12]$$

This result is the only allowed value for the magnitude of the spin angular momentum vector for an electron, so we usually do not include s in a list of quantum numbers describing states of the atom. Like orbital angular momentum, spin angular momentum is quantized in space as described in Figure 29.10. It can have two orientations, specified by the spin magnetic quantum number m_s, where m_s has two possible values, $\pm\frac{1}{2}$. In analogy with Equation 29.10, the z component of spin angular

Wolfgang Pauli and Niels Bohr watch a spinning top.

▪ **Spin angular momentum of an electron**

---

[5] The Stern–Gerlach experiment was performed in 1921, before spin was hypothesized, so orbital angular momentum was the only type of angular momentum in the quantum model at the time.

FIGURE 29.10 Spin angular momentum $\vec{\mathbf{S}}$ exhibits space quantization. This figure shows the two allowed orientations of the spin angular momentum vector $\vec{\mathbf{S}}$ and the spin magnetic moment vector $\vec{\boldsymbol{\mu}}_{\text{spin}}$ for a spin-$\frac{1}{2}$ particle such as the electron.

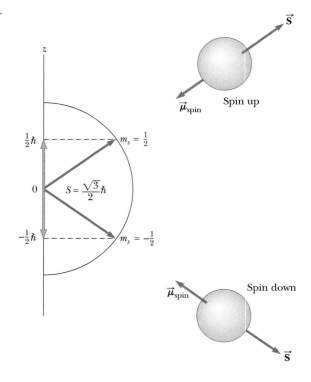

momentum is

$$S_z = m_s\hbar = \pm\tfrac{1}{2}\hbar \qquad [29.13]$$

The two values $\pm\hbar/2$ for S_z correspond to the two possible orientations for $\vec{\mathbf{S}}$ shown in Figure 29.10. The quantum number m_s is listed as the fourth quantum number describing a particular state of the atom.

The spin magnetic moment $\vec{\boldsymbol{\mu}}_s$ of the electron is related to its spin angular momentum $\vec{\mathbf{S}}$ by the expression

$$\vec{\boldsymbol{\mu}}_s = -\frac{e}{m_e}\,\vec{\mathbf{S}} \qquad [29.14]$$

Because $S_z = \pm\tfrac{1}{2}\hbar$, the z component of the spin magnetic moment can have the values

$$\mu_{sz} = \pm\frac{e\hbar}{2m_e} \qquad [29.15]$$

The quantity $e\hbar/2m_e$ is called the **Bohr magneton** μ_B and has the numerical value 9.274×10^{-24} J/T.

Today physicists explain the outcome of the Stern–Gerlach experiment as follows. The observed moments for both silver and hydrogen are due to spin angular momentum alone and not to orbital angular momentum. (The hydrogen atom in its ground state has $\ell = 0$; for silver, used in the Stern–Gerlach experiment, the net orbital angular momentum for all the electrons is $|\vec{\mathbf{L}}| = 0$.) A single-electron atom such as hydrogen has its electron spin quantized in the magnetic field in such a way that its z component of spin angular momentum is either $\tfrac{1}{2}\hbar$ or $-\tfrac{1}{2}\hbar$, corresponding to $m_s = \pm\tfrac{1}{2}$. Electrons with spin $+\tfrac{1}{2}$ are deflected in one direction by the nonuniform magnetic field, and those with spin $-\tfrac{1}{2}$ are deflected in the opposite direction.

The Stern–Gerlach experiment provided two important results. First, it verified the concept of space quantization. Second, it showed that spin angular momentum exists even though this property was not recognized until long after the experiments were performed.

▪ Thinking Physics 29.1

Does the Stern–Gerlach experiment differentiate between orbital angular momentum and spin angular momentum?

Reasoning A magnetic force on the magnetic moment arises from both orbital angular momentum and spin angular momentum. In this sense, the experiment does not differentiate between the two. The number of components on the screen does tell us something, however, because orbital angular momenta are described by an integral quantum number ℓ, whereas spin angular momentum depends on a half-integral quantum number s. If an odd number of components occur on the screen, three possibilities arise: the atom has (1) orbital angular momentum only, (2) an even number of electrons with spin angular momentum, or (3) a combination of orbital angular momentum and an even number of electrons with spin angular momentum. If an even number of components occurs on the screen, at least one unpaired spin angular momentum exists, possibly in combination with orbital angular momentum. The only numbers of components for which we can specify the type of angular momentum are one component (no orbital, no spin) and two components (spin of one electron). Once we see more than two components multiple possibilities arise because of various combinations of $\vec{\mathbf{L}}$ and $\vec{\mathbf{S}}$. ▪

EXAMPLE 29.7 Putting a Spin on Hydrogen

For a hydrogen atom, determine the quantum numbers associated with the possible states that correspond to the principal quantum number $n = 2$.

Solution With the results from Example 29.1 and the addition of the spin quantum number, we have the possibilities given in the table to the right. Therefore, there are eight possible states.

n	ℓ	m_ℓ	m_s	Subshell	Shell	Number of States in Subshell
2	0	0	$\frac{1}{2}$			
2	0	0	$-\frac{1}{2}$	$2s$	L	2
2	1	1	$\frac{1}{2}$			
2	1	1	$-\frac{1}{2}$			
2	1	0	$\frac{1}{2}$			
2	1	0	$-\frac{1}{2}$	$2p$	L	6
2	1	-1	$\frac{1}{2}$			
2	1	-1	$-\frac{1}{2}$			

29.5 THE EXCLUSION PRINCIPLE AND THE PERIODIC TABLE

The quantum model generated from the Schrödinger equation is based on the hydrogen atom, which is a system consisting of one electron and one proton. As soon as we consider the next atom, helium, we introduce complicating factors. The two electrons in helium both interact with the nucleus, so we can define a potential energy function for those interactions. They also interact with each other, however. The line of action of the electron–nucleus interaction is along a line between the electron and the nucleus. The line of action of the electron–electron interaction is along the line between the two electrons, which is different from that of the electron–nucleus interaction. Thus, the Schrödinger equation is extremely difficult to solve. As we consider atoms with more and more electrons, the possibility of an algebraic solution of the Schrödinger equation becomes hopeless.

We find, however, that despite our inability to solve the Schrödinger equation, **we can use the same four quantum numbers developed for hydrogen for the electrons in heavier atoms.** We are not able to calculate the quantized energy levels easily, but we can gain information about the levels from theoretical models and experimental measurements.

▦ **PITFALL PREVENTION 29.3**

QUANTUM NUMBERS DESCRIBE A SYSTEM The common usage is to assign the quantum numbers to an electron. Remember, however, that these quantum numbers arise from the Schrödinger equation, which involves a potential energy function for the *system* consisting of the electron and the nucleus. Therefore, it is more *proper* to assign the quantum numbers to the atom, but it is more *popular* to assign them to an electron. We will follow this latter usage because it is so common, but keep the notion of the system in the back of your mind.

WOLFGANG PAULI (1900–1958)

An extremely talented Austrian theoretical physicist, Pauli made important contributions in many areas of modern physics. Pauli gained public recognition at the age of 21 with a masterful review article on relativity, which is still considered one of the finest and most comprehensive introductions to the subject. Other major contributions were the discovery of the exclusion principle, the explanation of the connection between particle spin and statistics, and theories of relativistic quantum electrodynamics, the neutrino hypothesis, and the hypothesis of nuclear spin.

(AIP Emilio Segrè Visual Archives, Goudsmit Collection)

⊞ PITFALL PREVENTION 29.4

THE EXCLUSION PRINCIPLE IS MORE GENERAL The exclusion principle stated here is a limited form of the more general exclusion principle, which states that no two *fermions,* which are *all* particles with half-integral spin $\frac{1}{2}, \frac{3}{2}, \frac{5}{2}, \ldots$ can be in the same quantum state. The present form is satisfactory for our discussions of atomic physics, and we will discuss the general form further in Chapter 31.

Because a quantum state in any atom is specified by four quantum numbers, n, ℓ, m_ℓ, and m_s, an obvious and important question is, "How many electrons in an atom can have a particular set of quantum numbers?" Pauli provided an answer in 1925 in a powerful statement known as the **exclusion principle:**

No two electrons in an atom can ever be in the same quantum state; that is, no two electrons in the same atom can have the same set of quantum numbers.

It is interesting that if this principle were not valid, every atom would radiate energy by means of photons and end up with all electrons in the lowest energy state. The chemical behavior of the elements would be grossly modified because this behavior depends on the electronic structure of atoms. Nature as we know it would not exist! In reality, we can view the electronic structure of complex atoms as a succession of filled levels increasing in energy, where the outermost electrons are primarily responsible for the chemical properties of the element.

Imagine building an atom by forming the nucleus and then filling in the available quantum states with electrons until the atom is neutral. We shall use the common language here that "electrons go into available states." Keep in mind, however, that the states are those of the *system* of the atom. As a general rule, the order of filling of an atom's subshells with electrons is as follows. Once one subshell is filled, the next electron goes into the vacant subshell that is lowest in energy.

Before we discuss the electronic configurations of some elements, it is convenient to define an **orbital** as the state of an electron characterized by the quantum numbers n, ℓ, and m_ℓ. From the exclusion principle, we see that **at most two electrons can be in any orbital.** One of these electrons has $m_s = +\frac{1}{2}$ and the other has $m_s = -\frac{1}{2}$. Because each orbital is limited to two electrons, the numbers of electrons that can occupy the shells are also limited.

Table 29.3 shows the allowed quantum states for an atom up to $n = 3$. Each square in the bottom row of the table represents one orbital, with the ↑ arrows representing $m_s = +\frac{1}{2}$ and the ↓ arrows representing $m_s = -\frac{1}{2}$. The $n = 1$ shell can accommodate only two electrons because only one orbital is allowed with $m_\ell = 0$. The $n = 2$ shell has two subshells, with $\ell = 0$ and $\ell = 1$. The $\ell = 0$ subshell is limited to only two electrons because $m_\ell = 0$. The $\ell = 1$ subshell has three allowed orbitals, corresponding to $m_\ell = 1$, 0, and -1. Because each orbital can accommodate two electrons, the $\ell = 1$ subshell can hold six electrons (and the $n = 2$ shell can hold eight). The $n = 3$ shell has three subshells and nine orbitals and can accommodate up to 18 electrons. In general, each shell can accommodate up to $2n^2$ electrons.

The results of the exclusion principle can be illustrated by an examination of the electronic arrangement in a few of the lighter atoms. For example, **hydrogen** has only one electron, which, in its ground state, can be described by either of two sets of quantum numbers: 1, 0, 0, $+\frac{1}{2}$ or 1, 0, 0, $-\frac{1}{2}$. The electronic configuration of this atom is often designated as $1s^1$. The notation $1s$ refers to a state for which $n = 1$ and $\ell = 0$, and the superscript indicates that one electron is present in the s subshell.

Neutral **helium** has two electrons. In the ground state, the quantum numbers for these two electrons are 1, 0, 0, $+\frac{1}{2}$ and 1, 0, 0, $-\frac{1}{2}$. No other combinations of

---

TABLE 29.3		Allowed Quantum States for an Atom Up to $n = 3$												
n	1	2				3								
ℓ	0	0	1			0	1			2				
m_ℓ	0	0	1	0	-1	0	1	0	-1	2	1	0	-1	-2
m_s	↑↓	↑↓	↑↓	↑↓	↑↓	↑↓	↑↓	↑↓	↑↓	↑↓	↑↓	↑↓	↑↓	↑↓

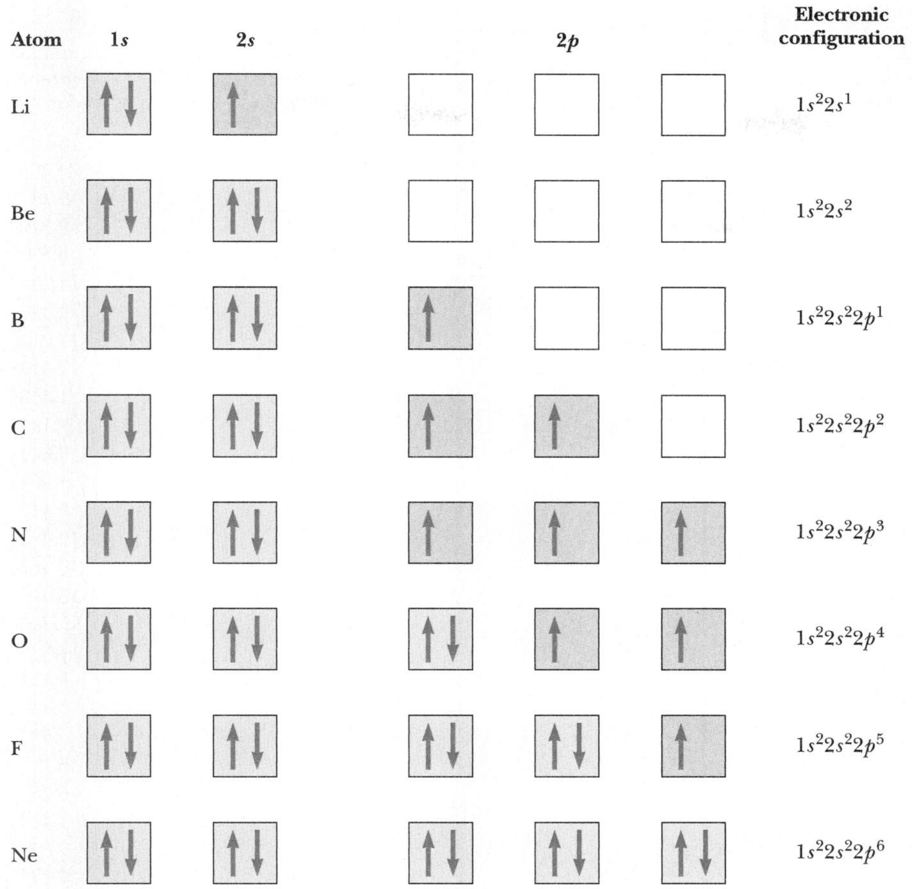

Atom	1s	2s		2p		Electronic configuration
Li	↑↓	↑				$1s^2 2s^1$
Be	↑↓	↑↓				$1s^2 2s^2$
B	↑↓	↑↓	↑			$1s^2 2s^2 2p^1$
C	↑↓	↑↓	↑	↑		$1s^2 2s^2 2p^2$
N	↑↓	↑↓	↑	↑	↑	$1s^2 2s^2 2p^3$
O	↑↓	↑↓	↑↓	↑	↑	$1s^2 2s^2 2p^4$
F	↑↓	↑↓	↑↓	↑↓	↑	$1s^2 2s^2 2p^5$
Ne	↑↓	↑↓	↑↓	↑↓	↑↓	$1s^2 2s^2 2p^6$

FIGURE 29.11 The filling of electronic states must obey both the exclusion principle and Hund's rules.

quantum numbers are possible for this level, and we say that the K shell is filled. The electronic configuration of helium is designated as $1s^2$.

The electronic configurations of some successive elements are given in Figure 29.11. Neutral **lithium** has three electrons. In the ground state, two of them are in the $1s$ subshell and the third is in the $2s$ subshell because this subshell is lower in energy than the $2p$ subshell. (In addition to the simple dependence of E on n in Eq. 29.2, there is an additional dependence on ℓ, which will be addressed in Section 29.6.) Hence, the electronic configuration for lithium is $1s^2 2s^1$.

Note that the electronic configuration of **beryllium,** with its four electrons, is $1s^2 2s^2$, and **boron** has a configuration of $1s^2 2s^2 2p^1$. The $2p$ electron in boron may be described by one of six sets of quantum numbers, corresponding to six states of equal energy.

Carbon has six electrons, and a question arises concerning how to assign the two $2p$ electrons. Do they go into the same orbital with paired spins ($\uparrow\downarrow$), or do they occupy different orbitals with unpaired spins ($\uparrow\uparrow$ or $\downarrow\downarrow$)? Experimental data show that the lowest energy configuration is the latter, where the spins are unpaired. Hence, the two $2p$ electrons in carbon and the three $2p$ electrons in nitrogen have unpaired spins in the ground state (see Fig. 29.11). The general rules that govern such situations throughout the periodic table are called **Hund's rules.** The rule appropriate for elements like carbon is that **when an atom has orbitals of equal energy, the order in which they are filled by electrons is such that a maximum number of electrons will have unpaired spins.** Some exceptions to this rule occur in elements having subshells close to being filled or half-filled.

A complete list of electronic configurations is provided in the tabular representation in Table 29.4. An early attempt to find some order among the elements was

TABLE 29.4 Electronic Configuration of the Elements

Atomic Number Z	Symbol	Ground-State Configuration	Ionization Energy (eV)
1	H	$1s^1$	13.595
2	He	$1s^2$	24.581
3	Li	[He] $2s^1$	5.39
4	Be	$2s^2$	9.320
5	B	$2s^22p^1$	8.296
6	C	$2s^22p^2$	11.256
7	N	$2s^22p^3$	14.545
8	O	$2s^22p^4$	13.614
9	F	$2s^22p^5$	17.418
10	Ne	$2s^22p^6$	21.559
11	Na	[Ne] $3s^1$	5.138
12	Mg	$3s^2$	7.644
13	Al	$3s^23p^1$	5.984
14	Si	$3s^23p^2$	8.149
15	P	$3s^23p^3$	10.484
16	S	$3s^23p^4$	10.357
17	Cl	$3s^23p^5$	13.01
18	Ar	$3s^23p^6$	15.755
19	K	[Ar] $4s^1$	4.339
20	Ca	$4s^2$	6.111
21	Sc	$3d^14s^2$	6.54
22	Ti	$3d^24s^2$	6.83
23	V	$3d^34s^2$	6.74
24	Cr	$3d^54s^1$	6.76
25	Mn	$3d^54s^2$	7.432
26	Fe	$3d^64s^2$	7.87
27	Co	$3d^74s^2$	7.86
28	Ni	$3d^84s^2$	7.633
29	Cu	$3d^{10}4s^1$	7.724
30	Zn	$3d^{10}4s^2$	9.391
31	Ga	$3d^{10}4s^24p^1$	6.00
32	Ge	$3d^{10}4s^24p^2$	7.88
33	As	$3d^{10}4s^24p^3$	9.81
34	Se	$3d^{10}4s^24p^4$	9.75
35	Br	$3d^{10}4s^24p^5$	11.84
36	Kr	$3d^{10}4s^24p^6$	13.996
37	Rb	[Kr] $5s^1$	4.176
38	Sr	$5s^2$	5.692
39	Y	$4d^15s^2$	6.377
40	Zr	$4d^25s^2$	
41	Nb	$4d^45s^1$	6.881
42	Mo	$4d^55s^1$	7.10
43	Tc	$4d^65s^1$	7.228
44	Ru	$4d^75s^1$	7.365
45	Rh	$4d^85s^1$	7.461
46	Pd	$4d^{10}$	8.33
47	Ag	$4d^{10}5s^1$	7.574
48	Cd	$4d^{10}5s^2$	8.991
49	In	$4d^{10}5s^25p^1$	
50	Sn	$4d^{10}5s^25p^2$	7.342
51	Sb	$4d^{10}5s^25p^3$	8.639
52	Te	$4d^{10}5s^25p^4$	9.01
53	I	$4d^{10}5s^25p^5$	10.454
54	Xe	$4d^{10}5s^25p^6$	12.127
55	Cs	[Xe] $6s^1$	3.893
56	Ba	$6s^2$	5.210
57	La	$5d^16s^2$	5.61

| TABLE 29.4 | Electronic Configuration of the Elements (Continued) | | |

Atomic Number Z	Symbol	Ground-State Configuration	Ionization Energy (eV)
58	Ce	$4f^15d^16s^2$	6.54
59	Pr	$4f^36s^2$	5.48
60	Nd	$4f^46s^2$	5.51
61	Pm	$4f^56s^2$	
62	Fm	$4f^66s^2$	5.6
63	Eu	$4f^76s^2$	5.67
64	Gd	$4f^75d^16s^2$	6.16
65	Tb	$4f^96s^2$	6.74
66	Dy	$4f^{10}6s^2$	
67	Ho	$4f^{11}6s^2$	
68	Er	$4f^{12}6s^2$	
69	Tm	$4f^{13}6s^2$	
70	Yb	$4f^{14}6s^2$	6.22
71	Lu	$4f^{14}5d^16s^2$	6.15
72	Hf	$4f^{14}5d^26s^2$	7.0
73	Ta	$4f^{14}5d^36s^2$	7.88
74	W	$4f^{14}5d^46s^2$	7.98
75	Re	$4f^{14}5d^56s^2$	7.87
76	Os	$4f^{14}5d^66s^2$	8.7
77	Ir	$4f^{14}5d^76s^2$	9.2
78	Pt	$4f^{14}5d^96s^1$	8.88
79	Au	[Xe, $4f^{14}5d^{10}$] $6s^1$	9.22
80	Hg	$6s^2$	10.434
81	Tl	$6s^26p^1$	6.106
82	Pb	$6s^26p^2$	7.415
83	Bi	$6s^26p^3$	7.287
84	Po	$6s^26p^4$	8.43
85	At	$6s^26p^5$	
86	Rn	$6s^26p^6$	10.745
87	Fr	[Rn] $7s^1$	
88	Ra	$7s^2$	5.277
89	Ac	$6d^17s^2$	6.9
90	Th	$6d^27s^2$	
91	Pa	$5f^26d^17s^2$	
92	U	$5f^36d^17s^2$	4.0
93	Np	$5f^46d^17s^2$	
94	Pu	$5f^67s^2$	
95	Am	$5f^77s^2$	
96	Cm	$5f^76d^17s^2$	
97	Bk	$5f^97s^2$	
98	Cf	$5f^{10}7s^2$	
99	Es	$5f^{11}7s^2$	
100	Fm	$5f^{12}7s^2$	
101	Md	$5f^{13}7s^2$	
102	No	$5f^{14}7s^2$	
103	Lr	$5f^{14}7s^27p^1$	
104	Rf	$5f^{14}6d^27s^2$	
105	Db	$5f^{14}6d^37s^2$	
106	Sg	$5f^{14}6d^47s^2$	
107	Bh	$5f^{14}6d^57s^2$	
108	Hs	$5f^{14}6d^67s^2$	
109	Mt	$5f^{14}6d^77s^2$	
110	Ds	$5f^{14}6d^97s^1$	

Note: The bracket notation is used as a shorthand method to avoid repetition in indicating inner-shell electrons. Therefore, [He] represents $1s^2$, [Ne] represents $1s^22s^22p^6$, [Ar] represents $1s^22s^22p^63s^23p^6$, and so on. Configurations for elements above $Z = 102$ are tentative.

made by a Russian chemist, Dmitri Mendeleev, in 1871. He developed a tabular representation of the elements, which has become one of the most important, as well as well-recognized, tools of science. He arranged the atoms in a table (similar to that in Appendix C) according to their atomic masses and chemical similarities. Thus was born the first **periodic table of the elements.** The first table Mendeleev proposed contained many blank spaces, and he boldly stated that the gaps were there only because the elements had not yet been discovered. By noting the columns in which these missing elements should be located, he was able to make rough predictions about their chemical properties. Within 20 years of Mendeleev's announcement, the missing elements were indeed discovered. The predictions made possible by this table represent an excellent example of the power of presenting information in an alternative representation.

The elements in the periodic table are arranged so that all those in a vertical column have similar chemical properties. For example, consider the elements in the last column: He (helium), Ne (neon), Ar (argon), Kr (krypton), Xe (xenon), and Rn (radon). The outstanding characteristic of all these elements is that they do not normally take part in chemical reactions; that is, they do not readily join with other atoms to form molecules. They are therefore called *inert gases.*

We can partially understand this behavior by looking at the electronic configurations in Table 29.4. The element helium is one in which the electronic configuration is $1s^2$; in other words, one shell is filled. Additionally, it is found that the energy associated with this filled shell is considerably lower than the energy of the next available level, the $2s$ level. Next, look at the electronic configuration for neon, $1s^2 2s^2 2p^6$. Again, the outermost shell is filled, and a gap in energy occurs between the $2p$ level and the $3s$ level. Argon has the configuration $1s^2 2s^2 2p^6 3s^2 3p^6$. Here, the $3p$ subshell is filled, and a gap in energy arises between the $3p$ subshell and the $3d$ subshell. We could continue this procedure through all the inert gases; the pattern remains the same. An inert gas is formed when either a shell or a subshell is filled and a gap in energy occurs before the next possible level is encountered.

If we consider the column to the left of the inert gases in the periodic table, we find a group of elements called the *halogens*: fluorine, chlorine, bromine, iodine, and astatine. At room temperature, fluorine and chlorine are gases, bromine is a liquid, and iodine and astatine are solids. In each of these atoms, the outer subshell is one electron short of being filled. As a result, the halogens are chemically very active, readily accepting an electron from another atom to form a closed shell. The halogens tend to from strong ionic bonds with atoms at the other side of the periodic table. In a halogen lightbulb, bromine or iodine atoms combine with tungsten atoms evaporated from the filament and return them to the filament, resulting in a longer-lasting bulb. In addition, the filament can be operated at a higher temperature than in ordinary lightbulbs, giving a brighter and whiter light.

At the left side of the periodic table, the Group I elements consist of hydrogen and the *alkali metals,* lithium, sodium, potassium, rubidium, cesium, and francium. Each of these atoms contains one electron in a subshell outside of a closed subshell. Therefore, these elements easily form positive ions because the lone electron is bound with a relatively low energy and is easily removed. Thus, the alkali metal atoms are chemically active and form very strong bonds with halogen atoms. For example, table salt, NaCl, is a combination of an alkali metal and a halogen. Because the outer electron is weakly bound, pure alkali metals tend to be good electrical conductors, although, because of their high chemical activity, pure alkali metals are not generally found in nature.

Table 29.4 also lists the ionization energies for certain elements. It is interesting to plot ionization energy versus the atomic number Z as in Figure 29.12. Note the pattern of differences in atomic numbers between the peaks in the graph: 8, 8, 18, 18, 32. This pattern follows from the Pauli exclusion principle and helps explain why the elements repeat their chemical properties in groups. For example, the

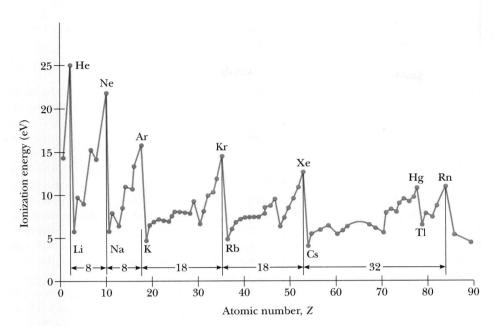

FIGURE **29.12** Ionization energy of the elements versus atomic number.

peaks at $Z = 2$, 10, 18, and 36 correspond to the elements He, Ne, Ar, and Kr, which have filled shells. These elements have similar chemical behavior.

QUICK QUIZ 29.4 Rank the energy necessary to remove the outermost electron from the following three elements, smallest to largest: lithium, potassium, cesium.

29.6 MORE ON ATOMIC SPECTRA: VISIBLE AND X-RAY

In Chapter 11, we briefly discussed the origin of the spectral lines for hydrogen and hydrogen-like ions. Recall that an atom in an excited state will emit electromagnetic radiation if it makes a transition to a lower energy state.

The energy level diagram for hydrogen is shown in Figure 29.13. This semigraphical representation is different from Figure 11.20 in that the individual states corresponding to different values of ℓ within a given value of n are spread out horizontally. Figure 29.13 shows only those states up to $\ell = 2$; the shells from $n = 4$ upward would have more sets of states to the right, which are not shown.

The diagonal lines in Figure 29.13 represent allowed transitions between stationary states. Whenever an atom makes a transition from a higher energy state to a lower one, a photon of light is emitted. The frequency of this photon is $f = \Delta E/h$,

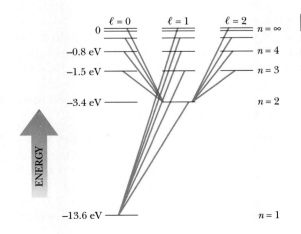

FIGURE **29.13** Some allowed electronic transitions for hydrogen, represented by the colored lines. These transitions must obey the selection rule $\Delta \ell = \pm 1$.

where ΔE is the energy difference between the two states and h is Planck's constant. The **selection rules** for the allowed transitions are

$$\Delta \ell = \pm 1 \quad \text{and} \quad \Delta m_\ell = 0 \text{ or } \pm 1 \qquad [29.16]$$

∎ Selection rules for allowed atomic transitions

Transitions that do not obey the above selection rules are said to be **forbidden.** (Such transitions can occur, but their probability is negligible relative to the probability of the allowed transitions.) For example, any transition represented by a vertical line in Figure 29.13 is forbidden because the quantum number ℓ does not change.

Because the orbital angular momentum of an atom changes when a photon is emitted or absorbed (i.e., as a result of a transition) and because angular momentum of the isolated system of the atom and the photon must be conserved, we conclude that **the photon involved in the process must carry angular momentum.** In fact, the photon has an intrinsic angular momentum equivalent to that of a particle with a spin of $s = 1$, compared with the electron with $s = \frac{1}{2}$. Hence, **a photon possesses energy, linear momentum, and angular momentum.** This example is the first one we have seen of a single particle with *integral* spin.

Equation 29.2 gives the energies of the allowed quantum states for hydrogen. We can also apply the Schrödinger equation to other one-electron systems, such as the He^+ and Li^{++} ions. The primary difference between these ions and the hydrogen atom is the different number of protons Z in the nucleus. The result is a generalization of Equation 29.2 for these other one-electron systems:

$$E_n = -\frac{(13.606 \text{ eV}) Z^2}{n^2} \qquad [29.17]$$

For outer electrons in multielectron atoms, the nuclear charge Ze is largely canceled or shielded by the negative charge of the inner-core electrons. Hence, the outer electrons interact with a net charge that is reduced below the actual charge of the nucleus. (According to Gauss's law, the electric field at the position of an outer electron depends on the net charge of the nucleus and the electrons closer to the nucleus.) The expression for the allowed energies for multielectron atoms has the same form as Equation 29.17, with Z replaced by an effective atomic number Z_{eff}. That is,

$$E_n \approx -\frac{(13.6 \text{ eV}) Z_{eff}^2}{n^2} \qquad [29.18]$$

where Z_{eff} depends on n and ℓ.

∎ Thinking Physics 29.2

A physics student is watching a meteor shower in the early morning hours. She notices that the streaks of light from the meteoroids entering the very high regions of the atmosphere last for up to 2 or 3 s before fading.

She also notices a lightning storm off in the distance. The streaks of light from the lightning fade away almost immediately after the flash, certainly in much less than 1 s. Both lightning and meteors cause the air to turn into a plasma because of the very high temperatures generated. The light is emitted from both sources when the stripped electrons in the plasma recombine with the ionized molecules. Why would this light last longer for meteors than for lightning?

Reasoning The answer lies in the subtle phrase in the description of the meteoroids "entering the very high regions of the atmosphere." In the very high regions of the atmosphere, the pressure of the air is very low. The *density* of the air is therefore very low, so molecules of the air are relatively far apart. Therefore, after the air is ionized by the passing meteoroid, the probability per unit time interval of freed electrons encountering an ionized molecule with which to recombine is relatively low. As a result, the recombination process for all freed electrons occurs over a relatively long time interval, measured in seconds.

On the other hand, lightning occurs in the lower regions of the atmosphere (the troposphere) where the pressure and density are relatively high. After the ionization by the lightning flash, the freed electrons and ionized molecules are much closer together than in the upper atmosphere. The probability per unit time interval of a recombination is much higher, and the time interval for the recombination of all the electrons and ions to occur is much shorter. ■

X-Ray Spectra

X-rays are emitted from a metal target that is being bombarded by high-energy electrons. If we consider the target as the system, the continuity equation for energy (see Eq. 6.20) for this process can be written as

$$\Delta E_{\text{system}} = \sum T \quad \rightarrow \quad \Delta E_{\text{int}} = T_{\text{MT}} + T_{\text{ER}}$$

The matter-transfer term on the right-hand side represents the process by which energy enters the target; it travels with the electron. The second term on the right has a negative value and represents the transfer of energy out of the system by x-rays. On the left, there is an increase in internal energy of the target, which recognizes that only a fraction of the incoming energy leaves as x-rays. A large fraction of the incoming energy results in an increase in temperature of the target.

The **x-ray spectrum** typically consists of a broad continuous band and a series of sharp lines that depend on the type of material used for the target as shown in Figure 29.14. In Chapter 24, we mentioned that an accelerated electric charge emits electromagnetic radiation. The x-rays we see in Figure 29.14 are the result of the slowing down of high-energy electrons as they strike the target. It may take several interactions with the atoms of the target before the electron loses all its kinetic energy. The amount of kinetic energy lost in any given interaction can vary from zero up to the entire kinetic energy of the electron. Therefore, the wavelength of radiation from these interactions lies in a continuous range from some minimum value up to infinity. It is this general slowing down of the electrons that provides the continuous curve in Figure 29.14, which shows the cutoff of x-rays below a minimum wavelength value that depends on the kinetic energy of the incoming electrons. X-radiation with its origin in the slowing down of electrons is called **bremsstrahlung,** German for "braking radiation."

The discrete lines in Figure 29.14, called **characteristic x-rays** and discovered in 1908, have a different origin. Their origin remained unexplained until the details of atomic structure were understood. The first step in the production of characteristic x-rays occurs when a bombarding electron collides with a target atom. The incoming electron must have sufficient energy to remove an inner-shell electron from the atom. The vacancy created in the shell is filled when an electron in a higher shell drops down into the shell containing the vacancy. The time interval required for this to happen is very short, less than 10^{-9} s. As usual, this transition is accompanied by the emission of a photon whose energy equals the difference in energy between the two shells. Typically, the energy of such transitions is greater than 1 000 eV, and the emitted x-ray photons have wavelengths in the range of 0.01 to 1 nm.

Let us assume that the incoming electron has dislodged an atomic electron from the innermost shell, the K shell. If the vacancy is filled by an electron dropping from the next higher shell, the L shell, the photon emitted in the process has an energy corresponding to the K_α line on the curve of Figure 29.14. If the vacancy is filled by an electron dropping from the M shell, the line produced is called the K_β line. In this notation, the letter K represents the final shell into which the electron drops and the subscript provides a Greek letter corresponding to the number of the shell above the final shell in which the electron originates. Therefore, K_α indicates that the final shell is the K shell, whereas the initial shell is

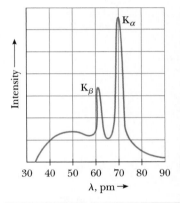

FIGURE 29.14 The x-ray spectrum of a metal target consists of a broad continuous spectrum *(bremsstrahlung)* plus a number of sharp lines, which are due to *characteristic x-rays*. The data shown were obtained when 37-keV electrons bombarded a molybdenum target.

the first shell above K (because α is the first letter in the Greek alphabet), which is the L shell.

Other characteristic x-ray lines are formed when electrons drop from upper shells to vacancies in shells other than the K shell. For example, L lines are produced when vacancies in the L shell are filled by electrons dropping from higher shells. An L_α line is produced as an electron drops from the M shell to the L shell, and an L_β line is produced by a transition from the N shell to the L shell.

Although multielectron atoms cannot be analyzed exactly using either the Bohr model or the Schrödinger equation, we can apply our knowledge of Gauss's law from Chapter 19 to make some surprisingly accurate estimates of expected x-ray energies and wavelengths. Consider an atom of atomic number Z in which one of the two electrons in the K shell has been ejected. Imagine that we draw a gaussian sphere just inside the most probable radius of the L electrons. The electric field at the position of the L electrons is a combination of that due to the nucleus, the single K electron, the other L electrons, and the outer electrons. The wave functions of the outer electrons are such that they have a very high probability of being farther from the nucleus than the L electrons are. Therefore, they are much more likely to be outside the gaussian surface than inside and, on the average, do not contribute significantly to the electric field at the position of the L electrons. The effective charge inside the gaussian surface is the positive nuclear charge and one negative charge due to the single K electron. If we ignore the interactions between L electrons, a single L electron behaves as if it experiences an electric field due to a charge enclosed by the gaussian surface of $(Z - 1)e$. The nuclear charge is in effect shielded by the electron in the K shell such that Z_{eff} in Equation 29.18 is $Z - 1$. For higher-level shells, the nuclear charge is shielded by electrons in all the inner shells.

We can now use Equation 29.18 to estimate the energy associated with an electron in the L shell:

$$E_L \approx -(Z - 1)^2 \frac{13.6 \text{ eV}}{2^2}$$

The final state of the atom after it makes the transition is such that there are two electrons in the K shell. We can use a similar argument by drawing a gaussian surface just inside the most probable radius for one K electron. The energy associated with one of these electrons is approximately that of a one-electron atom with the nuclear charge reduced by the negative charge of the other electron. Therefore,

$$E_K \approx -(Z - 1)^2(13.6 \text{ eV}) \qquad [29.19]$$

As we show in Example 29.8, the energy of the atom with an electron in an M shell can be estimated in a similar fashion. Taking the energy difference between the initial and final levels, the energy and wavelength of the emitted photon can then be calculated.

In 1914, Henry G. J. Moseley plotted $\sqrt{1/\lambda}$ versus the Z values for a number of elements, where λ is the wavelength of the K_α line of each element. He found that the curve is a straight line as in Figure 29.15. This finding is consistent with rough calculations of the energy levels given by Equation 29.19. From this plot, Moseley was able to determine the Z values of some missing elements, which provided a periodic chart in excellent agreement with the known chemical properties of the elements.

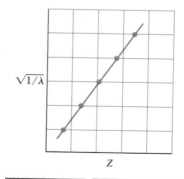

FIGURE 29.15 A Moseley plot of $\sqrt{1/\lambda}$ versus Z, where λ is the wavelength of the K_α x-ray line of the element with atomic number Z.

QUICK QUIZ 29.5 What are the initial and final shells for an M_β line in an x-ray spectrum?

QUICK QUIZ 29.6 In an x-ray tube, as you increase the energy of the electrons striking the metal target, (i) the wavelengths of the characteristic x-rays (a) increase, (b) decrease, or (c) do not change and (ii), the minimum wavelength of the bremsstrahlung (a) increases, (b) decreases, or (c) does not change.

EXAMPLE 29.8 | **Estimating the Energy of an X-Ray**

Estimate the energy of the characteristic x-ray emitted from a tungsten target when an electron drops from an M shell ($n = 3$ state) to a vacancy in the K shell ($n = 1$ state).

Solution The atomic number for tungsten is $Z = 74$. Using Equation 29.19, we see that the energy associated with the electron in the K shell is approximately

$$E_K \approx -(74 - 1)^2(13.6 \text{ eV}) = -7.2 \times 10^4 \text{ eV}$$

An electron in the M shell is subject to an effective nuclear charge that depends on the number of electrons in the $n = 1$ and $n = 2$ states, which shield the nucleus. Because eight electrons are in the $n = 2$ state and one electron is in the $n = 1$ state, nine electrons

shield the nucleus, and so $Z_{\text{eff}} = Z - 9$. Hence, the energy of the M shell, following Equation 29.18, is approximately

$$E_M \approx -\frac{(13.6 \text{ eV})(74 - 9)^2}{(3)^2} \approx -6.4 \times 10^3 \text{ eV}$$

The emitted x-ray therefore has an energy equal to $E_M - E_K \approx -6.4 \times 10^3 \text{ eV} - (-7.2 \times 10^4 \text{ eV}) \approx 6.6 \times 10^4 \text{ eV} = $ 66 keV. Consultation of x-ray tables shows that the M−K transition energies in tungsten vary from 66.9 to 67.7 keV, where the range of energies is due to slightly different energy values for states of different ℓ. Therefore, our estimate differs from the midpoint of this experimentally measured range by about 2%.

29.7 ATOMS IN SPACE

CONTEXT
CONNECTION

We have spent quite a bit of time on the hydrogen atom in this chapter. Let us now consider hydrogen atoms located in space. Because hydrogen is the most abundant element in the Universe, its role in astronomy and cosmology is very important.

Let us begin by considering pictures of some nebulae you might have seen in an astronomy text, such as Figure 29.16. Time-exposure photographs of these objects show a variety of colors. What causes the colors in these clouds of gas and grains of dust? Let us imagine a cloud of hydrogen atoms in space near a very hot star. The high-energy photons from the star can interact with the hydrogen atoms, either raising them to a high-energy state or ionizing them. As the atoms fall back to the lower states, many atoms emit the Balmer series of wavelengths. Therefore, these atoms provide red, green, blue, and violet colors to the nebula, corresponding to the colors seen in the hydrogen spectrum in Chapter 11.

In practice, nebulae are classified into three groups depending on the transitions occurring in the hydrogen atoms. **Emission nebulae** (Fig. 29.16a) are near a hot star, so hydrogen atoms are excited by light from the star as described above.

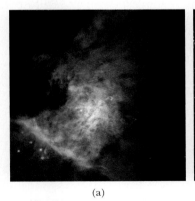

(a)

(b)

(c)

(a. C. R. O'Dell (Rice University) and NASA; b. © 1985 Royal Observatory Edinburgh/Anglo-Australian Observatory by David Malin; c. A. Caulet (ST-ECF, ESA) and NASA)

FIGURE 29.16 | Types of astronomical nebulae. (a) The central part of the Orion Nebula represents an emission nebula, from which colored light is emitted from atoms. (b) The Pleiades. The clouds of light surrounding the stars represent a reflection nebula, from which starlight is reflected by dust particles. (c) The Lagoon Nebula shows the effects of a dark nebula, in which clouds of dust block starlight and appear as a dark silhouette against the light from stars farther away.

Therefore, the light from an emission nebula is dominated by discrete emission spectral lines and contains colors. **Reflection nebulae** (Fig. 29.16b) are near a cool star. In these cases, most of the light from the nebula is the starlight reflected from larger grains of material in the nebula rather than emitted by excited atoms. Therefore, the spectrum of the light from the nebula is the same as that from the star: an absorption spectrum with dark lines corresponding to atoms and ions in the outer regions of the star. The light from these nebulae tends to appear white. Finally, **dark nebulae** (Fig. 29.16c) are not close to a star. Therefore, little radiation is available to excite atoms or reflect from grains of dust. As a result, the material in these nebulae screens out light from stars beyond them, and they appear as black patches against the brightness of the more distant stars.

In addition to hydrogen, some other atoms and ions in space are raised to higher energy states by radiation from stars and proceed to emit various colors. Some of the more prominent colors are violet (373 nm) from the O^+ ion and green (496 nm and 501 nm) from the O^{++} ion. Helium and nitrogen also provide strong colors.

In our discussion of the quantum numbers for the hydrogen atom, we claimed that two states are possible in the $1s$ shell, corresponding to up or down spin, and that these two states are equivalent in energy. If we modify our structural model to include the spin of the proton, however, we find that the two atomic states corresponding to the electron spin are not the same in energy. The state in which the electron and proton spins are parallel is slightly higher in energy than the state in which they are antiparallel. The energy difference is only 5.9×10^{-6} eV. Because these two states differ in energy, it is possible for the atom to make a transition between the states. If the transition is from the parallel state to the antiparallel state, a photon is emitted, with energy equal to the difference in energy between the states. The wavelength of this photon is

$$\lambda = \frac{c}{f} = \frac{hc}{hf} = \frac{hc}{E} = \frac{1\,240\ \text{eV}\cdot\text{nm}}{5.9 \times 10^{-6}\ \text{eV}} \left(\frac{10^{-9}\ \text{m}}{1\ \text{nm}}\right)$$
$$= 0.21\ \text{m} = 21\ \text{cm}$$

This radiation is called, for obvious reasons, **21-cm radiation.** It is radiation with a wavelength that is identifiable with the hydrogen atom. Therefore, by looking for this radiation in space, we can detect hydrogen atoms. Furthermore, if the wavelength of the observed radiation is not equal to 21 cm, we can infer that it has been Doppler shifted due to relative motion between the Earth and the source. This Doppler shift can then be used to measure the relative speed of the source toward or away from the Earth. This technique has been extensively used to study the hydrogen distribution in the Milky Way galaxy and to detect the presence of spiral arms in our galaxy, similar to the spiral arms in other galaxies.

Our study of atomic physics allows us to understand an important connection between the microscopic world of quantum physics and the macroscopic Universe. Atoms throughout the Universe act as transmitters of information to us about the local conditions. In Chapter 30, which deals with nuclear physics, we shall see how our understanding of microscopic processes helps us understand the local conditions at the center of a star.

SUMMARY

Physics⊗Now™ Take a practice test by logging into Physics-Now at **www.pop4e.com** and clicking on the Pre-Test link for this chapter.

The methods of quantum mechanics can be applied to the hydrogen atom using the appropriate potential energy function $U(r) = -k_e e^2/r$ in the Schrödinger equation. The solution to this equation yields the wave functions for the allowed states and the allowed energies, given by

$$E_n = -\left(\frac{k_e e^2}{2a_0}\right)\frac{1}{n^2} = -\frac{13.606\ \text{eV}}{n^2} \qquad n = 1, 2, 3, \ldots \quad [29.2]$$

which is precisely the result obtained in the Bohr theory. The allowed energy depends only on the **principal quantum number** n. The allowed wave functions depend on three quantum numbers, n, ℓ, and m_ℓ, where ℓ is the **orbital quantum number** and m_ℓ is the **orbital magnetic quantum number.** The restrictions on the quantum numbers are as follows:

$$n = 1, 2, 3, \ldots$$
$$\ell = 0, 1, 2, \ldots, (n-1)$$
$$m_\ell = -\ell, -\ell+1, \ldots, \ell-1, \ell$$

All states with the same principal quantum number n form a **shell,** identified by the letters K, L, M, . . . (corresponding to $n = 1, 2, 3, \ldots$). All states with the same values of both n and ℓ form a **subshell,** designated by the letters $s, p, d, f, \ldots$ (corresponding to $\ell = 0, 1, 2, 3, \ldots$).

An atom in a state characterized by a specific n can have the following values of **orbital angular momentum** L:

$$|\vec{\mathbf{L}}| = L = \sqrt{\ell(\ell+1)}\,\hbar \qquad \ell = 0, 1, 2, \ldots, n-1 \quad [29.9]$$

The allowed values of the projection of the angular momentum vector $\vec{\mathbf{L}}$ along the z axis are given by

$$L_z = m_\ell \hbar \qquad [29.10]$$

where m_ℓ is restricted to integer values lying between $-\ell$ and ℓ. Only discrete values of L_z are allowed, and they are determined by the restrictions on m_ℓ. This quantization of L_z is referred to as **space quantization.**

To describe a quantum state of the hydrogen atom completely, it is necessary to include a fourth quantum number m_s, called the **spin magnetic quantum number.** This quantum number can have only two values, $\pm\frac{1}{2}$. In effect, this additional quantum number doubles the number of allowed states specified by the quantum numbers n, ℓ, and m_ℓ.

The electron has an intrinsic angular momentum called **spin angular momentum.** That is, the total angular momentum of an atom can have two contributions: one arising from the spin of the electron ($\vec{\mathbf{S}}$) and one arising from the orbital motion of the electron ($\vec{\mathbf{L}}$).

Electronic spin can be described by a quantum number $s = \frac{1}{2}$. The **magnitude of the spin angular momentum** is

$$S = \frac{\sqrt{3}}{2}\hbar \qquad [29.12]$$

and the z component of $\vec{\mathbf{S}}$ is

$$S_z = m_s \hbar = \pm\tfrac{1}{2}\hbar \qquad [29.13]$$

The magnetic moment $\vec{\boldsymbol{\mu}}_s$ associated with the spin angular momentum of an electron is

$$\vec{\boldsymbol{\mu}}_s = -\frac{e}{m_e}\vec{\mathbf{S}} \qquad [29.14]$$

The z component of $\vec{\boldsymbol{\mu}}_s$ can have the values

$$\mu_{sz} = \pm\frac{e\hbar}{2m_e} \qquad [29.15]$$

The quantity $e\hbar/2m_e$ is called the **Bohr magneton** μ_B and has the numerical value 9.274×10^{-24} J/T.

The **exclusion principle** states that no two electrons in an atom can have the same set of quantum numbers n, ℓ, m_ℓ, and m_s. Using this principle, one can determine the electronic configuration of the elements. This procedure serves as a basis for understanding atomic structure and the chemical properties of the elements.

The allowed electronic transitions between any two states in an atom are governed by the **selection rules**

$$\Delta\ell = \pm 1 \quad \text{and} \quad \Delta m_\ell = 0 \text{ or } \pm 1 \qquad [29.16]$$

The **x-ray spectrum** of a metal target consists of a set of sharp characteristic lines superimposed on a broad, continuous spectrum. **Bremsstrahlung** is x-radiation with its origin in the slowing down of high-energy electrons as they encounter the target. **Characteristic x-rays** are emitted by atoms when an electron undergoes a transition from an outer shell into an electron vacancy in one of the inner shells.

QUESTIONS

☐ = answer available in the *Student Solutions Manual and Study Guide*

1. According to Bohr's model of the hydrogen atom, what is the uncertainty in the radial coordinate of the electron? What is the uncertainty in the radial component of the velocity of the electron? In what way does the model violate the uncertainty principle?

2. Why are three quantum numbers needed to describe the state of a one-electron atom (ignoring spin)?

3. Compare the Bohr theory and the Schrödinger treatment of the hydrogen atom. Comment on the total energy and orbital angular momentum.

4. Discuss why the term *electron cloud* is used to describe the electronic arrangement in the quantum mechanical model of an atom.

5. Why is the direction of the orbital angular momentum of an electron opposite to that of its magnetic moment?

6. Why is a *nonuniform* magnetic field used in the Stern–Gerlach experiment?

7. Could the Stern–Gerlach experiment be performed with ions rather than neutral atoms? Explain.

8. Describe some experiments that support the conclusion that the spin magnetic quantum number for electrons can only have the values $\pm\frac{1}{2}$.

9. Discuss some of the consequences of the exclusion principle.

10. How is it possible that electrons, whose positions are described by a probability distribution around a nucleus, can exist in atoms with states of *definite* energy (e.g., $1s$, $2p$, $3d$, . . .)?

11. Why do lithium, potassium, and sodium exhibit similar chemical properties?

12. An energy of about 21 eV is required to excite an electron in a helium atom from the $1s$ state to the $2s$ state. The same transition for the He^+ ion requires approximately twice as much energy. Explain.

13. The absorption or emission spectrum of a gas consists of lines that broaden as the density of gas molecules increases. Why do you suppose that occurs?

14. It is easy to understand how two electrons (one spin up, one spin down) can fill the $1s$ shell for a helium atom. How is it possible that eight more electrons can fit into the $2s$, $2p$ level to complete the $1s^2 2s^2 2p^6$ shell for a neon atom?

15. In 1914, Henry G. J. Moseley was able to define the atomic number of an element from its characteristic x-ray spectrum. How was that possible? (*Suggestion:* See Figs. 29.14 and 29.15.)

16. (a) "As soon as I define a particular direction as the z axis, precisely one half of the electrons in this part of the Universe have their magnetic moment vectors oriented at 54.735 61° to that axis, and all the rest have their magnetic moments at 125.264 39°." Argue for or against this statement. (b) "The Universe is not simply stranger than we suppose; it is stranger than we *can* suppose." Argue for or against this statement.

17. A message reads, "*All your base are belong to us!*" Argue for or against the view that a scientific discovery is like a communication from an utterly alien source, needing interpretation and susceptible to misunderstanding. Argue for or against the view that the human mind is not necessarily well adapted to understand the Universe. Argue for or against the view that education in science is the best preparation for life in a rapidly changing world.

PROBLEMS

1, 2, 3 = straightforward, intermediate, challenging

☐ = full solution available in the *Student Solutions Manual and Study Guide*

Physics⊗Now™ = coached problem with hints available at **www.pop4e.com**

🖥 = computer useful in solving problem

▭ = paired numerical and symbolic problems

▨ = biomedical application

Section 29.1 ∎ Early Structural Models of the Atom

1. Physics⊗Now™ According to classical physics, a charge e moving with an acceleration a radiates at a rate

$$\frac{dE}{dt} = -\frac{1}{6\pi\epsilon_0}\frac{e^2 a^2}{c^3}$$

(a) Show that an electron in a classical hydrogen atom (see Fig. 29.3) spirals into the nucleus at a rate

$$\frac{dr}{dt} = -\frac{e^4}{12\pi^2 \epsilon_0^2 r^2 m_e^2 c^3}$$

(b) Find the time interval over which the electron will reach $r = 0$, starting from $r_0 = 2.00 \times 10^{-10}$ m.

2. **Review problem.** In the Rutherford scattering experiment, 4.00-MeV alpha particles (^{4}He nuclei containing 2 protons and 2 neutrons) scatter off gold nuclei (containing 79 protons and 118 neutrons). Assume that a particular alpha particle makes a direct head-on collision with the gold nucleus and scatters backward at 180°. Determine (a) the distance of closest approach of the alpha particle to the gold nucleus and (b) the maximum force exerted on the alpha particle. Assume that the gold nucleus remains fixed throughout the entire process.

3. (a) Calculate the angular momentum of the Moon due to its orbital motion about the Earth. In your calculation, use 3.84×10^8 m as the average Earth–Moon distance and 2.36×10^6 s as the period of the Moon in its orbit. (b) Assume that the Moon's angular momentum is described by Bohr's assumption $mvr = n\hbar$. Determine the corresponding quantum number. (c) By what fraction would the Earth–Moon distance have to be increased to raise the quantum number by 1?

4. (a) An isolated atom of a certain element emits light of wavelength 520 nm when the atom falls from its fifth excited state into its second excited state. The atom emits a photon of wavelength 410 nm when it drops from its sixth excited state into its second excited state. Find the wavelength of the light radiated when the atom makes a transition from its sixth to its fifth excited state. (b) Solve the same problem again in symbolic terms. Letting λ_{BA} represent the wavelength emitted in the transition B to A and λ_{CA} the shorter wavelength emitted in the transition C to A, find λ_{CB}. This problem exemplifies the *Ritz combination principle*, an empirical rule formulated in 1908.

Section 29.2 ∎ The Hydrogen Atom Revisited

5. The Balmer series for the hydrogen atom corresponds to electronic transitions that terminate in the state with quantum number $n = 2$ as shown in Figure P29.5. (a) Consider the photon of longest wavelength; determine its energy and wavelength. (b) Consider the spectral line of shortest wavelength; find its photon energy and wavelength.

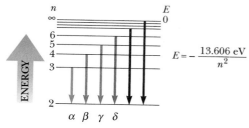

FIGURE P29.5 An energy level diagram for hydrogen showing the Balmer series (not drawn to scale).

6. A photon with energy 2.28 eV is barely capable of causing a photoelectric effect when it strikes a sodium plate. Suppose the photon is instead absorbed by hydrogen. Find (a) the minimum n for a hydrogen atom that can be ionized by such a photon and (b) the speed of the released electron far from the nucleus.

7. A general expression for the energy levels of one-electron atoms and ions is

$$E_n = -\frac{\mu k_e^2 q_1^2 q_2^2}{2\hbar^2 n^2}$$

where k_e is the Coulomb constant, q_1 and q_2 are the charges of the electron and the nucleus, and μ is the reduced mass of the atom, given by $\mu = m_1 m_2/(m_1 + m_2)$ where m_1 is the mass of the electron and m_2 is the mass of the nucleus. In Problem 29.5 we found that the wavelength for the $n = 3$ to $n = 2$ transition of the hydrogen atom is 656.3 nm (visible red light). What are the wavelengths for this same transition in (a) positronium, which consists of an electron and a positron, and (b) singly ionized helium? (*Note:* A positron is a positively charged electron.)

8. Ordinary hydrogen gas is a mixture of two kinds of atoms (isotopes) containing either one- or two-particle nuclei. These isotopes are hydrogen-1 with a proton nucleus and hydrogen-2, called deuterium, with a deuteron nucleus. A deuteron is one proton and one neutron bound together. Hydrogen-1 and deuterium have identical chemical properties, but can be separated via an ultracentrifuge or by other methods. Their emission spectra show lines of the same colors at very slightly different wavelengths. (a) Use the equation given in Problem 29.7 to show that the difference in wavelength, between the hydrogen-1 and deuterium spectral lines associated with a particular electron transition, is given by

$$\lambda_H - \lambda_D = \left(1 - \frac{\mu_H}{\mu_D}\right)\lambda_H$$

(b) Evaluate the wavelength difference for the Balmer alpha line of hydrogen, with wavelength 656.3 nm, emitted by an atom making a transition from an $n = 3$ state to an $n = 2$ state. Harold Urey observed this wavelength difference in 1931, confirming his discovery of deuterium.

9. An electron of momentum p is at a distance r from a stationary proton. The electron has kinetic energy $K = p^2/2m_e$. The atom has potential energy $U = -k_e e^2/r$ and total energy $E = K + U$. If the electron is bound to the proton to form a hydrogen atom, its average position is at the proton, but the uncertainty in its position is approximately equal to the radius r of its orbit. The electron's average vector momentum is zero, but its average squared momentum is approximately equal to the squared uncertainty in its momentum, as given by the uncertainty principle. Treating the atom as a one-dimensional system, (a) estimate the uncertainty in the electron's momentum in terms of r. (b) Estimate the electron's kinetic, potential, and total energies in terms of r. (c) The actual value of r is the one that *minimizes the total energy*, resulting in a stable atom. Find that value of r and the resulting total energy. Compare your answer with the predictions of the Bohr theory.

Section 29.3 ■ The Wave Functions for Hydrogen

10. Plot the wave function $\psi_{1s}(r)$ (see Eq. 29.3) and the radial probability density function $P_{1s}(r)$ (see Eq. 29.7) for hydrogen. Let r range from 0 to $1.5a_0$, where a_0 is the Bohr radius.

11. The ground-state wave function for a hydrogen atom is

$$\psi_{1s}(r) = \frac{1}{\sqrt{\pi a_0^3}} e^{-r/a_0}$$

where r is the radial coordinate of the electron and a_0 is the Bohr radius. (a) Show that the wave function as given is normalized. (b) Find the probability of locating the electron between $r_1 = a_0/2$ and $r_2 = 3a_0/2$.

12. The wave function for the $2p$ state of hydrogen is

$$\psi_{2p} = \frac{1}{\sqrt{3}(2a_0)^{3/2}} \frac{r}{a_0} e^{-r/2a_0}$$

What is the most likely distance from the nucleus to find an electron in the $2p$ state?

13. **Physics⊗Now**™ For a spherically symmetric state of a hydrogen atom, the Schrödinger equation in spherical coordinates is

$$-\frac{\hbar^2}{2m}\left(\frac{d^2\psi}{dr^2} + \frac{2}{r}\frac{d\psi}{dr}\right) - \frac{k_e e^2}{r}\psi = E\psi$$

Show that the $1s$ wave function for hydrogen,

$$\psi_{1s}(r) = \frac{1}{\sqrt{\pi a_0^3}} e^{-r/a_0}$$

satisfies the Schrödinger equation.

14. In an experiment, electrons are fired at a sample of neutral hydrogen atoms and observations are made of how the incident particles scatter. A large set of trials can be thought of as containing 1 000 observations of the electron in the ground state of a hydrogen atom being momentarily at a distance $a_0/2$ from the nucleus. How many times is the atomic electron observed at a distance $2a_0$ from the nucleus in this set of trials?

Section 29.4 ■ Physical Interpretation of the Quantum Numbers

15. List the possible sets of quantum numbers for the hydrogen atom associated with (a) the $3d$ subshell and (b) the $3p$ subshell.

16. Calculate the orbital angular momentum for a hydrogen atom in (a) the $4d$ state and (b) the $6f$ state.

17. If a hydrogen atom has orbital angular momentum 4.714×10^{-34} J·s, what is the orbital quantum number for the state of the atom?

18. A hydrogen atom is in its fifth excited state, with principal quantum number 6. The atom emits a photon with a wavelength of 1 090 nm. Determine the maximum possible orbital angular momentum of the atom after emission.

19. **Physics⊗Now**™ How many sets of quantum numbers are possible for a hydrogen atom for which (a) $n = 1$, (b) $n = 2$, (c) $n = 3$, (d) $n = 4$, and (e) $n = 5$? Check your results to show that they agree with the general rule

that the number of sets of quantum numbers for a shell is equal to $2n^2$.

20. Find all possible values of L, L_z, and θ for a hydrogen atom in a $3d$ state.

21. (a) Find the mass density of a proton, modeling it as a solid sphere of radius 1.00×10^{-15} m. (b) Consider a classical model of an electron as a solid sphere with the same density as the proton. Find its radius. (c) Imagine that this electron possesses spin angular momentum $I\omega = \hbar/2$ because of classical rotation about the z axis. Determine the speed of a point on the equator of the electron and (d) compare this speed to the speed of light.

22. An electron is in the N shell. Determine the maximum value the z component of its angular momentum could have.

23. The ρ^- meson has a charge of $-e$, a spin quantum number of 1, and a mass 1 507 times that of the electron. The possible values for its spin magnetic quantum number are -1, 0, and 1. Imagine that the electrons in atoms were replaced by ρ^- mesons. List the possible sets of quantum numbers for ρ^- mesons in the $3d$ subshell.

Section 29.5 ■ The Exclusion Principle and the Periodic Table

24. (a) Write out the electronic configuration for the ground state of oxygen ($Z = 8$). (b) Write out a set of possible values for the quantum numbers n, ℓ, m_ℓ, and m_s for each electron in oxygen.

25. As we go down the periodic table, which subshell is filled first, the $3d$ or the $4s$ subshell? Which electronic configuration has a lower energy: $[Ar]3d^44s^2$ or $[Ar]3d^54s^1$? Which has the greater number of unpaired spins? Identify this element and discuss Hund's rule in this case. (*Note:* The notation $[Ar]$ represents the filled configuration for argon.)

26. Devise a table similar to that shown in Figure 29.11 for atoms containing 11 through 19 electrons. Use Hund's rule and educated guesswork.

27. A certain element has its outermost electron in a $3p$ subshell. It has valence $+3$ because it has 3 more electrons than a certain inert gas. What element is it?

28. Two electrons in the same atom both have $n = 3$ and $\ell = 1$. (a) List the quantum numbers for the possible states of the atom. (b) How many states would be possible if the exclusion principle were inoperative?

29. Physics⊗Now™ (a) Scanning through Table 29.4 in order of increasing atomic number, note that the electrons usually fill the subshells in such a way that those subshells with the lowest values of $n + \ell$ are filled first. If two subshells have the same value of $n + \ell$, the one with the lower value of n is generally filled first. Using these two rules, write the order in which the subshells are filled through $n + \ell = 7$. (b) Predict the chemical valence for the elements that have atomic numbers 15, 47, and 86 and compare your predictions with the actual valences (which may be found in a chemistry text).

30. For a neutral atom of element 110, what would be the probable ground-state electronic configuration?

31. Review problem. For an electron with magnetic moment $\vec{\mu}_s$ in a magnetic field $\vec{B}$, the result of Problem 22.20 in

Chapter 22 shows the following. The electron-field system can be in a higher energy state with the z component of the magnetic moment of the electron opposite to the field or in a lower energy state with the z component of the magnetic moment in the direction of the field. The difference in energy between the two states is $2\mu_B B$.

Under high resolution, many spectral lines are observed to be doublets. The most famous of these are the two yellow lines in the spectrum of sodium (the D lines), with wavelengths of 588.995 nm and 589.592 nm. Their existence was explained in 1925 by Goudsmit and Uhlenbeck, who postulated that an electron has intrinsic spin angular momentum. When the sodium atom is excited with its outermost electron in a $3p$ subshell, the orbital motion of the outermost electron creates a magnetic field. The atom's energy is somewhat different depending on whether the electron is itself spin-up or spin-down in this field. Then the photon energy the atom radiates as it falls back into its ground state depends on the energy of the excited state. Calculate the magnitude of the internal magnetic field mediating this so-called spin-orbit coupling.

Section 29.6 ■ More on Atomic Spectra: Visible and X-ray

32. (a) Determine the possible values of the quantum numbers ℓ and m_ℓ for the He$^+$ ion in the state corresponding to $n = 3$. (b) What is the energy of this state?

33. If you wish to produce 10.0-nm x-rays in the laboratory, what is the minimum voltage you must use in accelerating the electrons?

34. In x-ray production, electrons are accelerated through a high voltage ΔV and then decelerated by striking a target. Show that the shortest wavelength of an x-ray that can be produced is

$$\lambda_{min} = \frac{1\,240 \text{ nm} \cdot \text{V}}{\Delta V}$$

35. Use the method illustrated in Example 29.8 to calculate the wavelength of the x-ray emitted from a molybdenum target ($Z = 42$) when an electron moves from the L shell ($n = 2$) to the K shell ($n = 1$).

36. The K series of the discrete x-ray spectrum of tungsten contains wavelengths of 0.018 5 nm, 0.020 9 nm, and 0.021 5 nm. The K-shell ionization energy is 69.5 keV. Determine the ionization energies of the L, M, and N shells. Draw a diagram of the transitions.

37. The wavelength of characteristic x-rays in the K$_\beta$ line from a particular source is 0.152 nm. Determine the material in the target.

Section 29.7 ■ Context Connection—Atoms in Space

38. In interstellar space, atomic hydrogen produces the sharp spectral line called the 21-cm radiation, which astronomers find most helpful in detecting clouds of hydrogen between stars. This radiation is useful because it is the only signal cold hydrogen emits and because interstellar dust that obscures visible light is transparent to these radio waves. The radiation is not generated by an electron transition between energy states characterized by different values of n.

Instead, in the ground state $(n = 1)$, the electron and proton spins may be parallel or antiparallel, with a resultant slight difference in these energy states. (a) Which condition has the higher energy? (b) More precisely, the line has wavelength 21.11 cm. What is the energy difference between the states? (c) The average lifetime in the excited state is about 10^7 yr. Calculate the associated uncertainty in energy of the excited energy level.

39. **Review problem.** Refer to Section 24.3. Prove that the Doppler shift in wavelength of electromagnetic waves is described by

$$\lambda' = \lambda \sqrt{\frac{1 + v/c}{1 - v/c}}$$

where λ' is the wavelength measured by an observer moving at speed v away from a source radiating waves of wavelength λ.

40. Astronomers observe a series of spectral lines in the light from a distant galaxy. On the hypothesis that the lines form the Lyman series for a (new?!) one-electron atom, they start to construct the energy level diagram shown in Figure P29.40, which gives the wavelengths of the first four lines and the short-wavelength limit of this series. Based on this information, calculate (a) the energies of the ground state and first four excited states for this one-electron atom and (b) the wavelengths of the first three lines and the short-wavelength limit in the Balmer series for this atom. (c) Show that the wavelengths of the first four lines and the short wavelength limit of the Lyman series for the hydrogen atom are all 60.0% of the wavelengths for the Lyman series in the one-electron atom described in part (b). (d) Based on this observation, explain why this atom could be hydrogen.

41. **Physics⊗Now™** A distant quasar is moving away from the Earth at such high speed that the blue 434-nm H_γ line of hydrogen is observed at 510 nm, in the green portion of the spectrum (Fig. P29.41). (a) How fast is the quasar receding? You may use the result of Problem 29.39. (b) Edwin Hubble discovered that all objects outside the local group of galaxies are moving away from us, with speeds proportional to their distances. Hubble's law is expressed as $v = HR$, where Hubble's constant has the approximate value $H = 17 \times 10^{-3}$ m/s · ly. Determine the distance from the Earth to this quasar.

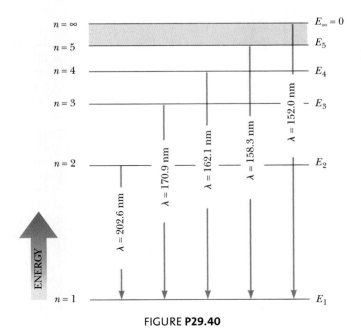

FIGURE **P29.40**

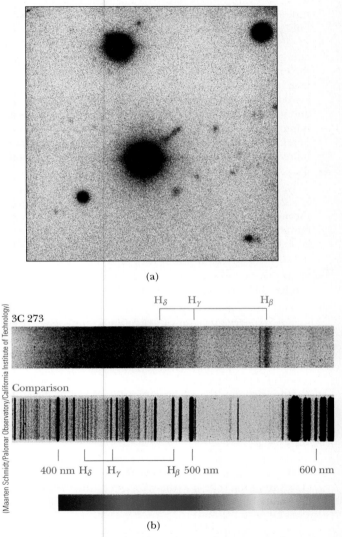

FIGURE **P29.41** (a) Image of the quasar 3C273. (b) Spectrum of the quasar above a comparison spectrum emitted by stationary hydrogen and helium atoms. Both parts of the figure are printed as black-and-white photographic negatives to reveal detail.

Additional Problems

42. (a) If a hydrogen atom makes a transition from the $n = 4$ state to the $n = 2$ state, determine the wavelength of the photon created in the process. (b) Assuming that the atom

was initially at rest, determine the recoil speed of the hydrogen atom when it emits this photon.

43. LENINGRAD, 1930—Four years after the publication of the Schrödinger equation, Lev Davidovich Landau, age 23, solved the equation for a charged particle moving in a uniform magnetic field. A single electron moving perpendicular to a field $\vec{B}$ can be considered as a model atom without a nucleus, or as the irreducible quantum limit of the cyclotron. Landau proved that its energy is quantized in uniform steps of $e\hbar B/m_e$.

CAMBRIDGE, MA, 1999—Gerald Gabrielse trapped a single electron in an evacuated centimeter-size metal can cooled to a temperature of 80 mK. In a magnetic field of magnitude 5.26 T, the electron circulated for hours in its lowest energy level, generating a measurable signal as it moved. (a) Evaluate the size of a quantum jump in the electron's energy. (b) For comparison, evaluate $k_B T$ as a measure of the energy available to the electron in blackbody radiation from the walls of its container. (c) Microwave radiation was introduced to excite the electron. Calculate the frequency and wavelength of the photon that the electron absorbs as it jumps to its second energy level. Measurement of the resonant absorption frequency verified the theory and permitted precise determination of properties of the electron.

44. **Review problem.** (a) How much energy is required to cause a hydrogen atom to move from the $n = 1$ state to the $n = 2$ state? (b) Suppose the atom gains this energy through collisions with other hydrogen atoms at a high temperature. At what temperature would the average atomic kinetic energy $3k_B T/2$ be great enough to excite the electron? Here k_B is the Boltzmann constant.

45. Show that the average value of r for the $1s$ state of hydrogen has the value $3a_0/2$. (*Suggestion:* Use Eq. 29.7.)

46. An elementary theorem in statistics states that the root-mean-square uncertainty in a quantity r is given by $\Delta r = \sqrt{\langle r^2 \rangle - \langle r \rangle^2}$. Evaluate the uncertainty in the radial position of the electron in the ground state of the hydrogen atom. Use the average value of r found in the previous problem: $\langle r \rangle = 3a_0/2$. The average value of the squared distance between the electron and the proton is given by

$$\langle r^2 \rangle = \int_{\text{all space}} |\psi|^2 r^2 \, dV = \int_0^\infty P(r) r^2 \, dr$$

47. *An example of the correspondence principle.* Use Bohr's model of the hydrogen atom to show that when the electron moves from the state n to the state $n - 1$, the frequency of the emitted light is

$$f = \left(\frac{2\pi^2 m_e k_e^2 e^4}{h^3 n^2} \right) \frac{2n - 1}{(n-1)^2}$$

Show that as $n \rightarrow \infty$, this expression varies as $1/n^3$ and reduces to the classical frequency one expects the atom to emit. (*Suggestion:* To calculate the classical frequency, note that the frequency of revolution is $v/2\pi r$, where r is given by Eq. 11.22.)

48. 🖥 Example 29.2 calculates the most probable value for the radial coordinate r of the electron in the ground state of a hydrogen atom. Problem 29.45 shows that the average value is $\langle r \rangle = 3a_0/2$. For comparison with these modal and

mean values, find the median value of r. Proceed as follows. (a) Derive an expression for the probability, as a function of r, that the electron in the ground state of hydrogen will be found outside a sphere of radius r centered on the nucleus. (b) Make a graph of the probability as a function of r/a_0. Choose values of r/a_0 ranging from 0 to 4.00 in steps of 0.250. (c) Find the value of r for which the probability of finding the electron outside a sphere of radius r is equal to the probability of finding the electron inside this sphere. You must solve a transcendental equation numerically, and your graph is a good starting point.

49. Suppose a hydrogen atom is in the $2s$ state, with its wave function given by Equation 29.8. Taking $r = a_0$, calculate values for (a) $\psi_{2s}(a_0)$, (b) $|\psi_{2s}(a_0)|^2$, and (c) $P_{2s}(a_0)$.

50. The states of matter are solid, liquid, gas, and plasma. Plasma can be described as a gas of charged particles or a gas of ionized atoms. Most of the matter in the Solar System is plasma (throughout the interior of the Sun). In fact, most of the matter in the Universe is plasma; so is a candle flame. Use the information in Figure 29.12 to make an order-of-magnitude estimate for the temperature to which a typical chemical element must be raised to turn into plasma by ionizing most of the atoms in a sample. Explain your reasoning.

51. Assume that three identical uncharged particles of mass m and spin $\frac{1}{2}$ are contained in a one-dimensional box of length L. What is the ground-state energy of this system?

52. The force on a magnetic moment μ_z in a nonuniform magnetic field B_z is given by $F_z = \mu_z(dB_z/dz)$. If a beam of silver atoms travels a horizontal distance of 1.00 m through such a field and each atom has a speed of 100 m/s, how strong must be the field gradient dB_z/dz to deflect the beam 1.00 mm?

53. (a) Show that the most probable radial position for an electron in the $2s$ state of hydrogen is $r = 5.236a_0$. (b) Show that the wave function given by Equation 29.8 is normalized.

54. **Review problem.** (a) Is the mass of a hydrogen atom in its ground state larger or smaller than the sum of the masses of a proton and an electron? (b) What is the mass difference? (c) How large is the difference as a percentage of the total mass? (d) Is it large enough to affect the value of the atomic mass listed to six decimal places in Table A.3 in Appendix A?

55. An electron in chromium moves from the $n = 2$ state to the $n = 1$ state without emitting a photon. Instead, the excess energy is transferred to an outer electron (one in the $n = 4$ state), which is then ejected by the atom. This phenomenon is called an Auger (pronounced "ohjay") process, and the ejected electron is referred to as an Auger electron. Use the Bohr theory to find the kinetic energy of the Auger electron.

56. Suppose the ionization energy of an atom is 4.10 eV. In the spectrum of this same atom, we observe emission lines with wavelengths 310 nm, 400 nm, and 1 377.8 nm. Use this information to construct the energy level diagram with the fewest levels. Assume that the higher levels are closer together.

57. For hydrogen in the 1s state, what is the probability of finding the electron farther than $2.50a_0$ from the nucleus?

58. All atoms have the same size, to an order of magnitude. (a) To show that, estimate the diameters for aluminum (with molar mass 27.0 g/mol and density 2.70 g/cm³) and uranium (molar mass 238 g/mol and density 18.9 g/cm³). (b) What do the results imply about the wave functions for inner-shell electrons as we progress to higher and higher atomic mass atoms? (*Suggestion:* The molar volume is approximately $D^3 N_A$, where D is the atomic diameter and N_A is Avogadro's number.)

59. In the technique known as electron spin resonance (ESR), a sample containing unpaired electrons is placed in a magnetic field. Consider the simplest situation, in which only one electron is present and therefore only two energy states are possible, corresponding to $m_s = \pm\frac{1}{2}$. In ESR, the absorption of a photon causes the electron's spin magnetic moment to flip from the lower energy state to the higher energy state. According to the result of Problem 22.20 in Chapter 22, the change in energy is $2\mu_B B$. (The lower energy state corresponds to the case where the z component of the magnetic moment $\vec{\boldsymbol{\mu}}_{\text{spin}}$ is aligned with the magnetic field, and the higher energy state is the case where the z component of $\vec{\boldsymbol{\mu}}_{\text{spin}}$ is aligned opposite to the field.) What is the photon frequency required to excite an ESR transition in a 0.350-T magnetic field?

60. Show that the wave function for a hydrogen atom in the 2s state

$$\psi_{2s}(r) = \frac{1}{4\sqrt{2\pi}}\left(\frac{1}{a_0}\right)^{3/2}\left(2 - \frac{r}{a_0}\right)e^{-r/2a_0}$$

satisfies the spherically symmetric Schrödinger equation given in Problem 29.13.

61. **Review problem.** Steven Chu, Claude Cohen-Tannoudji, and William Phillips received the 1997 Nobel Prize in Physics for "the development of methods to cool and trap atoms with laser light." One part of their work was with a beam of atoms (mass ~10^{-25} kg) that move at a speed on the order of 1 km/s, similar to the speed of molecules in air at room temperature. An intense laser light beam tuned to a visible atomic transition (assume 500 nm) is directed straight into the atomic beam. That is, the atomic beam and the light beam are traveling in opposite directions. An atom in the ground state immediately absorbs a photon. Total system momentum is conserved in the absorption process. After a lifetime on the order of 10^{-8} s, the excited atom radiates by spontaneous emission. It has an equal probability of emitting a photon in any direction. Therefore, the average "recoil" of the atom is zero over many absorption and emission cycles. (a) Estimate the average deceleration of the atomic beam. (b) What is the order of magnitude of the distance over which the atoms in the beam will be brought to a halt?

62. Find the average (expectation) value of $1/r$ in the 1s state of hydrogen. Note that the general expression is given by

$$\langle 1/r \rangle = \int_{\text{all space}} |\psi|^2 (1/r)\ dV = \int_0^\infty P(r)(1/r)\ dr$$

Is the result equal to the inverse of the average value of r?

ANSWERS TO QUICK QUIZZES

29.1 (b). The number of subshells is the same as the number of allowed values of ℓ. The allowed values of ℓ for $n = 4$ are $\ell = 0$, 1, 2, and 3, so there are four subshells.

29.2 (a) Five values (0, 1, 2, 3, 4) of ℓ and (b) nine different values $(-4, -3, -2, -1, 0, 1, 2, 3, 4)$ of m_ℓ as follows:

ℓ	m_ℓ
0	0
1	$-1, 0, 1$
2	$-2, -1, 0, 1, 2$
3	$-3, -2, -1, 0, 1, 2, 3$
4	$-4, -3, -2, -1, 0, 1, 2, 3, 4$

29.3 The vector model for $\ell = 1$ is shown at the top of the right column.

29.4 Cesium, potassium, lithium. The higher the value of Z, the closer to zero is the energy associated with the outermost electron and the smaller is the ionization energy.

29.5 Final: M. Initial: O (because the subscript β indicates that the initial shell is the second shell higher than M).

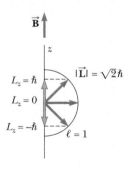

29.6 (i), (c). The wavelengths of the characteristic x-rays are determined by the separation between energy levels in the atoms of the target, which is unrelated to the energy with which electrons are fired at the target. The only dependence is that the incoming electrons must have enough energy to eject an atomic electron from an inner shell. (ii), (b). The minimum wavelength of the bremsstrahlung is associated with the highest-energy photon. This photon comes from an electron striking the target and giving up all its energy to electromagnetic radiation in one collision. Therefore, higher-energy incoming electrons will result in higher-energy photons with shorter wavelengths.

CHAPTER 30

Nuclear Physics

The Ice Man, discovered in 1991 when an Italian glacier melted enough to expose his remains. His possessions, particularly his tools, have shed light on the way people lived in the Bronze Age. A dating technique using radioactive carbon-14 was used to determine how long ago this person lived.

(Paul Hanny/Gamma Liaison)

In 1896, the year that marked the birth of nuclear physics, Antoine-Henri Becquerel (1852–1908) introduced the world of science to radioactivity in uranium compounds by accidentally discovering that uranyl potassium sulfate crystals emit an invisible radiation that can darken a photographic plate when the plate is covered to exclude light. After a series of experiments, he concluded that the radiation emitted by the crystals was of a new type, one that requires no external stimulation and is so penetrating that it can darken protected photographic plates and ionize gases.

A great deal of research followed as scientists attempted to understand the radiation emitted by radioactive nuclei. Pioneering work by Rutherford showed that the radiation was of three types, which he called alpha, beta, and gamma rays. Later experiments showed that alpha rays are helium nuclei, beta rays are electrons or related particles called positrons, and gamma rays are high-energy photons.

As we saw in Section 29.1, the 1911 experiments of Rutherford established that the nucleus of an atom has a very small volume and that most of the atomic mass is contained in the nucleus.

Furthermore, such studies demonstrated a new type of force, the nuclear force, first introduced in Section 5.5, that is predominant at distances on the order of 10^{-15} m and essentially zero at distances larger than that.

In this chapter, we discuss the structure of the atomic nucleus. We shall describe the basic properties of nuclei, nuclear forces, nuclear binding energy, the phenomenon of radioactivity, and nuclear reactions.

30.1 SOME PROPERTIES OF NUCLEI

In the commonly accepted structural model of the nucleus, all nuclei are composed of two types of particles: protons and neutrons. The only exception is the ordinary hydrogen nucleus, which is a single proton with no neutrons. In describing the atomic nucleus, we identify the following integer quantities:

- The **atomic number** Z (introduced in Chapter 29) equals the number of protons in the nucleus (the atomic number is sometimes called the charge number).
- The **neutron number** N equals the number of neutrons in the nucleus.
- The **mass number** A equals the number of nucleons (neutrons plus protons) in the nucleus. That is, $A = N + Z$.

In representing nuclei, it is convenient to have a symbolic representation that shows how many protons and neutrons are present. The symbol used is $_{Z}^{A}X$, where X represents the chemical symbol for the element. For example, $_{26}^{56}Fe$ (iron) has a mass number of 56 and an atomic number of 26; therefore, it contains 26 protons and 30 neutrons. When no confusion is likely to arise, we omit the subscript Z because the chemical symbol can always be used to determine Z. Therefore, $_{26}^{56}Fe$ is the same as ^{56}Fe and can also be expressed as "iron-56."

The nuclei of all atoms of a particular element contain the same number of protons but often contain different numbers of neutrons. Nuclei that are related in this way are called **isotopes. The isotopes of an element have the same Z value but different N and A values.** The natural abundances of isotopes can differ substantially. For example, $_{6}^{11}C$, $_{6}^{12}C$, $_{6}^{13}C$, and $_{6}^{14}C$ are four isotopes of carbon. The natural abundance of the $_{6}^{12}C$ isotope is about 98.9%, whereas that of the $_{6}^{13}C$ isotope is only about 1.1%. ($_{6}^{11}C$ and $_{6}^{14}C$ exist in trace amounts.) Even the simplest element, hydrogen, has isotopes: $_{1}^{1}H$, the ordinary hydrogen nucleus; $_{1}^{2}H$, deuterium; and $_{1}^{3}H$, tritium. Some isotopes do not occur naturally but can be produced in the laboratory through nuclear reactions.

QUICK QUIZ 30.1 **(i)** Consider the following three nuclei: ^{12}C, ^{13}N, ^{14}O. What is the same for these three nuclei? **(a)** number of protons **(b)** number of neutrons **(c)** number of nucleons. **(ii)** Consider the following three nuclei: ^{12}N, ^{13}N, ^{14}N. From the same list of choices, what is the same for these three nuclei? **(iii)** Consider the following three nuclei: ^{14}C, ^{14}N, ^{14}O. From the same list of choices, what is the same for these three nuclei?

Charge and Mass

The proton carries a single positive charge $+e$ and the electron carries a single negative charge $-e$, where $e = 1.60 \times 10^{-19}$ C. The neutron is electrically neutral, as its name implies. Because the neutron has no charge, it was difficult to detect with early experimental apparatus and techniques. Today we can detect neutrons relatively easily with modern detection devices.

A convenient unit for measuring mass on a nuclear scale is the **atomic mass unit** u. This unit is defined in such a way that the atomic mass of the isotope $_{6}^{12}C$ is exactly 12 u, where $1\,u = 1.660\,539 \times 10^{-27}$ kg. The proton and neutron each

TABLE 30.1	Masses of Selected Particles in Various Units		
	Mass		
Particle	**kg**	**u**	**MeV/c^2**
Proton	$1.672\,62 \times 10^{-27}$	1.007 276	938.28
Neutron	$1.674\,93 \times 10^{-27}$	1.008 665	939.57
Electron	$9.109\,39 \times 10^{-31}$	$5.48\,579 \times 10^{-4}$	0.510 999
$^1_1$H atom	$1.673\,53 \times 10^{-27}$	1.007 825	938.783
$^4_2$He atom	$6.646\,48 \times 10^{-27}$	4.002 603	3 728.40
$^{12}_6$C atom	$1.992\,65 \times 10^{-27}$	12.000 000	11 177.9

have a mass of approximately 1 u, and the electron has a mass that is only a small fraction of an atomic mass unit:

$$\text{Mass of proton} = 1.007\,276 \text{ u}$$
$$\text{Mass of neutron} = 1.008\,665 \text{ u}$$
$$\text{Mass of electron} = 0.000\,5486 \text{ u}$$

Because the rest energy of a particle is given by $E_R = mc^2$ (Section 9.7), it is often convenient to express the atomic mass unit in terms of its rest energy equivalent. For one atomic mass unit, we have

$$E_R = mc^2 = (1.660\,539 \times 10^{-27} \text{ kg})(2.997\,92 \times 10^8 \text{ m/s})^2 = 931.494 \text{ MeV/}c^2$$

where we have used the conversion 1 eV = $1.602\,176 \times 10^{-19}$ J. Using this equivalence, nuclear physicists often express mass in terms of the unit MeV/c^2. The masses of several simple particles are given in Table 30.1. The masses and some other properties of selected isotopes are provided in Table A.3 in Appendix A.

The Size of Nuclei

The size and structure of nuclei were first investigated in the scattering experiments of Rutherford, discussed in Section 29.1. Using the principle of conservation of energy, Rutherford found an expression for how close an alpha particle moving directly toward the nucleus can approach the nucleus before being turned around by Coulomb repulsion.

Let us consider the system of the incoming alpha particle ($Z = 2$) and the nucleus (arbitrary Z), and apply the energy version of the isolated system model. Because the nucleus is assumed to be much more massive than the alpha particle, we identify the kinetic energy of the system as the kinetic energy of the alpha particle alone. When the alpha particle and the nucleus are far apart, we can approximate the potential energy of the system as zero. If the collision is head-on, the alpha particle stops momentarily at some point (Active Fig. 30.1) and the energy of the system is entirely potential. Therefore, the initial kinetic energy of the incoming alpha particle is converted completely to electric potential energy of the system when the particle stops:

$$\tfrac{1}{2}mv^2 = k_e \frac{q_1 q_2}{r} = k_e \frac{(2e)(Ze)}{d}$$

where d is the distance of closest approach, Z is the atomic number of the target nucleus, and we have used the nonrelativistic expression for kinetic energy because speeds of alpha particles from radioactive decay are small relative to c. Solving for d, we find that

$$d = \frac{4k_e Ze^2}{mv^2}$$

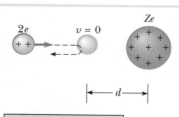

ACTIVE FIGURE 30.1

An alpha particle on a head-on collision course with a nucleus of charge Ze. Because of the Coulomb repulsion between charges of the same sign, the alpha particle approaches to a distance d from the target nucleus, called the distance of closest approach.

Physics Now™ By logging into PhysicsNow at **www.pop4e.com** and going to Active Figure 30.1, you can adjust the atomic number of the target nucleus and the kinetic energy of the alpha particle. Then observe the approach of the alpha particle toward the nucleus.

From this expression, Rutherford found that alpha particles approached to within 3.2×10^{-14} m of a nucleus when the foil was made of gold. Based on this calculation and his analysis of results for collisions that were not head-on, Rutherford argued that the radius of the gold nucleus must be less than this value. For silver atoms, the distance of closest approach was found to be 2×10^{-14} m. From these results, Rutherford reached his conclusion that the positive charge in an atom is concentrated in a small sphere called the nucleus, whose radius is no greater than about 10^{-14} m. Note that this radius is on the order of 10^{-4} of the Bohr radius, corresponding to a nuclear volume which is on the order of 10^{-12} of the volume of a hydrogen atom. The nucleus is an incredibly small part of the atom! Because such small lengths are common in nuclear physics, a convenient unit of length is the *femtometer* (fm), sometimes called the **fermi,** defined as

$$1 \text{ fm} \equiv 10^{-15} \text{ m}$$

FIGURE 30.2 A nucleus can be modeled as a cluster of tightly packed spheres, each of which is a nucleon.

Since the time of Rutherford's scattering experiments, a multitude of other experiments have shown that most nuclei can be geometrically modeled as being approximately spherical with an average radius of

$$r = r_0 A^{1/3} \qquad [30.1]$$

▮ Radius of a nucleus

where A is the mass number and r_0 is a constant equal to 1.2×10^{-15} m. Because the volume of a sphere is proportional to the cube of the radius, it follows from Equation 30.1 that the volume of a nucleus (assumed to be spherical) is directly proportional to A, the total number of nucleons, which suggests that **all nuclei have nearly the same density.** Nucleons combine to form a nucleus as though they were tightly packed spheres (Fig. 30.2).

EXAMPLE 30.1   Nuclear Volume and Density

A Find an approximate expression for the mass of a nucleus of mass number A.

Solution The mass of the proton is approximately equal to that of the neutron. Therefore, if the mass of one of these particles is m, the mass of the nucleus is approximately Am.

B Find an expression for the volume of this nucleus in terms of the mass number.

Solution Assuming that the nucleus is spherical and using Equation 30.1, we find that the volume is

$$V = \tfrac{4}{3} \pi r^3 = \tfrac{4}{3} \pi r_0^3 A$$

C Find a numerical value for the density of this nucleus.

Solution The nuclear density is

$$\rho_n = \frac{m_{\text{nucleus}}}{V} = \frac{Am}{\tfrac{4}{3} \pi r_0^3 A} = \frac{3m}{4\pi r_0^3}$$

$$= \frac{3(1.67 \times 10^{-27} \text{ kg})}{4\pi (1.2 \times 10^{-15} \text{ m})^3} = 2.3 \times 10^{17} \text{ kg/m}^3$$

Recalling that the density of water is 10^3 kg/m^3, note that the nuclear density is about 2.3×10^{14} times greater than that of water!

Nuclear Stability

Because the nucleus consists of a closely packed collection of protons and neutrons, you might be surprised that it can exist at all. The very large repulsive electrostatic forces between protons in close proximity should cause the nucleus to fly apart. Nuclei are stable, however, because of the presence of another force, the **nuclear force** (see Section 5.5). This short-range force (it is nonzero only for particle separations less than about 2 fm) is an attractive force that acts between all nuclear particles. The nuclear force also acts between pairs of neutrons and between neutrons and protons.

(a) Potential energy versus separation distance for the neutron–proton system. (b) Potential energy versus separation distance for the proton–proton system. The difference in the two curves is due to the Coulomb repulsion in the case of the proton–proton interaction. To display the difference in the curves on this scale, the height of the peak for the proton–proton curve has been exaggerated by a factor of 10.

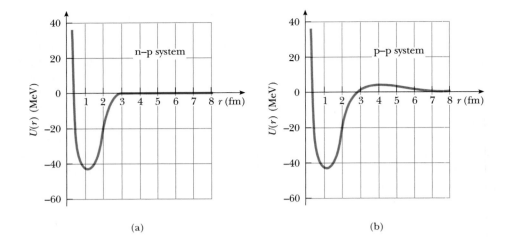

(a)   (b)

The nuclear force dominates the Coulomb repulsive force within the nucleus (at short ranges). If that were not the case, stable nuclei would not exist. Moreover, the nuclear force is independent of charge. In other words, the forces associated with the proton–proton, proton–neutron, and neutron–neutron interactions are the same, apart from the additional repulsive Coulomb force for the proton–proton interaction.

Evidence for the limited range of nuclear forces comes from scattering experiments and from studies of nuclear binding energies, which we shall discuss shortly. The short range of the nuclear force is shown in the neutron–proton (n–p) potential energy plot of Figure 30.3a obtained by scattering neutrons from a target containing hydrogen. The depth of the n–p potential energy well is 40 to 50 MeV, and a strong repulsive component prevents the nucleons from approaching much closer than 0.4 fm.

The nuclear force does not affect electrons, enabling energetic electrons to serve as point-like probes of the charge density of nuclei. The charge independence of the nuclear force also means that the main difference between the n–p and p–p interactions is that the p–p potential energy consists of a *superposition* of nuclear and Coulomb interactions as shown in Figure 30.3b. At distances less than 2 fm, the p–p and n–p potential energies are nearly identical, but for distances greater than this, the p–p potential has a positive energy barrier with a maximum at 4 fm.

About 260 stable nuclei exist; hundreds of other nuclei have been observed but are unstable. A useful graphical representation in nuclear physics is a plot of N versus Z for stable nuclei as shown in Figure 30.4. Note that light nuclei are stable if they contain equal numbers of protons and neutrons—that is, if $N = Z$—but heavy nuclei are stable if $N > Z$. This behavior can be partially understood by recognizing that as the number of protons increases, the strength of the Coulomb force increases, which tends to break the nucleus apart. As a result, more neutrons are needed to keep the nucleus stable because neutrons experience only the attractive nuclear force. Eventually, when $Z = 83$, the repulsive forces between protons cannot be compensated by the addition of more neutrons. Elements that contain more than 83 protons do not have stable nuclei.

Interestingly, most stable nuclei have even values of A. In fact, certain values of Z and N correspond to nuclei with unusually high stability. These values of Z and N, called **magic numbers,** are

$$Z \text{ or } N = 2, 8, 20, 28, 50, 82, 126 \qquad [30.2]$$

For example, the helium nucleus (two protons and two neutrons), which has $Z = 2$ and $N = 2$, is very stable. This stability is reminiscent of the chemical stability of inert gases and suggests quantized nuclear energy levels, which we indeed find to

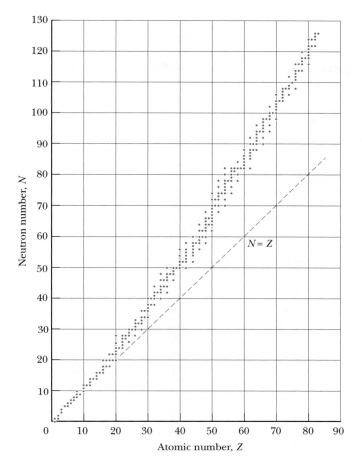

FIGURE 30.4 Neutron number N versus atomic number Z for the stable nuclei (blue dots). These nuclei lie in a narrow band called the line of stability. The dashed line corresponds to the condition $N = Z$.

be the case. Some structural models of the nucleus predict a shell structure similar to that for the atom.

Nuclear Spin and Magnetic Moment

In Chapter 29, we discussed that an electron has an intrinsic angular momentum called spin. Protons and neutrons, like electrons, also have an intrinsic angular momentum. Furthermore, a nucleus has a net intrinsic angular momentum that arises from the individual spins of the protons and neutrons. This angular momentum must obey the same quantum rules as orbital angular momentum and spin (Section 29.4). Therefore, the magnitude of the **nuclear angular momentum** is due to the combination of all nucleons and is equal to $\sqrt{I(I + 1)}\,\hbar$, where I is called the **nuclear spin quantum number** and may be an integer or a half-integer. The maximum component of the nuclear angular momentum projected along any direction is $I\hbar$. Figure 30.5 illustrates the possible orientations of the nuclear spin and its projections along the z axis for the case where $I = \frac{3}{2}$.

The nuclear angular momentum has a nuclear magnetic moment associated with it. The magnetic moment of a nucleus is measured in terms of the **nuclear magneton** μ_n, a unit of magnetic moment defined as

$$\mu_n \equiv \frac{e\hbar}{2m_p} = 5.05 \times 10^{-27}\,\text{J/T} \qquad [30.3]$$

This definition is analogous to Equation 29.15 for the z component of the spin magnetic moment for an electron, which is the Bohr magneton μ_B. Note that μ_n is smaller than μ_B by a factor of about 2 000 because of the large difference in masses of the proton and electron.

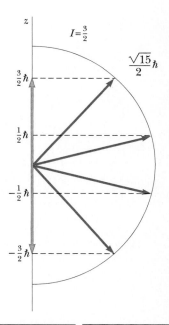

FIGURE 30.5 A vector model showing possible orientations of the nuclear spin angular momentum vector and its projections along the z axis for the case $I = \frac{3}{2}$.

■ **Nuclear magneton**

The magnetic moment of a free proton is $2.792\,8\mu_n$. Unfortunately, no general theory of nuclear magnetism explains this value. Another surprising point is that a neutron, despite having no electric charge, also has a magnetic moment, which has a value of $-1.913\,5\mu_n$. The negative sign indicates that the neutron's magnetic moment is opposite its spin angular momentum. Such a magnetic moment for a neutral particle suggests that we need to design a structural model for the neutron that explains such an observation. This structural model, the *quark model*, will be discussed in Chapter 31.

> **QUICK QUIZ 30.2** Which do you expect to show very little variation among different isotopes of an element? **(a)** atomic mass **(b)** nuclear spin magnetic moment **(c)** chemical behavior

Nuclear Magnetic Resonance and Magnetic Resonance Imaging

The potential energy of a system consisting of a magnetic dipole moment in a magnetic field is $-\vec{\mu} \cdot \vec{B}$. When the direction of $\vec{\mu}$ is along the field, the potential energy of the system has its minimum value $-\mu B$. When the direction of $\vec{\mu}$ is opposite the field, the potential energy has its maximum value μB. Because the direction of the magnetic moment for a particle is quantized, the energies of the system are also quantized. In addition, because the spin vector cannot align exactly with the direction of the magnetic field, the extreme values of the energy are $\pm \mu_z B$, where μ_z is the z component of the magnetic moment. The two energy states for a nucleus with a spin of $\frac{1}{2}$ are shown in Figure 30.6. These states are often called **spin states** because they differ in energy as a result of the direction of the spin.

It is possible to observe transitions between these two spin states in a sample using a technique known as **nuclear magnetic resonance** (NMR). A constant magnetic field changes the energy associated with the spin states, splitting them apart in energy (Fig. 30.6). In addition, the sample is irradiated with electromagnetic waves in the radio range of the electromagnetic spectrum. When the frequency of the radio waves is adjusted such that the photon energy matches the separation energy between spin states, the photon is absorbed by a nucleus in the ground state, raising the nucleus–magnetic field system to the higher-energy spin state. The result is a net absorption of energy by the system, which is detected by the experimental control and measurement system. A diagram of the apparatus used to detect an NMR signal is illustrated in Figure 30.7. The absorbed energy is supplied by the oscillator producing the radio waves. Nuclear magnetic resonance and a related technique called electron spin resonance are extremely important methods for studying nuclear and atomic systems and how these systems interact with their surroundings.

FIGURE 30.6 A nucleus with spin $\frac{1}{2}$ can occupy one of two energy states when placed in an external magnetic field. The lower energy state E_{min} corresponds to the case where the spin is aligned with the field as much as possible according to quantum mechanics, and the higher energy state E_{max} corresponds to the case where the spin is opposite the field as much as possible.

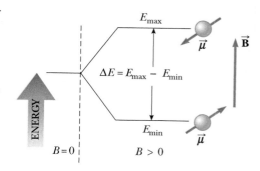

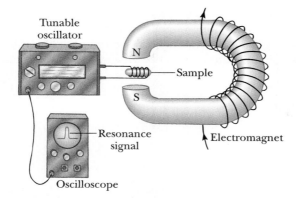

Tunable
oscillator

N

Sample

S

Resonance
signal

Electromagnet

Oscilloscope

FIGURE **30.7** Experimental arrangement for nuclear magnetic resonance. The radio-frequency
magnetic field created by the coil surrounding the sample and provided by the
variable-frequency oscillator is perpendicular to the constant magnetic field created by
the electromagnet. When the nuclei in the sample meet the resonance condition, the
nuclei absorb energy from the radio-frequency field of the coil, and this absorption
changes the characteristics of the circuit in which the coil is included. Most modern
NMR spectrometers use superconducting magnets at fixed field strengths and
operate at frequencies of approximately 200 MHz.

A widely used medical diagnostic technique called **MRI**, for **magnetic resonance imaging,** is based on nuclear magnetic resonance. In MRI, the patient is placed inside a large solenoid that supplies a spatially varying magnetic field. Because of the variation in the magnetic field across the patient's body, protons in hydrogen atoms in water molecules in different parts of the body have different splittings in energy between spin states, and the resonance signal can be used to provide information on the positions of the protons. A computer is used to analyze the position information to provide data for constructing a final image. An MRI scan showing incredible detail in internal body structure is shown in Figure 30.8. The main advantage of MRI over other imaging techniques in medical diagnostics is that it does not cause damage to cellular structures as x-rays do. Photons associated with the radio-frequency signals used in MRI have energies of only about 10^{-7} eV. Because molecular bond strengths are much larger (on the order of 1 eV), the radio-frequency radiation cannot cause cellular damage. In comparison, x-rays or γ-rays have energies ranging from 10^4 to 10^6 eV and can cause considerable cellular damage. Therefore, despite some individuals' fears of the word *nuclear* associated with magnetic resonance imaging, the radio-frequency radiation involved is overwhelmingly safer than x-rays!

 Magnetic resonance imaging

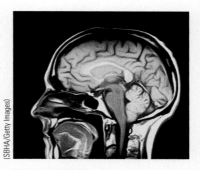

(SBHA/Getty Images)

FIGURE **30.8** A color-enhanced MRI scan of a human brain.

PITFALL PREVENTION 30.1

BINDING ENERGY When separate nucleons are combined to form a nucleus, the rest energy of the system is reduced. Therefore, the change in energy is negative. The absolute value of this change is called the binding energy. This difference in sign may be a source of confusion. For example, an *increase* in binding energy corresponds to a *decrease* in the rest energy of the system.

30.2 | BINDING ENERGY

It is found that the mass of a nucleus is always less than the sum of the masses of its nucleons. Because mass is a manifestation of energy, **the total rest energy of the bound system (the nucleus) is less than the combined rest energy of the separated nucleons.** This difference in energy is called the **binding energy** E_b of the nucleus and represents the energy that must be added to a nucleus to break it apart into its components:

$$E_b(\text{MeV}) = [ZM(\text{H}) + Nm_n - M({}_Z^A\text{X})] \times 931.494 \text{ MeV/u} \qquad [30.4]$$

▪ Binding energy of a nucleus

where $M(\text{H})$ is the atomic mass of the neutral hydrogen atom, $M({}_Z^A\text{X})$ represents the atomic mass of an atom of the isotope ${}_Z^A\text{X}$, m_n is the mass of the neutron, and the masses are all in atomic mass units. Note that the mass of the Z electrons included in $M(\text{H})$ cancels with the mass of the Z electrons included in the term

$M(^A_Z X)$ within a small difference associated with the atomic binding energy of the electrons. Because atomic binding energies are typically several electron volts and nuclear binding energies are several million electron volts, this difference is negligible, and we adopt a simplification model in which we ignore this difference.

| EXAMPLE 30.2 | The Binding Energy of the Deuteron |

Calculate the binding energy of the deuteron (the nucleus of a deuterium atom), which consists of a proton and a neutron, given that the atomic mass of deuterium is 2.014 102 u.

Solution From Table 30.1, we see that the mass of the hydrogen atom, representing the proton, is $M(\text{H}) = 1.007\ 825$ u and that the neutron mass $m_n = 1.008\ 665$ u. Therefore,

$$E_b(\text{MeV}) = [(1)(1.007\ 825\ \text{u}) + (1)(1.008\ 665\ \text{u})$$
$$- 2.014\ 102\ \text{u}] \times 931.494\ \text{MeV/u}$$

$$= 2.224\ \text{MeV}$$

This result tells us that separating a deuteron into its constituent proton and neutron requires adding 2.224 MeV of energy to the deuteron. One way of supplying the deuteron with this energy is by bombarding it with energetic particles.

A plot of binding energy per nucleon E_b/A as a function of mass number for various stable nuclei is shown in Figure 30.9. Note that the curve has a maximum in the vicinity of $A = 60$, corresponding to isotopes of iron, cobalt, and nickel. That is, nuclei having mass numbers either greater or less than 60 are not as strongly bound as those near the middle of the periodic table. The higher values of binding energy per nucleon near $A = 60$ imply that energy is released when a heavy nucleus splits, or *fissions*, into two lighter nuclei. Energy is released in fission because the nucleons in each product nucleus are more tightly bound to one another than are the nucleons in the original nucleus. The important process of fission and a second important process of *fusion*, in which energy is released as light nuclei combine, are considered in detail in Section 30.6.

The binding energy per nucleon in Figure 30.9 is approximately constant at 8 MeV for $A > 20$. In this case, the nuclear forces between a particular nucleon and all the other nucleons in the nucleus are said to be *saturated*; that is, a particular

FIGURE 30.9 Binding energy per nucleon versus mass number for nuclei that lie along the line of stability in Figure 30.4. Some representative nuclei appear as blue dots with labels. (Nuclei to the right of ^{208}Pb are unstable. The curve represents the binding energy for the most stable isotopes.)

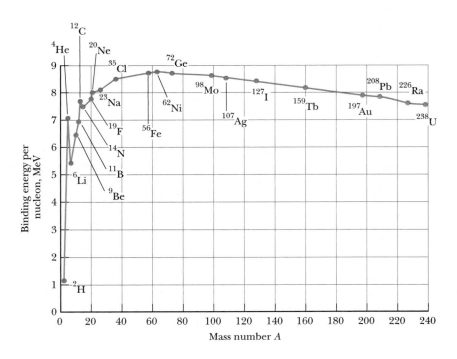

nucleon interacts with only a limited number of other nucleons because of the short-range character of the nuclear force. These other nucleons can be viewed as being the nearest neighbors in the closely packed structure shown in Figure 30.2.

Figure 30.9 provides insight into fundamental questions about the origin of the chemical elements. In the early life of the Universe, there were only hydrogen and helium. Clouds of cosmic gas coalesced under gravitational forces to form stars. As a star ages, it produces heavier elements from the lighter elements contained within it, beginning by fusing hydrogen atoms to form helium. This process continues as the star becomes older, generating atoms having larger and larger atomic numbers. The nuclide $^{62}_{28}$Ni has the largest binding energy per nucleon of 8.794 5 MeV/nucleon. It takes additional energy to create elements in a star with mass numbers larger than 62 because of their lower binding energies per nucleon. This energy comes from the supernova explosion that occurs at the end of some large stars' lives. Therefore, all the heavy atoms in your body were produced from the explosions of ancient stars. You are literally made of stardust!

■ Thinking Physics 30.1

Figure 30.9 shows a graph of the average amount of energy necessary to remove a nucleon from the nucleus. Figure 29.12 shows the energy necessary to remove an electron from an atom. Why does Figure 30.9 show an *approximately constant* amount of energy necessary to remove a nucleon (above about $A = 20$), but Figure 29.12 shows *widely varying* amounts of energy necessary to remove an electron from the atom?

Reasoning In the case of Figure 30.9, the approximately constant value of the nuclear binding energy is a result of the short-range nature of the nuclear force. A given nucleon interacts only with its few nearest neighbors, rather than with all the nucleons in the nucleus. Therefore, no matter how many nucleons are present in the nucleus, removing one nucleon involves separating it only from its nearest neighbors. The energy to do so is therefore approximately independent of how many nucleons are present.

On the other hand, the electric force holding the electrons to the nucleus in an atom is a long-range force. An electron in the atom interacts with all the protons in the nucleus. When the nuclear charge increases, a stronger attraction occurs between the nucleus and the electrons. As a result, as the nuclear charge increases, more energy is necessary to remove an electron, as demonstrated by the upward tendency of the ionization energy in Figure 29.12 for each period. ■

30.3 | RADIOACTIVITY

At the beginning of this chapter, we discussed the discovery of radioactivity by Becquerel, which indicated that nuclei emit particles and radiation. This spontaneous emission was soon to be called **radioactivity.**

The most significant investigations of this phenomenon were conducted by Marie Curie and Pierre Curie (1859–1906). After several years of careful and laborious chemical separation processes on tons of pitchblende, a radioactive ore, the Curies reported the discovery of two previously unknown elements, both of which were radioactive, named polonium and radium. Subsequent experiments, including Rutherford's famous work on alpha particle scattering, suggested that radioactivity was the result of the decay, or disintegration, of unstable nuclei.

Three types of radiation can be emitted by a radioactive substance: alpha (α) rays, where the emitted particles are ^{4}He nuclei; beta (β) rays, in which the emitted particles are either electrons or positrons; and gamma (γ) rays, in which the emitted rays are high-energy photons. A **positron** is a particle similar to the electron in all respects except that it has a charge of $+e$ (the positron is said to be the **antiparticle**

(FPG International)

MARIE CURIE (1867–1934)

A Polish scientist, Marie Curie shared the Nobel Prize in Physics in 1903 with her husband, Pierre, and with Henri Becquerel for their work on spontaneous radioactivity and the radiation emitted by radioactive substances. She wrote "I persist in believing that the ideas that then guided us are the only ones which can lead to the true social progress. We cannot hope to build a better world without improving the individual. Toward this end, each of us must work toward his own highest development, accepting at the same time his share of responsibility in the general life of humanity."

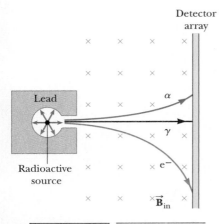

Lead

Radioactive
source

$\vec{B}_{in}$

FIGURE 30.10 The radiation from radioactive sources can be separated into three components by using a magnetic field to deflect the charged particles. The detector array at the right records the events. The gamma ray is not deflected by the magnetic field.

■ **PITFALL PREVENTION 30.2**

RAYS OR PARTICLES? Early in the history of nuclear physics, the term *radiation* was used to describe the emanations from radioactive nuclei. We now know that two out of the three types, namely alpha radiation and beta radiation, involve the emission of particles. Even though these particles are not examples of electromagnetic radiation, the use of the term *radiation* for all three types is deeply entrenched in our language. We will use this term because of its wide usage in the physics community.

■ Number of undecayed nuclei
   as a function of time

■ **PITFALL PREVENTION 30.3**

NOTATION WARNING In Section 30.1, we introduced the symbol N as an integer representing the number of neutrons in a nucleus. In this discussion, the symbol N represents the number of undecayed nuclei in a radioactive sample remaining after some time interval. As you read further, be sure to consider the context to determine the appropriate meaning for the symbol N.

of the electron; we shall discuss antiparticles further in Chapter 31). The symbol e^- is used to designate an electron and e^+ designates a positron.

It is possible to distinguish these three forms of radiation using the scheme illustrated in Figure 30.10. The radiation from a variety of radioactive samples is directed into a region with a magnetic field. The radiation is separated into three components by the magnetic field, two bending in opposite directions and the third experiencing no change in direction. From this simple observation, one can conclude that the radiation of the undeflected beam carries no charge (the gamma ray), the component deflected upward corresponds to positively charged particles (alpha particles), and the component deflected downward corresponds to negatively charged particles (e^-). If the beam includes positrons (e^+), these particles are deflected upward with a different radius of curvature from that of the alpha particles.

The three types of radiation have quite different penetrating powers. Alpha particles barely penetrate a sheet of paper, beta particles can penetrate a few millimeters of aluminum, and gamma rays can penetrate several centimeters of lead.

The rate at which a decay process occurs in a radioactive sample is proportional to the number of radioactive nuclei present in the sample (i.e., those nuclei that have not yet decayed). This dependence is similar to the behavior of population growth in that the rate at which babies are born is proportional to the number of people currently alive. If N is the number of radioactive nuclei present at some instant, the rate of change of N is

$$\frac{dN}{dt} = -\lambda N \qquad [30.5]$$

where λ is called either the **decay constant** or the **disintegration constant** and has a different value for different nuclei. The negative sign indicates that dN/dt is a negative number; that is, N decreases in time.

If we write Equation 30.5 in the form

$$\frac{dN}{N} = -\lambda \, dt$$

we can integrate from an arbitrary initial instant $t = 0$ to a later time t:

$$\int_{N_0}^{N} \frac{dN}{N} = -\lambda \int_0^t dt$$

$$\ln\left(\frac{N}{N_0}\right) = -\lambda t$$

$$N = N_0 e^{-\lambda t} \qquad [30.6]$$

The constant N_0 represents the number of undecayed radioactive nuclei at $t = 0$. We have seen exponential behaviors before, for example, with the discharging of a capacitor in Section 21.9. Based on these experiences, we can identify the inverse of the decay constant $1/\lambda$ as the time interval required for the number of undecayed nuclei to fall to $1/e$ of its original value. Therefore, $1/\lambda$ is the **time constant** for this decay, similar to the time constants we investigated for the decay of the current in an *RC* circuit in Section 21.9 and an *RL* circuit in Section 23.6.

The **decay rate** R is obtained by differentiating Equation 30.6 with respect to time:

$$R = \left|\frac{dN}{dt}\right| = N_0 \lambda e^{-\lambda t} = R_0 e^{-\lambda t} \qquad [30.7]$$

where $R = N\lambda$ and $R_0 = N_0\lambda$ is the decay rate at $t = 0$. The decay rate of a sample is often referred to as its **activity.** Note that both N and R decrease exponentially with time. The plot of N versus t in Active Figure 30.11 illustrates the exponential decay law.

A common unit of activity for a radioactive sample is the **curie** (Ci), defined as

$$1 \text{ Ci} \equiv 3.7 \times 10^{10} \text{ decays/s}$$

This unit was selected as the original unit of activity because it is the approximate activity of 1 g of radium. The SI unit of activity is called the **becquerel** (Bq):

$$1 \text{ Bq} \equiv 1 \text{ decay/s}$$

Therefore, $1 \text{ Ci} = 3.7 \times 10^{10} \text{ Bq}$. The most commonly used units of activity are millicuries (mCi) and microcuries (μCi).

A useful parameter for characterizing radioactive decay is the **half-life** $T_{1/2}$. **The half-life of a radioactive substance is the time interval required for half of a given number of radioactive nuclei to decay.** Setting $N = N_0/2$ and $t = T_{1/2}$ in Equation 30.6 gives

$$\frac{N_0}{2} = N_0 e^{-\lambda T_{1/2}}$$

Writing this equation in the form $e^{\lambda T_{1/2}} = 2$ and taking the natural logarithm of both sides, we have

$$T_{1/2} = \frac{\ln 2}{\lambda} = \frac{0.693}{\lambda} \qquad [30.8]$$

which is a convenient expression relating the half-life to the decay constant. Note that after a time interval of one half-life, $N_0/2$ radioactive nuclei remain (by definition); after two half-lives, half of these have decayed and $N_0/4$ radioactive nuclei remain; after three half-lives, $N_0/8$ remain; and so on. In general, after n half-lives, the number of radioactive nuclei remaining is $N_0/2^n$.

QUICK QUIZ 30.3 On your birthday, you measure the activity of a sample of ^{210}Bi, which has a half-life of 5.01 days. The activity you measure is 1.000 μCi. What is the activity of this sample on your next birthday? **(a)** 1.000 μCi **(b)** 0 **(c)** $\sim 0.2\ \mu$Ci **(d)** $\sim 0.01\ \mu$Ci **(e)** $\sim 10^{-22}\ \mu$Ci

QUICK QUIZ 30.4 Suppose you have a pure radioactive material with a half-life of $T_{1/2}$. You begin with N_0 undecayed nuclei of the material at $t = 0$. At $t = \frac{1}{2}T_{1/2}$, how many of the nuclei *have decayed*? **(a)** $\frac{1}{4}N_0$ **(b)** $\frac{1}{2}N_0$ **(c)** $\frac{3}{4}N_0$ **(d)** $0.707N_0$ **(e)** $0.293N_0$

■ Thinking Physics 30.2

The isotope $^{14}_{6}$C is radioactive and has a half-life of 5 730 years. If you start with a sample of 1 000 carbon-14 nuclei, how many remain (have not decayed) after 17 190 yr?

Reasoning In 5 730 yr, half the sample will have decayed, leaving 500 radioactive $^{14}_{6}$C nuclei. In another 5 730 yr (for a total elapsed time of 11 460 yr), the number remaining is 250 nuclei. After another 5 730 yr (total of 17 190 yr), 125 remain.

These numbers represent ideal circumstances. Radioactive decay is an averaging process over a very large number of atoms, and the actual outcome depends on statistics. Our original sample in this example contained only 1 000 nuclei, certainly not a very large number when we are dealing with atoms, for which we measure the numbers in macroscopic samples in terms of Avogadro's number. Therefore, if we were actually to count the number remaining after one half-life for this small sample, it probably would not be exactly 500. ■

■ The curie

■ The becquerel

⊞ PITFALL PREVENTION 30.4

HALF-LIFE It is *not* true that all the original nuclei have decayed after two half-lives! In one half-life, *half of those nuclei that are left* will decay.

■ Relationship between half-life and decay constant

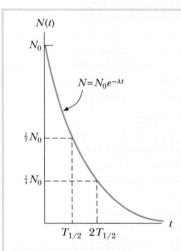

ACTIVE FIGURE 30.11

Plot of the exponential decay law for radioactive nuclei. The vertical axis represents the number of undecayed radioactive nuclei present at any time t, and the horizontal axis is time. The time $T_{1/2}$ is the half-life of the sample.

Physics⊗Now™ By logging into PhysicsNow at **www.pop4e.com** and going to Active Figure 30.11, you can observe the decay curves for nuclei with varying half-lives.

The half-life of the radioactive nucleus radium-226, $^{226}_{88}$Ra, is 1.6×10^3 yr.

A What is the decay constant λ of this nucleus?

Solution We can calculate λ using Equation 30.8 and that

$$T_{1/2} = 1.6 \times 10^3 \text{ yr} \left(\frac{3.16 \times 10^7 \text{ s}}{1 \text{ yr}} \right)$$

$$= 5.0 \times 10^{10} \text{ s}$$

Therefore,

$$\lambda = \frac{0.693}{T_{1/2}} = \frac{0.693}{5.0 \times 10^{10} \text{ s}} = \boxed{1.4 \times 10^{-11} \text{ s}^{-1}}$$

Note that this result is also the probability that any single $^{226}_{88}$Ra nucleus will decay in a time interval of 1 second.

B If a sample contains 3.0×10^{16} $^{226}_{88}$Ra nuclei at $t = 0$, determine its activity in curies at this time.

Solution By definition (Eq. 30.7), R_0, the activity at $t = 0$, is λN_0, where N_0 is the number of radioactive nuclei

present at $t = 0$. With $N_0 = 3.0 \times 10^{16}$, we have

$$R_0 = \lambda N_0 = (1.4 \times 10^{-11} \text{ s}^{-1})(3.0 \times 10^{16})$$

$$= (4.2 \times 10^5 \text{ Bq}) \left(\frac{1 \text{ Ci}}{3.7 \times 10^{10} \text{ Bq}} \right)$$

$$= \boxed{11 \mu\text{Ci}}$$

C What is the activity after the sample is 2.0×10^3 yr old?

Solution We use Equation 30.7 and that 2.0×10^3 yr $= 6.3 \times 10^{10}$ s:

$$R = R_0 e^{-\lambda t}$$

$$= (11 \ \mu\text{Ci}) e^{-(1.4 \times 10^{-11} \text{ s}^{-1})(6.3 \times 10^{10} \text{ s})}$$

$$= \boxed{4.7 \mu\text{Ci}}$$

Physics⊗Now™ By logging into PhysicsNow at **www.pop4e.com** and going to Interactive Example 30.3, you can practice evaluating the parameters for radioactive decay of various isotopes of radium.

EXAMPLE 30.4 | **A Radioactive Isotope of Iodine**

A sample of the isotope ^{131}I, which has a half-life of 8.04 days, has an activity of 5.0 mCi at the time of shipment. Upon receipt in a medical laboratory, the activity is 4.2 mCi. How much time has elapsed between the two measurements?

Solution To conceptualize this problem, consider that the sample is continuously decaying as it is in transit. The decrease in the activity is 16% during the time interval between shipment and receipt, so we expect the elapsed time to be less than the half-life of 8.04 d. The stated activity corresponds to many decays per second, so N is large and we can categorize this problem as one in which we can use our statistical analysis of radioactivity. To analyze the problem, we use Equation 30.7 in the form

$$\frac{R}{R_0} = e^{-\lambda t}$$

where the sample is shipped at $t = 0$, at which time the activity is R_0. Taking the natural logarithm of each side, we have

$$\ln\left(\frac{R}{R_0}\right) = -\lambda t$$

$$t = -\frac{1}{\lambda} \ln\left(\frac{R}{R_0}\right) \quad (1)$$

To find λ, we use Equation 30.8:

$$\lambda = \frac{0.693}{T_{1/2}} = \frac{0.693}{8.04 \text{ d}} = 8.62 \times 10^{-2} \text{ d}^{-1} \quad (2)$$

Substituting (2) into (1) gives

$$t = -\left(\frac{1}{8.62 \times 10^{-2} \text{ d}^{-1}}\right) \ln\left(\frac{4.2 \text{ mCi}}{5.0 \text{ mCi}}\right) = \boxed{2.0 \text{ d}}$$

To finalize this problem, note that this value is indeed less than the half-life, as we expected. This problem demonstrates the difficulty in shipping radioactive samples with short half-lives. If the shipment were to be delayed by several days, only a small fraction of the sample would remain upon receipt. This difficulty can be addressed by shipping a combination of isotopes in which the desired isotope is the product of a decay occurring within the sample. It is possible for the desired isotope to be in *equilibrium*, in which case it is created at the same rate as it decays. Therefore, the amount of the desired isotope remains constant during the shipping process. Upon receipt, the desired isotope can be separated from the rest of the sample, and its decay from the initial activity begins upon receipt rather than upon shipment.

30.4 THE RADIOACTIVE DECAY PROCESSES

When one nucleus changes into another without external influence, the process is called **spontaneous decay**. As we stated in Section 30.3, a radioactive nucleus spontaneously decays by one of three processes: alpha decay, beta decay, or gamma decay. Active Figure 30.12 shows a close-up view of a portion of Figure 30.4 from $Z = 65$ to $Z = 80$. The blue circles are the stable nuclei seen in Figure 30.4. In addition, unstable nuclei above and below the line of stability for each value of Z are shown. Above the line of stability, the red circles show unstable nuclei that are neutron-rich and undergo a beta decay process in which an electron is emitted. Below the blue circles are green circles corresponding to proton-rich unstable nuclei that primarily undergo a beta decay process in which a positron is emitted or a competing process called electron capture. Beta decay and electron capture are described in more detail below. Further below the line of stability (with a few exceptions) are yellow circles that represent very proton-rich nuclei for which the primary decay mechanism is alpha decay, which we will discuss first.

Alpha Decay

If a nucleus emits an alpha particle ($^4_2$He) in a spontaneous decay, it loses two protons and two neutrons. Therefore, N decreases by 2, Z decreases by 2, and A decreases by 4. The **alpha decay** can be written with a symbolic representation as

$$^A_Z X \rightarrow {}^{A-4}_{Z-2} Y + {}^4_2 He \qquad [30.9]$$

where X is called the **parent nucleus** and Y the **daughter nucleus**. As general rules, (1) the sum of the mass numbers must be the same on both sides of the symbolic representation and (2) the sum of the atomic numbers must be the same on both sides. As examples, ^{238}U and ^{226}Ra are both alpha emitters and decay according to the schemes

$$^{238}_{92} U \rightarrow {}^{234}_{90} Th + {}^4_2 He \qquad [30.10]$$

$$^{226}_{88} Ra \rightarrow {}^{222}_{86} Rn + {}^4_2 He \qquad [30.11]$$

The half-life for ^{238}U decay is 4.47×10^9 years, and the half-life for ^{226}Ra decay is 1.60×10^3 years. In both cases, note that the mass number A of the daughter nucleus is 4 less than that of the parent nucleus. Likewise, the atomic number Z is reduced by 2.

The decay of ^{226}Ra is shown in Active Figure 30.13. In addition to the rules for the mass number and the atomic number, the total energy of the system must be conserved in the decay. If we call M_X the mass of the parent nucleus, M_Y the mass of the daughter nucleus, and M_α the mass of the alpha particle, we can define the **disintegration energy** Q:

$$Q \equiv (M_X - M_Y - M_\alpha) c^2 \qquad [30.12]$$

Note that the value of Q will be in joules if the masses are in kilograms and $c = 3.00 \times 10^8$ m/s. When the nuclear masses are expressed in the more convenient atomic mass unit u, however, the value of Q can be calculated in MeV units using the expression

$$Q = (M_X - M_Y - M_\alpha) \times 931.494 \text{ MeV/u} \qquad [30.13]$$

The disintegration energy Q represents the decrease in binding energy of the system and appears in the form of kinetic energy of the daughter nucleus and the alpha particle. In this nuclear example of the energy version of the isolated system model, no energy is entering or leaving the system. The energy in the system simply transforms from rest energy to kinetic energy, and Equation 30.13 gives the amount of energy transformed in the process. This quantity is sometimes referred to as the **Q value** of the nuclear reaction.

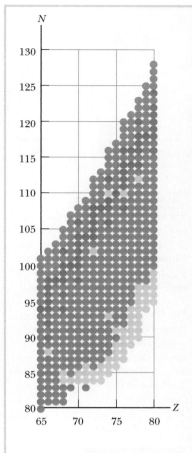

● Beta (electron)

● Stable

● Beta (positron) or electron capture

● Alpha

ACTIVE FIGURE 30.12

A close-up view of the line of stability in Figure 30.4 from $Z = 65$ to $Z = 80$. The blue dots represent stable nuclei as in Figure 30.4. The other colored dots represent unstable isotopes above and below the line of stability, with the color of the dot indicating the primary means of decay.

Physics⊗Now™ Study the decay modes and decay energies by logging into PhysicsNow at **www.pop4e.com** and going to Active Figure 30.12. Click on any of the colored dots to view information about the decay.

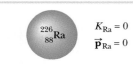

Before decay

After decay

ACTIVE FIGURE 30.13

The alpha decay of radium-226. The radium nucleus is initially at rest. After the decay, the radon nucleus has kinetic energy K_{Rn} and momentum $\vec{p}_{Rn}$, and the alpha particle has kinetic energy K_α and momentum $\vec{p}_\alpha$.

Physics⊗Now™ By logging into PhysicsNow at **www.pop4e.com** and going to Active Figure 30.13, you can observe the decay of radium-226. For a large number of decays, observe the development of the graph in Active Figure 30.14.

In addition to energy conservation, we can also apply the momentum version of the isolated system model to the decay. Because momentum of the isolated system must be conserved, the lighter alpha particle moves with a much higher speed than the daughter nucleus after the decay occurs. As a result, most of the available kinetic energy is associated with the alpha particle. Generally, light particles carry off most of the energy in nuclear decays.

Equation 30.13 suggests that the alpha particles are emitted with a discrete energy. Such an energy is calculated in Example 30.5. In practice, we find that alpha particles are emitted with a *set* of discrete energies (Active Fig. 30.14), with the *maximum* value calculated as in Example 30.5. This set of energies occurs because the energy of the nucleus is quantized, similar to the quantized energies in an atom. In Equation 30.13, we assume that the daughter nucleus is left in the ground state. If the daughter nucleus is left in an excited state, however, less energy is available for the decay and the alpha particle is emitted with less than the maximum kinetic energy. That the alpha particles have a discrete set of energies is direct evidence for the quantization of energy in the nucleus. This quantization is consistent with the model of a quantum particle under boundary conditions because the nucleons are quantum particles and they are subject to the constraints imposed by their mutual forces.

Finally, it is interesting to note that if one assumes that ^{238}U (or other alpha emitters) decays by emitting protons and neutrons, the mass of the decay products exceeds that of the parent nucleus, corresponding to negative Q values. Because that cannot occur for an isolated system, such spontaneous decays do not occur.

QUICK QUIZ 30.5 Which of the following is the correct daughter nucleus associated with the alpha decay of $^{157}_{72}$Hf? (a) $^{153}_{72}$Hf (b) $^{153}_{70}$Yb (c) $^{157}_{70}$Yb

EXAMPLE 30.5 | **The Energy Liberated When Radium Decays**

The ^{226}Ra nucleus undergoes alpha decay according to Equation 30.11. Calculate the Q value for this process.

Solution Using Equation 30.13 and the mass values in Table A.3 in Appendix A, we see that

$$Q = [M(^{226}\text{Ra}) - M(^{222}\text{Rn}) - M(^4\text{He})] \times 931.494 \text{ MeV/u}$$

$$= (226.025\ 403 \text{ u} - 222.017\ 570 \text{ u} - 4.002\ 603 \text{ u}) \times 931.494 \text{ MeV/u}$$

$$= (0.005\ 230 \text{ u}) \times (931.494 \text{ MeV/u}) = \boxed{4.87 \text{ MeV}}$$

It is left to Problem 30.49 to show that the kinetic energy of the alpha particle is about 4.8 MeV, whereas that of the recoiling daughter nucleus is only about 0.1 MeV.

PITFALL PREVENTION 30.5

ANOTHER Q We have seen the symbol Q before, but in this section we introduced a brand new meaning for this symbol: the disintegration energy. It is neither heat nor charge, for which we have used Q before.

We now turn to a structural model for the mechanism of alpha decay that allows some understanding of the decay process. Imagine that the alpha particle forms within the parent nucleus so that the parent nucleus is modeled as a system consisting of the alpha particle and the remaining daughter nucleus. Figure 30.15 is a graphical representation of the potential energy of this system as a function of the separation distance r between the alpha particle and the daughter nucleus. The distance R is the range of the nuclear force. The curve represents the combined effects of (1) the repulsive Coulomb force, which describes the curve for $r > R$, and (2) the attractive nuclear force, which causes the energy curve to be negative for $r < R$. As we saw in Example 30.5, a typical disintegration energy is a few MeV, which is the approximate kinetic energy of the emitted alpha particle, represented by the lower dotted line in Figure 30.15. According to classical physics, the alpha particle is trapped in the potential well. How, then, does it ever escape from the nucleus?

The answer to this question was provided by Gamow and, independently, Ronald Gurney and Edward Condon in 1928, using quantum mechanics. The view of quantum mechanics is that there is always some probability that the particle can *tunnel* through the barrier as we discussed in Section 28.13. Our model of the potential energy curve, combined with the possibility of tunneling, predicts that the probability of tunneling should increase as the particle energy increases because of the narrowing of the barrier for higher energies. This increased probability should be reflected as an increased activity and consequently a shorter half-life. Experimental data show just this relationship: nuclei with higher alpha particle energies have shorter half-lives. If the potential energy curve in Figure 30.15 is modeled as a series of square barriers whose heights vary with particle separation according to the curve, we can generate a theoretical relationship between particle energy and half-life that is in excellent agreement with the experimental results. This particular application of modeling and quantum physics is a very effective demonstration of the power of these approaches.

Beta Decay

When a radioactive nucleus undergoes **beta decay,** the daughter nucleus has the same number of nucleons as the parent nucleus, but the atomic number is changed by 1:

$$^{A}_{Z}\text{X} \quad \rightarrow \quad ^{A}_{Z+1}\text{Y} + \text{e}^{-} \qquad \text{(incomplete expression)} \qquad [30.14]$$

$$^{A}_{Z}\text{X} \quad \rightarrow \quad ^{A}_{Z-1}\text{Y} + \text{e}^{+} \qquad \text{(incomplete expression)} \qquad [30.15]$$

Again, note that nucleon number and total charge are both conserved in these decays. As we shall see later, however, these processes are not described completely by these expressions. We shall explain this incomplete description shortly.

The electron or positron involved in these decays is created within the nucleus as an initial step in the decay process. For example, during beta-minus decay, a neutron in the nucleus is transformed into a proton and an electron:

$$\text{n} \quad \rightarrow \quad \text{p} + \text{e}^{-} \qquad \text{(incomplete expression)}$$

For beta-plus decay, we have a proton transformed into a neutron and a positron:

$$\text{p} \quad \rightarrow \quad \text{n} + \text{e}^{+} \qquad \text{(incomplete expression)}$$

Outside the nucleus, this latter process will not occur because the neutron and electron have more total mass than the proton. This process can occur within the nucleus, however, because we consider the rest energy changes of the entire nuclear system, not just the individual particles. In beta-plus decay, the process $\text{p} \rightarrow \text{n} + \text{e}^{+}$ does indeed result in a decrease in the mass of the nucleus, so the process does occur spontaneously.

As with alpha decay, the energy of the isolated system of the nucleus and the emitted particle must be conserved in beta decay. Experimentally, one finds that the beta particles are emitted over a continuous range of energies (Active Fig. 30.16), unlike alpha particles, which are emitted with discrete energies (Active Fig. 30.14). The kinetic energy increase of the system must be balanced by the decrease in rest energy of the system; either of these changes is the Q value. Because all decaying nuclei have the same initial mass, however, **the Q value must be the same for each decay.** Then why do the emitted electrons have a range of kinetic energies? The energy version of the isolated system model seems to make an incorrect prediction! Further experimentation shows that, according to the decay processes given by Equations 30.14 and 30.15, the angular momentum (spin) and linear momentum versions of the isolated system model fail, too, and neither angular momentum nor linear momentum of the system is conserved!

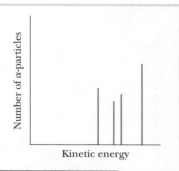

Distribution of alpha particle energies in a typical alpha decay. The energies of the alpha particles are discrete.

Physics ⊗ Now™ By logging into PhysicsNow at **www.pop4e.com** and going to Active Figure 30.14, you can observe the development of this graph for the decay in Active Figure 30.13.

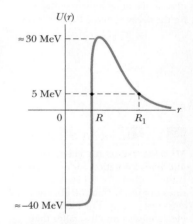

FIGURE 30.15 Potential energy versus separation distance for a system consisting of an alpha particle and a daughter nucleus. Classically, the energy associated with the alpha particle is not sufficiently large to overcome the energy barrier and so the particle should not be able to escape the nucleus. In reality, the alpha particle does escape by tunneling through the barrier.

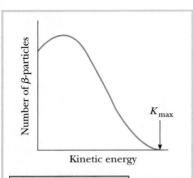

Clearly, the structural model for beta decay must differ from that for alpha decay. After a great deal of experimental and theoretical study, Pauli proposed in 1930 that a third particle must be involved in the decay to account for the "missing" energy and momentum. Enrico Fermi later named this particle the **neutrino** (little neutral one) because it has to be electrically neutral and have little or no rest energy. Although it eluded detection for many years, the neutrino (symbolized by ν) was finally detected experimentally in 1956 by Frederick Reines and Clyde Cowan. It has the following properties:

- It has zero electric charge.
- Its mass is much smaller than that of the electron. Recent experiments show that the mass of the neutrino is not 0 but is less than 2.8 eV/c^2.
- It has a spin of $\frac{1}{2}$, which allows the law of conservation of angular momentum to be satisfied in beta decay.
- It interacts very weakly with matter and is therefore very difficult to detect.

We can now write the beta decay processes (Eqs. 30.14 and 30.15) in their correct form:

$$^A_Z X \rightarrow \ ^A_{Z+1} Y + e^- + \bar{\nu} \qquad \text{(complete expression)} \qquad [30.16]$$

$$^A_Z X \rightarrow \ ^A_{Z-1} Y + e^+ + \nu \qquad \text{(complete expression)} \qquad [30.17]$$

where $\bar{\nu}$ represents the **antineutrino,** the antiparticle to the neutrino. We shall discuss antiparticles further in Chapter 31. For now, it suffices to say that **a neutrino is emitted in positron decay, and an antineutrino is emitted in electron decay.** The spin of the neutrino allows angular momentum to be conserved in the decay processes. Despite its small mass, the neutrino does carry momentum, which allows linear momentum to be conserved.

The decays of the neutron and proton within the nucleus are more properly written as

$$n \rightarrow p + e^- + \bar{\nu} \qquad \text{(complete expression)}$$

$$p \rightarrow n + e^+ + \nu \qquad \text{(complete expression)}$$

As examples of beta decay, we can write the decay schemes for carbon-14 and nitrogen-12:

$$^{14}_6 C \rightarrow \ ^{14}_7 N + e^- + \bar{\nu} \qquad \text{(complete expression)} \qquad [30.18]$$

$$^{12}_7 N \rightarrow \ ^{12}_6 C + e^+ + \nu \qquad \text{(complete expression)} \qquad [30.19]$$

Active Figure 30.17 shows a pictorial representation of the decays described by Equations 30.18 and 30.19.

$^{14}_6 C$ $K_C = 0$ $\vec{\mathbf{P}}_C = 0$

Before decay

K_{e^-} $\vec{\mathbf{P}}_{e^-}$

Electron

K_N

$^{14}_7 N$

$\vec{\mathbf{P}}_N$

Antineutrino

After decay $\vec{\mathbf{P}}_{\bar{\nu}}$ $K_{\bar{\nu}}$

(a)

$^{12}_7 N$ $K_N = 0$ $\vec{\mathbf{P}}_N = 0$

Before decay

K_{e^+} $\vec{\mathbf{P}}_{e^+}$

Positron

K_C

$^{12}_6 C$

$\vec{\mathbf{P}}_C$

Neutrino

After decay $\vec{\mathbf{P}}_{\nu}$ K_{ν}

(b)

In beta-plus decay, the final system consists of the daughter nucleus, the ejected positron and neutrino, and an electron shed from the atom to neutralize the daughter atom. In some cases, this process represents an overall increase in rest energy, so it does not occur. There is an alternative process that allows some proton-rich nuclei to decay and become more stable. This process, called **electron capture,** occurs when a parent nucleus captures one of its own orbital electrons and emits a neutrino. The final product after decay is a nucleus whose charge is $Z - 1$:

$$_{Z}^{A}X + e^- \rightarrow \ _{Z-1}^{A}Y + \nu \qquad [30.20]$$

■ Electron capture process

In most cases, an inner K-shell electron is captured, a process referred to as **K capture.** In this process, the only outgoing particles are the neutrino and x-ray photons, originating in higher-shell electrons falling into the vacancy left by the captured K electron.

> **QUICK QUIZ 30.6** Which of the following is the correct daughter nucleus associated with the beta decay of $_{72}^{184}$Hf? (a) $_{72}^{183}$Hf (b) $_{73}^{183}$Ta (c) $_{73}^{184}$Ta

Carbon Dating

The beta decay of ^{14}C given by Equation 30.18 is commonly used to date organic samples. Cosmic rays (high-energy particles from outer space) in the upper atmosphere cause nuclear reactions that create ^{14}C. The ratio of ^{14}C to ^{12}C in the carbon dioxide molecules of our atmosphere has a constant value of about 1.3×10^{-12}. All living organisms have the same ratio of ^{14}C to ^{12}C because they continuously exchange carbon dioxide with their surroundings. When an organism dies, however, it no longer absorbs ^{14}C from the atmosphere, and so the ratio of ^{14}C to ^{12}C decreases as the result of the beta decay of ^{14}C, which has a half-life of 5 730 yr. It is therefore possible to determine the age of a biological sample by measuring its activity per unit mass due to the decay of ^{14}C. Using carbon dating, samples of wood, charcoal, bone, and shell have been identified as having lived 1 000 to 25 000 yr ago.

A particularly interesting example is the dating of the Dead Sea Scrolls, a group of manuscripts discovered by a shepherd in 1947 (Fig. 30.18). Translation showed them to be religious documents, including most of the books of the Old Testament. Because of their historical and religious significance, scholars wanted to know their age. Carbon dating applied to the material in which they were wrapped established their age at approximately 1 950 yr.

 Carbon dating

(© CORBIS)

ENRICO FERMI (1901–1954)

An Italian physicist who immigrated to the United States to escape the Fascists, Fermi was awarded the Nobel Prize in Physics in 1938 for producing the transuranic elements by neutron irradiation and for his discovery of nuclear reactions brought about by slow neutrons. He made many other outstanding contributions to physics including his theory of beta decay, the free electron theory of metals, and the development of the world's first fission reactor in 1942. Fermi was truly a gifted theoretical and experimental physicist. He was also well known for his ability to present physics in a clear and exciting manner. He wrote, "Whatever Nature has in store for mankind, unpleasant as it may be, men must accept, for ignorance is never better than knowledge."

(Corbis SYGMA)

(a)

(M. Milner/Corbis SYGMA)

(b)

FIGURE 30.18 (a) A fragment of the Dead Sea Scrolls, which were discovered in the caves in the photograph (b). The packing material of the scrolls was analyzed by carbon dating to determine their age.

■ Thinking Physics 30.3

In 1991, a German tourist discovered the well-preserved remains of the Ice Man trapped in a glacier in the Italian Alps, shown in the opening photograph for this chapter. Radioactive dating of a sample of the Ice Man revealed an age of 5 300 yr. Why did scientists date the sample using the isotope ^{14}C rather than ^{11}C, a beta emitter with a half-life of 20.4 min?

Reasoning ^{14}C has a long half-life of 5 730 yr, so the fraction of ^{14}C nuclei remaining after one half-life is high enough to measure accurate changes in the sample's activity. The ^{11}C isotope, which has a very short half-life, is not useful because its activity decreases to a vanishingly small value over 5 300 yr, making it impossible to detect.

An isotope used to date a sample must be present in a known amount in the sample when it is formed. As a general rule, the isotope chosen to date a sample should also have a half-life with the same order of magnitude as the age of the sample. If the half-life is much less than the age of the sample, there won't be enough activity left to measure because almost all the original radioactive nuclei will have decayed. If the half-life is much greater than the age of the sample, the reduction in activity that has taken place since the sample died will be too small to measure. ■

INTERACTIVE EXAMPLE 30.6 **Radioactive Dating**

A piece of charcoal of mass 25.0 g is found in the ruins of an ancient city. The sample shows a ^{14}C activity of 250 decays/min. How long has the tree from which this charcoal came been dead?

Solution We begin by calculating the decay constant for ^{14}C, which has a half-life of 5 730 yr:

$$\lambda = \frac{0.693}{T_{1/2}} = \frac{0.693}{(5\ 730\ \text{yr})(3.16 \times 10^7\ \text{s/yr})}$$
$$= 3.83 \times 10^{-12}\ \text{s}^{-1}$$

The number of ^{14}C nuclei can be calculated in two steps. First, the number of ^{12}C nuclei in 25 g of carbon is

$$N(^{12}\text{C}) = \frac{6.02 \times 10^{23}\ \text{nuclei/mol}}{12.0\ \text{g/mol}}\ (25.0\ \text{g})$$
$$= 1.25 \times 10^{24}\ \text{nuclei}$$

Assuming that the initial ratio of ^{14}C to ^{12}C was 1.3×10^{-12}, we see that the number of ^{14}C nuclei in 25.0 g *before* decay is

$$N_0(^{14}\text{C}) = (1.3 \times 10^{-12})(1.25 \times 10^{24})$$
$$= 1.6 \times 10^{12}\ \text{nuclei}$$

Hence, the initial activity of the sample is

$$R_0 = \lambda N_0 = (3.83 \times 10^{-12}\ \text{s}^{-1})(1.6 \times 10^{12}\ \text{nuclei})$$
$$= 6.13\ \text{decays/s} = 368\ \text{decays/min}$$

We can now calculate the age of the charcoal using Equation 30.7, which relates the activity R at any time t to the initial activity R_0:

$$R = R_0 e^{-\lambda t} \quad \text{or} \quad e^{-\lambda t} = \frac{R}{R_0}$$

Because it is given that $R = 250$ decays/min and because we found that $R_0 = 368$ decays/min, we can calculate t by taking the natural logarithm of both sides of the last equation:

$$-\lambda t = \ln\left(\frac{R}{R_0}\right) = \ln\left(\frac{250}{368}\right) = -0.39$$

$$t = \frac{0.39}{\lambda} = \frac{0.39}{3.83 \times 10^{-12}\ \text{s}^{-1}}$$
$$= 1.0 \times 10^{11}\ \text{s} = \boxed{3.2 \times 10^3\ \text{yr}}$$

Physics⊗Now™ Practice using carbon dating on samples by logging into PhysicsNow at **www.pop4e.com** and going to Interactive Example 30.6.

Gamma Decay

Very often, a nucleus that undergoes radioactive decay is left in an excited quantum state. The nucleus can then undergo a second decay, **a gamma decay,** to a lower state, perhaps to the ground state, by emitting a photon:

■ Gamma decay

$$^A_Z\text{X*} \rightarrow\ ^A_Z\text{X} + \gamma \qquad\qquad [30.21]$$

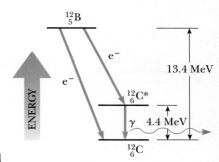

TABLE 30.2	Various Decay Pathways
Alpha decay	$^A_Z X \rightarrow ^{A-4}_{Z-2} Y + ^4_2 He$
Beta decay (e^-)	$^A_Z X \rightarrow ^A_{Z+1} Y + e^- + \bar{\nu}$
Beta decay (e^+)	$^A_Z X \rightarrow ^A_{Z-1} Y + e^+ + \nu$
Electron capture	$^A_Z X + e^- \rightarrow ^A_{Z-1} Y + \nu$
Gamma decay	$^A_Z X^* \rightarrow ^A_Z X + \gamma$

FIGURE 30.19 An energy level diagram showing the initial nuclear state of a ^{12}B nucleus and two possible lower-energy states of the ^{12}C nucleus. The beta decay of the ^{12}B nucleus can result in either of two situations, with the ^{12}C nucleus in the ground state or in the excited state, in which case the nucleus is denoted as ^{12}C*. In the latter case, the beta decay to ^{12}C* is followed by a gamma decay to ^{12}C as the excited nucleus makes a transition to the ground state.

where X* indicates a nucleus in an excited state. The typical half-life of an excited nuclear state is 10^{-10} s. Photons emitted in such a de-excitation process are called **gamma rays.** Such photons have very high energy (on the order of 1 MeV or higher) relative to the energy of visible light (on the order of a few electron volts). Recall from Chapter 29 that the energy of photons emitted (or absorbed) by an atom equals the difference in energy between the two atomic quantum states involved in the transition. Similarly, a gamma ray photon has an energy hf that equals the energy difference ΔE between two nuclear quantum states. When a nucleus decays by emitting a gamma ray, it ends up in a lower state, but its atomic mass A and atomic number Z do not change.

A nucleus may reach an excited state as the result of a violent collision with another particle. It is more common, however, for a nucleus to be in an excited state after it has undergone an alpha or beta decay. The following sequence of events represents a typical situation in which gamma decay occurs:

$$^{12}_5 B \rightarrow ^{12}_6 C^* + e^- + \bar{\nu} \qquad [30.22]$$

$$^{12}_6 C^* \rightarrow ^{12}_6 C + \gamma \qquad [30.23]$$

Figure 30.19 shows the decay scheme for ^{12}B, which undergoes beta decay with a half-life of 20.4 ms to either of two levels of ^{12}C. It can either (1) decay directly to the ground state of ^{12}C by emitting a 13.4-MeV electron or (2) undergo beta-minus decay to an excited state of ^{12}C*, followed by gamma decay to the ground state. The latter process results in the emission of a 9.0-MeV electron and a 4.4-MeV photon. Table 30.2 summarizes the pathways by which radioactive nuclei undergo decay.

30.5 | NUCLEAR REACTIONS

In Section 30.4, we discussed the processes by which nuclei can *spontaneously* change to another nucleus by undergoing a radioactive decay process. It is also possible to change the structures and properties of nuclei by bombarding them with energetic particles. Such changes are called **nuclear reactions.** In 1919, Rutherford was the first to observe nuclear reactions, using naturally occurring radioactive sources for the bombarding particles. Since then, thousands of nuclear reactions have been observed following the development of charged-particle accelerators in the 1930s. With today's advanced technology in particle accelerators and particle detectors, it is possible to achieve particle energies of more than $1\,000$ GeV = 1 TeV. These high-energy particles are used to create new particles whose properties are helping solve the mysteries of the nucleus.

Consider a reaction (Fig. 30.20) in which a target nucleus X is bombarded by an incoming particle a, resulting in a different nucleus Y and an outgoing particle b:

$$a + X \rightarrow Y + b \qquad [30.24]$$

Sometimes this reaction is written in the equivalent symbolic representation

$$X(a, b)Y$$

In the preceding section, the Q value, or disintegration energy, associated with radioactive decay was defined as the change in the rest energy, which is the amount

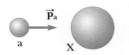

Before reaction

After reaction

FIGURE 30.20 A nuclear reaction. Before the reaction, an incoming particle a moves toward a target nucleus X. After the reaction, the target nucleus has changed to nucleus Y and an outgoing particle b moves away from the reaction site.

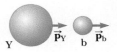

■ Nuclear reaction

of the rest energy transformed to kinetic energy during the decay process. In a similar way, we define the **reaction energy** Q associated with a nuclear reaction as the **total change in rest energy that results from the reaction:**

$$Q = (M_a + M_X - M_Y - M_b)c^2 \qquad [30.25]$$

A reaction for which Q is positive is called **exothermic.** After the reaction, the transformed rest energy appears as an increase in kinetic energy of Y and b over that of a and X.

A reaction for which Q is negative is called **endothermic** and represents an increase in rest energy. An endothermic reaction will not occur unless the bombarding particle has a kinetic energy greater than $|Q|$. The minimum kinetic energy of the incoming particle necessary for such a reaction to occur is called the **threshold energy.** The threshold energy is larger than $|Q|$ because we must also conserve linear momentum in the isolated system of the initial and final particles. If an incoming particle has just energy $|Q|$, enough energy is present to increase the rest energy of the system, but none is left over for kinetic energy of the final particles, that is, nothing is moving after the reaction. Therefore, the incoming particle has momentum before the reaction but there is no momentum of the system afterward, which is a violation of the law of conservation of momentum.

If particles a and b in a nuclear reaction are identical so that X and Y are also necessarily identical, the reaction is called a **scattering event.** If the kinetic energy of the system (a and X) before the event is the same as that of the system (b and Y) after the event, it is classified as *elastic scattering.* If the kinetic energies of the system before and after the event are not the same, the reaction is described as *inelastic scattering.* In this case, the difference in energy is accounted for by the target nucleus being raised to an excited state by the event. The final system now consists of b and an excited nucleus Y*, and eventually it will become b, Y, and γ, where γ is the gamma-ray photon that is emitted when the system returns to the ground state. This elastic and inelastic terminology is identical to that used in describing collisions between macroscopic objects (Section 8.3).

In addition to energy and momentum, the total charge and total number of nucleons must be conserved in the system of particles for a nuclear reaction. For example, consider the reaction $^{19}\text{F}(p, \alpha)^{16}\text{O}$, which has a Q value of 8.124 MeV. We can show this reaction more completely as

$$^{1}_{1}\text{H} + {}^{19}_{9}\text{F} \;\rightarrow\; {}^{16}_{8}\text{O} + {}^{4}_{2}\text{He}$$

We see that the total number of nucleons before the reaction $(1 + 19 = 20)$ is equal to the total number after the reaction $(16 + 4 = 20)$. Furthermore, the total charge $(Z = 10)$ is the same before and after the reaction.

30.6 | THE ENGINE OF THE STARS

One of the important features of nuclear reactions is that much more energy is released (i.e., converted from rest energy) than in normal chemical reactions such as in the burning of fossil fuels. Let us look back at our binding energy curve (see Fig. 30.9) and consider two important nuclear reactions that relate to that curve. If a heavy nucleus at the right of the graph splits into two lighter nuclei, the total binding energy within the system increases, representing energy released from the nuclei. This type of reaction was observed and reported in 1939 by Otto Hahn and Fritz Strassman. This reaction, known as **fission,** was of great scientific and political interest at the time of World War II because of the development of the first nuclear weapon.

In the fission reaction, a fissionable nucleus (the target nucleus X), which is often ^{235}U, absorbs a slowly moving neutron (the incoming particle a) and the nucleus splits into two smaller nuclei (two nuclei Y_1 and Y_2), releasing energy and

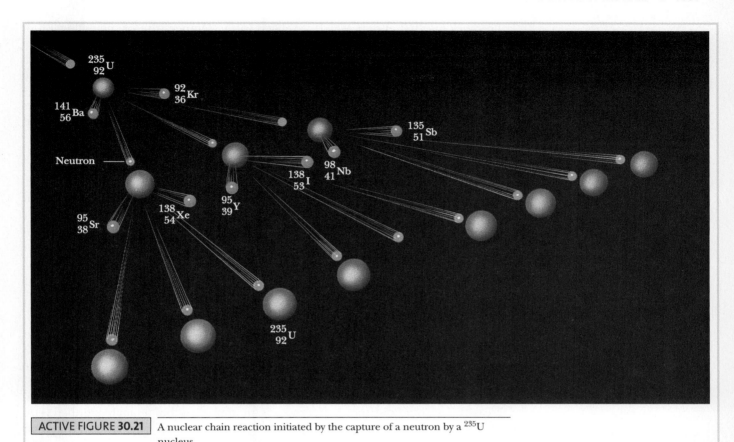

ACTIVE FIGURE 30.21 | A nuclear chain reaction initiated by the capture of a neutron by a ^{235}U nucleus.

Physics ⊗ Now™ By logging into PhysicsNow at **www.pop4e.com** and going to Active Figure 30.21, you can observe the chain reaction.

more neutrons (several particles b). These neutrons can then go on to be absorbed within other nuclei, causing other fissions. With no means of control, the result is a chain reaction explosion as suggested by Active Figure 30.21. With proper control, the fission process is used in nuclear power generating stations.

Examining the other end of the binding energy curve, we see that we could also increase the binding energy of the system and release energy by combining two light nuclei. This process of **fusion** is made difficult because the nuclei must overcome a very strong Coulomb repulsion before they become close enough together to fuse. One way to assist the nuclei in overcoming this repulsion is to cause them to move with very high kinetic energy by raising the system of nuclei to a very high temperature. If the density of nuclei is high also, the probability of nuclei colliding is high and fusion can occur. The technological problem of creating very high temperatures and densities is a major challenge in the area of Earth-based controlled fusion research.

At some natural locations (e.g., the cores of stars), the necessary high temperatures and densities exist. Consider a collection of gas and dust somewhere in the Universe to be an isolated system. What happens as this system collapses under its own gravitational attraction? Energy of the system is conserved, and the gravitational potential energy associated with the separated particles decreases while the kinetic energy of the particles increases, just like a falling ball with cosmic particles "falling" into a gravitational center. As the falling particles collide with the particles that have already fallen into the central region of collapse, their kinetic energy is distributed to the other particles by collisions and randomized; it becomes internal energy, which is related to the temperature of the collection of particles.

If the temperature and density of the system's core rise to the point where fusion can occur, the system becomes a star. The primary constituent of the Universe is hydrogen, so the fusion reaction at the center of a star combines hydrogen nuclei—protons—into helium nuclei. A common reaction process for stars with relatively cool cores ($T < 15 \times 10^6$ K) is the **proton–proton cycle.** In the first step of the process, two protons combine to form deuterium:

$$^1_1\text{H} + \,^1_1\text{H} \rightarrow \,^2_1\text{H} + e^+ + \nu$$

Notice the implicit ^2_2H nucleus that is formed but that does not appear in the reaction equation. This nucleus is highly unstable and decays very rapidly by beta-plus decay to the deuterium nucleus, a positron and a neutrino.

In the next step, the deuterium nucleus undergoes fusion with another proton to form a helium-3 nucleus:

$$^1_1\text{H} + \,^2_1\text{H} \rightarrow \,^3_2\text{He} + \gamma$$

Finally, two helium-3 nuclei formed in such reactions can fuse to form helium-4 and two protons:

$$^3_2\text{He} + \,^3_2\text{He} \rightarrow \,^4_2\text{He} + \,^1_1\text{H} + \,^1_1\text{H}$$

The net result of this cycle has been the joining of four protons to form a helium-4 nucleus, with the release of energy that eventually leaves the star as electromagnetic radiation from its surface. In addition, notice that the reaction releases neutrinos, which serve as a signal for beta decay occurring within the star. The observation of increased neutrino flow from a supernova is an important tool in analyzing the event.

For stars with hotter cores ($T > 15 \times 10^6$ K), another process, called the **carbon cycle,** dominates. At such high temperatures, hydrogen nuclei can fuse into nuclei heavier than helium such as carbon. In the first of six steps in the cycle, a carbon nucleus fuses with a proton to form nitrogen:

$$^1_1\text{H} + \,^{12}_6\text{C} \rightarrow \,^{13}_7\text{N}$$

The nitrogen nucleus is proton-rich and undergoes beta-plus decay:

$$^{13}_7\text{N} \rightarrow \,^{13}_6\text{C} + e^+ + \nu$$

The resulting carbon-13 nucleus fuses with another proton, with the emission of a gamma ray:

$$^1_1\text{H} + \,^{13}_6\text{C} \rightarrow \,^{14}_7\text{N} + \gamma$$

The nitrogen-14 fuses with another proton, with more gamma emission:

$$^1_1\text{H} + \,^{14}_7\text{N} \rightarrow \,^{15}_8\text{O} + \gamma$$

The oxygen nucleus undergoes beta-plus decay:

$$^{15}_8\text{O} \rightarrow \,^{15}_7\text{N} + e^+ + \nu$$

Finally, the nitrogen-15 fuses with another proton:

$$^1_1\text{H} + \,^{15}_7\text{N} \rightarrow \,^{12}_6\text{C} + \,^4_2\text{He}$$

Notice that the net effect of this process is to combine four protons into a helium nucleus, just like the proton–proton cycle. The carbon-12 with which we began the process is returned at the end, so it acts only as a catalyst to the process and is not consumed.

Depending on its mass, a star transforms energy in its core at a rate between 10^{23} and 10^{33} W. The energy transformed from the rest energy of the nuclei in the core is transferred outward through the surrounding layers by matter transfer in two forms. First, neutrinos carry energy directly through these layers to space because these particles interact only weakly with matter. Second, energy carried by photons from the core is absorbed by the gases in layers outside the core and slowly works its way to the surface by convection. This energy is eventually radiated from the surface of the star by electromagnetic radiation, mostly in the infrared, visible, and ultraviolet regions of the electromagnetic spectrum. The weight of the layers outside the core keeps the core from exploding. The whole system of a star is stable as long as the supply of hydrogen in the core lasts.

In the previous chapters, we presented examples of the applications of quantum physics and atomic physics to processes in space. In this chapter, we have seen that nuclear processes also have an important role in the cosmos. The formation of stars is a critical process in the development of the Universe. The energy provided by stars is crucial to life on planets such as the Earth. In our next, and final, chapter, we shall discuss the processes that occur on an even smaller scale, the scale of *elementary particles*. We shall find again that looking at a smaller scale allows us to advance our understanding of the largest scale system, the Universe.

SUMMARY

Physics ⊗ Now™ Take a practice test by logging into Physics-Now at **www.pop4e.com** and clicking on the Pre-Test link for this chapter.

A nuclear species can be represented by $^A_Z X$, where A is the **mass number,** the total number of nucleons, and Z is the **atomic number,** the total number of protons. The total number of neutrons in a nucleus is the **neutron number** N, where $A = N + Z$. Elements with the same Z but different A and N values are called **isotopes.**

Assuming that a nucleus is spherical, its radius is

$$r = r_0 A^{1/3} \qquad [30.1]$$

where $r_0 = 1.2$ fm.

Nuclei are stable because of the **nuclear force** between nucleons. This short-range force dominates the Coulomb repulsive force at distances of less than about 2 fm and is independent of charge.

Light nuclei are most stable when the number of protons equals the number of neutrons. Heavy nuclei are most stable when the number of neutrons exceeds the number of protons. In addition, many stable nuclei have Z and N values that are both even. Nuclei with unusually high stability have Z or N values of 2, 8, 20, 28, 50, 82, and 126, called **magic numbers.**

Nuclei have an intrinsic angular momentum (spin) of magnitude $\sqrt{I(I + 1)}\,\hbar$, where I is the **nuclear spin quantum number.** The magnetic moment of a nucleus is measured in terms of the **nuclear magneton** μ_n, where

$$\mu_n \equiv \frac{e\hbar}{2m_p} = 5.05 \times 10^{-27}\, \text{J/T} \qquad [30.3]$$

The difference in mass between the separate nucleons and the nucleus containing these nucleons, when multiplied by c^2, gives the **binding energy** E_b of the nucleus. We can calculate the binding energy of any nucleus $^A_Z X$ using the expression

$$E_b(\text{MeV}) = [ZM(\text{H}) + Nm_n - M(^A_Z X)] \times 931.494\ \text{MeV/u} \qquad [30.4]$$

Radioactive processes include alpha decay, beta decay, and gamma decay. An alpha particle is a ^{4}He nucleus, a beta particle is either an electron (e^-) or a positron (e^+), and a gamma particle is a high-energy photon.

If a radioactive material contains N_0 radioactive nuclei at $t = 0$, the number N of nuclei remaining at time t is

$$N = N_0 e^{-\lambda t} \qquad [30.6]$$

where λ is the **decay constant,** or **disintegration constant.** The **decay rate,** or **activity,** of a radioactive substance is given by

$$R = \left| \frac{dN}{dt} \right| = N_0 \lambda e^{-\lambda t} = R_0 e^{-\lambda t} \qquad [30.7]$$

where $R_0 = N_0 \lambda$ is the activity at $t = 0$. The **half-life** $T_{1/2}$ is defined as the time interval required for half of a given number of radioactive nuclei to decay, where

$$T_{1/2} = \frac{\ln 2}{\lambda} = \frac{0.693}{\lambda} \qquad [30.8]$$

Alpha decay can occur because according to quantum mechanics some nuclei have barriers that can be penetrated by the alpha particles (the tunneling process). This process is energetically more favorable for those nuclei having large excesses of neutrons. A nucleus can undergo **beta decay** in two ways. It can emit either an electron (e^-) and an antineutrino ($\bar{\nu}$) or a positron (e^+) and a neutrino (ν). In the **electron capture** process, the nucleus of an atom absorbs one of its own electrons (usually from the K shell) and emits a neutrino. In **gamma decay,** a nucleus in an excited state decays to its ground state and emits a gamma ray.

Nuclear reactions can occur when a target nucleus X is bombarded by a particle a, resulting in a nucleus Y and an outgoing particle b:

$$a + X \ \rightarrow \ Y + b \qquad \text{or} \qquad X(a, b)Y \qquad [30.24]$$

The rest energy transformed to kinetic energy in such a reaction, called the **reaction energy** Q, is

$$Q = (M_a + M_X - M_Y - M_b)c^2 \qquad [30.25]$$

A reaction for which Q is positive is called **exothermic.** A reaction for which Q is negative is called **endothermic.** The minimum kinetic energy of the incoming particle necessary for such a reaction to occur is called the **threshold energy.**

QUESTIONS

[ ] = answer available in the *Student Solutions Manual and Study Guide*

1. In Rutherford's experiment, assume that an alpha particle is headed directly toward the nucleus of an atom. Why doesn't the alpha particle make physical contact with the nucleus?

2. Why are very heavy nuclei unstable?

[3.] Why do nearly all the naturally occurring isotopes lie above the $N = Z$ line in Figure 30.4?

4. Explain why nuclei that are well off the line of stability in Figure 30.4 tend to be unstable.

5. From Table A.3 in Appendix A, identify the four stable nuclei that have magic numbers in both Z and N.

6. If a nucleus has a half-life of 1 year, does that mean that its whole life is 2 years? Will it be completely decayed after 2 years? Explain.

[7.] Two samples of the same radioactive nuclide are prepared. Sample A has twice the initial activity of sample B. How does the half-life of A compare with the half-life of B? After each has passed through five half-lives, what is the ratio of their activities?

8. "If no more people were to be born, the law of population growth would strongly resemble the radioactive decay law." Discuss this statement.

[9.] If a nucleus such as ^{226}Ra initially at rest undergoes alpha decay, which has more kinetic energy after the decay, the alpha particle or the daughter nucleus?

10. Can a nucleus emit alpha particles that have different energies? Explain.

[11.] Suppose it could be shown that the cosmic ray intensity at the Earth's surface was much greater 10 000 years ago. How would this difference affect what we accept as valid carbon-dated values of the age of ancient samples of once-living matter?

12. Explain why many heavy nuclei undergo alpha decay but do not spontaneously emit neutrons or protons.

13. Do all natural events have causes? Is the Universe intelligible? Give reasons for your answers. (*Note:* You may wish to consider again Question 5.17 in Chapter 5 on whether the future is determinate.)

14. Discuss the similarities and differences between fusion and fission.

15. *And swift, and swift past comprehension*
    Turn round Earth's beauty and her might.
    The heavens blaze in alternation
    With deep and chill and rainy night.
    In mighty currents foams the ocean
    Up from the rocks' abyssal base,
    With rock and sea torn into motion
    In ever-swift celestial race.
    Corrosive, choking smoke is spraying.
    Above infernos, lava flies.
    A perilous bridge, the land is swaying
    Between them and the gaping skies.
    And tempests bluster in a contest
    From sea to land, from land to sea.
    In rage they forge a chain around us
    Of primal meaning, energy.
    There flames a lightning disaster
    Before the thunder, in its way.
    But all Your servants honor, Master,
    The gentle order of Your day.

    Johann Wolfgang von Goethe wrote the song of the archangels in *Faust* half a century before the law of conservation of energy was recognized. Students often find it useful to think of a list of several "forms of energy," from kinetic to nuclear. Argue for or against the view that these lines of poetry make an obvious or oblique reference to every form of energy and energy transfer.

PROBLEMS

1, 2, 3 = straightforward, intermediate, challenging

[ ] = full solution available in the *Student Solutions Manual and Study Guide*

Physics⊗Now™ = coached problem with hints available at **www.pop4e.com**

🖥 = computer useful in solving problem

▬ = paired numerical and symbolic problems

🦓 = biomedical application

Note: Atomic masses are listed in Table A.3 in Appendix A.

Section 30.1 ∎ Some Properties of Nuclei

1. What is the order of magnitude of the number of protons in your body? Of the number of neutrons? Of the number of electrons?

2. **Review problem.** Singly ionized carbon is accelerated through 1 000 V and passed into a mass spectrometer to determine the isotopes present (see Chapter 22). The magnitude of the magnetic field in the spectrometer is 0.200 T. (a) Determine the orbit radii for the ^{12}C and the ^{13}C isotopes as they pass through the field. (b) Show that the ratio of radii may be written in the form

$$\frac{r_1}{r_2} = \sqrt{\frac{m_1}{m_2}}$$

and verify that your radii in part (a) agree with this equation.

3. In a Rutherford scattering experiment, alpha particles having kinetic energy of 7.70 MeV are fired toward a gold nucleus. (a) Use energy conservation to determine the distance of closest approach between the alpha particle and gold nucleus. Assume that the nucleus remains at rest.

(b) Calculate the de Broglie wavelength for the 7.70-MeV alpha particle and compare it with the distance obtained in part (a). (c) Based on this comparison, why is it proper to treat the alpha particle as a particle and not as a wave in the Rutherford scattering experiment?

4. Find the radius of (a) a nucleus of $_2^4$He and (b) a nucleus of $_{92}^{238}$U.

5. A star ending its life with a mass of two times the mass of the Sun is expected to collapse, combining its protons and electrons to form a neutron star. Such a star could be thought of as a gigantic atomic nucleus. If a star of mass $2 \times 1.99 \times 10^{30}$ kg collapsed into neutrons ($m_n = 1.67 \times 10^{-27}$ kg), what would its radius be? (Assume that $r = r_0 A^{1/3}$.)

6. Review problem. What would be the gravitational force exerted by each of two golf balls on the other, if they were made of nuclear matter? Assume that each has a 4.30-cm diameter and that the balls are 1.00 m apart.

7. The radio frequency at which a nucleus displays resonance absorption between spin states is called the Larmor precessional frequency and is given by

$$f = \frac{\Delta E}{h} = \frac{2\mu B}{h}$$

Calculate the Larmor frequency for (a) free neutrons in a magnetic field of 1.00 T, (b) free protons in a magnetic field of 1.00 T, and (c) free protons in the Earth's magnetic field at a location where the magnitude of the field is 50.0 μT.

Section 30.2 ∎ Binding Energy

8. Calculate the binding energy per nucleon for (a) ^{2}H, (b) ^{4}He, (c) ^{56}Fe, and (d) ^{238}U.

9. **Physics⊗Now™** A pair of nuclei for which $Z_1 = N_2$ and $Z_2 = N_1$ are called *mirror isobars* (the atomic and neutron numbers are interchanged). Binding energy measurements on these nuclei can be used to obtain evidence of the charge independence of nuclear forces (i.e., proton–proton, proton–neutron, and neutron–neutron nuclear forces are equal). Calculate the difference in binding energy for the two mirror isobars $_8^{15}$O and $_7^{15}$N. The electric repulsion among eight protons rather than seven accounts for the difference.

10. Nuclei having the same mass numbers are called *isobars*. The isotope $_{57}^{139}$La is stable. The radioactive isobar $_{59}^{139}$Pr is located below the line of stable nuclei in Figure 30.4 and decays by e^+ emission. Another radioactive isobar of $_{57}^{139}$La, $_{55}^{139}$Cs, decays by e^- emission and is located above the line of stable nuclei in Figure 30.4. (a) Which of these three isobars has the highest neutron-to-proton ratio? (b) Which has the greatest binding energy per nucleon? (c) Which do you expect to be heavier, $_{59}^{139}$Pr or $_{55}^{139}$Cs?

11. Using the graph in Figure 30.9, estimate how much energy is released when a nucleus of mass number 200 fissions into two nuclei each of mass number 100.

Section 30.3 ∎ Radioactivity

12. The half-life of ^{131}I is 8.04 days. On a certain day, the activity of an iodine-131 sample is 6.40 mCi. What is its activity 40.2 days later?

13. **Physics⊗Now™** A freshly prepared sample of a certain radioactive isotope has an activity of 10.0 mCi. After 4.00 h, its activity is 8.00 mCi. (a) Find the decay constant and half-life. (b) How many atoms of the isotope were contained in the freshly prepared sample? (c) What is the sample's activity 30.0 h after it is prepared?

14. A sample of radioactive material contains 1.00×10^{15} atoms and has an activity of 6.00×10^{11} Bq. What is its half-life?

15. What time interval elapses while 90.0% of the radioactivity of a sample of $_{33}^{72}$As disappears as measured by its activity? The half-life of $_{33}^{72}$As is 26 h.

16. A radioactive nucleus has half-life $T_{1/2}$. A sample containing these nuclei has initial activity R_0. Calculate the number of nuclei that decay during the interval between the times t_1 and t_2.

17. In an experiment on the transport of nutrients in the root structure of a plant, two radioactive nuclides X and Y are used. Initially 2.50 times more nuclei of type X are present than of type Y. Just three days later there are 4.20 times more nuclei of type X than of type Y. Isotope Y has a half-life of 1.60 d. What is the half-life of isotope X?

18. (a) The daughter nucleus formed in radioactive decay is often radioactive. Let N_{10} represent the number of parent nuclei at time $t = 0$, $N_1(t)$ the number of parent nuclei at time t, and λ_1 the decay constant of the parent. Suppose the number of daughter nuclei at time $t = 0$ is zero, let $N_2(t)$ be the number of daughter nuclei at time t, and let λ_2 be the decay constant of the daughter. Show that $N_2(t)$ satisfies the differential equation

$$\frac{dN_2}{dt} = \lambda_1 N_1 - \lambda_2 N_2$$

(b) Verify by substitution that this differential equation has the solution

$$N_2(t) = \frac{N_{10}\lambda_1}{\lambda_1 - \lambda_2} (e^{-\lambda_2 t} - e^{-\lambda_1 t})$$

This equation is the law of successive radioactive decays. (c) ^{218}Po decays into ^{214}Pb with a half-life of 3.10 min, and ^{214}Pb decays into ^{214}Bi with a half-life of 26.8 min. On the same axes, plot graphs of $N_1(t)$ for ^{218}Po and $N_2(t)$ for ^{214}Pb. Let $N_{10} = 1\,000$ nuclei, and choose values of t from 0 to 36 min in 2-min intervals. The curve for ^{214}Pb at first rises to a maximum and then starts to decay. At what instant t_m is the number of ^{214}Pb nuclei a maximum? (d) By applying the condition for a maximum $dN_2/dt = 0$, derive a symbolic equation for t_m in terms of λ_1 and λ_2. Does the value obtained in part (c) agree with this equation?

Section 30.4 ∎ The Radioactive Decay Processes

19. Find the energy released in the alpha decay

$$_{92}^{238}\text{U} \rightarrow _{90}^{234}\text{Th} + _2^4\text{He}$$

You will find Table A.3 useful.

20. Identify the missing nuclide or particle (X):

(a) X $\rightarrow$ $_{28}^{65}$Ni $+ \gamma$
(b) $_{84}^{215}$Po $\rightarrow$ X $+ \alpha$

(c) $X \rightarrow {}^{55}_{26}Fe + e^+ + \nu$
(d) ${}^{109}_{48}Cd + X \rightarrow {}^{109}_{47}Ag + \nu$
(e) ${}^{14}_{7}N + {}^{4}_{2}He \rightarrow X + {}^{17}_{8}O$

21. 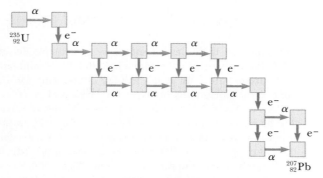 A living specimen in equilibrium with the atmosphere contains one atom of ${}^{14}C$ (half-life = 5 730 yr) for every 7.7×10^{11} stable carbon atoms. An archeological sample of wood (cellulose, $C_{12}H_{22}O_{11}$) contains 21.0 mg of carbon. When the sample is placed inside a shielded beta counter with 88.0% counting efficiency, 837 counts are accumulated in one week. Assuming that the cosmic-ray flux and the Earth's atmosphere have not changed appreciably since the sample was formed, find the age of the sample.

22. A ${}^3H$ nucleus beta decays into ${}^3He$ by creating an electron and an antineutrino according to the reaction

$${}^{3}_{1}H \rightarrow {}^{3}_{2}He + e^- + \bar{\nu}$$

The symbols in this reaction refer to nuclei. Write the reaction referring to neutral atoms by adding one electron to both sides. Then use Table A.3 to determine the total energy released in this reaction.

23. The nucleus ${}^{15}_{8}O$ decays by electron capture. The nuclear reaction is written

$${}^{15}_{8}O + e^- \rightarrow {}^{15}_{7}N + \nu$$

(a) Write the process going on for a single particle within the nucleus. (b) Write the decay process referring to neutral atoms. (c) Determine the energy of the neutrino. Disregard the daughter's recoil.

24. Enter the correct isotope symbol in each open square in Figure P30.24, which shows the sequences of decays in the natural radioactive series starting with the long-lived isotope uranium-235 and ending with the stable nucleus lead-207.

FIGURE P30.24

25. *Indoor air pollution.* Uranium is naturally present in rock and soil. At one step in its series of radioactive decays, ${}^{238}U$ produces the chemically inert gas radon-222, with a half-life of 3.82 days. The radon seeps out of the ground to mix into the atmosphere, typically making open air radioactive with activity 0.3 pCi/L. In homes, ${}^{222}Rn$ can be a serious pollutant, accumulating to reach much higher activities in enclosed spaces. If the radon activity exceeds 4 pCi/L, the Environmental Protection Agency suggests taking action to reduce it, such as by reducing infiltration of air from the ground. (a) Convert the activity 4 pCi/L to units of becquerel per cubic meter. (b) How many ${}^{222}Rn$ atoms are in one cubic meter of air displaying this activity? (c) What fraction of the mass of the air does the radon constitute?

Section 30.5 ■ Nuclear Reactions

Note: Problem 20.61 in Chapter 20 can be assigned with this section.

26. Identify the unknown nuclei and particles X and X′ in the following nuclear reactions:

(a) $X + {}^{4}_{2}He \rightarrow {}^{24}_{12}Mg + {}^{1}_{0}n$
(b) ${}^{235}_{92}U + {}^{1}_{0}n \rightarrow {}^{90}_{38}Sr + X + 2{}^{1}_{0}n$
(c) $2{}^{1}_{1}H \rightarrow {}^{2}_{1}H + X + X'$

27. **Physics⊗Now™** Natural gold has only one isotope, ${}^{197}_{79}Au$. If natural gold is irradiated by a flux of slow neutrons, electrons are emitted. (a) Write the reaction equation. (b) Calculate the maximum energy of the emitted electrons.

28. A beam of 6.61 MeV protons is incident on a target of ${}^{27}_{13}Al$. Those protons that collide with a target nucleus produce the reaction

$$p + {}^{27}_{13}Al \rightarrow {}^{27}_{14}Si + n$$

(${}^{27}_{14}Si$ has mass 26.986 705 u.) Ignoring any recoil of the product nucleus, determine the kinetic energy of the emerging neutrons.

29. **Review problem.** Suppose enriched uranium containing 3.40% of the fissionable isotope ${}^{235}_{92}U$ is used as fuel for a ship. The water exerts an average friction force of magnitude 1.00×10^5 N on the ship. How far can the ship travel per kilogram of fuel? Assume that the energy released per fission event is 208 MeV and that the ship's engine has an efficiency of 20.0%.

30. (a) The following fission reaction is typical of those occurring in a nuclear electric generating station:

$${}^{1}_{0}n + {}^{235}_{92}U \rightarrow {}^{141}_{56}Ba + {}^{92}_{36}Kr + 3({}^{1}_{0}n)$$

Find the energy released. The required masses are

$$M({}^{1}_{0}n) = 1.008\ 665\ u$$
$$M({}^{235}_{92}U) = 235.043\ 923\ u$$
$$M({}^{141}_{56}Ba) = 140.914\ 4\ u$$
$$M({}^{92}_{36}Kr) = 91.926\ 2\ u$$

(b) What fraction of the initial mass of the system is transformed?

31. **Physics⊗Now™** It has been estimated that on the order of 10^9 tons of natural uranium is available at concentrations exceeding 100 parts per million, of which 0.7% is the fissionable isotope ${}^{235}U$. Assume that all the world's energy use $(7 \times 10^{12}$ J/s) were supplied by ${}^{235}U$ fission in conventional nuclear reactors, releasing 208 MeV for each reaction. How long would the supply last? The estimate of uranium supply is taken from K. S. Deffeyes and I. D. MacGregor, "World Uranium Resources," *Scientific American* 242(1):66, 1980.

32. Of all the hydrogen in the oceans, 0.030 0% of the mass is deuterium. The oceans have a volume of 317 million mi^3. (a) If nuclear fusion were controlled and all the deuterium in the oceans were fused to $^4_2$He, how many joules of energy would be released? (b) World power consumption is about 7.00×10^{12} W. If consumption were 100 times greater, how many years would the energy calculated in part (a) last?

Section 30.6 ▮ Context Connection—The Engine of the Stars

33. The Sun radiates energy at the rate of 3.85×10^{26} W. Suppose the net reaction

$$4(^1_1H) + 2(_{-1}^0e) \rightarrow {}^4_2He + 2\nu + \gamma$$

accounts for all the energy released. Calculate the number of protons fused per second.

34. In addition to the proton–proton cycle, the carbon cycle, first proposed by Hans Bethe in 1939, is another cycle by which energy is released in stars as hydrogen is converted to helium. The carbon cycle requires higher temperatures than the proton–proton cycle. The series of reactions is

$$^{12}C + {}^1H \rightarrow {}^{13}N + \gamma$$
$$^{13}N \rightarrow {}^{13}C + e^+ + \nu$$
$$e^+ + e^- \rightarrow 2\gamma$$
$$^{13}C + {}^1H \rightarrow {}^{14}N + \gamma$$
$$^{14}N + {}^1H \rightarrow {}^{15}O + \gamma$$
$$^{15}O \rightarrow {}^{15}N + e^+ + \nu$$
$$e^+ + e^- \rightarrow 2\gamma$$
$$^{15}N + {}^1H \rightarrow {}^{12}C + {}^4He$$

(a) Assuming that the proton–proton cycle requires a temperature of 1.5×10^7 K, estimate by proportion the temperature required for the carbon cycle. (b) Calculate the Q value for each step in the carbon cycle and the overall energy released. (c) Do you think that the energy carried off by the neutrinos is deposited in the star? Explain.

35. Consider the two nuclear reactions

$$A + B \rightarrow C + E \quad (I)$$
$$C + D \rightarrow F + G \quad (II)$$

(a) Show that the net disintegration energy for these two reactions ($Q_{net} = Q_I + Q_{II}$) is identical to the disintegration energy for the net reaction

$$A + B + D \rightarrow E + F + G$$

(b) One chain of reactions in the proton–proton cycle in the Sun's core is

$$^1_1H + {}^1_1H \rightarrow {}^2_1H + {}^0_1e + \nu$$
$$^0_1e + {}^0_{-1}e \rightarrow 2\gamma$$
$$^1_1H + {}^2_1H \rightarrow {}^3_2He + \gamma$$
$$^1_1H + {}^3_2He \rightarrow {}^4_2He + {}^0_1e + \nu$$
$$^0_1e + {}^0_{-1}e \rightarrow 2\gamma$$

Based on part (a), what is Q_{net} for this sequence?

36. After determining that the Sun has existed for hundreds of millions of years but before the discovery of nuclear physics, scientists could not explain why the Sun has continued to burn for such a long time. For example, if it were a coal fire, it would have burned up in about 3 000 yr. Assume that the Sun, whose mass is 1.99×10^{30} kg, originally consisted entirely of hydrogen and that its total power output is 3.85×10^{26} W. (a) Assuming the energy-generating mechanism of the Sun is the fusion of hydrogen into helium via the net reaction

$$4(^1_1H) + 2(e^-) \rightarrow {}^4_2He + 2\nu + \gamma$$

calculate the energy (in joules) given off by this reaction. (b) Determine how many hydrogen atoms constitute the Sun. Take the mass of one hydrogen atom to be 1.67×10^{-27} kg. (c) If the total power output remains constant, after what time interval will all the hydrogen be converted into helium, making the Sun die? The actual projected lifetime of the Sun is about 10 billion years, because only the hydrogen in a relatively small core is available as a fuel. Only in the core are temperatures and densities high enough for the fusion reaction to be self-sustaining.

37. Carbon detonations are powerful nuclear reactions that temporarily tear apart the cores inside massive stars late in their lives. These blasts are produced by carbon fusion, which requires a temperature of about 6×10^8 K to overcome the strong Coulomb repulsion between carbon nuclei. (a) Estimate the repulsive energy barrier to fusion, using the temperature required for carbon fusion. (In other words, what is the average kinetic energy of a carbon nucleus at 6×10^8 K?) (b) Calculate the energy (in MeV) released in each of these "carbon-burning" reactions:

$$^{12}C + {}^{12}C \rightarrow {}^{20}Ne + {}^4He$$
$$^{12}C + {}^{12}C \rightarrow {}^{24}Mg + \gamma$$

(c) Calculate the energy (in kWh) given off when 2.00 kg of carbon completely fuses according to the first reaction.

38. A theory of nuclear astrophysics proposes that all the elements heavier than iron are formed in supernova explosions ending the lives of massive stars. Assume that at the time of the explosion the amounts of ^{235}U and ^{238}U were equal. How long ago did the star(s) explode that released the elements that formed our Earth? The present $^{235}U/^{238}U$ ratio is 0.007 25. The half-lives of ^{235}U and ^{238}U are 0.704×10^9 yr and 4.47×10^9 yr.

Additional Problems

39. (a) One method of producing neutrons for experimental use is bombardment of light nuclei with alpha particles. In the method used by James Chadwick in 1932, alpha particles emitted by polonium are incident on beryllium nuclei:

$$^4_2He + {}^9_4Be \rightarrow {}^{12}_6C + {}^1_0n$$

What is the Q value? (b) Neutrons are also often produced by small particle accelerators. In one design, deuterons accelerated in a Van de Graaff generator bombard other deuterium nuclei:

$$^2_1H + {}^2_1H \rightarrow {}^3_2He + {}^1_0n$$

Is this reaction exothermic or endothermic? Calculate its Q value.

40. As part of his discovery of the neutron in 1932, Chadwick determined the mass of the newly identified particle by firing a beam of fast neutrons, all having the same speed, at two different targets and measuring the maximum recoil speeds of the target nuclei. The maximum speeds arise when an elastic head-on collision occurs between a neutron and a stationary target nucleus. (a) Represent the masses and final speeds of the two target nuclei as m_1, v_1, m_2, and v_2 and assume that Newtonian mechanics applies. Show that the neutron mass can be calculated from the equation

$$m_n = \frac{m_1 v_1 - m_2 v_2}{v_2 - v_1}$$

(b) Chadwick directed a beam of neutrons (produced from a nuclear reaction) on paraffin, which contains hydrogen. The maximum speed of the protons ejected was found to be 3.3×10^7 m/s. Because the velocity of the neutrons could not be determined directly, a second experiment was performed using neutrons from the same source and nitrogen nuclei as the target. The maximum recoil speed of the nitrogen nuclei was found to be 4.7×10^6 m/s. The masses of a proton and a nitrogen nucleus were taken as 1 u and 14 u, respectively. What was Chadwick's value for the neutron mass?

41. When the nuclear reaction represented by Equation 30.24 is endothermic, the reaction energy Q is negative. For the reaction to proceed, the incoming particle must have a minimum energy called the threshold energy, E_{th}. Some fraction of the energy of the incident particle is transferred to the compound nucleus to conserve momentum. Therefore, E_{th} must be greater than Q. (a) Show that

$$E_{th} = -Q\left(1 + \frac{M_a}{M_X}\right)$$

(b) Calculate the threshold energy of the incident alpha particle in the reaction

$$^4_2\text{He} + {}^{14}_7\text{N} \rightarrow {}^{17}_8\text{O} + {}^1_1\text{H}$$

42. (a) Find the radius of the $^{12}_6\text{C}$ nucleus. (b) Find the force of repulsion between a proton at the surface of a $^{12}_6\text{C}$ nucleus and the remaining five protons. (c) How much work (in MeV) has to be done to overcome this electric repulsion to put the last proton into the nucleus? (d) Repeat parts (a), (b), and (c) for $^{238}_{92}\text{U}$.

43. (a) Why is the beta decay p → n + e$^+$ + ν forbidden for a free proton? (b) Why is the same reaction possible if the proton is bound in a nucleus? For example, the following reaction occurs:

$$^{13}_7\text{N} \rightarrow {}^{13}_6\text{C} + \text{e}^+ + \nu$$

(c) How much energy is released in the reaction given in part (b)? [Suggestion: Add seven electrons to both sides of the reaction to write it for neutral atoms. You may use the masses $m(\text{e}^+) = 0.000\ 549$ u, $M(^{13}\text{C}) = 13.003\ 355$ u, and $M(^{13}\text{N}) = 13.005\ 739$ u.]

44. ▨ The activity of a radioactive sample was measured over 12 h, with the net count rates shown in the table.

Time (h)	Counting Rate (counts/min)
1.00	3 100
2.00	2 450
4.00	1 480
6.00	910
8.00	545
10.0	330
12.0	200

(a) Plot the logarithm of counting rate as a function of time. (b) Determine the decay constant and half-life of the radioactive nuclei in the sample. (c) What counting rate would you expect for the sample at $t = 0$? (d) Assuming the efficiency of the counting instrument to be 10.0%, calculate the number of radioactive atoms in the sample at $t = 0$.

45. When, after a reaction or disturbance of any kind, a nucleus is left in an excited state, it can return to its normal (ground) state by emission of a gamma-ray photon (or several photons). This process is illustrated by Equation 30.21. The emitting nucleus must recoil to conserve both energy and momentum. (a) Show that the recoil energy of the nucleus is

$$E_r = \frac{(\Delta E)^2}{2Mc^2}$$

where ΔE is the difference in energy between the excited and ground states of a nucleus of mass M. (b) Calculate the recoil energy of the ^{57}Fe nucleus when it decays by gamma emission from the 14.4-keV excited state. For this calculation, take the mass to be 57 u. [Suggestions: When writing the equation for conservation of energy, use $(Mv)^2/2M$ for the kinetic energy of the recoiling nucleus. Also, assume that $hf \ll Mc^2$ and use the binomial expansion.]

46. ▨ After the sudden release of radioactivity from the Chernobyl nuclear reactor accident in 1986, the radioactivity of milk in Poland rose to 2 000 Bq/L due to iodine-131 present in the grass eaten by dairy cattle. Radioactive iodine, with half-life 8.04 days, is particularly hazardous because the thyroid gland concentrates iodine. The Chernobyl accident caused a measurable increase in thyroid cancers among children in Belarus. (a) For comparison, find the activity of milk due to potassium. Assume that one liter of milk contains 2.00 g of potassium, of which 0.011 7% is the isotope ^{40}K with half-life 1.28×10^9 yr. (b) After what time interval would the activity due to iodine fall below that due to potassium?

47. Europeans named a certain direction in the sky as between the horns of Taurus the Bull. On the day they named as A.D. July 4, 1054, a brilliant light appeared there. Europeans left no surviving record of the supernova, which could be seen in daylight for some days. As it faded it remained visible for years, dimming for a time with the 77.1-day half-life of the radioactive cobalt-56 that had been created in the explosion. (a) The remains of the star now form the Crab Nebula. (See Fig. 10.23 and the

opening photographs of Chapter 24.) In it, the cobalt-56 has now decreased to what fraction of its original activity? (b) Suppose an American, of the people called the Anasazi, made a charcoal drawing of the supernova. The carbon-14 in the charcoal has now decayed to what fraction of its original activity?

48. In a piece of rock from the Moon, the ^{87}Rb content is assayed to be 1.82×10^{10} atoms per gram of material and the ^{87}Sr content is found to be 1.07×10^9 atoms per gram. (a) Calculate the age of the rock. (b) Could the material in the rock actually be much older? What assumption is implicit in using the radioactive dating method? (The relevant decay is ^{87}Rb $\rightarrow$ ^{87}Sr $+ e^- + \bar{\nu}$. The half-life of the decay is 4.75×10^{10} yr.)

49. **Physics Now™** The decay of an unstable nucleus by alpha emission is represented by Equation 30.9. The disintegration energy Q given by Equation 30.12 must be shared by the alpha particle and the daughter nucleus to conserve both energy and momentum in the decay process. (a) Show that Q and K_α, the kinetic energy of the alpha particle, are related by the expression

$$Q = K_\alpha \left(1 + \frac{M_\alpha}{M}\right)$$

where M is the mass of the daughter nucleus. (b) Use the result of part (a) to find the energy of the alpha particle emitted in the decay of ^{226}Ra. (See Example 30.5 for the calculation of Q.)

50. *Student determination of the half-life of ^{137}Ba.* The radioactive barium isotope ^{137}Ba has a relatively short half-life and can be easily extracted from a solution containing its parent cesium (^{137}Cs). This barium isotope is commonly used in an undergraduate laboratory exercise for demonstrating the radioactive decay law. Undergraduate students using modest experimental equipment took the data presented in Figure P30.50. Determine the half-life for the decay of ^{137}Ba using their data.

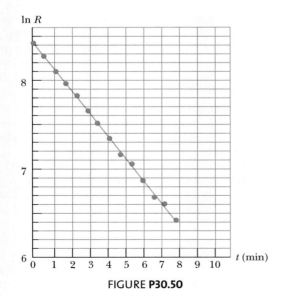

FIGURE P30.50

51. 🖼 A small building has become accidentally contaminated with radioactivity. The longest-lived material in the building is strontium-90. ($^{90}_{38}$Sr has an atomic mass 89.907 7 u, and its half-life is 29.1 yr. It is particularly dangerous because it substitutes for calcium in bones.) Assume that the building initially contained 5.00 kg of this substance uniformly distributed throughout the building and that the safe level is defined as less than 10.0 decays/min (to be small in comparison to background radiation). How long will the building be unsafe?

52. *Lead shielding.* When gamma rays are incident on matter, the intensity of the gamma rays passing through the material varies with depth x as $I(x) = I_0 e^{-\mu x}$, where μ is the absorption coefficient and I_0 is the intensity of the radiation at the surface of the material. For 0.400-MeV gamma rays in lead, the absorption coefficient is 1.59 cm^{-1}. (a) Determine the "half-thickness" for lead, that is, the thickness of lead that would absorb half the incident gamma rays. (b) What thickness will reduce the radiation by a factor of 10^4?

53. *A thickness gauge.* When gamma rays are incident on matter, the intensity of the gamma rays passing through the material varies with depth x as $I(x) = I_0 e^{-\mu x}$, where μ is the absorption coefficient and I_0 is the intensity of the radiation at the surface of the material. For low-energy gamma rays in steel, take the absorption coefficient to be 0.720 mm^{-1}. (a) Determine the "half-thickness" for steel, that is, the thickness of steel that would absorb half the incident gamma rays. (b) In a steel mill, the thickness of sheet steel passing into a roller is measured by monitoring the intensity of gamma radiation reaching a detector below the rapidly moving metal from a small source just above the metal. If the thickness of the sheet changes from 0.800 mm to 0.700 mm, by what percentage will the gamma-ray intensity change?

54. During the manufacture of a steel engine component, radioactive iron (^{59}Fe) is included in the total mass of 0.200 kg. The component is placed in a test engine when the activity due to this isotope is 20.0 μCi. After a 1 000-h test period, some of the lubricating oil is removed from the engine and found to contain enough ^{59}Fe to produce 800 disintegrations/min/L of oil. The total volume of oil in the engine is 6.50 L. Calculate the total mass worn from the engine component per hour of operation. (The half-life of ^{59}Fe is 45.1 days.)

55. *Neutron activation analysis* is a method for chemical analysis at the level of isotopes. When a sample is irradiated by neutrons, radioactive atoms are produced continuously and then decay according to their characteristic half-lives. (a) Assume that one species of radioactive nuclei is produced at a constant rate R and that its decay is described by the conventional radioactive decay law. Defining $t = 0$ as the time irradiation begins, show that the number of radioactive atoms accumulated at time t is

$$N = \frac{R}{\lambda}(1 - e^{-\lambda t})$$

(b) What is the maximum number of radioactive atoms that can be produced?

56. On August 6, 1945, the United States dropped on Hiroshima a nuclear bomb that released 5×10^{13} J of energy, equivalent to that from 12 000 tons of TNT. The fission of one $^{235}_{92}$U nucleus releases an average of 208 MeV. Estimate (a) the number of nuclei fissioned and (b) the mass of this $^{235}_{92}$U.

57. **Review problem.** A nuclear power plant operates by using the energy released in nuclear fission to convert 20°C water into 400°C steam. How much water could theoretically be converted to steam by the complete fissioning of 1.00 gram of ^{235}U at 200 MeV/fission?

58. **Review problem.** The first nuclear bomb was a fissioning mass of plutonium-239, exploded in the Trinity test, before dawn on July 16, 1945, at Alamogordo, New Mexico. Enrico Fermi was 14 km away, lying on the ground facing away from the bomb. After the whole sky had flashed with unbelievable brightness, Fermi stood up and began dropping bits of paper to the ground. They first fell at his feet in the calm and silent air. As the shock wave passed, about 40 s after the explosion, the paper then in flight jumped about 5 cm away from ground zero. (a) Assume that the shock wave in air propagated equally in all directions without absorption. Find the change in volume of a sphere of radius 14 km as it expands by 5 cm. (b) Find the work $P \Delta V$ done by the air in this sphere on the next layer of air farther from the center. (c) Assume that the shock wave carried on the order of one tenth of the energy of the explosion. Make an order-of-magnitude estimate of the bomb yield. (d) One ton of exploding trinitrotoluene (TNT) releases energy 4.2 GJ. What was the order of magnitude of the energy of the Trinity test in equivalent tons of TNT? The dawn revealed the mushroom cloud. Fermi's immediate knowledge of the bomb yield agreed with that determined days later by analysis of elaborate measurements.

59. About 1 of every 3 300 water molecules contains one deuterium atom. (a) If all the deuterium nuclei in 1 L of water are fused in pairs according to the D–D reaction ^{2}H + ^{2}H → ^{3}He + n + 3.27 MeV, how much energy in joules is liberated? (b) Burning gasoline produces about 3.40×10^7 J/L. Compare the energy obtainable from the fusion of the deuterium in 1 L of water with the energy liberated from the burning of 1 L of gasoline.

60. The alpha-emitter polonium-210 ($^{210}_{84}$Po) is used in a nuclear energy source on a spacecraft (Fig. P30.60). Determine the initial power output of the source. Assume that it contains 0.155 kg of ^{210}Po and that the efficiency for conversion of radioactive decay energy to energy transferred by electrical transmission is 1.00%.

61. ▨ Natural uranium must be processed to produce uranium enriched in ^{235}U for bombs and power plants. The processing yields a large quantity of nearly pure ^{238}U as a by-product, called "depleted uranium." Because of its high mass density, it is used in armor-piercing artillery shells. (a) Find the edge dimension of a 70.0-kg cube of ^{238}U. The density of uranium is 18.7×10^3 kg/m^3. (b) The isotope ^{238}U has a long half-life of 4.47×10^9 yr. As soon as one nucleus decays, it begins a relatively rapid series of 14 steps that together constitute the net reaction

$$^{238}_{92}\text{U} \; \rightarrow \; 8(^4_2\text{He}) + 6(^{\;\;0}_{-1}\text{e}) + ^{206}_{82}\text{Pb} + 6\,\bar{\nu} + Q_{net}$$

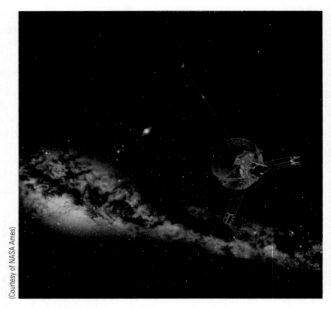

FIGURE P30.60 The *Pioneer 10* spacecraft leaves the Solar System. It carries radioactive power supplies at the ends of two booms. Solar panels would not work far from the Sun.

Find the net decay energy. (Refer to Table A.3.) (c) Argue that a radioactive sample with decay rate R and decay energy Q has power output $\mathcal{P} = QR$. (d) Consider an artillery shell with a jacket of 70.0 kg of ^{238}U. Find its power output due to the radioactivity of the uranium and its daughters. Assume that the shell is old enough that the daughters have reached steady-state amounts. Express the power in joules per year. (e) A 17-year-old soldier of mass 70.0 kg works in an arsenal where many such artillery shells are stored. Assume that his radiation exposure is limited to absorbing 45.5 mJ per year per kilogram of body mass. Find the net rate at which he can absorb energy of radiation, in joules per year.

62. ▨ A sealed capsule containing the radiopharmaceutical phosphorus-32 ($^{32}_{15}$P), an e$^-$ emitter, is implanted into a patient's tumor. The average kinetic energy of the beta particles is 700 keV. The initial activity is 5.22 MBq. Determine the energy absorbed during a 10.0-day period. Assume that the beta particles are completely absorbed within the tumor. (*Suggestion:* Find the number of beta particles emitted.)

63. ▨ To destroy a cancerous tumor, a dose of gamma radiation totaling an energy of 2.12 J is to be delivered in 30.0 days from implanted sealed capsules containing palladium-103. Assume that this isotope has half-life 17.0 d and emits gamma rays of energy 21.0 keV, which are entirely absorbed within the tumor. (a) Find the initial activity of the set of capsules. (b) Find the total mass of radioactive palladium that these "seeds" should contain.

64. (a) Calculate the energy (in kilowatt-hours) released if 1.00 kg of ^{239}Pu undergoes complete fission and the energy released per fission event is 200 MeV. (b) Calculate the energy (in electron volts) released in the deuterium–tritium

fusion reaction

$$_1^2H + _1^3H \;\rightarrow\; _2^4He + _0^1n$$

(c) Calculate the energy (in kilowatt-hours) released if 1.00 kg of deuterium undergoes fusion according to this reaction. (d) Calculate the energy (in kilowatt-hours) released by the combustion of 1.00 kg of coal if each $C + O_2 \rightarrow CO_2$ reaction yields 4.20 eV. (e) List advantages and disadvantages of each of these methods of energy generation.

ANSWERS TO QUICK QUIZZES

30.1 (i),(b). The value of $N = A - Z$ is the same for all three nuclei. (ii), (a). The value of Z is the same for all three nuclei because they are all nuclei of nitrogen. (iii), (c). The value of A is the same for all three nuclei, as seen by the unchanging preceding superscript.

30.2 (c). Isotopes of a given element correspond to nuclei with different numbers of neutrons. The result is different masses of the atom, and different magnetic moments because the neutron, despite being uncharged, has a magnetic moment. The chemical behavior, however, is governed by the electrons. All isotopes of a given element have the same number of electrons and therefore the same chemical behavior.

30.3 (e). A year of 365 days is equivalent to 365 d/5.01 d $\approx$ 73 half-lives. Therefore, the activity will be reduced after one year to approximately $(1/2)^{73}(1.000\ \mu Ci)$ $\sim 10^{-22}\ \mu Ci$.

30.4 (e). The time we are interested in is half of a half-life. Therefore, the number of *remaining* nuclei is $(\frac{1}{2})^{1/2}N_0 = (1/\sqrt{2})N_0 = 0.707N_0$. The number of nuclei that *have decayed* is $N_0 - 0.707N_0 = 0.293N_0$.

30.5 (b). In alpha decay, the atomic number decreases by two and the atomic mass number decreases by four.

30.6 (c). In e^- decay, the atomic number increases by one and the atomic mass number stays fixed. None of the choices is consistent with e^+ decay, so we assume that the decay must be by e^-.

CHAPTER 31

Particle Physics

In this image from the NA49 experiment at CERN, hundreds of subatomic particles are created in the collision of high-energy nuclei with a lead target. The aim of the experiment is to create a quark-gluon plasma, in which the force that normally locks quarks within protons and neutrons is broken.

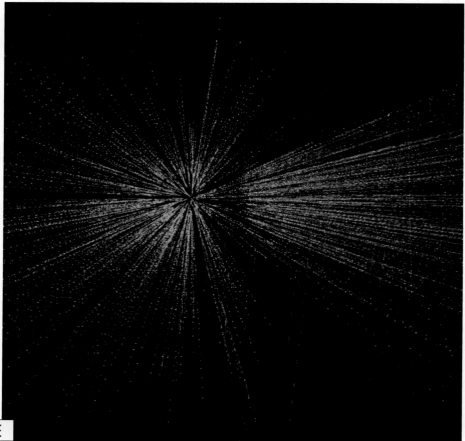

(Courtesy of CERN)

CHAPTER OUTLINE

In the early chapters of this book, we discussed the particle model, which treats an object as a particle of zero size with no structure. Some behaviors of objects, such as thermal expansion, can be understood by modeling the object as a collection of particles: atoms. In these models, any internal structure of the atom is ignored. We could not ignore the internal structure of the atom to understand such phenomena as atomic spectra, however. Modeling the hydrogen atom as a system of an electron in orbit about a particle-like nucleus helped in this regard (Section 11.5). In Chapter 30, however, we could not model the nucleus as a particle and ignore its structure to understand behavior such as nuclear stability and radioactive decay. We had to model the nucleus as a collection of smaller particles, nucleons. What about these nuclear constituents, the protons and neutrons? Can we apply the particle model to these entities? As we shall see, even protons and neutrons have structure, which leads to a puzzling question. As we continue to investigate the structure of smaller and smaller "particles," will we ever reach a level at which the building blocks are truly and completely described by the particle model?

In this concluding chapter, we explore this question by examining the properties and classifications of the various known subatomic particles and the fundamental interactions that govern their behavior. We also discuss the current model of elementary particles, in which all matter is believed to be constructed from only two families of particles: quarks and leptons.

The word *atom* is from the Greek *atomos,* which means "indivisible." At one time, atoms were thought to be the indivisible constituents of matter; that is, they were regarded as elementary particles. After 1932, physicists viewed all matter as consisting of only three constituent particles: electrons, protons, and neutrons. (The neutron was observed and identified in 1932.) With the exception of the free neutron (as opposed to a neutron within a nucleus), these particles are very stable. Beginning in 1945, many new particles were discovered in experiments involving high-energy collisions between known particles. These new particles are characteristically very unstable and have very short half-lives, ranging between 10^{-6} s and 10^{-23} s. So far, more than 300 of these unstable, temporary particles have been catalogued.

Since the 1930s, many powerful particle accelerators have been constructed throughout the world, making it possible to observe collisions of highly energetic particles under controlled laboratory conditions so as to reveal the subatomic world in finer detail. Until the 1960s, physicists were bewildered by the large number and variety of subatomic particles being discovered. They wondered if the particles were like animals in a zoo, having no systematic relationship connecting them, or whether a pattern was emerging that would provide a better understanding of the elaborate structure in the subnuclear world. Since that time, physicists have advanced our knowledge of the structure of matter tremendously by developing a structural model in which most of the particles in the ever-growing particle zoo are made of smaller particles called quarks. Therefore, protons and neutrons, for example, are not truly elementary but are systems of tightly bound quarks.

31.1 | THE FUNDAMENTAL FORCES IN NATURE

As we learned in Chapter 5, all natural phenomena can be described by four fundamental forces between particles. In order of decreasing strength, they are the **strong** force, the **electromagnetic** force, the **weak** force, and the **gravitational** force. In current models, the electromagnetic and weak forces are considered to be two manifestations of a single interaction, the **electroweak force,** as discussed in Section 31.11.

The **nuclear force,** as we mentioned in Chapter 30, holds nucleons together. It is very short range and is negligible for separations greater than about 2 fm (about the size of the nucleus). The electromagnetic force, which binds atoms and molecules together to form ordinary matter, has about 10^{-2} times the strength of the nuclear force. It is a long-range force that decreases in strength as the inverse square of the separation between interacting particles. The weak force is a short-range force that accounts for radioactive decay processes such as beta decay, and its strength is only about 10^{-5} times that of the nuclear force. Finally, the gravitational force is a long-range force that has a strength of only about 10^{-41} times that of the nuclear force. Although this familiar interaction is the force that holds the planets, stars, and galaxies together, its effect on elementary particles is negligible.

In modern physics, interactions between particles are often described in terms of a structural model that involves the exchange of **field particles,** or **quanta.** In the case of the familiar electromagnetic interaction, for instance, the field particles are photons. In the language of modern physics, we say that the electromagnetic force is *mediated* by photons and that photons are the quanta of the electromagnetic field. Likewise, the nuclear force is mediated by field particles called **gluons,** the weak

■ Field particles

TABLE 31.1	Fundamental Forces			
Force	**Relative Strength**	**Range of Force**	**Mediating Field Particle**	**Mass of Field Particle (GeV/c^2)**
Nuclear	1	Short (~1 fm)	Gluon	0
Electromagnetic	10^{-2}	∞	Photon	0
Weak	10^{-5}	Short (~10^{-3} fm)	$W^{\pm}$, Z^0 bosons	80.4, 80.4, 91.2
Gravitational	10^{-41}	∞	Graviton	0

force is mediated by particles called the W and Z **bosons** (in general, all particles with integral spin are called *bosons*), and the gravitational force is mediated by quanta of the gravitational field called **gravitons.** These forces, their ranges, and their relative strengths are summarized in Table 31.1.

31.2 POSITRONS AND OTHER ANTIPARTICLES

In the 1920s, English theoretical physicist Paul Adrien Maurice Dirac developed a version of quantum mechanics that incorporated special relativity. Dirac's theory explained the origin of electron spin and its magnetic moment. It also presented a major difficulty, however. Dirac's relativistic wave equation required solutions corresponding to negative energy states even for free electrons. If negative energy states existed, however, one would expect an electron in a state of positive energy to make a rapid transition to one of these states, emitting a photon in the process. Dirac avoided this difficulty by postulating a structural model in which all negative energy states are filled. The electrons occupying these negative energy states are collectively called the *Dirac sea*. Electrons in the Dirac sea are not directly observable because the Pauli exclusion principle does not allow them to react to external forces; there are no states available to which an electron can make a transition in response to an external force. Therefore, an electron in such a state acts as an isolated system unless an interaction with the environment is strong enough to excite the electron to a positive energy state. Such an excitation causes one of the negative energy states to be vacant, as in Figure 31.1, leaving a hole in the sea of filled states. (Notice that positive energy states exist only for $E > m_e c^2$, representing the rest energy of the electron. Similarly, negative energy states exist only for $E < -m_e c^2$.) *The hole can react to external forces and is observable.* The hole reacts in a way similar to that of the electron, except that it has a positive charge. It is the **antiparticle** to the electron.

The profound implication of this model is that *every particle has a corresponding antiparticle*. The antiparticle has the same mass as the particle, but the opposite charge. For example, the electron's antiparticle, called a **positron,** has a mass of 0.511 MeV/c^2 and a positive charge of 1.60×10^{-19} C.

Carl Anderson (1905–1991) observed and identified the positron in 1932, and in 1936 he was awarded the Nobel Prize in Physics for that achievement. Anderson discovered the positron while examining tracks in a cloud chamber created by electron-like particles of positive charge. (A cloud chamber contains a gas that has been supercooled to just below its usual condensation point. An energetic radioactive particle passing through ionizes the gas and leaves a visible track. These early experiments used cosmic rays—mostly energetic protons passing through interstellar space—to initiate high-energy reactions in the upper atmosphere, which resulted in the production of positrons at ground level.) To discriminate between positive and negative charges, Anderson placed the cloud chamber in a magnetic field, causing moving charged particles to follow curved paths as discussed in Section 22.3. He

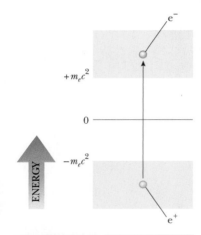

FIGURE 31.1 Dirac's model for the existence of antielectrons (positrons). The states lower in energy than $-m_e c^2$ are filled with electrons (the Dirac sea). One of these electrons can make a transition out of its state only if it is provided with energy equal to or larger than $2m_e c^2$. That leaves a vacancy in the Dirac sea, which can behave as a particle identical to the electron except for its positive charge.

⊞ PITFALL PREVENTION 31.1

ANTIPARTICLES An antiparticle is not identified solely on the basis of opposite charge; even neutral particles have antiparticles, which are defined in terms of other properties, such as spin magnetic moment.

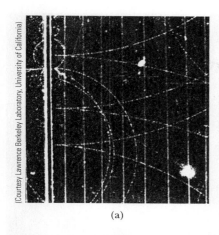

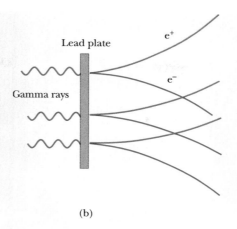

FIGURE 31.2 (a) Bubble-chamber tracks of electron–positron pairs produced by 300-MeV gamma rays striking a lead plate. (b) Sketch of the pertinent pair-production events. Note that the positrons deflect upward and the electrons deflect downward in an applied magnetic field.

(a)   (b)

noted that some of the electron-like tracks deflected in a direction corresponding to a positively charged particle.

Since Anderson's discovery, the positron has been observed in a number of experiments. A common process for producing positrons is **pair production.** In this process, a gamma-ray photon with sufficiently high energy interacts with a nucleus and an electron–positron pair is created. In the Dirac sea model, an electron in a negative energy state is excited to a positive energy state, resulting in a new observable electron and a hole, which is the positron. Because the total rest energy of the electron–positron pair is $2m_e c^2 = 1.022$ MeV, the photon must have at least this much energy to create an electron–positron pair. Therefore, energy in the form of a gamma-ray photon is converted to rest energy in accordance with Einstein's relationship $E_R = mc^2$. We can use the isolated system model to describe this process. The energy of the system of the photon and the nucleus is conserved and transformed to rest energy of the electron and positron, kinetic energy of these particles, and some small amount of kinetic energy associated with the nucleus. Figure 31.2a shows tracks of electron–positron pairs created by 300-MeV gamma rays striking a lead plate.

PAUL ADRIEN MAURICE DIRAC
(1902–1984)

British physicist Dirac was instrumental in the understanding of antimatter and the unification of quantum mechanics and relativity. He made many contributions to the development of quantum physics and cosmology. In 1933, he won the Nobel Prize in Physics.

> **QUICK QUIZ 31.1** Given the identification of the particles in Figure 31.2b, what is the direction of the external magnetic field in Figure 31.2a? **(a)** into the page **(b)** out of the page **(c)** impossible to determine

The reverse process can also occur. Under the proper conditions, an electron and positron can annihilate each other to produce two gamma-ray photons (see Thinking Physics 31.1) that have a combined energy of at least 1.022 MeV:

$$e^- + e^+ \rightarrow 2\gamma$$

Electron–positron annihilation is used in the medical diagnostic technique called *positron-emission tomography* (PET). The patient is injected with a glucose solution containing a radioactive substance that decays by positron emission, and the material is carried by the blood throughout the body. A positron emitted during a decay event in one of the radioactive nuclei in the glucose solution annihilates with an electron in the immediately surrounding tissue, resulting in two gamma-ray photons emitted in opposite directions. A gamma detector surrounding the patient pinpoints the source of the photons and, with the assistance of a computer, displays an image of the sites at which the glucose accumulates. (Glucose is metabolized rapidly in cancerous tumors and accumulates in these sites, providing a strong signal for a PET detector system.) The images from a PET scan can indicate a wide

 Positron-emission tomography (PET)

FIGURE 31.3 PET scans of the brain of a healthy older person (*left*) and that of a patient suffering from Alzheimer's disease (*right*). Lighter regions contain higher concentrations of radioactive glucose, indicating higher metabolism rates and therefore increased brain activity.

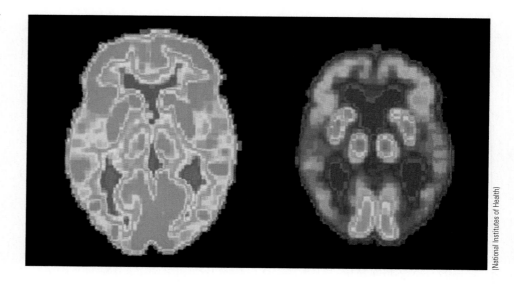

variety of disorders in the brain, including Alzheimer's disease (Fig. 31.3). In addition, because glucose metabolizes more rapidly in active areas of the brain, a PET scan can indicate which areas of the brain are involved when the patient is engaging in such activities as language use, music, or vision.

Prior to 1955, on the basis of the Dirac theory, it was expected that every particle has a corresponding antiparticle, but antiparticles such as the antiproton and antineutron had not been detected experimentally. Because the relativistic Dirac theory had some failures (it predicted the wrong-size magnetic moment for the photon) as well as many successes, it was important to determine whether the antiproton really existed. In 1955, a team led by Emilio Segrè (1905–1989) and Owen Chamberlain (b. 1920) used the Bevatron particle accelerator at the University of California–Berkeley to produce antiprotons and antineutrons. They therefore established with certainty the existence of antiparticles. For this work, Segrè and Chamberlain received the Nobel Prize in Physics in 1959. It is now established that **every particle has a corresponding antiparticle with equal mass and spin, and with charge, magnetic moment, and strangeness of equal magnitude but opposite sign.** (The property of strangeness is explained in Section 31.6.) The only exception to these rules for particles and antiparticles are the neutral photon, pion, and eta, each of which is its own antiparticle.

An intriguing aspect of the existence of antiparticles is that if we replace every proton, neutron, and electron in an atom with its antiparticle, we can create a stable antiatom; combinations of antiatoms should form antimolecules and eventually antiworlds. As far as we know, everything would behave in the same way in an antiworld as in our world. In principle, it is possible that some distant antimatter galaxies exist, separated from normal-matter galaxies by millions of lightyears. Unfortunately, because the photon is its own antiparticle, the light emitted from an antimatter galaxy is no different from that from a normal-matter galaxy, so astronomical observations cannot determine if the galaxy is composed of matter or antimatter. Although no evidence of antimatter galaxies exists at present, it is awe-inspiring to imagine the cosmic spectacle that would result if matter and antimatter galaxies were to collide: a gigantic eruption of jets of annihilation radiation, transforming the entire galactic mass into energetic particles fleeing the collision point.

■ Thinking Physics 31.1

When an electron and a positron meet at low speed in free space, why are two 0.511-MeV gamma rays produced rather than one gamma ray with an energy of 1.022 MeV?

Reasoning Gamma rays are photons, and photons carry momentum. We apply the momentum version of the isolated system model to the system, which consists initially of the electron and positron. If the system, assumed to be at rest, transformed to only one photon, momentum would not be conserved because the initial momentum of the electron–positron system is zero, whereas the final system consists of a single photon of energy 1.022 MeV and nonzero momentum. On the other hand, the two gamma-ray photons travel in *opposite* directions, so the total momentum of the final system—two photons—is zero, and momentum is conserved. ▪

31.3 | MESONS AND THE BEGINNING OF PARTICLE PHYSICS

In the mid-1930s, physicists had a fairly simple view of the structure of matter. The building blocks were the proton, the electron, and the neutron. Three other particles were known or had been postulated at the time: the photon, the neutrino, and the positron. These six particles were considered the fundamental constituents of matter. With this marvelously simple picture of the world, however, no one was able to answer an important question. Because many protons in proximity in any nucleus should strongly repel one another due to their positive charges, what is the nature of the force that holds the nucleus together? Scientists recognized that this mysterious force, which we now call the nuclear force, must be much stronger than anything encountered in nature up to that time.

In 1935, Japanese physicist Hideki Yukawa proposed the first theory to successfully explain the nature of the nuclear force, an effort that later earned him the Nobel Prize in Physics. To understand Yukawa's theory, it is useful to first recall that in the modern structural model of electromagnetic interactions, charged particles interact by exchanging photons. Yukawa used this idea to explain the nuclear force by proposing a new particle whose exchange between nucleons in the nucleus produces the nuclear force. Furthermore, he established that the range of the force is inversely proportional to the mass of this particle and predicted that the mass would be about 200 times the mass of the electron. Because the new particle would have a mass between that of the electron and that of the proton, it was called a meson (from the Greek *meso*, meaning "middle").

In an effort to substantiate Yukawa's predictions, physicists began an experimental search for the meson by studying cosmic rays entering the Earth's atmosphere. In 1937, Anderson and his collaborators discovered a particle of mass 106 MeV/c^2, about 207 times the mass of the electron. Subsequent experiments showed that the particle interacted very weakly with matter, however, and hence could not be the carrier of the nuclear force. The puzzling situation inspired several theoreticians to propose that two mesons existed with slightly different masses. This idea was confirmed by the discovery in 1947 of the **pi (π) meson**, or simply **pion,** by Cecil Frank Powell (1903–1969) and Giuseppe P. S. Occhialini (1907–1993). The particle discovered by Anderson in 1937, the one thought to be Yukawa's meson, is not really a meson. (We shall discuss the requirements for a particle to be a meson in Section 31.4). Instead, it takes part in the weak and electromagnetic interactions only and is now called the **muon (μ)**. We first discussed the muon in Section 9.4, with regard to time dilation.

The pion, Yukawa's carrier of the nuclear force, comes in three varieties corresponding to three charge states: π^+, π^-, and π^0. The π^+ and π^- particles have masses of 139.6 MeV/c^2, and the π^0 particle has a mass of 135.0 MeV/c^2. Pions and muons are very unstable particles. For example, the π^-, which has a mean lifetime of 2.6×10^{-8} s, first decays to a muon and an antineutrino. The muon, which has a mean lifetime of 2.2 μs, then decays into an electron, a neutrino, and

---

📶 **PITFALL PREVENTION 31.2**

THE NUCLEAR FORCE AND THE STRONG FORCE The nuclear force that we discussed in Chapter 30 and continue to discuss here was originally called the strong force. Once the quark theory (Section 31.9) was established, however, the phrase *strong force* was identified as the force between quarks. Currently, the strong force is associated both with the force between quarks and the force between particles made up of quarks. If those particles happen to be neutrons and protons, the strong force is often called the nuclear force because these particles make up the nucleus.

(UPI/Corbis-Bettman)

HIDEKI YUKAWA (1907–1981)

Japanese physicist Yukawa was awarded the Nobel Prize in Physics in 1949 for predicting the existence of mesons. This photograph of him at work was taken in 1950 in his office at Columbia University. Yukawa came to Columbia in 1949 after spending the early part of his career in Japan.

FIGURE 31.4 Feynman diagram representing a photon mediating the electromagnetic force between two electrons.

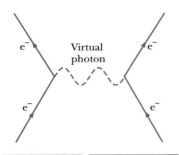

RICHARD FEYNMAN (1918–1988)

Inspired by Dirac, Feynman developed quantum electrodynamics, the theory of the interaction of light and matter on a relativistic and quantum basis. Feynman won the Nobel Prize in Physics in 1965. The prize was shared by Feynman, Julian Schwinger, and Sin Itiro Tomonaga. Early in his career, Feynman was a leading member of the team developing the first nuclear weapon in the Manhattan Project. Toward the end of his career, he worked on the commission investigating the 1986 *Challenger* tragedy and demonstrated the effects of cold temperatures on the rubber O-rings used in the space shuttle.

an antineutrino:

$$\pi^- \rightarrow \mu^- + \bar{\nu} \qquad [31.1]$$
$$\mu^- \rightarrow e^- + \nu + \bar{\nu}$$

Note that for chargeless particles (as well as some charged particles such as the proton), a bar over the symbol indicates an antiparticle.

The interaction between two particles can be represented in a simple qualitative graphical representation called a **Feynman diagram,** developed by American physicist Richard P. Feynman. Figure 31.4 is such a diagram for the electromagnetic interaction between two electrons approaching each other. A Feynman diagram is a qualitative graph of time in the vertical direction versus space in the horizontal direction. It is qualitative in the sense that the actual values of time and space are not important, but the overall appearance of the graph provides a representation of the process. The time evolution of the process can be approximated by starting at the bottom of the diagram and moving your eyes upward.

In the simple case of the electron–electron interaction in Figure 31.4, a photon is the field particle that mediates the electromagnetic force between the electrons. Notice that the entire interaction is represented in such a diagram as if it occurs at a single point in time. Therefore, the paths of the electrons appear to undergo a discontinuous change in direction at the moment of interaction. This representation is correct on a microscopic level over a time interval that includes the exchange of one photon. It is different from the paths produced over the much longer interval during which we watch the interaction from a macroscopic point of view. In this case, the paths would be curved (as in Fig. 31.2) due to the continuous exchange of large numbers of field particles, illustrating another aspect of the qualitative nature of Feynman diagrams.

In the electron–electron interaction, the photon, which transfers energy and momentum from one electron to the other, is called a *virtual photon* because it vanishes during the interaction without having been detected. In Chapter 28, we discussed that a photon has energy $E = hf$, where f is its frequency. Consequently, for a system of two electrons initially at rest, the system has energy $2m_e c^2$ before a virtual photon is released and energy $2m_e c^2 + hf$ after the virtual photon is released (plus any kinetic energy of the electron resulting from the emission of the photon). Is that a violation of the law of conservation of energy for an isolated system? No; this process does *not* violate the law of conservation of energy because the virtual photon has a very short lifetime Δt that makes the uncertainty in the energy $\Delta E \approx \hbar/2\,\Delta t$ of the system consisting of two electrons and the photon greater than the photon energy. Therefore, within the constraints of the uncertainty principle, the energy of the system is conserved.

Now consider a pion exchange between a proton and a neutron according to Yukawa's model (Fig. 31.5a). The energy ΔE_R needed to create a pion of mass m_π is given by Einstein's equation $\Delta E_R = m_\pi c^2$. As with the photon in Figure 31.4, the very existence of the pion would appear to violate the law of conservation of energy

FIGURE 31.5 (a) Feynman diagram representing a proton and a neutron interacting via the nuclear force with a neutral pion mediating the force. (This model is *not* the most fundamental model for nucleon interaction.) (b) Feynman diagram for an electron and a neutrino interacting via the weak force with a Z^0 boson mediating the force.

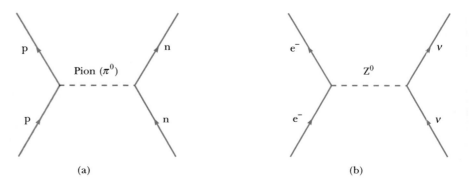

(a)   (b)

if the particle existed for a time greater than $\Delta t \approx \hbar/2\,\Delta E_R$ (from the uncertainty principle), where Δt is the time interval required for the pion to transfer from one nucleon to the other. Therefore,

$$\Delta t \approx \frac{\hbar}{2\,\Delta E_R} = \frac{\hbar}{2 m_\pi c^2} \qquad [31.2]$$

Because the pion cannot travel faster than the speed of light, the maximum distance d it can travel in a time interval Δt is $c\,\Delta t$. Therefore, using Equation 31.2 and $d = c\,\Delta t$, we find this maximum distance to be

$$d = c\,\Delta t \approx \frac{\hbar}{2 m_\pi c} \qquad [31.3]$$

From Chapter 30, we know that the range of the nuclear force is on the order of 10^{-15} fm. Using this value for d in Equation 31.3, we estimate the rest energy of the pion to be

$$m_\pi c^2 \approx \frac{\hbar c}{2d} = \frac{(1.055 \times 10^{-34}\,\text{J·s})(3.00 \times 10^8\,\text{m/s})}{2(1 \times 10^{-15}\,\text{m})}$$
$$= 1.6 \times 10^{-11}\,\text{J} \approx 100\,\text{MeV}$$

which corresponds to a mass of $100\,\text{MeV}/c^2$ (approximately 250 times the mass of the electron). This value is in reasonable agreement with the observed pion mass.

The concept we have just described is quite revolutionary. In effect, it says that a system of two nucleons can change into two nucleons plus a pion as long as it returns to its original state in a very short time interval. (Remember that this model is the older, historical one, which assumes that the pion is the field particle for the nuclear force.) Physicists often say that a nucleon undergoes *fluctuations* as it emits and absorbs pions. As we have seen, these fluctuations are a consequence of a combination of quantum mechanics (through the uncertainty principle) and special relativity (through Einstein's mass–energy relationship $E_R = mc^2$).

This section has dealt with the particles that mediate the nuclear force, pions, and the mediators of the electromagnetic force, photons. **Current ideas indicate that the nuclear force is more fundamentally described as an average or residual effect of the force between quarks,** as will be explained in Section 31.10. The graviton, which is the mediator of the gravitational force, has yet to be observed. The $W^\pm$ and Z^0 particles that mediate the weak force were discovered in 1983 by Italian physicist Carlo Rubbia (b. 1934) and his associates using a proton–antiproton collider. Rubbia and Simon van der Meer (b. 1925), both at CERN (European Organization for Nuclear Research), shared the 1984 Nobel Prize in Physics for the detection and identification of the $W^\pm$ and Z^0 particles and the development of the proton–antiproton collider. In this accelerator, protons and antiprotons undergo head-on collisions with each other. In some of the collisions, $W^\pm$ and Z^0 particles are produced, which in turn are identified by their decay products. Figure 31.5b shows a Feynman diagram for a weak interaction mediated by a Z^0 boson.

31.4 CLASSIFICATION OF PARTICLES

All particles other than field particles can be classified into two broad categories, *hadrons* and *leptons*. The criterion for separating these particles into categories is whether or not they interact via a force called the **strong force**. This force (discussed in Section 31.10) increases with separation distance, similar to the force exerted by a stretched spring. The nuclear force between nucleons in a nucleus is a particular manifestation of the strong force, but, as mentioned in Pitfall Prevention 31.2, we will use the term *strong force* in general to refer to any interaction between particles made up of more elementary units called quarks. (Today it is believed that hadrons are not elementary particles, but rather are composed of more elementary

TABLE 31.2	Some Particles and Their Properties										
Category	Particle Name	Symbol	Anti-particle	Mass (MeV/c^2)	B	L_e	L_μ	L_τ	S	Lifetime(s)	Principal Decay Modes[a]
Leptons	Electron	e^-	e^+	0.511	0	+1	0	0	0	Stable	
	Electron–neutrino	ν_e	$\bar{\nu}_e$	$< 7\,eV/c^2$	0	+1	0	0	0	Stable	
	Muon	μ^-	μ^+	105.7	0	0	+1	0	0	2.20×10^{-6}	$e^- \bar{\nu}_e \nu_\mu$
	Muon–neutrino	ν_μ	$\bar{\nu}_\mu$	< 0.3	0	0	+1	0	0	Stable	
	Tau	τ^-	τ^+	1 784	0	0	0	+1	0	$<4 \times 10^{-13}$	$\mu^- \bar{\nu}_\mu \nu_\tau, e^- \bar{\nu}_e \nu_\tau$
	Tau–neutrino	ν_τ	$\bar{\nu}_\tau$	< 30	0	0	0	+1	0	Stable	
Hadrons											
Mesons	Pion	π^+	π^-	139.6	0	0	0	0	0	2.60×10^{-8}	$\mu^+ \nu_\mu$
		π^0	Self	135.0	0	0	0	0	0	0.83×10^{-16}	2γ
	Kaon	K^+	K^-	493.7	0	0	0	0	+1	1.24×10^{-8}	$\mu^+ \nu_\mu, \pi^+ \pi^0$
		K_s^0	$\bar{K}_s^0$	497.7	0	0	0	0	+1	0.89×10^{-10}	$\pi^+ \pi^-, 2\pi^0$
		K_L^0	$\bar{K}_L^0$	497.7	0	0	0	0	+1	5.2×10^{-8}	$\pi^\pm e^\mp \bar{\nu}_e, 3\pi^0$ $\pi^\pm \mu^\mp \bar{\nu}_\mu$
	Eta	η	Self	548.8	0	0	0	0	0	$<10^{-18}$	$2\gamma, 3\pi^0$
		η'	Self	958	0	0	0	0	0	2.2×10^{-21}	$\eta\pi^+ \pi^-$
Baryons	Proton	p	$\bar{p}$	938.3	+1	0	0	0	0	Stable	
	Neutron	n	$\bar{n}$	939.6	+1	0	0	0	0	614	$pe^- \bar{\nu}_e$
	Lambda	Λ^0	$\bar{\Lambda}^0$	1 115.6	+1	0	0	0	−1	2.6×10^{-10}	$p\pi^-, n\pi^0$
	Sigma	Σ^+	$\bar{\Sigma}^-$	1 189.4	+1	0	0	0	−1	0.80×10^{-10}	$p\pi^0, n\pi^+$
		Σ^0	$\bar{\Sigma}^0$	1 192.5	+1	0	0	0	−1	6×10^{-20}	$\Lambda^0 \gamma$
		Σ^-	$\bar{\Sigma}^+$	1 197.3	+1	0	0	0	−1	1.5×10^{-10}	$n\pi^-$
	Delta	Δ^{++}	$\bar{\Delta}^{--}$	1 230	+1	0	0	0	0	6×10^{-24}	$p\pi^+$
		Δ^+	$\bar{\Delta}^-$	1 231	+1	0	0	0	0	6×10^{-24}	$p\pi^0, n\pi^+$
		Δ^0	$\bar{\Delta}^0$	1 232	+1	0	0	0	0	6×10^{-24}	$n\pi^0, p\pi^-$
		Δ^-	$\bar{\Delta}^+$	1 234	+1	0	0	0	0	6×10^{-24}	$n\pi^-$
	Xi	Ξ^0	$\bar{\Xi}^0$	1 315	+1	0	0	0	−2	2.9×10^{-10}	$\Lambda^0 \pi^0$
		Ξ^-	Ξ^+	1 321	+1	0	0	0	−2	1.64×10^{-10}	$\Lambda^0 \pi^-$
	Omega	Ω^-	Ω^+	1 672	+1	0	0	0	−3	0.82×10^{-10}	$\Xi^- \pi^0, \Xi^0 \pi^-, \Lambda^0 K^-$

[a]Notations in this column such as $p\pi^-$, $n\pi^0$ mean two possible decay modes. In this case, the two possible decays are $\Lambda^0 \rightarrow p + \pi^-$ and $\Lambda^0 \rightarrow n + \pi^0$.

units called quarks. We shall discuss quarks in Section 31.9.) Table 31.2 provides a summary of the properties of some of these particles.

Hadrons

Particles that interact through the strong force are called **hadrons.** The two classes of hadrons—*mesons* and *baryons*—are distinguished by their masses and spins.

Mesons all have zero or integer spin (0 or 1).[1] As indicated in Section 31.3, the origin of the name comes from the expectation that Yukawa's proposed meson mass would lie between the mass of the electron and the mass of the proton. Several meson masses do lie in this range, although there are heavier mesons that have masses larger than that of the proton.

All mesons are known to decay into final products including electrons, positrons, neutrinos, and photons. The pions are the lightest of the known mesons; they have masses of about 140 MeV/c^2 and a spin of 0. Another is the K meson, with a mass of approximately 500 MeV/c^2 and a spin of 0.

[1]Thus, the particle discovered by Anderson in 1937, the muon, is not a meson; the muon has spin $\frac{1}{2}$. It belongs in the *lepton* classification described shortly.

Baryons, the second class of hadrons, have masses equal to or greater than the proton mass (*baryon* means "heavy" in Greek), and their spins are always an odd half-integer value ($\frac{1}{2}$ or $\frac{3}{2}$). Protons and neutrons are baryons, as are many other particles. With the exception of the proton, all baryons decay in such a way that the end products include a proton. For example, the baryon called the Ξ hyperon decays to the Λ^0 baryon in about 10^{-10} s. The Λ^0 baryon then decays to a proton and a π^- in approximately 3×10^{-10} s.

Today it is believed that hadrons are not elementary particles, but rather are composed of more elementary units called quarks. We shall discuss quarks in Section 31.9.

Leptons

Leptons (from the Greek *leptos,* meaning "small" or "light") are a group of particles that participate in the electromagnetic (if charged) and weak interactions. All leptons have spins of $\frac{1}{2}$. Unlike hadrons, which have size and structure, **leptons appear to be truly elementary particles with no structure.**

Quite unlike hadrons, the number of known leptons is small. Currently, scientists believe that only six leptons exist: the electron, the muon, and the tau, e^-, μ^-, τ^-, and a neutrino associated with each, ν_e, ν_μ, ν_τ. The tau lepton, discovered in 1975, has a mass equal to about twice that of the proton. Direct experimental evidence for the neutrino associated with the tau was announced by the Fermi National Accelerator Laboratory (Fermilab) in July 2000. Each of these six leptons has an antiparticle.

Current studies indicate that neutrinos may have a small but nonzero mass. If they do have mass, they cannot travel at the speed of light. Also, so many neutrinos exist that their combined mass may be sufficient to cause all the matter in the Universe to eventually collapse to infinite density and then explode and create a completely new Universe! We shall discuss this concept in more detail in Section 31.12.

31.5 | CONSERVATION LAWS

We have seen the importance of conservation laws for isolated systems many times in earlier chapters and have solved problems using conservation of energy, linear momentum, angular momentum, and electric charge. Conservation laws are important in understanding why certain decays and reactions occur but others do not. In general, our familiar conservation laws provide us with a set of rules that all processes must follow.

Certain new conservation laws have been identified through experimentation and are important in the study of elementary particles. The members of the isolated system change identity during a decay or reaction. The initial particles before the decay or reaction are different from the final particles afterward.

Baryon Number

Experimental results tell us that whenever a baryon is created in a nuclear reaction or decay, an antibaryon is also created. This scheme can be quantified by assigning a baryon number $B = +1$ for all baryons, $B = -1$ for all antibaryons, and $B = 0$ for all other particles. Therefore, the **law of conservation of baryon number** states that **whenever a reaction or decay occurs, the sum of the baryon numbers of the system before the process must equal the sum of the baryon numbers after the process.** An equivalent statement is that the net number of baryons remains constant in any process.

If baryon number is absolutely conserved, the proton must be absolutely stable. For example, a decay of the proton to a positron and a neutral pion would satisfy

■ Conservation of baryon number

conservation of energy, momentum, and electric charge. Such a decay has never been observed, however. At present, we can say only that the proton has a half-life of at least 10^{33} years (the estimated age of the Universe is only 10^{10} years). There-fore, it is extremely unlikely that one would see a given proton undergo a decay process. If we collect a huge number of protons, however, perhaps we might see *some* proton in the collection undergo a decay, as addressed in Interactive Example 31.2.

QUICK QUIZ 31.2 Consider the following decay: $n \rightarrow \pi^+ + \pi^- + \mu^+ + \mu^-$. What conservation laws are violated by this decay? **(a)** energy **(b)** electric charge **(c)** baryon number **(d)** angular momentum **(e)** no conservation laws

---

QUICK QUIZ 31.3 Consider the following decay: $n \rightarrow p + \pi^-$. What conservation laws are violated by this decay? **(a)** energy **(b)** electric charge **(c)** baryon number **(d)** angular momentum **(e)** no conservation laws

---

EXAMPLE 31.1 **Checking Baryon Numbers**

A Use the law of conservation of baryon number to determine whether the reaction $p + n \rightarrow p + p + n + \bar{p}$ can occur.

Solution The left side of the equation gives a total baryon number of $1 + 1 = 2$. The right side gives a total baryon number of $1 + 1 + 1 + (-1) = 2$. Therefore, baryon number is conserved and the reaction can occur (provided the incoming proton has sufficient kinetic energy so that energy conservation is satisfied).

B Use the law of conservation of baryon numbers to determine whether the reaction $p + n \rightarrow p + p + \bar{p}$ can occur.

Solution The left side of the equation gives a total baryon number of $1 + 1 = 2$; the right side, however, gives $1 + 1 + (-1) = 1$. Because baryon number is not conserved, the reaction cannot occur.

INTERACTIVE EXAMPLE 31.2 **Detecting Proton Decay**

Measurements taken at the Super Kamiokande neutrino detection facility in Japan (Fig. 31.6) indicate that the half-life of protons is at least 10^{33} years.

A Estimate how long we would have to watch, on average, to see a proton in a glass of water decay.

Solution To conceptualize the problem, imagine the number of protons in a glass of water. Although this number is huge, we know that the probability of a single proton undergoing decay is small, so we would expect to wait a long time before observing a decay. Because a half-life is provided in the problem, we categorize this problem as one in which we can apply our statistical analysis techniques from Section 30.3. To analyze the problem, let us estimate that a glass contains about 250 g of water. The number of molecules of water is

$$\frac{(250 \text{ g})(6.02 \times 10^{23} \text{ molecules/mol})}{18 \text{ g/mol}}$$
$$= 8.4 \times 10^{24} \text{ molecules}$$

Each water molecule contains one proton in each of its two hydrogen atoms plus eight protons in its oxygen atom, for a total of ten. Therefore, 8.4×10^{25} protons are in the glass of water. The decay constant is given by Equation 30.8:

$$\lambda = \frac{0.693}{T_{1/2}} = \frac{0.693}{10^{33} \text{ yr}} = 6.9 \times 10^{-34} \text{ yr}^{-1}$$

This result is the probability that any one proton will decay in a year. The probability that *any* proton in our glass of water will decay in the one-year interval is (Eqs. 30.5 and 30.7)

$$R = (8.4 \times 10^{25})(6.9 \times 10^{-34} \text{ yr}^{-1}) = 5.8 \times 10^{-8} \text{ yr}^{-1}$$

To finalize this part of the problem, note that we have to watch our glass of water for $1/R \approx$ 17 million years! This answer is indeed a long time, as we suspected.

B The Super Kamiokande neutrino facility contains 50 000 metric tons of water. Estimate the average time interval between detected proton decays in this much water if the half-life of a proton is 10^{33} yr.

Solution We find the ratio of the number of molecules in 50 000 metric tons of water to that in the glass of water in part A, which will be same as the ratio of masses:

$$\frac{N_{\text{Kamiokande}}}{N_{\text{glass}}} = \frac{m_{\text{Kamiokande}}}{m_{\text{glass}}}$$

$$= \frac{50\,000\,\text{metric ton}}{250\,\text{g}} \left(\frac{1\,000\,\text{kg}}{1\,\text{metric ton}}\right)\left(\frac{1\,000\,\text{g}}{1\,\text{kg}}\right)$$

$$= 2.0 \times 10^8$$

$$N_{\text{Kamiokande}} = (2.0 \times 10^8)\,N_{\text{glass}}$$
$$= (2.0 \times 10^8)\,(8.4 \times 10^{24}\,\text{molecules})$$
$$= 1.7 \times 10^{33}\,\text{molecules}$$

Each of these molecules contains ten protons. The probability that one of these protons will decay in one year is

$$R = (10)(1.7 \times 10^{33})(6.9 \times 10^{-34}\,\text{yr}^{-1}) \approx 12\,\text{yr}^{-1}$$

To finalize this part of the problem, note that the average time interval between decays is about one twelfth of a year, or approximately one month. This result is much shorter than the time interval in part A due to the tremendous amount of water in the detector facility.

Physics⊗Now™ Practice the statistics of proton decay by logging into PhysicsNow at **www.pop4e.com** and going to Interactive Example 31.2.

FIGURE 31.6 (Interactive Example 31.2) This detector at the Super Kamiokande neutrino facility in Japan is used to study photons and neutrinos. It holds 50 000 metric tons of highly purified water and 13 000 photomultipliers. The photograph was taken while the detector was being filled. Technicians use a raft to clean the photodetectors before they are submerged. (Courtesy of ICRR [Institute for Cosmic Ray Research], University of Tokyo)

Lepton Number

From observations of commonly occurring decays of the electron, muon, and tau, we arrive at three conservation laws involving lepton numbers, one for each variety of lepton. The **law of conservation of electron-lepton number** states that **the sum of the electron-lepton numbers of the system before a reaction or decay must equal the sum of the electron-lepton numbers after the reaction or decay.**

∎ Conservation of electron-lepton number

The electron and the electron neutrino are assigned a positive electron-lepton number $L_e = +1$, the antileptons e^+ and $\bar{\nu}_e$ are assigned a negative electron-lepton number $L_e = -1$; all others have $L_e = 0$. For example, consider the decay of the neutron

$$n \rightarrow p + e^- + \bar{\nu}_e$$

Before the decay, the electron-lepton number is $L_e = 0$; after the decay, it is $0 + 1 + (-1) = 0$. Therefore, the electron-lepton number is conserved. It is important to recognize that the baryon number must also be conserved; which can easily be checked by noting that before the decay $B = +1$ and after the decay B is $+1 + 0 + 0 = +1$.

Similarly, when a decay involves muons, the muon-lepton number L_μ is conserved. The μ^- and the ν_μ are assigned positive numbers, $L_\mu = +1$, the antimuons μ^+ and $\overline{\nu}_\mu$ are assigned negative numbers, $L_\mu = -1$; all others have $L_\mu = 0$. Finally, the tau-lepton number L_τ is conserved, and similar assignments can be made for the tau lepton and its neutrino.

> **QUICK QUIZ 31.4** Consider the following decay: $\pi^0 \rightarrow \mu^- + e^+ + \nu_\mu$. What conservation laws are violated by this decay? **(a)** energy **(b)** angular momentum **(c)** electric charge **(d)** baryon number **(e)** electron-lepton number **(f)** muon-lepton number **(g)** tau-lepton number **(h)** no conservation laws

> **QUICK QUIZ 31.5** Suppose a claim is made that the decay of the neutron is given by $n \rightarrow p + e^-$. What conservation laws are violated by this decay? **(a)** energy **(b)** angular momentum **(c)** electric charge **(d)** baryon number **(e)** electron-lepton number **(f)** muon-lepton number **(g)** tau-lepton number **(h)** no conservation laws

EXAMPLE 31.3 Checking Lepton Numbers

A Use the law of conservation of electron-lepton number to determine if the decay scheme $\mu^- \rightarrow e^- + \overline{\nu}_e + \nu_\mu$ can occur.

Solution Because this decay involves a muon and an electron, L_μ and L_e must both be conserved. Before the decay, $L_\mu = +1$ and $L_e = 0$. After the decay, $L_\mu = 0 + 0 + 1 = +1$ and $L_e = +1 + (-1) + 0 = 0$. Therefore, both numbers are conserved, and on this basis the decay is possible.

B Use the law of conservation of electron-lepton number to determine if the decay scheme $\pi^+ \rightarrow \mu^+ + \nu_\mu + \nu_e$ can occur.

Solution Before the decay, $L_\mu = 0$ and $L_e = 0$. After the decay, $L_\mu = -1 + 1 + 0 = 0$, but $L_e = 0 + 0 + 1 = 1$. Therefore, the decay is not possible because electron-lepton number is not conserved.

31.6 | STRANGE PARTICLES AND STRANGENESS

Many particles discovered in the 1950s were produced by the nuclear interaction of pions with protons and neutrons in the atmosphere. A group of these particles—the kaon (K), lambda (Λ), and sigma (Σ) particles—exhibited unusual properties in production and decay and hence were called *strange particles*.

One unusual property is that these particles are always produced in pairs. For example, when a pion collides with a proton, two neutral strange particles are produced with high probability:

$$\pi^- + p \rightarrow \Lambda^0 + K^0$$

On the other hand, the reaction $\pi^- + p \rightarrow n^0 + K^0$ in which only one of the final particles is strange never occurs, even though no conservation laws known in the 1950s are violated and the energy of the pion is sufficient to initiate the reaction.

The second peculiar feature of strange particles is that, although they are produced by the strong force at a high rate, they do not decay at a very high rate into particles that interact via the strong force. Instead, they decay very slowly, which is characteristic of the weak interaction as shown in Table 31.1. Their half-lives are in the range 10^{-10} s to 10^{-8} s; most other particles that interact via the strong force have very short lifetimes, on the order of 10^{-20} s or less.

Such observations indicate the necessity to make modifications in our model. To explain these unusual properties of strange particles, a new quantum number S, called **strangeness,** was introduced into our model of elementary particles, together with a new conservation law. The strangeness numbers for some particles are given in Table 31.2. The production of strange particles in pairs is handled by assigning $S = +1$ to one of the particles and $S = -1$ to the other. All nonstrange particles are assigned strangeness $S = 0$. The **law of conservation of strangeness** states that **whenever a reaction or decay occurs via the strong force, the sum of the strangeness numbers of the system before the process must equal the sum of the strangeness numbers after the process.**

The low decay rate of strange particles can be explained by assuming that the nuclear and electromagnetic interactions obey the law of conservation of strangeness, but the weak interaction does not. Because the decay reaction involves the loss of one strange particle, it violates strangeness conservation and hence proceeds slowly via the weak interaction.

■ Conservation of strangeness

EXAMPLE 31.4   **Is Strangeness Conserved?**

A Determine whether the following reaction occurs on the basis of conservation of strangeness.

$$\pi^0 + n \quad \rightarrow \quad K^+ + \Sigma^-$$

Solution From Table 31.2, we see that the initial system has strangeness $S = 0 + 0 = 0$. Because the strangeness of the K^+ is $S = +1$ and the strangeness of the Σ^- is $S = -1$, the strangeness of the final sysstem is $+1 - 1 = 0$. Therefore, strangeness is conserved and the reaction is allowed.

B Show that the following reaction does not conserve strangeness.

$$\pi^- + p \quad \rightarrow \quad \pi^- + \Sigma^+$$

Solution The initial system has strangeness $S = 0 + 0 = 0$, and the final system has strangeness $S = 0 + (-1) = -1$. Therefore, strangeness is not conserved.

31.7 | MEASURING PARTICLE LIFETIMES

The bewildering array of entries in Table 31.2 leaves one yearning for firm ground. In fact, it is natural to wonder about an entry, for example, that shows a particle (Σ^0) that exists for 10^{-20} s and has a mass of $1\,192.5$ MeV/c^2. How is it possible to detect a particle that exists for only 10^{-20} s?

Most particles are unstable and are created in nature only rarely, in cosmic ray showers. In the laboratory, however, large numbers of these particles are created in controlled collisions between high-energy particles and a suitable target. The incident particles must have very high energy, and it takes a considerable time interval for electromagnetic fields to accelerate particles to high energies. Therefore, stable charged particles such as electrons or protons generally make up the incident beam. Similarly, targets must be simple and stable, and the simplest target, hydrogen, serves nicely as both target (the proton) and detector.

Figure 31.7 shows a typical event in which hydrogen in a bubble chamber served as both target source and detector. (A bubble chamber is a device in which the tracks of charged particles are made visible in liquid hydrogen that is maintained near its boiling point.) Many parallel tracks of negative pions are visible entering the photograph from the bottom. As the labels in the inset drawing show, one of the pions has hit a stationary proton in the hydrogen, producing two strange particles, Λ^0 and K^0, according to the reaction

$$\pi^- + p \quad \rightarrow \quad \Lambda^0 + K^0$$

Neither neutral strange particle leaves a track, but their subsequent decays into charged particles can be clearly seen as indicated in Figure 31.7. A magnetic field directed into the plane of the photograph causes the track of each charged particle to curve, and from the measured curvature one can determine the particle's charge

FIGURE 31.7 This bubble-chamber photograph shows many events, and the inset is a drawing of identified tracks. The strange particles Λ^0 and K^0 are formed at the bottom as the π^- interacts with a proton according to $\pi^- + p \rightarrow \Lambda^0 + K^0$. (Note that the neutral particles leave no tracks, as indicated by the dashed lines.) The Λ^0 and K^0 then decay according to $\Lambda^0 \rightarrow \pi^- + p$ and $K^0 \rightarrow \pi^0 + \mu^- + \bar{\nu}_\mu$.

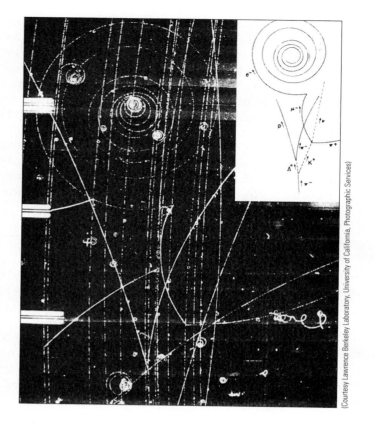

and linear momentum. If the mass and momentum of the incident particle are known, we can then usually calculate the product particle mass, kinetic energy, and speed from conservation of momentum and energy. Finally, by combining a product particle's speed with a measurable decay track length, we can calculate the product particle's lifetime. Figure 31.7 shows that sometimes one can use this lifetime technique even for a neutral particle, which leaves no track. As long as the beginning and end points of the missing track are known as well as the particle speed, one can infer the missing track length and find the lifetime of the neutral particle.

Resonance Particles

With clever experimental technique and much effort, decay track lengths as short as 10^{-6} m can be measured. Thus, lifetimes as short as 10^{-16} s can be measured for high-energy particles traveling at about the speed of light. We arrive at this result by assuming that a decaying particle travels 1 μm at a speed of $0.99c$ in the reference frame of the laboratory, yielding a lifetime of $\Delta t_{\text{lab}} = 1 \times 10^{-6}$ m$/0.99c \approx 3.4 \times 10^{-15}$ s. This result is not our final one, however, because we must account for the relativistic effects of time dilation. Because the proper lifetime Δt_p as measured in the decaying particle's reference frame is shorter than the laboratory frame value Δt_{lab} by a factor of $\sqrt{1 - (v^2/c^2)}$ (see Eq. 9.6), we can calculate the proper lifetime:

$$\Delta t_p = \Delta t_{\text{lab}} \sqrt{1 - \frac{v^2}{c^2}} = (3.4 \times 10^{-15} \text{ s}) \sqrt{1 - \frac{(0.99c)^2}{c^2}} = 4.8 \times 10^{-16} \text{ s}$$

Unfortunately, even with Einstein's help, the best answer we can obtain with the track length method is several orders of magnitude away from lifetimes of 10^{-20} s. How then can we detect the presence of particles that exist for time intervals like 10^{-20} s? For such short-lived particles, known as **resonance particles,** all we can do is infer their masses, their lifetimes, and, indeed, their very existence from data on their decay products.

31.8 | FINDING PATTERNS IN THE PARTICLES

A tool scientists use to help understand nature is the detection of patterns in data. One of the best examples of the use of this tool is the development of the periodic table, which provides fundamental understanding of the chemical behavior of the elements. The periodic table explains how more than a hundred elements can be formed from three particles: the electron, proton, and neutron. The number of observed particles and resonances observed by particle physicists is even larger than the number of elements. Is it possible that a small number of entities could exist from which all these particles could be built? Motivated by the success of the periodic table, let us explore the historical search for patterns among the particles.

Many classification schemes have been proposed for grouping particles into families. Consider, for instance, the baryons listed in Table 31.2 that have spins of $\frac{1}{2}$: p, n, Λ^0, Σ^+, Σ^0, Σ^-, Ξ^0, and Ξ^-. If we plot strangeness versus charge for these baryons using a sloping coordinate system, as in Figure 31.8a, we observe a fascinating pattern. Six of the baryons form a hexagon, and the remaining two are at the hexagon's center.[2]

As a second example, consider the following nine spin-zero mesons listed in Table 31.2: π^+, π^0, π^-, K^+, K^0, K^-, η, η', and the antiparticle $\overline{K}^0$. Figure 31.8b is a plot of strangeness versus charge for this family. Again, a hexagonal pattern emerges. In this case, each particle on the perimeter of the hexagon lies opposite its antiparticle, and the remaining three (which form their own antiparticles) are at its center. These and related symmetric patterns were developed independently in 1961 by Murray Gell-Mann and Yuval Ne'eman (b. 1925). Gell-Mann called the patterns the **eightfold way,** after the eightfold path to nirvana in Buddhism.

MURRAY GELL-MANN (b. 1929)

American physicist Gell-Mann was awarded the Nobel Prize in Physics in 1969 for his theoretical studies dealing with subatomic particles.

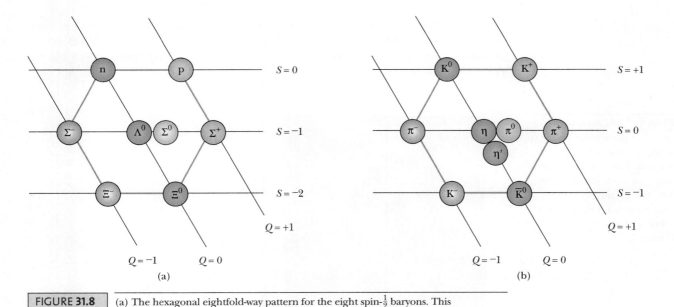

FIGURE 31.8 (a) The hexagonal eightfold-way pattern for the eight spin-$\frac{1}{2}$ baryons. This strangeness-versus-charge plot uses a sloping axis for charge number Q and a horizontal axis for strangeness S. (b) The eightfold-way pattern for the nine spin-zero mesons.

---

[2]The reason for the sloping coordinate system is so that a *regular* hexagon is formed, one with equal sides. If a normal orthogonal coordinate system is used, the pattern still appears, but the hexagonal shape does not have equal sides. Try it!

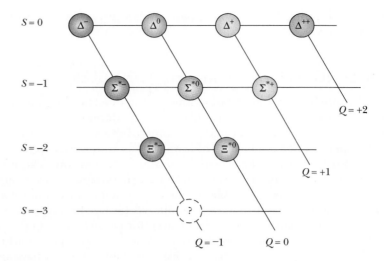

FIGURE 31.9 The pattern for the higher-mass, spin-$\frac{3}{2}$ baryons known at the time the pattern was proposed. The three Σ^* and two Ξ^* particles are excited states of the corresponding spin-$\frac{1}{2}$ particles in Figure 31.8. These excited states have higher mass and spin $\frac{3}{2}$. The absence of a particle in the bottom position was evidence of a new particle yet to be discovered, the Ω^-.

Groups of baryons and mesons can be displayed in many other symmetric patterns within the framework of the eightfold way. For example, the family of spin-$\frac{3}{2}$ baryons known in 1961 contains nine particles arranged in a pattern like that of the pins in a bowling alley as in Figure 31.9. [The particles Σ^{*+}, Σ^{*0}, Σ^{*-}, Ξ^{*0}, and Ξ^{*-} are excited states of the particles Σ^+, Σ^0, Σ^-, Ξ^0, and Ξ^-. In these higher-energy states, the spins of the three quarks (see Section 31.9) making up the particle are aligned so that the total spin of the particle is $\frac{3}{2}$.] When this pattern was proposed, an empty spot occurred in it (at the bottom position), corresponding to a particle that had never been observed. Gell-Mann predicted that the missing particle, which he called the omega minus (Ω^-), should have spin $\frac{3}{2}$, charge -1, strangeness -3, and rest energy of approximately 1 680 MeV. Shortly thereafter, in 1964, scientists at the Brookhaven National Laboratory found the missing particle through careful analyses of bubble-chamber photographs (Fig. 31.10) and confirmed all its predicted properties.

The prediction of the missing particle from the eightfold way has much in common with the prediction of missing elements in the periodic table. Whenever a vacancy occurs in an organized pattern of information, experimentalists have a guide for their investigations.

FIGURE 31.10 Discovery of the Ω^- particle. The photograph on the left shows the original bubble-chamber tracks. The drawing on the right isolates the tracks of the important events. The K^- particle at the bottom collides with a proton to produce the first detected Ω^- particle plus a K^0 and a K^+.

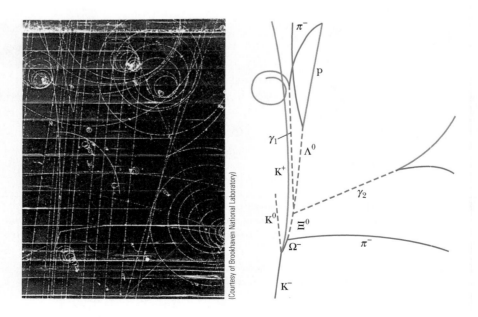

31.9 | QUARKS

As we have noted, leptons appear to be truly elementary particles because they occur in a small number of types, have no measurable size or internal structure, and do not seem to break down to smaller units. Hadrons, on the other hand, are complex particles having size and structure. The existence of the eightfold-way patterns suggests that hadrons have a more elemental substructure. Furthermore, we know that hundreds of types of hadrons exist and that many of them decay into other hadrons. These facts strongly suggest that hadrons cannot be truly elementary. In this section, we show that the complexity of hadrons can be explained by a simple substructure.

The Original Quark Model: A Structural Model for Hadrons

In 1963, Gell-Mann and George Zweig (b. 1937) independently proposed that hadrons have a more elemental substructure. According to their structural model, all hadrons are composite systems of two or three fundamental constituents called **quarks** (pronounced to rhyme with *forks*). (Gell-Mann borrowed the word *quark* from the passage "Three quarks for Muster Mark" in James Joyce's *Finnegan's Wake.*) The model proposes that three types of quarks exist, designated by the symbols u, d, and s. They are given the arbitrary names **up, down,** and **strange.** The various types of quarks are called **flavors.** Baryons consist of three quarks, and mesons consist of a quark and an antiquark. Active Figure 31.11 is a pictorial representation of the quark composition of several hadrons.

An unusual property of quarks is that they carry a fractional electronic charge. The u, d, and s quarks have charges of $+\frac{2}{3}e$, $-\frac{1}{3}e$, and $-\frac{1}{3}e$, respectively, where e is the elementary charge 1.6×10^{-19} C. These and other properties of quarks and antiquarks are given in Table 31.3. Notice that quarks have spin $\frac{1}{2}$, which means that all quarks are *fermions,* defined as any particle having half-integral spin. As Table 31.3 shows, associated with each quark is an antiquark of opposite charge, baryon number, and strangeness.

The composition of all hadrons known when Gell-Mann and Zweig presented their models can be completely specified by three simple rules:

• A meson consists of one quark and one antiquark, giving it a baryon number of 0, as required.
• A baryon consists of three quarks.
• An antibaryon consists of three antiquarks.

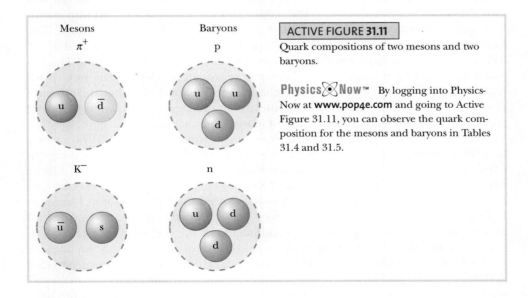

ACTIVE FIGURE **31.11**
Quark compositions of two mesons and two baryons.

Physics⊗Now™ By logging into Physics-Now at **www.pop4e.com** and going to Active Figure 31.11, you can observe the quark composition for the mesons and baryons in Tables 31.4 and 31.5.

TABLE 31.3				**Properties of Quarks and Antiquarks**				

Quarks

Name	Symbol	Spin	Charge	Baryon Number	Strangeness	Charm	Bottomness	Topness
Up	u	$\frac{1}{2}$	$+\frac{2}{3}e$	$\frac{1}{3}$	0	0	0	0
Down	d	$\frac{1}{2}$	$-\frac{1}{3}e$	$\frac{1}{3}$	0	0	0	0
Strange	s	$\frac{1}{2}$	$-\frac{1}{3}e$	$\frac{1}{3}$	-1	0	0	0
Charmed	c	$\frac{1}{2}$	$+\frac{2}{3}e$	$\frac{1}{3}$	0	$+1$	0	0
Bottom	b	$\frac{1}{2}$	$-\frac{1}{3}e$	$\frac{1}{3}$	0	0	$+1$	0
Top	t	$\frac{1}{2}$	$+\frac{2}{3}e$	$\frac{1}{3}$	0	0	0	$+1$

Antiquarks

Name	Symbol	Spin	Charge	Baryon Number	Strangeness	Charm	Bottomness	Topness
Anti-up	$\bar{u}$	$\frac{1}{2}$	$-\frac{2}{3}e$	$-\frac{1}{3}$	0	0	0	0
Anti-down	$\bar{d}$	$\frac{1}{2}$	$+\frac{1}{3}e$	$-\frac{1}{3}$	0	0	0	0
Anti-strange	$\bar{s}$	$\frac{1}{2}$	$+\frac{1}{3}e$	$-\frac{1}{3}$	$+1$	0	0	0
Anti-charmed	$\bar{c}$	$\frac{1}{2}$	$-\frac{2}{3}e$	$-\frac{1}{3}$	0	-1	0	0
Anti-bottom	$\bar{b}$	$\frac{1}{2}$	$+\frac{1}{3}e$	$-\frac{1}{3}$	0	0	-1	0
Anti-top	$\bar{t}$	$\frac{1}{2}$	$-\frac{2}{3}e$	$-\frac{1}{3}$	0	0	0	-1

The theory put forth by Gell-Mann and Zweig is referred to as the *original quark model.*

QUICK QUIZ 31.6 Using a coordinate system like that in Figure 31.8, draw an eightfold-way diagram for the three quarks in the original quark model.

Charm and Other Developments

Although the original quark model was highly successful in classifying particles into families, some discrepancies were evident between predictions of the model and certain experimental decay rates. It became clear that the structural model needed to be modified to remove these discrepancies. Consequently, several physicists proposed a fourth quark in 1967. They argued that if four leptons exist (as was thought at the time: the electron, the muon, and a neutrino associated with each), four quarks should also exist because of an underlying symmetry in nature. The fourth quark, designated by c, was given a property called **charm.** A **charmed** quark has charge $+\frac{2}{3}e$, but its charm distinguishes it from the other three quarks. This addition introduces a new quantum number C, representing charm. The new quark has charm $C = +1$, its antiquark has charm $C = -1$, and all other quarks have $C = 0$ as indicated in Table 31.3. Charm, like strangeness, is conserved in strong and electromagnetic interactions, but not in weak interactions.

Evidence that the charmed quark exists began to accumulate in 1974 when a new heavy particle called the J/Ψ particle (or simply Ψ) was discovered independently by two groups, one led by Burton Richter (b. 1931) at the Stanford Linear Accelerator (SLAC), and the other led by Samuel Ting (b. 1936) at the Brookhaven National Laboratory. Richter and Ting were awarded the Nobel Prize in Physics in 1976 for this work. The J/Ψ particle does not fit into the three-quark structural model; instead, it has properties of a combination of the proposed charmed quark and its antiquark ($c\bar{c}$). It is much more massive than the other known mesons ($\sim 3\ 100\ \text{MeV}/c^2$), and its lifetime is much longer than the lifetimes of particles that decay via the strong force. Soon, related mesons were discovered, corresponding to such quark combinations as $\bar{c}d$ and $c\bar{d}$, which all have large masses and long

TABLE 31.4	Quark Composition of Mesons									
		Antiquarks								
		$\bar{b}$		$\bar{c}$		$\bar{s}$		$\bar{d}$		$\bar{u}$	
Quarks	b	Υ	$(\bar{b}b)$	B_c^-	$(\bar{c}b)$	B_s^0	$(\bar{s}b)$	$\bar{B}^0$	$(\bar{d}b)$	B^-	$(\bar{u}b)$
	c	B_c^+	$(\bar{b}c)$	J/Ψ	$(\bar{c}c)$	D_s^+	$(\bar{s}c)$	D^+	$(\bar{d}c)$	D^0	$(\bar{u}c)$
	s	B_s^0	$(\bar{b}s)$	D_s^-	$(\bar{c}s)$	η, η'	$(\bar{s}s)$	$\bar{K}^0$	$(\bar{d}s)$	K^-	$(\bar{u}s)$
	d	B^0	$(\bar{b}d)$	D^-	$(\bar{c}d)$	K^0	$(\bar{s}d)$	π^0, η, η'	$(\bar{d}d)$	π^-	$(\bar{u}d)$
	u	B^+	$(\bar{b}u)$	$\bar{D}^0$	$(\bar{c}u)$	K^+	$(\bar{s}u)$	π^+	$(\bar{d}u)$	π^0, η, η'	$(\bar{u}u)$

Note: The top quark does not form mesons because it decays too quickly.

lifetimes. The existence of these new mesons provided firm evidence for the fourth quark flavor.

In 1975, researchers at Stanford University reported strong evidence for the tau (τ) lepton with a mass of 1 784 MeV/c^2. It is the fifth type of lepton to be discovered, which led physicists to propose that more flavors of quarks may exist, based on symmetry arguments similar to those leading to the proposal of the charmed quark. These proposals led to more elaborate quark models and the prediction of two new quarks: **top** (t) and **bottom** (b). To distinguish these quarks from the original four, quantum numbers called *topness* and *bottomness* (with allowed values $+1$, 0, -1) are assigned to all quarks and antiquarks (Table 31.3). In 1977, researchers at the Fermi National Laboratory, under the direction of Leon Lederman (b. 1922), reported the discovery of a very massive new meson Υ whose composition is considered to be $b\bar{b}$, providing evidence for the bottom quark. In March 1995, researchers at Fermilab announced the discovery of the top quark (supposedly the last of the quarks to be found), with a mass of 173 GeV/c^2.

Table 31.4 lists the quark compositions of mesons formed from the up, down, strange, charmed, and bottom quarks. Table 31.5 shows the quark combinations for the baryons listed in Table 31.2. Note that only two flavors of quarks, u and d, are contained in all hadrons encountered in ordinary matter (protons and neutrons).

You are probably wondering if such discoveries will ever end. How many "building blocks" of matter really exist? At present, physicists believe that the fundamental particles in nature are six quarks and six leptons (together with their antiparticles)

TABLE 31.5	Quark Composition of Several Baryons
Particle	**Quark Composition**
p	uud
n	udd
Λ^0	uds
Σ^+	uus
Σ^0	uds
Σ^-	dds
Δ^{++}	uuu
Δ^+	uud
Δ^0	udd
Δ^-	ddd
Ξ^0	uss
Ξ^-	dss
Ω^-	sss

Note: Some baryons have the same quark composition, such as the p and the Δ^+ and the n and the Δ^0. In these cases, the Δ particles are considered to be excited states of the proton and neutron.

TABLE **31.6**	The Elementary Particles and Their Rest Energies and Charges	
Particle	**Rest Energy**	**Charge**
Quarks		
u	360 MeV	$+\frac{2}{3}e$
d	360 MeV	$-\frac{1}{3}e$
s	540 MeV	$-\frac{1}{3}e$
c	1 500 MeV	$+\frac{2}{3}e$
b	5 GeV	$-\frac{1}{3}e$
t	173 GeV	$+\frac{2}{3}e$
Leptons		
e^-	511 keV	$-e$
μ^-	105.7 MeV	$-e$
τ^-	1 784 MeV	$-e$
ν_e	< 7 eV	0
ν_μ	< 0.3 MeV	0
ν_τ	< 30 MeV	0

listed in Table 31.6 and the field particles listed in Table 31.1. Table 31.6 lists the rest energies and charges of the quarks and leptons.

Despite extensive experimental effort, no isolated quark has ever been observed. Physicists now believe that quarks are permanently confined inside hadrons because of the strong force, which prevents them from escaping. Current efforts are under way to form a **quark-gluon plasma,** a state of matter in which the quarks are freed from neutrons and protons. In 2000, scientists at CERN announced evidence for a quark-gluon plasma formed by colliding lead nuclei. Experiments continue at CERN as well as at the Relativistic Heavy Ion Collider (RHIC) at Brookhaven to verify the production of a quark-gluon plasma.

▮ Thinking Physics 31.2

We have seen a law of conservation of *lepton number* and a law of conservation of *baryon number*. Why isn't there a law of conservation of *meson number*?

Reasoning We can argue from the point of view of creating particle–antiparticle pairs from available energy. (Review pair production in Section 31.2.) If energy is converted to rest energy of a lepton–antilepton pair, no net change occurs in lepton number because the lepton has a lepton number of $+1$ and the antilepton -1. Energy can also be transformed into rest energy of a baryon–antibaryon pair. The baryon has baryon number $+1$, the antibaryon -1, and no net change in baryon number occurs.

Now, however, suppose energy is transformed into rest energy of a quark–antiquark pair. By definition in quark theory, a quark–antiquark pair *is a meson*. Therefore, we have created a meson from energy because no meson existed before, now one does. Therefore, meson number is not conserved. With more energy, we can create more mesons, with no restriction from a conservation law other than that of energy. ▮

31.10 COLORED QUARKS

Shortly after the concept of quarks was proposed, scientists recognized that certain particles had quark compositions that violated the Pauli exclusion principle. As noted in Pitfall Prevention 29.4 in Chapter 29, all fermions obey the exclusion principle. Because all quarks are fermions with spin $\frac{1}{2}$, they are expected to follow the exclusion principle. One example of a particle that appears to violate the exclusion principle is the Ω^- (sss) baryon that contains three s quarks having parallel spins, giving it a total spin of $\frac{3}{2}$. Other examples of baryons that have identical quarks with parallel spins are the Δ^{++} (uuu) and the Δ^- (ddd). To resolve this problem, in 1965 Moo-Young Han (b. 1934) and Yoichiro Nambu (b. 1921) suggested a modification of the structural model of quarks in which quarks possess a new property called **color** or **color charge.** This property is similar in many respects to electric charge except that it occurs in three varieties called **red, green,** and **blue.** The antiquarks have the colors **antired, antigreen,** and **antiblue.** To satisfy the exclusion principle, all three quarks in a baryon must have different colors. Just as a combination of actual colors of light can produce the neutral color white, a combination of three quarks with different colors is also described as white, or colorless. A meson consists of a quark of one color and an antiquark of the corresponding anticolor. The result is that baryons and mesons are always colorless (or white).

Although the concept of color in the quark model was originally conceived to satisfy the exclusion principle, it also provided a better theory for explaining certain experimental results. For example, the modified theory correctly predicts the lifetime of the π^0 meson. The theory of how quarks interact with one another is called **quantum chromodynamics,** or QCD, to parallel quantum electrodynamics (the theory of interaction between electric charges). In QCD, the quark is said to carry a **color charge,** in analogy to electric charge. The strong force between quarks is often called the **color force.**

The color force between quarks is analogous to the electric force between charges; like colors repel and opposite colors attract. Therefore, two green quarks repel each other, but a green quark is attracted to an antigreen quark. The attraction between quarks of opposite color to form a meson (q$\bar{\text{q}}$) is indicated in Figure 31.12a. Differently colored quarks also attract one another, but with less strength than opposite colors of quark and antiquark. For example, a cluster of red, blue, and green quarks all attract one another to form a baryon as indicated in Figure 31.12b. Therefore, every baryon contains three quarks of three different colors.

As stated earlier, the strong force between quarks is carried by massless particles that travel at the speed of light called **gluons.** According to QCD, there are eight gluons, all carrying two color charges, a color and an anticolor such as a "blue–antired" gluon. When a quark emits or absorbs a gluon, its color changes. For example, a blue quark that emits a blue–antired gluon becomes a red quark, and a red quark that absorbs this gluon becomes a blue quark.

Figure 31.13a shows the interaction between a neutron and a proton by means of Yukawa's pion, in this case a π^-. In Figure 31.13a, the charged pion carries charge from one nucleon to the other, so the nucleons change identities and the

▦ **PITFALL PREVENTION 31.3**

COLOR IS NOT REALLY COLOR The description of color for a quark has nothing to do with visual sensation from light. It is simply a convenient name for a property analogous to electric charge, except that we need to combine three types of this property to achieve neutrality.

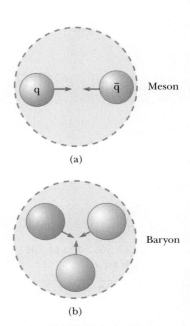

(a)

(b)

FIGURE 31.12 (a) A green quark is attracted to an antigreen quark, forming a meson whose quark structure is (q$\bar{\text{q}}$). (b) Three quarks of different colors attract one another to form a baryon.

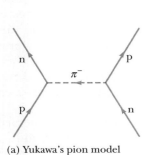

(a) Yukawa's pion model

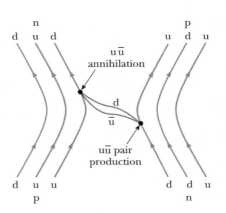

(b) Quark model

FIGURE 31.13 (a) A nuclear interaction between a proton and a neutron explained in terms of Yukawa's pion-exchange model. Because the pion carries charge, the proton and neutron switch identities. (b) The same interaction, explained in terms of quarks and gluons. Note that the exchanged $\bar{\text{u}}$d quark pair makes up a π^- meson.

proton becomes a neutron and the neutron becomes a proton. (This process differs from Fig. 31.5, in which the field particle is a π^0, resulting in no transfer of charge from one nucleon to the other.)

Let us look at the same interaction from the viewpoint of the quark model shown in Figure 31.13b. In this Feynman diagram, the proton and neutron are represented by their quark constituents. Each quark in the neutron and proton is continuously emitting and absorbing gluons. The energy of a gluon can result in the creation of quark–antiquark pairs. This is similar to the creation of electron–positron pairs in pair production, which we investigated in Section 31.2. When the neutron and proton approach to within 1 to 2 fm of each other, these gluons and quarks can be exchanged between the two nucleons, and such exchanges produce the strong force. Figure 31.13b depicts one possibility for the process shown in Figure 31.13a. A down quark in the neutron on the right emits a gluon. The energy of the gluon is then transformed to create a $u\bar{u}$ pair. The u quark stays within the nucleon (which has now changed to a proton), and the recoiling d quark and the $\bar{u}$ antiquark are transmitted to the proton on the left side of the diagram. Here the $\bar{u}$ annihilates a u quark within the proton and the d is captured. Therefore, the net effect is to change a u quark to a d quark, and the proton has changed to a neutron.

As the d quark and $\bar{u}$ antiquark in Figure 31.13 transfer between the nucleons, the d and $\bar{u}$ exchange gluons with each other and can be considered to be bound to each other by means of the strong force. If we look back at Table 31.4, we see that this combination is a π^-, which is Yukawa's field particle! Therefore, the quark model of interactions between nucleons is consistent with the pion-exchange model.

31.11 THE STANDARD MODEL

Scientists now believe that there are three classifications of truly elementary particles: leptons, quarks, and field particles. These three particles are further classified as either fermions or bosons. Quarks and leptons have spin $\frac{1}{2}$ and hence are fermions, whereas the field particles have integral spin of 1 or higher and are bosons.

Recall from Section 31.1 that the weak force is believed to be mediated by the W^+, W^-, and Z^0 bosons. These particles are said to have *weak charge* just as quarks have color charge. Therefore, each elementary particle can have mass, electric charge, color charge, and weak charge. Of course, one or more of these could be zero.

In 1979, Sheldon Glashow (b. 1932), Abdus Salam (1926–1996), and Steven Weinberg (b. 1933) won the Nobel Prize in Physics for developing a theory that unified the electromagnetic and weak interactions. This **electroweak theory** postulates that the weak and electromagnetic interactions have the same strength at very high particle energies. The two interactions are viewed as two different manifestations of a single unifying electroweak interaction. The photon and the three massive bosons ($W^\pm$ and Z^0) play a key role in the electroweak theory. The theory makes many concrete predictions, but perhaps the most spectacular is the prediction of the masses of the W and Z particles at about 82 GeV/c^2 and 93 GeV/c^2, respectively. The 1984 Nobel Prize in Physics was awarded to Carlo Rubbia and Simon van der Meer for their work leading to the discovery of these particles at these energies at the CERN Laboratory in Geneva, Switzerland.

The combination of the electroweak theory and QCD for the strong interaction form what is referred to in high-energy physics as the **Standard Model.** Although the details of the Standard Model are complex, its essential ingredients can be summarized with the help of Figure 31.14. (The Standard Model does not include the gravitational force at present; we include gravity in Fig. 31.14, however, because physicists hope to eventually incorporate this force into a unified theory.) This

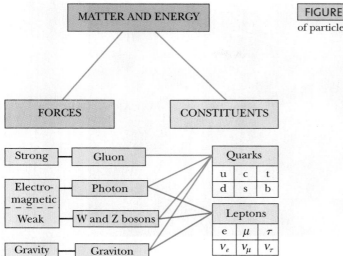

FIGURE 31.14 The Standard Model of particle physics.

diagram shows that quarks participate in all the fundamental forces and that leptons participate in all except the strong force.

The Standard Model does not answer all questions. A major question that is still unanswered is why, of the two mediators of the electroweak interaction, the photon has no mass but the W and Z bosons do. Because of this mass difference, the electromagnetic and weak forces are quite distinct at low energies but become similar at very high energies, when the rest energy is negligible relative to the total energy. The behavior as one goes from high to low energies is called *symmetry breaking* because the forces are similar, or symmetric, at high energies but are very different at low energies. The nonzero rest energies of the W and Z bosons raise the question of the origin of particle masses. To resolve this problem, a hypothetical particle called the **Higgs boson,** which provides a mechanism for breaking the electroweak symmetry, has been proposed. The Standard Model, modified to include the Higgs mechanism, provides a logically consistent explanation of the massive nature of the W and Z bosons. Unfortunately, the Higgs boson has not yet been found, but physicists know that its rest energy should be less than 1 TeV. To determine whether the Higgs boson exists, two quarks of at least 1 TeV of energy must collide. Calculations show, however, that this process requires injecting 40 TeV of energy within the volume of a proton.

Scientists are convinced that because the energy available in conventional accelerators using fixed targets is too limited, it is necessary to build colliding-beam accelerators called **colliders.** The concept of colliders is straightforward. Particles with equal masses and kinetic energies, traveling in opposite directions in an accelerator ring, collide head-on to produce the required reaction and the formation of new particles. Because the total momentum of the isolated system of interacting particles is zero, all their kinetic energy is available for the reaction. The Large Electron–Positron (LEP) Collider at CERN (Fig. 31.15), near Geneva, Switzerland, and the Stanford Linear Collider in California collide both electrons and positrons. The Super Proton Synchrotron at CERN accelerates protons and antiprotons to energies of 270 GeV. The world's highest energy proton accelerator, the Tevatron located at Fermilab in Illinois, produces protons at almost 1 000 GeV (1 TeV). CERN expects a 2007 completion date for the Large Hadron Collider (LHC), a proton–proton collider that will provide a center of mass energy of 14 TeV and allow an exploration of Higgs boson physics. The accelerator will be constructed in the same 27-km circumference tunnel now housing the LEP collider, and many countries will participate in the project.

(Courtesy of CERN)

FIGURE 31.15 A view from inside the Large Electron–Positron (LEP) Collider tunnel, which is 27 km in circumference.

FIGURE 31.16 Computers at Fermilab create a pictorial representation such as this one of the paths of particles after a collision.

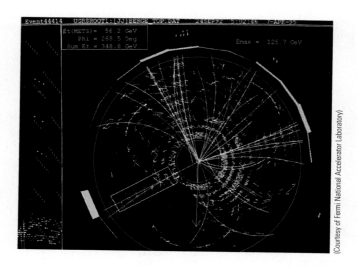

(Courtesy of Fermi National Accelerator Laboratory)

In addition to increasing energies in modern accelerators, detection techniques have become increasingly sophisticated. Figure 31.16 shows the computer-generated pictorial representation of the tracks of particles after a collision from a modern particle detector.

∎ Thinking Physics 31.3

Consider a car making a head-on collision with an identical car moving in the opposite direction at the same speed. Compare that collision with one of the cars making a collision with the second car at rest. In which collision is the transformation of kinetic energy to other forms larger? How does this example relate to particle accelerators?

Reasoning In the head-on collision with both cars moving, conservation of momentum for the system of two cars requires that the cars come to rest during the collision. Therefore, *all* the original kinetic energy is transformed to other forms. In the collision between a moving car and a stationary car, the cars are still moving with reduced speed after the collision, in the direction of the initially moving car. Therefore, *only part* of the kinetic energy is transformed to other forms.

This example suggests the importance of colliding beams in a particle accelerator as opposed to firing a beam into a stationary target. When particles moving in opposite directions collide, all the kinetic energy is available for transformation into other forms, which in this case is the creation of new particles. When a beam is fired into a stationary target, only part of the energy is available for transformation, so higher mass particles cannot be created. ∎

31.12 INVESTIGATING THE SMALLEST SYSTEM TO UNDERSTAND THE LARGEST

CONTEXT CONNECTION

In this section, we shall describe further one of the most fascinating theories in all science—the Big Bang theory of the creation of the Universe, introduced in the Context Connection of Chapter 28—and the experimental evidence that supports it. This theory of cosmology states that the Universe had a beginning and, further, that the beginning was so cataclysmic that it is impossible to look back beyond it. According to this theory, the Universe erupted from a singularity with infinite density about 15 to 20 billion years ago. The first few fractions of a second after the Big Bang saw such extremes of energy that all four fundamental forces of physics were believed to be unified and all matter was contained in a quark-gluon plasma.

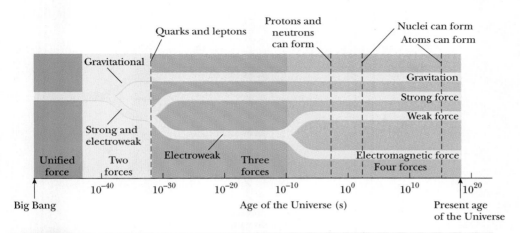

FIGURE 31.17 A brief history of the Universe from the Big Bang to the present. The four forces became distinguishable during the first nanosecond. Following that, all the quarks combined to form particles that interact via the strong force. The leptons remained separate, however, and exist as individually observable particles to this day.

The evolution of the four fundamental forces from the Big Bang to the present is shown in Figure 31.17. During the first 10^{-43} s (the ultrahot epoch, $T \sim 10^{32}$ K), it is presumed that the strong, electroweak, and gravitational forces were joined to form a completely unified force. In the first 10^{-35} s following the Big Bang (the hot epoch, $T \sim 10^{29}$ K), gravity broke free of this unification while the strong and electroweak forces remained unified. During this period, particle energies were so great ($> 10^{16}$ GeV) that very massive particles as well as quarks, leptons, and their antiparticles existed. Then, after 10^{-35} s, the Universe rapidly expanded and cooled (the warm epoch, $T \sim 10^{29} - 10^{15}$ K), and the strong and electroweak forces parted company. As the Universe continued to cool, the electroweak force split into the weak force and the electromagnetic force about 10^{-10} s after the Big Bang.

After a few minutes, protons condensed out of the plasma. For half an hour the Universe underwent thermonuclear detonation, exploding like a hydrogen bomb and producing most of the helium nuclei that now exist. The Universe continued to expand and its temperature dropped. Until about 700 000 years after the Big Bang, the Universe was dominated by radiation. Energetic radiation prevented matter from forming single hydrogen atoms because collisions would instantly ionize any atoms that happened to form. Photons experienced continuous Compton scattering from the vast numbers of free electrons, resulting in a Universe that was opaque to radiation. By the time the Universe was about 700 000 years old, it had expanded and cooled to about 3 000 K, and protons could bind to electrons to form neutral hydrogen atoms. Because of the quantized energies of the atoms, far more wavelengths of radiation were not absorbed by atoms than were, and the Universe suddenly became transparent to photons. Radiation no longer dominated the Universe, and clumps of neutral matter steadily grew, first atoms, followed by molecules, gas clouds, stars, and finally galaxies.

Evidence for the Expanding Universe

In Chapter 28, we discussed the observation of blackbody radiation by Penzias and Wilson that represents the leftover glow from the Big Bang. We discuss here additional relevant astronomical observations. Vesto Melvin Slipher (1875–1969), an American astronomer, reported that most nebulae are receding from the Earth at speeds up to several million miles per hour. Slipher was one of the first to use the methods of Doppler shifts in spectral lines to measure galactic speeds.

FIGURE 31.18 Hubble's law. The speed of recession is directly proportional to distance. Data points for four galaxies are shown here.

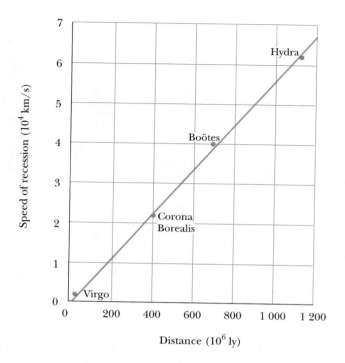

In the late 1920s, Edwin P. Hubble (1889–1953) made the bold assertion that the whole Universe is expanding. From 1928 to 1936, he and Milton Humason (1891–1972) toiled at the Mount Wilson Observatory in California to prove this assertion until they reached the limits of that 100-in. telescope. The results of this work and its continuation on a 200-in. telescope in the 1940s showed that the speeds of galaxies increase in direct proportion to their distance R from us (Fig. 31.18). This linear relationship, known as **Hubble's law,** may be written as

■ Hubble's law

$$v = HR \qquad [31.7]$$

where H, called the **Hubble parameter,** has the approximate value

$$H \approx 17 \times 10^{-3} \, \text{m/(s·ly)}$$

EXAMPLE 31.5 Recession of a Quasar

A quasar is an object that appears similar to a star and that is very distant from the Earth. Its speed can be measured from Doppler shift measurements in the light it emits.

A A certain quasar recedes from the Earth at a speed of $0.55c$. How far away is it?

Solution We can find the distance from Hubble's law:

$$R = \frac{v}{H} = \frac{(0.55)(3.00 \times 10^8 \, \text{m/s})}{17 \times 10^{-3} \, \text{m/(s·ly)}} = \boxed{9.7 \times 10^9 \, \text{ly}}$$

B Suppose we assume that the quasar has moved at this speed ever since the Big Bang. With this assumption, estimate the age of the Universe.

Solution We approximate the distance from the Earth to the quasar as the distance that the quasar has moved from the singularity since the Big Bang. We can then find the time interval from a calculation as performed in Chapter 2: $\Delta t = \Delta x / v = R / v = 1/H \approx 18$ billion years, which is in approximate agreement with other calculations.

Will the Universe Expand Forever?

In the 1950s and 1960s, Allan R. Sandage (b. 1926) used the 200-in. telescope at the Mount Palomar Observatory in California to measure the speeds of galaxies at distances of up to 6 billion lightyears from the Earth. These measurements showed

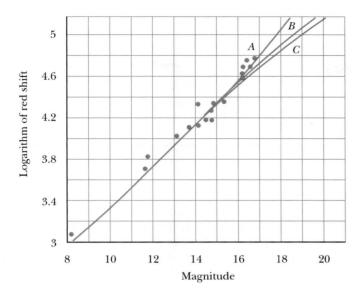

FIGURE 31.19 Red shift, or speed of recession, versus magnitude (which is related to brightness) of 18 faint galaxy clusters. Significant scatter of the data occurs, so the extrapolation of the curve to the upper right is uncertain. Curve A is the trend suggested by the six faintest clusters. Curve C corresponds to a Universe having a constant rate of expansion. If more data are taken and the complete set of data indicates a curve that falls between B and C, the expansion will slow but never stop. If the data fall to the left of B, expansion will eventually stop and the Universe will begin to contract.

that these very distant galaxies were moving about 10 000 km/s faster than Hubble's law predicted. According to this result, the Universe must have been expanding more rapidly 1 billion years ago, and consequently the expansion is slowing (Fig. 31.19). Today, astronomers and physicists are trying to determine the rate of slowing.

If the average mass density of atoms in the Universe is less than some critical density (about 3 atoms/m^3), the galaxies will slow in their outward rush but still escape to infinity. If the average density exceeds the critical value, the expansion will eventually stop and contraction will begin, possibly leading to a new superdense state and another expansion. In this scenario, we have an **oscillating Universe.**

EXAMPLE 31.6 **The Critical Density of the Universe**

Estimate the critical mass density ρ_c of the Universe, using energy considerations.

Solution Figure 31.20 shows a large section of the Universe with radius R, containing galaxies with a total mass M. Let us apply the isolated system model to an escaping galaxy and the section of the Universe; a galaxy of mass m and speed v at R will just escape to infinity with zero speed if the sum of its kinetic energy and the gravitational potential energy of the system is zero. The Universe may be infinite in extent, but a theorem such as the gravitational form of Gauss's law implies that only the mass inside the sphere contributes to the gravitational potential energy of the system of the sphere and the galaxy. Therefore,

$$E_{\text{total}} = 0 = K + U = \tfrac{1}{2}mv^2 - \frac{GmM}{R}$$

$$\tfrac{1}{2}mv^2 = \frac{Gm\tfrac{4}{3}\pi R^3 \rho_c}{R}$$

$$(1) \quad v^2 = \frac{8\pi G}{3}R^2\rho_c$$

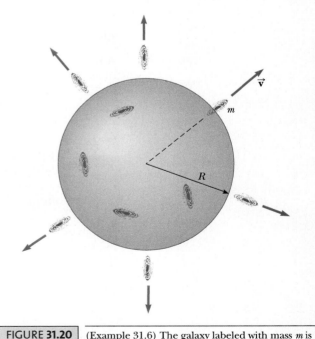

FIGURE 31.20 (Example 31.6) The galaxy labeled with mass m is escaping from a large cluster of galaxies contained within a spherical volume of radius R. Only the mass within the sphere slows the escaping galaxy.

Because the galaxy of mass m obeys the Hubble law, $v = HR$, (1) becomes

$$H^2 = \frac{8\pi G}{3}\rho_c$$

$$(2)\quad \rho_c = \frac{3H^2}{8\pi G}$$

Using $H = 17 \times 10^{-3}\,\text{m}/(\text{s}\cdot\text{ly})$, where $1\,\text{ly} = 9.46 \times 10^{12}\,\text{km}$, and $G = 6.67 \times 10^{-11}\,\text{N}\cdot\text{m}^2/\text{kg}^2$ yields the critical density $\rho_c = 6 \times 10^{-30}\,\text{g/cm}^3$. Because the mass of a hydrogen atom is $1.67 \times 10^{-24}\,\text{g}$, the value calculated for ρ_c corresponds to 3×10^{-6} hydrogen atoms per cubic centimeter or 3 atoms per cubic meter.

Missing Mass in the Universe?

The luminous matter in galaxies averages out to a Universe density of about $5 \times 10^{-33}\,\text{g/cm}^3$. The radiation in the Universe has a mass equivalent of approximately 2% of the visible matter. The total mass of all nonluminous matter (such as interstellar gas and black holes) may be estimated from the speeds of galaxies orbiting one another in a cluster. The higher the galaxy speeds, the more mass in the cluster. Measurements on the Coma cluster of galaxies indicate that the amount of nonluminous matter is 20 to 30 times the amount of luminous matter present in stars and luminous gas clouds. Yet even this large invisible component of dark matter, if extrapolated to the Universe as a whole, leaves the observed mass density a factor of 10 less than ρ_c. The deficit, called *missing mass,* has been the subject of intense theoretical and experimental work. Exotic particles such as axions, photinos, and superstring particles have been suggested as candidates for the missing mass. More mundane proposals argue that the missing mass is present in certain galaxies as neutrinos. In fact, neutrinos are so abundant that a tiny neutrino rest energy on the order of only 20 eV would furnish the missing mass and "close" the Universe. Therefore, current experiments designed to measure the rest energy of the neutrino will affect predictions for the future of the Universe, showing a clear connection between one of the smallest pieces of the Universe and the Universe as a whole!

Mysterious Energy in the Universe?

A surprising twist in the story of the Universe arose in 1998 with the observation of a class of supernovae that have a fixed absolute brightness. By combining the apparent brightness and the redshift of light from these explosions, their distance and speed of recession of the Earth can be determined. These observations led to the conclusion that the expansion of the Universe is not slowing down but rather is accelerating! Observations by other groups also led to the same interpretation.

To explain this acceleration, physicists have proposed *dark energy,* which is energy possessed by the vacuum of space. In the early life of the Universe, gravity dominated over the dark energy. As the Universe expanded and the gravitational force between galaxies became smaller because of the great distances between them, the dark energy became more important. The dark energy results in an effective repulsive force that causes the expansion rate to increase.[3]

---

[3]For a discussion of dark energy, see S. Perlmutter, "Supernovae, Dark Energy, and the Accelerating Universe," *Physics Today,* 56(4): 53–60, April 2003.

Although we have some degree of certainty about the beginning of the Universe, we are uncertain about how the story will end. Will the Universe keep on expanding forever, or will it someday collapse and then expand again, perhaps in an endless series of oscillations? Results and answers to these questions remain inconclusive, and the exciting controversy continues.

SUMMARY

Physics⊗Now™ Take a practice test by logging into Physics-Now at **www.pop4e.com** and clicking on the Pre-Test link for this chapter.

There are four fundamental forces in nature: **strong, electromagnetic, weak,** and **gravitational.** The strong force is the force between quarks. A residual effect of the strong force is the **nuclear force** between nucleons that keeps the nucleus together. The weak force is responsible for beta decay. The electromagnetic and weak forces are now considered to be manifestations of a single force called the **electroweak force.** Every fundamental interaction is mediated by the exchange of **field particles.** The electromagnetic interaction is mediated by the photon; the weak interaction is mediated by the $W^{\pm}$ and Z^0 **bosons;** the gravitational interaction is mediated by **gravitons;** the strong interaction is mediated by **gluons.**

An **antiparticle** and a particle have the same mass, but opposite charge, and other properties may have opposite values such as lepton number and baryon number. It is possible to produce particle–antiparticle pairs in nuclear reactions if the available energy is greater than $2mc^2$, where m is the mass of the particle (or antiparticle).

Particles other than field particles are classified as hadrons or leptons. **Hadrons** interact through the strong force. They have size and structure and are not elementary particles. Hadrons are of two types, baryons and mesons. **Mesons** have baryon number zero and have either zero or integral spin. **Baryons,** which generally are the most massive particles, have nonzero baryon number and a spin of $\frac{1}{2}$ or $\frac{3}{2}$. The neutron and proton are examples of baryons.

Leptons have no structure or size and are considered truly elementary. They interact through the weak and electromagnetic forces. The six leptons are the electron e^-, the muon μ^-, the tau τ^-; and their neutrinos ν_e, ν_μ, and ν_τ.

In all reactions and decays, quantities such as energy, linear momentum, angular momentum, electric charge, baryon number, and lepton number are strictly conserved. Certain particles have properties called **strangeness** and **charm.** These unusual properties are conserved only in those reactions and decays that occur via the strong force.

Theories in elementary particle physics have postulated that all hadrons are composed of smaller units known as **quarks.** Quarks have fractional electric charge and come in six "flavors": **up** (u), **down** (d), **strange** (s), **charmed** (c), **top** (t), and **bottom** (b). Each baryon contains three quarks, and each meson contains one quark and one antiquark.

According to the theory of **quantum chromodynamics,** quarks have a property called **color charge,** and the strong force between quarks is referred to as the **color force.**

QUESTIONS

☐ = answer available in the *Student Solutions Manual and Study Guide*

1. Name the four fundamental forces and the field particle that mediates each.

2. Describe the quark model of hadrons, including the properties of quarks.

3. What are the differences between hadrons and leptons?

4. Describe the properties of baryons and mesons and the important differences between them.

5. Particles known as resonances have very short lifetimes, on the order of 10^{-23} s. From this information, would you guess that they are hadrons or leptons? Explain.

6. Kaons all decay into final states that contain no protons or neutrons. What is the baryon number of kaons?

7. Two protons in a nucleus interact via the nuclear interaction. Are they also subject to the weak interaction?

8. The Ξ^0 particle decays by the weak interaction according to the decay mode $\Xi^0 \rightarrow \Lambda^0 + \pi^0$. Would you expect this decay to be fast or slow? Explain.

9. Identify the particle decays in Table 31.2 that occur by the weak interaction. Justify your answers.

10. Identify the particle decays in Table 31.2 that occur by the electromagnetic interaction. Justify your answers.

11. Discuss the following conservation laws: energy, linear momentum, angular momentum, electric charge, baryon number, lepton number, and strangeness. Are all these laws based on fundamental properties of nature? Explain.

12. An antibaryon interacts with a meson. Can a baryon be produced in such an interaction? Explain.

13. Describe the essential features of the Standard Model of particle physics.

14. How many quarks are in each of the following: (a) a baryon, (b) an antibaryon, (c) a meson, (d) an antimeson? How do you explain that baryons have half-integral spins, whereas mesons have spins of 0 or 1? (*Note:* Quarks have spin $\frac{1}{2}$.)

15. In the theory of quantum chromodynamics, quarks come in three colors. How would you justify the statement that "all baryons and mesons are colorless"?

16. Which baryon did Murray Gell-Mann predict in 1961? What is the quark composition of this particle?

17. What is the quark composition of the Ξ^- particle? (See Table 31.5.)

18. The W and Z bosons were first produced at CERN in 1983 by causing a beam of protons and a beam of antiprotons to meet at high energy. Why was this discovery important?

19. How did Edwin Hubble determine in 1928 that the Universe is expanding?

20. Neutral atoms did not exist until hundreds of thousands of years after the Big Bang. Why?

21. What does the infinite range of the electromagnetic and gravitational interactions tell you about the masses of the photon and the graviton?

22. If high-energy electrons, with deBroglie wavelengths smaller than the size of the nucleus, are scattered from nuclei, the behavior of the electrons is consistent with scattering from very dense structures much smaller in size than the nucleus—quarks. Is this experiment similar to another classic experiment that detected small structures in atoms? Explain.

23. Observations of galaxies outside our Local Group show that they are all moving away from us. Is it therefore correct to propose that we are at the center of the Universe?

PROBLEMS

1, 2, 3 = straightforward, intermediate, challenging
☐ = full solution available in the *Student Solutions Manual and Study Guide*

Physics⊗Now™ = coached problem with hints available at **www.pop4e.com**

🖥 = computer useful in solving problem

▨ = paired numerical and symbolic problems

▨ = biomedical application

Section 31.1 ∎ The Fundamental Forces in Nature

Section 31.2 ∎ Positrons and Other Antiparticles

1. A photon produces a proton–antiproton pair according to the reaction $\gamma \rightarrow p + \bar{p}$. What is the minimum possible frequency of the photon? What is its wavelength?

2. ▨ At some time in your past or future, you may find yourself in a hospital to have a PET scan. The acronym stands for *positron-emission tomography*. In the procedure, a radioactive element that undergoes e^+ decay is introduced into your body. The equipment detects the gamma rays that result from pair annihilation when the emitted positron encounters an electron in your body's tissue. Suppose you receive an injection of glucose containing on the order of 10^{10} atoms of ^{14}O. Assume that the oxygen is uniformly distributed through 2 L of blood after 5 min. What will be the order of magnitude of the activity of the oxygen atoms in 1 cm^3 of the blood?

3. Model a penny as 3.10 g of copper. Consider an anti-penny minted from 3.10 g of copper anti-atoms, each with 29 positrons in orbit around a nucleus comprising 29 antiprotons and 34 or 36 antineutrons. (a) Find the energy released if the two coins collide. (b) Find the value of this energy at the unit price of

0.14/kWh, a representative retail rate for energy from the electric company.

4. Two photons are produced when a proton and antiproton annihilate each other. In the reference frame in which the center of mass of the proton–antiproton system is stationary, what are the minimum frequency and corresponding wavelength of each photon?

5. A photon with an energy $E_\gamma = 2.09$ GeV creates a proton–antiproton pair in which the proton has a kinetic energy of 95.0 MeV. What is the kinetic energy of the antiproton? ($m_p c^2 = 938.3$ MeV.)

Section 31.3 ∎ Mesons and the Beginning of Particle Physics

6. Occasionally, high-energy muons collide with electrons and produce two neutrinos according to the reaction $\mu^+ + e^- \rightarrow 2\nu$. What kind of neutrinos are they?

7. Physics⊗Now™ One of the mediators of the weak interaction is the Z^0 boson, with mass 91.2 GeV/c^2. Use this information to find the order of magnitude of the range of the weak interaction.

8. Calculate the range of the force that might be produced by the virtual exchange of a proton.

9. Physics⊗Now™ A neutral pion at rest decays into two photons according to

$$\pi^0 \rightarrow \gamma + \gamma$$

Find the energy, momentum, and frequency of each photon.

10. When a high-energy proton or pion traveling near the speed of light collides with a nucleus, it travels an average distance of 3×10^{-15} m before interacting. From this information, find the order of magnitude of the time interval required for the strong interaction to occur.

11. A free neutron beta decays by creating a proton, an electron, and an antineutrino according to the reaction $n \rightarrow p + e^- + \bar{\nu}$. Imagine that a free neutron were to decay by creating a proton and electron according to the reaction

$$n \rightarrow p + e^-$$

and assume that the neutron is initially at rest in the laboratory. (a) Determine the energy released in this reaction. (b) Determine the speeds of the proton and electron after the reaction. (Energy and momentum are conserved in the reaction.) (c) Is either of these particles moving at a relativistic speed? Explain.

Section 31.4 ∎ Classification of Particles

12. Identify the unknown particle on the left side of the reaction

$$? + p \rightarrow n + \mu^+$$

13. Name one possible decay mode (see Table 31.2) for Ω^+, $\overline{K}_S^0$, $\overline{\Lambda}^0$, and $\bar{n}$.

Section 31.5 ∎ Conservation Laws

14. Each of the following reactions is forbidden. Determine a conservation law that is violated for each reaction.
(a) $p + \bar{p} \rightarrow \mu^+ + e^-$ (b) $\pi^- + p \rightarrow p + \pi^+$
(c) $p + p \rightarrow p + \pi^+$ (d) $p + p \rightarrow p + p + n$
(e) $\gamma + p \rightarrow n + \pi^0$

15. (a) Show that baryon number and charge are conserved in the following reactions of a pion with a proton.

$$(1) \quad \pi^+ + p \rightarrow K^+ + \Sigma^+$$
$$(2) \quad \pi^+ + p \rightarrow \pi^+ + \Sigma^+$$

(b) The first reaction is observed, but the second never occurs. Explain.

16. The first of the following two reactions can occur, but the second cannot. Explain.

$$K_S^0 \rightarrow \pi^+ + \pi^- \quad \text{(can occur)}$$
$$\Lambda^0 \rightarrow \pi^+ + \pi^- \quad \text{(cannot occur)}$$

17. Physics⊗Now™ The following reactions or decays involve one or more neutrinos. In each case, supply the missing neutrino (ν_e, ν_μ, or ν_τ) or antineutrino.
(a) $\pi^- \rightarrow \mu^- + ?$ (b) $K^+ \rightarrow \mu^+ + ?$
(c) $? + p \rightarrow n + e^+$ (d) $? + n \rightarrow p + e^-$
(e) $? + n \rightarrow p + \mu^-$ (f) $\mu^- \rightarrow e^- + ? + ?$

18. A K_S^0 particle at rest decays into a π^+ and a π^-. What will be the speed of each of the pions? The mass of the K_S^0 is 497.7 MeV/c^2, and the mass of each π is 139.6 MeV/c^2.

19. Physics⊗Now™ Determine which of the following reactions can occur. For those that cannot occur, determine the conservation law (or laws) violated.
(a) $p \rightarrow \pi^+ + \pi^0$ (b) $p + p \rightarrow p + p + \pi^0$
(c) $p + p \rightarrow p + \pi^+$ (d) $\pi^+ \rightarrow \mu^+ + \nu_\mu$
(e) $n \rightarrow p + e^- + \bar{\nu}_e$ (f) $\pi^+ \rightarrow \mu^+ + n$

20. (a) Show that the proton-decay reaction

$$p \rightarrow e^+ + \gamma$$

cannot occur because it violates conservation of baryon number. (b) Imagine that this reaction does occur and that the proton is initially at rest. Determine the energy and momentum of the positron and photon after the reaction. (*Suggestion:* Recall that energy and momentum must be conserved in the reaction.) (c) Determine the speed of the positron after the reaction.

21. Determine the type of neutrino or antineutrino involved in each of the following processes.
    (a) $\pi^+ \rightarrow \pi^0 + e^+ + ?$ (b) $? + p \rightarrow \mu^- + p + \pi^+$
    (c) $\Lambda^0 \rightarrow p + \mu^- + ?$ (d) $\tau^+ \rightarrow \mu^+ + ? + ?$

Section 31.6 ▪ Strange Particles and Strangeness

22. The neutral meson ρ^0 decays by the strong interaction into two pions: $\rho^0 \rightarrow \pi^+ + \pi^-$, half-life 10^{-23} s. The neutral kaon also decays into two pions: $K_S^0 \rightarrow \pi^+ + \pi^-$, half-life 10^{-10} s. How do you explain the difference in half-lives?

23. Determine whether or not strangeness is conserved in the following decays and reactions.
    (a) $\Lambda^0 \rightarrow p + \pi^-$ (b) $\pi^- + p \rightarrow \Lambda^0 + K^0$
    (c) $\bar{p} + p \rightarrow \bar{\Lambda}^0 + \Lambda^0$ (d) $\pi^- + p \rightarrow \pi^- + \Sigma^+$
    (e) $\Xi^- \rightarrow \Lambda^0 + \pi^-$ (f) $\Xi^0 \rightarrow p + \pi^-$

24. For each of the following forbidden decays, determine which conservation law is violated.
    (a) $\mu^- \rightarrow e^- + \gamma$ (b) $n \rightarrow p + e^- + \nu_e$
    (c) $\Lambda^0 \rightarrow p + \pi^0$ (d) $p \rightarrow e^+ + \pi^0$
    (e) $\Xi^0 \rightarrow n + \pi^0$

25. Which of the following processes are allowed by the strong interaction, the electromagnetic interaction, the weak interaction, or no interaction at all?
    (a) $\pi^- + p \rightarrow 2\eta$ (b) $K^- + n \rightarrow \Lambda^0 + \pi^-$
    (c) $K^- \rightarrow \pi^- + \pi^0$ (d) $\Omega^- \rightarrow \Xi^- + \pi^0$
    (e) $\eta \rightarrow 2\gamma$

26. Identify the conserved quantities in the following processes.
    (a) $\Xi^- \rightarrow \Lambda^0 + \mu^- + \nu_\mu$ (b) $K_S^0 \rightarrow 2\pi^0$
    (c) $K^- + p \rightarrow \Sigma^0 + n$ (d) $\Sigma^0 \rightarrow \Lambda^0 + \gamma$
    (e) $e^+ + e^- \rightarrow \mu^+ + \mu^-$ (f) $\bar{p} + n \rightarrow \bar{\Lambda}^0 + \Sigma^-$

27. Fill in the missing particle. Assume that (a) occurs via the strong interaction and that (b) and (c) involve the weak interaction.
    (a) $K^+ + p \rightarrow ? + p$ (b) $\Omega^- \rightarrow ? + \pi^-$
    (c) $K^+ \rightarrow ? + \mu^+ + \nu_\mu$

Section 31.7 ▪ Measuring Particle Lifetimes

28. The particle decay $\Sigma^+ \rightarrow \pi^+ + n$ is observed in a bubble chamber. Figure P31.28 represents the curved tracks of the particles Σ^+ and π^+, and the invisible track of the neutron, in the presence of a uniform

magnetic field of 1.15 T directed out of the page. The measured radii of curvature are 1.99 m for the Σ^+ particle and 0.580 m for the π^+ particle. (a) Find the momenta of the Σ^+ and the π^+ particles in units of MeV/c. (b) The angle between the momenta of the Σ^+ and the π^+ particles at the moment of decay is 64.5°. Find the momentum of the neutron. (c) Calculate the total energy of the π^+ particle, and of the neutron, from their known masses ($m_\pi = 139.6$ MeV/c^2, $m_n = 939.6$ MeV/c^2) and the relativistic energy-momentum relation. What is the total energy of the Σ^+ particle? (d) Calculate the mass and speed of the Σ^+ particle.

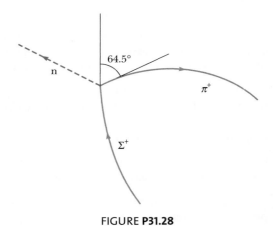

FIGURE **P31.28**

29. If a K_S^0 meson at rest decays in 0.900×10^{-10} s, how far will a K_S^0 meson travel if it is moving at $0.960c$?

30. A particle of mass m_1 is fired at a stationary particle of mass m_2, and a reaction takes place in which new particles are created out of the incident kinetic energy. Taken together, the product particles have total mass m_3. The minimum kinetic energy that the bombarding particle must have to induce the reaction is called the threshold energy. At this energy, the kinetic energy of the products is a minimum, so the fraction of the incident kinetic energy that is available to create new particles is a maximum. This situation occurs when all the product particles have the same velocity; then the particles have no kinetic energy of motion relative to one another. (a) By using conservation of relativistic energy and momentum, and the relativistic energy-momentum relation, show that the threshold energy is given by

$$K_{\min} = \frac{[m_3^2 - (m_1 + m_2)^2]c^2}{2m_2}$$

Calculate the threshold energy for each of the following reactions:

(b) $p + p \rightarrow p + p + p + \bar{p}$

   (One of the initial protons is at rest. Antiprotons are produced.)

(c) $\pi^- + p \rightarrow K^0 + \Lambda^0$

   (The proton is at rest. Strange particles are produced.)

(d) $p + p \rightarrow p + p + \pi^0$

   (One of the initial protons is at rest. Pions are produced.)

(e) $p + \bar{p} \rightarrow Z^0$

   (One of the initial particles is at rest. Z^0 particles (mass 91.2 GeV/c^2) are produced.)

Section 31.8 ▪ Finding Patterns in the Particles

Section 31.9 ▪ Quarks

Section 31.10 ▪ Colored Quarks

Section 31.11 ▪ The Standard Model

> *Note:* Problem 9.59 in Chapter 9 can be assigned with Section 31.11.

31. (a) Find the number of electrons and the number of each species of quark in 1 L of water. (b) Make an order-of-magnitude estimate of the number of each kind of fundamental matter particle in your body. State your assumptions and the quantities you take as data. Note that the t and b quarks were sometimes called "truth" and "beauty."

32. The quark composition of the proton is uud and that of the neutron is udd. Show that in each case the charge, baryon number, and strangeness of the particle equal, respectively, the sums of these numbers for the quark constituents.

33. Imagine that binding energies could be ignored. Find the masses of the u and d quarks from the masses of the proton and neutron.

34. The quark compositions of the K^0 and Λ^0 particles are $\bar{s}d$ and uds, respectively. Show that the charge, baryon number, and strangeness of these particles equal, respectively, the sums of these numbers for the quark constituents.

35. Analyze each reaction in terms of constituent quarks.

   (a) $\pi^- + p \rightarrow K^0 + \Lambda^0$

   (b) $\pi^+ + p \rightarrow K^+ + \Sigma^+$

   (c) $K^- + p \rightarrow K^+ + K^0 + \Omega^-$

   (d) $p + p \rightarrow K^0 + p + \pi^+ + ?$

   In the last reaction, identify the mystery particle.

36. The text states that the reaction $\pi^- + p \rightarrow K^0 + \Lambda^0$ occurs with high probability, whereas the reaction $\pi^- + p \rightarrow K^0 + n$ never occurs. Analyze these reactions at the quark level. Show that the first reaction conserves the total number of each type of quark and that the second reaction does not.

37. A Σ^0 particle traveling through matter strikes a proton; then a Σ^+ and a gamma ray emerge, as well as a third particle. Use the quark model of each to determine the identity of the third particle.

38. Identify the particles corresponding to the quark combinations (a) suu, (b) $\bar{u}d$, (c) $\bar{s}d$, and (d) ssd.

39. What is the electrical charge of the baryons with the quark compositions (a) $\bar{u}\bar{u}\underline{d}$ and (b) $\bar{u}\,\underline{d}\,\underline{d}$? What are these baryons called?

Section 31.12 ▪ Context Connection—Investigating the Smallest System to Understand the Largest

> *Note:* Problem 24.14 in Chapter 24, Problems 29.39 and 29.41 in Chapter 29, and Problems 28.53 and 28.54 in Chapter 28 can be assigned with this section.

40. Imagine that all distances expand at a rate described by the Hubble constant of 17.0×10^{-3} m/s·ly. (a) At what rate would the 1.85-m height of a basketball player be increasing? (b) At what rate would the distance between the Earth and the Moon be increasing? In fact, gravitation and other forces prevent the Hubble's-law expansion from taking place except in systems larger than clusters of galaxies.

41. Using Hubble's law, find the wavelength of the 590-nm sodium line emitted from galaxies (a) 2.00×10^6 ly away from the Earth, (b) 2.00×10^8 ly away, and (c) 2.00×10^9 ly away. You may use the result of Problem 29.39 in Chapter 29.

42. The various spectral lines observed in the light from a distant quasar have longer wavelengths $\lambda_n{'}$ than the wavelengths λ_n measured in light from a stationary source. Here n is an index taking different values for different spectral lines. The fractional change in wavelength toward the red is the same for all spectral lines. That is, the redshift parameter Z defined by

$$Z = \frac{\lambda_n{'} - \lambda_n}{\lambda_n}$$

is common to all spectral lines for one object. In terms of Z, determine (a) the speed of recession of the quasar and (b) the distance from the Earth to this quasar. Use the result of Problem 29.39 in Chapter 29 and Hubble's law.

43. Assume that dark matter exists throughout space with a uniform density of 6.00×10^{-28} kg/m^3. (a) Find the amount of such dark matter inside a sphere centered on the Sun, having the Earth's orbit as its equator. (b) Would the gravitational field of this dark matter have a measurable effect on the Earth's revolution?

44. It is mostly your roommate's fault. Nosy astronomers have discovered enough junk and clutter in your dorm room to constitute the missing mass required to close the Universe. After observing your floor, closet, bed, and computer files, they extrapolate to slobs in other galaxies and calculate the average density of the observable Universe as $1.20\rho_c$. How many times larger will the Universe become before it begins to collapse? That is, by what factor will the distance between remote galaxies increase in the future?

45. The early Universe was dense with gamma-ray photons of energy $\sim k_B T$ and at such a high temperature that protons and antiprotons were created by the process $\gamma \rightarrow p + \bar{p}$ as rapidly as they annihilated each other. As the Universe cooled in adiabatic expansion, its temperature fell below a certain value and proton pair production became rare. At that time slightly more protons than antiprotons existed, and essentially all the protons in the Universe today date from that time. (a) Estimate the order of magnitude of the temperature of the Universe when protons condensed out. (b) Estimate the order of magnitude of the temperature of the Universe when electrons condensed out.

46. If the average density of the Universe is small compared with the critical density, the expansion of the Universe described by Hubble's law proceeds with speeds that are nearly constant over time. (a) Prove that in this case the age of the Universe is given by the inverse of Hubble's constant. (b) Calculate $1/H$ and express it in years.

47. Assume that the average density of the Universe is equal to the critical density. (a) Prove that the age of the Universe is given by $2/3H$. (b) Calculate $2/3H$ and express it in years.

48. Hubble's law can be stated in vector form as $\vec{\mathbf{v}} = H\vec{\mathbf{R}}$. Outside the local group of galaxies, all objects are moving away from us with velocities proportional to their displacements from us. In this form, it sounds as if our location in the Universe is specially privileged. Prove that Hubble's law would be equally true for an observer elsewhere in the Universe. Proceed as follows. Assume that we are at the origin of coordinates, that one galaxy cluster is at location $\vec{\mathbf{R}}_1$ and has velocity $\vec{\mathbf{v}}_1 = H\vec{\mathbf{R}}_1$ relative to us, and that another galaxy cluster has position vector $\vec{\mathbf{R}}_2$ and velocity $\vec{\mathbf{v}}_2 = H\vec{\mathbf{R}}_2$. Suppose the speeds are nonrelativistic. Consider the frame of reference of an observer in the first of these galaxy clusters. Show that our velocity relative to her, together with the position vector of our galaxy cluster relative to hers, satisfies Hubble's law. Show that the position and velocity of cluster 2 relative to cluster 1 satisfy Hubble's law.

Additional Problems

49. **Review problem.** Supernova Shelton 1987A, located about 170 000 ly from the Earth, is estimated to have emitted a burst of neutrinos carrying energy $\sim 10^{46}$ J

FIGURE P31.49 (Problems 31.49 and 31.50) The giant star catalogued as Sanduleak $-69°$ 202 in the "before" picture (*top*) became Supernova Shelton 1987A in the "after" picture (*bottom*).

(Fig. P31.49). Suppose the average neutrino energy was 6 MeV and your mother's body presented cross-sectional area 5 000 cm². To an order of magnitude, how many of these neutrinos passed through your mother?

50. The most recent naked-eye supernova was Supernova Shelton 1987A (Fig. P31.49). It was 170 000 ly away in the next galaxy to ours, the Large Magellanic Cloud. About 3 h before its optical brightening was noticed, two continuously running neutrino detection experiments simultaneously registered the first neutrinos from an identified source other than the Sun. The Irvine-Michigan-Brookhaven experiment in a salt mine in Ohio registered eight neutrinos over a 6-s period, and the Kamiokande II experiment in a zinc mine in Japan counted eleven neutrinos in 13 s. (Because the supernova is far south in the sky, these neutrinos entered the detectors from below. They passed through the Earth before they were by chance absorbed by nuclei in the detectors.) The neutrino energies were between about 8 MeV and 40 MeV. If neutrinos have no mass, neutrinos of all energies should travel together at the speed of light, and the data are consistent with this possibility. The arrival times could show scatter simply because neutrinos were created at different moments as the core of the star collapsed into a neutron star. If neutrinos have nonzero mass, lower-energy neutrinos should move comparatively slowly. The data are consistent with a 10 MeV neutrino requiring at most about 10 s more than a photon would require to travel from the supernova to us. Find the upper limit that this observation sets on the mass of a neutrino. (Other evidence sets an even tighter limit.)

51. **Physics⊗Now™** The energy flux carried by neutrinos from the Sun is estimated to be on the order of 0.4 W/m^2 at the Earth's surface. Estimate the fractional mass loss of the Sun over 10^9 yr due to the emission of neutrinos. (The mass of the Sun is 2×10^{30} kg. The Earth–Sun distance is 1.5×10^{11} m.)

52. Name at least one conservation law that prevents each of the following reactions: (a) $\pi^- + p \rightarrow \Sigma^+ + \pi^0$, (b) $\mu^- \rightarrow \pi^- + \nu_e$, (c) $p \rightarrow \pi^+ + \pi^+ + \pi^-$.

53. Assume that the half-life of free neutrons is 614 s. What fraction of a group of free thermal neutrons with kinetic energy 0.040 0 eV will decay before traveling a distance of 10.0 km?

54. Two protons approach each other head-on, each with 70.4 MeV of kinetic energy, and engage in a reaction in which a proton and positive pion emerge at rest. What third particle, obviously uncharged and therefore difficult to detect, must have been created?

55. Determine the kinetic energies of the proton and pion resulting from the decay of a Λ^0 at rest:

$$\Lambda^0 \rightarrow p + \pi^-$$

56. A rocket engine for space travel using photon drive and matter–antimatter annihilation has been suggested. Suppose the fuel for a short-duration burn consists of N protons and N antiprotons, each with mass m. (a) Assume that all the fuel is annihilated to produce photons. When the photons are ejected from the rocket, what momentum can be imparted to it? (b) If half of the protons and antiprotons annihilate each other and the energy released is used to eject the remaining particles, what momentum could be given to the rocket? Which scheme results in the greatest change in speed for the rocket?

57. An unstable particle, initially at rest, decays into a proton (rest energy 938.3 MeV) and a negative pion (rest energy 139.6 MeV). A uniform magnetic field of 0.250 T exists perpendicular to the velocities of the created particles. The radius of curvature of each track is found to be 1.33 m. What is the mass of the original unstable particle?

58. A gamma-ray photon strikes a stationary electron. Determine the minimum gamma-ray energy to make this reaction occur:

$$\gamma + e^- \rightarrow e^- + e^- + e^+$$

59. Two protons approach each other with velocities of equal magnitude in opposite directions. What is the minimum kinetic energy of each of the protons if they are to produce a π^+ meson at rest in the following reaction?

$$p + p \rightarrow p + n + \pi^+$$

60. A Σ^0 particle at rest decays according to

$$\Sigma^0 \rightarrow \Lambda^0 + \gamma$$

Find the gamma-ray energy.

61. **Review problem.** Use the Boltzmann distribution function $e^{-E/k_B T}$ to calculate the temperature at which 1.00% of a population of photons will have energy greater than 1.00 eV. The energy required to excite an atom is on the order of 1 eV. Therefore, as the temperature of the Universe fell below the value you calculate, neutral atoms could form from plasma and the Universe became transparent. The cosmic background radiation represents our vastly red-shifted view of the opaque fireball of the Big Bang as it was at this time and temperature. The fireball surrounds us; we are embers.

62. A π-meson at rest decays according to $\pi^- \rightarrow \mu^- + \overline{\nu}_\mu$. What is the energy carried off by the neutrino? (Assume

that the neutrino has no mass and moves off with the speed of light. Take $m_\pi c^2 = 139.6\,\text{MeV}$ and $m_\mu c^2 = 105.7\,\text{MeV}$.)

63. Identify the mediators for the two interactions described in the Feynman diagrams shown in Figure P31.63.

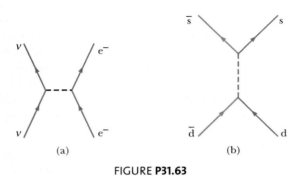

FIGURE **P31.63**

64. What processes are described by the Feynman diagrams in Figure P31.64? What is the exchanged particle in each process?

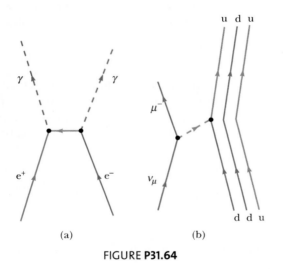

FIGURE **P31.64**

65. The cosmic rays of highest energy are mostly protons, accelerated by unknown sources. Their spectrum shows a cutoff at an energy on the order of 10^{20} eV. Above that energy, a proton will interact with a photon of cosmic microwave background radiation to produce mesons, for example, according to

$$p + \gamma \;\rightarrow\; p + \pi^0$$

Demonstrate this fact by taking the following steps. (a) Find the minimum photon energy required to produce this reaction in the reference frame where the total momentum of the photon–proton system is zero. The reaction was observed experimentally in the 1950s with photons of a few hundred MeV. (b) Use Wien's displacement law to find the wavelength of a photon at the peak of the blackbody spectrum of the primordial microwave background radiation, with a temperature of 2.73 K. (c) Find the energy of this photon. (d) Consider the reaction in part (a) in a moving reference frame so that the photon is the same as that in part (c). Calculate the energy of the proton in this frame, which represents the Earth reference frame.

ANSWERS TO QUICK QUIZZES

31.1 (a). The right-hand rule for the positive particle tells you that this direction is the one that leads to a force directed toward the center of curvature of the path.

31.2 (c), (d). There is a baryon, the neutron, on the left of the reaction, but no baryon on the right. Therefore, baryon number is not conserved. The neutron has spin $\frac{1}{2}$. On the right side of the reaction, the pions each have integral spin, and the combination of two muons must also have integral spin. Therefore, the total spin of the

particles on the right-hand side is integral and angular momentum is not conserved.

31.3 (a). The sum of the proton and pion masses is larger than the mass of the neutron, so energy conservation is violated.

31.4 (b), (e), (f). The pion on the left has integral spin, whereas the three spin-$\frac{1}{2}$ leptons on the right must result in a total spin that is half-integral. Therefore, angular momentum (b) is not conserved. There is an electron on the right but no lepton on the left, so electron lepton number (e) is not conserved. There are no muons on the left, but a muon and its neutrino on the right (both with $L_\mu = +1$). Therefore, muon lepton number (f) is not conserved.

31.5 (b), (e). There is one spin-$\frac{1}{2}$ particle on the left and two on the right, so angular momentum is not conserved. There are no leptons on the left and an electron on the right, so electron lepton number is not conserved.

31.6 The diagram would look like this one:

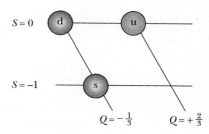

Problems and Perspectives

We have now investigated the principles of quantum physics and have seen many connections to our central question for the *Cosmic Connection* Context:

How can we connect the physics of microscopic particles to the physics of the Universe?

While particle physicists have been exploring the realm of the very small, cosmologists have been exploring cosmic history back to the first second of the Big Bang. Observation of events that occur when two particles collide in an accelerator is essential in reconstructing the early moments in cosmic history. The key to understanding the early Universe is first to understand the world of elementary particles. Cosmologists and physicists now find that they have many common goals and are joining hands to attempt to understand the physical world at its most fundamental level.

Problems

We have made great progress in understanding the Universe and its underlying structure, but a multitude of questions remain unanswered. Why does so little anti-matter exist in the Universe? Do neutrinos have a small rest energy, and if so, how do they contribute to the "dark matter" of the Universe? Is there "dark energy" in the Universe? Is it possible to unify the strong and electroweak forces in a logical and consistent manner? Can gravity be unified with the other forces? Why do quarks and leptons form three similar but distinct families? Are muons the same as electrons (apart from their difference in mass), or do they have other subtle differences that have not been detected? Why are some particles charged and others neutral? Why do quarks carry a fractional charge? What determines the masses of the fundamental constituents? Can isolated quarks exist? Do leptons and quarks have a substructure?

String Theory: A New Perspective

Let us briefly discuss one current effort at answering some of these questions by proposing a new perspective on particles. As you read this book, you may recall starting off with the particle model and doing quite a bit of physics with it. In the *Earthquakes* Context, we introduced the wave model, and more physics was used to investigate the properties of waves. We used a wave model for light in the *Lasers* Context. Early in this Context, however, we saw the need to return to the particle model for light. Furthermore, we found that material particles had wave-like characteristics. The quantum particle model of Chapter 28 allowed us to build particles out of waves, suggesting that a wave is the fundamental entity. In Chapter 31, however, we discussed the elementary particles as the fundamental entities. It seems as if we cannot make up our mind! In some sense, that is true because the wave–particle duality is still an area of active research. In this final Context Conclusion, we shall discuss a current research effort to build particles out of waves and vibrations.

String theory is an effort to unify the four fundamental forces by modeling all particles as various quantized vibrational modes of a single entity, an incredibly small string. The typical length of such a string is on the order of 10^{-35} m, called the **Planck length.** We have seen quantized modes before with the frequencies of vibrating guitar strings in Chapter 14 and the quantized energy levels of atoms in

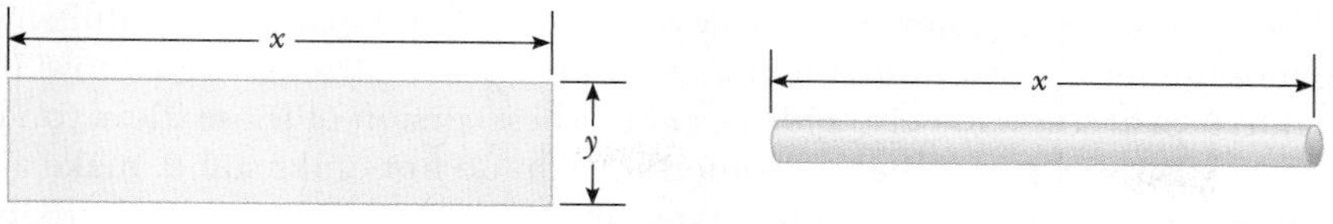

FIGURE 1 (a) A piece of paper is cut into a rectangular shape. As a rectangle, the shape has two dimensions. (b) The paper is rolled up into a soda straw. From far away, it appears to be one-dimensional. The curled-up second dimension is not visible when viewed from a distance that is large compared with the diameter of the straw.

Chapter 29. In string theory, each quantized mode of vibration of the string corresponds to a different elementary particle in the Standard Model.

One complicating factor in string theory is that it requires space–time to have ten dimensions. Despite the theoretical and conceptual difficulties in dealing with ten dimensions, string theory holds promise in incorporating gravity with the other forces. Four of the ten dimensions are visible to us—three space dimensions and one time dimension—and the other six are *compactified*. In other words, the six dimensions are curled up so tightly that they are not visible in the macroscopic world.

As an analogy, consider a soda straw. We can build a soda straw by cutting a rectangular piece of paper (Fig. 1a), which clearly has two dimensions, and rolling it up into a small tube (Fig. 1b). From far away, the soda straw looks like a one-dimensional straight line. The second dimension has been curled up and is not visible. String theory claims that six space–time dimensions are curled up in an analogous way, with the curling on the size of the Planck length and impossible to see from our viewpoint.

Another complicating factor with string theory is that it is difficult for string theorists to guide experimentalists in how and what to look for in an experiment. The Planck length is so incredibly small that direct experimentation on strings is impossible. Until the theory has been further developed, string theorists are restricted to applying the theory to known results and testing for consistency.

One of the predictions of string theory is called **supersymmetry** (SUSY), which suggests that every elementary particle has a superpartner that has not yet been observed. It is believed that supersymmetry is a broken symmetry (like the broken electroweak symmetry at low energies) and that the masses of the superpartners are above our current capabilities of detection by accelerators. Some theorists claim that the mass of superpartners is the missing mass discussed in the Context Conclusion of Chapter 31. Keeping with the whimsical trend in naming particles and their properties that we saw in Chapter 31, superpartners are given names such as the *squark* (the superpartner to a quark), the *selectron* (electron), and the *gluinos* (gluon).

Other theorists are working on **M-theory,** which is an 11-dimensional theory based on membranes rather than strings. In a way reminiscent of the correspondence principle, M-theory is claimed to reduce to string theory if one compactifies from 11 dimensions to 10.

The questions that we listed at the beginning of this Context Conclusion go on and on. Because of the rapid advances and new discoveries in the field of particle physics, by the time you read this book some of these questions may be resolved and other new questions may emerge.

Question

1. **Review question.** A girl and her grandmother grind corn while the woman tells the girl stories about what is most important. A boy keeps crows away from ripening corn while his grandfather sits in the shade and explains to him the Universe and his place in it. What the children do not understand this year they

will better understand next year. Now you must take the part of the adults. State the most general, most fundamental, most universal truths that you know. If you need to repeat someone else's ideas, get the best version of those ideas you can and state your source. If there is something you do not understand, make a plan to understand it better within the next year.

Problem

1. Classical general relativity views the structure of space–time as deterministic and well defined down to arbitrarily small distances. On the other hand, quantum general relativity forbids distances smaller than the Planck length given by $L = (\hbar G/c^3)^{1/2}$. (a) Calculate the value of the Planck length. The quantum limitation suggests that after the Big Bang, when all the presently observable section of the Universe was contained within a point-like singularity, nothing could be observed until that singularity grew larger than the Planck length. Because the size of the singularity grew at the speed of light, we can infer that no observations were possible during the time interval required for light to travel the Planck length. (b) Calculate this time interval, known as the Planck time T, and compare it with the ultrahot epoch mentioned in the text. (c) Does this answer suggest that we may never know what happened between the time $t = 0$ and the time $t = T$?

The Meaning of Success

To earn the respect of intelligent people and to win the affection of children;
To appreciate the beauty in nature and all that surrounds us;
To seek out and nurture the best in others;
To give the gift of yourself to others without the slightest thought of return, for it is in giving that we receive;
To have accomplished a task, whether it be saving a lost soul, healing a sick child, writing a book, or risking your life for a friend;
To have celebrated and laughed with great joy and enthusiasm and sung with exultation;
To have hope even in times of despair, for as long as you have hope, you have life;
To love and be loved;
To be understood and to understand;
To know that even one life has breathed easier because you have lived;
This is the meaning of success.

Ralph Waldo Emerson and modified by Ray Serway

Tables

| TABLE **A.1** | Conversion Factors |

Length

	m	cm	km	in.	ft	mi
1 meter	1	10^2	10^{-3}	39.37	3.281	6.214×10^{-4}
1 centimeter	10^{-2}	1	10^{-5}	0.393 7	3.281×10^{-2}	6.214×10^{-6}
1 kilometer	10^3	10^5	1	3.937×10^4	3.281×10^3	0.621 4
1 inch	2.540×10^{-2}	2.540	2.540×10^{-5}	1	8.333×10^{-2}	1.578×10^{-5}
1 foot	0.304 8	30.48	3.048×10^{-4}	12	1	1.894×10^{-4}
1 mile	1 609	1.609×10^5	1.609	6.336×10^4	5 280	1

Mass

	kg	g	slug	u
1 kilogram	1	10^3	6.852×10^{-2}	6.024×10^{26}
1 gram	10^{-3}	1	6.852×10^{-5}	6.024×10^{23}
1 slug	14.59	1.459×10^4	1	8.789×10^{27}
1 atomic mass unit	1.660×10^{-27}	1.660×10^{-24}	1.137×10^{-28}	1

Note: 1 metric ton = 1 000 kg.

Time

	s	min	h	day	yr
1 second	1	1.667×10^{-2}	2.778×10^{-4}	1.157×10^{-5}	3.169×10^{-8}
1 minute	60	1	1.667×10^{-2}	6.994×10^{-4}	1.901×10^{-6}
1 hour	3 600	60	1	4.167×10^{-2}	1.141×10^{-4}
1 day	8.640×10^4	1 440	24	1	2.738×10^{-5}
1 year	3.156×10^7	5.259×10^5	8.766×10^3	365.2	1

Speed

	m/s	cm/s	ft/s	mi/h
1 meter per second	1	10^2	3.281	2.237
1 centimeter per second	10^{-2}	1	3.281×10^{-2}	2.237×10^{-2}
1 foot per second	0.304 8	30.48	1	0.681 8
1 mile per hour	0.447 0	44.70	1.467	1

Note: 1 mi/min = 60 mi/h = 88 ft/s.

Force

	N	lb
1 newton	1	0.224 8
1 pound	4.448	1

(Continued)

TABLE A.1 Conversion Factors (*Continued*)

Work, Energy, Heat

	J	ft · lb	eV
1 joule	1	0.737 6	6.242×10^{18}
1 foot-pound	1.356	1	8.464×10^{18}
1 electron volt	1.602×10^{-19}	1.182×10^{-19}	1
1 calorie	4.186	3.087	2.613×10^{19}
1 British thermal unit	1.055×10^{3}	7.779×10^{2}	6.585×10^{21}
1 kilowatt-hour	3.600×10^{6}	2.655×10^{6}	2.247×10^{25}

	cal	Btu	kWh
1 joule	0.238 9	9.481×10^{-4}	2.778×10^{-7}
1 foot-pound	0.323 9	1.285×10^{-3}	3.766×10^{-7}
1 electron volt	3.827×10^{-20}	1.519×10^{-22}	4.450×10^{-26}
1 calorie	1	3.968×10^{-3}	1.163×10^{-6}
1 British thermal unit	2.520×10^{2}	1	2.930×10^{-4}
1 kilowatt-hour	8.601×10^{5}	3.413×10^{2}	1

Pressure

	Pa	atm
1 pascal	1	9.869×10^{-6}
1 atmosphere	1.013×10^{5}	1
1 centimeter mercury[a]	1.333×10^{3}	1.316×10^{-2}
1 pound per square inch	6.895×10^{3}	6.805×10^{-2}
1 pound per square foot	47.88	4.725×10^{-4}

	cm Hg	lb/in.^{2}	lb/ft^2
1 pascal	7.501×10^{-4}	1.450×10^{-4}	2.089×10^{-2}
1 atmosphere	76	14.70	2.116×10^{3}
1 centimeter mercury[a]	1	0.194 3	27.85
1 pound per square inch	5.171	1	144
1 pound per square foot	3.591×10^{-2}	6.944×10^{-3}	1

[a]At 0°C and at a location where the free-fall acceleration has its "standard" value, 9.806 65 m/s^2.

TABLE A.2 Symbols, Dimensions, and Units of Physical Quantities

Quantity	Common Symbol	Unit[a]	Dimensions[b]	Unit in Terms of Base SI Units
Acceleration	$\vec{a}$	m/s^2	L/T^2	m/s^2
Amount of substance	n	MOLE		mol
Angle	θ, ϕ	radian (rad)	1	
Angular acceleration	$\vec{\alpha}$	rad/s^2	T^{-2}	s^{-2}
Angular frequency	ω	rad/s	T^{-1}	s^{-1}
Angular momentum	$\vec{L}$	kg · m^2/s	ML^2/T	kg · m^2/s
Angular velocity	$\vec{\omega}$	rad/s	T^{-1}	s^{-1}
Area	A	m^2	L^2	m^2
Atomic number	Z			

(Continued)

TABLE A.2   Symbols, Dimensions, and Units of Physical Quantities *(Continued)*

Quantity	Common Symbol	Unit[a]	Dimensions[b]	Unit in Terms of Base SI Units
Capacitance	C	farad (F)	Q^2T^2/ML^2	$A^2\cdot s^4/kg\cdot m^2$
Charge	q, Q, e	coulomb (C)	Q	$A\cdot s$
Charge density				
Line	λ	C/m	Q/L	$A\cdot s/m$
Surface	σ	C/m^2	Q/L^2	$A\cdot s/m^2$
Volume	ρ	C/m^3	Q/L^3	$A\cdot s/m^3$
Conductivity	σ	$1/\Omega\cdot m$	Q^2T/ML^3	$A^2\cdot s^3/kg\cdot m^3$
Current	I	AMPERE	Q/T	A
Current density	$\vec{J}$	A/m^2	Q/TL^2	A/m^2
Density	ρ	kg/m^3	M/L^3	kg/m^3
Dielectric constant	κ			
Electric dipole moment	$\vec{p}$	C·m	QL	$A\cdot s\cdot m$
Electric field	$\vec{E}$	V/m	ML/QT^2	$kg\cdot m/A\cdot s^3$
Electric flux	Φ_E	V·m	ML^3/QT^2	$kg\cdot m^3/A\cdot s^3$
Electromotive force	$\mathcal{E}$	volt (V)	ML^2/QT^2	$kg\cdot m^2/A\cdot s^3$
Energy	E, U, K	joule (J)	ML^2/T^2	$kg\cdot m^2/s^2$
Entropy	S	J/K	$ML^2/T^2\cdot K$	$kg\cdot m^2/s^2\cdot K$
Force	$\vec{F}$	newton (N)	ML/T^2	$kg\cdot m/s^2$
Frequency	f	hertz (Hz)	T^{-1}	s^{-1}
Heat	Q	joule (J)	ML^2/T^2	$kg\cdot m^2/s^2$
Inductance	L	henry (H)	ML^2/Q^2	$kg\cdot m^2/A^2\cdot s^2$
Length	ℓ, L	METER	L	m
Displacement	$\Delta x, \Delta\vec{r}$			
Distance	d, h			
Position	$x, y, z, \vec{r}$			
Magnetic dipole moment	$\vec{\mu}$	N·m/T	QL^2/T	$A\cdot m^2$
Magnetic field	$\vec{B}$	tesla (T) (= Wb/m^2)	M/QT	$kg/A\cdot s^2$
Magnetic flux	Φ_B	weber (Wb)	ML^2/QT	$kg\cdot m^2/A\cdot s^2$
Mass	m, M	KILOGRAM	M	kg
Molar specific heat	C	J/mol·K		$kg\cdot m^2/s^2\cdot mol\cdot K$
Moment of inertia	I	kg·m^2	ML^2	$kg\cdot m^2$
Momentum	$\vec{p}$	kg·m/s	ML/T	$kg\cdot m/s$
Period	T	s	T	s
Permeability of free space	μ_0	N/A^2 (= H/m)	ML/Q^2	$kg\cdot m/A^2\cdot s^2$
Permittivity of free space	ϵ_0	C^2/N·m^2 (= F/m)	Q^2T^2/ML^3	$A^2\cdot s^4/kg\cdot m^3$
Potential	V	volt (V) (= J/C)	ML^2/QT^2	$kg\cdot m^2/A\cdot s^3$
Power	$\mathcal{P}$	watt (W) (= J/s)	ML^2/T^3	$kg\cdot m^2/s^3$
Pressure	P	pascal (Pa) (= N/m^2)	M/LT^2	$kg/m\cdot s^2$
Resistance	R	ohm (Ω) (= V/A)	ML^2/Q^2T	$kg\cdot m^2/A^2\cdot s^3$
Specific heat	c	J/kg·K	$L^2/T^2\cdot K$	$m^2/s^2\cdot K$
Speed	v	m/s	L/T	m/s
Temperature	T	KELVIN	K	K
Time	t	SECOND	T	s
Torque	$\vec{\tau}$	N·m	ML^2/T^2	$kg\cdot m^2/s^2$
Velocity	$\vec{v}$	m/s	L/T	m/s
Volume	V	m^3	L^3	m^3
Wavelength	λ	m	L	m
Work	W	joule (J) (= N·m)	ML^2/T^2	$kg\cdot m^2/s^2$

[a]The base SI units are given in uppercase letters.
[b]The symbols M, L, T, and Q denote mass, length, time, and charge, respectively.

TABLE A.3 Table of Atomic Masses

Atomic Number Z	Element	Symbol	Chemical Atomic Mass (u)	Mass Number (*indicates radioactive) A	Atomic Mass (u)	Percent Abundance	Half-Life (if radioactive) $T_{1/2}$
0	(Neutron)	n		1*	1.008 665		10.4 min
1	Hydrogen	H	1.007 94	1	1.007 825	99.988 5	
	Deuterium	D		2	2.014 102	0.011 5	
	Tritium	T		3*	3.016 049		12.33 yr
2	Helium	He	4.002 602	3	3.016 029	0.000 137	
				4	4.002 603	99.999 863	
				6*	6.018 888		0.81 s
3	Lithium	Li	6.941	6	6.015 122	7.5	
				7	7.016 004	92.5	
				8*	8.022 487		0.84 s
4	Beryllium	Be	9.012 182	7*	7.016 929		53.3 days
				9	9.012 182	100	
				10*	10.013 534		1.5×10^6 yr
5	Boron	B	10.811	10	10.012 937	19.9	
				11	11.009 306	80.1	
				12*	12.014 352		0.020 2 s
6	Carbon	C	12.010 7	10*	10.016 853		19.3 s
				11*	11.011 434		20.4 min
				12	12.000 000	98.93	
				13	13.003 355	1.07	
				14*	14.003 242		5 730 yr
				15*	15.010 599		2.45 s
7	Nitrogen	N	14.006 7	12*	12.018 613		0.011 0 s
				13*	13.005 739		9.96 min
				14	14.003 074	99.632	
				15	15.000 109	0.368	
				16*	16.006 101		7.13 s
				17*	17.008 450		4.17 s
8	Oxygen	O	15.999 4	14*	14.008 595		70.6 s
				15*	15.003 065		122 s
				16	15.994 915	99.757	
				17	16.999 132	0.038	
				18	17.999 160	0.205	
				19*	19.003 579		26.9 s
9	Fluorine	F	18.998 403 2	17*	17.002 095		64.5 s
				18*	18.000 938		109.8 min
				19	18.998 403	100	
				20*	19.999 981		11.0 s
				21*	20.999 949		4.2 s
10	Neon	Ne	20.179 7	18*	18.005 697		1.67 s
				19*	19.001 880		17.2 s
				20	19.992 440	90.48	
				21	20.993 847	0.27	
				22	21.991 385	9.25	
				23*	22.994 467		37.2 s
11	Sodium	Na	22.989 77	21*	20.997 655		22.5 s
				22*	21.994 437		2.61 yr
				23	22.989 770	100	
				24*	23.990 963		14.96 h
12	Magnesium	Mg	24.305 0	23*	22.994 125		11.3 s
				24	23.985 042	78.99	
				25	24.985 837	10.00	

(Continued)

TABLE A.3	Table of Atomic Masses	(Continued)

Atomic Number Z	Element	Symbol	Chemical Atomic Mass (u)	Mass Number (*indicates radioactive) A	Atomic Mass (u)	Percent Abundance	Half-Life (if radioactive) $T_{1/2}$
(12)	Magnesium			26	25.982 593	11.01	
				27*	26.984 341		9.46 min
13	Aluminum	Al	26.981 538	26*	25.986 892		7.4×10^5 yr
				27	26.981 539	100	
				28*	27.981 910		2.24 min
14	Silicon	Si	28.085 5	28	27.976 926	92.229 7	
				29	28.976 495	4.683 2	
				30	29.973 770	3.087 2	
				31*	30.975 363		2.62 h
				32*	31.974 148		172 yr
15	Phosphorus	P	30.973 761	30*	29.978 314		2.50 min
				31	30.973 762	100	
				32*	31.973 907		14.26 days
				33*	32.971 725		25.3 days
16	Sulfur	S	32.066	32	31.972 071	94.93	
				33	32.971 458	0.76	
				34	33.967 869	4.29	
				35*	34.969 032		87.5 days
				36	35.967 081	0.02	
17	Chlorine	Cl	35.452 7	35	34.968 853	75.78	
				36*	35.968 307		3.0×10^5 yr
				37	36.965 903	24.22	
18	Argon	Ar	39.948	36	35.967 546	0.336 5	
				37*	36.966 776		35.04 days
				38	37.962 732	0.063 2	
				39*	38.964 313		269 yr
				40	39.962 383	99.600 3	
				42*	41.963 046		33 yr
19	Potassium	K	39.098 3	39	38.963 707	93.258 1	
				40*	39.963 999	0.011 7	1.28×10^9 yr
				41	40.961 826	6.730 2	
20	Calcium	Ca	40.078	40	39.962 591	96.941	
				41*	40.962 278		1.0×10^5 yr
				42	41.958 618	0.647	
				43	42.958 767	0.135	
				44	43.955 481	2.086	
				46	45.953 693	0.004	
				48	47.952 534	0.187	
21	Scandium	Sc	44.955 910	41*	40.969 251		0.596 s
				45	44.955 910	100	
22	Titanium	Ti	47.867	44*	43.959 690		49 yr
				46	45.952 630	8.25	
				47	46.951 764	7.44	
				48	47.947 947	73.72	
				49	48.947 871	5.41	
				50	49.944 792	5.18	
23	Vanadium	V	50.941 5	48*	47.952 254		15.97 days
				50*	49.947 163	0.250	1.5×10^{17} yr
				51	50.943 964	99.750	
24	Chromium	Cr	51.996 1	48*	47.954 036		21.6 h
				50	49.946 050	4.345	

(Continued)

| TABLE A.3 | Table of Atomic Masses *(Continued)* |

Atomic Number Z	Element	Symbol	Chemical Atomic Mass (u)	Mass Number (*indicates radioactive) A	Atomic Mass (u)	Percent Abundance	Half-Life (if radioactive) $T_{1/2}$
(24)	Chromium			52	51.940 512	83.789	
				53	52.940 654	9.501	
				54	53.938 885	2.365	
25	Manganese	Mn	54.938 049	54*	53.940 363		312.1 days
				55	54.938 050	100	
26	Iron	Fe	55.845	54	53.939 615	5.845	
				55*	54.938 298		2.7 yr
				56	55.934 942	91.754	
				57	56.935 399	2.119	
				58	57.933 280	0.282	
				60*	59.934 077		1.5×10^6 yr
27	Cobalt	Co	58.933 200	59	58.933 200	100	
				60*	59.933 822		5.27 yr
28	Nickel	Ni	58.693 4	58	57.935 348	68.076 9	
				59*	58.934 351		7.5×10^4 yr
				60	59.930 790	26.223 1	
				61	60.931 060	1.139 9	
				62	61.928 349	3.634 5	
				63*	62.929 673		100 yr
				64	63.927 970	0.925 6	
29	Copper	Cu	63.546	63	62.929 601	69.17	
				65	64.927 794	30.83	
30	Zinc	Zn	65.39	64	63.929 147	48.63	
				66	65.926 037	27.90	
				67	66.927 131	4.10	
				68	67.924 848	18.75	
				70	69.925 325	0.62	
31	Gallium	Ga	69.723	69	68.925 581	60.108	
				71	70.924 705	39.892	
32	Germanium	Ge	72.61	70	69.924 250	20.84	
				72	71.922 076	27.54	
				73	72.923 459	7.73	
				74	73.921 178	36.28	
				76	75.921 403	7.61	
33	Arsenic	As	74.921 60	75	74.921 596	100	
34	Selenium	Se	78.96	74	73.922 477	0.89	
				76	75.919 214	9.37	
				77	76.919 915	7.63	
				78	77.917 310	23.77	
				79*	78.918 500		$\leq 6.5 \times 10^4$ yr
				80	79.916 522	49.61	
				82*	81.916 700	8.73	1.4×10^{20} yr
35	Bromine	Br	79.904	79	78.918 338	50.69	
				81	80.916 291	49.31	
36	Krypton	Kr	83.80	78	77.920 386	0.35	
				80	79.916 378	2.28	
				81*	80.916 592		2.1×10^5 yr
				82	81.913 485	11.58	
				83	82.914 136	11.49	
				84	83.911 507	57.00	
				85*	84.912 527		10.76 yr
				86	85.910 610	17.30	

(Continued)

TABLE A.3   **Table of Atomic Masses** *(Continued)*

Atomic Number Z	Element	Symbol	Chemical Atomic Mass (u)	Mass Number (*indicates radioactive) A	Atomic Mass (u)	Percent Abundance	Half-Life (if radioactive) $T_{1/2}$
37	Rubidium	Rb	85.467 8	85	84.911 789	72.17	
				87*	86.909 184	27.83	4.75×10^{10} yr
38	Strontium	Sr	87.62	84	83.913 425	0.56	
				86	85.909 262	9.86	
				87	86.908 880	7.00	
				88	87.905 614	82.58	
				90*	89.907 738		29.1 yr
39	Yttrium	Y	88.905 85	89	88.905 848	100	
40	Zirconium	Zr	91.224	90	89.904 704	51.45	
				91	90.905 645	11.22	
				92	91.905 040	17.15	
				93*	92.906 476		1.5×10^6 yr
				94	93.906 316	17.38	
				96	95.908 276	2.80	
41	Niobium	Nb	92.906 38	91*	90.906 990		6.8×10^2 yr
				92*	91.907 193		3.5×10^7 yr
				93	92.906 378	100	
				94*	93.907 284		2×10^4 yr
42	Molybdenum	Mo	95.94	92	91.906 810	14.84	
				93*	92.906 812		3.5×10^3 yr
				94	93.905 088	9.25	
				95	94.905 842	15.92	
				96	95.904 679	16.68	
				97	96.906 021	9.55	
				98	97.905 408	24.13	
				100	99.907 477	9.63	
43	Technetium	Tc		97*	96.906 365		2.6×10^6 yr
				98*	97.907 216		4.2×10^6 yr
				99*	98.906 255		2.1×10^5 yr
44	Ruthenium	Ru	101.07	96	95.907 598	5.54	
				98	97.905 287	1.87	
				99	98.905 939	12.76	
				100	99.904 220	12.60	
				101	100.905 582	17.06	
				102	101.904 350	31.55	
				104	103.905 430	18.62	
45	Rhodium	Rh	102.905 50	103	102.905 504	100	
46	Palladium	Pd	106.42	102	101.905 608	1.02	
				104	103.904 035	11.14	
				105	104.905 084	22.33	
				106	105.903 483	27.33	
				107*	106.905 128		6.5×10^6 yr
				108	107.903 894	26.46	
				110	109.905 152	11.72	
47	Silver	Ag	107.868 2	107	106.905 093	51.839	
				109	108.904 756	48.161	
48	Cadmium	Cd	112.411	106	105.906 458	1.25	
				108	107.904 183	0.89	
				109*	108.904 986		462 days
				110	109.903 006	12.49	
				111	110.904 182	12.80	

(Continued)

TABLE A.3	Table of Atomic Masses *(Continued)*

Atomic Number Z	Element	Symbol	Chemical Atomic Mass (u)	Mass Number (*indicates radioactive) A	Atomic Mass (u)	Percent Abundance	Half-Life (if radioactive) $T_{1/2}$
(48)	Cadmium			112	111.902 757	24.13	
				113*	112.904 401	12.22	9.3×10^{15} yr
				114	113.903 358	28.73	
				116	115.904 755	7.49	
49	Indium	In	114.818	113	112.904 061	4.29	
				115*	114.903 878	95.71	4.4×10^{14} yr
50	Tin	Sn	118.710	112	111.904 821	0.97	
				114	113.902 782	0.66	
				115	114.903 346	0.34	
				116	115.901 744	14.54	
				117	116.902 954	7.68	
				118	117.901 606	24.22	
				119	118.903 309	8.59	
				120	119.902 197	32.58	
				121*	120.904 237		55 yr
				122	121.903 440	4.63	
				124	123.905 275	5.79	
51	Antimony	Sb	121.760	121	120.903 818	57.21	
				123	122.904 216	42.79	
				125*	124.905 248		2.7 yr
52	Tellurium	Te	127.60	120	119.904 020	0.09	
				122	121.903 047	2.55	
				123*	122.904 273	0.89	1.3×10^{13} yr
				124	123.902 820	4.74	
				125	124.904 425	7.07	
				126	125.903 306	18.84	
				128*	127.904 461	31.74	$> 8 \times 10^{24}$ yr
				130*	129.906 223	34.08	$\leq 1.25 \times 10^{21}$ yr
53	Iodine	I	126.904 47	127	126.904 468	100	
				129*	128.904 988		1.6×10^{7} yr
54	Xenon	Xe	131.29	124	123.905 896	0.09	
				126	125.904 269	0.09	
				128	127.903 530	1.92	
				129	128.904 780	26.44	
				130	129.903 508	4.08	
				131	130.905 082	21.18	
				132	131.904 145	26.89	
				134	133.905 394	10.44	
				136*	135.907 220	8.87	$\geq 2.36 \times 10^{21}$ yr
55	Cesium	Cs	132.905 45	133	132.905 447	100	
				134*	133.906 713		2.1 yr
				135*	134.905 972		2×10^{6} yr
				137*	136.907 074		30 yr
56	Barium	Ba	137.327	130	129.906 310	0.106	
				132	131.905 056	0.101	
				133*	132.906 002		10.5 yr
				134	133.904 503	2.417	
				135	134.905 683	6.592	
				136	135.904 570	7.854	
				137	136.905 821	11.232	
				138	137.905 241	71.698	
57	Lanthanum	La	138.905 5	137*	136.906 466		6×10^{4} yr
				138*	137.907 107	0.090	1.05×10^{11} yr

(Continued)

TABLE A.3 **Table of Atomic Masses** *(Continued)*

Atomic Number Z	Element	Symbol	Chemical Atomic Mass (u)	Mass Number (*indicates radioactive) A	Atomic Mass (u)	Percent Abundance	Half-Life (if radioactive) $T_{1/2}$
(57)	Lanthanum			139	138.906 349	99.910	
58	Cerium	Ce	140.116	136	135.907 144	0.185	
				138	137.905 986	0.251	
				140	139.905 434	88.450	
				142*	141.909 240	11.114	$>5 \times 10^{16}$ yr
59	Praseodymium	Pr	140.907 65	141	140.907 648	100	
60	Neodymium	Nd	144.24	142	141.907 719	27.2	
				143	142.909 810	12.2	
				144*	143.910 083	23.8	2.3×10^{15} yr
				145	144.912 569	8.3	
				146	145.913 112	17.2	
				148	147.916 888	5.7	
				150*	149.920 887	5.6	$>1 \times 10^{18}$ yr
61	Promethium	Pm		143*	142.910 928		265 days
				145*	144.912 744		17.7 yr
				146*	145.914 692		5.5 yr
				147*	146.915 134		2.623 yr
62	Samarium	Sm	150.36	144	143.911 995	3.07	
				146*	145.913 037		1.0×10^{8} yr
				147*	146.914 893	14.99	1.06×10^{11} yr
				148*	147.914 818	11.24	7×10^{15} yr
				149*	148.917 180	13.82	$>2 \times 10^{15}$ yr
				150	149.917 272	7.38	
				151*	150.919 928		90 yr
				152	151.919 728	26.75	
				154	153.922 205	22.75	
63	Europium	Eu	151.964	151	150.919 846	47.81	
				152*	151.921 740		13.5 yr
				153	152.921 226	52.19	
				154*	153.922 975		8.59 yr
				155*	154.922 889		4.7 yr
64	Gadolinium	Gd	157.25	148*	147.918 110		75 yr
				150*	149.918 656		1.8×10^{6} yr
				152*	151.919 788	0.20	1.1×10^{14} yr
				154	153.920 862	2.18	
				155	154.922 619	14.80	
				156	155.922 120	20.47	
				157	156.923 957	15.65	
				158	157.924 100	24.84	
				160	159.927 051	21.86	
65	Terbium	Tb	158.925 34	159	158.925 343	100	
66	Dysprosium	Dy	162.50	156	155.924 278	0.06	
				158	157.924 405	0.10	
				160	159.925 194	2.34	
				161	160.926 930	18.91	
				162	161.926 795	25.51	
				163	162.928 728	24.90	
				164	163.929 171	28.18	
67	Holmium	Ho	164.930 32	165	164.930 320	100	
				166*	165.932 281		1.2×10^{3} yr
68	Erbium	Er	167.6	162	161.928 775	0.14	
				164	163.929 197	1.61	

(Continued)

| TABLE A.3 | Table of Atomic Masses *(Continued)* |

Atomic Number Z	Element	Symbol	Chemical Atomic Mass (u)	Mass Number (*indicates radioactive) A	Atomic Mass (u)	Percent Abundance	Half-Life (if radioactive) $T_{1/2}$
(68)	Erbium			166	165.930 290	33.61	
				167	166.932 045	22.93	
				168	167.932 368	26.78	
				170	169.935 460	14.93	
69	Thulium	Tm	168.934 21	169	168.934 211	100	
				171*	170.936 426		1.92 yr
70	Ytterbium	Yb	173.04	168	167.933 894	0.13	
				170	169.934 759	3.04	
				171	170.936 322	14.28	
				172	171.936 378	21.83	
				173	172.938 207	16.13	
				174	173.938 858	31.83	
				176	175.942 568	12.76	
71	Lutecium	Lu	174.967	173*	172.938 927		1.37 yr
				175	174.940 768	97.41	
				176*	175.942 682	2.59	3.78×10^{10} yr
72	Hafnium	Hf	178.49	174*	173.940 040	0.16	2.0×10^{15} yr
				176	175.941 402	5.26	
				177	176.943 220	18.60	
				178	177.943 698	27.28	
				179	178.945 815	13.62	
				180	179.946 549	35.08	
73	Tantalum	Ta	180.947 9	180	179.947 466	0.012	
				181	180.947 996	99.988	
74	Tungsten (Wolfram)	W	183.84	180	179.946 706	0.12	
				182	181.948 206	26.50	
				183	182.950 224	14.31	
				184	183.950 933	30.64	
				186	185.954 362	28.43	
75	Rhenium	Re	186.207	185	184.952 956	37.40	
				187*	186.955 751	62.60	4.4×10^{10} yr
76	Osmium	Os	190.23	184	183.952 491	0.02	
				186*	185.953 838	1.59	2.0×10^{15} yr
				187	186.955 748	1.96	
				188	187.955 836	13.24	
				189	188.958 145	16.15	
				190	189.958 445	26.26	
				192	191.961 479	40.78	
				194*	193.965 179		6.0 yr
77	Iridium	Ir	192.217	191	190.960 591	37.3	
				193	192.962 924	62.7	
78	Platinum	Pt	195.078	190*	189.959 930	0.014	6.5×10^{11} yr
				192	191.961 035	0.782	
				194	193.962 664	32.967	
				195	194.964 774	33.832	
				196	195.964 935	25.242	
				198	197.967 876	7.163	
79	Gold	Au	196.966 55	197	196.966 552	100	
80	Mercury	Hg	200.59	196	195.965 815	0.15	
				198	197.966 752	9.97	
				199	198.968 262	16.87	
				200	199.968 309	23.10	
				201	200.970 285	13.18	

(Continued)

TABLE A.3	Table of Atomic Masses *(Continued)*

Atomic Number Z	Element	Symbol	Chemical Atomic Mass (u)	Mass Number (*indicates radioactive) A	Atomic Mass (u)	Percent Abundance	Half-Life (if radioactive) $T_{1/2}$
(80)	Mercury			202	201.970 626	29.86	
				204	203.973 476	6.87	
81	Thallium	Tl	204.383 3	203	202.972 329	29.524	
				204*	203.973 849		3.78 yr
				205	204.974 412	70.476	
		(Ra E″)		206*	205.976 095		4.2 min
		(Ac C″)		207*	206.977 408		4.77 min
		(Th C″)		208*	207.982 005		3.053 min
		(Ra C″)		210*	209.990 066		1.30 min
82	Lead	Pb	207.2	202*	201.972 144		5×10^4 yr
				204*	203.973 029	1.4	$\geq 1.4 \times 10^{17}$ yr
				205*	204.974 467		1.5×10^7 yr
				206	205.974 449	24.1	
				207	206.975 881	22.1	
				208	207.976 636	52.4	
		(Ra D)		210*	209.984 173		22.3 yr
		(Ac B)		211*	210.988 732		36.1 min
		(Th B)		212*	211.991 888		10.64 h
		(Ra B)		214*	213.999 798		26.8 min
83	Bismuth	Bi	208.980 38	207*	206.978 455		32.2 yr
				208*	207.979 727		3.7×10^5 yr
				209	208.980 383	100	
		(Ra E)		210*	209.984 105		5.01 days
		(Th C)		211*	210.987 258		2.14 min
				212*	211.991 272		60.6 min
		(Ra C)		214*	213.998 699		19.9 min
				215*	215.001 832		7.4 min
84	Polonium	Po		209*	208.982 416		102 yr
		(Ra F)		210*	209.982 857		138.38 days
		(Ac C′)		211*	210.986 637		0.52 s
		(Th C′)		212*	211.988 852		0.30 μs
		(Ra C′)		214*	213.995 186		164 μs
		(Ac A)		215*	214.999 415		0.001 8 s
		(Th A)		216*	216.001 905		0.145 s
		(Ra A)		218*	218.008 966		3.10 min
85	Astatine	At		215*	214.998 641		≈ 100 μs
				218*	218.008 682		1.6 s
				219*	219.011 297		0.9 min
86	Radon	Rn					
		(An)		219*	219.009 475		3.96 s
		(Tn)		220*	220.011 384		55.6 s
		(Rn)		222*	222.017 570		3.823 days
87	Francium	Fr					
		(Ac K)		223*	223.019 731		22 min
88	Radium	Ra					
		(Ac X)		223*	223.018 497		11.43 days
		(Th X)		224*	224.020 202		3.66 days
		(Ra)		226*	226.025 403		1 600 yr
		(Ms Th$_1$)		228*	228.031 064		5.75 yr
89	Actinium	Ac		227*	227.027 747		21.77 yr
		(Ms Th$_2$)		228*	228.031 015		6.15 h
90	Thorium	Th	232.038 1				

(Continued)

TABLE A.3	Table of Atomic Masses *(Continued)*

Atomic Number Z	Element	Symbol	Chemical Atomic Mass (u)	Mass Number (*indicates radioactive) A	Atomic Mass (u)	Percent Abundance	Half-Life (if radioactive) $T_{1/2}$
(90)	Thorium	(Rd Ac)		227*	227.027 699		18.72 days
		(Rd Th)		228*	228.028 731		1.913 yr
				229*	229.031 755		7 300 yr
		(Io)		230*	230.033 127		75.000 yr
		(UY)		231*	231.036 297		25.52 h
		(Th)		232*	232.038 050	100	1.40×10^{10} yr
		(UX$_1$)		234*	234.043 596		24.1 days
91	Protactinium	Pa	231.035 88	231*	231.035 879		32.760 yr
		(Uz)		234*	234.043 302		6.7 h
92	Uranium	U	238.028 9	232*	232.037 146		69 yr
				233*	233.039 628		1.59×10^5 yr
				234*	234.040 946	0.005 5	2.45×10^5 yr
		(Ac U)		235*	235.043 923	0.720 0	7.04×10^8 yr
				236*	236.045 562		2.34×10^7 yr
		(UI)		238*	238.050 783	99.274 5	4.47×10^9 yr
93	Neptunium	Np		235*	235.044 056		396 days
				236*	236.046 560		1.15×10^5 yr
				237*	237.048 167		2.14×10^6 yr
94	Plutonium	Pu		236*	236.046 048		2.87 yr
				238*	238.049 553		87.7 yr
				239*	239.052 156		2.412×10^4 yr
				240*	240.053 808		6 560 yr
				241*	241.056 845		14.4 yr
				242*	242.058 737		3.73×10^6 yr
				244*	244.064 198		8.1×10^7 yr

Sources: Chemical atomic masses are from T. B. Coplen, "Atomic Weights of the Elements 1999," a technical report to the International Union of Pure and Applied Chemistry, and published in *Pure and Applied Chemistry* 73(4), 667–683, 2001. Atomic masses of the isotopes are from G. Audi and A. H. Wapstra, "The 1995 Update to the Atomic Mass Evaluation," *Nuclear Physics* A595, vol. 4, 409–480, December 25, 1995. Percent abundance values are from K. J. R. Rosman and P. D. P. Taylor, "Isotopic Compositions of the Elements 1999," a technical report to the International Union of Pure and Applied Chemistry, and published in *Pure and Applied Chemistry* 70(1), 217–236, 1998.

Mathematics Review

This appendix in mathematics is intended as a brief review of operations and methods. Early in this course, you should be totally familiar with basic algebraic techniques, analytic geometry, and trigonometry. The sections on differential and integral calculus are more detailed and are intended for those students who have difficulty applying calculus concepts to physical situations.

B.1 SCIENTIFIC NOTATION

Many quantities that scientists deal with often have very large or very small values. The speed of light, for example, is about 300 000 000 m/s, and the ink required to make the dot over an i in this textbook has a mass of about 0.000 000 001 kg. Obviously, it is very cumbersome to read, write, and keep track of such numbers. We avoid this problem by using a method dealing with powers of the number ten:

$$10^0 = 1$$

$$10^1 = 10$$

$$10^2 = 10 \times 10 = 100$$

$$10^3 = 10 \times 10 \times 10 = 1\ 000$$

$$10^4 = 10 \times 10 \times 10 \times 10 = 10\ 000$$

$$10^5 = 10 \times 10 \times 10 \times 10 \times 10 = 100\ 000$$

and so on. The number of zeros corresponds to the power to which ten is raised, called the **exponent** of ten. For example, the speed of light, 300 000 000 m/s, can be expressed as 3×10^8 m/s.

In this method, some representative numbers smaller than unity are the following:

$$10^{-1} = \frac{1}{10} = 0.1$$

$$10^{-2} = \frac{1}{10 \times 10} = 0.01$$

$$10^{-3} = \frac{1}{10 \times 10 \times 10} = 0.001$$

$$10^{-4} = \frac{1}{10 \times 10 \times 10 \times 10} = 0.000\ 1$$

$$10^{-5} = \frac{1}{10 \times 10 \times 10 \times 10 \times 10} = 0.000\ 01$$

In these cases, the number of places the decimal point is to the left of the digit 1 equals the value of the (negative) exponent. Numbers expressed as some power of ten multiplied by another number between one and ten are said to be in **scientific notation.** For example, the scientific notation for 5 943 000 000 is 5.943×10^9 and that for 0.000 083 2 is 8.32×10^{-5}.

When numbers expressed in scientific notation are being multiplied, the following general rule is very useful:

$$10^n \times 10^m = 10^{n+m} \qquad [B.1]$$

where n and m can be *any* numbers (not necessarily integers). For example, $10^2 \times 10^5 = 10^7$. The rule also applies if one of the exponents is negative: $10^3 \times 10^{-8} = 10^{-5}$.

When dividing numbers expressed in scientific notation, note that

$$\frac{10^n}{10^m} = 10^n \times 10^{-m} = 10^{n-m} \qquad [B.2]$$

Exercises

With help from the preceding rules, verify the answers to the following equations.

1. $86\ 400 = 8.64 \times 10^4$
2. $9\ 816\ 762.5 = 9.816\ 762\ 5 \times 10^6$
3. $0.000\ 000\ 039\ 8 = 3.98 \times 10^{-8}$
4. $(4.0 \times 10^8)(9.0 \times 10^9) = 3.6 \times 10^{18}$
5. $(3.0 \times 10^7)(6.0 \times 10^{-12}) = 1.8 \times 10^{-4}$
6. $\dfrac{75 \times 10^{-11}}{5.0 \times 10^{-3}} = 1.5 \times 10^{-7}$
7. $\dfrac{(3 \times 10^6)(8 \times 10^{-2})}{(2 \times 10^{17})(6 \times 10^5)} = 2 \times 10^{-18}$

B.2 | ALGEBRA

Some Basic Rules

When algebraic operations are performed, the laws of arithmetic apply. Symbols such as x, y, and z are usually used to represent unspecified quantities, called the **unknowns.**

First, consider the equation

$$8x = 32$$

If we wish to solve for x, we can divide (or multiply) each side of the equation by the same factor without destroying the equality. In this case, if we divide both sides by 8, we have

$$\frac{8x}{8} = \frac{32}{8}$$

$$x = 4$$

Next consider the equation

$$x + 2 = 8$$

In this type of expression, we can add or subtract the same quantity from each side. If we subtract 2 from each side, we have

$$x + 2 - 2 = 8 - 2$$

$$x = 6$$

In general, if $x + a = b$, then $x = b - a$.

Now consider the equation

$$\frac{x}{5} = 9$$

If we multiply each side by 5, we are left with x on the left by itself and 45 on the right:

$$\left(\frac{x}{5}\right)(5) = 9 \times 5$$

$$x = 45$$

In all cases, *whatever operation is performed on the left side of the equality must also be performed on the right side.*

The following rules for multiplying, dividing, adding, and subtracting fractions should be recalled, where a, b, c, and d are four numbers:

	Rule	Example
Multiplying	$\left(\dfrac{a}{b}\right)\left(\dfrac{c}{d}\right) = \dfrac{ac}{bd}$	$\left(\dfrac{2}{3}\right)\left(\dfrac{4}{5}\right) = \dfrac{8}{15}$
Dividing	$\dfrac{(a/b)}{(c/d)} = \dfrac{ad}{bc}$	$\dfrac{2/3}{4/5} = \dfrac{(2)(5)}{(4)(3)} = \dfrac{10}{12}$
Adding	$\dfrac{a}{b} \pm \dfrac{c}{d} = \dfrac{ad \pm bc}{bd}$	$\dfrac{2}{3} - \dfrac{4}{5} = \dfrac{(2)(5)-(4)(3)}{(3)(5)} = -\dfrac{2}{15}$

Exercises

In the following exercises, solve for x:

Answers

1. $a = \dfrac{1}{1 + x}$ $\quad x = \dfrac{1 - a}{a}$

2. $3x - 5 = 13$ $\quad x = 6$

3. $ax - 5 = bx + 2$ $\quad x = \dfrac{7}{a - b}$

4. $\dfrac{5}{2x + 6} = \dfrac{3}{4x + 8}$ $\quad x = -\dfrac{11}{7}$

Powers

When powers of a given quantity x are multiplied, the following rule applies:

$$x^n x^m = x^{n+m} \qquad \text{[B.3]}$$

For example, $x^2 x^4 = x^{2+4} = x^6$.

When dividing the powers of a given quantity, the rule is

$$\frac{x^n}{x^m} = x^{n-m} \qquad \text{[B.4]}$$

For example, $x^8/x^2 = x^{8-2} = x^6$.

A power that is a fraction, such as $\frac{1}{3}$, corresponds to a root as follows:

$$x^{1/n} = \sqrt[n]{x} \qquad \text{[B.5]}$$

For example, $4^{1/3} = \sqrt[3]{4} = 1.5874$. (A scientific calculator is useful for such calculations.)

Finally, any quantity x^n raised to the mth power is

$$(x^n)^m = x^{nm} \qquad \text{[B.6]}$$

Table B.1 summarizes the rules of exponents.

TABLE **B.1**	Rules of Exponents
$x^0 = 1$	
$x^1 = x$	
$x^n x^m = x^{n+m}$	
$x^n/x^m = x^{n-m}$	
$x^{1/n} = \sqrt[n]{x}$	
$(x^n)^m = x^{nm}$	

Exercises

Verify the following equations.

1. $3^2 \times 3^3 = 243$
2. $x^5 x^{-8} = x^{-3}$
3. $x^{10}/x^{-5} = x^{15}$
4. $5^{1/3} = 1.709\ 975$ (Use your calculator.)
5. $60^{1/4} = 2.783\ 158$ (Use your calculator.)
6. $(x^4)^3 = x^{12}$

Factoring

Some useful formulas for factoring an equation are the following:

$$ax + ay + az = a(x + y + x) \qquad \text{common factor}$$
$$a^2 + 2ab + b^2 = (a + b)^2 \qquad \text{perfect square}$$
$$a^2 - b^2 = (a + b)(a - b) \qquad \text{differences of squares}$$

Quadratic Equations

The general form of a quadratic equation is

$$ax^2 + bx + c = 0 \qquad \text{[B.7]}$$

where x is the unknown quantity and a, b, and c are numerical factors referred to as **coefficients** of the equation. This equation has two roots, given by

$$x = \frac{-b \pm \sqrt{b^2 - 4ac}}{2a} \qquad \text{[B.8]}$$

If $b^2 \geq 4ac$, the roots are real.

EXAMPLE B.1

The equation $x^2 + 5x + 4 = 0$ has the following roots corresponding to the two signs of the square-root term:

$$x = \frac{-5 \pm \sqrt{5^2 - (4)(1)(4)}}{2(1)} = \frac{-5 \pm \sqrt{9}}{2} = \frac{-5 \pm 3}{2}$$

$$x_+ = \frac{-5 + 3}{2} = -1 \qquad x_- = \frac{-5 - 3}{2} = -4$$

where x_+ refers to the root corresponding to the positive sign and x_- refers to the root corresponding to the negative sign.

Exercises

Solve the following quadratic equations.

Answers

1. $x^2 + 2x - 3 = 0$ $x_+ = 1$ $x_- = -3$
2. $2x^2 - 5x + 2 = 0$ $x_+ = 2$ $x_- = \frac{1}{2}$
3. $2x^2 - 4x - 9 = 0$ $x_+ = 1 + \sqrt{22}/2$ $x_- = 1 - \sqrt{22}/2$

Linear Equations

A linear equation has the general form

$$y = mx + b \qquad \text{[B.9]}$$

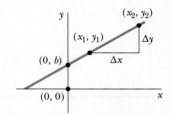

where m and b are constants. This equation is referred to as being linear because the graph of y versus x is a straight line as shown in Figure B.1. The constant b, called the **y-intercept,** represents the value of y at which the straight line intersects the y axis. The constant m is equal to the **slope** of the straight line. If any two points on the straight line are specified by the coordinates (x_1, y_1) and (x_2, y_2) as in Figure B.1, the slope of the straight line can be expressed as

$$\text{Slope} = \frac{y_2 - y_1}{x_2 - x_1} = \frac{\Delta y}{\Delta x} \qquad \text{[B.10]}$$

FIGURE B.1   A straight line graphed on an x-y coordinate system. The slope of the line is the ratio of Δy to Δx.

Note that m and b can have either positive or negative values. If $m > 0$, the straight line has a *positive* slope as in Figure B.1. If $m < 0$, the straight line has a *negative* slope. In Figure B.1, both m and b are positive. Three other possible situations are shown in Figure B.2.

Exercises

1. Draw graphs of the following straight lines: (a) $y = 5x + 3$, (b) $y = -2x + 4$, (c) $y = -3x - 6$.
2. Find the slopes of the straight lines described in Exercise 1.

Answers   (a) 5   (b) -2 (c) -3

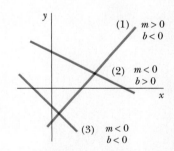

3. Find the slopes of the straight lines that pass through the following sets of points: (a) $(0, -4)$ and $(4, 2)$, (b) $(0, 0)$ and $(2, -5)$, (c) $(-5, 2)$ and $(4, -2)$.

Answers   (a) $\frac{3}{2}$ (b) $-\frac{5}{2}$ (c) $-\frac{4}{9}$

FIGURE B.2   The brown line has a positive slope and a negative y-intercept. The blue line has a negative slope and a positive y-intercept. The green line has a negative slope and a negative y-intercept.

Solving Simultaneous Linear Equations

Consider the equation $3x + 5y = 15$, which has two unknowns, x and y. Such an equation does not have a unique solution. For example, note that $(x = 0, y = 3)$, $(x = 5, y = 0)$, and $\left(x = 2, y = \frac{9}{5}\right)$ are all solutions to this equation.

If a problem has two unknowns, a unique solution is possible only if we have *two* equations. In general, if a problem has n unknowns, its solution requires n equations. To solve two simultaneous equations involving two unknowns, x and y, we solve one of the equations for x in terms of y and substitute this expression into the other equation.

EXAMPLE B.2

Solve the two simultaneous equations

$$(1) \quad 5x + y = -8$$

$$(2) \quad 2x - 2y = 4$$

Solution From (2), $x = y + 2$. Substitution of this equation into (1) gives

$$5(y + 2) + y = -8$$

$$6y = -18$$

$$y = \boxed{-3}$$

$$x = y + 2 = \boxed{-1}$$

Alternative Solution Multiply each term in (1) by the factor 2 and add the result to (2):

$$10x + 2y = -16$$

$$\underline{2x - 2y = 4}$$

$$12x \qquad = -12$$

$$x = \boxed{-1}$$

$$y = x - 2 = \boxed{-3}$$

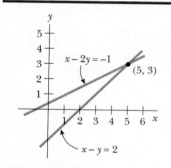

FIGURE B.3   A graphical solution for two linear equations.

Two linear equations containing two unknowns can also be solved by a graphical method. If the straight lines corresponding to the two equations are plotted in a conventional coordinate system, the intersection of the two lines represents the solution. For example, consider the two equations

$$x - y = 2$$

$$x - 2y = -1$$

These equations are plotted in Figure B.3. The intersection of the two lines has the coordinates $x = 5$ and $y = 3$, which represents the solution to the equations. You should check this solution by the analytical technique discussed earlier.

Exercises

Solve the following pairs of simultaneous equations involving two unknowns.

Answers

1. $x + y = 8$ $x = 5, y = 3$
    $x - y = 2$

2. $98 - T = 10a$ $T = 65, a = 3.27$
    $T - 49 = 5a$

3. $6x + 2y = 6$ $x = 2, y = -3$
    $8x - 4y = 28$

Logarithms

Suppose a quantity x is expressed as a power of some quantity a:

$$\boxed{x = a^y} \qquad\qquad \text{[B.11]}$$

The number a is called the **base** number. The **logarithm** of x with respect to the base a is equal to the exponent to which the base must be raised to satisfy the expression $x = a^y$:

$$\boxed{y = \log_a x} \qquad\qquad \text{[B.12]}$$

Conversely, the **antilogarithm** of y is the number x:

$$\boxed{x = \text{antilog}_a y} \qquad\qquad \text{[B.13]}$$

In practice, the two bases most often used are base 10, called the *common* logarithm base, and base $e = 2.718\,282$, called Euler's constant or the *natural* logarithm

base. When common logarithms are used,

$$y = \log_{10} x \qquad (\text{or } x = 10^y) \qquad \text{[B.14]}$$

When natural logarithms are used,

$$y = \ln x \qquad (\text{or } x = e^y) \qquad \text{[B.15]}$$

For example, $\log_{10} 52 = 1.716$, so antilog$_{10}$ $1.716 = 10^{1.716} = 52$. Likewise, $\ln 52 = 3.951$, so antiln $3.951 = e^{3.951} = 52$.

In general, you can convert between base 10 and base e with the equality

$$\ln x = (2.302\ 585) \log_{10} x \qquad \text{[B.16]}$$

Finally, some useful properties of logarithms are the following:

$$\left.\begin{array}{l} \log(ab) = \log a + \log b \\ \log(a/b) = \log a - \log b \\ \log(a^n) = n \log a \end{array}\right\} \text{any base}$$

$$\ln e = 1$$

$$\ln e^a = a$$

$$\ln\left(\frac{1}{a}\right) = -\ln a$$

B.3 | GEOMETRY

The **distance** d between two points having coordinates (x_1, y_1) and (x_2, y_2) is

$$d = \sqrt{(x_2 - x_1)^2 + (y_2 - y_1)^2} \qquad \text{[B.17]}$$

Radian measure: The arc length s of a circular arc (Fig. B.4) is proportional to the radius r for a fixed value of θ (in radians):

$$s = r\theta$$
$$\theta = \frac{s}{r} \qquad \text{[B.18]}$$

Table B.2 gives the **areas** and **volumes** for several geometric shapes used throughout this text.

The equation of a **straight line** (Fig. B.5) is

$$y = mx + b \qquad \text{[B.19]}$$

where b is the y-intercept and m is the slope of the line.

The equation of a **circle** of radius R centered at the origin is

$$x^2 + y^2 = R^2 \qquad \text{[B.20]}$$

The equation of an **ellipse** having the origin at its center (Fig. B.6) is

$$\frac{x^2}{a^2} + \frac{y^2}{b^2} = 1 \qquad \text{[B.21]}$$

where a is the length of the semimajor axis (the longer one) and b is the length of the semiminor axis (the shorter one).

The equation of a **parabola** the vertex of which is at $y = b$ (Fig. B.7) is

$$y = ax^2 + b \qquad \text{[B.22]}$$

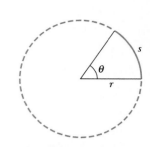

FIGURE **B.4** The angle θ in radians is the ratio of the arc length s to the radius r of the circle.

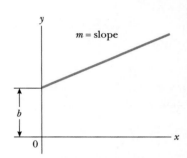

FIGURE **B.5** A straight line with a slope of m and a y-intercept of b.

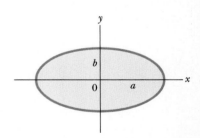

FIGURE **B.6** An ellipse with semimajor axis a and semiminor axis b.

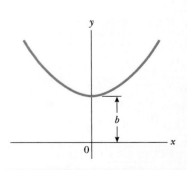

FIGURE **B.7** A parabola.

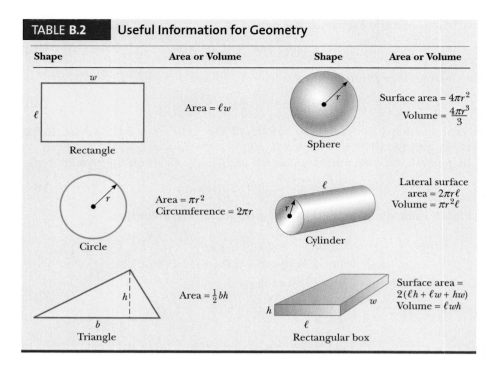

TABLE **B.2**   **Useful Information for Geometry**

Shape	Area or Volume	Shape	Area or Volume
Rectangle	Area $= \ell w$	Sphere	Surface area $= 4\pi r^2$ Volume $= \frac{4\pi r^3}{3}$
Circle	Area $= \pi r^2$ Circumference $= 2\pi r$	Cylinder	Lateral surface area $= 2\pi r \ell$ Volume $= \pi r^2 \ell$
Triangle	Area $= \frac{1}{2}bh$	Rectangular box	Surface area $=$ $2(\ell h + \ell w + hw)$ Volume $= \ell wh$

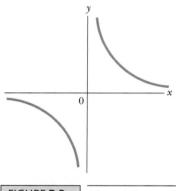

FIGURE **B.8**   A hyperbola.

The equation of a **rectangular hyperbola** (Fig. B.8) is

$$xy = \text{constant} \qquad [\text{B.23}]$$

B.4 | TRIGONOMETRY

That portion of mathematics based on the special properties of the right triangle is called trigonometry. By definition, a right triangle is a triangle containing a 90° angle. Consider the right triangle shown in Figure B.9, where side a is opposite the angle θ, side b is adjacent to the angle θ, and side c is the hypotenuse of the triangle. The three basic trigonometric functions defined by such a triangle are the sine (sin), cosine (cos), and tangent (tan) functions. In terms of the angle θ, these functions are defined by

$$\sin \theta = \frac{\text{side opposite } \theta}{\text{hypotenuse}} = \frac{a}{c} \qquad [\text{B.24}]$$

$$\cos \theta = \frac{\text{side adjacent to } \theta}{\text{hypotenuse}} = \frac{b}{c} \qquad [\text{B.25}]$$

$$\tan \theta = \frac{\text{side opposite } \theta}{\text{side adjacent to } \theta} = \frac{a}{b} \qquad [\text{B.26}]$$

The Pythagorean theorem provides the following relationship among the sides of a right triangle:

$$c^2 = a^2 + b^2 \qquad [\text{B.27}]$$

From the preceding definitions and the Pythagorean theorem, it follows that

$$\sin^2 \theta + \cos^2 \theta = 1$$

$$\tan \theta = \frac{\sin \theta}{\cos \theta}$$

$a =$ opposite side
$b =$ adjacent side
$c =$ hypotenuse

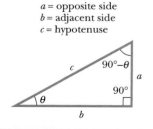

FIGURE **B.9**   A right triangle, used to define the basic functions of trigonometry.

TABLE B.3	Some Trigonometric Identities
$\sin^2\theta + \cos^2\theta = 1$	$\csc^2\theta = 1 + \cot^2\theta$
$\sec^2\theta = 1 + \tan^2\theta$	$\sin^2\dfrac{\theta}{2} = \tfrac{1}{2}(1 - \cos\theta)$
$\sin 2\theta = 2\sin\theta\cos\theta$	$\cos^2\dfrac{\theta}{2} = \tfrac{1}{2}(1 + \cos\theta)$
$\cos 2\theta = \cos^2\theta - \sin^2\theta$	$1 - \cos\theta = 2\sin^2\dfrac{\theta}{2}$
$\tan 2\theta = \dfrac{2\tan\theta}{1 - \tan^2\theta}$	$\tan\dfrac{\theta}{2} = \sqrt{\dfrac{1 - \cos\theta}{1 + \cos\theta}}$

$\sin(A \pm B) = \sin A\cos B \pm \cos A\sin B$
$\cos(A \pm B) = \cos A\cos B \mp \sin A\sin B$
$\sin A \pm \sin B = 2\sin\left[\tfrac{1}{2}(A \pm B)\right]\cos\left[\tfrac{1}{2}(A \mp B)\right]$
$\cos A + \cos B = 2\cos\left[\tfrac{1}{2}(A + B)\right]\cos\left[\tfrac{1}{2}(A - B)\right]$
$\cos A - \cos B = 2\sin\left[\tfrac{1}{2}(A + B)\right]\sin\left[\tfrac{1}{2}(B - A)\right]$

The cosecant, secant, and cotangent functions are defined by

$$\csc\theta = \frac{1}{\sin\theta} \qquad \sec\theta = \frac{1}{\cos\theta} \qquad \cot\theta = \frac{1}{\tan\theta}$$

The following relationships are derived directly from the right triangle shown in Figure B.9:

$$\sin\theta = \cos(90° - \theta)$$
$$\cos\theta = \sin(90° - \theta)$$
$$\cot\theta = \tan(90° - \theta)$$

Some properties of trigonometric functions are

$$\sin(-\theta) = -\sin\theta$$
$$\cos(-\theta) = \cos\theta$$
$$\tan(-\theta) = -\tan\theta$$

The following relationships apply to *any* triangle, as shown in Figure B.10:

$$\alpha + \beta + \gamma = 180°$$

Law of cosines
$$\begin{cases} a^2 = b^2 + c^2 - 2bc\cos\alpha \\ b^2 = a^2 + c^2 - 2ac\cos\beta \\ c^2 = a^2 + b^2 - 2ab\cos\gamma \end{cases}$$

Law of sines
$$\frac{a}{\sin\alpha} = \frac{b}{\sin\beta} = \frac{c}{\sin\gamma}$$

Table B.3 lists a number of useful trigonometric identities.

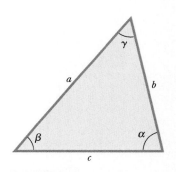

FIGURE B.10 An arbitrary, non-right triangle.

EXAMPLE B.3

Consider the right triangle in Figure B.11 in which $a = 2.00$, $b = 5.00$, and c is unknown. From the Pythagorean theorem we have

$$c^2 = a^2 + b^2 = 2.00^2 + 5.00^2 = 4.00 + 25.0 = 29.0$$

$$c = \sqrt{29.0} = \boxed{5.39}$$

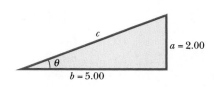

FIGURE B.11 (Example B.3)

To find the angle θ, note that

$$\tan \theta = \frac{a}{b} = \frac{2.00}{5.00} = 0.400$$

Using a calculator, we find that

$$\theta = \tan^{-1}(0.400) = \boxed{21.8°}$$

where $\tan^{-1}(0.400)$ is the notation for "angle whose tangent is 0.400," sometimes written as arctan(0.400).

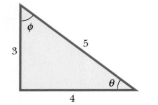

FIGURE **B.12** (Exercise 1)

Exercises

1. In Figure B.12, identify (a) the side opposite θ and (b) the side adjacent to ϕ and then find (c) $\cos \theta$, (d) $\sin \phi$, and (e) $\tan \phi$.

Answers (a) 3 (b) 3 (c) $\frac{4}{5}$ (d) $\frac{4}{5}$ (e) $\frac{4}{3}$

2. In a certain right triangle, the two sides that are perpendicular to each other are 5.00 m and 7.00 m long. What is the length of the third side?

Answer 8.60 m

3. A right triangle has a hypotenuse of length 3.0 m, and one of its angles is 30°. (a) What is the length of the side opposite the 30° angle? (b) What is the length of the side adjacent to the 30° angle?

Answers (a) 1.5 m (b) 2.6 m

B.5 | SERIES EXPANSIONS

$$(a + b)^n = a^n + \frac{n}{1!} a^{n-1}b + \frac{n(n - 1)}{2!} a^{n-2}b^2 + \cdots$$

$$(1 + x)^n = 1 + nx + \frac{n(n - 1)}{2!} x^2 + \cdots$$

$$e^x = 1 + x + \frac{x^2}{2!} + \frac{x^3}{3!} + \cdots$$

$$\ln(1 \pm x) = \pm x - \tfrac{1}{2}x^2 \pm \tfrac{1}{3}x^3 - \cdots$$

$$\left.\begin{array}{l} \sin x = x - \dfrac{x^3}{3!} + \dfrac{x^5}{5!} - \cdots \\[2mm] \cos x = 1 - \dfrac{x^2}{2!} + \dfrac{x^4}{4!} - \cdots \\[2mm] \tan x = x + \dfrac{x^3}{3} + \dfrac{2x^5}{15} + \cdots \qquad |x| < \dfrac{\pi}{2} \end{array}\right\} x \text{ in radians}$$

For $x \ll 1$, the following approximations can be used:[1]

$$(1 + x)^n \approx 1 + nx \qquad \sin x \approx x$$

$$e^x \approx 1 + x \qquad \cos x \approx 1$$

$$\ln(1 \pm x) \approx \pm x \qquad \tan x \approx x$$

B.6 | DIFFERENTIAL CALCULUS

In various branches of science, it is sometimes necessary to use the basic tools of calculus, invented by Newton, to describe physical phenomena. The use of calculus is fundamental in the treatment of various problems in Newtonian mechanics,

---

[1]The approximations for the functions $\sin x$, $\cos x$, and $\tan x$ are for $x \leq 0.1$ rad.

electricity, and magnetism. In this section, we simply state some basic properties and "rules of thumb" that should be a useful review to the student.

First, a **function** must be specified that relates one variable to another (e.g., a coordinate as a function of time). Suppose one of the variables is called y (the dependent variable) and the other x (the independent variable). We might have a function relationship such as

$$y(x) = ax^3 + bx^2 + cx + d$$

If a, b, c, and d are specified constants, y can be calculated for any value of x. We usually deal with continuous functions, that is, those for which y varies "smoothly" with x.

The **derivative** of y with respect to x is defined as the limit, as Δx approaches zero, of the slopes of chords drawn between two points on the y versus x curve. Mathematically, we write this definition as

$$\frac{dy}{dx} = \lim_{\Delta x \to 0} \frac{\Delta y}{\Delta x} = \lim_{\Delta x \to 0} \frac{y(x + \Delta x) - y(x)}{\Delta x} \qquad \text{[B.28]}$$

where Δy and Δx are defined as $\Delta x = x_2 - x_1$ and $\Delta y = y_2 - y_1$ (Fig. B.13). It is important to note that dy/dx does *not* mean dy divided by dx, but rather is simply a notation of the limiting process of the derivative as defined by Equation B.28.

A useful expression to remember when $y(x) = ax^n$, where a is a *constant* and n is *any* positive or negative number (integer or fraction), is

$$\frac{dy}{dx} = nax^{n-1} \qquad \text{[B.29]}$$

If $y(x)$ is a polynomial or algebraic function of x, we apply Equation B.29 to *each* term in the polynomial and take $d[\text{constant}]/dx = 0$. In Examples 4 through 7, we evaluate the derivatives of several functions.

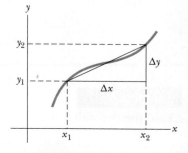

FIGURE B.13 The lengths Δx and Δy are used to define the derivative of this function at a point.

Special Properties of the Derivative

A. Derivative of the product of two functions If a function $f(x)$ is given by the product of two functions—say, $g(x)$ and $h(x)$—the derivative of $f(x)$ is defined as

$$\frac{d}{dx} f(x) = \frac{d}{dx} [g(x) h(x)] = g \frac{dh}{dx} + h \frac{dg}{dx} \qquad \text{[B.30]}$$

B. Derivative of the sum of two functions If a function $f(x)$ is equal to the sum of two functions, the derivative of the sum is equal to the sum of the derivatives:

$$\frac{d}{dx} f(x) = \frac{d}{dx} [g(x) + h(x)] = \frac{dg}{dx} + \frac{dh}{dx} \qquad \text{[B.31]}$$

C. Chain rule of differential calculus If $y = f(x)$ and $x = g(z)$, then dy/dz can be written as the product of two derivatives:

$$\frac{dy}{dz} = \frac{dy}{dx} \frac{dx}{dz} \qquad \text{[B.32]}$$

D. The second derivative The second derivative of y with respect to x is defined as the derivative of the function dy/dx (the derivative of the derivative). It is usually written as

$$\frac{d^2 y}{dx^2} = \frac{d}{dx} \left(\frac{dy}{dx} \right) \qquad \text{[B.33]}$$

EXAMPLE B.4

Suppose $y(x)$ (that is, y as a function of x) is given by

$$y(x) = ax^3 + bx + c$$

where a and b are constants. Then it follows that

$$y(x + \Delta x) = a(x + \Delta x)^3 + b(x + \Delta x) + c$$
$$= a(x^3 + 3x^2 \Delta x + 3x \Delta x^2 + \Delta x^3)$$
$$+ b(x + \Delta x) + c$$

so

$$\Delta y = y(x + \Delta x) - y(x)$$
$$= a(3x^2 \Delta x + 3x \Delta x^2 + \Delta x^3) + b \Delta x$$

Substituting this equation into Equation B.28 gives

$$\frac{dy}{dx} = \lim_{\Delta x \to 0} \frac{\Delta y}{\Delta x} = \lim_{\Delta x \to 0} a[3x^2 + 3x \Delta x + \Delta x^2] + b$$

$$\frac{dy}{dx} = 3ax^2 + b$$

EXAMPLE B.5

Find the derivative of

$$y(x) = 8x^5 + 4x^3 + 2x + 7$$

Solution By applying Equation B.29 to each term independently and remembering that d/dx (constant) $= 0$,

we have

$$\frac{dy}{dx} = 8(5)x^4 + 4(3)x^2 + 2(1)x^0 + 0$$

$$\frac{dy}{dx} = 40x^4 + 12x^2 + 2$$

EXAMPLE B.6

Find the derivative of $y(x) = x^3/(x + 1)^2$ with respect to x.

Solution We can rewrite this function as $y(x) = x^3(x + 1)^{-2}$ and apply Equation B.30:

$$\frac{dy}{dx} = (x + 1)^{-2} \frac{d}{dx} (x^3) + x^3 \frac{d}{dx} (x + 1)^{-2}$$

$$= (x + 1)^{-2} 3x^2 + x^3(-2)(x + 1)^{-3}$$

$$\frac{dy}{dx} = \frac{3x^2}{(x + 1)^2} - \frac{2x^3}{(x + 1)^3}$$

EXAMPLE B.7

A useful formula that follows from Equation B.30 is the derivative of the quotient of two functions. Show that

$$\frac{d}{dx} \left[\frac{g(x)}{h(x)} \right] = \frac{h \dfrac{dg}{dx} - g \dfrac{dh}{dx}}{h^2}$$

Solution We can write the quotient as gh^{-1} and then apply Equations B.29 and B.30:

$$\frac{d}{dx} \left(\frac{g}{h} \right) = \frac{d}{dx} (gh^{-1}) = g \frac{d}{dx} (h^{-1}) + h^{-1} \frac{d}{dx} (g)$$

$$= -gh^{-2} \frac{dh}{dx} + h^{-1} \frac{dg}{dx}$$

$$= \frac{h \dfrac{dg}{dx} - g \dfrac{dh}{dx}}{h^2}$$

Some of the more commonly used derivatives of functions are listed in Table B.4.

B.7 │ INTEGRAL CALCULUS

We think of integration as the inverse of differentiation. As an example, consider the expression

$$f(x) = \frac{dy}{dx} = 3ax^2 + b \qquad \text{[B.34]}$$

which was the result of differentiating the function

$$y(x) = ax^3 + bx + c$$

in Example 4. We can write Equation B.34 as $dy = f(x)\,dx = (3ax^2 + b)\,dx$ and obtain $y(x)$ by "summing" over all values of x. Mathematically, we write this inverse operation

$$y(x) = \int f(x)\,dx$$

For the function $f(x)$ given by Equation B.34, we have

$$y(x) = \int (3ax^2 + b)\,dx = ax^3 + bx + c$$

where c is a constant of the integration. This type of integral is called an *indefinite integral* because its value depends on the choice of c.

A general **indefinite integral** $I(x)$ is defined as

$$I(x) = \int f(x)\,dx \qquad [\text{B.35}]$$

where $f(x)$ is called the *integrand* and $f(x) = dI(x)/dx$.

For a *general continuous* function $f(x)$, the integral can be described as the area under the curve bounded by $f(x)$ and the x axis, between two specified values of x, say, x_1 and x_2, as in Figure B.14.

The area of the blue element in Figure B.14 is approximately $f(x_i)\,\Delta x_i$. If we sum all these area elements between x_1 and x_2 and take the limit of this sum as $\Delta x_i \to 0$, we obtain the *true* area under the curve bounded by $f(x)$ and the x axis, between the limits x_1 and x_2:

$$\text{Area} = \lim_{\Delta x_i \to 0} \sum_i f(x_i)\Delta x_i = \int_{x_1}^{x_2} f(x)\,dx \qquad [\text{B.36}]$$

Integrals of the type defined by Equation B.36 are called **definite integrals.**

One common integral that arises in practical situations has the form

$$\int x^n\,dx = \frac{x^{n+1}}{n+1} + c \qquad (n \neq -1) \qquad [\text{B.37}]$$

This result is obvious because differentiation of the right-hand side with respect to x gives $f(x) = x^n$ directly. If the limits of the integration are known, this integral becomes a *definite integral* and is written

$$\int_{x_1}^{x_2} x^n\,dx = \frac{x^{n+1}}{n+1}\Big|_{x_1}^{x_2} = \frac{x_2^{n+1} - x_1^{n+1}}{n+1} \qquad (n \neq -1) \qquad [\text{B.38}]$$

TABLE **B.4**	Derivatives for Several Functions
$\dfrac{d}{dx}(a) = 0$	
$\dfrac{d}{dx}(ax^n) = nax^{n-1}$	
$\dfrac{d}{dx}(e^{ax}) = ae^{ax}$	
$\dfrac{d}{dx}(\sin ax) = a\cos ax$	
$\dfrac{d}{dx}(\cos ax) = -a\sin ax$	
$\dfrac{d}{dx}(\tan ax) = a\sec^2 ax$	
$\dfrac{d}{dx}(\cot ax) = -a\csc^2 ax$	
$\dfrac{d}{dx}(\sec x) = \tan x \sec x$	
$\dfrac{d}{dx}(\csc x) = -\cot x \csc x$	
$\dfrac{d}{dx}(\ln ax) = \dfrac{1}{x}$	

Note: The letters a and n are constants.

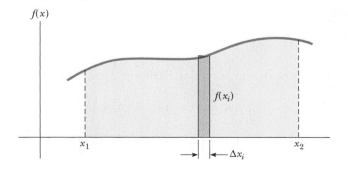

FIGURE B.14 The definite integral of a function is the area under the curve of the function between the limits x_1 and x_2.

1. $\displaystyle\int_0^a x^2\,dx = \frac{x^3}{3}\bigg]_0^a = \frac{a^3}{3}$

2. $\displaystyle\int_0^b x^{3/2}\,dx = \frac{x^{5/2}}{5/2}\bigg]_0^b = \tfrac{2}{5}b^{5/2}$

3. $\displaystyle\int_3^5 x\,dx = \frac{x^2}{2}\bigg]_3^5 = \frac{5^2 - 3^2}{2} = 8$

Partial Integration

Sometimes it is useful to apply the method of *partial integration* (also called "integrating by parts") to evaluate certain integrals. The method uses the property that

$$\int u\ dv = uv - \int v\ du \qquad\qquad [B.39]$$

where u and v are *carefully* chosen so as to reduce a complex integral to a simpler one. In many cases, several reductions have to be made. Consider the function

$$I(x) = \int x^2 e^x\,dx$$

which can be evaluated by integrating by parts twice. First, if we choose $u = x^2$, $v = e^x$, we obtain

$$\int x^2 e^x\,dx = \int x^2\,d(e^x) = x^2 e^x - 2\int e^x x\,dx + c_1$$

Now, in the second term, choose $u = x$, $v = e^x$, which gives

$$\int x^2 e^x\,dx = x^2 e^x - 2xe^x + 2\int e^x\,dx + c_1$$

or

$$\int x^2 e^x\,dx = x^2 e^x - 2xe^x + 2e^x + c_2$$

The Perfect Differential

Another useful method to remember is the use of the *perfect differential*, in which we look for a change of variable such that the differential of the function is the differential of the independent variable appearing in the integrand. For example, consider the integral

$$I(x) = \int \cos^2 x \sin x\,dx$$

This integral becomes easy to evaluate if we rewrite the differential as $d(\cos x) = -\sin x\,dx$. The integral then becomes

$$\int \cos^2 x \sin x\,dx = -\int \cos^2 x\,d(\cos x)$$

If we now change variables, letting $y = \cos x$, we obtain

$$\int \cos^2 x \sin x\,dx = -\int y^2\,dy = -\frac{y^3}{3} + c = -\frac{\cos^3 x}{3} + c$$

Table B.5 lists some useful indefinite integrals. Table B.6 gives Gauss's probability integral and other definite integrals. A more complete list can be found in

| TABLE B.5 | Some Indefinite Integrals (An arbitrary constant should be added to each of these integrals.) |

$$\int x^n \, dx = \frac{x^{n+1}}{n+1} \quad (\text{provided } n \neq -1)$$

$$\int \frac{dx}{x} = \int x^{-1} dx = \ln x$$

$$\int \frac{dx}{a+bx} = \frac{1}{b} \ln(a+bx)$$

$$\int \frac{x\,dx}{a+bx} = \frac{x}{b} - \frac{a}{b^2} \ln(a+bx)$$

$$\int \frac{dx}{x(x+a)} = -\frac{1}{a} \ln \frac{x+a}{x}$$

$$\int \frac{dx}{(a+bx)^2} = -\frac{1}{b(a+bx)}$$

$$\int \frac{dx}{a^2+x^2} = \frac{1}{a} \tan^{-1} \frac{x}{a}$$

$$\int \frac{dx}{a^2-x^2} = \frac{1}{2a} \ln \frac{a+x}{a-x} \quad (a^2-x^2 > 0)$$

$$\int \frac{dx}{x^2-a^2} = \frac{1}{2a} \ln \frac{x-a}{x+a} \quad (x^2-a^2 > 0)$$

$$\int \frac{x\,dx}{a^2 \pm x^2} = \pm\tfrac{1}{2} \ln(a^2 \pm x^2)$$

$$\int \frac{dx}{\sqrt{a^2-x^2}} = \sin^{-1} \frac{x}{a} = -\cos^{-1} \frac{x}{a} \quad (a^2-x^2 > 0)$$

$$\int \frac{dx}{\sqrt{x^2 \pm a^2}} = \ln\left(x + \sqrt{x^2 \pm a^2}\right)$$

$$\int \frac{x\,dx}{\sqrt{a^2-x^2}} = -\sqrt{a^2-x^2}$$

$$\int \frac{x\,dx}{\sqrt{x^2 \pm a^2}} = \sqrt{x^2 \pm a^2}$$

$$\int \sqrt{a^2-x^2} \, dx = \tfrac{1}{2}\left(x\sqrt{a^2-x^2} + a^2 \sin^{-1} \frac{x}{a}\right)$$

$$\int x\sqrt{a^2-x^2} \, dx = -\tfrac{1}{3}(a^2-x^2)^{3/2}$$

$$\int \sqrt{x^2 \pm a^2} \, dx = \tfrac{1}{2}\left[x\sqrt{x^2 \pm a^2} \pm a^2 \ln\left(x + \sqrt{x^2 \pm a^2}\right)\right]$$

$$\int x\left(\sqrt{x^2 \pm a^2}\right) dx = \tfrac{1}{3}(x^2 \pm a^2)^{3/2}$$

$$\int e^{ax} \, dx = \frac{1}{a} e^{ax}$$

$$\int \ln ax \, dx = (x \ln ax) - x$$

$$\int xe^{ax} \, dx = \frac{e^{ax}}{a^2}(ax - 1)$$

$$\int \frac{dx}{a+be^{cx}} = \frac{x}{a} - \frac{1}{ac} \ln(a + be^{cx})$$

$$\int \sin ax \, dx = -\frac{1}{a} \cos ax$$

$$\int \cos ax \, dx = \frac{1}{a} \sin ax$$

$$\int \tan ax \, dx = -\frac{1}{a} \ln(\cos ax) = \frac{1}{a} \ln(\sec ax)$$

$$\int \cot ax \, dx = \frac{1}{a} \ln(\sin ax)$$

$$\int \sec ax \, dx = \frac{1}{a} \ln(\sec ax + \tan ax) = \frac{1}{a} \ln\left[\tan\left(\frac{ax}{2} + \frac{\pi}{4}\right)\right]$$

$$\int \csc ax \, dx = \frac{1}{a} \ln(\csc ax - \cot ax) = \frac{1}{a} \ln\left(\tan \frac{ax}{2}\right)$$

$$\int \sin^2 ax \, dx = \frac{x}{2} - \frac{\sin 2ax}{4a}$$

$$\int \cos^2 ax \, dx = \frac{x}{2} + \frac{\sin 2ax}{4a}$$

$$\int \frac{dx}{\sin^2 ax} = -\frac{1}{a} \cot ax$$

$$\int \frac{dx}{\cos^2 ax} = \frac{1}{a} \tan ax$$

$$\int \tan^2 ax \, dx = \frac{1}{a}(\tan ax) - x$$

$$\int \cot^2 ax \, dx = -\frac{1}{a}(\cot ax) - x$$

$$\int \sin^{-1} ax \, dx = x(\sin^{-1} ax) + \frac{\sqrt{1-a^2x^2}}{a}$$

$$\int \cos^{-1} ax \, dx = x(\cos^{-1} ax) - \frac{\sqrt{1-a^2x^2}}{a}$$

$$\int \frac{dx}{(x^2+a^2)^{3/2}} = \frac{x}{a^2\sqrt{x^2+a^2}}$$

$$\int \frac{x\,dx}{(x^2+a^2)^{3/2}} = -\frac{1}{\sqrt{x^2+a^2}}$$

various handbooks, such as *The Handbook of Chemistry and Physics* (Boca Raton, FL: CRC Press, published annually).

B.8 | PROPAGATION OF UNCERTAINTY

In laboratory experiments, a common activity is to take measurements that act as raw data. These measurements are of several types—length, time interval, temperature, voltage, and so on—and are taken by a variety of instruments. Regardless of the measurement and the quality of the instrumentation, **there is always uncertainty associated with a physical measurement.** This uncertainty is a combination of that associated with the instrument and that related to the system being measured.

TABLE B.6	Gauss's Probability Integral and Other Definite Integrals

$$\int_0^\infty x^n e^{-ax}\,dx = \frac{n!}{a^{n+1}}$$

$$I_0 = \int_0^\infty e^{-ax^2}\,dx = \tfrac{1}{2}\sqrt{\frac{\pi}{a}} \qquad \text{(Gauss's probability integral)}$$

$$I_1 = \int_0^\infty x e^{-ax^2}\,dx = \frac{1}{2a}$$

$$I_2 = \int_0^\infty x^2 e^{-ax^2}\,dx = -\frac{dI_0}{da} = \tfrac{1}{4}\sqrt{\frac{\pi}{a^3}}$$

$$I_3 = \int_0^\infty x^3 e^{-ax^2}\,dx = -\frac{dI_1}{da} = \frac{1}{2a^2}$$

$$I_4 = \int_0^\infty x^4 e^{-ax^2}\,dx = \frac{d^2 I_0}{da^2} = \tfrac{3}{8}\sqrt{\frac{\pi}{a^5}}$$

$$I_5 = \int_0^\infty x^5 e^{-ax^2}\,dx = \frac{d^2 I_1}{da^2} = \frac{1}{a^3}$$

$$\vdots$$

$$I_{2n} = (-1)^n \frac{d^n}{da^n} I_0$$

$$I_{2n+1} = (-1)^n \frac{d^n}{da^n} I_1$$

An example of the former is the inability to determine exactly the position of a length measurement between the lines on a meter stick. An example of uncertainty related to the system being measured is the variation of temperature within a sample of water so that a single temperature for the sample is difficult to determine.

Uncertainties can be expressed in two ways. **Absolute uncertainty** refers to an uncertainty expressed in the same units as the measurement. Thus, the length of a computer disk label might be expressed as (5.5 ± 0.1) cm. The uncertainty of ± 0.1 cm by itself is not descriptive enough for some purposes, however. This uncertainty is large if the measurement is 1.0 cm, but it is small if the measurement is 100 m. To give a more descriptive account of the uncertainty, **fractional uncertainty** or **percent uncertainty** is used. In this type of description, the uncertainty is divided by the actual measurement. Therefore, the length of the computer disk label could be expressed as

$$\ell = 5.5\,\text{cm} \pm \frac{0.1\,\text{cm}}{5.5\,\text{cm}} = 5.5\,\text{cm} \pm 0.018 \qquad \text{(fractional uncertainty)}$$

or as

$$\ell = 5.5\,\text{cm} \pm 1.8\% \qquad \text{(percent uncertainty)}$$

When combining measurements in a calculation, the percent uncertainty in the final result is generally larger than the uncertainty in the individual measurements. This **propagation of uncertainty** is one of the challenges of experimental physics.

Some simple rules can provide a reasonable estimate of the uncertainty in a calculated result.

Multiplication and division: When measurements with uncertainties are multiplied or divided, add the *percent uncertainties* to obtain the percent uncertainty in the result.

Example: The Area of a Rectangular Plate

$$A = \ell w = (5.5\text{ cm} \pm 1.8\%) \times (6.4\text{ cm} \pm 1.6\%) = 35\text{ cm}^2 \pm 3.4\%$$
$$= (35 \pm 1)\text{ cm}^2$$

Addition and subtraction: When measurements with uncertainties are added or subtracted, add the *absolute uncertainties* to obtain the absolute uncertainty in the result.

Example: A Change in Temperature

$$\Delta T = T_2 - T_1 = (99.2 \pm 1.5)°\text{C} - (27.6 \pm 1.5)°\text{C} = (71.6 \pm 3.0)°\text{C}$$
$$= 71.6°\text{C} \pm 4.2\%$$

Powers: If a measurement is taken to a power, the percent uncertainty is multiplied by that power to obtain the percent uncertainty in the result.

Example: The Volume of a Sphere

$$V = \tfrac{4}{3}\pi r^3 = \tfrac{4}{3}\pi(6.20\text{ cm} \pm 2.0\%)^3 = 998\text{ cm}^3 \pm 6.0\%$$
$$= (998 \pm 60)\text{ cm}^3$$

For complicated calculations, many uncertainties are added together. This can cause the uncertainty in the final result to be undesirably large. Experiments should be designed such that calculations are as simple as possible.

Notice that uncertainties in a calculation always add. As a result, an experiment involving a subtraction should be avoided if possible, especially if the measurements being subtracted are close together. The result of such a calculation is a small difference in the measurements and uncertainties that add together. It is possible that the uncertainty in the result could be larger than the result itself!

Periodic Table of the Elements

Group I — Group II — Transition elements

Legend:
- Symbol — **Ca** — Atomic number 20
- Atomic mass † — 40.078
- Electron configuration — $4s^2$

Group I	Group II							
H 1 1.007 9 $1s$								
Li 3 6.941 $2s^1$	**Be** 4 9.0122 $2s^2$							
Na 11 22.990 $3s^1$	**Mg** 12 24.305 $3s^2$							
K 19 39.098 $4s^1$	**Ca** 20 40.078 $4s^2$	**Sc** 21 44.956 $3d^14s^2$	**Ti** 22 47.867 $3d^24s^2$	**V** 23 50.942 $3d^34s^2$	**Cr** 24 51.996 $3d^54s^1$	**Mn** 25 54.938 $3d^54s^2$	**Fe** 26 55.845 $3d^64s^2$	**Co** 27 58.933 $3d^74s^2$
Rb 37 85.468 $5s^1$	**Sr** 38 87.62 $5s^2$	**Y** 39 88.906 $4d^15s^2$	**Zr** 40 91.224 $4d^25s^2$	**Nb** 41 92.906 $4d^45s^1$	**Mo** 42 95.94 $4d^55s^1$	**Tc** 43 (98) $4d^55s^2$	**Ru** 44 101.07 $4d^75s^1$	**Rh** 45 102.91 $4d^85s^1$
Cs 55 132.91 $6s^1$	**Ba** 56 137.33 $6s^2$	57–71*	**Hf** 72 178.49 $5d^26s^2$	**Ta** 73 180.95 $5d^36s^2$	**W** 74 183.84 $5d^46s^2$	**Re** 75 186.21 $5d^56s^2$	**Os** 76 190.23 $5d^66s^2$	**Ir** 77 192.2 $5d^76s^2$
Fr 87 (223) $7s^1$	**Ra** 88 (226) $7s^2$	89–103**	**Rf** 104 (261) $6d^27s^2$	**Db** 105 $(262)_1$ $6d^37s^2$	**Sg** 106 (266)	**Bh** 107 (264)	**Hs** 108 (269)	**Mt** 109 (268)

*Lanthanide series

La 57 138.91 $5d^16s^2$	**Ce** 58 140.12 $5d^14f^16s^2$	**Pr** 59 140.91 $4f^36s^2$	**Nd** 60 144.24 $4f^46s^2$	**Pm** 61 (145) $4f^56s^2$	**Sm** 62 150.36 $4f^66s^2$

**Actinide series

Ac 89 (227) $6d^17s^2$	**Th** 90 232.04 $6d^27s^2$	**Pa** 91 231.04 $5f^26d^17s^2$	**U** 92 238.03 $5f^36d^17s^2$	**Np** 93 (237) $5f^46d^17s^2$	**Pu** 94 (244) $5f^66d^07s^2$

Note: Atomic mass values given are averaged over isotopes in the percentages in which they exist in nature.
†For an unstable element, mass number of the most stable known isotope is given in parentheses.
††Elements 111, 112, and 114 have not yet been named
†††For a description of the atomic data, visit **physics.nist.gov/atomic**.

		Group III	Group IV	Group V	Group VI	Group VII	Group 0
						H 1 1.007 9 $1s^1$	**He** 2 4.002 6 $1s^2$
		B 5 10.811 $2p^1$	**C** 6 12.011 $2p^2$	**N** 7 14.007 $2p^3$	**O** 8 15.999 $2p^4$	**F** 9 18.998 $2p^5$	**Ne** 10 20.180 $2p^6$
		Al 13 26.982 $3p^1$	**Si** 14 28.086 $3p^2$	**P** 15 30.974 $3p^3$	**S** 16 32.066 $3p^4$	**Cl** 17 35.453 $3p^5$	**Ar** 18 39.948 $3p^6$
Ni 28 58.693 $3d^84s^2$	**Cu** 29 63.546 $3d^{10}4s^1$	**Zn** 30 65.39 $3d^{10}4s^2$	**Ga** 31 69.723 $4p^1$	**Ge** 32 72.61 $4p^2$	**As** 33 74.922 $4p^3$	**Se** 34 78.96 $4p^4$	**Br** 35 79.904 $4p^5$
Pd 46 106.42 $4d^{10}$	**Ag** 47 107.87 $4d^{10}5s^1$	**Cd** 48 112.41 $4d^{10}5s^2$	**In** 49 114.82 $5p^1$	**Sn** 50 118.71 $5p^2$	**Sb** 51 121.76 $5p^3$	**Te** 52 127.60 $5p^4$	**I** 53 126.90 $5p^5$
Pt 78 195.08 $5d^96s^1$	**Au** 79 196.97 $5d^{10}6s^1$	**Hg** 80 200.59 $5d^{10}6s^2$	**Tl** 81 204.38 $6p^1$	**Pb** 82 207.2 $6p^2$	**Bi** 83 208.98 $6p^3$	**Po** 84 (209) $6p^4$	**At** 85 (210) $6p^5$
Ds 110 (271)	111†† (272)	112†† (285)		114†† (289)			

Further right in the table: **Kr** 36 (83.80, $4p^6$); **Xe** 54 (131.29, $5p^6$); **Rn** 86 (222, $6p^6$).

Eu 63 151.96 $4f^76s^2$	**Gd** 64 157.25 $5d^14f^76s^2$	**Tb** 65 158.93 $5d^14f^86s^2$	**Dy** 66 162.50 $4f^{10}6s^2$	**Ho** 67 164.93 $4f^{11}6s^2$	**Er** 68 167.26 $4f^{12}6s^2$	**Tm** 69 168.93 $4f^{13}6s^2$	**Yb** 70 173.04 $4f^{14}6s^2$	**Lu** 71 174.97 $5d^14f^{14}6s^2$
Am 95 (243) $5f^76d^07s^2$	**Cm** 96 (247) $5f^76d^17s^2$	**Bk** 97 (247) $5f^86d^17s^2$	**Cf** 98 (251) $5f^{10}6d^07s^2$	**Es** 99 (252) $5f^{11}6d^07s^2$	**Fm** 100 (257) $5f^{12}6d^07s^2$	**Md** 101 (258) $5f^{13}6d^07s^2$	**No** 102 (259) $6d^07s^2$	**Lr** 103 (262) $6d^17s^2$

SI Units

TABLE D.1	SI Base Units	
	SI Base Unit	
Base Quantity	**Name**	**Symbol**
Length	meter	m
Mass	kilogram	kg
Time	second	s
Electric current	ampere	A
Temperature	kelvin	K
Amount of substance	mole	mol
Luminous intensity	candela	cd

TABLE D.2	Some Derived SI Units			
Quantity	**Name**	**Symbol**	**Expression in Terms of Base Units**	**Expression in Terms of Other SI Units**
Plane angle	radian	rad	m/m	
Frequency	hertz	Hz	s^{-1}	
Force	newton	N	$kg \cdot m/s^2$	J/m
Pressure	pascal	Pa	$kg/m \cdot s^2$	N/m^2
Energy; work	joule	J	$kg \cdot m^2/s^2$	$N \cdot m$
Power	watt	W	$kg \cdot m^2/s^3$	J/s
Electric charge	coulomb	C	$A \cdot s$	
Electric potential	volt	V	$kg \cdot m^2/A \cdot s^3$	W/A
Capacitance	farad	F	$A^2 \cdot s^4/kg \cdot m^2$	C/V
Electric resistance	ohm	w	$kg \cdot m^2/A^2 \cdot s^3$	V/A
Magnetic flux	weber	Wb	$kg \cdot m^2/A \cdot s^2$	$V \cdot s$
Magnetic field	tesla	T	$kg/A \cdot s^2$	
Inductance	henry	H	$kg \cdot m^2/A^2 \cdot s^2$	$T \cdot m^2/A$

Nobel Prizes

All Nobel Prizes in Physics are listed (and marked with a P), as well as relevant Nobel Prizes in Chemistry (C). The key dates for some of the scientific work are supplied; they often antedate the prize considerably.

1901   (P) *Wilhelm Roentgen* for discovering x-rays (1895).

1902   (P) *Hendrik A. Lorentz* for predicting the Zeeman effect and *Pieter Zeeman* for discovering the Zeeman effect, the splitting of spectral lines in magnetic fields.

1903   (P) *Antoine-Henri Becquerel* for discovering radioactivity (1896) and *Pierre Curie* and *Marie Curie* for studying radioactivity.

1904   (P) *Lord Rayleigh* for studying the density of gases and discovering argon.

(C) *William Ramsay* for discovering the inert gas elements helium, neon, xenon, and krypton, and placing them in the periodic table.

1905   (P) *Philipp Lenard* for studying cathode rays, electrons (1898–1899).

1906   (P) *J. J. Thomson* for studying electrical discharge through gases and discovering the electron (1897).

1907   (P) *Albert A. Michelson* for inventing optical instruments and measuring the speed of light (1880s).

1908   (P) *Gabriel Lippmann* for making the first color photographic plate, using interference methods (1891).

(C) *Ernest Rutherford* for discovering that atoms can be broken apart by alpha rays and for studying radioactivity.

1909   (P) *Guglielmo Marconi* and *Carl Ferdinand Braun* for developing wireless telegraphy.

1910   (P) *Johannes D. van der Waals* for studying the equation of state for gases and liquids (1881).

1911   (P) *Wilhelm Wien* for discovering Wien's law giving the peak of a blackbody spectrum (1893).

(C) *Marie Curie* for discovering radium and polonium (1898) and isolating radium.

1912   (P) *Nils Dalén* for inventing automatic gas regulators for lighthouses.

1913   (P) *Heike Kamerlingh Onnes* for the discovery of superconductivity and liquefying helium (1908).

1914   (P) *Max T. F. von Laue* for studying x-rays from their diffraction by crystals, showing that x-rays are electromagnetic waves (1912).

(C) *Theodore W. Richards* for determining the atomic weights of 60 elements, indicating the existence of isotopes.

1915   (P) *William Henry Bragg* and *William Lawrence Bragg*, his son, for studying the diffraction of x-rays in crystals.

1917   (P) *Charles Barkla* for studying atoms by x-ray scattering (1906).

1918   (P) *Max Planck* for discovering energy quanta (1900).

1919   (P) *Johannes Stark* for discovering the Stark effect, the splitting of spectral lines in electric fields (1913).

1920 (P) *Charles-Édouard Guillaume* for discovering invar, a nickel–steel alloy with low coefficient of expansion.

(C) *Walther Nernst* for studying heat changes in chemical reactions and formulating the third law of thermodynamics (1918).

1921 (P) *Albert Einstein* for explaining the photoelectric effect and for his services to theoretical physics (1905).

(C) *Frederick Soddy* for studying the chemistry of radioactive substances and discovering isotopes (1912).

1922 (P) *Niels Bohr* for his model of the atom and its radiation (1913).

(C) *Francis W. Aston* for using the mass spectrograph to study atomic weights, thus discovering 212 of the 287 naturally occurring isotopes.

1923 (P) *Robert A. Millikan* for measuring the charge on an electron (1911) and for studying the photoelectric effect experimentally (1914).

1924 (P) *Karl M. G. Siegbahn* for his work in x-ray spectroscopy.

1925 (P) *James Franck* and *Gustav Hertz* for discovering the Franck–Hertz effect in electron–atom collisions.

1926 (P) *Jean-Baptiste Perrin* for studying Brownian motion to validate the discontinuous structure of matter and measure the size of atoms.

1927 (P) *Arthur Holly Compton* for discovering the Compton effect on x-rays, their change in wavelength when they collide with matter (1922), and *Charles T. R. Wilson* for inventing the cloud chamber, used to study charged particles (1906).

1928 (P) *Owen W. Richardson* for studying the thermionic effect and electrons emitted by hot metals (1911).

1929 (P) *Louis Victor de Broglie* for discovering the wave nature of electrons (1923).

1930 (P) *Chandrasekhara Venkata Raman* for studying Raman scattering, the scattering of light by atoms and molecules with a change in wavelength (1928).

1932 (P) *Werner Heisenberg* for creating quantum mechanics (1925).

1933 (P) *Erwin Schrödinger* and *Paul A. M. Dirac* for developing wave mechanics (1925) and relativistic quantum mechanics (1927).

(C) *Harold Urey* for discovering heavy hydrogen, deuterium (1931).

1935 (P) *James Chadwick* for discovering the neutron (1932).

(C) *Irène Joliot-Curie* and *Frédéric Joliot-Curie* for synthesizing new radioactive elements.

1936 (P) *Carl D. Anderson* for discovering the positron in particular and antimatter in general (1932) and *Victor F. Hess* for discovering cosmic rays.

(C) *Peter J. W. Debye* for studying dipole moments and diffraction of x-rays and electrons in gases.

1937 (P) *Clinton Davisson* and *George Thomson* for discovering the diffraction of electrons by crystals, confirming de Broglie's hypothesis (1927).

1938 (P) *Enrico Fermi* for producing the transuranic radioactive elements by neutron irradiation (1934–1937).

1939 (P) *Ernest O. Lawrence* for inventing the cyclotron.

1943 (P) *Otto Stern* for developing molecular-beam studies (1923) and using them to discover the magnetic moment of the proton (1933).

1944 (P) *Isidor I. Rabi* for discovering nuclear magnetic resonance in atomic and molecular beams.

(C) *Otto Hahn* for discovering nuclear fission (1938).

1945 (P) *Wolfgang Pauli* for discovering the exclusion principle (1924).

1946 (P) *Percy W. Bridgman* for studying physics at high pressures.

1947 (P) *Edward V. Appleton* for studying the ionosphere.

1948 (P) *Patrick M. S. Blackett* for studying nuclear physics with cloud-chamber photographs of cosmic-ray interactions.

1949 (P) *Hideki Yukawa* for predicting the existence of mesons (1935).

1950 (P) *Cecil F. Powell* for developing the method of studying cosmic rays with photographic emulsions and discovering new mesons.

1951 (P) *John D. Cockcroft* and *Ernest T. S. Walton* for transmuting nuclei in an accelerator (1932).

(C) *Edwin M. McMillan* for producing neptunium (1940) and *Glenn T. Seaborg* for producing plutonium (1941) and further transuranic elements.

1952 (P) *Felix Bloch* and *Edward Mills Purcell* for discovering nuclear magnetic resonance in liquids and gases (1946).

1953 (P) *Frits Zernike* for inventing the phase-contrast microscope, which uses interference to provide high contrast.

1954 (P) *Max Born* for interpreting the wave function as a probability (1926) and other quantum-mechanical discoveries and *Walther Bothe* for developing the coincidence method to study subatomic particles (1930–1931), producing, in particular, the particle interpreted by Chadwick as the neutron.

1955 (P) *Willis E. Lamb Jr.*, for discovering the Lamb shift in the hydrogen spectrum (1947) and *Polykarp Kusch* for determining the magnetic moment of the electron (1947).

1956 (P) *John Bardeen, Walter H. Brattain*, and *William Shockley* for inventing the transistor (1956).

1957 (P) *T.-D. Lee* and *C.-N. Yang* for predicting that parity is not conserved in beta decay (1956).

1958 (P) *Pavel A. Čerenkov* for discovering Čerenkov radiation (1935) and *Ilya M. Frank* and *Igor Tamm* for interpreting it (1937).

1959 (P) *Emilio G. Segrè* and *Owen Chamberlain* for discovering the antiproton (1955).

1960 (P) *Donald A. Glaser* for inventing the bubble chamber to study elementary particles (1952).

(C) *Willard Libby* for developing radiocarbon dating (1947).

1961 (P) *Robert Hofstadter* for discovering internal structure in protons and neutrons and *Rudolf L. Mössbauer* for discovering the Mössbauer effect of recoilless gamma-ray emission (1957).

1962 (P) *Lev Davidovich Landau* for studying liquid helium and other condensed matter theoretically.

1963 (P) *Eugene P. Wigner* for applying symmetry principles to elementary-particle theory and *Maria Goeppert Mayer* and *J. Hans D. Jensen* for studying the shell model of nuclei (1947).

1964 (P) *Charles H. Townes, Nikolai G. Basov*, and *Alexandr M. Prokhorov* for developing masers (1951–1952) and lasers.

1965 (P) *Sin-itiro Tomonaga, Julian S. Schwinger*, and *Richard P. Feynman* for developing quantum electrodynamics (1948).

1966 (P) *Alfred Kastler* for his optical methods of studying atomic energy levels.

1967 (P) *Hans Albrecht Bethe* for discovering the routes of energy production in stars (1939).

1968 (P) *Luis W. Alvarez* for discovering resonance states of elementary particles.

1969 (P) *Murray Gell-Mann* for classifying elementary particles (1963).

1970 (P) *Hannes Alfvén* for developing magnetohydrodynamic theory and *Louis Eugène Félix Néel* for discovering antiferromagnetism and ferrimagnetism (1930s).

1971 (P) *Dennis Gabor* for developing holography (1947).

(C) *Gerhard Herzberg* for studying the structure of molecules spectroscopically.

1972 (P) *John Bardeen, Leon N. Cooper,* and *John Robert Schrieffer* for explaining superconductivity (1957).

1973 (P) *Leo Esaki* for discovering tunneling in semiconductors, *Ivar Giaever* for discovering tunneling in superconductors, and *Brian D. Josephson* for predicting the Josephson effect, which involves tunneling of paired electrons (1958–1962).

1974 (P) *Anthony Hewish* for discovering pulsars and *Martin Ryle* for developing radio interferometry.

1975 (P) *Aage N. Bohr, Ben R. Mottelson,* and *James Rainwater* for discovering why some nuclei take asymmetric shapes.

1976 (P) *Burton Richter* and *Samuel C. C. Ting* for discovering the J/psi particle, the first charmed particle (1974).

1977 (P) *John H. Van Vleck, Nevill F. Mott,* and *Philip W. Anderson* for studying solids quantum-mechanically.

(C) *Ilya Prigogine* for extending thermodynamics to show how life could arise in the face of the second law.

1978 (P) *Arno A. Penzias* and *Robert W. Wilson* for discovering the cosmic background radiation (1965) and *Pyotr Kapitsa* for his studies of liquid helium.

1979 (P) *Sheldon L. Glashow, Abdus Salam,* and *Steven Weinberg* for developing the theory that unified the weak and electromagnetic forces (1958–1971).

1980 (P) *Val Fitch* and *James W. Cronin* for discovering CP (charge-parity) violation (1964), which possibly explains the cosmological dominance of matter over antimatter.

1981 (P) *Nicolaas Bloembergen* and *Arthur L. Schawlow* for developing laser spectroscopy and *Kai M. Siegbahn* for developing high-resolution electron spectroscopy (1958).

1982 (P) *Kenneth G. Wilson* for developing a method of constructing theories of phase transitions to analyze critical phenomena.

1983 (P) *William A. Fowler* for theoretical studies of astrophysical nucleosynthesis and *Subramanyan Chandrasekhar* for studying physical processes of importance to stellar structure and evolution, including the prediction of white dwarf stars (1930).

1984 (P) *Carlo Rubbia* for discovering the W and Z particles verifying the electroweak unification, and *Simon van der Meer* for developing the method of stochastic cooling of the CERN beam that allowed the discovery (1982–1983).

1985 (P) *Klaus von Klitzing* for the quantized Hall effect, relating to conductivity in the presence of a magnetic field (1980).

1986 (P) *Ernst Ruska* for inventing the electron microscope (1931) and *Gerd Binnig* and *Heinrich Rohrer* for inventing the scanning-tunneling electron microscope (1981).

1987 (P) *J. Georg Bednorz* and *Karl Alex Müller* for the discovery of high-temperature superconductivity (1986).

1988 (P) *Leon M. Lederman, Melvin Schwartz,* and *Jack Steinberger* for a collaborative experiment that led to the development of a new tool for studying the weak nuclear force, which affects the radioactive decay of atoms.

1989 (P) *Norman Ramsay* for various techniques in atomic physics and *Hans Dehmelt* and *Wolfgang Paul* for the development of techniques for trapping single-charge particles.

1990 (P) *Jerome Friedman, Henry Kendall,* and *Richard Taylor* for experiments important to the development of the quark model.

1991 (P) *Pierre-Gilles de Gennes* for discovering that methods developed for studying order phenomena in simple systems can be generalized to more complex forms of matter, in particular to liquid crystals and polymers.

1992 (P) *George Charpak* for developing detectors that trace the paths of evanescent subatomic particles produced in particle accelerators.

1993 (P) *Russell Hulse* and *Joseph Taylor* for discovering evidence of gravitational waves.

1994 (P) *Bertram N. Brockhouse* and *Clifford G. Shull* for pioneering work in neutron scattering.

1995 (P) *Martin L. Perl* and *Frederick Reines* for discovering the tau particle and the neutrino, respectively.

1996 (P) *David M. Lee, Douglas C. Osheroff,* and *Robert C. Richardson* for developing a superfluid using helium-3.

1997 (P) *Steven Chu, Claude Cohen-Tannoudji,* and *William D. Phillips* for developing methods to cool and trap atoms with laser light.

1998 (P) *Robert B. Laughlin, Horst L. Störmer,* and *Daniel C. Tsui* for discovering a new form of quantum fluid with fractionally charged excitations.

1999 (P) *Gerardus 'T Hooft* and *Martinus J. G. Veltman* for studies in the quantum structure of electroweak interactions in physics.

2000 (P) *Zhores I. Alferov* and *Herbert Kroemer* for developing semiconductor heterostructures used in high-speed electronics and optoelectronics and *Jack St. Clair Kilby* for participating in the invention of the integrated circuit.

2001 (P) *Eric A. Cornell, Wolfgang Ketterle,* and *Carl E. Wieman* for the achievement of Bose–Einstein condensation in dilute gases of alkali atoms.

2002 (P) *Raymond Davis Jr.* and *Masatoshi Koshiba* for the detection of cosmic neutrinos and *Riccardo Giacconi* for contributions to astrophysics that led to the discovery of cosmic x-ray sources.

2003 *Alexei A. Abrikosov, Vitaly L. Ginzburg,* and *Anthony J. Leggett* for pioneering contributions to the theory of superconductors and superfluids.

2004 *David J. Gross, H. David Politzer,* and *Frank Wilczeck* for the discovery of asymptotic freedom in the theory of the strong interaction.

Answers to Odd-Numbered Problems

Chapter 1

1. $5.52 \times 10^3 \text{ kg/m}^3$, between the density of aluminum and that of iron and greater than the densities of typical surface rocks

3. $4\pi\rho(r_2{}^3 - r_1{}^3)/3$

5. No

7. (b) only

9. (a) 0.071 4 gal/s   (b) $2.70 \times 10^{-4} \text{ m}^3/\text{s}$
(c) 1.03 h

11. 667 lb/s

13. 151 μm

15. 2.86 cm

17. (a) 2.07 mm   (b) 8.62×10^{13} times as large

19. $\sim 10^6$ balls

21. $\sim 10^2$ tuners

23. (a) 3   (b) 4   (c) 3   (d) 2

25. 31 556 926.0 s

27. 5.2 m^3, 3%

29. 108° and 288°

31. 3.46 or -3.46

33. (a) 2.24 m   (b) 2.24 m at 26.6°

35. (a) r, $180° - \theta$ (b) $2r$, $180° + \theta$ (c) $3r$, $-\theta$

37. (a) 10.0 m   (b) 15.7 m   (c) 0

39. Approximately 420 ft at $-3°$

41. 47.2 units at 122°

43. 196 cm at 345°

45. (a) $2.00\hat{\mathbf{i}} - 6.00\hat{\mathbf{j}}$ (b) $4.00\hat{\mathbf{i}} + 2.00\hat{\mathbf{j}}$ (c) 6.32
(d) 4.47   (e) 288°; 26.6°

47. 240 m at 237°

49. (a) 10.4 cm   (b) 35.5°

51. (a) $8.00\hat{\mathbf{i}} + 12.0\hat{\mathbf{j}} - 4.00\hat{\mathbf{k}}$ (b) $2.00\hat{\mathbf{i}} + 3.00\hat{\mathbf{j}} - 1.00\hat{\mathbf{k}}$
(c) $-24.0\hat{\mathbf{i}} - 36.0\hat{\mathbf{j}} + 12.0\hat{\mathbf{k}}$

53. (a) $49.5\hat{\mathbf{i}} + 27.1\hat{\mathbf{j}}$ (b) 56.4 units at 28.7°

55. 70.0 m

57. 0.141 nm

59. 4.50 m^2

61. 0.449%

63. (a) 0.529 cm/s   (b) 11.5 cm/s

65. $\sim 10^{11}$ stars

67. (a) 185 N at 77.8° from the $+x$ axis
(b) $(-39.3\hat{\mathbf{i}} - 181\hat{\mathbf{j}})$ N

69. (a) (10.0 m, 16.0 m)

71. (a) $\vec{\mathbf{R}}_1 = a\hat{\mathbf{i}} + b\hat{\mathbf{j}}$; $R_1 = \sqrt{a^2 + b^2}$
(b) $\vec{\mathbf{R}}_2 = a\hat{\mathbf{i}} + b\hat{\mathbf{j}} + c\hat{\mathbf{k}}$; $R_2 = \sqrt{a^2 + b^2 + c^2}$

Chapter 2

1. (a) 2.30 m/s   (b) 16.1 m/s   (c) 11.5 m/s

3. (a) 5 m/s   (b) 1.2 m/s   (c) -2.5 m/s
(d) -3.3 m/s   (e) 0

5. (a) -2.4 m/s   (b) -3.8 m/s   (c) 4.0 s

7. (b) $v_{t\,=\,5.0\,\text{s}} = 23$ m/s, $v_{t\,=\,4.0\,\text{s}} = 18$ m/s,
$v_{t\,=\,3.0\,\text{s}} = 14$ m/s, $v_{t\,=\,2.0\,\text{s}} = 9.0$ m/s
(c) 4.6 m/s^2 (d) 0

9. 5.00 m

11. (a) 20.0 m/s, 5.00 m/s   (b) 262 m

13. (a) 2.00 m   (b) -3.00 m/s   (c) -2.00 m/s^2

15. (a) 1.3 m/s^2 (b) 2.0 m/s^2 at 3 s
(c) at $t = 6$ s and for $t > 10$ s   (d) -1.5 m/s^2 at 8 s

17. (a) 6.61 m/s   (b) -0.448 m/s^2

19. -16.0 cm/s^2

21. (a) 20.0 s   (b) no

23. 3.10 m/s

25. (a) 35.0 s   (b) 15.7 m/s

27. yes; 212 m, 11.4 s

29. (a) 29.4 m/s   (b) 44.1 m

31. (a) 10.0 m/s up   (b) 4.68 m/s down

33. (a) 7.82 m   (b) 0.782 s

35. (b) 7.4 m/s^2 and 2.1 m/s^2 (c) 48 m and 170 m
(d) 2.74 s

37. (a) $70.0 \text{ mi/h} \cdot \text{s} = 31.3 \text{ m/s}^2 = 3.19g$
(b) 321 ft = 97.8 m

39. (a) -202 m/s^2 (b) 198 m

41. $2.74 \times 10^5 \text{ m/s}^2$, which is $2.79 \times 10^4 \, g$

43. (a) 3.00 m/s   (b) 6.00 s   (c) -0.300 m/s^2
(d) 2.05 m/s

45. 1.60 m/s^2

47. (a) 41.0 s   (b) 1.73 km   (c) -184 m/s

49. (a) 5.43 m/s^2 and 3.83 m/s^2
(b) 10.9 m/s and 11.5 m/s
(c) Maggie by 2.62 m

51. (a) 3.00 s   (b) -15.3 m/s   (c) 31.4 m/s down and 34.8 m/s down

53. (c) $v_{boy}^2/h, 0$ (d) $v_{boy}, 0$

55. (a) 26.4 m   (b) 6.82%

57. $0.577v$

Chapter 3

1. (a) 4.87 km at 209° from east   (b) 23.3 m/s
   (c) 13.5 m/s at 209°

3. (a) $(0.800\hat{\mathbf{i}} - 0.300\hat{\mathbf{j}})$m/s²   (b) 339°
   (c) $(360\hat{\mathbf{i}} - 72.7\hat{\mathbf{j}})$m, $-15.2°$

5. (a) $\vec{\mathbf{r}} = (5.00t\,\hat{\mathbf{i}} + 1.50t^2\,\hat{\mathbf{j}})$m, $\vec{\mathbf{v}} = (5.00\hat{\mathbf{i}} + 3.00t\,\hat{\mathbf{j}})$m/s
   (b) (10.0 m, 6.00 m), 7.81 m/s

7. (a) $3.34\hat{\mathbf{i}}$ m/s   (b) $-50.9°$

9. 12.0 m/s

11. 22.4° or 89.4°

13. 67.8°

15. (a) The ball clears by 0.889 m while (b) descending

17. (a) 18.1 m/s   (b) 1.13 m   (c) 2.79 m

19. 9.91 m/s

21. $\tan^{-1}[(2gh)^{1/2}/v]$

23. 377 m/s²

25. 10.5 m/s, 219 m/s² inward

27. 7.58×10^3 m/s, 5.80×10^3 s

29. 1.48 m/s² inward and 29.9° backward

31. (a) 13.0 m/s²   (b) 5.70 m/s   (c) 7.50 m/s²

33. 2.02×10^3 s; 21.0% longer

35. 153 km/h at 11.3° north of west

37. 15.3 m

39. $0.975g$

41. (a) 101 m/s   (b) 32 700 ft   (c) 20.6 s
    (d) 180 m/s

43. 54.4 m/s²

45. (a) 41.7 m/s   (b) 3.81 s   (c) $(34.1\hat{\mathbf{i}} - 13.4\hat{\mathbf{j}})$m/s; 36.7 m/s

47. 10.7 m/s

49. (a) 6.80 km   (b) 3.00 km vertically above the impact point   (c) 66.2°

51. (a) 20.0 m/s, 5.00 s   (b) $(16.0\hat{\mathbf{i}} - 27.1\hat{\mathbf{j}})$m/s
    (c) 6.53 s   (d) $24.5\hat{\mathbf{i}}$ m

53. (a) 22.9 m/s   (b) 360 m from the base of the cliff
    (c) $\vec{\mathbf{v}} = (114\hat{\mathbf{i}} - 44.3\hat{\mathbf{j}})$m/s

55. (a) 1.52 km   (b) 36.1 s   (c) 4.05 km

57. (a) 43.2 m   (b) $(9.66\hat{\mathbf{i}} - 25.6\hat{\mathbf{j}})$m/s

59. 4.00 km/h

61. Safe distances are less than 270 m and greater than 3.48×10^3 m from the western shore.

Chapter 4

1. (a) 1/3   (b) 0.750 m/s²

3. $(6.00\hat{\mathbf{i}} + 15.0\hat{\mathbf{j}})$ N; 16.2 N

5. (a) $(2.50\hat{\mathbf{i}} + 5.00\hat{\mathbf{j}})$ N   (b) 5.59 N

7. (a) 5.00 m/s² at 36.9°   (b) 6.08 m/s² at 25.3°

9. (a) 534 N down   (b) 54.5 kg

11. 2.55 N for an 88.7-kg person

13. (a) 3.64×10^{-18} N   (b) 8.93×10^{-30} N is 408 billion times smaller

15. (a) $\sim10^{-22}$ m/s²   (b) $\sim10^{-23}$ m

17. (a) 15.0 lb up   (b) 5.00 lb up   (c) 0

21. (a) From a free-body diagram of the forces on the bit of string touching the weight hanger we have $\Sigma F_y = 0$: $-F_g + T\sin\theta = 0$, so $T = F_g/\sin\theta$. The force the child feels gets smaller, changing from T to $T\cos\theta$ when the counterweight hangs from the string. On the other hand, the kite does not notice what you are doing and the tension in the main part of the string stays constant. You do not need a level because you learned in physics lab to sight to a horizontal line in a building. Share with the parents your estimate of the experimental uncertainty, which you made by thinking critically about the measurement, repeating trials, practicing in advance, and looking for variations and improvements in technique, including using other observers. You will then be glad to have the parents themselves repeat your measurements.
    (b) 1.79 N

23. (a) $a = g\tan\theta$ (b) 4.16 m/s²

25. 100 N and 204 N

27. 8.66 N east

29. 3.73 m

31. A is in compression 3.83 kN and B is in tension 3.37 kN

33. 950 N

35. (a) $F_x > 19.6$ N   (b) $F_x \leq -78.4$ N

(c)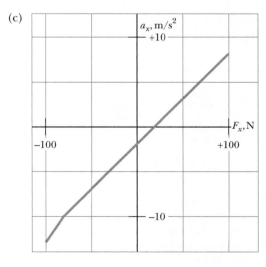

37. (a) 706 N   (b) 814 N   (c) 706 N   (d) 648 N

39. (a) Removing mass   (b) 13.7 mi/h·s

41. (a)

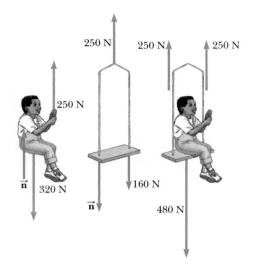

(b) 0.408 m/s^2 (c) 83.3 N

43. (a) 2.00 m/s^2 forward   (b) 4.00 N forward on 2 kg, 6.00 N forward on 3 kg, 8.00 N forward on 4 kg (c) 14.0 N between 2 kg and 3 kg, 8.00 N between 4 kg and 3 kg   (d) The 3-kg block models the heavy block of wood. The contact force on your back is represented by Q, which is much less than F. The difference between F and Q is the net force causing acceleration of the 5-kg pair of objects. The acceleration is real and nonzero but lasts for so short a time interval that it is never associated with a large velocity. The frame of the building and your legs exert forces, small compared with the hammer blow, to bring the partition, block, and you to rest again over a time interval large compared with the duration of the hammer blow.

45. (a) $Mg/2$, $Mg/2$, $Mg/2$, $3Mg/2$, Mg (b) $Mg/2$

47. $(M + m_1 + m_2)(m_2g/m_1)$

49. (c) 3.56 N

51. 1.16 cm

53. (a) $30.7°$ (b) 0.843 N

55. $mg \sin \theta \cos \theta \hat{\mathbf{i}} + (M + m \cos^2 \theta)g\hat{\mathbf{j}}$

57. (a) $T_1 = \dfrac{2mg}{\sin \theta_1}$, $T_2 = \dfrac{mg}{\sin \theta_2} = \dfrac{mg}{\sin [\tan^{-1}(\frac{1}{2} \tan \theta_1)]}$,

$T_3 = \dfrac{2\,mg}{\tan \theta_1}$

(b) $\theta_2 = \tan^{-1}\left(\dfrac{\tan \theta_1}{2}\right)$

Chapter 5

1. $\mu_s = 0.306$; $\mu_k = 0.245$

3. (a) 3.34 (b) The car would flip over backwards; or the wheels would skid, spinning in place, and the time would increase.

5. (a) 1.11 s (b) 0.875 s

7. $\mu_s = 0.727$, $\mu_k = 0.577$

9. (a) 1.78 m/s^2 (b) 0.368 (c) 9.37 N
(d) 2.67 m/s

11. (a)

(b) 27.2 N, 1.29 m/s^2

13. any value between 31.7 N and 48.6 N

15. any speed up to 8.08 m/s

17. $v \le 14.3 \text{ m/s}$

19. (a) 68.6 N toward the center of the circle and 784 N up
(b) 0.857 m/s^2

21. No. The jungle-lord needs a vine of tensile strength 1.38 kN.

23. 3.13 m/s

25. (a) 32.7 s^{-1} (b) 9.80 m/s^2 down
(c) 4.90 m/s^2 down

27. (a) $1.47 \text{ N} \cdot \text{s/m}$ (b) $2.04 \times 10^{-3} \text{ s}$
(c) $2.94 \times 10^{-2} \text{ N}$

29. (a) $0.034\ 7 \text{ s}^{-1}$ (b) 2.50 m/s (c) $a = -cv$

31. 2.97 nN

33. 0.613 m/s^2 toward the Earth

35. -0.212 m/s^2

37. (a) $M = 3m \sin \theta$ (b) $T_1 = 2mg \sin \theta$, $T_2 = 3mg \sin \theta$

(c) $a = \dfrac{g \sin \theta}{1 + 2 \sin \theta}$

(d) $T_1 = 4mg \sin \theta \left(\dfrac{1 + \sin \theta}{1 + 2 \sin \theta}\right)$

$T_2 = 6mg \sin \theta \left(\dfrac{1 + \sin \theta}{1 + 2 \sin \theta}\right)$

(e) $M_{\max} = 3m(\sin \theta + \mu_s \cos \theta)$

(f) $M_{\min} = 3m(\sin \theta - \mu_s \cos \theta)$

(g) $T_{2,\max} - T_{2,\min} = (M_{\max} - M_{\min})g = 6\mu_s mg \cos \theta$

39. (b)

θ	0	15°	30°	45°	60°
P (N)	40.0	46.4	60.1	94.3	260

41. (a) $0.087\ 1$ (b) 27.4 N

43. (a) 2.13 s (b) 1.67 m

45. (a)

$v_{\min} = \sqrt{\dfrac{Rg(\tan \theta - \mu_s)}{1 + \mu_s \tan \theta}}$

$v_{\max} = \sqrt{\dfrac{Rg(\tan \theta + \mu_s)}{1 - \mu_s \tan \theta}}$

(b) $\mu_s = \tan \theta$
(c) $8.57 \text{ m/s} \le v \le 16.6 \text{ m/s}$

47. 0.835 rev/s

49. (b) 732 N down at the equator and 735 N down at the poles

51. (a) 1.58 m/s^2 (b) 455 N (c) 329 N
(d) 397 N upward and 9.15° inward

53. 2.14 rev/min

55. (b) 2.54 s; 23.6 rev/min

57. (a) 0.013 2 m/s (b) 1.03 m/s (c) 6.87 m/s

59. 12.8 N

Chapter 6

1. (a) 31.9 J (b) 0 (c) 0 (d) 31.9 J

3. − 4.70 kJ

5. 5.33 W

7. (a) 16.0 J (b) 36.9°

9. (a) 11.3° (b) 156° (c) 82.3°

11. (a) 7.50 J (b) 15.0 J (c) 7.50 J (d) 30.0 J

13. (a) 0.938 cm (b) 1.25 J

15. (a) 575 N/m (b) 46.0 J

17. 12.0 J

19. (b) mgR

21. (a) 1.20 J (b) 5.00 m/s (c) 6.30 J

23. (a) 60.0 J (b) 60.0 J

25. 878 kN up

27. 0.116 m

29. (a) 650 J (b) 588 J (c) 0 (d) 0 (e) 62.0 J
(f) 1.76 m/s

31. (a) − 168 J (b) 184 J (c) 500 J (d) 148 J
(e) 5.65 m/s

33. 2.04 m

35. 875 W

37. $46.2

39. (a) 423 mi/gal (b) 776 mi/gal

41. 830 N

43. 2.92 m/s

45. (a) $(2 + 24t^2 + 72t^4)$ J (b) $12t \text{ m/s}^2$; $48t$ N
(c) $(48t + 288t^3)$ W (d) 1 250 J

47. (a) $\dfrac{mgnhh_s}{v + nh_s}$ (b) $\dfrac{mgvh}{v + nh_s}$

49. 7.37 N/m

51. (b) 240 W

53. (a) 4.12 m (b) 3.35 m

55. 1.68 m/s

57. $- 1.37 \times 10^{-21}$ J

59. 0.799 J

61. (a) 2.17 kW (b) 58.6 kW

Chapter 7

1. (a) 259 kJ, 0, − 259 kJ (b) 0, − 259 kJ, − 259 kJ

3. 22.0 kW

5. (a) $v = (3gR)^{1/2}$ (b) 0.098 0 N down

7. 1.84 m

9. (a) 4.43 m/s (b) 5.00 m

11. (b) 60.0°

13. (a) 1.24 kW (b) 20.9%

15. (a) 125 J (b) 50.0 J (c) 66.7 J
(d) Nonconservative; the work done depends on the path.

17. 10.2 m

19. (a) 22.0 J, 40.0 J (b) Yes; the total mechanical energy changes.

21. 26.5 m/s

23. 3.74 m/s

25. (a) − 160 J (b) 73.5 J (c) 28.8 N (d) 0.679

27. (a) 1.40 m/s (b) 4.60 cm after release
(c) 1.79 m/s

29. (a) 0.381 m (b) 0.143 m (c) 0.371 m

31. (a) 40.0 J (b) − 40.0 J (c) 62.5 J

33. (A/r^2) away from the other particle

35. (a) − 4.77 × 10⁹ J (b) 569 N (c) 569 N up

37. 2.52×10^7 m

39. (a) + at Ⓑ, − at Ⓓ, 0 at Ⓐ, Ⓒ, and Ⓔ (b) Ⓒ stable;
Ⓐ and Ⓔ unstable
(c)

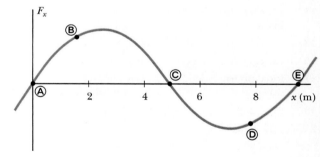

41. (b)

Equilibrium at $x = 0$. (c) 0.823 m/s

43. 0.27 MJ/kg for a battery. 17 MJ/kg for hay is 63 times larger. 44 MJ/kg for gasoline is 2.6 times larger still. 142 MJ/kg for hydrogen is 3.2 times larger than that.

45. $\sim 10^3$ W peak or $\sim 10^2$ W sustainable

47. $(8gh/15)^{1/2}$

49. (a) 0.225 J (b) $\Delta E_{mech} = -0.363$ J (c) No; the normal force changes in a complicated way.

51. 0.328

53. 1.24 m/s

55. (a) 0.400 m (b) 4.10 m/s (c) The block stays on the track.

57. (a) 6.15 m/s (b) 9.87 m/s

59. (a) 11.1 m/s (b) 19.6 m/s^2 upward (c) 2.23×10^3 N upward (d) 1.01×10^3 J (e) 5.14 m/s (f) 1.35 m (g) 1.39 s

63. (a) 14.1 m/s (b) -7.90 kJ (c) 800 N (d) 771 N (e) 1.57 kN up

Context 1 Conclusion

1. (a) 315 kJ (b) 220 kJ (c) 187 kJ (d) 127 kJ (e) 14.0 m/s (f) 40.5% (g) 187 kJ

Chapter 8

1. (a) $(9.00\hat{\mathbf{i}} - 12.0\hat{\mathbf{j}})$ kg·m/s (b) 15.0 kg·m/s at 307°

3. 40.5 g

5. (a) 6.00 m/s toward the left (b) 8.40 J

7. (a) 13.5 N·s (b) 9.00 kN (c) 18.0 kN

9. 260 N normal to the wall

11. 15.0 N in the direction of the initial velocity of the exiting water stream

13. (a) 2.50 m/s (b) 37.5 kJ

15. (a) $v_{gx} = 1.15$ m/s (b) $v_{px} = -0.346$ m/s

17. force on truck driver $= 1.78 \times 10^3$ N; force on car driver $= 8.89 \times 10^3$ N in the opposite direction

19. (a) 0.284 (b) 115 fJ and 45.4 fJ

21. 91.2 m/s

23. (a) 4.85 m/s (b) 8.41 m

25. orange: $v_i \cos\theta$; yellow: $v_i \sin\theta$

27. 2.50 m/s at $-60.0°$

29. $(3.00\hat{\mathbf{i}} - 1.20\hat{\mathbf{j}})$ m/s

31. (a) $(-9.33\hat{\mathbf{i}} - 8.33\hat{\mathbf{j}})$ Mm/s (b) 439 fJ

33. $\vec{\mathbf{r}}_{CM} = (11.7\hat{\mathbf{i}} + 13.3\hat{\mathbf{j}})$ cm

35. (b) 3.57×10^8 J

37. (a) $(1.40\hat{\mathbf{i}} + 2.40\hat{\mathbf{j}})$ m/s (b) $(7.00\hat{\mathbf{i}} + 12.0\hat{\mathbf{j}})$ kg·m/s

39. 0.700 m

41. (a) 39.0 MN (b) 3.20 m/s^2 up

43. (a) 442 metric tons (b) 19.2 metric tons

45. 4.41 kg

47. (a) $1.33\hat{\mathbf{i}}$ m/s (b) $-235\hat{\mathbf{i}}$ N (c) 0.680 s (d) $-160\hat{\mathbf{i}}$ N·s and $+160\hat{\mathbf{i}}$ N·s (e) 1.81 m (f) 0.454 m (g) -427 J (h) $+107$ J (i) Equal friction forces act through different distances on person and cart to do different amounts of work on them. The total work on both together, -320 J, becomes $+320$ J of extra internal energy in this perfectly inelastic collision.

49. (a) 2.07 m/s^2 (b) 3.88 m/s

51. (a) -0.667 m/s (b) 0.952 m

53. (a) $-0.256\hat{\mathbf{i}}$ m/s and $0.128\hat{\mathbf{i}}$ m/s (b) $-0.064\ 2\hat{\mathbf{i}}$ m/s and 0 (c) 0 and 0

55. $2v_i$ and 0

57. (a) $m/M = 0.403$ (b) no changes; no difference

59. (a) 3.75 kg·m/s^2 to the right (b) 3.75 N to the right (c) 3.75 N (d) 2.81 J (e) 1.41 J (f) Friction between sand and belt causes half of the input work to appear as extra internal energy.

Chapter 9

5. $0.866c$

7. (a) 25.0 yr (b) 15.0 yr (c) 12.0 ly

9. 1.54 ns

11. $0.800c$

13. (a) 20.0 m (b) 19.0 m (c) $0.312c$

15. (a) 21.0 yr (b) 14.7 ly (c) 10.5 ly (d) 35.7 yr

17. (a) 17.4 m (b) 3.30°

19. (a) 2.50×10^8 m/s (b) 4.97 m (c) -1.33×10^{-8} s

21. $0.960c$

23. (a) 2.73×10^{-24} kg·m/s (b) 1.58×10^{-22} kg·m/s (c) 5.64×10^{-22} kg·m/s

25. 4.50×10^{-14}

27. $0.285c$

29. (a) 0.582 MeV (b) 2.45 MeV

31. (a) 3.07 MeV (b) $0.986c$

33. (a) 938 MeV (b) 3.00 GeV (c) 2.07 GeV

35. (a) $0.979c$ (b) $0.065\ 2c$ (c) $0.914c = 274$ Mm/s (d) $0.999\ 999\ 97c$; $0.948c$; $0.052\ 3c = 15.7$ Mm/s

39. 4.08 MeV and 29.6 MeV

41. 4.28×10^9 kg/s

43. 1.02 MeV

45. (a) 3.87 km/s (b) -8.36×10^{-11} (c) 5.29×10^{-10} (d) $+4.46 \times 10^{-10}$

47. (a) $v/c = 1 - 1.12 \times 10^{-10}$ (b) 6.00×10^{27} J (c) \$$2.17 \times 10^{20}$

49. (a) a few hundred seconds (b) $\sim 10^8$ km

51. 0.712%

53. (a) $0.946c$ (b) 0.160 ly (c) 0.114 yr (d) 7.50×10^{22} J

55. yes, with 18.8 m to spare

57. (b) For u small compared to c, the relativistic expression agrees with the classical expression. As u approaches c, the acceleration approaches zero, so the object can never reach or surpass the speed of light. (c) Perform $\int (1 - u^2/c^2)^{-3/2}\,du = (qE/m)\int dt$ to obtain $u = qEct(m^2c^2 + q^2E^2t^2)^{-1/2}$ and then $\int dx = \int qEct(m^2c^2 + q^2E^2t^2)^{-1/2}\,dt$ to obtain $x = (c/qE)[(m^2c^2 + q^2E^2t^2)^{1/2} - mc]$.

63. (a) The refugees conclude that Tau Ceti exploded 16.0 yr before the Sun. (b) A stationary observer at the midpoint concludes that they exploded simultaneously.

Chapter 10

1. (a) 5.00 rad, 10.0 rad/s, 4.00 rad/s^2
   (b) 53.0 rad, 22.0 rad/s, 4.00 rad/s^2
3. (a) 5.24 s (b) 27.4 rad
5. 50.0 rev
7. (a) 7.27×10^{-5} rad/s (b) 2.57×10^4 s = 428 min
9. (a) 126 rad/s (b) 3.77 m/s (c) 1.26 km/s^2
   (d) 20.1 m
11. (a) 0.605 m/s (b) 17.3 rad/s (c) 5.82 m/s
    (d) The crank length is unnecessary.
13. 0.572
17. (a) $\sqrt{\dfrac{2(m_1 - m_2)gh}{m_1 + m_2 + I/R^2}}$ (b) $\sqrt{\dfrac{2(m_1 - m_2)gh}{m_1 R^2 + m_2 R^2 + I}}$
19. 24.5 m/s
21. -3.55 N·m
23. $\vec{\tau} = (2.00\hat{\mathbf{k}})$ N·m
27. $[(m_1 + m_b)d + m_1\ell/2]/m_2$
29. (a) 1.04 kN at 60.0° (b) $(370\hat{\mathbf{i}} + 900\hat{\mathbf{j}})$ N
31. (a) $T = F_g(L + d)/\sin\theta(2L + d)$
    (b) $R_x = F_g(L + d)\cot\theta/(2L + d)$; $R_y = F_g L/(2L + d)$
33. (a) 21.6 kg·m^2 (b) 3.60 N·m (c) 52.4 rev
35. 21.5 N
37. (a) 118 N and 156 N (b) 1.17 kg·m^2
39. (a) 11.4 N, 7.57 m/s^2, 9.53 m/s down (b) 9.53 m/s
41. $(60.0\hat{\mathbf{k}})$ kg·m^2/s
43. (a) 0.433 kg·m^2/s (b) 1.73 kg·m^2/s
45. (a) $\omega_f = \omega_i I_1/(I_1 + I_2)$ (b) $I_1/(I_1 + I_2)$
47. (a) 0.360 rad/s counterclockwise (b) 99.9 J
49. (a) 7.20×10^{-3} kg·m^2/s (b) 9.47 rad/s
51. 5.99×10^{-2} J
53. (a) 500 J (b) 250 J (c) 750 J
55. (a) 2.38 m/s. Its weight is insufficient to provide the centripetal acceleration. (b) 4.31 m/s
    (c) The ball does not reach the top of the loop.
57. 131 s
59. (a) $(3g/L)^{1/2}$ (b) $3g/2L$ (c) $-\frac{3}{2}g\hat{\mathbf{i}} - \frac{3}{4}g\hat{\mathbf{j}}$
    (d) $-\frac{3}{2}Mg\hat{\mathbf{i}} + \frac{1}{4}Mg\hat{\mathbf{j}}$
61. (a) $\sqrt{\dfrac{2mgd\sin\theta + kd^2}{I + mR^2}}$ (b) 1.74 rad/s
67. (a) 61.2 J (b) 50.8 J
69. (a) Mvd (b) Mv^2 (c) Mvd (d) $2v$
    (e) $4Mv^2$ (f) $3Mv^2$
71. $T = 2.71$ kN, $R_x = 2.65$ kN
73. (a) 20.1 cm to the left of the front edge; $\mu_k = 0.571$
    (b) 0.501 m
75. (a) 133 N (b) $n_A = 429$ N and $n_B = 257$ N
    (c) $R_x = 133$ N and $R_y = -257$ N
77. $\frac{3}{8}F_g$

Chapter 11

1. 2.67×10^{-7} m/s^2
3. 7.41×10^{-10} N

5. (a) 4.39×10^{20} N toward the Sun (b) 1.99×10^{20} N away from the Sun (c) 3.55×10^{22} N toward the Sun
7. $\rho_M/\rho_E = 2/3$
9. (a) 7.61 cm/s^2 (b) 363 s (c) 3.08 km
   (d) 28.9 m/s at 72.9° below the horizontal
11. $\vec{\mathbf{g}} = 2MGr(r^2 + a^2)^{-3/2}$ toward the center of mass
13. (a) 4.23×10^7 m (b) 0.285 s
15. 1.90×10^{27} kg
17. 1.26×10^{32} kg
19. After 3.93 yr, Mercury would be farther from the Sun than Pluto.
21. (a) 1.84×10^9 kg/m^3 (b) 3.27×10^6 m/s^2
    (c) -2.08×10^{13} J
23. 1.78 km
25. 1.66×10^4 m/s
29. 1.58×10^{10} J
31. (b) 1.00×10^7 m (c) 1.00×10^4 m/s
33. (a) 0.980 (b) 127 yr (c) -2.13×10^{17} J
35. (a) 5 (b) no; no
37. (a) ii (b) i (c) ii and iii
39. (a) 0.212 nm (b) 9.95×10^{-25} kg·m/s
    (c) 2.11×10^{-34} kg·m^2/s (d) 3.40 eV
    (e) -6.80 eV (f) -3.40 eV
41. 4.42×10^4 m/s
43. (a) 29.3% (b) no change
45. 2.26×10^{-7}
47. (c) 1.85×10^{-5} m/s^2
49. $v = 492$ m/s
51. (a) 7.79 km/s (b) 7.85 km/s (c) -3.04 GJ
    (d) -3.08 GJ (e) loss = 46.9 MJ (f) A component of the Earth's gravity pulls forward on the satellite on its downward-banking trajectory.
53. (a) $m_2(2G/d)^{1/2}(m_1 + m_2)^{-1/2}$ and $m_1(2G/d)^{1/2}(m_1 + m_2)^{-1/2}$; relative speed $(2G/d)^{1/2}(m_1 + m_2)^{1/2}$
    (b) 1.07×10^{32} J and 2.67×10^{31} J
55. (a) 200 Myr (b) $\sim 10^{41}$ kg; $\sim 10^{11}$ stars
57. $(GM_E/4R_E)^{1/2}$
61. $r_n = (0.106 \text{ nm})n^2$, $E_n = -6.80$ eV$/n^2$, for $n = 1, 2, 3, \ldots$

Context 2 Conclusion

1. (a) 146 d (b) Venus 53.9° behind the Earth
3. (a) 2.95 km/s (b) 2.65 km/s (c) 10.7 km/s
   (d) 4.80 km/s

Chapter 12

1. (a) The motion repeats precisely. (b) 1.81 s
   (c) No, the force is not in the form of Hooke's law.
3. (a) 1.50 Hz, 0.667 s (b) 4.00 m (c) π rad
   (d) 2.83 m
5. (b) 18.8 cm/s, 0.333 s (c) 178 cm/s^2, 0.500 s
   (d) 12.0 cm
9. 40.9 N/m

11. (a) 40.0 cm/s, 160 cm/s^2
(b) 32.0 cm/s, $-$ 96.0 cm/s^2 (c) 0.232 s

13. 2.23 m/s

15. (a) 0.542 kg   (b) 1.81 s   (c) 1.20 m/s^2

17. (a) 28.0 mJ   (b) 1.02 m/s   (c) 12.2 mJ
(d) 15.8 mJ

19. (a) E increases by a factor of 4   (b) v_{max} is doubled.
(c) a_{max} is doubled.   (d) The period is unchanged.

21. 2.60 cm and $-$ 2.60 cm

23. Assume simple harmonic motion: (a) 0.820 m/s
(b) 2.57 rad/s^2 (c) 0.641 N   More precisely:
(a) 0.817 m/s   (b) 2.54 rad/s^2 (c) 0.634 N

27. 0.944 kg·m^2

31. 1.00×10^{-3} s^{-1}

33. (a) 1.00 s   (b) 5.09 cm

37. 1.74 Hz

39. If the cyclist goes over them at one certain speed, the washboard bumps can excite a resonance vibration of the bike, so large in amplitude as to make the rider lose control. $\sim 10^1$ m

41. 6.62 cm

43. 9.19×10^{13} Hz

45. (b) 1.04 m/s   (c) four times larger, 3.40 m

47. $f = (2\pi L)^{-1}(gL + kh^2/M)^{1/2}$

49. (b) 1.23 Hz

51. (a) 3.00 s   (b) 14.3 J   (c) 25.5°

57. (a) 5.20 s   (b) 2.60 s

Chapter 13

1. $y = 6\,[(x - 4.5t)^2 + 3]^{-1}$

3. 0.319 m

5. (a) $(3.33\hat{\mathbf{i}})$ m/s   (b) -5.48 cm
(c) 0.667 m, 5.00 Hz   (d) 11.0 m/s

7. (a) 31.4 rad/s   (b) 1.57 rad/m
(c) $y = (0.120\text{ m})\sin(1.57x - 31.4t)$ (d) 3.77 m/s
(e) 118 m/s^2

9. (a) $y = (8.00\text{ cm})\sin(7.85x + 6\pi t)$
(b) $y = (8.00\text{ cm})\sin(7.85x + 6\pi t - 0.785)$

11. (a) 0.021 5 m   (b) 1.95 rad   (c) 5.41 m/s
(d) $y(x, t) = (0.021\text{ 5 m})\sin(8.38x + 80.0\pi t + 1.95)$

13. 80.0 N

15. 13.5 N

17. 0.329 s

19. 1.07 kW

21. 55.1 Hz

23. 5.56 km

25. (a) 23.2 cm   (b) 1.38 cm

27. (a) 4.16 m   (b) 0.455 μs   (c) 0.158 mm

29. 5.81 m

31. $\Delta P = (0.200\text{ N/m}^2)\sin(62.8x/\text{m} - 2.16 \times 10^4 t/\text{s})$

33. (a) 3.04 kHz   (b) 2.08 kHz   (c) 2.62 kHz; 2.40 kHz

35. 26.4 m/s

37. 19.3 m

39. (a) 0.364 m   (b) 0.398 m   (c) 941 Hz
(d) 938 Hz

41. 184 km

43. $(Lm/Mg\sin\theta)^{1/2}$

45. 0.084 3 rad

49. (a) $\dfrac{\mu\omega^3}{2k}A_0^2 e^{-2bx}$ (b) $\dfrac{\mu\omega^3}{2k}A_0^2$ (c) e^{-2bx}

51. (a) $\mu_0 + (\mu_L - \mu_0)x/L$

55. 6.01 km

57. (a) 55.8 m/s   (b) 2 500 Hz

59. The gap between bat and insect is closing at 1.69 m/s.

Chapter 14

1. (a) -1.65 cm   (b) -6.02 cm   (c) 1.15 cm

3. (a) $+x, -x$ (b) 0.750 s   (c) 1.00 m

5. (a) 9.24 m   (b) 600 Hz

7. 91.3°

9. (a) 156°   (b) 0.058 4 cm

11. (a) To reach the receiver, waves from the more distant source must travel an extra distance $\Delta r = \lambda/2$ and interfere destructively with waves from the closer source.
(b) It should move along the hyperbola represented by $9.00x^2 - 16.0y^2 = 144$.

13. at 0.089 1 m, 0.303 m, 0.518 m, 0.732 m, 0.947 m, and 1.16 m from one speaker

15. (a) 4.24 cm   (b) 6.00 cm   (c) 6.00 cm
(d) 0.500 cm, 1.50 cm, 2.50 cm

17. 0.786 Hz, 1.57 Hz, 2.36 Hz, 3.14 Hz

19. 15.7 Hz

21. (a) reduced by $\frac{1}{2}$ (b) reduced by $1/\sqrt{2}$
(c) increased by $\sqrt{2}$

23. (a) 163 N   (b) 660 Hz

25. $\dfrac{Mg}{4Lf^2\tan\theta}$

27. (a) 0.357 m   (b) 0.715 m

29. 57.9 Hz

31. n(206 Hz) for $n = 1$ to 9 and n(84.5 Hz) for $n = 2$ to 23

33. 50.0 Hz, 1.70 m

35. n(0.252 m) with $n = 1, 2, 3, \ldots$

37. (a) 350 m/s   (b) 1.14 m

39. 5.64 beats/s

41. (a) 1.99 beats/s   (b) 3.38 m/s

43. The second harmonic of E is close to the third harmonic of A, and the fourth harmonic of C$^{\#}$ is close to the fifth harmonic of A.

45. The condition for resonance is satisfied because the 12 h 24 min period of free oscillation agrees precisely with the period of the lunar excitation.

47. (a) 34.8 m/s   (b) 0.977 m

49. 3.85 m/s away from the station and 3.77 m/s toward the station

51. 21.5 m

53. (a) 59.9 Hz (b) 20.0 cm

55. (a) $\frac{1}{2}$ (b) $[n/(n+1)]^2T$ (c) $\frac{9}{16}$

57. $y_1 + y_2 = 11.2 \sin(2.00x - 10.0t + 63.4°)$

59. (a) 78.9 N (b) 211 Hz

Context 3 Conclusion

1. 3.5 cm

2. The speed decreases by a factor of 25.

3. Station 1: 15:46:32; Station 2: 15:46:22; Station 3: 15:46:08, all with uncertainties of ±1 s

Chapter 15

1. 0.111 kg

3. 6.24 MPa

5. 1.62 m

7. 7.74×10^{-3} m^2

9. 271 kN horizontally backward

11. 2.31 lb

13. 10.5 m; no because some alcohol and water evaporate

15. 98.6 kPa

17. (a) 7.54 kg (b) 39.8 N (c) 41.9 N up (d) zero (e) The tension decreases and the normal force increases.

19. 0.258 N

21. (a) $1.017\ 9 \times 10^3$ N down, $1.029\ 7 \times 10^3$ N up (b) 86.2 N (c) 11.8 N

23. (a) 7.00 cm (b) 2.80 kg

25. 1 430 m^3

27. 1 250 kg/m^3 and 500 kg/m^3

29. 1.01 kJ

31. 12.8 kg/s

33. $2\sqrt{h(h_0 - h)}$

35. (a) 27.9 N (b) 3.32×10^4 kg (c) 7.26×10^4 Pa

37. 0.247 cm

39. (a) 1 atm + 15.0 MPa (b) 2.95 m/s (c) 4.34 kPa

41. 347 m/s

43. (a) 4.43 m/s (b) The siphon can be no higher than 10.3 m.

45. 12.6 m/s

47. 1.61×10^4 m^2

51. 0.604 m

55. The top scale reads $(1 - \rho_0/\rho_{Fe})\,m_{Fe}g$. The bottom scale reads $[m_b + m_0 + \rho_0 m_{Fe}/\rho_{Fe}]g$.

57. (a) 2.79 μm/s (b) 7.95 h (c) 8.88×10^3 m/s^2 (d) 31.6 s

59. 4.43 m/s

61. (a) 1.25 cm (b) 13.8 m/s

63. (a) 3.307 g (b) 3.271 g (c) 3.48×10^{-4} N

Context 4 Conclusion

1. 9.8×10^9 N·m

2. (a) 1.30 MPa (b) yes, but only with specialized equipment and techniques

3. (a) 0.42 m/s (b) greater

4. (a) 16 knots at 56° west of south (b) 47%

Chapter 16

1. (a) −273°C (b) 1.27 atm (c) 1.74 atm

3. (a) −320°F (b) 77.3 K

5. 1.54 km. The pipeline can be supported on rollers. Ω-shaped loops can be built between straight sections. They bend as the steel changes length.

7. 0.001 58 cm

9. (a) 0.176 mm (b) 8.78 μm (c) 0.093 0 cm^3

11. (a) 0.109 cm^2 (b) increase

13. (a) 99.4 cm^3 (b) 0.943 cm

15. 8.72×10^{11} atoms/s

17. (a) 400 kPa (b) 449 kPa

19. 1.50×10^{29} molecules

21. 472 K

23. (a) 7.13 m (b) The open end of the tube should be at the bottom after the bird surfaces so that the water can drain out. There is no other requirement. Air does not tend to bubble out of a narrow tube.

25. 4.39 kg

27. 3.55 L

29. $m_1 - m_2 = \dfrac{P_0 VM}{R}\left(\dfrac{1}{T_1} - \dfrac{1}{T_2}\right)$

31. 17.6 kPa

33. (a) 3.54×10^{23} atoms (b) 6.07×10^{-21} J (c) 1.35 km/s

35. (a) 8.76×10^{-21} J for both (b) 1.62 km/s for helium and 514 m/s for argon

39. (a) 2.37×10^4 K (b) 1.06×10^3 K

41. (a) −9.73°C/km (b) As rising air drops in temperature, water vapor in it condenses into liquid. It releases energy in this process to reduce the net temperature drop. (c) −4.60°C/km (d) 4.34 km (e) Dust aloft absorbs sunlight to raise the temperature there. *Mariner* occurred in dustier conditions.

43. 0.523 kg

45. (a) Expansion makes density drop. (b) 5×10^{-5}/°C

47. (a) $h = nRT/(mg + P_0A)$ (b) 0.661 m

49. We assume that $\alpha \Delta T$ is much less than 1.

51. (a) 0.340% (b) 0.480%

53. 2.74 m

55. (a) It increases. As the disk cools, its radius and hence its moment of inertia decrease. Conservation of angular momentum then requires that its angular speed increase. (b) 25.7 rad/s

57. (b) 1.33 kg/m^3

59. 1.12 atm

61. (d) 0.275 mm (e) The plate creeps down the roof each day by an amount given by the same expression.

63. $1.09 \times 10^{-3}, 2.69 \times 10^{-2}, 0.529, 1.00, 0.199,$
$1.01 \times 10^{-41}, 1.25 \times 10^{-1\,082}$

Chapter 17

1. 0.281°C

3. 87.0°C

5. 29.6°C

7. (a) 16.1°C   (b) 16.1°C

9. 23.6°C

11. 1.22×10^5 J

13. 0.294 g

15. (a) 0°C   (b) 114 g

17. liquid lead at 805°C

19. -1.18 MJ

21. -466 J

23. $Q = -720$ J

25.

	Q	W	ΔE_{int}
BC	$-$	0	$-$
CA	$-$	$+$	$-$
AB	$+$	$-$	$+$

27. (a) 7.50 kJ   (b) 900 K

29. -3.10 kJ; 37.6 kJ

31. (a) 0.041 0 m³   (b) $+5.48$ kJ   (c) -5.48 kJ

33. (a) 3.46 kJ   (b) 2.45 kJ   (c) -1.01 kJ

35. (a) 209 J   (b) zero   (c) 317 K

37. between 10^{-2}°C and 10^{-3}°C

39. $13.5PV$

41. (a) 1.39 atm   (b) 366 K, 253 K
(c) 0, -4.66 kJ, -4.66 kJ

43. (a)

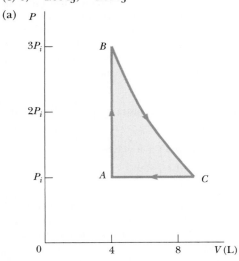

  (b) 8.77 L   (c) 900 K   (d) 300 K   (e) -336 J

45. 25.0 kW

47. (a) 9.95 cal/K, 13.9 cal/K   (b) 13.9 cal/K, 17.9 cal/K

49. 51.2°C

51. 3.85×10^{26} J/s

53. 74.8 kJ

55. 279 K = 6°C

57. (a) 0.964 kg or more   (b) The test samples and the inner surface of the insulation can be preheated to 37.0°C as the box is assembled. Then nothing changes in temperature during the test period, and the masses of the test samples and insulation make no difference.

59. (a) 13.0°C   (b) -0.532 °C/s

61. $c = \mathscr{P}/\rho R \Delta T$

63. (a) 9.31×10^{10} J   (b) -8.47×10^{12} J
(c) 8.38×10^{12} J

65. 5.31 h

67. (a) 15.0 mg; block: $Q = 0$, $W = -5.00$ J, $\Delta E_{int} = 0$,
$\Delta K = -5.00$ J; ice: $Q = 0$, $W = +5.00$ J; $\Delta E_{int} = 5.00$ J,
$\Delta K = 0$ (b) 15.0 mg; block: $Q = 0$, $W = 0$,
$\Delta E_{int} = 5.00$ J, $\Delta K = -5.00$ J; metal: $Q = 0$, $W = 0$,
$\Delta E_{int} = 0$, $\Delta K = 0$ (c) 0.004 04°C; moving block: $Q = 0$,
$W = -2.50$ J, $\Delta E_{int} = 2.50$ J, $\Delta K = -5.00$ J; stationary
block: $Q = 0$, $W = +2.50$ J, $\Delta E_{int} = 2.50$ J, $\Delta K = 0$

69. 38.6 m³/d

71. (a) 100 kPa, 66.5 L, 400 K; 5.82 kJ; 7.48 kJ; -1.66 kJ
(b) 133 kPa, 49.9 L, 400 K; 5.82 kJ; 5.82 kJ; 0
(c) 120 kPa, 41.6 L, 300 K; 0; -909 J; $+909$ J
(d) 120 kPa, 43.3 L, 312 K; 722 J; 0; $+722$ J

73. (a) 300 K   (b) 1.00 atm

75. (a) 0.203 mol   (b) $T_B = T_C = 900$ K, $V_C = 15.0$ L

(c, d)	P, atm	V, L	T, K	E_{int}, kJ
A	1.00	5.00	300	0.760
B	3.00	5.00	900	2.28
C	1.00	15.0	900	2.28
A	1.00	5.00	300	0.760

(e) Lock the piston in place and put the cylinder into an oven at 900 K. Keep the gas in the oven while gradually letting the gas expand to lift a load on the piston as far as it can. Move the cylinder from the oven back to the 300-K room and let the gas cool and contract.

(f, g)	Q, kJ	W, kJ	ΔE_{int}, kJ
AB	1.52	0	1.52
BC	1.67	-1.67	0
CA	-2.53	$+1.01$	-1.52
ABCA	0.656	-0.656	0

Chapter 18

1. (a) 6.94%   (b) 335 J

3. (a) 10.7 kJ   (b) 0.533 s

5. (a) 67.2%   (b) 58.8 kW

7. (a) 741 J   (b) 459 J

9. 0.330

11. (b) $1 - T_c/T_h$ (c) $(T_c + T_h)/2$ (d) $(T_hT_c)^{1/2}$

13. (a) 24.0 J   (b) 144 J

15. (a) 2.93   (b) coefficient of performance for a refrigerator   (c) $300 is twice as large as $150

19. 1.17 J

21. 72.2 J

23. 195 J/K

25. (a) isobaric   (b) 402 kJ   (c) 1.20 kJ/K

27. (a) 1   (b) 6

29. (a)

Result	Number of ways to draw
All R	1
2R, 1G	3
1R, 2G	3
All G	1

(b)

Result	Number of ways to draw
All R	1
4R, 1G	5
3R, 2G	10
2R, 3G	10
1R, 4G	5
All G	1

31. 1.02 kJ/K

33. $\sim 10^0$ W/K from metabolism; much more if you are using high-power electric appliances or an automobile, or if your taxes are paying for a war.

35. 0.507 J/K

37. (a) 5.2×10^{17} J   (b) 1.8×10^3 s

39. (a) 5.00 kW   (b) 763 W

41. 32.9 kJ

43. (a) $2nRT_i \ln 2$ (b) 0.273

45. 5.97×10^4 kg/s

49. (a) 4.11 kJ   (b) 14.2 kJ   (c) 10.1 kJ   (d) 28.9%

51. (a) $10.5nRT_i$ (b) $8.50nRT_i$ (c) 0.190
    (d) 0.833

53. (a) $nC_P \ln 3$ (b) Both ask for the change in entropy between the same two states of the same system. Entropy is a state variable. The change in entropy does not depend on path, but only on original and final states.

55. (a) $V_A = 1.97$ L, $V_B = 11.9$ L, $V_C = 32.8$ L, $V_D = 5.44$ L, $P_B = 4.14$ atm, $P_D = 6.03$ atm   (b) 2.99 kJ
    (c) 0.333

57. 1.18 J/K

Context 5 Conclusion

1. 298 K

2. 60 km

3. (c) 336 K   (d) The troposphere and stratosphere are too thick to be accurately modeled as having uniform temperatures.   (e) 227 K   (f) 107   (g) The multilayer model should be better for Venus than for the Earth. There are many layers, so the temperature of each can be reasonably uniform.

Chapter 19

1. (a) + 160 zC, 1.01 u   (b) + 160 zC, 23.0 u
   (c) − 160 zC, 35.5 u   (d) + 320 zC, 40.1 u

(e) − 480 zC, 14.0 u   (f) + 640 zC, 14.0 u
(g) + 1.12 aC, 14.0 u   (h) − 160 zC, 18.0 u

3. The force is $\sim 10^{26}$ N.

5. 0.872 N at 330°

7. (a) 2.16×10^{-5} N toward the other
   (b) 8.99×10^{-7} N away from the other

9. (a) 82.2 nN   (b) 2.19 Mm/s

11. 1.82 m to the left of the negative charge

13. (a) $(- 0.599\hat{\mathbf{i}} - 2.70\hat{\mathbf{j}})$ kN/C
    (b) $(-3.00\hat{\mathbf{i}} - 13.5\hat{\mathbf{j}})$ μN

15. (a) $5.91 \, k_e q / a^2$ at 58.8°   (b) $5.91 \, k_e q^2 / a^2$ at 58.8°

17. 1.59×10^6 N/C toward the rod

19. (a) $6.64\hat{\mathbf{i}}$ MN/C   (b) $24.1\hat{\mathbf{i}}$ MN/C
    (c) $6.40\hat{\mathbf{i}}$ MN/C   (d) $0.664\hat{\mathbf{i}}$ MN/C, taking the axis of the ring as the x axis

21. $- 21.6\hat{\mathbf{i}}$ MN/C

23. (a) 2.00×10^{-10} C   (b) 1.41×10^{-10} C
    (c) 5.89×10^{-11} C

25.

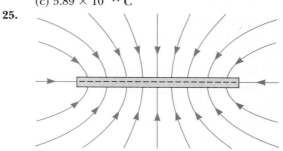

27. (a) 61.3 Gm/s^2 (b) 19.5 μs   (c) 11.7 m
    (d) 1.20 fJ

29. (a) 111 ns   (b) 5.68 mm   (c) $(450\hat{\mathbf{i}} + 102\hat{\mathbf{j}})$ km/s

31. 4.14 MN/C

33. (a) $+ Q/2\epsilon_0$ (b) $- Q/2\epsilon_0$

35. (a) 0   (b) 365 kN/C radially outward
    (c) 1.46 MN/C outward   (d) 649 kN/C radially outward

37. (a) 913 nC   (b) 0

39. $\vec{\mathbf{E}} = \rho r/2\epsilon_0$ away from the axis

41. 3.50 kN

43. $\vec{\mathbf{E}} = Q/2\epsilon_0 A$ vertically upward in each case if $Q > 0$

45. (a) 0   (b) 79.9 MN/C radially outward   (c) 0
    (d) 7.34 MN/C radially outward

47. (a) $- \lambda, + 3\lambda$ (b) $3\lambda/2\pi\epsilon_0 r$ radially outward

49. (a) 80.0 nC/m^2 on each face   (b) $9.04\hat{\mathbf{k}}$ kN/C
    (c) $- 9.04\hat{\mathbf{k}}$ kN/C

51. 1.77×10^{-12} C/m^3, positive

53. possible only with a charge of $+ 51.3$ μC at $x = - 16.0$ cm

55. 40.9 N at 263°

57. 26.7 μC

59. (a) $\theta_1 = \theta_2$

61. (b) in the $+ z$ direction

63. (a) σ/ϵ_0 away from both plates   (b) 0   (c) σ/ϵ_0 away from both plates

65. (a) $\rho r/3\epsilon_0$; $Q/4\pi\epsilon_0 r^2$; 0; $Q/4\pi\epsilon_0 r^2$, all radially outward
(b) $-Q/4\pi b^2$ and $+Q/4\pi c^2$

Chapter 20

1. (a) 152 km/s   (b) 6.49 Mm/s

3. (a) $-600\ \mu\text{J}$ (b) -50.0 V

5. 38.9 V; the origin

7. (a) 1.44×10^{-7} V   (b) -7.19×10^{-8} V
(c) -1.44×10^{-7} V, $+7.19 \times 10^{-8}$ V

9. (a) -4.83 m   (b) 0.667 m and -2.00 m

11. -11.0 MV

15. (a) 10.8 m/s and 1.55 m/s   (b) greater

17. (a) no point at a finite distance from the charges
(b) $2k_eq/a$

19. $5k_eq^2/9d$

21. (a) 10.0 V, -11.0 V, -32.0 V
(b) 7.00 N/C in the $+x$ direction

23. $\vec{E} = (-5 + 6xy)\hat{i} + (3x^2 - 2z^2)\hat{j} - 4yz\hat{k}$; 7.07 N/C

25. (a) coulombs per square meter
(b) $k_e\alpha[L - d\ln(1 + L/d)]$

27. -1.51 MV

29. (a) 0, 1.67 MV   (b) 5.84 MN/C away, 1.17 MV
(c) 11.9 MN/C away, 1.67 MV

31. (a) $48.0\ \mu\text{C}$ (b) $6.00\ \mu\text{C}$

33. (a) $1.33\ \mu\text{C/m}^2$ (b) 13.3 pF

35. (a) 11.1 kV/m toward the negative plate
(b) $98.3\ \text{nC/m}^2$ (c) 3.74 pF   (d) 74.7 pC

37. $mgd\tan\theta/q$

39. (a) $17.0\ \mu\text{F}$ (b) 9.00 V   (c) $45.0\ \mu\text{C}$ and $108\ \mu\text{C}$

41. (a) $5.96\ \mu\text{F}$ (b) $89.5\ \mu\text{C}$ on $20\ \mu\text{F}$, $63.2\ \mu\text{C}$ on $6\ \mu\text{F}$,
$26.3\ \mu\text{C}$ on $15\ \mu\text{F}$ and on $3\ \mu\text{F}$

43. $120\ \mu\text{C}$; $80.0\ \mu\text{C}$ and $40.0\ \mu\text{C}$

45. (a) $398\ \mu\text{F}$ in series   (b) $2.20\ \mu\text{F}$ in parallel

47. (a) $216\ \mu\text{J}$ (b) $54.0\ \mu\text{J}$

49. (a) circuit diagram:

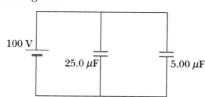

stored energy = 0.150 J

(b) potential difference = 268 V

circuit diagram:

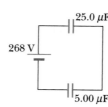

53. (a) 81.3 pF   (b) 2.40 kV

55. 1.04 m

57. (a) 369 pC   (b) 118 pF, 3.12 V   (c) -45.5 nJ

59. 9.79 kg

61. 253 MeV

63 $k_eQ^2/2R$

65. 579 V

67. (a) volume 9.09×10^{-16} m^3, area 4.54×10^{-10} m^2
(b) 2.01×10^{-13} F
(c) 2.01×10^{-14} C; 1.26×10^5 electronic charges

71. (a) $-2Q/3$ on upper plate, $-Q/3$ on lower plate
(b) $2Qd/3\epsilon_0 A$

73. 0.188 m^2

75. (a) $\dfrac{\epsilon_0}{d}\left(\ell^2 + \ell x(\kappa - 1)\right)$

(b) $\dfrac{Q^2 d}{2\epsilon_0(\ell^2 + \ell x(\kappa - 1))}$

(c) $\dfrac{Q^2 d\ell(\kappa - 1)}{2\epsilon_0(\ell^2 + \ell x(\kappa - 1))^2}$ to the right

(d) $205\ \mu\text{N}$ to the right

77. $\frac{4}{3}C$

Chapter 21

1. 7.50×10^{15} electrons

3. (a) $0.632\ I_0\tau$ (b) $0.999\ 95\ I_0\tau$ (c) $I_0\tau$

5. 0.130 mm/s

7. 6.43 A

9. (a) $31.5\ \text{n}\Omega\cdot\text{m}$ (b) 6.35 MA/m^2 (c) 49.9 mA
(d) $659\ \mu\text{m/s}$ (e) 0.400 V

11. $1.71\ \Omega$

13. 0.181 V/m

15. 448 A

17. 36.1%

19. (a) 184 W   (b) 461°C

21. (a) $1.61   (b) $0.005 82   (c) $0.416

23. (a) 667 A   (b) 50.0 km

25. (a) $6.73\ \Omega$ (b) $1.97\ \Omega$

27. (a) $17.1\ \Omega$ (b) 1.99 A for $4\ \Omega$ and $9\ \Omega$, 1.17 A for $7\ \Omega$,
0.818 A for $10\ \Omega$

29. (a) 227 mA   (b) 5.68 V

31. 14.2 W to $2\ \Omega$, 28.4 W to $4\ \Omega$, 1.33 W to $3\ \Omega$,
4.00 W to $1\ \Omega$

33. (a) 470 W   (b) 1.60 mm or more
(c) 2.93 mm or more

35. 846 mA down in the $8\text{-}\Omega$ resistor; 462 mA down in the
middle branch; 1.31 A up in the right-hand branch

37. (a) -222 J and 1.88 kJ   (b) 687 J, 128 J, 25.6 J, 616 J,
205 J   (c) 1.66 kJ of chemical energy is transformed
into internal energy

39. 50.0 mA from a to e

41. (a) 5.00 s   (b) $150\ \mu\text{C}$ (c) $4.06\ \mu\text{A}$

43. (a) 1.50 s   (b) 1.00 s   (c) $(200 + 100e^{-t/1.00\ \text{s}})\ \mu\text{A}$

45. (a) 6.00 V   (b) $8.29\ \mu\text{s}$

47. $6.00 \times 10^{-15}/\Omega \cdot m$

49. (a) 576 Ω, 144 Ω (b) 4.80 s. The charge is the same. It is at a location of lower potential energy. (c) 0.040 0 s. Energy entering by electrical transmission exits by heat and electromagnetic radiation. (d) \$1.26, energy at 1.94×10^{-8} \$/J

51. (a) $(8.00\hat{\mathbf{i}})$ V/m   (b) 0.637 Ω (c) 6.28 A (d) $(200\hat{\mathbf{i}})$ MA/m^2

53. (a) 12.5 A, 6.25 A, 8.33 A (b) No; together they would require 27.1 A.

55. 2.22 h

57. (a) $R \to \infty$ (b) $R \to 0$ (c) $R = r$

59. (a) 9.93 μC   (b) 33.7 nA   (c) 334 nW (d) 337 nW

61. (a) 222 μC   (b) increases by 444 μC

63. (a) 0.991   (b) 0.648 (c) Insulation should be added to the ceiling.

Context 6 Conclusion

1. (a) 87.0 s   (b) 261 s   (c) $t \to \infty$

2. (a) 0.01 s   (b) 7×10^6

3. (a) 3×10^6 (b) 9×10^6

Chapter 22

1. (a) up   (b) toward you, out of the plane of the paper (c) no deflection   (d) into the plane of the paper

3. (a) 8.67×10^{-14} N   (b) 5.19×10^{13} m/s^2

5. 8.93×10^{-30} N down, 1.60×10^{-17} N up, 4.80×10^{-17} N down

7. 115 keV

9. 7.88 pT

11. 0.278 m

13. 70.1 mT

15. $(-2.88\hat{\mathbf{j}})$ N

17. $2\pi r I B \sin \theta$ up

19. (a) 5.41 mA $\cdot$ m^2 (b) 4.33 mN $\cdot$ m

21. 9.98 N $\cdot$ m clockwise as seen looking down from above

23. 12.5 T

25. $\dfrac{\mu_0 I}{4\pi x}$ into the paper

27. $\left(1 + \dfrac{1}{\pi}\right) \dfrac{\mu_0 I}{2R}$ directed into the page

29. (a) $2I_1$ out of the page   (b) $6I_1$ into the page

31. 261 nT into the page

33. (a) 21.5 mA   (b) 4.51 V   (c) 96.7 mW

35. $(-27.0\hat{\mathbf{i}})$ μN

37. 20.0 μT toward the bottom of the page

39. (a) 6.34 mN/m inward   (b) greater

41. (a) 3.60 T   (b) 1.94 T

43. 500 A

45. 31.8 mA

47. 207 W

49. (a) 8.63×10^{45} electrons   (b) 4.01×10^{20} kg

51. (a) 1.4 MJ/mi   (b) 5.7 MJ/mi   (c) 1/400

53. $\vec{\mathbf{B}} = \dfrac{\mu_0 J_s}{2} \hat{\mathbf{k}}$ for $x > 0$ and $\vec{\mathbf{B}} = -\dfrac{\mu_0 J_s}{2} \hat{\mathbf{k}}$ for $x < 0$

55. (a) The electric current experiences a magnetic force. (c) no, no, no

57. (a) $(3.52\hat{\mathbf{i}} - 1.60\hat{\mathbf{j}})$ aN   (b) 24.4°

59. $B \sim 10^{-1}$ T, $\tau \sim 10^{-1}$ N $\cdot$ m, $I \sim 10^0$ A, $A \sim 10^{-3}$ m^2, $N \sim 10^3$

61. (a) 1.04×10^{-4} m   (b) 1.89×10^{-4} m

63. $\dfrac{\mu_0 I}{2\pi w} \ln\left(1 + \dfrac{w}{b}\right) \hat{\mathbf{k}}$

65. $\dfrac{\mu_0 q\omega}{2.5\pi R\sqrt{5}}$

67. (a) 2.46 N up   (b) 107 m/s^2 up

Chapter 23

1. 0.800 mA

3. 160 A

5. (a) $(\mu_0 IL/2\pi) \ln(1 + w/h)$ (b) -4.80 μV; current is counterclockwise

7. 61.8 mV

9. (b) The emf induced in the coil is proportional to the line integral of the magnetic field around the circular axis of the toroid. By Ampère's law, this line integral depends only on the current the circle encloses.

11. (a) eastward   (b) 458 μV

13. (a) 3.00 N to the right   (b) 6.00 W

15. $mvR/B^2\ell^2$

17. 24.1 V with the outer contact positive

19. 2.83 mV

21. (b) Larger R makes current smaller, so the loop must travel faster to maintain equality of magnetic force and weight.   (c) The magnetic force is proportional to the product of field and current, whereas the current is itself proportional to field. If B becomes two times smaller, the speed must become four times larger to compensate.

23. (a) 7.54 kV   (b) The plane of the coil is parallel to $\vec{\mathbf{B}}$.

25. 1.80 mN/C upward and to the left, perpendicular to r_1

27. 19.5 mV

29. $-(18.8$ V$) \cos(377t)$

31. (a) 360 mV   (b) 180 mV   (c) 3.00 s

33. (a) 0.139 s   (b) 0.461 s

35. (a) 2.00 ms   (b) 0.176 A   (c) 1.50 A   (d) 3.22 ms

37. (a) 20.0%   (b) 4.00%

39. $(500$ mA$)(1 - e^{-10t/s})$, 1.50 A $- (0.250$ A$)e^{-10t/s}$

41. (a) 5.66 ms   (b) 1.22 A   (c) 58.1 ms

43. 2.44 μJ

45. 44.2 nJ/m^3 for the $\vec{\mathbf{E}}$ field and 995 μJ/m^3 for the $\vec{\mathbf{B}}$ field

47. (a) 2.93 mT up   (b) 3.42 Pa   (c) clockwise (d) up   (e) 1.30 mN

49. -7.22 mV $\cos(2\pi 523\ t/s)$

51. $\sim 10^{-4}$ V, by reversing a 20-turn coil of diameter 3 cm in 0.1 s in a field of 10^{-3} T

53. (a) 254 km/s   (b) 215 V
55. 6.00 A
59. $(-87.1 \text{ mV}) \cos(200\pi t + \phi)$
61. (a) $L \approx (\pi/2)N^2\mu_0 R$ (b) ~100 nH   (c) ~1 ns
63. $3.97 \times 10^{-25} \ \Omega$
65. (a) 50.0 mT   (b) 20.0 mT   (c) 2.29 MJ
    (d) 318 Pa

Context 7 Conclusion

1. 5.56 Hz
2. Both are correct.

Chapter 24

1. 1.85 aT up
3. $(-2.87\hat{\mathbf{j}} + 5.75\hat{\mathbf{k}}) \ \text{Gm/s}^2$
5. 2.25×10^8 m/s
7. (a) 6.00 MHz   (b) $(-73.3\hat{\mathbf{k}})$ nT
    (c) $\vec{\mathbf{B}} = [(-73.3\hat{\mathbf{k}}) \text{ nT}] \cos(0.126x - 3.77 \times 10^7 t)$
11. 2.9×10^8 m/s $\pm 5\%$
13. (c) 2.00 kHz   (d) $\pm 0.075\ 0$ m/s ≈ 0.2 mi/h
15. $0.220c = 6.59 \times 10^7$ m/s
17. 608 pF
19. (a) 503 Hz   (b) 12.0 μC   (c) 37.9 mA   (d) 72.0 μJ
21. 307 μW/m^2
23. 3.33×10^3 m^2
25. (a) 332 kW/m^2 radially inward
    (b) 1.88 kV/m and 222 μT
27. 5.16 m
29. (a) 1.90 kN/C   (b) 50.0 pJ   (c) 1.67×10^{-19} kg·m/s
31. The radio audience hears it 8.41 ms sooner.
33. 545 THz
35. (a) 6.00 pm   (b) 7.50 cm
37. 56.2 m
39. (a) 0.690 wavelengths   (b) 58.9 wavelengths
41. (a) 54.7°   (b) 63.4°   (c) 71.6°
45. $\frac{1}{8}$
49. (a) 4.24 PW/m^2 (b) 1.20 pJ = 7.50 MeV
51. 3.49×10^{16} photons
53. (a) three: 632.808 57 nm, 632.809 14 nm, and 632.809 71 nm   (b) 697 m/s   (c) For an atom moving away from the observer at the rms speed, the wavelength is increased by 0.001 47 nm. For an approaching atom, the wavelength is decreased by this amount. Many atoms are moving at speeds higher than the rms speed.
55. (a) 3.85×10^{26} W   (b) 1.02 kV/m and 3.39 μT
57. (a) $2\pi^2 r^2 f B_{max} \cos\theta$, where θ is the angle between the magnetic field and the normal to the loop
    (b) The loop should be in the vertical plane containing the line of sight to the transmitter.
59. (a) 6.67×10^{-16} T   (b) 5.31×10^{-17} W/m^2
    (c) 1.67×10^{-14} W   (d) 5.56×10^{-23} N
61. 95.1 mV/m

63. (a) 625 kW/m^2 (b) 21.7 kN/C, 72.4 μT
    (c) 17.8 min
65. (b) 17.6 Tm/s^2, 1.75×10^{-27} W   (c) 1.80×10^{-24} W
67. (a) 388 K   (b) 363 K
69. (a) 22.6 h   (b) 30.6 s

Chapter 25

1. (a) 1.94 m   (b) 50.0° above the horizontal
3. six times from the mirror on the left and five times from the mirror on the right
5. 15.4°; 2.56 m
7. 19.5° above the horizon
9. (a) 2.0×10^8 m/s   (b) 474 THz   (c) 4.2×10^{-7} m
11. (a) 181 Mm/s   (b) 225 Mm/s   (c) 136 Mm/s
13. 30.0° and 19.5° at entry; 19.5° and 30.0° at exit
15. $\tan^{-1} n$
17. 3.88 mm
19. 30.4° and 22.3°
21. $\sim 10^{-11}$ s; between 10^3 and 10^4 wavelengths
23. 0.171°
25. 27.9°
27. 4.61°
29. (a) 24.4°   (b) 37.0°   (c) 49.8°
31. 1.000 08
33. 67.2°
35. 82 reflections
37. 23.1°
39. (a) $\frac{h}{c}\left(\frac{n+1.00}{2}\right)$ (b) $\left(\frac{n+1.00}{2}\right)$ times longer
41. 2.27 m
43. (a) 0.172 mm/s   (b) 0.345 mm/s   (c) northward at 50.0° below the horizontal   (d) northward at 50.0° below the horizontal
45. 62.2%
47. (a) $0.042\ 6 = 4.26\%$ (b) no difference
49. 70.6%
51. 27.5°
53. (a) It always happens.   (b) 30.3°   (c) It cannot happen.
55. 2.36 cm
57. 1.93
59. (a) 1.20   (b) 3.40 ns

Chapter 26

1. $\sim 10^{-9}$ s younger
3. 35.0 in.
5. 10.0 ft, 30.0 ft, 40.0 ft
7. (a) 13.3 cm, real and inverted, -0.333 (b) 20.0 cm, real and inverted, -1.00 (c) No image is formed.
9. (a) -12.0 cm; 0.400   (b) -15.0 cm; 0.250
    (c) upright

11. (a) $q = 45.0$ cm; $M = -0.500$ (b) $q = -60.0$ cm; $M = 3.00$ (c) Image (a) is real, inverted, and diminished. Image (b) is virtual, upright, and enlarged.

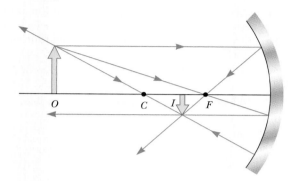

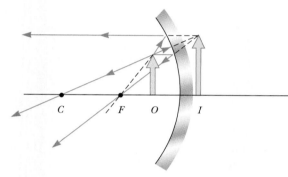

13. At 0.708 cm in front of the reflecting surface. Image is virtual, upright, and diminished.

15. 7.90 mm

17. (a) a concave mirror with radius of curvature 2.08 m (b) 1.25 m from the object

19. (a) 25.6 m (b) 0.058 7 rad (c) 2.51 m (d) 0.023 9 rad (e) 62.8 m from your eyes

21. 38.2 cm below the top surface of the ice

23. 8.57 cm

25. (a) 45.0 cm (b) -90.0 cm (c) -6.00 cm

27. (a) 16.4 cm (b) 16.4 cm

29. (a) 650 cm from the lens on the opposite side from the object; real, inverted, enlarged (b) 600 cm from the lens on the same side as the object; virtual, upright, enlarged

31. 2.84 cm

35. (a) -12.3 cm, to the left of the lens (b) 0.615 (c)

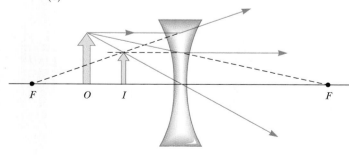

37. 1.16 mm/s toward the lens

39. (a) $p = \dfrac{d}{2} \pm \sqrt{\dfrac{d^2}{4} - fd}$ (b) Both images are real and inverted. One is enlarged, the other diminished.

41. (a) 0.833 mm (b) 0.820 mm

43. $f = \dfrac{-Md}{(1 - M)^2}$ if $M < 1$, $f = \dfrac{Md}{(M - 1)^2}$ if $M > 1$

45. -25.0 cm

47. (a) 67.5 cm (b) The lenses can be displaced in two ways. The first lens can be displaced 1.28 cm farther away from the object and the second lens 17.7 cm toward the object. Alternatively, the first lens can be displaced 0.927 cm toward the object and the second lens 4.44 cm toward the object.

49. 0.107 m to the right of the vertex of the hemispherical face

51. 8.00 cm

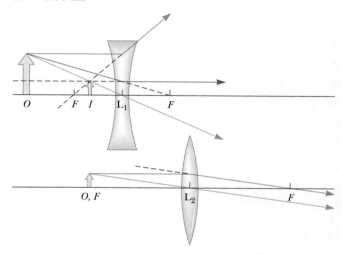

53. 1.50 m in front of the mirror; 1.40 cm (inverted)

55. (a) 30.0 cm and 120 cm (b) 24.0 cm (c) real, inverted, diminished with $M = -0.250$

57. (a) 263 cm (b) 79.0 cm

59. The image is real, inverted, and actual size.

Chapter 27

1. 515 nm

3. (a) 55.7 m (b) 124 m

5. 1.54 mm

7. 641

9. (a) 13.2 rad (b) 6.28 rad (c) 0.012 7° (d) 0.059 7°

11. 48.0 μm

13. 0.968

15. (a) green (b) violet

17. 96.2 m

19. 4.35 μm

21. 0.230 mm

23. 91.2 cm

25. 51.8 μm wide and 949 μm high

27. 3.09 m
29. 13.1 m
31. 105 m
33. 5.91° in first order, 13.2° in second order, 26.5° in third order
35. (a) 5 orders (b) 10 orders in the short-wavelength region
37. three, at 0° and at 45.2° to the right and left
39. 14.4°
41. (a) 0.738 mm (b) Individual waves from all the transparent zones will add crest-on-crest to interfere constructively at the slit images. The grating equation $d \sin \theta = m\lambda$ is satisfied at the slit images. Elsewhere on the screen destructive interference will prevent light from reaching the screen.
43. number of antinodes = number of constructive interference zones = 1 plus 2 times the greatest positive integer $\le d/\lambda$; number of nodes = number of destructive interference zones = 2 times the greatest positive integer $< (d/\lambda + \frac{1}{2})$
45. $20.0 \times 10^{-6}\,°C^{-1}$
47. 2.50 mm
49. 113 dark fringes
53. 632.8 nm
55. (a) 25.6° (b) 19.0°
57. (a) $3.53 \times 10^3\,cm^{-1}$ (b) 11
59. $4.58\,\mu m < d < 5.23\,\mu m$

Context 8 Conclusion

1. 130 nm
2. 74.2 grooves/mm
3. 1.8 μm/bit
4. 48 059
5. $\sim 10^8\,W/m^2$

Chapter 28

1. 1.69%
3. About 5 200 K. A firefly cannot be at this temperature, so its light cannot be blackbody radiation.
5. 2.27×10^{30} photons/s
7. 1.32×10^{31}
9. (a) 296 nm, 1.01 PHz (b) 2.71 V
11. (a) 1.90 eV (b) 0.216 V
13. 8.41 pC
15. (a) 488 fm (b) 268 keV (c) 31.5 keV
17. 70.0°
19. By this definition, ionizing radiation is the ultraviolet light, x-rays and γ rays with wavelength shorter than 124 nm; that is, with frequency higher than 2.41×10^{15} Hz.
21. (a) 0.709 nm (b) 414 nm
23. (a) ~100 MeV or more (b) No. With kinetic energy much larger than the magnitude of its negative electric

potential energy, the electron would immediately escape.
25. (a) 14.9 keV (b) 124 keV
29. (a) 993 nm (b) 4.96 mm (c) If its detection forms part of an interference pattern, the neutron must have passed through both slits. If we test to see which slit a particular neutron passes through, it will not form part of the interference pattern.
31. within 1.16 mm for the electron, 5.28×10^{-32} m for the bullet
33. 3.79×10^{28} m, 190 times the diameter of the visible Universe
35. (b) 519 am
37. (a) 126 pm (b) $5.27 \times 10^{-24}\,kg \cdot m/s$ (c) 95.5 eV
39. (a)

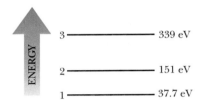

(b) 2.20 nm, 2.75 nm, 4.12 nm, 4.71 nm, 6.60 nm, 11.0 nm
41. (a) $(15h\lambda/8m_ec)^{1/2}$ (b) 1.25λ
45. (a) L/2 (b) 5.26×10^{-5} (c) 3.99×10^{-2} (d) The probability density has peaks around L/4 and 3L/4, and a zero at L/2. Because the probability density is symmetric about L/2, the average experimental value has to be L/2.
47. 0.250
49. (a) 0.010 3 (b) 0.990
51. 85.9
53. (a) 1.06 mm (b) microwave
55. length 0.333 m, radius 19.8 μm
57. (a)

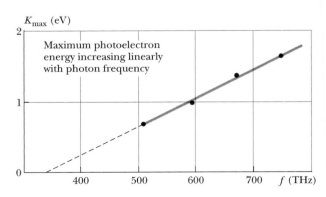

(b) $6.4 \times 10^{-34}\,J \cdot s \pm 8\%$ (c) 1.4
59. (a) 2.82×10^{-37} m (b) 1.06×10^{-32} J (c) 2.87×10^{-35} % or more

61.

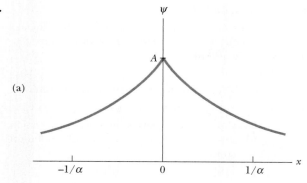

(a)

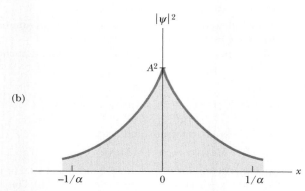

(b)

(c) The wave function is continuous. It shows localization by approaching zero as $x \rightarrow \pm \infty$. It is everywhere finite and can be normalized.　(d) $A = \sqrt{\alpha}$　(e) 0.632

65. (a)

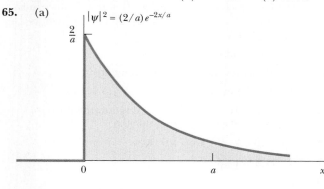

$|\psi|^2 = (2/a)e^{-2x/a}$

(b) 0　(c) 0.865

Chapter 29

1. (b) 0.846 ns

3. (a) 2.89×10^{34} kg·m²/s　(b) 2.74×10^{68}
(a) 7.30×10^{-69}

5. (a) 1.89 eV, 656 nm　(b) 3.40 eV, 365 nm

7. (a) 1.31 μm　(b) 164 nm

9. (a) $\Delta p \geq \hbar/2r$　(b) Choosing $p \approx \hbar/r$, we find that $E = K + U = \hbar^2/2m_e r^2 - k_e e^2/r$.
(c) $r = \hbar^2/m_e k_e e^2 = a_0$ and $E = -13.6$ eV, in agreement with the Bohr theory

11. (b) 0.497

13. It does, with $E = -k_e e^2/2a_0$.

15. (a)

n	ℓ	m_ℓ	m_s
3	2	2	$\frac{1}{2}$
3	2	2	$-\frac{1}{2}$
3	2	1	$\frac{1}{2}$
3	2	1	$-\frac{1}{2}$
3	2	0	$\frac{1}{2}$
3	2	0	$-\frac{1}{2}$
3	2	-1	$\frac{1}{2}$
3	2	-1	$-\frac{1}{2}$
3	2	-2	$\frac{1}{2}$
3	2	-2	$-\frac{1}{2}$

(b)

n	ℓ	m_ℓ	m_s
3	1	1	$\frac{1}{2}$
3	1	1	$-\frac{1}{2}$
3	1	0	$\frac{1}{2}$
3	1	0	$-\frac{1}{2}$
3	1	-1	$\frac{1}{2}$
3	1	-1	$-\frac{1}{2}$

17. $\ell = 4$

19. (a) 2　(b) 8　(c) 18　(d) 32　(e) 50

21. (a) 3.99×10^{17} kg/m³　(b) 81.7 am　(c) 1.77 Tm/s
(d) $5.91 \times 10^3 c$

23. $n = 3$; $\ell = 2$; $m_\ell = -2, -1, 0, 1,$ or 2; $s = 1$; $m_s = -1,$ 0, or 1, for a total of 15 states

25. The 4s subshell is filled first. We would expect $[Ar]3d^4 4s^2$ to have lower energy, but $[Ar]3d^5 4s^1$ has more unpaired spins and lower energy according to Hund's rule. It is the ground-state configuration of chromium.

27. aluminum

29. (a) 1s, 2s, 2p, 3s, 3p, 4s, 3d, 4p, 5s, 4d, 5p, 6s, 4f, 5d, 6p, 7s
(b) Element 15 should have valence +5 or -3, and it does. Element 47 should have valence -1, but it has valence +1. Element 86 should be inert, and it is.

31. 18.4 T

33. 124 V

35. 0.072 5 nm

37. iron

41. (a) 0.160c　(b) 2.82×10^9 ly

43. (a) 609 μeV　(b) 6.9 μeV　(c) 147 GHz, 2.04 mm

47. The classical frequency is $4\pi^2 m_e k_e^2 e^4/h^3 n^3$.

49. (a) 1.57×10^{14} m$^{-3/2}$　(b) 2.47×10^{28} m^{-3}
(c) 8.69×10^8 m^{-1}

51. $3h^2/4mL^2$

55. 5.39 keV

57. 0.125

59. 9.79 GHz

61. (a) $\sim -10^6$ m/s²　(b) ~1 m

Chapter 30

1. $\sim 10^{28}$; $\sim 10^{28}$; $\sim 10^{28}$

3. (a) 29.5 fm   (b) 5.18 fm   (c) The wavelength is much less than the distance of closest approach.

5. 16.0 km

7. (a) 29.2 MHz   (b) 42.6 MHz   (c) 2.13 kHz

9. greater for $^{15}_{7}$N by 3.54 MeV

11. 200 MeV

13. (a) 1.55×10^{-5}/s, 12.4 h   (b) 2.39×10^{13} atoms
    (c) 1.88 mCi

15. 86.4 h

17. 2.66 d

19. 4.27 MeV

21. 9.96×10^{3} yr

23. (a) $e^{-} + p \rightarrow n + \nu$
    (b) $^{15}_{8}$O atom $\rightarrow$ $^{15}_{7}$N atom $+ \nu$ (c) 2.75 MeV

25. (a) 148 Bq/m^3 (b) 7.05×10^{7} atoms/m^3
    (c) 2.17×10^{-17}

27. (a) $^{197}_{79}$Au $+$ $^{1}_{0}$n $\rightarrow$ $^{198}_{80}$Hg $+$ $^{0}_{-1}$e $+ \bar{\nu}$
    (b) 7.89 MeV

29. 5.80 Mm

31. about 3 000 yr

33. 3.60×10^{38} protons/s

35. (b) 26.7 MeV

37. (a) 8×10^{4} eV   (b) 4.62 MeV and 13.9 MeV
    (c) 1.03×10^{7} kWh

39. (a) 5.70 MeV   (b) exothermic; 3.27 MeV

41. (b) 1.53 MeV

43. (a) conservation of energy   (b) electric potential energy of the nucleus   (c) 1.20 MeV

45. (b) 1.94 meV

47. (a) $\sim 10^{-1356}$ (b) 0.891

49. (b) 4.78 MeV

51. 1.66×10^{3} yr

53. (a) 0.963 mm   (b) It increases by 7.47%

55. (b) R/λ

57. 2.56×10^{4} kg

59. (a) 2.65 GJ   (b) The fusion energy is 78.0 times larger.

61. (a) 15.5 cm   (b) 51.7 MeV   (c) The number of decays per second is the decay rate R, and the energy released in each decay is Q. Then the energy released per unit time interval is $\mathcal{P} = QR$.   (d) 227 kJ/yr
    (e) 3.18 J/yr

63. (a) 422 MBq   (b) 153 ng

Chapter 31

1. 453 ZHz; 662 am

3. (a) 558 TJ   (b) 2.17×10^{7}

5. 118 MeV

7. $\sim 10^{-18}$ m

9. 67.5 MeV, 67.5 MeV/c, 16.3 ZHz

11. (a) 0.782 MeV   (b) $v_e = 0.919c$, $v_p = 380$ km/s
    (c) The electron is relativistic; the proton is not.

13. $\Omega^{+} \rightarrow \overline{\Lambda}^{0} + K^{+}$, $\overline{K}_{S}^{0} \rightarrow \pi^{+} + \pi^{-}$, $\overline{\Lambda}^{0} \rightarrow \overline{p} + \pi^{+}$,
    $\overline{n} \rightarrow \overline{p} + e^{+} + \nu_{e}$

15. (b) The second violates strangeness conservation.

17. (a) $\overline{\nu}_{\mu}$ (b) ν_{μ} (c) $\overline{\nu}_{e}$ (d) ν_{e} (e) ν_{μ} (f) $\overline{\nu}_{e} + \nu_{\mu}$

19. (a), (c), and (f) violate baryon number conservation.
    (b), (d), and (e) can occur. (f) violates muon-lepton number conservation.

21. (a) ν_{e} (b) ν_{μ} (c) $\overline{\nu}_{\mu}$ (d) $\nu_{\mu} + \overline{\nu}_{\tau}$

23. (b) and (c) conserve strangeness. (a), (d), (e), and (f) violate strangeness conservation.

25. (a) not allowed; violates conservation of baryon number
    (b) strong interaction   (c) weak interaction
    (d) weak interaction   (e) electromagnetic interaction

27. (a) K^{+} (b) Ξ^{0} (c) π^{0}

29. 9.26 cm

31. (a) 3.34×10^{26} e^{-}, 9.36×10^{26} u, 8.70×10^{26} d
    (b) $\sim 10^{28}$ e^{-}, $\sim 10^{29}$ u, $\sim 10^{29}$ d. You have zero strangeness, charm, truth, and beauty.

33. $m_{\mathrm{u}} = 312$ MeV/c^2, $m_{\mathrm{d}} = 314$ MeV/c^2

35. (a) The reaction $\overline{u}d + uud \rightarrow \overline{s}d + uds$ has a total of 1 u, 2 d, and 0 s quarks originally and finally.   (b) The reaction $\overline{d}u + uud \rightarrow \overline{s}u + uus$ has a net of 3 u, 0 d, and 0 s before and after.   (c) $\overline{u}s + uud \rightarrow \overline{s}u + \overline{s}d + sss$ shows conservation at 1 u, 1 d, and 1 s quark.
    (d) The process $uud + uud \rightarrow \overline{s}d + uud + \overline{d}u + uds$ nets 4 u, 2 d, and 0 s initially and finally; the mystery particle is a Λ^{0} or a Σ^{0}.

37. a neutron, udd

39. (a) $-e$, antiproton   (b) 0, antineutron

41. (a) 590.07 nm   (b) 597 nm   (c) 661 nm

43. (a) 8.41×10^{6} kg   (b) No. It is only the fraction 4.23×10^{-24} of the mass of the Sun.

45. (a) $\sim 10^{13}$ K   (b) $\sim 10^{10}$ K

47. (b) 11.8 Gyr

49. $\sim 10^{14}$

51. one part in 50 000 000

53. 0.407%

55. 5.35 MeV and 32.3 MeV

57. 1 116 MeV/c^2

59. 70.4 MeV

61. 2.52×10^{3} K

63. (a) Z^{0} boson   (b) gluon or photon

65. (a) 127 MeV   (b) 1.06 mm   (c) 1.17 meV
    (d) 58.1 EeV

Context 9 Conclusion

1. (a) 1.61×10^{-35} m   (b) 5.38×10^{-44} s   (c) yes

Credits

Photographs

This page constitutes an extension of the copyright page. We have made every effort to trace the ownership of all copyrighted material and to secure permission from copyright holders. In the event of any question arising as to the use of any material, we will be pleased to make the necessary corrections in future printings. Thanks are due to the following authors, publishers, and agents for permission to use the material indicated.

Invitation.   **1:** © Stockbyte **3:** © David Parker Photo Researchers, Inc.

Chapter 1.   **4:** Mark Wagner/Stone/Getty Images **6:** Courtesy of National Institute of Standards and Technology, U.S. Department of Commerce **10:** Phil Boorman/Getty Images **14:** Mack Henley/Visuals Unlimited

Context 1.   **34:** Courtesy of The Exhibition Alliance, Hamilton, N.Y. **35:** top left, © Bettmann/CORBIS; bottom right, © Martin Bond/Photo Researchers, Inc. **36:** © Mehau Kulyk/ Photo Researchers, Inc.

Chapter 2.   **37:** Jean Y. Ruszniewski/Getty Images **56:** top left, North Wind Picture Archive; bottom, © 1993 James Sugar/Black Star **57:** George Semple **60:** George Lepp/ Stone/Getty **66:** top left, Courtesy of the U.S. Air Force; top right, Photri, Inc., **67:** Courtesy Amtrak NEC Media Relations

Chapter 3.   **69:** © Arndt/Premium Stock/PictureQuest **74:** © The Telegraph Colour Library/Getty Images **79:** Tony Duffy/Getty Images **89:** Frederick McKinney/FPG/Getty **90:** top left, Jed Jacobsohn/Getty Images; middle left, Bill Lee/Dembinsky Photo Associates; bottom left, Sam Sargent/ Liaison International **91:** Courtesy of NASA **92:** Courtesy of NASA

Chapter 4.   **96:** Steve Raymer/CORBIS **99:** Giraudon/Art Source **104:** NASA **105:** top right, John Gillmoure, The Stock Market **116:** Roger Viollet, Mill Valley, CA, University Science Books, 1982 **118:** © Tony Arruza/CORBIS

Chapter 5.   **125:** Paul Hardy/CORBIS **134:** top, Robin Smith/Getty Images; bottom left, © Tom Carroll/Index Stock Imagery/Picture Quest **143:** Jump Run Productions/Image Bank **146:** a) Courtesy of GM; b) Courtesy of GM-Hummer **148:** Mike Powell/Getty Images **150:** Frank Cezus/FPG International

Chapter 6.   **156:** Billy Hustace/Getty Images **170:** a–c, e, f) George Semple; d) Digital Vision/Getty Images **172:** Sinclair Stammers/Science Photo Library/Photo Researchers, Inc. **185:** Ron Chapple/FPG/Getty

Chapter 7.   **188:** © Harold E. Edgerton/Courtesy of Palm Press, Inc. **213:** Gamma **219:** Engraving from Scientific American, July 1888

Context Conclusion 1.   **220:** Courtesy of Honda Motor Co., Inc **222:** top left, Photo by Brent Romans/www.Edmunds.com; bottom left, © Adam Hart-Davis/Photo Researchers, Inc.

Context 2.   **223:** Japanese Aerospace Exploration Agency (JAXA) **224:** top, courtesy of NASA/JPL; bottom, Courtesy of NASA/JPL/Cornell **225:** Pierre Mion/National Geographic Image Collection

Chapter 8.   **226:** © Harold and Esther Edgerton Foundation 2002, courtesy of Palm Press, Inc. **232:** Courtesy of Saab **233:** Tim Wright/CORBIS **246:** Richard Megna, Fundamental Photographs **251:** © Bill Stormont/The Stock Market

Chapter 9.   **259:** Emily Serway **262:** AIP Emilio Segré Visual Archives, Michelson Collection **264:** AIP Niels Bohr Library **288:** Courtesy of Garmin Ltd.

Chapter 10.   **291:** Courtesy of Tourism Malaysia **317:** top left, © Stuart Franklin/Getty Images; bottom, David Malin, Anglo-Australian Observatory **320:** Courtesy of Henry Leap and Jim Lehman **327:** John Lawrence/Stone/Getty Images

Chapter 11.   **337:** © 1987 Royal Observatory/Anglo-Australian Observatory, by David F. Mahlin from U.K. Schmidt plates **342:** Art Resource **346:** U.S. Space Command, NORAD **350:** bottom, H. Ford et al. & NASA **352:** K. W. Whitten, R. E. Davis, M. L. Peck, and G. G. Stanley, General Chemistry, 7th ed., Belmont, CA, Brooks/Cole, 2004 **353:** Photo courtesy of AIP Niels Bohr Library, Margarethe Bohr Collection **361:** Courtesy of NASA/JPL **365:** NASA

Context Conclusion 3.   **371:** top right, Guillermo Aldana Espinosa/National Geographic Image Collection; bottom right, Joseph Sohm/ChromoSohm Inc./CORBIS **372:** T. Campion/SYGMA

Chapter 12.   **373:** © Simon Kwong/Reuters/CORBIS **390:** Special Collections Division, Univ. of Wash. Libraries, Photo by Farquharson **394:** Telegraph Colour Library/FPG International

Chapter 24. **806:** upper left, NASA/CXC/SAO; upper right, Palomar Observatory; lower right, VLA/NRAO; lower left, WM Keck Observatory **808:** North Wind Picture Archives **815:** The Bettman Archive/CORBIS **823:** Ron Chapple/Getty Images **828:** Courtesy of Mark Helfer/National Institute of Standards and Technology **831:** George Semple **832:** Trent Steffler/David R. Frazier Photo Library **835:** Philippe Plaily/SPL/Photo Researchers **836:** Amos Morgan/Getty Images **837:** © Bill Banaszewski/Visuals Unlimited

Chapter 25. **839:** Patrick J. Endres/Visuals Unlimited **842:** c,d) Courtesy of Henry Leap and Jim Lehman **843:** David Parker/Photo Researchers, Inc. **844:** a,b) Courtesy of Texas Instruments **845:** top, Courtesy of Henry Leap and Jim Lehman; bottom, Jim Lehman **850:** David Parker/Science Photo Library/Photo Researchers, Inc. **852:** top left, Courtesy of Rijksmuseum voor de Geschiedenis der Natuurwetenschappen. Courtesy of Niels Bohr Library; middle left, Erich Schrempp/Photo Researchers, Inc. **854:** Courtesy of Henry Leap and Jim Lehman **856:** Dennis O'Clair/Stone/Getty Images **861:** Courtesy of Sony Disc Manufacturing **862:** Ray Atkeson/Image Archive **863:** Courtesy of Edwin Lo

Chapter 26. **867:** © Don Hammond/CORBIS **869:** George Semple **872:** Henry Leap and Jim Lehman **873:** Courtesy of Thompson Consumer Electronics **875:** Photos courtesy of David Rogers **876:** top, © Bo Zaunders/CORBIS; bottom, NASA **881:** Courtesy of Henry Leap and Jim Lehman **886:** Courtesy of Henry Leap and Jim Lehman **890:** Richard Megna/Fundamental Photographs, NYC **891:** M. C. Escher/Cordon Art–Baarn–Holland. All rights reserved. **892:** © Paul Silverman 1990, Fundamental Photographs **896:** © Michael Levin/Optigone Associates

Chapter 27. **898:** Dr. Jeremy Burgess/SPL/Photo Researchers, Inc. **900:** M. Cagnet, M. Francon, J.C. Thierr, *Atlas of Optical Phenomena,* Berlin, Springer-Verlag, 1962 **904:** From M. Cagnet, M. Francon, and J.C. Thierr, *Atlas of Optical Phenomena,* Berlin, Springer-Verlag, 1962 **908:** top, Kristen Brochmann/Fundamental Photographs; bottom, Richard Megna/Fundamental Photographs **909:** top right, Douglas C. Johnson/Cal Poly Pomona; middle right, Courtesy of P. M. Rinard, from *Am. J. Phys.* 44: 70, 1976; bottom, From M. Cagnet, M. Francon, and J.C. Thierr, *Atlas of Optical Phenomena,* Berlin, Springer-Verlag, 1962, plate 18 **913:** From M. Cagnet, M. Francon, J.C. Thierr, *Atlas of Optical Phenomena,* Berlin, Springer-Verlag, 1962 **915:** a, U.S. Naval Observatory/James W. Christy, U.S. Navy photograph; b, Photo courtesy of Gemini Observatory **917:** Silicon Light Machines **918:** © Kristen Brochmann/Fundamental Photographs **919:** a, Used with permission of Eastman Kodak Company; b, © I. Anderson, Oxford Molecular Biophysics Laboratory/Photo Researchers, Inc. **920:** Ronald Erickson/Media Interface **926:** SuperStock **927:** Courtesy of CENCO Scientific Company **928:** bottom left, © Doug Pensinger/Getty Images; right, © Danny Lehman **929:** © Richard Kolar/Animals Animals/Earth Scenes

Context 8 Conclusion. **932:** Courtesy of University of Miami, Music Engineering

Context 9 Opener. **935:** top right, Comstock Royalty Free/Getty; bottom, 1987 Anglo-Australian Observatory, photo by David Malin **936:** NASA, ESA, and The Hubble Heritage Team

Chapter 28. **937:** © Eye of Science/Science Source/Photo Researchers, Inc. **938:** Corbis **939:** © Bettmann/CORBIS **940:** left, Photodisc/Getty Images; right, John Chumack/Photo Researchers, Inc. **947:** Courtesy of AIP Niels Bohr Library **950:** AIP Niels Bohr Library **953:** © David Parker/Photo Researchers, Inc. **958:** a–d, From C. Jonsson, *Zeitschrift fur Physik* 161:454, 1961; used with permission Springer-Verlag **959:** Courtesy of the University of Hamburg **967:** AIP Emilio Segré Visual Archives **969:** IBM Research, Almaden Research Center. Unauthorized use prohibited **976:** a–b, Alexandra Héder

Chapter 29. **983:** © Jeff Hunter/Image Bank/Getty Images **995:** Courtesy of AIP Niels Bohr Library, Margarethe Bohr Collection **998:** AIP Emilio Segré Visual Archives, Goudsmit Collection **1007:** a, C. R. O'Dell (Rice University) and NASA; b, © 1985 Royal Observatory Edinburgh/Anglo-Australian Observatory by David Malin; c, A. Caulet (ST-ECF, ESA) and NASA **1013:** Maarten Schmidt/Palomar Observatory/California Institute of Technology

Chapter 30. **1016:** Paul Hanny/Gamma Liaison **1023:** SBHA/Getty Images **1025:** FPG International **1033:** middle right, © CORBIS; bottom left, Corbis SYGMA; bottom right, M. Milner/Corbis SYGMA **1046:** Courtesy of NASA Ames

Chapter 31. **1048:** Courtesy of CERN **1051:** top left, Courtesy Lawrence Berkeley Laboratory, University of California; middle right, Courtesy of AIP Emilio Segré Visual Archives **1052:** National Institutes of Health **1053:** UPI/Corbis-Bettmann **1054:** © Shelly Gazin/CORBIS **1059:** Courtesy of ICRR (Institute for Cosmic Ray Research), University of Tokyo **1062:** Courtesy Lawrence Berkeley Laboratory, University of California, Photographic Services **1063:** AIP Meggers Gallery of Nobel Laureates **1064:** Courtesy of Brookhaven National Laboratory **1071:** Courtesy of CERN **1072:** Courtesy of Fermi National Accelerator Laboratory **1081:** Anglo-Australian Telescope Board

Tables and Illustrations

This page constitutes an extension of the copyright page. We have made every effort to trace the ownership of all copyrighted material and to secure permission from copyright holders. In the event of any question arising as to the use of any material, we will be pleased to make the necessary corrections in future printings. Thanks are due to the following authors, publishers, and agents for permission to use the material indicated.

Chapter 1. **33:** By permission of John L. Hart FLP, and Creators Syndicate, Inc.

Chapter 11. **363:** By permission of John L. Hart FLP, and Creators Syndicate, Inc.

4 4

4 4

Chapter 14. **452:** Adapted from C. A. Culver, *Musical Acoustics,* 4th Edition, New York, McGraw-Hill, 1956, p. 128. **453:** Adapted from C. A. Culver, Musical Acoustic, 4th Edition, New York, McGraw-Hill, 1956.

Chapter 26. **893:** The Far Side ® by Gary Larson © 1985 FarWorks, Inc. All rights reserved. Used with permission.

Chapter 29. **989:** From E. U. Condon and G. H. Shortley, *The Theory of Atomic Spectra,* Cambridge, Cambridge University Press, 1953, used with permission.

Index

Page numbers in *italics* indicate figures; page numbers followed by "n" indicate footnotes; page numbers followed by "t" indicate tables.

Radioactive nucleus, 971–972
Radioactive process(es), 1039
Radioactivity, 1016, 1025–1028
   lead shielding from, 1045
   of radium-226, 1028
   unit of activity in, 1027
Radio-frequency radiation, 1023
Radio-frequency wave(s), 806
Radium, activity of, 1028
   discovery of, 1025
Radium-226, alpha decay of, *1030*
   energy liberated in, 1030
Radon, 1042
Rail guns, 764
Rainbow, double, 851
   formation of, *851*
   light rays in, 850
   secondary, *839*
Rainbow hologram, 921
Raindrop(s), light entering, 851
   light rays passing through, *867*
Ramp, crate sliding down, 198
Rare-earth magnets, 753
Rarefactions, 415
Ray approximation, 841–842, 858
Ray diagram(s), 868
   for flat mirror, 868
   for spherical mirrors, 873–876
   for thin lenses, 883–886
Ray model, 841–842
Rayleigh wave, 422, 424
Rayleigh's criterion, 913, 922
RC circuit(s), 708–712, 714, 782
   charging capacitor in, 708–710, 712
   discharging capacitor in, 710–712, 808
   in roadway construction flasher, *711*
Reaction energy, 1039
   in nuclear reaction, 1036
Reaction force, 104–106, 107, 226
Rearview mirror, daytime and nighttime
      settings of, *870*
Reasonable values, 6
Rectangular coordinate system, 13
Rectangular loop, induced emf in, 772
Red shift, 813, 832–833, *1075*
Reference clock, 6
Reference frames, absolute, 262
   inertial, 99, 115
   noninertial, 99
   time measurement and, 264
Reflected ray(s), *843, 844*
Reflection, angle of, 843
   images formed by, 867
      in flat mirror, 868–870
   law of, 843, 852–853, 858
   mechanical wave, 411–413
   phase change due to, 904–905
   total internal, 853–855
   wave under, 842–845
Reflection nebula(e), *1007,* 1008
Refracting surface(s), curved, 878–879
   in lenses, 881
   sign conventions for, 879t
Refraction, angle of, 845, 850
   images formed by, 867, 878–881
   in material, 845–848
   in prism, 850
   index of, 846, 848, 858, 922
      for various substances, 847t
      of thin film, 906

Refraction *(Continued)*
   of water, 855
   total internal reflection and, 854
   variation of, *850*
   law of, 847–848, 852–853, 858
      of light rays, 870
   wave under, 845–849
Refrigerant fluid, 578n
Refrigerator(s), 578–579
Reines, Frederick, 1032
Relative velocity, 83–85, 87
Relativistic energy, 276–279
Relativistic Heavy Ion Collider (RHIC), 1068
Relativistic momentum, 275–276
Relativistic particle, total energy of, 278
Relativistic wave equation, 1050
Relativity, 259–284. *See also* General relativity;
      Special relativity
   Einstein's principle of, 263–264
   general theory of, 280–283, 284
   in space travel, 283–284
   length contraction and, 269–272
   Lorentz transformation equations and,
      272–275
   Michelson-Morley experiment and,
      262–263
   Newtonian, 259–263
   special theory of, 260, 284
      consequences of, 264–272
   theory of, 2
   time dilation and, 265–269
   twin paradox and, 268–269
Repulsive force(s), 205, 607–608, 728, 788
Repulsive magnetic levitation model,
      787–788
Resistance, color code for determining, *690*
   internal, 699, 700
      in battery, 714
   microscopic origin of, 692–693
   of conductor, 687–690, 714
   of fluid flowing through pipe, 688–689
   of lightbulb filament, 697
   of Nichrome wire, 690
Resistance thermometer, platinum, 691
Resistive force, 147
   magnitude of, 140
   mathematical representation of, 141
   proportional to object speed, 140–142
   proportional to object speed squared,
      142–143
   velocity-dependent, 140–143
Resistivity, 688, 714
   change in with temperature, 691
   for various materials, 689t
   high temperature, 691–692
   microscopic parameters of, 694
Resistor(s), 683, 688
   color code for, 690t
   composition, 690
   energy delivered to, 696–697
   energy transferred to, 786–787
   in electric circuit, 696
   in parallel, 702–705, 705
   in series, 700–701, 703–704
   rule for determining sign of potential
      difference across, 707
   wire-wound, 690
Resolution, limiting angle of, 913
   of single-slit and circular apertures, 912–914
   of telescope, 914

Resonance, 389, 391, 450
   in structures, 390–391
Resonance frequency, 389–390, 817
Resonance particle(s), 1062–1063
Rest energy, 278, 284
   of elementary particles, 1067–1068
   of nucleons, 1023
   transformed to kinetic energy, 1039
Restoring force, 163
Resultant force, 101
Resultant vector, 16
Reversible process(es), 575, 589
   entropy change in, 583
   in Carnot cycle, 577n
Richter, Burton, 1066
Rigel, blue glow of, *940*
Right-hand rule, 294, 766
   for direction of angular momentum vector,
      294
   for direction of area vector, 742
   for direction of magnetic field of long wire,
      744
   for direction of vector product, 304
Rigid object, angular position, speed, and
      acceleration of, 292–294
   definition of, 291
   in equilibrium, 306–309
   modeling of, 23, 293–294
   moment of inertia of, 298–300
   rolling motion of, 320–423
   rotational kinetic energy of, 298–302
   under constant angular acceleration,
      295–296
   under net torque, 309–313
Ring galaxy, *936*
RL circuit(s), 782–785
   current versus time plot for, *782*
   dI/dt versus time plot for, *783*
   emf induced in, *782*
   energy storage in inductor in, *786*
   iron bar inserted into solenoid of, 783–784
   switch positions in, *783*
   time constant of, 783, 784–785, 789
Roadways, switchbacks on, 159–160
Robotic device, laser in, *805*
Rocket propulsion, 248–250
Rod, rotating, 302
Roentgen, Wilhelm, 918
Rogowski coil, 792
Rolling motion, 320–423, 324
Rolling object, translational and rotational
      variables of, 320–321
Rolling sound of thunder, 416–417
Root-mean-square speed, 522
   of gas molecules, 517
   of various gas molecules, 517t
Rosette Nebula, *337*
Rotating ball, 139–140
Rotating bar, motional emf induced in,
      772–773
Rotational equilibrium, 306
Rotational motion, 291, 324, 551, 552–553
   angular momentum and, 313–316
   angular position, speed, and acceleration
      in, 292–294
   conservation of angular momentum in,
      316–319
   dynamic equations of, 315t
   equilibrium and, 306–309
   kinematic equations of, 295–296

Standard Abbreviations and Symbols for Units

Symbol	Unit	Symbol	Unit
A	ampere	K	kelvin
u	atomic mass unit	kg	kilogram
atm	atmosphere	kmol	kilomole
Btu	British thermal unit	L	liter
C	coulomb	lb	pound
°C	degree Celsius	ly	lightyear
cal	calorie	m	meter
d	day	min	minute
eV	electron volt	mol	mole
°F	degree Fahrenheit	N	newton
F	farad	Pa	pascal
ft	foot	rad	radian
G	gauss	rev	revolution
g	gram	s	second
H	henry	T	tesla
h	hour	V	volt
hp	horsepower	W	watt
Hz	hertz	Wb	weber
in.	inch	yr	year
J	joule	Ω	ohm

Mathematical Symbols Used in the Text and Their Meaning

Symbol	Meaning
$=$	is equal to
$\equiv$	is defined as
$\neq$	is not equal to
$\propto$	is proportional to
$\sim$	is on the order of
$>$	is greater than
$<$	is less than
$\gg (\ll)$	is much greater (less) than
$\approx$	is approximately equal to
Δx	the change in x
$\displaystyle\sum_{i=1}^{N} x_i$	the sum of all quantities x_i from $i = 1$ to $i = N$
$\lvert x \rvert$	the magnitude of x (always a nonnegative quantity)
$\Delta x \to 0$	Δx approaches zero
$\dfrac{dx}{dt}$	the derivative of x with respect to t
$\dfrac{\partial x}{\partial t}$	the partial derivative of x with respect to t
$\displaystyle\int$	integral

DATE DUE

~~SEP 25 1971~~		
~~XXXXXX~~		
~~XX X 1973~~		
~~SEP 29 1977~~		
NOV 22 1981 lam		
DEC 14 1981		
MAY 21 1982 mlf		
JUNE 15 Phone		

THE MOUSE

ITS REPRODUCTION AND DEVELOPMENT

by

ROBERTS RUGH, Ph.D.

Radiological Research Laboratories
Radiology Department
College of Physicians and Surgeons
Columbia University

Mrs. Rhoda H. Van Dyke, Chief Illustrator

Burgess Publishing Company

426 South Sixth Street • Minneapolis, Minn. 55415

Other books by the author:

"Experimental Embryology", 1962, Burgess.
"Lab. Man. of Vertebrate Embryology", 1961, Burgess.
"Frog: Its Reproduction and Development", 1953, McGraw-Hill.
"Vertebrate Embryology", 1964, Harcourt, Brace & World.

Preface

This mouse embryology text was inevitable. The authorship was pure chance. During the last 19 years in Radiobiological Research for the Atomic Energy Commission, we have provided control material for hundreds of thousands of mouse embryos and fetuses subjected to X rays. The controls have gradually accumulated until we now have a complete and detailed series of normal embryos, whole and sectioned sagitally, frontally and transversely. Since the early stages of development were found to be particularly radiosensitive, some studies began with fertilization and terminated with the pre-parturition 18-day fetus. A variety of stains and techniques was devised to bring out certain morphological effects, among which the most graphic were probably those in which the skeleton was cleared.

After its initial cleavage the embryo seems to accelerate in divisions and after the onset of organogenesis and differentiation the mosaic of development changes so rapidly that it became imperative that we time the pregnancies very accurately. As it was known that ovulation generally occurs during the night, earlier studies dealt with pregnancies resulting from overnight exposure of females to sexually mature males. The criterion of successful mating was not the vaginal smear but the vaginal plug, a coagulum of semen which causes the sperm to be retained within the female genital tract. But, since a 5 P.M. to 9 A.M. exposure of females introduces a time variable of 16 hours in development, we were forced to shorten the exposure time of the females to 45 minutes, from 8:00 A.M. until 8:45 A.M., and to search for vaginal plugs immediately thereafter. It is now believed that, although ovulation likely occurs between midnight and 2 A.M., a 45 minute period of early morning mating produces embryos of more precisely determined age than those produced by any other technique. Thus the material here presented is based upon studies of the CFI-S mouse under the most rigidly controlled conditions.

The technical preparation of embryos and slides began with Miss Erica Grupp with whom I have published papers in teratology. It was continued energetically with Mrs. Ludmila Skaredoff, who has had years of experience in histopathological laboratories. Much of the data was collected, and certainly most of the actual handling and direct observations on embryos and fetuses was done by Miss Marlis Wohlfromm, and some skeletal data was collected by Miss Lyse Duhamel. Other members of the research staff made important contributions.

Photographs of whole embryos and fetuses, and even of sections, are valuable, but since they are largely two-dimensional, they do not always include certain details. These can be shown only in drawings. Mrs. Rhoda Van Dyke, who has an M.S. in biology, has taught embryology, and is also an accomplished artist, has made practically all of the new drawings for this book. Because she has a first-hand knowledge and understanding of the subject, her drawings are neither rigidly presented nor "touched up" for artistic purposes. They are based on projections of microscopic sections at various magnifications but with all proportions maintained. Since I believe so strongly in accurately illustrated teaching, I have been most fortunate to have Mrs. Van Dyke's assistance.

The question might arise as to why rat development was not included in this book, or a section on abnormalities of mouse development. There are basic differences between mouse and rat development, particularly with respect to time but also with respect to certain organogenies, so that coverage of both within a single volume would be impractical. There are, of course, also minor differences in development among the many species of mice, but the species chosen here is a very satisfactory representative of all. A section on anomalies of development might shift the emphasis from the normal to the abnormal. The vast majority of fertilized mouse eggs develop normally and for the research worker and student of embryology an accurate and detailed description of normal development is most desirable. After all, normality is in itself an exciting revelation. Since I have concerned myself during the last two decades with radiation effects on the mammalian embryo and fetus, a separate treatise on this subject will follow.

As both teaching aids and ready references, particularly for courses in embryology and the research laboratory, I have included a complete bibliography of titles on normal development of the mouse, and a glossary of embryological terms. In a few instances the titles deal with related rodents but are listed because there is no parallel reference on the mouse or because they describe special techniques that would be applicable to the mouse. The completeness of the bibliography is due to the help of Dr. Joan Staats of the Jackson Memorial Laboratory, Bar Harbor, Maine, and Suzanne Kriss of Medlars Service of the National Library of Medicine, Department of Health, Education, and Welfare, Bethesda, Maryland. The glossary is a composite from my other books, corrected and increased from the literature pertaining to the mouse.

As a teacher of embryology I have been dissatisfied with the use of the pig as a representative of the mammals, largely because it is available only after most of the organs have been formed (*i.e.*, 4 mm stage). I believe that the mouse will supplant the pig for teaching purposes within a few years. The mouse may be examined alive and studied from fertilization through cleavage, blastulation, implantation, germ layer development, and organogenesis with a minimum of expense and at any laboratory in the world. It is hoped that this book will be a beginning, a foundation upon which others can build even a more thorough description of the normal development of the mouse.

November 1967   R. R.

Table of Contents

Chapter

INTRODUCTION

The mouse is proving to be a boon to embryological research and hence to a better understanding of normal mammalian embryology. It is available the world around; it is easy to feed, raise, mate and handle; and it has a short gestation period (18 to 21 days) and a long period of reproductive activity (from 2 to about 14 months of age) during which it can produce over 10 litters and 100 offspring. Furthermore, strains or species may be crossed, either naturally or artificially, to produce hybrids that exhibit typical heterosis with longer natural and reproductive lives, healthier and larger litters, and better resistance to disease than most pure bred strains.

The subject chosen as representative of the species is the inbred CFI-S mouse strain. Its members have a life span of $2\frac{1}{2}$ to 3 years, and, if kept at uniform temperature (around 72° F.), with regulated humidity, and protection from drafts and from invasion by common mouse diseases, they will remain healthy in their caged environment for their lifetime. The food is generally a standardized synthetic diet, supplemented during pregnancy and lactation with rolled oats and whole wheat bread. Water must always be available, as it is as important as food for survival. When there is evidence of systemic infection, the drinking water may be treated with an antibiotic such as streptomycin, chloromycin, or tetracycline. Other deterrents to infectious conditions may be neomycin, sulfamerazine, terramycin, tylan (tylocentrartrate), polyotic, piperizine and PRL. Sterilization of cages and drinking bottles should be routine and regular.

Large mice appear to have a longer mean life span than small mice, even within a litter, and hybrids have the longest of all in life span and in survival. The CFI-S as an inbred strain is among the best available in this respect. Genetic constitution therefore plays a part in the life of the mouse.

The production of the CFI-S mouse* used in these embryological studies begins with the young which are delivered by hysterectomy-hysterotomy to become the F_1 axenic generation. After weaning and confirmation of their germfree status, the surgically-acquired young are transferred to a large breeding isolator. The F_1 mice are associated with a defined autochthonous flora, indigenous to the mouse, and are maintained as gnotobiotes. Here they are bred and their offspring, the F_2 gnotobiote generation, is derived. The F_2 mice are in turn transferred in disposable, germfree transporters into breeding rooms where they are maintained and bred under rigidly-controlled, micro-barrier conditions. The food, bedding, and water are sterilized, filter caps control airborne contaminants and technicians observe strict sanitary precautions.

* From Carworth Farms, New City, N. Y. This strain of mouse may be considered as quite representative of most mice, in its embryological development.

These F_2 mice become the breeders of the primary colony producing the F_3 mice. These F_3 primary-colony mice are moved on to become mass production breeding colonies, comprising the F_4 specific-pathogen-free (SPF) generation. Some of the F_3 generation of mice return to the cycle to become the parent generation from which another F_1 generation of axenic mice is derived. In this way colonies of mice with controlled and indigenous flora are provided, giving a uniformity which is so desirable for research. Such mice seem to be an improved product in terms of litter size and health.

Although we cannot simply extrapolate findings from mouse embryos to human embryos or vice versa, there is sufficient similarity in the development of these divergent mammals that findings are at least qualitatively suggestive. When comparable developmental stages of mouse and man are placed side by side, only the well informed can distinguish between them. Moreover, comparison of organ primordia and differentiation in the two forms yields a graph (Otis and Brent 1952) emphasizing the likeness. In summary, then, the accessible, abundant, and prolific mouse provides embryonic material for study of normal development and for basic experimentation leading to more critical and urgent studies on man, with some suggestion as to outcome.

A. GESTATION PERIOD: The gestation period is usually 19 days, although the range, in different strains is 18 to 21 days, with variations occurring even in mice simultaneously mated. The differences are sometimes related to litter size, not to the number of corpora lutea left in the ovary but to the total number (volume) of conceptuses. Apparently the total mass of fetal and placental tissue rather than the number of implants affects the length of the gestation period, so that heavier fetuses are associated with shorter periods. It seems, therefore, that a humoral factor, possibly from the placentae or the fetuses, may regulate the duration of pregnancy. There is some evidence that within a given litter the mean weight of the fetuses and their placentae decreases from the ovarian toward the cervical end of the uterus.

Intrauterine development of all vertebrates falls naturally into three consecutive phases: (1) Primary development from fertilization through germ layer derivation, (2) Basic organogenesis, and (3) Tissue differentiation with functional maturity and organismic integration (through nervous and circulatory systems, primarily). During the first, but more specially the second phase, the embryo is particularly labile so that congenital anomalies can result from extrinsic imposed hazards. The first period in the mouse lasts about 6 days, and the second about 6 more, although some organ systems are not fully differentiated until after birth (*e.g.*, cerebellum, gonads). After about day 13 gross congenital anomalies cannot be imposed because the major organ systems have been developed.

Parturition generally occurs between midnight and 4 A.M. in these nocturnal animals, but may occur at any time. Estrus begins again in 12 to 20 hours, depending upon the time of delivery with respect to the diurnal light cycle. Successful matings can then resume, proving that lactation is not a deterrent to ovulation in the mouse. When a lactating mouse becomes pregnant, however, its gestation period may be up to 2 weeks longer than usual. The extension of the gestation period may also be due to delays in implantation.

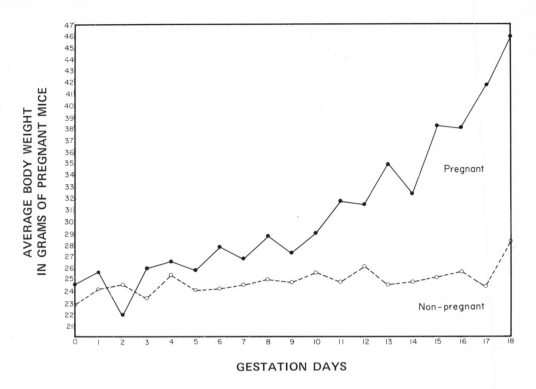

GESTATION DAYS

B. HEMATOLOGICAL AND WEIGHT CHANGES DURING NORMAL PREG-NANCY IN THE MOUSE:

A detailed study of 15 pregnant mice tested daily for blood and weight changes revealed that there was little change in the white cell count, but the hemoglobin dropped appreciably at about the sixth day of pregnancy to a low of 11.3 (compared with 14.97 for the non-pregnant controls), with a corresponding drop in red cell count from 9,561,017 at conception to 7,593,333 at the time of delivery. During pregnancy the platelet count increased a bit at times, especially on day 16, but this may not be statistically significant. The total neutrophil count fluctuated, but did not deviate seriously from the controls. Thus, it appears that the hemoglobin and red cell counts were the most definitely affected. In addition the total body weight was increased from 24.56 grams to a maximum of 45.7 grams just before birth. Even after birth the weight did not return to the pre-pregnancy level, remaining around 6 grams in excess for a period of a month. This may be due largely to lactation. By the time of weaning the mother's hemoglobin and red cell counts, but not body weight, had returned to normal.

C. LITTER SIZE:

Factors in litter size include (1) the strain of the mouse, (2) whether it is the first or a later pregnancy, (3) the age, and (4) the health and vigor of the mother. When a female is pushed to maximum fetal production, it seems that her uteri become physiologically exhausted. In the CFI-S strain litters may range in size from 1 to 19 with the average between 10 and 11. The first litter is generally the smallest (average of 8.4) and the fourth or fifth the largest (average of 10.28), with a plateau maintained to 6 or 7 months of age thereafter and then showing a slow decline in

TABLE 1

HEMATOLOGICAL CHANGES DURING GESTATION

G.D.	#	AV. WT.	AV. HGB.	AV. WBC.	AV. RBC.	AV. PLAT.	TOT. NEUT.	STATS.	SEGS.	EO.	LYMPH.	MON.	D	T
CONTROL	21	24.92	14.97	8,980	8,923,273	1,299,127	26.6	0.19	20.5	2.9	65	4.7	.17	
0.0	59	24.56	15.6	7,671	9,561,017	1,293,051	33.1	0.30	32.1	4.3	60	2.2	.1	
1.0	15	25.56	14.57	8,373	9,120,000	1,367,333	22.1	0	22.1	3.5	69	5.1	.5	
2.0	14	22.0	14.8	9,571	9,270,000	1,282,143	16.9	0.14	16.9	4.5	72	6.0	.6	.07
3.0	15	25.93	15.1	9,800	9,372,000	1,372,000	20.7	0.13	20.6	2.6	71	4.8	.3	
4.0	15	26.57	15.5	8,546	9,492,000	1,490,000	22.0	0.26	21.8	2.4	71	3.8	.12	.6
5.0	15	25.80	15.1	8,840	9,405,333	1,270,000	22.0	0.2	21.8	3.8	69	4.6	.3	.06
6.0	15	27.76	14.3	8,466	8,866,666	1,392,000	14.5	0.26	24.3	2.8	67	5.2	.2	
7.0	15	26.71	14.1	7,866	8,694,666	1,352,666	27.0	0.46	26.5	4.1	64	4.8	.3	
8.0	15	28.7	13.6	8,120	8,064,000	1,145,000	40.4	0.46	39.9	3.4	51	5.1	0.06	.06
9.0	15	27.33	12.9	9,706	8,029,333	1,329,333	33.5	0.33	33.2	3.1	57	5.4	.6	.2
10.0	15	29.02	13.3	9,533	7,942,666	1,246,000	31.6	0.33	31.4	3.7	58	6.3	.3	.06
11.0	15	31.84	12.66	8,240	7,420,666	1,200,000	25.6	0.13	25.5	2.6	63	7.8	.4	
12.0	15	31.44	12.5	7,480	7,401,333	1,253,333	30.8	0.26	30.6	2.3	60	6.9		
13.0	15	34.76	12.76	7,120	7,646,666	1,371,333	26.6	0.20	26.4	2.4	65	.05	.13	.66
14.0	15	33.4	11.56	8.720	7,049,333	1,480,666	25.2	0.13	25.1	1.8	66	7.2	.13	
15.0	15	38.28	12.01	7,285	7,248,000	1,243,000	23.3	0.26	23.6	2.0	69	6.1	.06	
16.0	15	38.1	12.1	8,200	7,454,666	1,546,666	29.2	0.06	29.1	1.6	63	4.73		
17.0	15	41.68	10.83	7,293	6,717,333	1,440,666	32.8	0.26	32.5	1.7	62	3.4	.06	
18.0	15	46.1	11.07	7,028	7,196,000	1,446,000	34.8	0.2	34.6	1.5	59	5.1	.13	
19.0	3	45.7	11.3	7,833	7,593,333	1,326,666	22.6	0	22.6	3.0	68	6.3		

G.D. — gestation day
Av. Wt. — average weight
Av. HGB — average hemoglobin
Av. WBC — average number of white blood cells
Av. RBC — average number of red blood cells
Av. Plat. — average number of platelets
Tot. Neut. — total neutrophils

Stats. — stabophils
Segs. — segmentals
Eo. — eosinophils
Lymph. — lymphocytes
Mon. — monocytes
D — double nucleated cells
T — triple nucleated cells

(Data collected by Csilla Somogyi)

litter size. The mating and breeding period lasts from 2 to 14 months of age, and even longer in males. A count of the corpora lutea is a clue to the number of ova ovulated but not, of course, to the number of implantations or to the number of fetuses that reach term. These numbers are almost invariably less than the number of corpora lutea. Abnormal offspring rarely exceed 3% in this strain. Embryos implanted nearest the cervix appear to be resorbed more frequently than others and their mean weight is less, and those nearest the oviduct seem, at times, to be slightly more advanced in development. This may be related to the average larger placenta found toward the oviduccal end.

TABLE 2

REPRODUCTIVE PERFORMANCE OF VIRGINS AND MULTIPARA FEMALES

	VIRGINS (3—5 months)	VIRGINS (7—9 months)	MULTIPARAS (7—9 months)	EX-BREEDERS (10—12 months)
Number of litters	164	168	128	92
Average implantations	11.42	11.04	12.36	10.37
Average litter size	9.48	9.01	10.35	7.63
Normal offspring %	83.03	81.57	83.70	73.65
Stunted offspring %	1.97	3.17	2.52	6.36
Dead fetuses %	1,31	1.02	1.07	1.88
Resorbed in utero %	33.18	13.90	12.57	17.89
Anomalous %	0.48	0.32	0.12	0.19
Males %	53.80	52.60	50.90	51.70
Females %	46.20	47.40	49.10	48.30

Virgin mice, whether young or older, do not have as many implantation sites as do multipara mice of 7 to 9 months of age, and the ex-breeders have the smallest average number of implantation sites. This is probably because of physiological fatigue since these ex-breeders had been kept pregnant rather constantly for some 10 months. Likewise, the ex-breeders of 10—12 months of age had the highest percentage of stunted offspring.

D. SEX RATIO: In data from approximately 200,000 births of normal (control) mice the ratio of males to females was close to 52% to 48%. Theoretically, if all fertilized ova resulted in living offspring, the ratio would be 1:1 since the heterologous spermatozoa determine sex and spermatogenesis yields equal numbers of (dimorphic) male and of female producing spermatozoa. The 1:1 ratio represents an over-all mean probability and never applies to numbers less than 1,000, certainly not to single matings. The slight imbalance in favor of males may be related to the slightly smaller Y chromosome, as compared with the X chromosome, in the male-producing spermatozoon giving it an infinitesimally lighter chromosome burden to carry toward the matured ovum waiting to be fertilized in the ampulla of the oviduct.

TABLE 3
SIZE, NORMALITY, AND SEX RATIOS OF SUCCESSIVE LITTERS

	FIRST LITTER	SECOND LITTER	THIRD LITTER	FOURTH LITTER
Total litters	350	350	350	350
Total offspring	2940	3416	3560	3591
Average litter size	8.40	9.76	10.17	10.28
Total males	1601	1748	1878	1903
Total females	1339	1669	1682	1688
Ratio: males/females	54.5/45.5	51.2/48.8	52.8/47.2	53.0/47.0
Abnormals:				
Eaten by mother	0.47%	0.48%	0.63%	0.70%
Dead at birth	1.33	0.71	0.93	0.73
Persistent amnions	0.33	1.40	1.41	1.51
CNS anomalies	0.10	0.08	0.08	0.32
Other anomalies	0.06	0.0	0.05	0.0
Total not normal	2.29%	2.67%	3.10%	3.26%

The 350 females used in this study were the same for the four pregnancies. It will be noted that with each pregnancy the litter size was increased from an average of 8.40 to 10.28 for the fourth litter. The sex ratios varied slightly, but in all instances males were in excess of females. Total anomalies also increased with each successive litter, but never exceeded 3.26%. Among the 13,508 offspring examined 52.6% were males and 47.4% were females.

E. THE NEO-NATAL MOUSE: The mouse is born hairless, with its eyes and ears closed, and the vagina covered by a membrane. They may be handled gently from the beginning with the mother apparently unconcerned. After 2 or 3 days hair appears, and after 3 or 4 days the ears open. Sex can be determined at birth, or even earlier, by the spatial relations of the genital papilla or opening and anal opening and after 9 or 10 days the mammary nipples of the female can be identified. By 17 days the first maturation spindles are seen in the ovarian ova, the mice are very active, and begin the weaning process. Weaning may be forced at 3 to 4 weeks, but a young mouse is usually healthier if weaned naturally somewhat later. The eyes open at about 2 weeks, the ears grow rapidly, and the rather abundant hair undergoes its first moult. The vagina opens at about 35 days, and the first estrus follows. Such weanling females are generally reluctant to accept the male in mating, and even if mating does occur, it may not result in fertilization, implantation, or the production of viable fetuses. The first healthy mating takes place when a female is at least 7 to 8 weeks of age.

F. SEX DISTINCTION: The distance between the anus and the genital papilla or opening is greater in a male mouse than in a female. The anus and clitoris are roughly one-half to two-thirds as far apart as the anus and penis. The male penis may of course be withdrawn into the scrotal sac and into the body cavity. Adult mice exhibit other distinguishing secondary sex characters. Generally males are larger and heavier than females of similar age. At 2 months males average 27.8 grams and at 24 months 34.8 grams in total weight. Females at the same ages average 22.4 grams and 29.8 grams. A female is generally slenderer than a male, unless she has been multiparous, in which case she tends to be fatter. She also has more prominent mammary glands, whether or not she is lactating. Usually males are more aggressive, and females are docile.

Chapter  REPRODUCTIVE SYSTEMS OF ADULT MICE

It is logical for us to begin our study with the matured reproductive organs of the adult mouse from which the germ cells are derived, and then to proceed to the normal development from fertilization to birth.

THE ADULT MALE

The male reproductive system consists of the testes and enclosing scrotal sac, epididymis and vas deferens, remnants of the embryonic excretory system that function in sperm transport, accessory glands, the urethra and the penis. Except for the urethra and penis, all these structures are paired.

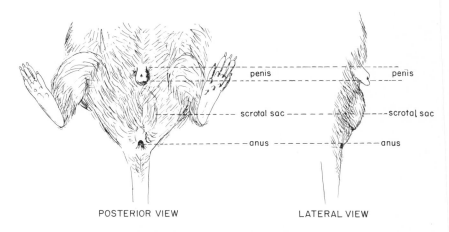

POSTERIOR VIEW   LATERAL VIEW

EXTERNAL GENITALIA OF ADULT MALE MOUSE

A. TESTES: Each testis is covered with a fibrous connective tissue, the tunica albuginea, from which thin partitions, or septa, project into the organ to divide it into lobules, containing many convoluted tubules. These tubules are called seminiferous because within them are produced all the functional germ cells of the male. The region from which the tunica projects into the testis, and at which the testicular arteries enter, is known as the hilus. The arteries nourish every part of the testis, and then they connect with the testicular veins which leave it by the hilus.

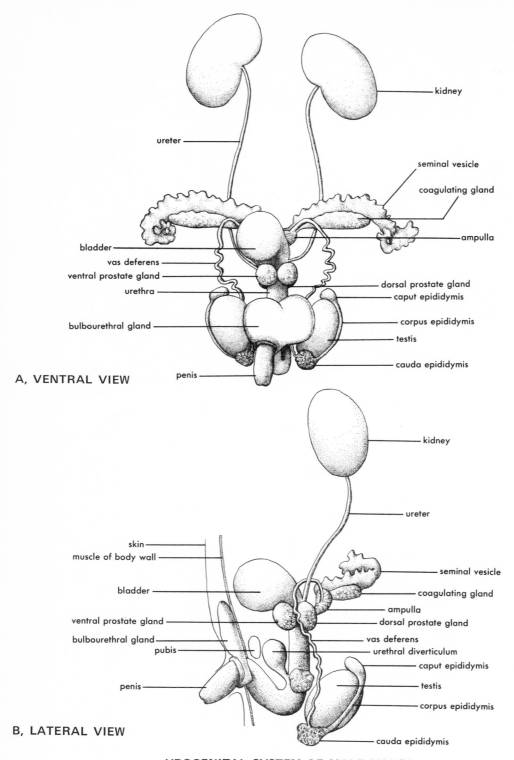

A, VENTRAL VIEW

B, LATERAL VIEW

UROGENITAL SYSTEM OF MALE MOUSE:

(From R. Rugh, "Vertebrate Embryology", Harcourt, Brace & World, Inc., New York, 1964.)

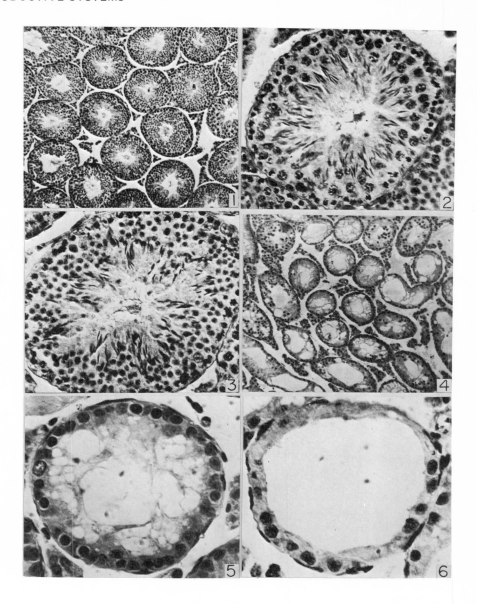

THE MOUSE TESTIS

Fig. 1 — Low power view of tubules within the testis as they are seen in transverse section. Note sparse interstitial tissue.

Fig. 2 — Enlarged view of single seminiferous tubule in section, one in which there are abundant large primary spermatocytes and some mature spermatozoa.

Fig. 3 — Tubule of sexually mature mouse showing all stages of spermatogenesis.

Fig. 4 — Low power view of section through testis of aged male, in which spermatogenesis is almost non-existent.

Fig. 5 — Seminiferous tubule of aged male, showing persistent Sertoli cells but no spermatogenesis. Coagulum within the tubule.

Fig. 6 — Tubule of aged male with most of the Sertoli cells also gone.

The seminiferous epithelium of the tubules lies against a basement membrane that is surrounded by thin fibrous connective tissue. Between the tubules is interstitial stroma, consisting of clumps of Leydig or interstitial cells and rich in blood and lymph. The interstitial cells of the testis have large round nuclei, each with one or more nucleoli containing coarse granules. Their cytoplasm is eosinophilic. It is believed that the interstitial tissue elaborates the male hormone testosterone. The seminiferous epithelium does not consist exclusively of spermatogenic cells, but also has sustaining nutritive or nurse (Sertoli) cells, found nowhere else in the body. Sertoli cells are attached by their bases to the basement membrane and project toward the lumen of a seminiferous tubule. They are elongate cells with large oval nuclei that may appear to be indented. Within the nucleus of a Sertoli cell is a compound or multiple nucleolus, one part composed of a central acidophilic body and the other of two or more peripheral basophilic bodies. The Sertoli cell may assume several forms, depending upon its activity. In the resting state it is closely associated with the basement membrane to which it is attached, and its oval nucleus is parallel to that membrane. As a supporting cell for the metamorphosis of a spermatid to a spermatozoon and the temporary retention of the mature spermatozoa, it is elongate, pyramidal, and its nucleus lies perpendicular to the basement membrane. The cytoplasm near the lumen generally contains the heads of many mature spermatozoa, the tails of which lie free within the lumen.

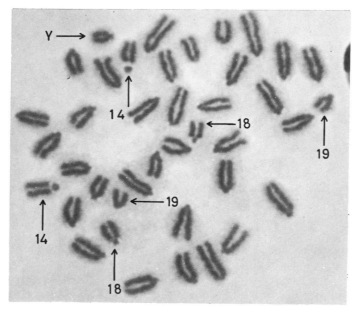

Chromosomes at mitotic metaphase in a cell from the spleen of a male CBA mouse. Arrows indicate the Y chromosome and the three pairs of autosomes that can be distinguished morphologically. The chromosomes of pair 19 are the shortest autosomes and commonly have a prominent proximal secondary constriction like those of pair 14. The X chromosome cannot be distinguished morphologically at this stage. Air-dried preparation. Stained in lactic-acetic orcein.

(Courtesy Drs. C. E. Ford and E. P. Evans)

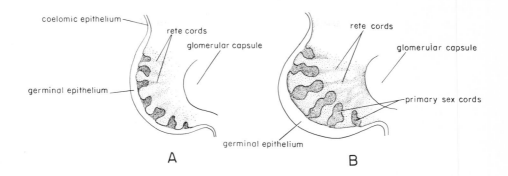

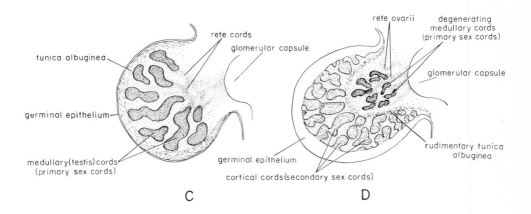

EMBRYOGENESIS OF THE MAMMALIAN GONAD

A — Origin of primary sex cords (medullary cords) from the germinal epithelium.

B — The gonad at an indifferent stage of sexual differentiation. There are well developed primary sex cords for the presumptive male or the medullary component, with the germinal epithelium representing the cortical component.

C — Differentiation of the testis, with further development of the primary sex cords and reduction of the germinal epithelium and development of the tunica albuginea.

D — Differentiation of an ovary which consists in the reduction of the primary sex cords to the medullary cords of the ovary, whereas the cortex is formed by continued development of the cortical cords from the germinal epithelium.

Redrawn from R. K. Burns in "Sex and Internal Secretions", 1961 (W. C. Young, Ed.)

B. SPERMATOGENESIS: The potential (primordial) germ cells of the male appear at about 8 days gestation, at which time there may be only about 100. They are the ancestors of all the millions of spermatozoa to be produced by the male (and there is no positive evidence of any other source for spermatozoa). They are first seen in the extra-gonadal endodermal yolk sac epithelium near the base of the allantois, far from their ultimate destination. Paired genital ridges arise independently at 9 days gestation, adherent to the paired mesonephroi, toward which the primordial germ cells migrate by ameboid movement. Since the germ cells are richly endowed with alkaline phosphatase which supplies the energy for their movement through the embryonic tissues, and which is not found in any other cells of the embryo, they are readily identifiable by appropriate staining techniques. Their route on days 9 and 10 is from yolk sac epithelium to hindgut endoderm to dorsal mesentery to root of the mesentery to coelomic angles during which passage many degenerate while others multiply and eventually migrate (at 11 or 12 days gestation) to the genital ridges. By that time the number of survivors has increased to probably 5,000 and identification of the testis can usually be made. Until that time gonad development in the two sexes is so similar that sex differentiation is not possible. In the testis subsequent proliferation and differentiation are medullary, while in the ovary they are cortical. Histological sex differentiation proceeds very rapidly. In cases of genetic sterility loss of germ cells seems to occur during this passage from the extra-gonadal region of origin toward the genital ridges.

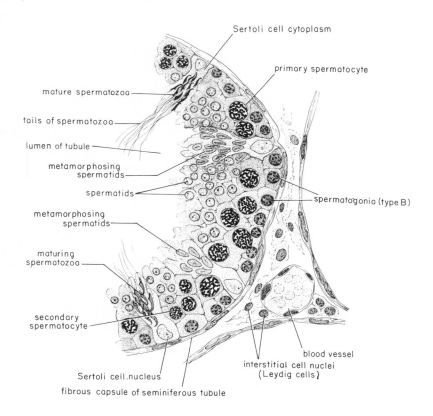

Sertoli cell cytoplasm

primary spermatocyte

mature spermatozoa

tails of spermatozoa

lumen of tubule

metamorphosing spermatids

spermatids

spermatogonia (type B)

metamorphosing spermatids

maturing spermatozoa

secondary spermatocyte

blood vessel

interstitial cell nuclei (Leydig cells)

Sertoli cell nucleus

fibrous capsule of seminiferous tubule

MATURATION OF SPERMATOZOA IN THE MOUSE

Toward the latter part of fetal life the mitotic activity of the primordial germ cells in the genital ridges declines, and some of the cells begin to degenerate by 19 days gestation. Shortly after birth larger cells, the spermatogonia are seen. Thereafter spermatogonia may be seen in the mouse testes throughout life. There are three types: type A, intermediate, and type B.

Type A is the ancestral stem cell: it is capable of mitosis or of giving rise to the other types and ultimately to spermatozoa. Type A spermatogonia are the largest and contain fine dust like particles of nuclear chromatin, and a single eccentrically placed chromatin nucleolus. Their metaphase chromosomes are long and slender. They may give rise, through intermediate spermatogonia to type B spermatogonia which are smaller, more numerous, and contain nuclear chromatin in coarse flakes or clumps on or near the inner surface of the nuclear membrane. There is a centrally placed plasmosome-like nucleolus. The metaphase chromosomes are usually short, rounded, and bean shaped. Type B spermatogonia may divide to give rise to more type B cells or change into primary spermatocytes, farther from the basement membrane. It has been estimated that the time lapse from spermatogonial metaphase to early meiotic prophase is 3 to 9 days, that diakinesis to second metaphase takes 4 days or less, and diakenesis to immature spermatozoa takes 7 or more days. Therefore, the time lapse from spermatogonial metaphase to immature spermatozoa is at least 10 days.

Type A cells first appear 3 days after birth. As they increase in number, the primordial germ cells, from which they are derived and which normally lie next to the basement membrane, decrease in number. Meiotic divisions in the testes begin about 8 days after birth.

The first indication that a type B spermatogonium will metamorphose into a primary spermatocyte is that it enlarges noticeably and moves away from the basement membrane. The primary spermatocyte divides into two smaller secondary spermatocytes, which in turn divide into four spermatids. They undergo a radical metamorphosis into an equal number of mature spermatozoa, losing most of their cytoplasm and changing form characteristically.

Between the primary and secondary spermatocyte stages, the chromatin material must divide. Premeiotic synthesis of DNA (deoxyribonucleotide) occurs in primary spermatocytes during the resting phase and is terminated just before the onset of meiotic prophase, with an average duration of 14 hours. No DNA synthesis occurs in the later stages of spermatogenesis. The first spermatocyte division reduces its volume, either without altering its quality, (equational division), or by actually separating members of allelomorphic pairs

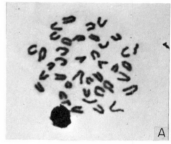
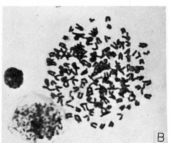

MOUSE CHROMOSOMES

A — Smear from spleen showing diploid chromosome number

B — Smear from bone marrow showing tetraploid chromosome number.

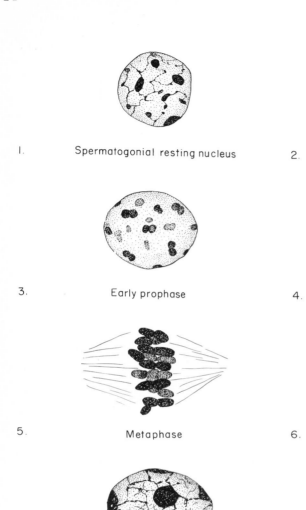

1.   Spermatogonial resting nucleus

2.   Early reproductive phase

3.   Early prophase

4.   Late prophase

5.   Metaphase

6.   Early differentiation

7.   Early differentiation showing prominent reticulum

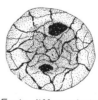

8.   Early differentiation showing orientation of reticulum

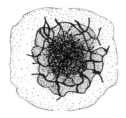

9.   Prophase – like stage

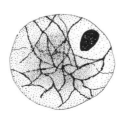

10.   Early spermatocyte

CYTOLOGIC CHANGES IN SPERMATOGONIAL NUCLEI IN MOUSE
(Redrawn from Fogg and Cowing, Exp. Cell Research, Vol. 4, 1953)

CYTOLOGIC CHANGES IN SPERMATOGONIAL NUCLEI IN MOUSE

Fig. 1 — Resting spermatogonium with finely granular chromatin mesh-work evenly distributed within the nucleus, a faintly basophilic nucleoplasm, and a well-defined nuclear membrane.

Fig. 2 — Spireme is lost, and the granular chromatin is assuming the form of compact bodies. These bodies tend to orient themselves peripherally but are not attached to the nuclear membrane. Nucleoli are still present.

Fig. 3 — The chromatin clumps have increased in number but not in size. This is a transitional phase, the orientation of the chromatin clumps tends to be peripheral and remain so until the beginning of nuclear breakdown in late prophase. The nuclear membrane in this figure seems to be fading out, the nucleus appears to be enlarging and the nucleoplasm is less definitely stainable.

Figs. 4 & 5 — These represent typical spermatogonial mitotic activity.

Fig. 6 — One of the first of the phases of differentiation, the nuclear reticulum is accentuated and clearly apparent, but the nucleolus, nuclear membrane, and staining capacity of the nucleoplasm are similar to the resting nucleus.

Fig. 7 — The next step in nuclear differentiation, with a more prominent linin network, slight increase in nuclear size, a reduction in the number of large-size chromatin staining particles, loss of morphological integrity of the nucleolus, and a decrease in the staining affinity of the nucleoplasm.

Fig. 8 — A further stage in nuclear differentiation showing an increase in the size of the reticulum and a gradual loss of the nucleolus. The nuclear membrane remains intact but the general picture of the nucleus shows wide variations at this time.

Fig. 9 — This is a key phase in the differentiation process, and may be confused with the late prophase. The reticulum is thick, more or less oriented in a mass, and there is no demonstrable nucleolus. Often the chromatin is massed to one side, leaving a non-stainable nuclear area and a faintly stainable nuclear membrane.

Fig. 10 — This is an early spermatocyte, with an enlarged reticulum which is breaking up into units, the nuceolus has reappeared and is surrounded by a clear zone, and the nuclear membrane is intact. The nucleus has increased in size and continues until the primary spermatocyte is formed.

(From L. C. Fogg and R. F. Cowing, 1953: Exp. Cell Research 4:107-115)

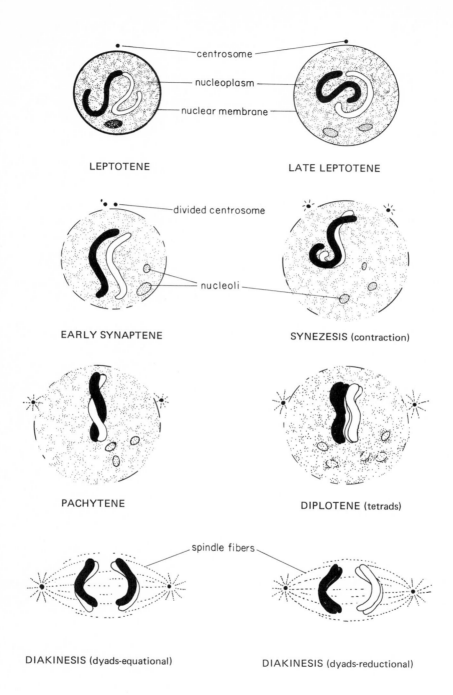

LEPTOTENE   LATE LEPTOTENE

EARLY SYNAPTENE   SYNEZESIS (contraction)

PACHYTENE   DIPLOTENE (tetrads)

DIAKINESIS (dyads-equational)   DIAKINESIS (dyads-reductional)

MEIOSIS

(reductional division).   The equational or quantitative division is essentially mitotic whereas the reductional or qualitative division, is characteristic only of meiosis, never seen in any other tissue or organ.   Whichever type of division occurs, the other follows, making the secondary spermatocyte truly haploid (divided both qualitatively and quantitatively).   There are 20 tetraploid chromosomes prior to the first spermatocyte division, and a spermatid has one-fourth of those, or 20 chromosomes, the haploid number.   Should the reductional division not take place, there would be a doubling of the chromosome number with each generation.

Following is a schematic representation of meiosis (maturation)as illustrated by spermatogenesis.   The following estimates have been made for the various stages of spermatogenesis (Oakberg 1957).

STAGE	DURATION: HOURS
Spermatogonia	
Type A	Always present
Intermediate	27.3
Type B	29.4
Primary spermatocytes	
Resting preleptotene	31.0
Leptotene	31.2
Zygotene	37.5
Pachytene	175.3
Diplotene	21.4
Diakenesis + metaphase	10.4
Secondary spermatocytes	10.4
Spermatids	229.2

Note that in diakenesis the chromosomes may be aligned in either of two ways. One of these results in their separation as pairs (equational), and the other in the separation of the members of allelomorphic pairs (reductional) of chromosomes.

The transformation of a spermatid into a spermatozoon involves no divisions.   Most of the cytoplasm disappears carrying with it certain residual bodies.   (See figure on page 18.)

The cytoplasm of the spermatid that is to be sloughed off contains lipid droplets, mitochondria, ribosomes, endoplasmic reticulum, the caudally migrated Golgi apparatus, and numerous multivesicular and multigranular bodies. These membrane-limited bodies and the Golgi zone stain heavily for acid phophatase.   Following extrusion, the residual bodies undergo a series of alterations: 1) disruption of the multigranular bodies with the release of free granules, 2) sequestration of granules, ribosomes, and reticulum inside double membrane-limited vacuoles derived from Golgi lamellae, 3) appearance of numerous single-membrane bound, cytoplasmic vacuoles, 4) fragmentation,

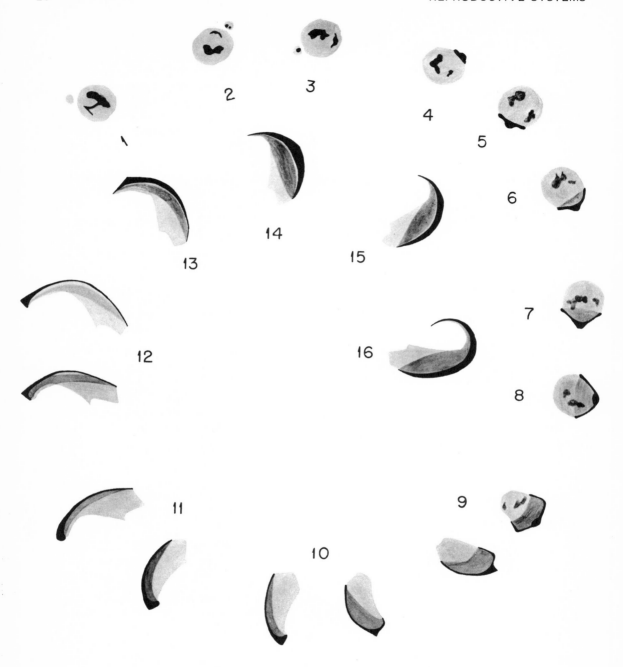

STAGES IN SPERMIOGENESIS

Spermiogenesis of the mouse as seen with periodic acid Schiff and hematoxylin staining of Zenker-formol fixed testis. Drawings are arranged in a spiral to demonstrate stages which overlap in a cycle of the seminiferous epithelium. Orientation of spermatids in relation to the basement membrane also is shown. Note especially the change between stages VII and VIII. 1—3 is the Golgi phase, 4—7 the cap phase, 8—12 the acrosome phase, and 13—16 the maturation phase.

STAGES IN SPERMIOGENESIS*

(The 16 stages below are based on changes in the acrosome and nucleus.)

Stage 1 — begins with the formation of a new group of spermatids, arising from the second meiotic division. The weakly staining idiosome may be seen close to the nucleus.

Stage 2 — this begins with the appearance of proacrosomic granules in the idiosome. The most frequent number of granules is two, with one being slightly larger than the other. The granules increase in size until they fuse.

Stage 3 — there is fusion of the proacrosomic granules into a single large granule adjacent to the nucleus.

Stage 4 — the granule formed in stage #3 becomes enlarged and flattens onto the nucleus, and begins its lateral extension over the nucleus, initiating the "cap" phase of spermiogenesis.

Stage 5 — there is extension of the cap so that a lateral view shows two projections from the acrosome granule.

Stage 6 — development of the cap has progressed so that its outer surface is visible in side view.

Stage 7 — there is further development of the head cap to cover from one-third to one-half of the nucleus.

Stage 8 — here the acrosomic phase of spermiogenesis is initiated. The young spermatids orient themselves with the acrosomic system toward the basement membrane, and elongation of the spermatid nucleus begins.

Stage 9 — there is now a definite change in the shape of the spermatid nucleus, with the caudal end appearing both narrower and angular. The nucleus begins to flatten, and the head cap begins its caudal progression over the dorsal or rounded side of the nucleus.

Stage 10 — migration of the acrosomic material has reached the dorsal, caudal angle of the nucleus. Both flattening and elongation continue, and the spermatid becomes narrower at its anterior end.

Stage 11 — there is now a transformation of the caudal angles of the spermatid from their previously rounded shape to sharp, acute angles. Flattening is more extreme, nuclear elongation continues, and the acrosomic material at the tip of the nucleus begins to shift caudally.

Stage 12 — the spermatid now reaches its greatest total length. The acrosome has a square anterior end, and appears as a wedge-shaped structure overlying the nucleus. The anterior extension of the nucleus begins to thin out, so that there remains only a thin thread of nuclear material underlying the anterior portion of the acrosome.

Stage 13 — there is now an abrupt shortening of the length of the spermatid by about 20%. The caudal angles assume the same shape as in the mature sperm. The acrosomic material migrates caudally, giving the appearance of a hook.

Stage 14 — the general shape of mature sperm is now attained. The acrosome appears as a crescent, and elongation at the tip results in a slender, sharp point.

Stage 15 — the nucleus now narrows, and the tip of the maturing sperm continues to develop. The acrosome is not wide, and resists staining.

Stage 16 — this is the condition of the spermatozoon at the time it is liberated from the seminiferous tubule. Both the acrosomic material and the nucleus extend to the extreme tip of the spermatozoon. A perforatiorium is probably present but not easily stained, or revealed.

* Based on work by E. P. Oakberg, 1956, Am. Jour. Anat. 99:391–413.

5) peripheral migration toward the tubular wall, and 6) phagocytosis of these migrating fragments by the Sertoli cells. The demonstration of acid phosphatase activity within free granules, the sequestration of Golgi lamellae, and both classes of vacuoles suggest that the initial body degradation occurs through liposomal cytoplasmic autophagy. (Pers. Com. S. E. Dietert) The nuclear material loses its identity and becomes lodged in a distinct head, covered by a bag-like acrosome, over the perforatorium. The acrosome carries the enzyme hyaluronidase or a zymogen-like precursor which, at fertilization, depolymerizes the hyaluronic acid jelly of the cumulus, and the exposed perforatorium carries a lysin to alter the chemical properties of the zona so that the sperm head can penetrate it. Enclosing the acrosome is the plasma membrane which extends around the entire spermatozoon. Over the distal half of the sperm head the plasma membrane carries a thickened inner aggregation of fine particles. Although the content of the sperm head is homogeneous, the DNA molecules of the haploid chromosomes are present in some form that preserves their gene sequences. A middle piece contains the mitochondria, the Golgi apparatus, and two centrioles; and the tail is made up of many flagella-like strands. The heads of many such spermatozoa lie embedded in the cytoplasm of a Sertoli cell, deriving nutrition therefrom until they are liberated during coitus.

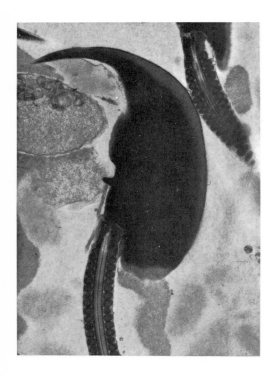

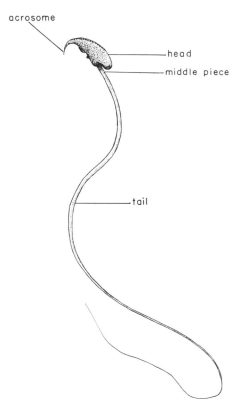

ELECTRON MICROGRAPH OF MOUSE
SPERM HEAD
(Courtesy Dr. D. W. Fawcett)

MATURE MOUSE SPERMATOZOAN

The spermatozoon varies in length, width, and shape with the mouse strain. It generally has a hooked head about 0.0080 mm long, a short middle piece, and a very long tail, for an overall length averaging 0.1226 mm. Enzyme machinery controlled by the mitochondria in the middle piece facilitates the movement of the tail. The swimming of the spermatozoon depends on a waving or bending motion originating in the base of the tail, probably in the distal centriole of the middle piece, and is propagated distally.

As stated, in the process of transformation into a spermatozoon, a spermatid sloughs off a cytoplasmic tag but small vesicles appear within the retained Golgi apparatus, each containing a homogeneous granule. These coalesce to form an acrosome granule, which becomes attached to the surface of the nucleus. The two spermatid centrioles move to the plasma membrane to which the distal one becomes attached. A fine thread grows out from this distal centriole as a core for the developing tail. The two centrioles then align themselves in the direction of the nucleus, free from the surface and to the side opposite the acrosome. The base of the tail is thus drawn into the cytoplasm, along with the distal centriole, but the plasma membrane is also indented to form a sheath around it. Later the distal centriole forms a ring, still associated with the base of the tail, and finally lodges near the plasma membrane. Mitochrondria aid in development of the middle piece, and an outer ring of nine coarse fibers grows from the proximal centriole to form a sheath around the axial filament emanating from the distal centriole. All the cytoplasm of the spermatid is then shed except for a minute droplet that is lost in transit through the epididymis. After extrusion, the cytoplasmic masses undergo the alterations which are accompanied by fragmentation of the Sertoli site of indentation and phagocytosis of the fragments by the Sertoli cells.

DNA (deoxyribonucleotide) synthesis occurs only in spermatogonia and primary spermatocytes, since the succeeding stages do not involve mitotic divisions. The average life span of the spermatogonia is 27 to 30.5 hours, and DNA synthesis takes longer in type B than in type A. The nuclei of spermatids show a noticeable change in DNA pattern during the metamorphosis into spermatozoa. The DNA eventually becomes evenly distributed, and then resistant to desoxyribonuclease, so that the chromosomes undergo an orderly rearrangement. RNA may be found in the chromatoid body of a spermatid.

The process of spermatogenesis in the mouse is basically similar to that in any other mammal. One cycle of the seminiferous epithelium takes 207 ± 6 hours, and four such cycles occur between type A spermatogonium and mature spermatozoon. The production of mature spermatozoa from the original spermatogonial cell takes about five weeks in the mouse (and about twice as long in man). The testes, and particularly the mature spermatozoa, are the richest sources of animal hyaluronidase, and this enzyme effectively disperses the cumulus cells surrounding the mature ovum at the time of fertilization. Each individual spermatozoon carries enough of the enzyme to clear a path through the cumulus cells to the gel matrix of the ovum. The hyaluronic acid cement substance tends to bind together the granulosa cells of the cumulus, so that the sperm head must be supplied with abundant enzyme.

In summary the best evidence suggests the following major intervals:

Meiotic prophase - 12.5 days

Spermatid stages - 9.5 days

Last four stages of spermatogenesis - 5.5 days and the maximum interval between type A spermatogonium and its release as mature spermatozoa from the seminiferous tubule is 35.5 days.

C. DUCTS: Remnants of the embryonic excretory system that became functional parts of the male reproductive system are the rete testis, the efferent ducts, the tripartitite epididymis (caput, corpus, and cauda), and the ductus deferens. Each of these structures is paired. The rete testis is an anastomosing system of ducts into which the seminiferous tubules ultimately empty their contents. It is lined with low simple cuboidal epithelium. The rete opens into the collecting chamber (lacuna) located outside the tunica albuginea, which in turn opens into the three to seven connecting efferent ducts. Each duct has two parts, the first is short, convoluted, and surrounded by fatty tissue, and the second is more convoluted and surrounded by a connective tissue capsule continuous with that of the epididymis. The ducts join to form the first part of the catput of the epididymis. An efferent duct is lined with both low and high columnar epithelial cells, and hence its lumen is irregular in contour. Below the epithelial cells is a basement membrane, and outside this are some smooth muscle fibers. The caput of the epididymis is convoluted and divided into seven or eight segments (lobules), the second of which is lined with high columnar epithelial cells. These cells have no cilia, and their oval nuclei are variously placed. In the third segment of the caput the epithelium is lower, the nuclei are more uniformly situated, and the lumen is narrower. The lumen widens toward the cauda, and smooth muscle cells may be seen in the outer wall. The ductus deferens, which extends from the cauda of the epididymis is lined with high columnar epithelium, slightly stratified. The mucosal layer consists of deep longitudinal folds, whereas the lamina propria is made up of fibrous connective tissue. The outer longitudinal and inner circular smooth muscle fibers constitute a rather thick enclosing wall. The adventitia, or loose connective tissue, surrounds the whole structure. The ductus deferens enters an ampulla and then the urethra. The ampulla is lined with low columnar cells having little cytoplasm and large oval, darkly staining nuclei.

D. THE ACCESSORY GLANDS: The accessory glands do not contain or carry germ cells but are adjuncts to their proper functioning and transport. They include the seminal vesicles, (vesicular secretory glands), three pairs of prostate or coagulating glands, ampullary glands, bulbourethral glands, and preputial glands.

The paired seminal vesicles are long, lobulated glands curved at the lateral tips, and located next to the first pair of prostate glands. Each vesicle has a lumen with alveolar outpocketings and a lining of high columnar epithelium with oval nuclei near the base. The cytoplasm is basophilic and contains heavy, eosinophilic secretion granules. Smooth muscles and a connective tissue sheath surround the vesicle.

The coagulating glands, attached to the posterior margins of the seminal vesicles are the first of the three pairs of prostate glands. They secrete a substance that, when mixed with the secretions of the vesicular glands, forms a coagulum the presence of which in the vaginal orifice is considered proof of successful copulation. This usually means insemination and fertilization except in cases where the male has been vasectomized. Seen grossly, a coagulating gland appears to be homogeneous; yet it actually consists of a multi-folded mucous membrane with many projections into a central lumen. The lining is simple columnar epithelium with centrally placed nuclei and eosinophilic cytoplasm. The gland has two ducts, both lined with low cuboidal epithelium having slightly basophilic cytoplasm. As with most accessory glands, there are smooth muscles and an enclosing connective tissue sheath. The dorsal prostate glands are smaller and more rounded than the coagulating glands. Each has several ducts. Moreover, their mucous membrane is smoother, and depending upon the amount and accumulation of secretion, mucous folds may or may not be present in the ventral prostate glands. Their ducts are lined with low cuboidal epithelium, having slightly basophilic cytoplasm and deeply staining nuclei.

The paired ampullary glands are found around the base of the ductus deferens and open into the vestibule of the ampulla. They are lined with low cuboidal epithelium having large and oval nuclei and are thrown into delicate longitudinal folds, The tubules contain a dense, red-staining homogeneous secretion, which, on fixation, tends to coagulate toward the center of the lumen.

The paired bulbourethral glands (of Cowper) are very large and closely adherent to the penis, just outside the body wall. A duct from each gland appears to enter the anterior wall of the urethral diverticulum. The bulbourethral glands are both tubular and alveolar, surrounded by striated muscle, and lined with columnar epithelium having primarily basophilic cytoplasm. Their secretion has a staining reaction similar to that of mucin.

E. URETHRA: The connection of the bladder is lined with thinner and thinner layers of transitional epithelium, until it joins the urethra, which has a ventral lining of stratified squamous epithelium and a dorsal lining of low cuboidal epithelium. The major portion of the lining is the stratified squamous epithelium. The lamina propria is loose connective tissue, rich in blood vessels, and it is enveloped by a thick layer of striated muscle. Urethral glands (of Littré) consist of small alveoli lined with cells having predominantly granular and basophilic cytoplasm.

The preputial glands are large, flat, leaf shaped sebaceous-type glands. They may be homologues of the clitoral glands of the female. Their lining is polyhedral epithelium with pale staining nuclei. As the cells degenerate, they form a fatty secretion. Each preputial gland opens separately through a long duct at the tip of the prepuce (foreskin) and its function is probably lubrication.

F. PENIS: The penis consists of one thin corpus cavernosa and two thick corpora cavernosa. The thin corpus is an extension of the urethra, surrounded by a tunica albuginea (dense fibrous connective tissue) within which is a layer of circular smooth muscle fibers. The lumen of the urethra expands into the urethral bulb, forming paired lateral diverticuli. The two thick corpora cavernosa are also surrounded by the tunica, which separates proximally and allows the two cavernosa to join distally. The os penis, a small bone, may be found within the fibrous septum between the two thick corpora cavernosa and projects beyond the orifice of the penis. The glans penis (terminal) is covered with the prepuce or foreskin, consisting of stratified squamous epithelium that may contain a few scattered hair follicles. The root of the penis is attached to the pubic bone by the ends of the corpora cavernosa, associated with the ischio-cavernosus muscle.

THE ADULT FEMALE

The female reproductive system consists of paired ovaries and oviducts, a bicornuate uterus, a cervix, vagina, clitoral gland, and clitoris.

A. OVARIES: The ovaries are suspended by ligaments from the dorsal body wall, lateral to the kidneys. This bulge into the peritoneal cavity is covered by germinal epithelium instead of mesothelium. Each ovary is within a bursa from which liberated ova cannot escape. The suspensory ligaments are invested with smooth muscle fibers, which seem to extend into the ovarian coverings. Other ligaments connect each ovary to the anterior end of a uterine horn. These contain smooth muscles, which supply the uterine horn and the in-fundibulum of the oviduct. They also contain the epoöphoron, vestiges of the Wolffian bodies. The infundibular muscle connects with the hilus of the ovary. Each uterine horn is supported by a dorsal broad ligament (mesometrium) which contains some fat, as well as some smooth muscle fibers continuous with the muscles of the uterus itself.

An ovary is a small, pink structure with its surfaces covered by a thin, transparent, connective tissue membrane, the tunica albuginea or ovarian cap-sule. The whole is enveloped by mesothelium. The ovary of a mature mouse has an inner medullary portion (the zona vasculosa and stroma) and a more peripheral portion, the cortex, within which growing follicles may be seen.

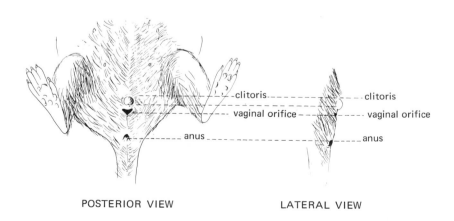

POSTERIOR VIEW   LATERAL VIEW

EXTERNAL GENITALIA OF ADULT FEMALE MOUSE

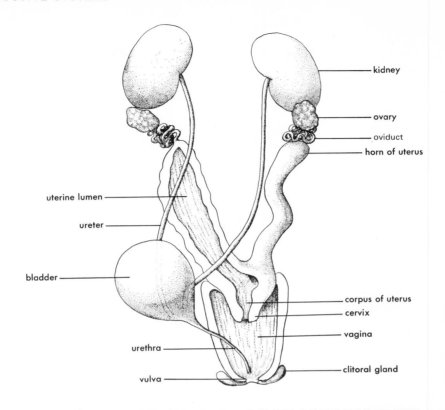

VENTRAL VIEW OF UROGENITAL SYSTEM OF FEMALE MOUSE
(From R. Rugh, "Vertebrate Embryology", Harcourt, Brace & World, Inc., New York, 1964.)

The small primary follicles, found just beneath the tunica, consist of oöcytes and their surrounding follicle cells, which appear at first to be squamous. The oöcyte nucleus is vesicular, with chromatin granules and a distinct nucleolus. As a follicle enlarges, the surrounding follicle cells become cuboidal, then layered, and finally are separated from the oöcyte by a clear, noncellular follicle cell secretion known as the zona pellucida. This plays an important role in the fertilization process. Enclosing each enlarging follicle are connective tissue fibers in the stroma, which together form the theca folliculi. As the follicle enlarges further, a distinction can be made between the theca interna, which has a rich blood supply and rather loosely arranged, constituent cells, and the outer and denser theca externa, in which the fibers are arranged concentrically.

The stroma is made up of dense fibrous connective tissue. Blood vessels penetrate the entire ovary, entering and leaving by the hilus. Outside the cortex is the single layer of cuboidal epithelium known as the germinal epithelium, and just outside this is the tunica.

The follicle continues to enlarge, since it is accessible to all the essential food elements from the blood (such as vitamins, and steroid hormones) but inaccessible to most enzymes, antigens, antibodies, and protein hormones. Small and irregular lacunae appear among the cells, and merge into an antrum, which becomes filled with follicular fluid, or liquor folliculi. The lining of the antrum

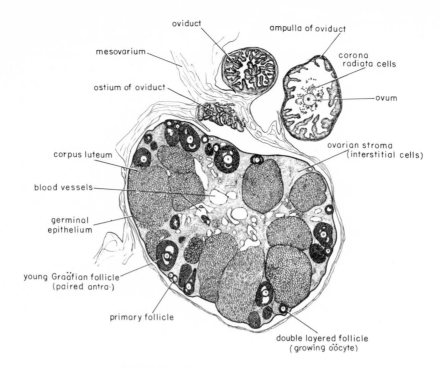

MOUSE OVARY POST-OVULATION
SHOWING MANY CORPORA LUTEA

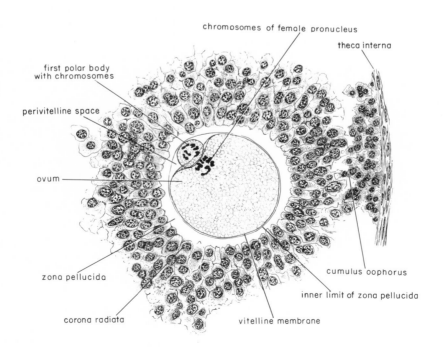

MOUSE EGG IN OVARY
(nearly ready for discharge)

consists of stratified follicle cells that are conspicuously granular and hence are called granulosa cells.   Granulosa cells surround the growing oöcyte and the zona pellucida to form the cumulus oöphorus, the matrix of which contains protein and hyaluronic acid, to be liquefied by the enzyme hyaluronidase from the spermatozoon.   (The hyaluronidase probably comes from the acrosome, which is discarded at fertilization.) The zona pellucida accumulates around the growing ovum, tending to separate it more and more from the nutrition-bearing cumulus cells.   The zona is a weakly acidic mucoprotein material. Since peroxide, trypsin, chymotrypsin, pronase or mold protease tend to dissolve it, it is believed that its main component is hyaluronic acid.   The zona pellucida is a secondary membrane which is glossy, tough, resilient, elastic, and the product of follicle cells.   While it is homogeneous, it has an irregular surface with microvilli from the surface of the vitelline membrane. Some cellular processes from the granulosa cell surfaces recede, due to the thickening of the zona, but maintain contact with the vitelline membrane.   The protoplasmic extensions from the zona radiata penetrate the zona pellucida and channel yolk nutrition to the egg through its membrane.   The zona is sloughed off during blastulation, probably owing to the expansion of the blastocyst as it acquires its blastocoel. Until then it may aid in the maintenance of a normal cleavage pattern and prevent the fusion of closely placed ova.   It can be removed at any early stage of development by digestion with the enzyme pronase, which also disperses the cumulus cell.

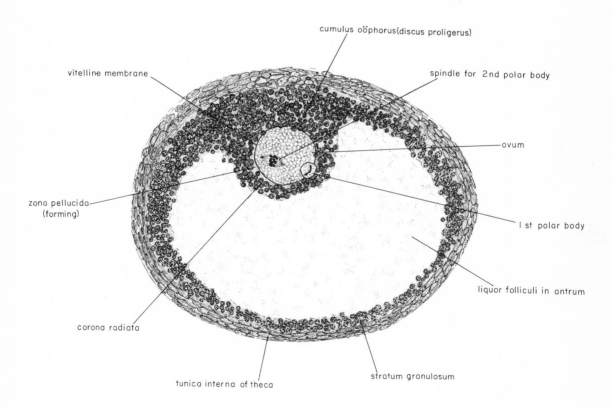

MATURING MOUSE OVUM IN ENLARGING FOLLICLE

The cumulus cells immediately around the zona pellucida are radially arranged elongate cells, often attached to the ovum by delicate tubule-like cytoplasmic structures, and are collectively called the zona radiata. It is possible that the radially arranged cells aid in directing the spermatozoon to the ovum after its liberation at ovulation. They may also provide a sticky target to entrap the spermatozoon initially. An intact cumulus is believed essential to successful sperm penetration. As the antrum increases in size, the entire follicle enlarges and moves toward the surface of the ovary to project into the periovarial space. The developing ovum and its surrounding cells are then known as a Graäfian follicle, with an average diameter of over 500 microns. Often the mature ovum and its cumulus cells can be seen floating freely within the enlarged antrum, just prior to ovulation or liberation from the ovary. A Graäfian follicle can be seen with the naked eye as a bulbous projection from the surface of the ovary.

B. OÖGENESIS:
At 8 days gestation the primordial germ cells of the female appear in the yolk sac splanchnopleure and are rich in alkaline phosphatase. They migrate by ameboid and undulating movement (as do the primordial germ cells in the males) along the dorsal mesentery to the mesenteric folds and arrive at the genital (germinal) ridges by 9 to 10 days gestation. By 11 days gestation the potential ovary shows its characteristic cortical proliferation in contrast with the medullary development of the potential testis. The controversy has not been resolved as to whether the migrating primordial germ cells are the lineal ancestors of all future ova or whether some ova are derived from the germinal epithelium of the genital ridge. The first theory is favored by most embryologists. These primordial germ cells are elongated, have definite clear cell membranes with globular mitochondria around the nucleus, nuclei of varying shapes apparently related to movement, and two or more nucleoli of high contrast. Beginning at about 13 days gestation meiotic prophase may be found, and this leads to ovum formation. Leptotene and zygotene stages may be seen in oöcytes at 14 and 15 days gestation and a high rate of oögonial division begins at this time. Numerous pachytene stages may be seen from 16 and 17 days to birth. Some continue through diplotene and diakenesis. DNA may be recognized in the meiotic prophases by 13 days and until 16 days gestation.

At about the time of birth some primordial ova acquire follicle cells, start on the maturation process, and shortly thereafter all have follicle cells. The total number of oöcytes at this has been estimated as up to 75,000, far in excess of the number that could ever mature. Many degenerate almost immediately, and others degenerate later or become follicle cells so that the stock is reduced to a fraction of the original number. The primary oöcytes may be distinguished from other cells of the ovarian cortex by their relatively large size, correspondingly large spherical nuclei, and by yolk particles in the cytoplasm. Although it has been suggested that some ova proliferate from the germinal epithelium of the ovary and that regeneration is possible after ovariectomy, this theory has not been confirmed. Young ova are large, have a spherical and heavily stained nucleus, and may occur in pairs. In the female mouse the germ cells pass through all of the oögonial divisions and reach the oöcyte stage while still in the embryo. About 3 days after birth the oöcytes reach a static state known as the dictyate stage, and this is maintained until a few hours (12) before ovulation. This interim may be as much as a year.

At 12 to 15 days after birth some antra appear, and at 17 days some follicles are almost maximum size. The ovum reaches its maximum size at the time that antrum formation begins. Follicular growth continues, and may even do so without the presence of an ovum. But as the ovarian egg increases, and as ovulation approaches, the cytoplasmic RNA (ribonucleicacid) is augumented sharply and many nucleoli can be seen. These early small nucleoli are low in RNA. Then the first ovulation occurs. The atretic follicles also increase in number, reaching a maximum at about 18.5 days. Once oögenesis has begun, it continues in regular $4\frac{1}{2}$ to 5 day cycles throughout the reproductive life to about 12 or 14 months of age. Ova degeneration occurs concomitantly. A fully formed and normal ovum consists of a few small Golgi granules, a thin layer of yolk, large Golgi granules, a nucleus, and abundant mitochondria. These mitochondria generally are concentrated in the periphery, and at fertilization they migrate to the region of the developing pronuclei and aggregate around them. During the growth of the oöcyte the DNA in its nucleus is reduced and a perinuclear band of ribonucleic acid makes its appearance in the cytoplasm. The mature ovum is slightly polarized in that on its dorsal side is a cortical zone of ribonucleic acid and on the ventral side appear some vacuoles.

According to some estimates at each estrus 1,000 or more ova are available for oögenesis, but only about 1% ever mature, for a 99% loss in potential. With estrus every $4\frac{1}{2}$ to 5 days, this means that in an average reproductive life of 2 to 12 months of age some 60,000 ova are available, of which only about 500 mature and only about 100 could possibly result in offspring.

Anomalies in oöcytes, aside from atretic ones, include giant oöcytes and polynuclear oöcytes. Polyovular follicles appear frequently, particularly in immature mice.

The first meiotic division of an oöcyte in a mature ovary begins 9 to 10 hours before ovulation, presumably stimulated by the luteinizing hormone from the previous ovulations. Its prophase is sometimes called the dictyate or leptoene stage. The first metaphase lasts roughly 6 hours. The second meiotic division in initiated immediately, but is arrested in metaphase where it remains until the ovum is fertilized. Thus the interval between the first and second meiotic divisions is entirely dependent on the time between ovulation and fertilization.

The DNA content of the female pronucleus is reduced to 26% of the primary oöcyte (which was tetraploid). The recently ovulated mouse egg has 5 to 10 times as much DNA as the ultimate normal diploid somatic cell. Some of the DNA is found in the mitochondria. Protein synthesis occurring in the developing mouse ovum prior to the RNA production by the nucleoli suggests ribosomes may be of maternal origin. The mature ovum has finely granular, homogeneous cytoplasm limited by a plasma membrane generally called the vitelline membrane (not to be confused with the membrane of the same name in invertebrates). The nucleoplasm is enclosed by a double membrane, perforated by pores. The mature ovum has a diameter of about 95 microns and a volume of about 200,000 cubic microns. Its fertilizable life span is 10 to 15 hours, and the loss of fertilizability is due to changes in the vitelline membrane, and the cortical cytoplasmic granules, occurring even before the zona pellucida loses its penetrability.

Ova are liberated from the adult female mouse ovary approximately every 5 days. In this interval two changes take place, maturation of the ovum and growth of the follicle. Correlating changes in the vaginal mucosa can be used to estimate the time of ovulation. Many of the stages, but not all, in the maturation of the ovum can be seen in any mature ovary and at any phase of the estrous cycle. A composite drawing of the ovary is given showing all the stages of oögenesis as well as a corpus luteum. The stages are as follows:

STAGES OF OÖGENESIS

Stage 1 — Oögonium, hardly distinguishable from other cortical cells of the ovary, and with no follicle cells. The amount of DNA is constant, but is diluted with the enlargement of the nucleus.

Stage 2 — Primary oöcyte, invested with a single loose layer of squamous epithelial (follicle) cells and having a nucleus slightly larger than those of the adjacent cells.

Stage 3 — Primary follicle, with a single layer of cuboidal follicle cells surrounding the oöcyte, the nucleus of which is enlarging.

Stage 4 — Double layer of follicle cells around the enlarging oöcyte.

Stage 5 — Many-layers of follicle cells around the enlarging oöcyte. Near the germinal vesicle is a yolk nucleus (Balbiani's body), and near it is a Golgi apparatus.

Stage 6 — Antral spaces are scattered among the follicle cells. Mitochondria form centers for yolk concentration; the diameter of the follicle is about 200 microns.

Stage 7 — Distinct antral spaces; the first polar body forms in the first maturation (meiotic) division, leaving a secondary oöcyte. Rodent polar bodies are characteristically large.

Stage 8 — Single fused antrum, with the oöcyte suspended in the cumulus oöphorus and the first polar body in the perivelline space.

Stage 9 — Antrum swollen with follicular fluid, and the ovum ready to erupt from the ovary, with its nucleus in metaphase of the second meiotic division; the diameter of the follicle about 500 microns. (See Peters and Borum 1961 for illustrations)

The first of the two maturation (meiotic) divisions of the ovum occurs at stage 7 and the second after invasion by the spermatozoon. Upon successful insemination and syngamy restoration of the diploid state of 40 chromosomes is accomplished.

With specific reference to the nucleus of the maturing ovum, another table of maturation may be presented. This relates to stages beginning at stage 7 in the preceding table.

1 — leptotene (sometimes called dictyate)
2 — late leptotene (or dictyate)
3 — chromatin mass (pachytene, diplotene)
4 — diakenesis
5 — first pre-metaphase I
6 — first meiotic metaphase I
7 — first anaphase I and telophase I, first polar body formation

8 — second pre-metaphase II
9 — second metaphase II (time of ovulation) and fertilization
10 — second polar body formation (penetration of the ovum by the spermatozoon and syngamy of the male and female pronuclei follow)

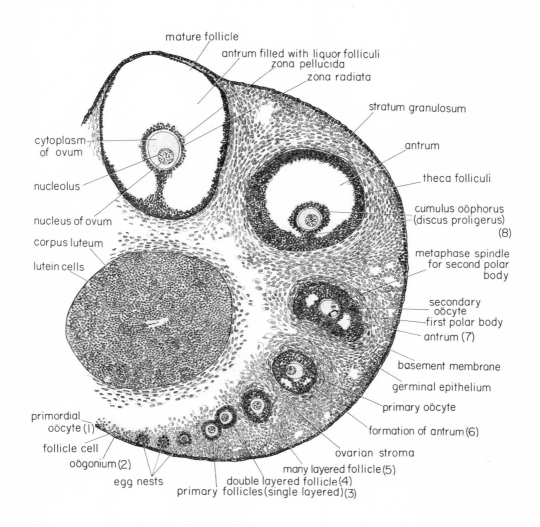

mature follicle
antrum filled with liquor folliculi
zona pellucida
zona radiata
stratum granulosum
cytoplasm of ovum
antrum
theca folliculi
nucleolus
cumulus oöphorus (discus proligerus) (8)
nucleus of ovum
metaphase spindle for second polar body
corpus luteum
lutein cells
secondary oöcyte
first polar body
antrum (7)
basement membrane
germinal epithelium
primary oöcyte
formation of antrum (6)
primordial oöcyte (1)
follicle cell
oögonium (2)
egg nests
ovarian stroma
many layered follicle (5)
double layered follicle (4)
primary follicles (single layered) (3)

DEVELOPMENT OF THE MOUSE OVUM AND OVARIAN FOLLICLE
(Parenthetical numbers refer to maturation stages — see text)

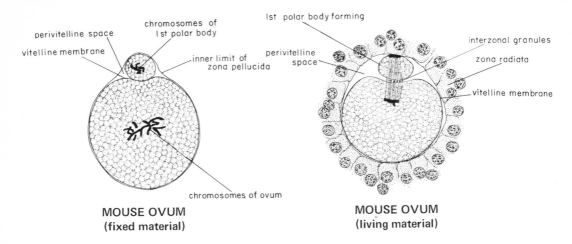

MOUSE OVUM
(fixed material)

MOUSE OVUM
(living material)

C. OVULATION: Ovulation is the liberation of the mature ovum from its follicle into the periovarial space. This process is not cataclysmic,
as was once thought, but takes from 30 to 45 minutes. The ovary itself pulsates,
most frequently and vigorously during estrus.   The fluid within the enlarging
antrum, the liquor folliculi, becomes more viscous as the time for rupture of
the follicle approaches.   There is some evidence that a second grade of liquor
folliculi appears, first among cells of the cumulus oöphorus, causing the cumulus to become detached from its base and to float freely with its ovum in the
antrum.   During these preovulation changes the nuclear membrane of the ovum
disappears, and the scattered chromatin granules aggregate as small, dense

chromosomes. Unlike most animal
cells an ovum often appears to have
no centrioles or astral rays. Nevertheless, a spindle forms, and the
newly assembled (tetraploid) chromosome line up in pairs along the
equatorial plate. The chromosome
pairs then divide and the two members of each pair move toward opposite spindle poles. One pole with
its chromosomes becomes the first
polar body, to be extruded and to
lie within the vitelline membrane.
(Stage 7). Since the first polar body
is not always seen, it is believed to
either escape the perivitelline space
or become fragmented, or cytolyzed.
Immediately the remaining chromosomes, which are diploid, anticipate
the next division, which will give
rise to the second polar body. The
second polar body spindle is forming at the time of ovulation, and remains in metaphase until fertilization.

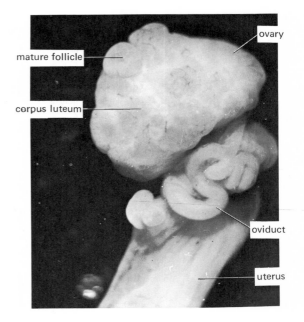

ACTIVELY OVULATING MOUSE OVARY

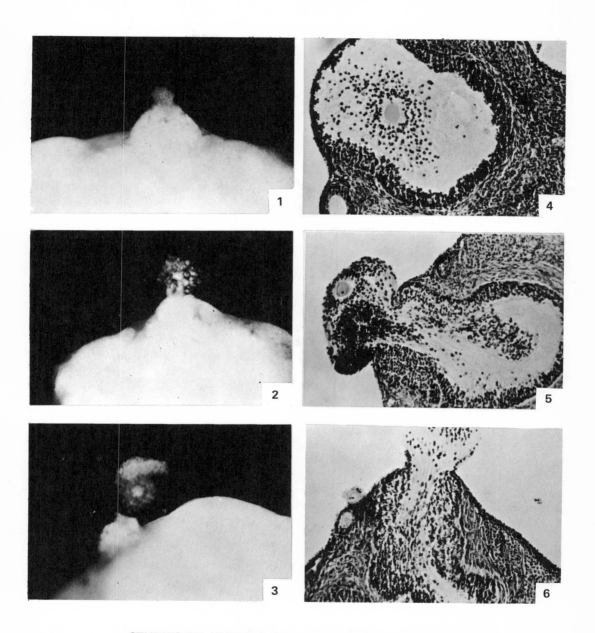

STUDIES ON *IN VITRO* OVULATION IN VERTEBRATES
S. NADAMITSU
(Jour. Sci. Hiroshima Univ., Ser. B. Div. 1, Vol. 20; 27-32, 1961)

Both in the vicinity of the matured follicle and in the medulla of the ovary will be seen large vessels engorged with blood.   Each ovum must rupture through the granulosa cells, the stretched tunica albuginea, and the much flattened germinal epithelium.   The periovarial space becomes congested with cells, fluid, and the ovum.   Opposite to the area of rupture the theca interna and the granulosa cells may be thrown into folds, owing to the collapse of the follicle and the reduction in fluid pressure.   Up to 10 ova may be liberated from a single ovary during a short period of time, to aggregate in the region of the infundibulum.   The many cilia of the infundibulum quickly transport the mature ova into the ampulla of the oviduct, where fertilization can occur.   Because of the slight stickiness of the liquor folliculi the ova tend to clump together.

The mean time for the onset of estrus in a normal female mouse is 4 to 6 hours after the onset of darkness in these nocturnal animals.   Ovulation occurs from 2 to 3 hours after the onset of estrus.   Both events are therefore correlated with the diurnal light cycle and can be shifted if that cycle is shifted.   In general, ovulation occurs at about the mid-point of the dark period, sometime between 2 and 4 A.M. under normal conditions.   The secondary oöcyte stays in metaphase for some 6 hours and then goes into anaphase, which takes 1.2 hours, and on into telophase, which takes only 0.2 hours.   The separation of the second polar body depends upon the time of fertilization.   The first sign of the approach of the final division is the condensation of the chromatin, which may be seen in the first hours of normal darkness on the night when ovulation is to occur.

Prepuberal mice can be induced to ovulate by treatment with hormones and generally respond by superovulating, producing up to 100 ova.   Gonadotrophic hormones cause ovulation and render a female receptive to a male.   A daily dose of 0.125 to 0.25 milligrams of progesterone ensures implantation and a dose of 1.0 to 2.0 milligrams maintains pregnancy.   Relaxin facilitates delivery, administered at 13, 16, and 19 days gestation.   A combination of progesterone and relaxin stimulates lactation.   Since the uterus of a prepuberal female is spatially inadequate and ill prepared for such large numbers of ova, pre-implantation and fetal mortality are high and the fetuses that survive are best delivered by Caesarian section.   In practice a female of 3 to 6 weeks of age is injected intraperitoneally with 10-15 international units (I.U.) of follicle stimulating pregnant mare serum (PMS) in 0.9% NaCl and 35 to 40 hours later with 10-15 I.U. of human gonadotropic hormone (HCG).   In 12 to 16 hours she will be actively ovulating and may be exposed to sexually mature males to insure fertilization of the ovulated ova.   This method is ideal for providing demonstration or teaching material of ova, or at about 24 to 32 hours after fertilization two cell embryos may be obtained from the ampulla of the oviduct. *

The rupture of the ovarian follicle is not associated with any appreciable hemorrhage in the mouse.   There simply remains a small gap in the follicle wall.   But the loss of tension following the escape of fluid allows the blood

*A basic culture medium for the 2 cell mouse embryo, as reported by Brinster (1965) follows. Ova should be cultured in small drops of medium under liquid paraffin oi.

	Gms/liter		Gms/liter
NaCl	6.97	NaHCO3	2.106
KCl	0.356	Ca lactate	1.147
CaCl	0.189	Penicillin	100 u/ml
KH2PO4	0.162	Streptomycin	50 ug/ml
MgSO4	0.294	Crystalline bovine serum albumin	1.000

capillaries in the surrounding area to repair the damage in about 2 hours, after which the vestiges of the follicle are known as the corpus luteum. The cells of the theca interna project into the follicle, along with the remaining granulosa cells. They are soon invaded by capillaries to form radially arranged trabeculae which occupy the original antrum. The cells are later filled with a yellowish lutein substance. These changes require active cell proliferation in both the theca interna and the granulosa layers, as well as the growth of capillaries. The granulosa cells then hypertrophy to increase the volume of the corpus luteum. The transformation from granulosa cells to lutein cells is gradual. The granulosa cells are small with darkly staining nuclei and basophilic cytoplasm, while the lutein cells are large and polyhedral, with eosinophilic cytoplasm.

The corpus luteum marks the site of a follicle that has liberated its ovum. The presence of a number of such lutein masses in an ovary does not inhibit further ovulation, and they may be seen in an ovary with mature follicles. The presence of actively secreting corpora lutea is essential for the continued nutrition of the free blastocyst, and it prevents the degeneration of ova. However, as estrus approaches, the fat and lipoid content of the corpora lutea increases, and the lipid granules coarsen. On the other hand, after ovulation there is very little lipid found in the previous corpus luteum. If fertilization does not take place the corpora lutea begin to degenerate in 10 to 12 days, leaving only fibrous and fatty scar tissue. If fertilization does take place, lipids do not accumulate in the corpora until about halfway through gestation (8 or 9 days), and the granules are smaller than in the corpora of a non-pregnant animal. At 13 days of gestation a corpus has reached its maximum diameter of about 1 mm, and at 18 days it begins to shrink. It does not completely disappear for some days after parturition, remnants persisting during lactation and for 5 to 6 weeks. Evidence exists for corpora lutea of lactation, which are formed after the birth of a litter. These generally remain small, with their cells having small nuclei and cytoplasm relatively free of fat.

There are cyclic fluctuations in the gonadotropic hormone content of the pituitary gland during pregnancy, with maxima at about 12.5 and 15.5 days, and a gradual increase in the release of the hormone. Gonadotropic hormone is augmented during the last half of pregnancy by luteinizing hormone. Simultaneously the acidophilic granules of the pituitary tend to disappear, an event suggesting that they may be one source of the luteinizing hormone during pregnancy.

As the corpora lutea degenerate so do many follicles. Frequently degeneration begins in the ovum itself and proceeds to the surrounding cells and tissues. The ovum and its nucleus may exhibit bizarre configurations. If the zona pellucida has already formed, it remains as a halo around the disappearing follicle. The vitelline membrane arises from the ovum itself; the zona pellucida comes from the surrounding follicle cells; the cumulus oöphorus consists of follicle cells and an intercellular matrix of acidic mucopolysaccharide, hyaluronic acid, and protein. The corona radiata are the innermost layer of cumulus cells.

D. THE OVIDUCTS:
The oviducts are tubes extending from the periovarial spaces to the uterine horns. They have been described as transport tunnels through which the fertilizing spermatozoon moves in one direction and

the fertilized ovum in the other.   Each begins with a ciliated and fimbriated
infundibulum (or ostium) within the periovarial space.   The ciliated epithelium
of the infundibulum beats rapidly and forms a current in the basic (pH 8.05)
oviduccal fluid that draws liberated ova into it and thence to the bulbous, and
thin-walled ampulla.   The ampulla itself is not highly ciliated; it appears to be
an expandable sac, dilating during estrus, in which the ova may accumulate to
await fertilization.   The ampulla is continuous with a narrow looped tube of the
oviduct lined with simple, low columnar non-ciliated epithelium.   The second
loop of the oviduct exhibits peristaltic contractions some 12 to 16 seconds apart
during ova transport.   This coiled duct joins a uterine horn eccentrically at its
cephalic end, projecting into it.   The entire oviduct is invested with a coat of
smooth muscle fibers, which aid in propelling the ova to the uterus.   There is
probably a specific pattern of muscular contractions of the oviduct which causes
the eggs to rotate as they progress downward.   There is also deposited onto the
eggs, from the glandular cells of the oviduct, a mucous coating outside the zona
pellucida, which may aid in the adhesion of the eggs to the uterine mucosa at
implantation.   Adhesion may precede actual invasion by several hours.

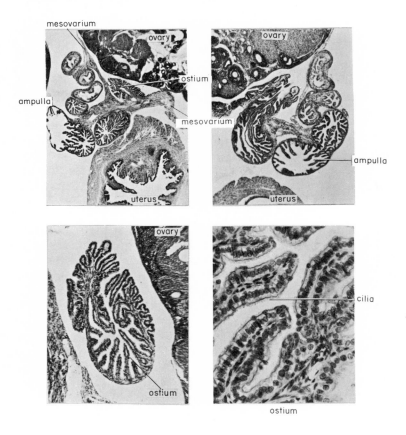

FIMBRIATED OSTIUM OF THE MOUSE

E. THE UTERUS: The uterus has two horns and a caudal section, corpus uteri, that is undivided.   In other words, it is shaped like a "Y" with a very short stem.   The bulk of its tissue is muscular; it has an outer layer of longitudinal smooth muscle fibers and an inner layer of circular smooth muscle fibers.   The lining of its folds is simple columnar epithelium, with numerous spiral tubular uterine glands.   The lamina propria contains small polyhedral cells with large, round nuclei as well as clusters of lymphocytes. The endometrium is really the mucosal layer in the nonpregnant animal, consisting of the lamina propria, the lining epithelium, the uterine glands, and many blood vessels.   The small polyhedral cells of the endometrium change into the large decidual cells of the placenta during pregnancy.   The fluid of the uterine lumen is slightly more alkaline than the surrounding peritoneal fluid.

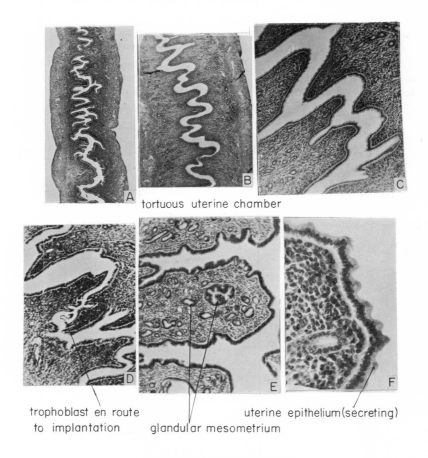

tortuous uterine chamber

trophoblast en route
to implantation   glandular mesometrium   uterine epithelium(secreting)

UTERUS OF THE MOUSE

The myometrium (peripheral to the endometrium) consists of the compact circular muscles, an enclosing layer of loose connective tissue with blood and lymph vessels, and finally the longitudinal muscles.   There the outermost enclosing layer of the uterus is a serious membrane which connects the uterine horns to the broad ligaments.

At their caudal ends the two horns are separated only by a septum consisting of longitudinal muscle and connective tissue. The tissue elements for implantation are absent from this region, which is lined with cuboidal cells. The corpus uteri projects into the short vagina, its mid-dorsal and mid-ventral wall being fused to the vaginal walls, to form a traplike space on either side (the fornix). The opening of the uterus into the vagina is through the cervix, which is lined with stratified squamous epithelium.

The maximum growth of the uterus occurs between 2.5 and 5 months of age, with the maximum RNA/DNA ratio at the latter time. The RNA content is correlated with the water content of the uterus and the amount of protein nitrogen synthesized. In a pregnant uterus the DNA content increases up to 15 days gestation and then levels off at 1400 to 1700 micrograms. The first pregnancy brings about the final maturation of the uterus. Electrical (EMG) techniques have been used to record the phasic activity in the non-pregnant as well as the early pregnant uterus, and changes in the intra-amniotic pressures of gravid mice. Spontaneous uterine contractions average one in 48 seconds on gestational day 10.5, and also at parturition, with a gradual increase in rate to days 19.5 and 20.5 when a mean interval of 32 seconds can be recorded. Pressures are greater in the earlier (11.5 day) gestation periods. Uterine contractions are autogenic in origin, and are not related to litter size in the pregnant mice. Strain specificity differences exist only during the early stages of pregnancy. Contraction rate does increase gradually as pregnancy progresses. (Pers. Com. M. L. Wood).

F. THE ESTROUS CYCLE:
The stages of maturation and estrus can be determined by analysis of vaginal smears. The changes are related to the diurnal light cycle and can be experimentally altered. The diurnal response may be controlled by the eyes, the central nervous system, and/or the anterior pituitary gland. The major normal stages and their characteristics are as follows:

PROESTRUS   — anabolic, active growth in the genital tract; a swollen and congested uterus; an open vaginal orifice; largely nucleated, and some cornified, epithelium in the vaginal smear. The duration is 1 to 1.5 days.

ESTRUS   — or heat; anabolic, active growth in the genital tract, a swollen and congested vulva, an open vaginal orifice, no leukocytes but both nucleated and cornified (not clumped) epithelia in the vaginal smear. Duration is 1 to 3 days.

METESTRUS 1 — catabolic, degenerative changes in the genital tract, clumped cornified epithelium exclusively in the vaginal smear.

METESTRUS 2 — catabolic, degenerative changes in the genital tract; nucleated and cornified epithelium and leukocytes in the vaginal smear. Both metestrus stages take from 1 to 5 days.

DIESTRUS   — quiescent period of slow growth; nucleated epithelium, leukocytes, and some mucous in the vaginal smear. The duration is 2 to 4 days.

Vaginal smears are best obtained by means of an ordinary pipette, the tip of which has been flamed to a smooth, reduced aperture. A few drops of 0.9% sodium chloride solution are drawn into the pipette, introduced into the vagina and then retracted into the pipette. The fluid is transferred to a slide and

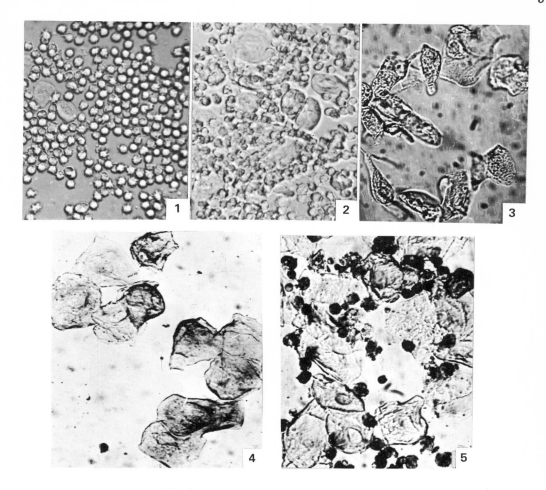

PHASES OF ESTRUS IN THE MOUSE

1 — Diestrus   — almost exclusively leukocytes, from vaginal smear.
2 — Pro-Estrus   — showing both leukocytes and nucleated epithelial cells in approximately
                    equal numbers.
3 — Early Estrus — showing clearly defined epithelial cells, some with distinct nuclei.
4 — Estrus   — large, squamous-type epithelial cells without nuclei.
5 — Post-Estrus   — showing approximately equal numbers of leukocytes and epithelial cells,
                    but the latter are large, folded, and with translucent nuclei.

Mating generally occurs during stages 2 to 4 above, but these stages have relatively short duration. The major portion of the 5-day cycle is spent in diestrus.

(From R. Rugh, "Experimental Embryology", Burgess Publishing Co., Minneapolis, 1962.)

mounted under a coverslip with a trace of methylene blue to add contrast and
bring out the nuclei. Examination for cell types is carried out under low and
then high power magnification, with reduced lighting. Cells may be nucleated
or cornified (old, non-nucleated) epithelial cells or leukocytes. The nucleated
epithelium is generally oval or polygonal, with obvious nuclei that stain readily.
The cornified epithelium appears to be very thin and much folded. As estrus
approaches, there may also be some mucous present, easily identified by the
proper stain. The phases through which the vaginal cells go represent parallel
changes in the entire reproductive tract and are hence diagnostic.

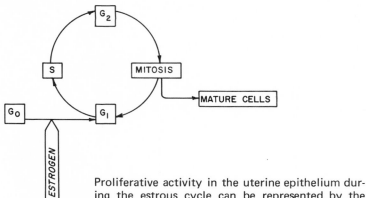

Proliferative activity in the uterine epithelium during the estrous cycle can be represented by the accompanying diagram. During diestrous, most of the cells are in what is called a G_0 phase — that is, cells that can synthesize DNA and subsequently undergo mitosis, but will not do so until the appropriate output of ovarian estrogen is attained. When this level of estrogen is reached there is a transition to a presynthetic or postmitotic interphase (G_1) — that is, to cells that will synthesize DNA (S phase) in the near future. These cells then enter the S phase and subsequently divide. Some of these cells progress through another generative cycle; others mature. The post synthetic or premitotic interphase is G_2. (See Perrotta '62).

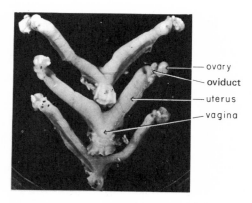

CHANGES IN THE UTERUS ATTENDANT UPON ESTRUS

Three entire genital structures of female mice.
Above — pro-estrus
Middle — estrus, note swelling of uteri
Lower — post-estrus, note shrinkage of uteri

G. VAGINA, CLITORIS, AND CLITORAL GLANDS:
As noted the vagina is lined with stratified squamous epithelium which undergoes cyclic changes. The mucous membrane of the vagina displays no glands; the lamina propria is vascular and fibrous; the thin muscular coat contains both circular and longitudinal fibers; and the outer wall consists of loose connective tissue. The vagina is dorso-ventrally flattened. Its opening to the exterior is the vulva, anterior to which is the clitoris, homologous to the penis of the male but lacking in erectile tissue. There is a small clitoral pouch (fossa) into which open the urethra dorsally and the two clitoral glands laterally. The clitoral glands are comparable to the preputial glands of the male, except that each contains a single hair follicle and elaborates a sebaceous-like secretion.

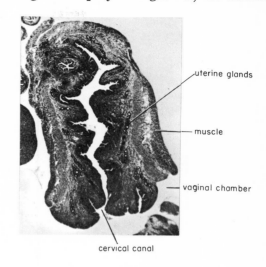

uterine glands

muscle

vaginal chamber

cervical canal

THE CERVIX

H. MAMMARY GLANDS:
The mouse has five pairs of mammary glands, three thoracic and two inguino-abdominal. In the female they undergo changes associated with estrus, pregnancy, and lactation. The glands are rudimentary in the male.

The nipple of each mammary gland consists of three epidermal layers; the stratum germanitivum, the stratum granulosum, and the stratum corneum, covered by elastic skin. A single major duct in the stratum germanitivum leads into subcutaneous fat pads, where it forms a framework of ducts, none of which is connected with any other mammary gland. Each duct is lined with cuboidal epithelium and surrounded by circular connective tissue fibers. Just before puberty (at 6 weeks of age) and just before estrus in the mature mouse the subcutaneous ducts extend and expand, and their lining epithelium becomes mitotically active. A "spreading factor" from the end bulbs of the growing ducts helps break down some component of the surrounding connective tissue, possibly the ground substance.

The amount of "spreading factor" in the mammary gland during pregnancy closely parallels growth of the gland, reaching a maximum at two-thirds of the way through the gestation period and declining during the last third of the period, when the cells of the gland begin their secretion. Practically speaking the elaboration or activation of the factor ceases as secretion begins.

At about 11 days gestation the epithelial elements of the mammary gland start increasing, to form alveoli, and at 14 days an alveolar system is well established, in anticipation of lactation. Secretory activity begins in the alveoli near the nipple and progresses distally, until at 17 days gestation the entire gland is involved. Vascularization of the gland is concomitant with alveolar

TABLE 4

CHANGES IN THE REPRODUCTIVE TRACT CORRELATED WITH ESTRUS

STAGE	VAGINAL SMEAR	OVARY & OVIDUCT	UTERUS	VAGINA
PROESTRUS	Epithelium, cornified cells and leukocytes	Follicles large (380μ) with liquor folliculi. Few mitoses.	Some hyperemia and hydration. Mitosis, few leukocytes. Glandular	Cell proliferation, many mitoses, few leukocytes. Gaping vulva. Vaginal weight maximal.
ESTRUS	More cornified than nucleated epithelial cells.	Follicles 550μ in diameter. Ovulation: Oviduct enlarged (distended). Mitoses in germinal epithelium and follicular cells. Plasma progesterone maximum.	No leukocytes: maximum mitosis and hydration . Glands active.	Outer nucleated layer lost, replaced by cornified cells. Deep cellular proliferation. Gaping vulva.
METESTRUS I	Exclusively and abundant cornified cells.	Corpora lutea; ova in oviduct; some follicular atresia.	Hydration and distension decreased; leukocytic invasion.	Cornified cells desquamated; leukocytes begin to appear.
METESTRUS II	Abundant cornified and nucleated epithelial cells; and leukocytes begin to appear.	Corpora lutea enlarging; ova moving toward uterus. Less activity in germinal epithelium.	Leukoctyic invasion; mitosis rare; uterine wall and epithelium degenerating. Glands least active.	Many leukocytes and layers of true epithelial cells.
DIESTRUS	Both cornified and nucleated epithelial cells, plus mucous	Follicles begin rapid growth for next ovulation.	Mucous, glands and walls collapsed; many leukocytes, anemic. No gland activity, beginning of regeneration.	Leukocytes and epithelial cells; begin active proliferation. Vaginal weight minimal.

development, and the fat pads tend to disappear. During lactation, which reaches its peak at 14 days after parturition, the ducts and alveoli are dilated with milk. Suckling generally continues for 3 weeks. Any unused glands (and all the glands at the end of suckling) regress. In a resting gland fat droplets accumulate in the cytoplasm of the fibroblasts, the fat pads reform, the lumina of the ducts narrow, and the surrounding connective tissue sheaths thicken. The gland remains at rest until the next pregnancy. When senility sets in, it begins a gradual involution.

Estradiol - 17ß alone promotes proliferation of the mammary epithelium but causes little alveolar differentiation. Progesterone alone promotes both epithelial proliferation and alveolar differentiation. The two hormones together exercise an additive action on cell proliferation and greatly augment alveolar differentiation. Testosterone administered to a female at 12 days gestation inhibits development of the mammary glands. It has no effect on the mammary glands of a male. Curiously, the second (or thoracic) and fourth (or inguinal) pairs of glands are the most affected.

Chapter  NORMAL DEVELOPMENT OF THE MOUSE

GESTATION DAYS	STAGE
1	1 to 2 cell stage in ampulla of oviduct
2	2 to 16 cell, in transit through oviduct to uterus
3	Morula, in upper uterus
4	Free blastocysts in uterus, shedding of zona pellucida
4.5	Implantation beginning, inner cell mass, trophoblastic cone
5	Pendant inner cell mass, endoderm, proamniotic cavity, primitive streak
6	Implantation complete, extraembryonic parts developing, uterine reaction
7	Ectoplacental cone, amniotic folds, primitive streak, mesenchyme, heart, pericardium forming, head process
7.5	Early neurula, neural plate, chorioamniotic stalk, embryonic lordosis, allantoic stalk beginning, pendant inner cell mass with 3 cavities, exocoelom, amniotic cavity, somites beginning to differentiate, foregut
8	Somites 1 to 4, visceral arch I, Reichert's membrane, pre-germ cells in yolk sac endoderm, embryonic lordosis, ectochorionic cyst fused with ectoplacenta and also with allantoic stalk; early regression of yolk sac; heart primordia, thyroid, optic sulcus, 1st aortic arch.
9	Somites 5 to 12, visceral arch II, disc and yolk sac placenta, embryo begins to reverse lordosis to curve ventrally with germ layers in proper relation, otic invagination, liver, 2 pharyngeal pouches, nephrogenic cord.
9.5	Somites 21 to 25, yolk stalk closes, primary germ cells migrating via mesentery to final site, primitive streak gone, tail, limb and lung buds forming, mesonephric tubules, 3 pharyngeal pouches.
10	Somites 26 to 28, visceral arch III, lung buds, pronephros reaches cloaca, posterior limb bud and lens forming, GI tract developing, sense organs differentiating, aortic arches I, II, and III.
11	Somites 29 to 42, total length 6.2 mm., thyroid, umbilical hernia, meso- and metanephros in early stages of formation; ventral pancreatic rudiment, uretric bud and mesonephric ducts to U.G. sinus, endocardial cushion fused, epiphysis and hypophysis evaginate, subcardinals formed, olfactory fibers to the brain, pigment in retina, lens cells elongate, aortic arches IV and V.

GESTATION DAYS

12	Somites 43 to 48, bronchi, aortic arch $\underline{V}$ gone, and $\underline{VI}$ reduced, vitreous humor, pancreatic rudiments, mammary welts, ribs and centrum chondrify, secondary bronchi, posterior cardinals degenerate, epithelial cords in testis, choroid fissure closed, superior vena cava enters heart.
13	Somites 49 to 60, cephalization resulting in brain differentiation, spinal ganglia, histological sex differentiation, active and complete circulation, atrioventricular valve, interventricular septum complete, nerves in optic stalk, otic capsule pre-cartilaginous, esophageal sub-mucosa thickens, neuroblasts in retina, enucleate red cells 1%.
14	Somites 61 to 63, total length 9.6 mm., digital development, umbilical hernia receding, mesonephros degenerating and metanephros becoming functional, diaphragm completed, gonad primordia becoming vascular, intestinal villi, ossification of frontal and zygomatic, saccule and utricle separated, enucleate red cells 25%, aortic pulmonary semilunars.
15	Somites 64 and 65, snout protruding from face and lifts off chest, hair follicles developing, digits clear, body contour more rounded, cartilage in humerus, centrum and ribs ossifying, nucleated red cells 5%, stratum granulosum, cerebellum fused at mid-line.
16	All somites formed, differentiating from anterior to posterior, fetal stage, eyelids, pinnae cover ears, umbilical hernia withdrawn, ossification proceeding, 16 mm. length, corpus callosum formed, centrum ossified, nucleated red cells down to 1%, proliferation of gastric glands.
17	Eyelids sealed, extra embryonic membranes reach maximum development, tail alone now 10 mm. length.
19 to 20	Birth

Thus far we have described the genital anatomy of male and female mice, and given a brief chronology of development. Now we may proceed with the details of development from mating and fertilization, through cleavage, blastulation, gastrulation, implantation, and organogenesis, to birth of the fully formed, relatively independent mouse.

A. MATING: The female mouse, like most other female mammals (except the anthropoids and man), copulates only during estrus when ova are or become ready for fertilization. Since estrus usually begins around midnight, mating is most common during the night hours generally about 2 A.M. However, it can occur in the early morning or late evening, during short exposures of female to male. Thus the time variable in estimating embryonic or post-fertilization age can be reduced. Evening matings resulting in fertilization probably depend upon the survival of the spermatozoa in the female genital tract until the subsequent ovulation, and morning matings resulting in fertilization upon the presence of ova in the ampulla of the oviduct. Our practice is to mate from 8 to 8:45 A.M., to catch ripe eggs ovulated 6 to 8 hours earlier. Overnight matings give a time range of some 16 hours, instead of two or less.

Generally a male is placed in a box containing five or six females and removed 45 minutes or more later. Evidence of successful mating is a vaginal plug, a coagulum of fluid from the vesicular and coagulating glands of the male

that occludes the vaginal orifice. The plug can be produced even by a vasectomized male. It usually hardens to such a degree that mechanical removal can
injure the vaginal mucosa and the uterine ligaments. Our experience with this
short period of mating has shown that we get an average of 6.98% vaginal plugs,
and 92.4% of these result in pregnancies. When sexually experienced males
are available an average of 8.5% plugs may be achieved in a randomly exposed
group of females having various stages of estrous. When neither male or fe-

male is sexually experienced,
but sexually mature (10 + weeks
of age), the average percentage
of plugs may be as low as 3.5%
Theoretically only about 10% of
a large group of sexually mature females might be found in
estrous at the time of mating,
hence receptive of the male.
Spermatozoa introduced into the
vagina may be found in the ampulla of the oviduct within minutes, but they retain their motility and fertilizing power so
that as much as 8 hours may
elapse between copulation and
fertilization of the ova.

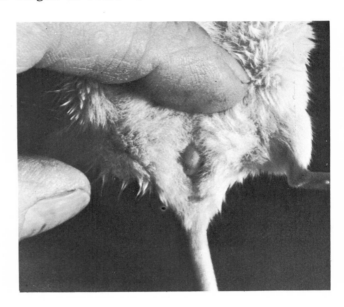

VAGINAL ORIFICE OF MOUSE,
SHOWING VAGINAL PLUG

Mating involves active
inspection of the female genitalia by the male and lack of
resistance by the female, with
a tendency toward lordosis.
Courtship continues for 15 to
20 minutes or less if the male
is vigorous and sexually experienced. Mounting is attempted and, if successful, repeated a number of times until intromission has been accomplished and
semen has been deposited in the vagina. It is estimated that an average of
60,000,000 sperm may be deposited in an ejaculate. A brief period of quiescence, particularly on the part of the male follows, after which normal activities
are resumed. Other males present may attempt to mount the female subsequently but usually fail. Litters have been produced fathered by two males.
Some males can mate with two (in 45 minutes) or even three (in 2 hours) susceptible females in succession making all such females pregnant. Under normal conditions coitus precedes ovulation by sometimes as much as 5 hours but
may follow ovulation by as much as 8 hours. Strain differences in frequency of
mating or time for recovery before a second mating can be achieved by a male
vary from 1 hour to 4 days. Hybrid mice are most vigorous and recover most
rapidly.

Some semen passes out through the cervix, but since the vaginal plug may
persist for several days, more remains in the uterus. Leukocytes rapidly in-
filtrate the lumen when it is filled with semen and during the first day after
mating most of the spermatozoa disappear owing to the phagocytic action of the
scavenging white cells. Apparently only 100 or so spermatozoa survive to
reach the ampulla of the oviduct to fertilize the available ova.

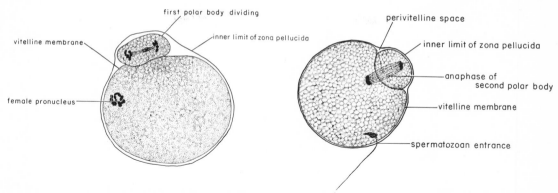

first polar body dividing

vitelline membrane

inner limit of zona pellucida

female pronucleus

perivitelline space

inner limit of zona pellucida

anaphase of second polar body

vitelline membrane

spermatozoan entrance

PREFERTILIZATION — MATURE OVUM   **FERTILIZATION — ½ HOUR AFTER MATING**

The progress of spermatozoa to the ampulla is aided by the peristaltic action of the muscles of the oviduct wall. Sperm can pass from cervix to ampulla in 15 minutes.

B. FERTILIZATION:
Fertilization consists in the activation of the ovum by a spermatozoon and the union of the male and female pronuclei, a process known as syngamy. It is a means of preventing the natural death of the ovum. The entire operation occurs in the ampulla of the oviduct, where the fertilizable life of the ovum has been estimated at 15 hours. Activation stimulates the ovum to complete its interrupted second meiotic division, by which it becomes haploid, and syngamy restores the normal diploid number of chromosomes. Second polar body formation may take as long as 2 hours.

Since ova are surrounded by a slightly sticky secretion, they tend to clump together but the clumping does not seem to interfere with fertilization. However, the cumulus oöphorus cells and the zona pellucida must undergo certain changes before fertilization can take place. The zona pellucida is essentially a homogeneous but layered matrix with irregular areas of varying density, and both inner and outer surfaces ragged. * The cumulus (corona) cells have extensions embedded in the zona which break after a few hours in the ampulla, possibly as a result of dispersal by the enzyme hyaluronidase. The corona cells retract their cytoplasmic extensions from the zona canaliculi.

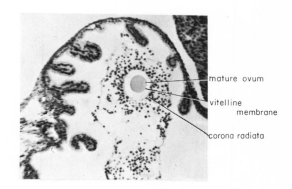

mature ovum

vitelline membrane

corona radiata

AMPULLA OF MOUSE OVIDUCT
Mature mouse ovum in ampulla awaiting fertilization by mature spermatozoon which must penetrate the surrounding zone radiata (cumulus oöphorus cells). This is aided by the elaboration of the enzyme hyaluronidase from the head of the sperm.

* The zona pellucida can be preserved best by glutaraldehyde-osmium or permanganate.

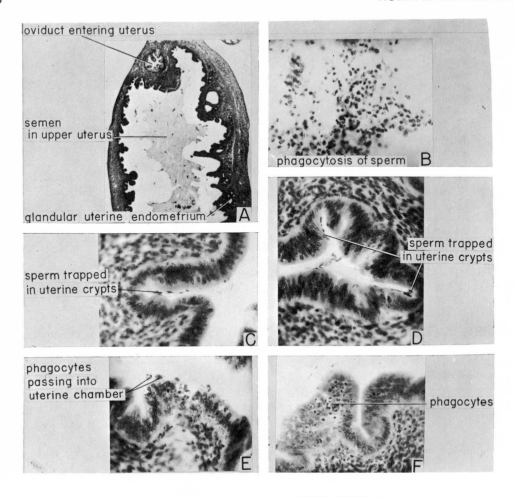

MOUSE UTERUS 1 HOUR AFTER MATING

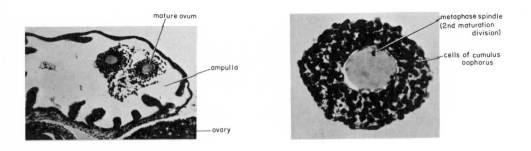

**MOUSE OVA IN AMPULLA
AWAITING FERTILIZATION**

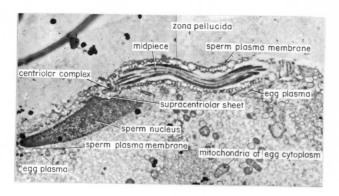

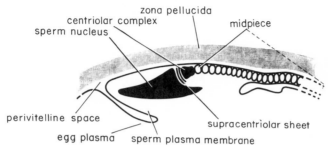

Upper figure - Rat sperm in process of penetrating egg, shown in electron microscopy.

Lower figure - A diagrammatic representation of sperm seen above, illustrating the behaviour of the egg and sperm plasma membranes during sperm entrance.

(Courtesy of D. G. Szollosi and H. Ris, 1961)

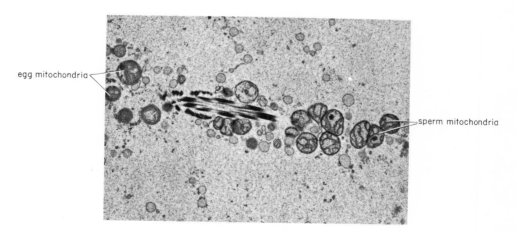

Electron micrograph of mouse egg one day after fertilization showing connection between mid-piece and principal piece of sperm tail. Sperm mitochondria to right and egg mitochondria to left.

(Courtesy of Dr. D. Szollosi)

Originally these extensions or processes have knoblike connections with the egg surface, and are presumed to convey nutriments to the egg during its development. Also, egg cortex microvilli pass into the zona. Both the extensions from the follicle cells and the microvilli are retracted upon explusion of the first polar body and the appearance of the perivitelline space. Remnants of the microvilli are seen to be most numerous at the point of polar body explusion, and at the site of sperm head entrance into the vitellus. About an hour elapses as sperm pass through the cumulus and zona pellucida. There is some evidence that fertilizin is present in the zona pellucida, and there may be some species specificity although hybrid crosses are easily accomplished. If present, it is probably similar to the fertilizin in other forms, consisting of a glyco-protein of high (82,000+) molecular weight. It presumably reacts with an antifertilizin substance identified as an acidic protein in a spermatozoon, its major function would be to attach a homologous spermatozoon to the coating of the ovum. If such a sperm agglutinin exists, it is in the zona. It is possible that the cortical granular response of the ovum releases an agent into the perivitelline space that reduces the penetrability of the zona pellucida to additional spermatozoa. It is believed that with the emission (abstriction) of the first polar body some perivitelline fluid is formed, and then when the sperm enters the vitellus causing the emission of the second polar body, further perivitelline fluid accumulates with the contraction of the vitellus. Such a "zona reaction", believed to take from 10 minutes to several hours, would be entirely independent of the second polar body spindle and would tend to block polyspermy although it is not completely effective. Some 20% of mouse eggs are found to have supplementary

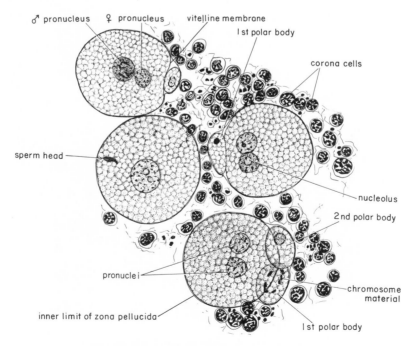

MOUSE OVA IN AMPULLA OF OVIDUCT
(10 hours after mating)

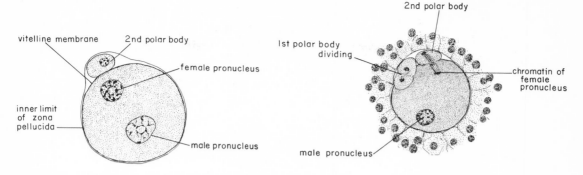

FERTILIZED OVUM (living material)   **MOUSE OVUM (fixed material)**

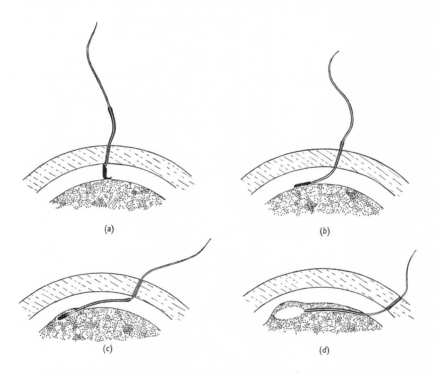

The figures illustrate four stages in the penetration of a rodent egg by a spermatozoon. (a) The spermatozoon head has just passed through the zona pellucida and made contact with the vitellus. (b) The spermatozoon head is lying flat upon the vitelline surface to which it is now attached. (c) The whole of the spermatozoon mid-piece has entered the egg and the head has passed through the surface of the vitellus. The spermatozoon head shows an early phase in its transformation to a male pronucleus—the posterior end of the head is becoming indistinguishable from the egg cytoplasm. (d) The head and mid-piece of the spermatozoon have now entered the vitellus. Transformation of the head has proceeded to the stage immediately before the appearance of nucleoli. The cytoplasmic elevation over the spermatozoon head, just evident in (c) has now become much larger.

(From Austin & Braden '56, J. Exp. Biol. 33:358-365)

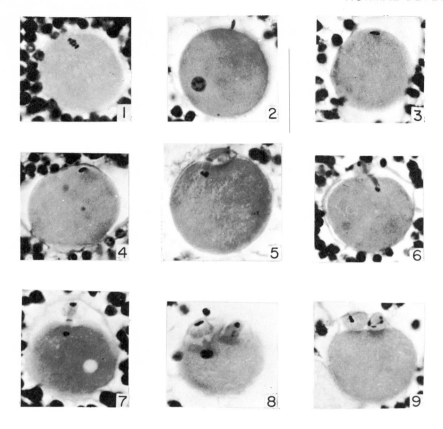

SPERM ENTRANCE AND SECOND
POLAR BODY FORMATION

Fig. 1 — Metaphase chromosomes of second maturation spindle at periphery of ovum found in ampulla surrounded by cumulus oöphorus cells.

Fig. 2 — Sperm head making contact at egg surface and female pronucleus seen at opposite pole, following second maturation division.

Fig. 3 — Sperm head (alone) just beneath surface of egg.

Fig. 4 — Sperm head moving into egg from surface.

Fig. 5 — Second maturation (metaphase) spindle seen tangentially.

Fig. 6 — Second maturation spindle in anaphase showing second polar body formation.

Fig. 7 — Same as Fig. 6 but direct view showing interzonal granules on spindle, and everted second polar body.

Fig. 8 — Two polar bodies in perivitelline space and mature egg nucleus within cytoplasm.

Fig. 9 — Clear view of two polar bodies surrounded by vitelline membrane.

spermatozoa. Another device for preventing polyspermy is the cumulus oöphorus cells which disappear after invasion by a spermatozoon and seem to alter the penetrability of the vitelline membrane.

The spindle for the formation of the second polar body, which has been lying parallel to the surface, turns 90 degrees so that one pole of the spindle is near the surface and the other deep within the ovum. The more peripheral pole attracts half of the chromosome material into the second polar body. The polar body has little cytoplasm. A nucleus occasionally reconstitutes within it, distinguishing it from the first polar body and its division products. The two polar bodies are rarely seen together in a mouse egg because of the plane of the section.

A female may be artificially inseminated by injection of semen through a 28 gauge needle into the periovarial space, the ampulla, the oviduct, or the uterus 1.5 to 4.5 hours after mating with a vasectomized male. Mid-ventral laparotomy is required unless insemination of only one side is proposed.

An active spermatozoon in the ampulla of the oviduct retains its capacity for fertilization for 8 hours, and generally all of the eggs of a single female are fertilized by 6 hours after mating. The delay is sometimes due to the necessity for the maturation of the cumulus cells. Some sperm-egg collisions occur within 15 minutes of mating. Cooled sperm can be used for fertilization up to 24 hours.

There is no evidence for the necessity of sperm capacitation in the mouse, as there seems to be in the rat. The mature spermatozoon passes rapidly through the zona pellucida and loses its acrosome, then comes into immediate contact with the vitelline membrane. There may be some evidence of a solid sperm penetration filament (SPF) which extends from the apex of the sperm head as it progresses through the zona pellucida, causing it to take a curved course. The presence of the SPF in the mouse has not been conclusively demonstrated as it has in the rabbit, pig, and sheep. The sperm head largely consists of deoxyribonucleoprotein, and does not penetrate the vitelline membrane at right angles but tangentially. The vitelline membrane may outpush somewhat, but the major effort is made by the spermatozoon. The acrosome probably aids in penetration. The fertilizing spermatozoon often remains attached to the surface of the egg for 30-40 minutes before proceeding. Penetration has been described as (1) a sort of specific phagocytic engulfing of the spermatozoon by the egg membrane (2) a brief rupture in the membrane permitting entrance of the spermatozoon, followed by closure of the membrane over the spermatozoon. The latter method appears to be the more likely. Penetration requires about 30 minutes. Usually the head separates from the middle piece and tail, and the tail does not necessarily enter the ovum. The tail undulates, propelling the sperm head forward and that part of the tail which penetrates the egg stops this movement, but the portion still in the perivitelline space continues to undulate. The forward motion averages 10 to 20 microns per lash of the tail. Also, the sperm plasma membrane remains intact around that portion of the spermatozoon still outside the vitellus, but at the surface of the ovum it is continuous with the egg plasma membrane. The sperm head which penetrates the vitellus lacks both the nuclear and plasma membranes.

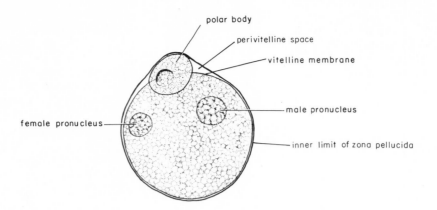

FORMATION OF MALE AND FEMALE PRONUCLEI

The activation of the ovum by the fertilizing spermatozoon starts before the enlargement of the head of the spermatozoon which occurs from 1 to 2 hours after penetration. The chromatin elements of the head disappear for a short while during this process. Swelling of the head begins at the posterior end and progresses anteriorly. The volume of the resulting pronucleus is several hundred times the original head volume, and usually two or three times the volume of the female pronucleus. The pronuclear volume depends upon material drawn from the cytoplasm, which limits the ultimate sizes. Both pronuclei appear to have double walls, and uniformly fine granules. The interval between penetration and formation of the male pronucleus is short in the mouse as compared with other rodents, but the interval between penetration and the first cleavage is long.

After fertilization, the zona pellucida expands, to give an overall diameter to the zona and ovum of about 114 microns. Since the ovum tends to shrink about 15%, a space appears, known as the perivitelline space, between it and the zona pellucida. The first polar body is occasionally visible in this space. The second polar body is discharged into it within 2 or 3 hours after fertilization. Then begins a boiling motion of the egg cytoplasm.

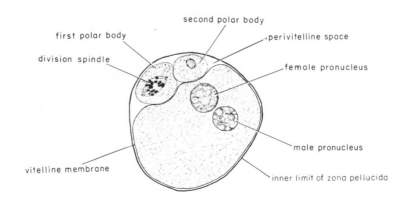

COMPLETION OF POLAR BODY FORMATION

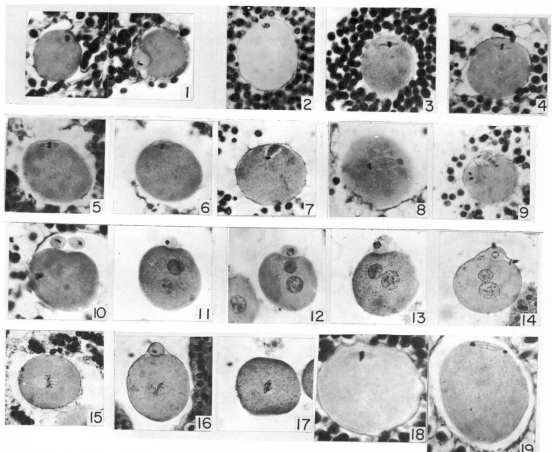

SECOND MATURATION DIVISION AND FIRST CLEAVAGE IN AMPULLA OF MOUSE

Fig. 1 — Two mouse ova surrounded by cumulus cells. One to left shows metaphase plate of second maturation spindle, hence is as yet unfertilized and one to right shows prominent first polar body within vitelline membrane.

Fig. 2 — Distinct chromosomes in metaphase at periphery anticipating first maturation division following fertilization.

Fig. 3 to 6 — Lateral views of metaphase spindle for second maturation division; condition of all ova in ampulla, awaiting fertilization.

Fig. 7 — Polar view of second maturation spindle.

Fig. 8 — View of entire spindle in anaphase of second maturation division, at surface of egg.

Fig. 9 — Tangential view of second maturation spindle in process of everting second polar body alongside first polar body, both within perivitelline space.

Fig. 10— First and second polar bodies free within the perivitelline space.

Fig. 11— Section showing male and female pronuclei (female nearest polar body) and everted second polar body.

Fig. 12 to 14 —Pronuclei approaching each other, and persistent polar body between the ovum and the perivitelline membrane (zona pellucida).

Fig. 15 — Metaphase spindle for first cleavage division of mouse egg about 14 hours after fertilization.

Fig. 16 — Same as Fig. 15 but showing polar body.

Fig. 17 — Beginning of cleavage furrow and early anaphase of chromosomes.

Fig. 18 — Enlarged view of mouse egg at time of fertilization, when the chromosomes are in metaphase prior to the second maturation division which occurs following the stimulation of fertilization (as in Figs. 3 to 6).

Fig. 20 — Lateral view of polar body formation showing entire spindle highly enlarged, with interzonal granules (as in Fig. 5).

Both male and female pronuclei may be seen as early as 6 hours after mating. The nucleus to cytoplasmic volume ratio of 1:30 is consistent for all mouse eggs, and is large compared with those of other mammals. The nucleus has a prominent nucleolus. The two pronuclei synthesize DNA before their fusion and each, with many distinctive acidophilic nucleoli and devoid of RNA, move toward each other, meeting near the center of the ovum. Occasionally the nucleoli may be found indented into the nuclear membrane. As they do so, they are considerably reduced in size. There is some question whether the primary mechanism in the cytoplasmic union of the gametes is a fusion of their membranes or a form of specific phagocytosis. Fertilization is considered to be complete when the pronuclei are almost contiguous and the first cleavage spindle is forming. Before the first cleavage the membranes of the pronuclei disappear, and the respective chromosomes form and split longitudinally. At the first cleavage two members of each chromosome tetrad move into each of the blastomeres so that a distinction between male and female chromatin elements is no longer possible. In other words representatives of each chromosome pass into the resulting blastomeres.

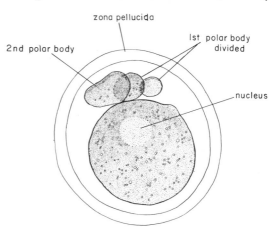

MOUSE EMBRYO — ONE CELL
2½ hours
(living material)

Anomalies associated with fertilization include anengamy (an abnormal number of pronuclei); *polyandry* (extra male pronuclei); *polygony* (extra female pronuclei); *dimegaly* (two sizes of spermatozoa) or *polymegaly* (many sizes of spermatozoa).

C. EARLY DEVELOPMENT:

a. *Cleavage:* Cleavage is total (holobastic) but slightly unequal in this meiolecithal egg. Its plane is believed to pass through the positions occupied by the centers of the two pronuclei in syngamy. But even in the earliest stages of development, patterns may be discerned that are peculiar to the species, and these may be related to cytological characteristics later to develop. Visible changes occur in the cristae of mitochondria of the early embryonic cells. Thus, there is no experimental evidence of the regulative capacity (totipotency) of the early mouse blastomere except that later blastocysts can be mechanically fused to derive an oversized blastocyst. The first of the cleavages begins in the ampulla of the oviduct about 24 hours after fertilization and continue for 2 to 3 days, even as the embryo moves into the uterus. Factors influencing its form are entirely maternal but the rate of cleavage is the inherent property of the zygote. The spermatozoon supplies the kinetic center in its proximal centriole and may affect the time to the second cleavage. The time interval to the first cleavage from fertilization ranges from 17 to 57 hours in different strains of mice. Difficulties in getting in-vitro zygotes to pass from the 1 to the 2 cell

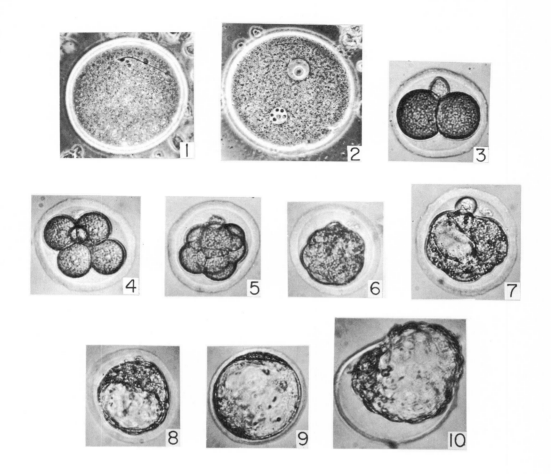

EARLY DEVELOPMENT OF THE MOUSE
(In vitro culture)

Fig. 1 — Fertilized egg 6 hours after ovulation, slightly compressed for better phase contrast photography. Note spermatozoon recently penetrated, lying beneath the vitelline membrane.

Fig. 2 — Zygote at 12 hours after ovulation showing male and female pronuclei, a polar body, remains of sperm middle piece and tail, and dispersing cumulus oöphorous.

Fig. 3 — Two-cell stage at 36 hours after ovulation, with polar body, within zona pellucida.

Fig. 4 — Four-cell stage at 58 hours, with polar body and zona pellucida.

Fig. 5 — Eight-cell stage, with polar body at 67 hours after ovulation, still in zona pellucida.

Fig. 6 — Morula stage at 82 hours after ovulation.

Fig. 7 — Early blastocyst stage at 93 hours with small blastocoel, and persistent polar body.

Fig. 8 — Blastocyst showing inner cell mass at 105 hours.

Fig. 9 — Blastocyst expanding with enlarging blastocoel to fill the zona pellucida and stretch it.

Fig. 10 — Blastocyst emerging from the zona pellucida in a hatching reaction which causes the rupture of the zona.

(Courtesy A. H. Gates, 1965, Ciba Foundation Symposium on Preimplantation Stages of Pregnancy, p. 270–288, eds. G. F. W. Wolstenholme and M. O'Connor; Pub. J. & A. Churchill, London.)

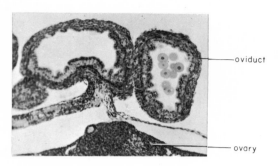

TWO CELL MOUSE EMBRYOS
32 hours after conception
(en route to the uterus)

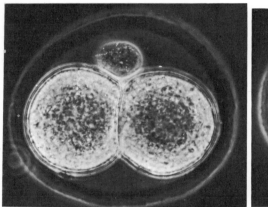
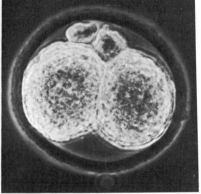

**TWO-CELL MOUSE EMBRYOS PHOTOGRAPHED BY PHASE,
SHOWING SINGLE & DOUBLE POLAR BODIES**

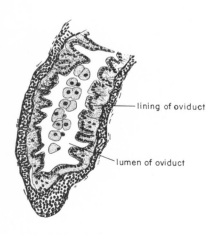
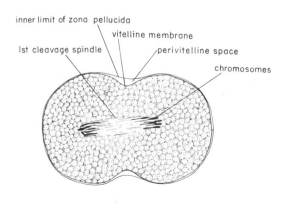

MOUSE OVA IN OVIDUCT
(2 cells — 24 hours)

BEGINNING OF FIRST CLEAVAGE

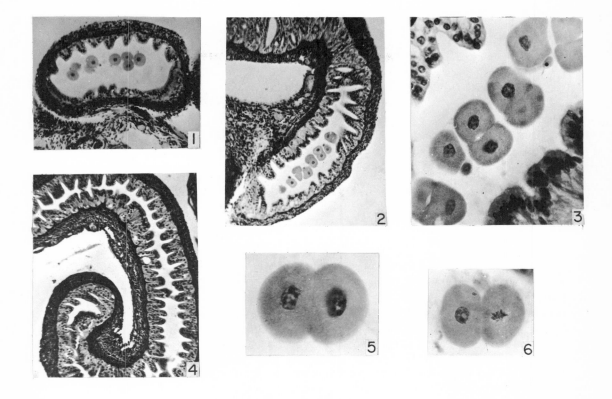

TWO CELL MOUSE EMBRYO
24 hours after fertilization

Fig. 1 — Ampulla of oviduct of mouse showing presence of five fertilized eggs in 1 and 2 cell stages.

Fig. 2 — Longitudinal section of oviduct showing mostly 2-cell mouse ova enroute to the uterus.

Fig. 3 — Enlarged view of two-cell mouse eggs showing distinct nuclei and cleavage furrow (space) between blastomeres. Note persistent polar body.

Fig. 4 — Longitudinal section of major portion of mouse oviduct showing its glandular but non-ciliated epithelium.

Fig. 5 — Enlarged view of two-cell mouse embryo showing clear nuclei. Zona pellucida was present but did not stain.

Fig. 6 — Two-cell stage with one blastomere anticipating the second cleavage division by metaphase spindle formation.

stage suggest that there is something in the oviducal environment requisite to this initial cleavage. It may take as long as $3\frac{1}{2}$ hours for all of the mature ova from a single female to be fertilized. This may contribute to the range of development within the members of the preimplantation ova of any female, but it is also possible that development could be impeded or arrested and the rate of cleavage altered by other means. The initial elongation of the fertilized ovum, anticipating cleavage, is probably the result of the arrangement of the spindle and asters although the latter structures are not readily demonstrable in the mouse zygote. The spindle fibers appear to be fine straight tubules while the chromosomes are ill-defined, electron-dense masses. There is some question as to whether the centrioles responsible for the first cleavage spindle arise de novo in the egg

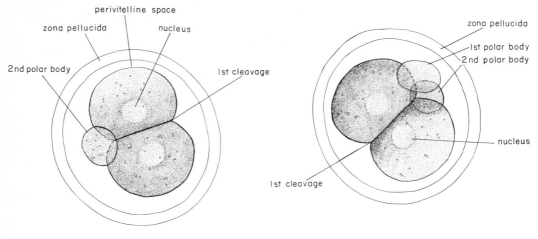

MOUSE EMBRYO – TWO CELLS
24 hours – 1 polar body
(living material)

MOUSE EMBRYO – TWO CELLS
24 hours – 2 polar bodies
(living material)

cytoplasm, but under some influence from the sperm nucleus. Before the first cleavage, the chromatin contents of the two pronuclei are not mixed, but thereafter, nuclear contents combine. The amount of DNA in each nucleus doubles before each division and the nucleoli become increasingly active centers of RNA synthesis. The nuclei also contain a considerable amount of protein, some of which is synthesized during early cleavage.

Succeeding cleavages occur after shorter and shorter intervals, soon becoming asynchronous. The second cleavage (to four cells) occurs at about 37 hours after fertilization; the third (to eight cells) at about 47 hours after fertilization, etc. The blastomeres of the 8 cell stage are labile and shift with considerable motility and yet they are sufficiently adhesive to retain their contigual relations with each other.* There is some evidence that by this cleavage the cells are committed to either embryonic or trophoblastic development. The fourth cleavage, at about 60 hours after fertilization, results in a solid ball of cells known as the morula. This is seen enroute to the uterus, or in the upper part of the uterus at 3 to 4 days after fertilization. The second cleavage takes the longest time, about 6 hours. Later divisions are reduced to about 10 minutes. An estimated early cleavage time table follows:

Coitus - 0	Sixteen cell stage - 60 to 70 hrs.
First Cleavage spindle - 21 to 28 hrs.	Blastocyst stage - 66 to 82 hrs.
Two cell stage - 21 to 43 hrs.	Transport to uterus - 66 to 72 hrs.
Four cell stage - 38 to 50 hrs.	Implantation - 4 to 5 days
Eight cell stage - 50 to 64 hrs.	

*Bovine serum albumen (BSA) alone will support development of the 8-cell mouse embryo. It may also survive on glucose or malate alone, without albumen. It seems that there is an ability to utilize different substrates during various stages of development of the mouse embryo. At the 2-cell stage both pyruvate and BSA are necessary. Probably the best medium for the development of the 2-cell mouse embryo is 2.5 to 5.0×10^{-4} M pyruvate, plus 2.5 to 5.0×10^{-2} M$_2$ lactate. Waymouth's medium (MB 752/1) allowed 2 and 4 cell stages to develop to the blastocyst stage. Glucose is not necessary for the early cleavages.

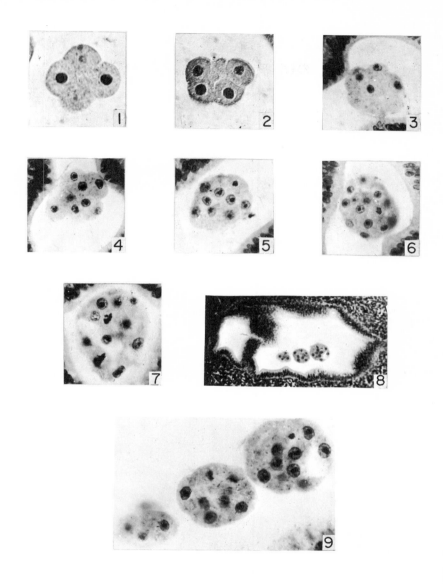

EARLY CLEAVAGE MOUSE EMBRYO

Fig. 1 — Four cell mouse embryo, two cells of which show their nuclei in this section.

Fig. 2 — Four plus cells with persistent polar body. Probably 6 or 8 cells since this was a section.

Fig. 3 — Third cleavage, eight or more cells.

Fig. 4 — Later than third cleavage, 8 nuclei showing in this section.

Fig. 5 — Probably 16 cell stage, nine nuclei showing plus the polar body.

Fig. 6 — Morula stage showing earliest indication of blastocoel formation (beneath topmost nucleus). This stage is en route to the uterus.

Fig. 7 — Earliest blastula (trophoblast) stage. Note blastocoel, and blastomeres in mitotic division.

Fig. 8 — Low power view of sections of three morula-blastula stages in upper uterus. Sections are at different levels but two at left were probably at stage represented by median section of stage at right.

Fig. 9 — Enlarged view of three morula-blastula stages in uterus at 3.5 days.

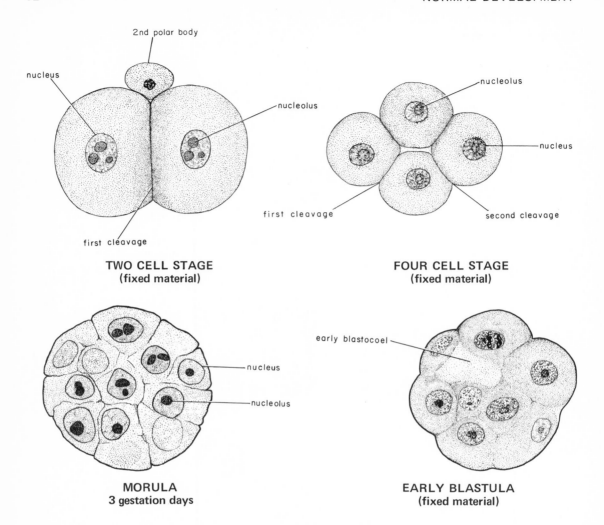

TWO CELL STAGE
(fixed material)

FOUR CELL STAGE
(fixed material)

MORULA
3 gestation days

EARLY BLASTULA
(fixed material)

Eggs do not all cleave at the same time intervals, nor are all the cleavages of a single egg complete, so that many early embryos possess uneven numbers of cells. There may be as many as two cleavages difference between the most advanced and most retarded eggs by the time they reach the uterus of any female. Some of this delay is due to variations in sperm penetration time, and may occasionally be so out of synchrony with the uterine endometrium as to complicate the process of implantation. As division proceeds, the cells become progressively smaller. The nuclei decrease in volume, the nucleoli diminish in size and number and disappear, and the chromosomes condense before each cleavage. Material associated with the nucleoli is hardly visible in the two-cell stage, but becomes increasingly prominent until by the 16 cell stage it almost obscures the nucleolus. Extranucleolar nuclear RNA production continues and the nucleoli become very active centers of RNA synthesis. Both nucleoli and cytoplasm synthesize protein.

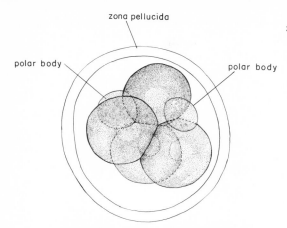

MOUSE EMBRYO — FOUR CELLS
48 hours
(living material)

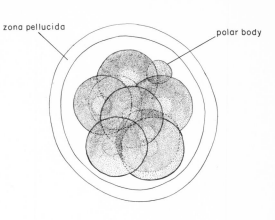

MOUSE EMBRYO — EIGHT CELLS
2½ days
(living material)

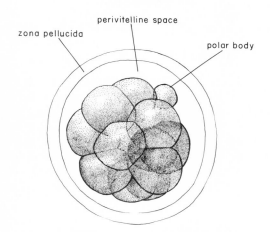

MOUSE EMBRYO — SIXTEEN CELLS
3 days
(living material)

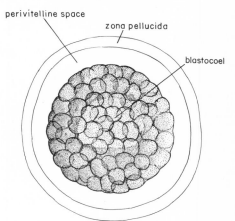

MOUSE EMBRYO — BLASTULA
3+ days
(living material)

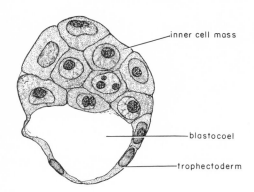

32 — 64 CELL STAGE

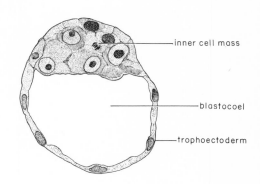

LATE BLASTULA

b. *Blastulation:* In the 32 to 64 cell stage the morula (in the uterus) acquires an eccentrically placed, slit-like cavity filled with fluid. This is the
beginning of the blastocoel and of the process of blastulation, deriving the
blastocyst stage which undergoes cycles of expansion and contraction. The
blastocoel enlarges but the total protoplasm does not increase, since the embryo
is unable to absorb any nutriment. Cytoplasmic structure alters a great deal
during blastulation. A single layer of lining cells, the trophoblast, encloses

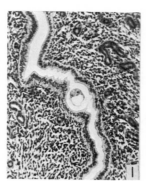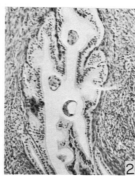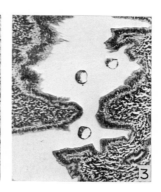

MOUSE MORULAE AND BLASTULAE IN UTERUS — 3.5 g.d.

the blastocoel except at one side, where a knob of cells, the inner cell mass,
forms. It has been suggested that the rapidly dividing cells of the blastocyst
may be the precursors of the trophoblast while the more slowly dividing cells
are the precursors of the inner cell mass, or the embryo proper. In any case,
all of the blastocysts possess short, relatively uniform microvilli on their
outermost surfaces, and all trophoblast cells have ribosomes in clusters and
rosettes. Glycogen, lipid granules and crystalloid inclusions can be found in
the early mouse blastocyst cells. Blastocoelic fluid first arises from the blastomeres at the end of the fifth cleavage.

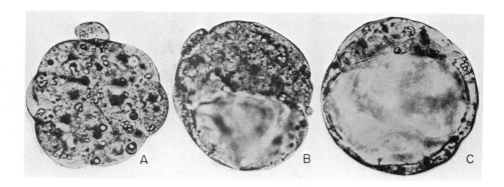

Fig. A — Morula stage, note persistent polar body.
Fig. B — Blastocyst at 76 hours; note inner cell mass and early blastocoel.
Fig. C — Large blastocyst at about 5 days, note trophoblast surrounding
             inner cell mass.   q

(Photographs from Carnegie Institute of Washington Publication Embryology # 148,
1935; W. H. Lewis and E. S. Wright.)

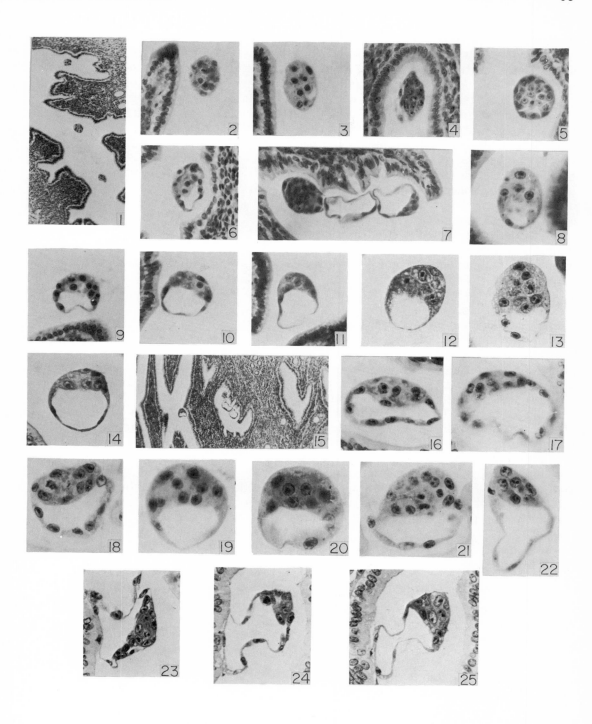

MOUSE MORULA TO TROPHOBLAST
3.5 to 4.5 days

The embryo is free within the lumen of the uterus at $4\frac{1}{2}$ days after fertilization but the inner cell mass, blastocoel, and trophoblast are undergoing
changes in preparation for implantation. These changes may be triggered by a
secretion from the ovary; they do not take place in an ovariectomized mouse or
in one subcutaneously injected with 2.5 milligrams of progesterone in 0.1 cubic
centimeter of corn oil about 4 days after mating. The abembryonic portion of
the blastocyst is a syncitium. The blastocyst (blastula) exhibits a high rate of

respiratory metabolism, which must con-
sume much of its nutrient reserve, and
starts a "hatching" action by which it
sheds the zona pellucida. This action includes both an enlargement and a rhythmic
undulating movement. It is not caused by
any secretion or activity of the uterus.
The initial volume changes of the blastocyst are noted at 4 days post-fertilization.
Single large contractions of the blastocyst
almost result in its disappearance, and
these are interspersed with several partial contractions. The frequency of the
large contractions is every 6 to 8 hours,
and of the smaller contractions every 20
to 100 minutes. Some contractions are
slow (5 to 6 minutes), while others are

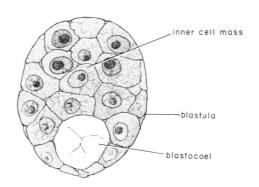

LATE BLASTULA

relatively fast (15 to 20 seconds). Such cycles are seen in liberated or denuded
blastocysts, and it is believed that hatching cannot occur without these pulsa-
tions. (Cole and Paul '63). It is preceded by the appearance of slender and
sticky protoplasmic processes (alkaline secreted) extending through the zona
pellucida from the abembryonal pole cells of the blastocyst. At the time of
hatching the blastocyst is no longer spherical but slightly ovoid, and it varies
considerably in size, measuring an average of 96 microns in length, or about
108 microns with the intact zona pellucida. The denuded blastocysts are very
sticky. The uterus is slightly more acid than the oviducts and this may contribute to the dissolution of the zona pellucida.

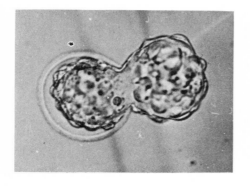
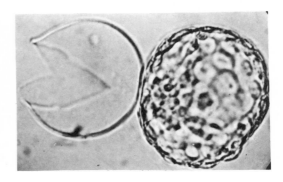

LATE MOUSE BLASTOCYST ESCAPING FROM ITS ZONA PELLUCIDA
(Two magnifications: Exp. Cell Res. 32:205-208, 1963. Courtesy Dr. R. L. Brinster)

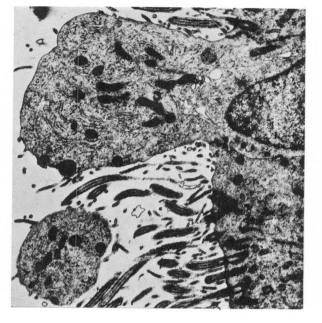

Infundibulum of mouse oviduct at time of egg transport. Apical part of ciliary and secretory cell, the latter having a smooth surface membrane with a few microvilli, and some dense protein-like granules. The endoplasmic reticulum has parallel membranes with ribosomes and well developed Golgi apparatus. x 15,000.

(Courtesy S. Reinius, originally published in Proc. Vth World Congress on Fertility and Sterility, Stockholm 1966, Excerpta Medica Foundation, Amsterdam.)

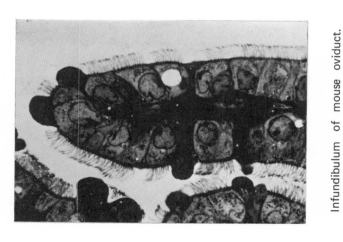

Infundibulum of mouse oviduct. Ciliate cells dominate, secretory cells among them ("peg cells"). x 1,100.

(Courtesy S. Reinius, originally published in Proc. Vth World Congress on Fertility and Sterility, Stockholm 1966, Excerpta Medica Foundation, Amsterdam.)

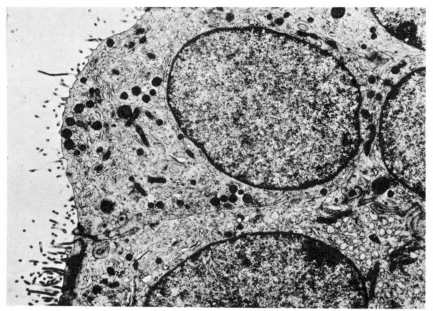

Secretory cell in ampulla of mouse oviduct at time of egg transport. Secretory granules, granular and agranular endoplasmic reticulum as well as Golgi apparatus are well developed.

(Courtesy S. Reinius, originally published in Proc. Vth World Congress on Fertility and Sterility, Stockholm 1966, Excerpta Medica Foundation, Amsterdam.)

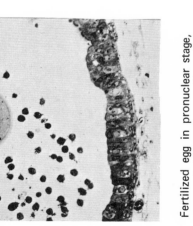

Fertilized egg in pronuclear stage, surrounded by corona radiata cells and found in ampulla of mouse oviduct. Toluidine blue. x 320.

(Courtesy S. Reinius, originally published in Proc. Vth World Congress on Fertility and Sterility, Stockholm 1966, Excerpta Medica Foundation, Amsterdam.)

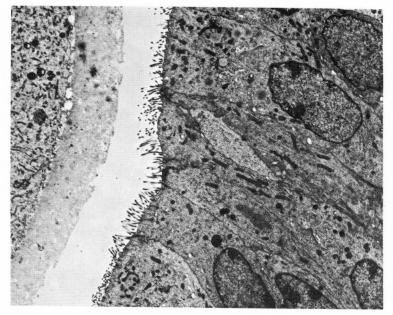

Portion of two-cell mouse egg with zona pellucida in relation to the epithelium in the isthmus of oviduct. Microvilli are long and regular. The endoplasmic reticulum is granular and forms parallel membranes aggregated in groups. × 8,960.

(Courtesy S. Reinius, originally published in Proc. Vth World Congress on Fertility and Sterility, Stockholm 1966, Excerpta Medica Foundation, Amsterdam.)

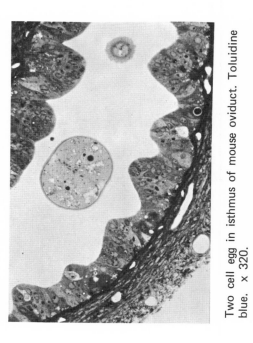

Two cell egg in isthmus of mouse oviduct. Toluidine blue. × 320.

(Courtesy S. Reinius, originally published in Proc. Vth World Congress on Fertility and Sterility, Stockholm 1966, Excerpta Medica Foundation, Amsterdam.)

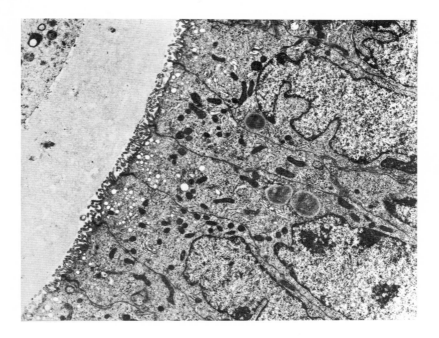

Mouse egg — epithelial relationship in the utero-tubal junction. Microvilli are low and regular, apical vesicles are present. x 11,000.

(Courtesy S. Reinius, Excerpta Medica, in press.)

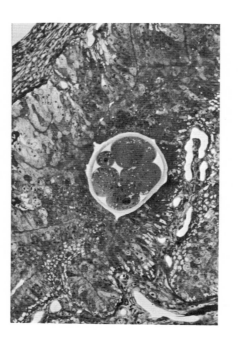

Mouse egg in utero-tubal junction. Note firm contact with surrounding epithelium. Toluidine blue. x 320.

(Courtesy S. Reinius, Excerpta Medica, in press.)

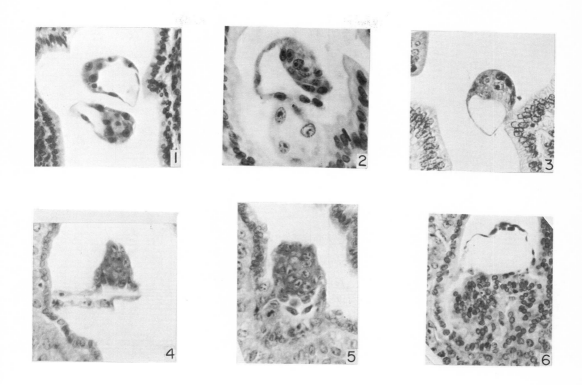

INITIAL CONTACT OF MOUSE EMBRYO WITH UTERINE WALL
(3.5 gestation days)

Fig. 1 — Two blastocysts in uterine cavity prior to implantation contact.

Fig. 2 — Later blastocyst and beneath it three cells of a morula, both in uterine cavity.

Fig. 3 — Blastocyst showing contact of lateral trophectoderm with uterine epithelium, prior to any obvious erosion.

Fig. 4 — Distal contact of trophectoderm of later blastocyst, indicating point of implantation.

Fig. 5 — Proliferating inner cell mass and invasion of trophectoderm into uterine epithelium.

Fig. 6 — Erosion and invasion of uterine epithelium and mucosa by trophoblast.

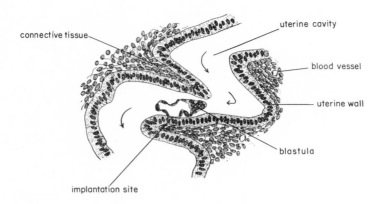

connective tissue

uterine cavity

blood vessel

uterine wall

blastula

implantation site

IMPLANTATION OF BLASTULA IN MOUSE
4 g.d. (after ovulation)

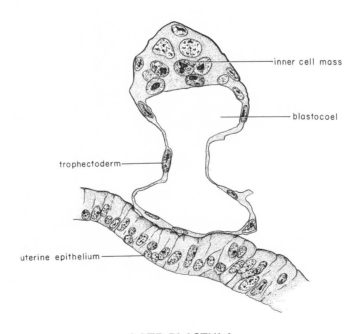

inner cell mass

blastocoel

trophectoderm

uterine epithelium

LATE BLASTULA
(site of implantation)

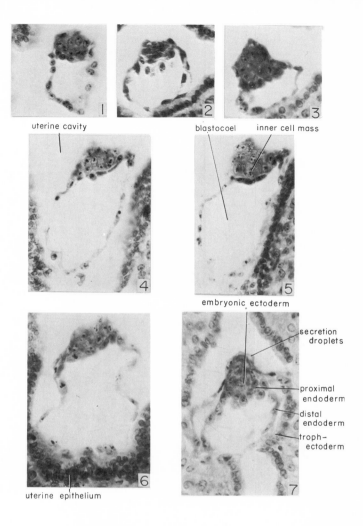

MOUSE IMPLANTATION
4.5 to 5.0 days

Fig. 1 — Blastocyst free within the uterine lumen showing distinct layer of endoderm cells beneath inner cell mass.

Fig. 2 — Trophectoderm making first contact with uterine epithelium. Note endoderm cells which appear to be free within the blastocoel early distal endoderm.

Fig. 3 — Inner cell mass increasing by mitosis.

Fig. 4 — Larger blastocyst, still free within the uterine lumen, but endoderm layer distinct.

Fig. 5 — Lateral contact of trophectoderm with uterine epithelium over wide area.

Fig. 6 — Blastocyst trapped in an epithelial crypt, with implantation contact at pole opposite inner cell mass — the most frequent situation.

Fig. 7 — Implantation in crypt, with contact on two sides of trophectoderm. Note extensive proliferation of inner cell mass, and distal endoderm.

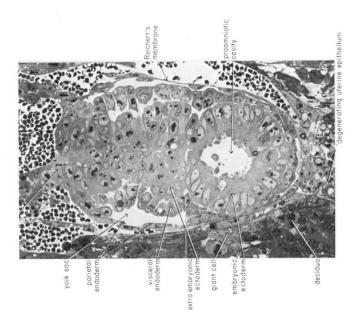

MOUSE EMBRYO
6.5 days

By a combination of electron and light micro-scopy the 6.5 day mouse embryo is shown.

(Courtesy S. Reinius, Zeit. Zellforsch. 68:711-723, 1965.)

MOUSE EMBRYO
4.5 days

By a combination of electron and light micro-scopy the 4.5 day mouse embryo is shown.

(Courtesy S. Reinius, Zeit. Zellforsch. 68:711-723, 1965.)

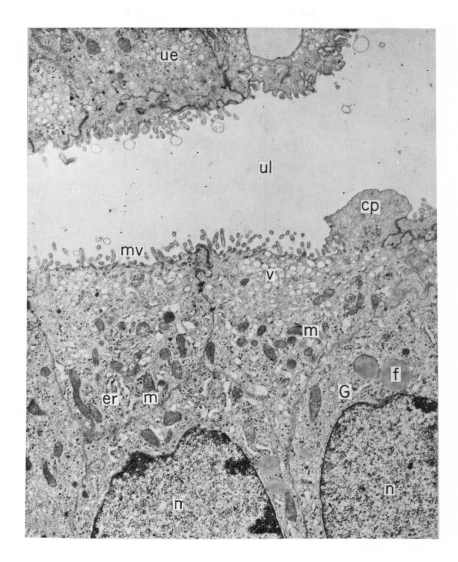

The surface of the uterine epithelium in pre-attachment stage gestation day 4½; cp — cytoplasmic protrusion; er — endoplasmic reticulum; f — fat granule; G — Golgi apparatus; m — mitochondria; mv — microvilli; n — nucleus; ue — uterine epithelium; ul — uterine lumen; v — apical vesicles. x 10,700.

(Courtesy S. Reinius, Z. Zellforsch. 77:257-266, 1967.)

The trophoblastic cells which surround the blastocoel of the blastocyst are transformed by the giant cells which appear in the contact and invasion area. This usually begins at the abembryonic pole, and in any litter will be seen in various stages of progress in its individual members. Blastocysts at this time may measure as much as 186 microns average, and the decidual swellings may be seen. Nucleolar activity of the embryonic cells is accelerated, deriving cytoplasmic (ribosomal) RNA which is of the high guanine-cytosine type. It seems that this giant cell transformation of the trophoblasts and changes in the size and form of the inner cell mass are initiated by a secretion from the ovary, because ovariectomized mice do not show these reactions. This concept is supported by the reaction to the subcutaneous injection of progesterone about 4 days after insemination.

Blastocysts obtained from old mice, from 13 to 24 months of age, fail to implant and develop when transferred to still older uterine environments. However, when transferred to uteri of young mice 3 to 7 months of age, just as many blastocysts develop as from reproductively active females. Reduction in litter size with increasing maternal age is therefore probably due to an increasingly less favorable uterine environment rather than to a decline in viability of the ova.

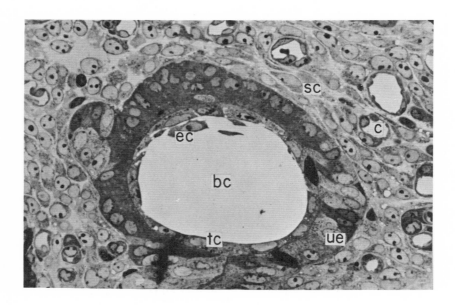

An attached blastocyst, gestation day 5, showing no decidual reaction. bc — blastocyst cavity; c — capillary; ec — endoderm cell; sc — stromal cells; tc — trophoblast cell; ue — uterine epithelium. Toluidine blue staining. x 3,700.

(Courtesy S. Reinius, Z. Zellforsch. 77:257-266, 1967.)

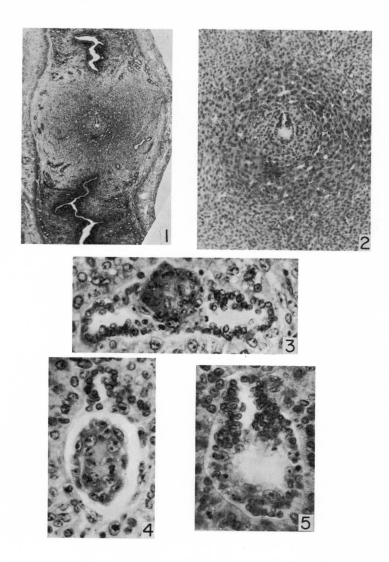

MOUSE EMBRYO
5 days

Fig. 1 — Low power view of mouse embryo at 5 days gestation, showing extensive decidual reaction of the uterus. Note lumen to either side of implantation site.

Fig. 2 — Higher power view of 5 day embryo and surrounding decidua.

Fig. 3 — Transverse section through cells of embryonic ectoderm and on either side portions of the blastocoel or yolk cavity.

Fig. 4 — Tangential section through 5 day embryo showing yolk cavity, and split between the inner embryonic ectoderm and outer endoderm.

Fig. 5 — Five day egg cylinder well embedded into uterine epithelium, and early development of central proamniotic cavity.

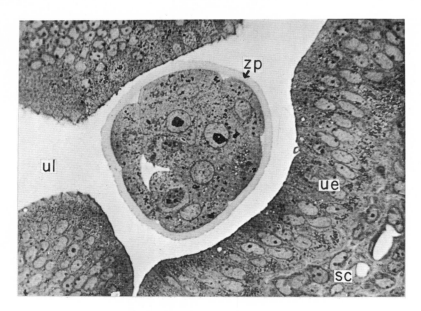

An early blastocyst on gestation day 4, free in uterine lumen. sc —
stromal cells; ue — uterine epithelium; ul — uterine lumen; zp — zona
pellucida. Toluidine blue stain. x 590.

(Courtesy S. Reinius, Z. Zellforsch. in press.)

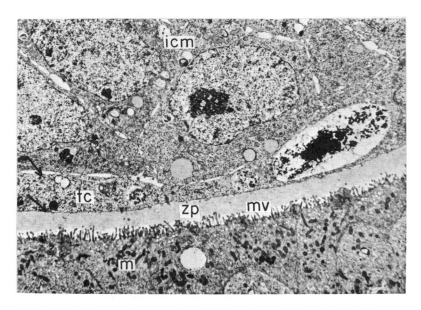

Part of the inner cell mass of a blastocyst, gestation day 5, still surrounded by a thin zona pellucida. Note relation to the uterine epithelial cell surface. icm — inner cell mass; m — mitochondria; mv —
microvilli; tc — trophoblast cell; zp — zona pellucida. Arrows indicate
outer and inner cell membrane of the trophoblast cell. x 3,700.

(Courtesy S. Reinius, Z. Zellforsch. 77:257-266, 1967.)

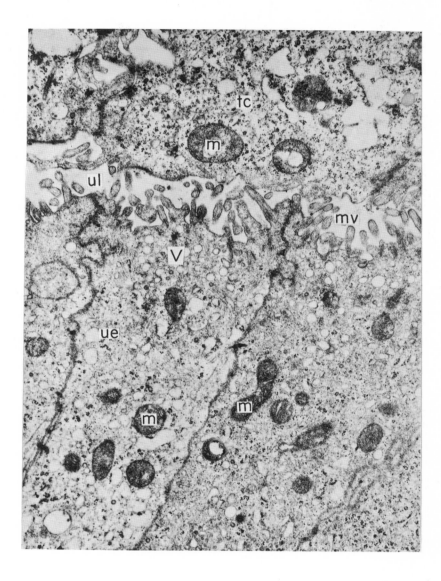

Blastocyst — uterine cell contact just prior to attachment, gestation day 5 when the zona pellucida is lost. m — mitochondria; mv — microvilli; tc — trophoblast cell; ue — uterine epithelium; ul — uterine lumen; v — apical vesicles. x 19,000.

(Courtesy S. Reinius, Z. Zellforsch. 77:257-266, 1967.)

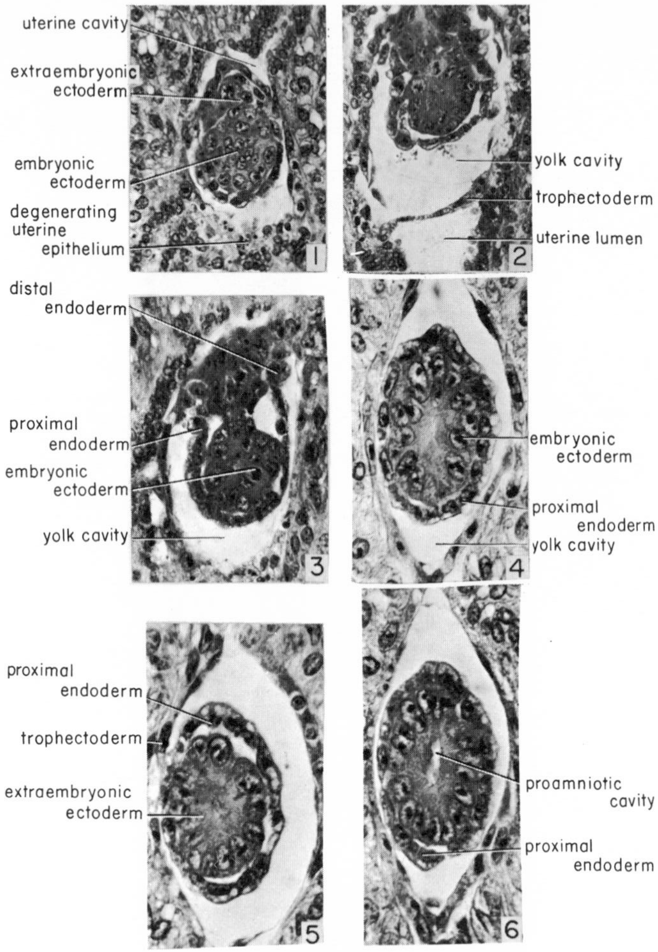

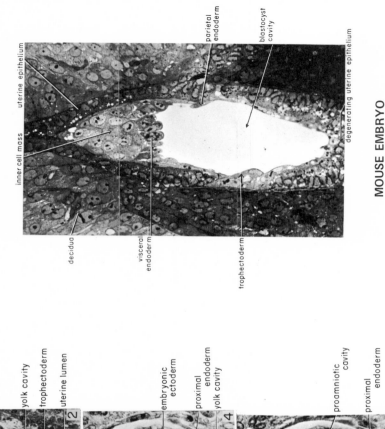

MOUSE EMBRYO
5.5 days

Shown by a combination of electron and light microscopy.
(Courtesy Dr. S. Reinius, Zeit. f. Zellforsch. 68:711–723, 1965)

MOUSE EMBRYO
5.5 days development

Figs. 1, 2, 3 — Longitudinal sections
Figs. 4, 5, 6 — Transverse sections at
               different levels

MOUSE DECIDUAL REACTION
5.5 days

Fig. 1 — Low power view of entire cross section of uterus containing 5.5 day mouse embryo. Note extent of decidual reaction within the distended uterus.

Fig. 2 — Enlarged view of embryo from Fig. 1. Note uterine lumen above and degenerating uterine epithelium below the embryo.

Fig. 3 — Transverse section through the extra embryonic level showing no proamniotic cavity, but distinct proximal endoderm.

Fig. 4 — Longitudinal section of embryo showing ectoplacental cone (above) and split of proamniotic cavity extending toward the cone. Note slight indentation at mid-embryo level between embryonic and extra embryonic regions.

Fig. 5 — Transverse section at extra-embryonic level showing separated proximal endoderm, and spacious yolk cavity.

Fig. 6 — Tangential section showing the difference between the bubbly proximal endoderm and the more squamous-like embryonic endoderm.

Fig. 7 — Slightly younger embryo showing proximal and distal endoderm, embryonic and extra-embryonic ectoderm, and degenerating uterine epithelium (below), and maternal vascular bed above.

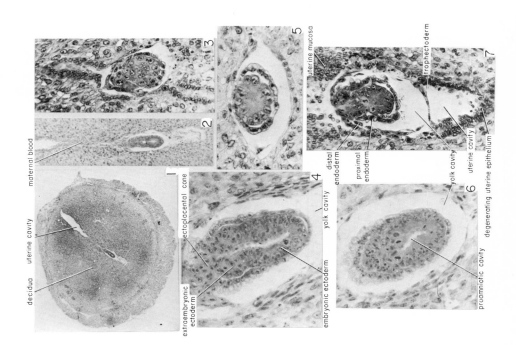

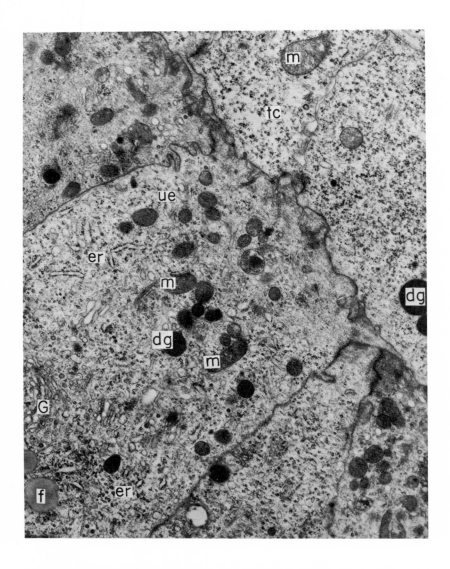

Blastocyst attachment, gestation day 5½. er — endoplasmic reticulum;
dg — dense granule; f — fat granule; G — Golgi apparatus; m — mitochondria; tc — trophoblast cell; ue — uterine epithelium; x 15,400.

(Courtesy S. Reinius, Z. Zellforsch. 77:257-266, 1967.)

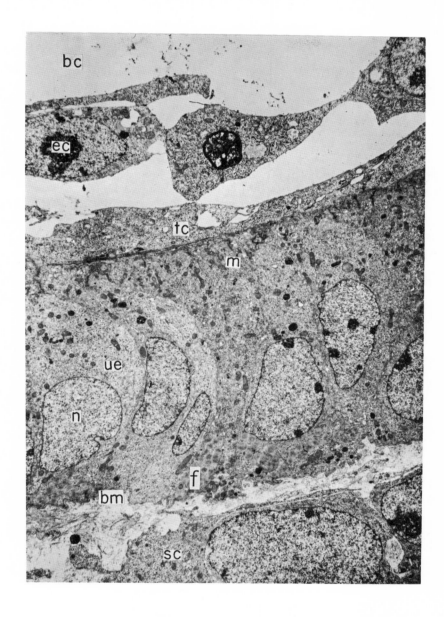

Blastocyst attachment, gestation day 5½. bc — blastocyst cavity; bm — basal membrane; ec — endoderm cell; f — fat granule; m — mitochondria; n — nucleus; sc — stromal cell; tc — trophoblast cell; ue — uterine epithelium. x 4,500.

(Courtesy S. Reinius, Z. Zellforsch. 77:257-266, 1967.)

c. *Gastrulation:* Gastrulation, or the formation of two primary germ layers occurs as the embryo is being implanted. The part of the inner cell mass nearest to the blastocoel splits off to form the endoderm. The remaining cells make up the ectoderm.

The developing embryo comes to lie within a crypt in the uterine mucosa on the ventral or anti-mesometrial side of the lumen. It is the uterus and not the blastocyst that determines the ventral or anti-mesometrial site for implantation. The mucosa is thrown into numerous folds, with those of the opposite sides closely interdigitated, so that every embryo will be trapped in a crypt. The factors that control the spacing of embryos within the uterus are not known, but with a normal litter of about 10 it seems to be most efficient. In experimental super-ovulation many of the embryos die at the time of attempted implantation. The blastocyst implanting in a endocrinologically prepared uterus, causes the nearby endometrium to develop a refractory zone in which no other blastocysts can implant. The onset of degenerative changes in nearby ova is coincidental with the rupture of blood vessels in the area of the implanting blastocyst. The initial stages of implantation appear to be the entrapment of and a secretion from the trophoblast, which adheres to the mucosa. Leukocytes of the uterus rush to the site of contact, and mucosal cells loosen and seem to degenerate (or be digested away). The embryo, minus its zona, its engulfed by the mucosa, to begin its parasitic-type relation with the maternal tissues.

Growth of the embryo as a whole is virtually impossible until implantation because no nutrition is available to its cells. Hence the total embryonic mass has been stabilized, even though cleavage has resulted in an increasing number

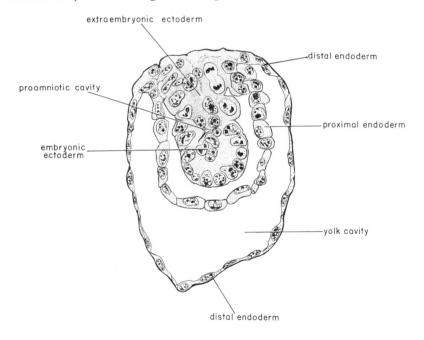

GASTRULATION
5.5 days

of smaller and smaller cells. Nevertheless, these important changes have been in progress; the blastocoel now known as the yolk cavity, has further enlarged; the inner cell mass, now known as the egg cylinder, has divided transversely into an outer layer of small extraembryonic ectoderm, an underlying layer of large embryonic ectoderm cells, and a central core of proximal endoderm cells, from which a tongue of distal endoderm extends into the blastocoel. There is some evidence of nutritional uterine milk elaborated at $4\frac{1}{2}$ days at the mesometrial pole of the implanting embryo. Reichert's membrane, the yolk cavity and the yolk sac effectively separate the embryo from the surrounding maternal blood. Lactic dehydrogenase activity in the mouse embryo decreases tenfold during the first five days of development.

   d. *Implantation:* Implantation depends upon a delicately balanced, synergistic action of estrogen and progesterone on the uterine endometrium to provide the optimal conditions for attachment and embedding of the embryo. There appears to be an "estrogenic surge" at about $4\frac{1}{2}$ days, just before the time for implantation, initiated by secretion of the lutenizing hormone. Ova will not implant when transplanted into uteri that are not thus prepared. Actually there is only a very short period (24 hours) during which a transplanted blastocyst can survive in the mouse uterus, this organ being generally inimical to implantation. On postconceptive days 4 or 6 the uterus will not accept the blastocysts. Best results are achieved when the donors' post-conception time is slightly in advance of that of the recipient. Progesterone from the corpora lutea prepares the endometrium for implantation, while estrogens and progesterone are balanced for maintenance of the implantation. Implantation may consist of five steps: adhesion of the trophoblast to the uterine mucosa, penetration of the mucosa by the trophoblast, invasion and spread of the embryonic components in the mucosa, active response of the maternal tissues, arrest of proliferation of the maternal tissues when optimum conditions have been reached and active corpora lutea secure the implantation. The zona pellucida is dissolved gradually around the blastocyst prior to its attachment, so that the zona-free blastocyst exists for only a very short time. The blastocyst attachment to the uterine epithelium is established when the trophoblast and uterine cell membranes lie only 150 Angstroms apart. The epithelium of the uterus does not immediately show any degenerative response, and the invasion precedes the decidual reaction.

   The uterine mucosa reacts quickly to invasion by an embryo at $4\frac{1}{2}$ to 5 days gestation by growth of the decidua which is rich in nutrient glycogen. The decidual reaction, which can be invoked by inanimate objects and does not involve any destruction of mucosa, is distinct from the active invasion of the endometrium by the trophoblast by a considerable interval of time. Possible functions of the decidua are suggested.

   a. Parturitional aid
   b. Nutritional source
   c. Protective (most likely)
   d. Hormonal (secretes prolactin)

Those who favor the protective function suggest the decidua protects the fetus against immunological attack by the mother, or defends the mother against the invasive activities of the trophoblast. At $5\frac{1}{2}$ days the embryo measures about 250 microns in diameter, and the egg cylinder about 70 microns in diameter.

MOUSE EMBRYO
6 days gestation

Fig. 1 — Transverse section of embryo at extra-embryonic level, showing surrounding decidual reaction of the uterus.

Fig. 2, 3, and 4 — Longitudinal sections of the same embryo at several levels. Note extent of maternal hemorrhage (above) and uterine degeneration (below).

Fig. 5 — Slightly enlarged view of tangential section of embryo showing extra-embryonic ectoderm and proximal endoderm. Note surrounding leukocyte activity.

Fig. 6 — Enlarged view above ectoplacental cone showing maternal vascular bed and a few secondary giant cells.

Fig. 7. — Transverse section just at level of proamniotic cavity and proximal endoderm.

Fig. 8 — Longitudinal section of typical 6 day embryo which is beginning to show the line of demarcation between the extra-embryonic and embryonic regions.

Fig. 9 — The egg cylinder showing some extra-embryonic ectoderm (above), bubbly proximal endoderm, compact embryonic ectoderm within, and faint proamniotic cavity.

Fig. 10 — Enlarged view of transverse section through extra-embryonic level showing the nature of the proximal endoderm, and the mitotic activity of the extra-embryonic ectoderm.

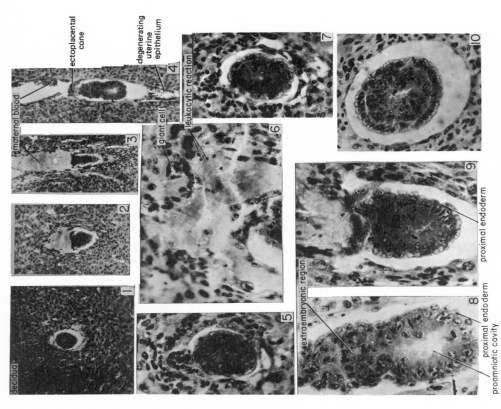

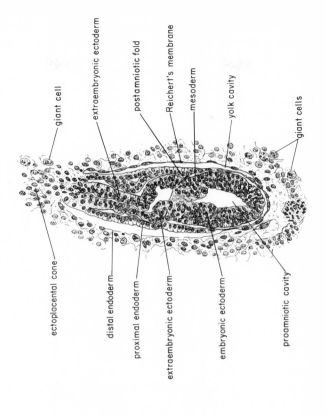

giant cell

extraembryonic ectoderm

postamniotic fold

Reichert's membrane

mesoderm

yolk cavity

giant cells

ectoplacental cone

distal endoderm

proximal endoderm

extraembryonic ectoderm

embryonic ectoderm

proamniotic cavity

MOUSE EMBRYO – 6.5 DAYS
(sagittal section)

ectoplacental cone

distal endoderm

proximal endoderm

yolk cavity

embryonic ectoderm

trophectoderm

extraembryonic ectoderm

line of demarcation between embryonic and extraembryonic ectoderm

proamniotic cavity

MOUSE EMBRYO – 6.0 DAYS
(sagittal section)

But considerable variation in development is seen in mouse blastocysts as they reach the uterus. The decidua is darkly staining with some lipid granules visible. At $6\frac{1}{2}$ days the embryo measures about 300 microns in diameter. Except for some degenerating cells anti-mesometrially, the uterine epithelium in this region has disappeared, leaving a hyperemia which may encourage implantation.

The uterine mucosa dorsal to the embryo is the site of the discoid hemochorial placenta, which divides the uterine lumen in two. By 8 days gestation a new connection is established between the two resulting cavities, but it is now ventral to the embryo. Active proliferation of the uterine mucosa cuts off the decidua from the uterine muscle ventrally, so that the embryo is suspended in a new portion of the lumen.

The decidua capsularis is ventral to the embryo, on the antimesometrial side, and contains many large, bi-, tri-, and even tetranucleate cells. When first formed, it is relatively thick, but, as the embryo grows, it is stretched and becomes thin. It eventually partitions the embryo from the uterine lumen. The decidua basalis, which looks like mucosa, is dorsal (mesometrial) to the embryo, and gives rise to much of the placenta. At 5 days gestation a vascular area can be identified between the decidual zones, in which blood is loose in lacunae or sinusoids, bathing the embryo almost directly. At 7 days gestation the decidua encloses the embryo and separates it completely from the lumen of the uterus. The impression is that many maternal capillaries have been ruptured by the invasion of the embryo, but the two blood systems never unite. They are effectively separated by Reichert's and yolk sac membranes. Some of the more peripheral sinusoids become so engorged that they shed their blood into the uterine lumen at about 8 days gestation, causing bleeding which reaches the vagina at 12 or 13 days gestation. This bleeding is natural and a certain sign of pregnancy.

During implantation the embryo may derive some nourishment from degenerating mucosal cells at the implantation site. There is a widespread occurrence of glucose, glycogen, lipids, phosphatases, iron, calcium, and many other nutritional necessities such as vitamins and enzymes in the endometrium which may provide the nutritional requirements of the early stages of blastocyst implantation. Both decidua and trophoblast contribute glycogen, with the peak at about 15 days gestation. The decidua is rich in glycogen and the enzyme glucose-6-phosphatase. The glycogen content of the trophoblast increases from the time of implantation to about 17 days gestation. The yolk sac is rudimentary, there being little or no yolk, but it is involved in the embryonic circulation, absorbing nutrition from the maternal blood bath. It also provides glycogen, with the peak at about 18 days gestation. The cytoplasm of the embryonic cells is basophilic, and their nucleoli have concentrations of RNA as implantation approaches, suggesting that protein synthesis, although demonstrated in unovulated ova and blastocysts, is not quantitatively significant.

The placenta is formed by the fusion of the decidua basalis, the ectoplacental cone, the chorion, and parts of the allantois, all so interfused that they can no longer be distinguished. Estrogens have not been detected in the mouse placenta, perhaps owing to technical difficulties or too low concentrations.

Placental fusion occurs very rarely in the mouse. This is probably due to the same factors which control the efficient spacing of the implantations. Even closely approximated blastocysts in the same uterine crypt can form their independent placentae. Foreign material in the uterus prevents implantation because it inhibits the decidual reaction. It is however a most effective contraceptive when the uterus is preparing for implantation. There is some evidence that females with large, heavy pituitary glands have a greater number of successful implantations than other females, but the reverse relation does not hold.

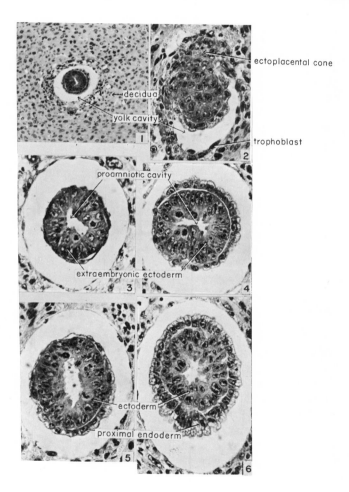

SECTIONS OF MOUSE EMBRYO
6.5 days gestation

Fig. 1 — Low power showing decidua surrounding embryo.

Fig. 2 — Longitudinal section showing yolk cavity and ectoplacental cone.

Fig. 3 — 6 — Transverse sections at various levels of the embryo at 6.5 days showing the early formation of the proamniotic cavity.

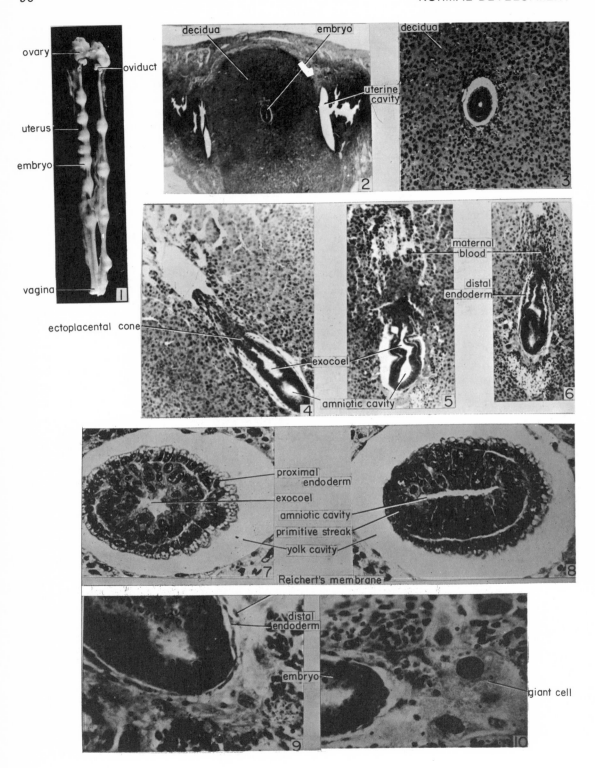

ovary

oviduct

uterus

embryo

vagina

1

decidua   embryo
2
uterine cavity

decidua
3

ectoplacental cone

exocoel

amniotic cavity
4

5

maternal blood

distal endoderm
6

proximal endoderm

exocoel

amniotic cavity

primitive streak

yolk cavity
7
Reichert's membrane
8

distal endoderm

embryo
9
giant cell
10

MOUSE EMBRYO — 6.5 days

The egg cylinder is divided into two regions, one dorsal with darkly staining high columnar cells having elongated nuclei and one ventral with lightly staining, smaller cells with rounded nuclei. The dorsal region is extra-embryonic ectoderm, which gives rise to the extra-embryonic structures (such as membranes), and the ventral region is the embryonic ectoderm, which gives rise to various structures of the embryo proper. Even at $5\frac{1}{2}$ days gestation, when the staining differences disappear, there is a sharp line of demarcation between the two regions. A proamniotic cavity appears in the center of the embryonic ectoderm, followed by a similar cavity in the extra-embryonic ectoderm. The two cavities join to form an elongated narrow lumen. The growing ectodermal mass of the egg cylinder remains separated from the yolk cavity by proximal endoderm. Hence the relations of the cell layers of the embryo in rodents are just the reverse of those in most other vertebrate embryos; the thick inner mass is ectoderm, which gives rise primarily to neural structures; and the thinner outer layer is endoderm, which gives rise to the gastointestinal tract lining. Both project deeper and deeper into the yolk cavity to obliterate it. In rare instances a slitlike extension of the proamniotic cavity through the ectoplacental cone to the outside is seen suggesting that the inversion of the germ layers is due to limitations on growth ventrally into the yolk sac, which causes invagination. As the proamniotic cavity enlarges, the embryo gradually fills the yolk cavity.

Cells proliferated from the extra-embryonic ectoderm dorsalward make up the ectoplacental cone, which approaches the lumen of the uterus and by $6\frac{1}{2}$ days gestation comprises about half the length of the embryo. The cone invades the maternal tissues as it grows, rupturing blood vessels in its path and producing

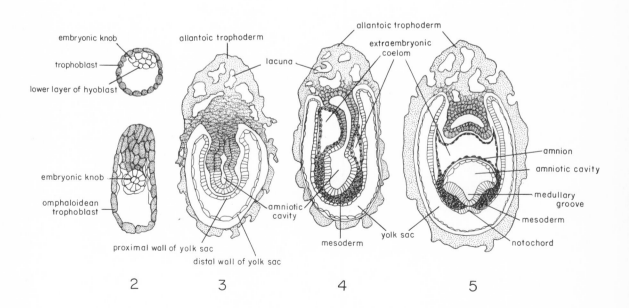

FORMATION OF THE AMNION IN THE MOUSE

(Redrawn after Jenkinson in "Vertebrate Embryology", Oxford & London, 1913.)

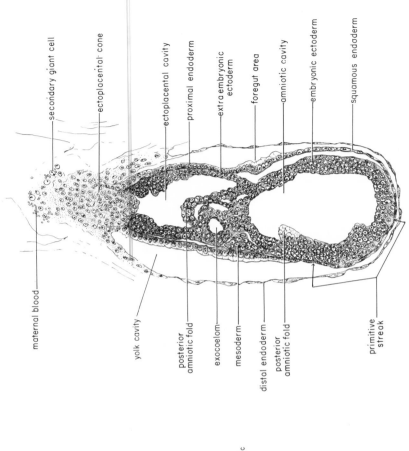

MOUSE EMBRYO — 7.5 days
(sagittal section)

secondary giant cell

ectoplacental cone

ectoplacental cavity

proximal endoderm

extra embryonic ectoderm

foregut area

amniotic cavity

embryonic ectoderm

squamous endoderm

maternal blood

yolk cavity

posterior amniotic fold

exocoelom

mesoderm

distal endoderm

posterior amniotic fold

primitive streak

MOUSE EMBRYO — 6.5 days

ectoplacental cone

distal endoderm

proximal endoderm

extraembryonic ectoderm

embryonic ectoderm

secondary giant cell

maternal blood

Reichert's membrane

yolk cavity

posterior amniotic fold

mesoderm

proamniotic cavity

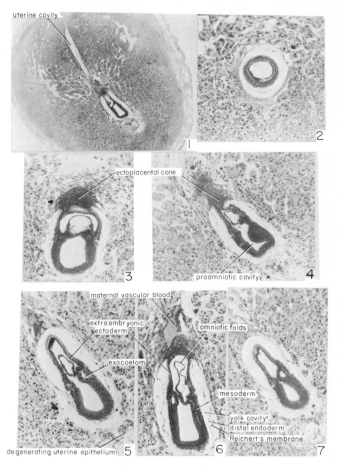

MOUSE EMBRYO
7 days gestation

Fig. 1 — Transverse section through entire uterus showing embedded 7 day mouse embryo. Above it
is a portion of the uterine lumen; near the
ectoplacental cone is the maternal vascular
bed; and below the embryo is the degenerating
uterine epithelium.

Fig. 2 — Transverse section through the extra embryonic level showing large proamniotic cavity
and relatively thin extra-embryonic ectoderm.
The distal endoderm is seen as an enclosing
membrane-like structure in the yolk cavity.

Fig. 3, 4 — Longitudinal sections at different regions
showing (3) exocoelom and mesoderm inter-
rupting the proamniotic cavity and this cavity
as continuous (4) in both embryonic and
extra-embryonic levels.

Figs. 5, 6, and 7 — Note clear distinction between embryonic and extra-embryonic levels, enlarged
exocoelom and the amniotic folds (anterior
and posterior). Reichert's membrane is becoming clearer.

some scattered giant cells. It later contributes to the placenta. The primitive streak begins at the posterior margin of the egg cylinder as a thickening of embryonic ectoderm. It establishes the primary axis of the embryo. Possibly the streak is homologous with the dorsal lip of the blastopore in amphibians as organizational center. It is a center of rapid growth and a derivative of all the primary germ layers; and there is no remnant of it in a later embryo. During implantation the embryo is oriented in a crypt with its long axis at right angles to the long axis of the uterus. Since the embryo develops ventrally to the egg cylinder, its dorsoventral axis is at right angles (perpendicular) to the long axis of the uterus, and its anterior-posterior axis is at right angles to the mesometrium. This orientation persists until organo genesis starts at 8 days gestation.

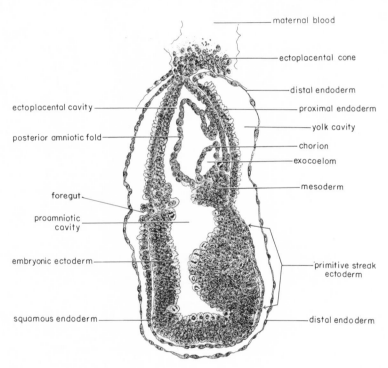

MOUSE EMBRYO — 7.0 DAYS
(sagittal section)

At $6\frac{1}{2}$ days gestation the third germ layer, the mesoderm appears as scattered mesenchyme cells between the primitive streak and the proximal endoderm. The cells move between the ectoderm and endoderm, even toward the extraembryonic region, where they acquire a cavity known as the exocoelom. They also form the yolk sac membrane, which envelops later the embryo and is discarded at birth. By 7 days they have all but separated the two other primary germ layers except near the primitive streak. Dorsal to the exocoelom is a diverticulum in the extraembryonic ectoderm, resulting from the proliferation of mesoderm, known as the proamniotic fold. This is continuous with lateral and posterior amniotic folds, all products of mesodermal activity. The proamniotic fold constricts the middle of the egg cylinder.

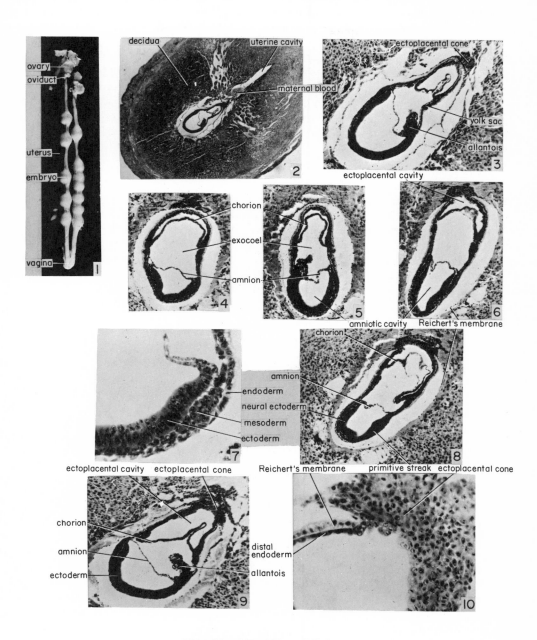

MOUSE EMBRYO — 7.5 days

As stated, the proamniotic fold arises posteriorly within the proamniotic cavity but shortly becomes continuous across the cavity. As it does so, it acquires small lumina (lacunae), which coalesce to form the exocoelom lined with mesoderm and surrounded by ectoderm. The closed off portion of the proamniotic cavity is the amniotic cavity, lined with embryonic ectoderm surrounded by mesoderm. A third cavity persists dorsally as the ectoplacental cavity. The dual membrane between the exocoelom and the amniotic cavity is the amnion, or amniotic membrane. It separates extra-embryonic from embryonic regions, and, with the later complete reversal of the embryo, comes with its cavity, to enclose the embryo from outside. The chorion separates the exocoelom from the ectoplacental cavity and is nonfunctional. Both amnion and chorion are composed of ectoderm and mesoderm but not in the same arrangement.

e. *Head Process Formation:* Mesoderm originating from the primitive streak moves laterally and posteriorly between the other germ layers, never anteriorly. At 7 days gestation, however, the embryonic ectoderm at the ventral tip of the egg cylinder thickens to begin forming the head process, cells of which are continuous with those of the primitive streak but move anteriorly away from the streak and laterally almost around the anterior half of the egg cylinder. The endoderm over and anterior to the head process changes gradually from squamous type to almost columnar type and indents near the point separating the embryonic and extraembryonic regions. The indentation is the earliest indication of the foregut.

The head process, therefore, constitutes a distinct head-like projection. The development of the cephalic structures is due largely to the formation of the foregut, which tends to lift the anterior end of the embryo upward above the heart area. As the head process grows anteriorly, it extends downward and away from the amniotic cavity, forming a head fold and trapping the cephalic end of the foregut as a blind pocket. A similar process, but in the opposite direction, forms a tail fold and traps the hindgut at the posterior end of the embryo.

f. *Early Organogenesis:* Beginning at about $7\frac{1}{2}$ days gestation the mouse embryo shows signs of organ differentiation. Between the thickened ectoderm of the head process and the related endoderm appears the notochord probably derived from endoderm, from which it is indistinguishable in some regions. Mesenchyme spreads fanlike outward from the sides of the notochord, filling the spaces between the other two primary germ layers. At 7 days the ectoderm anterior to the primitive streak and above the notochord thickens to form the neural or medullary plate and at 8 days it acquires a depression known as the neural groove. The primitive streak, head process, neural groove and notochord establish the anterior-posterior axis of the embryo.

The head process actively extends itself anteriorly, carrying with it the related and underlying endoderm, which will constitute the lining of the foregut. Head process ectoderm, foregut endoderm, and notochord are not always clearly delineated in the mouse so that some investigators believe that foregut endoderm is at least in part derived from head process ectoderm and notochord.

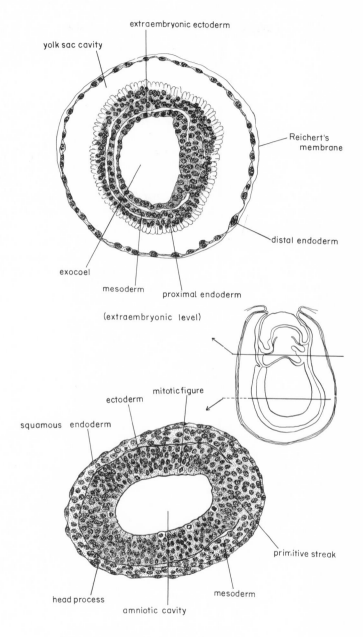

yolk sac cavity

extraembryonic ectoderm

Reichert's membrane

distal endoderm

exocoel

mesoderm

proximal endoderm

(extraembryonic level)

ectoderm

mitotic figure

squamous endoderm

primitive streak

head process

amniotic cavity

mesoderm

(head process and primitive streak level)

MOUSE EMBRYO — 7.5 days

Mesenchyme arising from the posterior limit of the primitive streak grows anteriorly in the exocoelom to form the allantois, which contains numerous small lacunae. Thus the mouse allantois lacks the endodermal lining characteristic of the allantois in most vertebrates. The allantois expands until it fills the exocoelom, and by 8 days it is fused with the chorion. It joins the primitive streak to the ectoplacental cone, whose blood vessels link the embryo to the uterus.

The foregut, first seen at 7 days, is a pocket beneath the cephalic neural primordia at 7 days. Directly beneath the foregut is loose mesenchyme which forms the heart primordia, at this time. The hindgut differentiates, by 7 3/4 days. Thus the two ends are the first portions to appear. Their openings into the intervening region are the anterior and posterior intestinal portals. Eventually the anterior ectoderm breaks through the stomodeum to the foregut, and the posterior ectoderm breaks through the proctodeum to the hindgut. The midgut forms through a downward growth of the endoderm on either side, connecting the foregut and hindgut regions in a zipper-like action. The entire embryo exhibits a lordosis curve, to be rectified when the three germ layers assume their proper relationships, with the ectoderm outermost, the mesoderm next, and the endoderm innermost. This is a reversal of the situation in the embryo at 7 days. The reversal starts at the foregut.

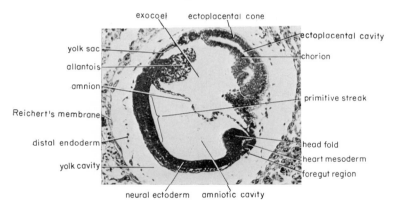

MOUSE EMBRYO — 7.5 days
(sagittal section)

Almost as soon as the mesenchyme aggregates adjacent to the notochord (the paraxial mesoderm), it is organized into paired, segmental (metameric) somites. The first pair to appear at 7 3/4 days is the most anterior, just anterior to the primitive streak and just posterior to the future hindbrain. The second pair forms immediately behind the first but is cleanly separated from it and lags behind it slightly in differentiation. By 8 days there are at least 4 pairs of somites. Eventually there are 65 pairs, each sharply delineated from its neighbors. The chronological and linear appearance of the somites can be taken as an accurate guide to the embryonic age.

At 8 days the intermediate cell mass (nephrotome) arises as the precursor of the excretory system. Laterally it is continuous with the parietal (or lateral plate) mesoderm, which splits into two layers, forming an intervening

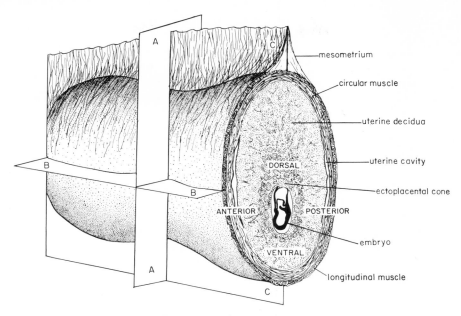

**SCHEMATIC REPRESENTATION OF THE 7.5 day
MOUSE EMBRYO IN THE UTERUS**

A — Sagittal to embryo   B — Transverse to embryo   C — Frontal to embryo
     Transverse to uterus   Horizontal to uterus   Sagittal to uterus

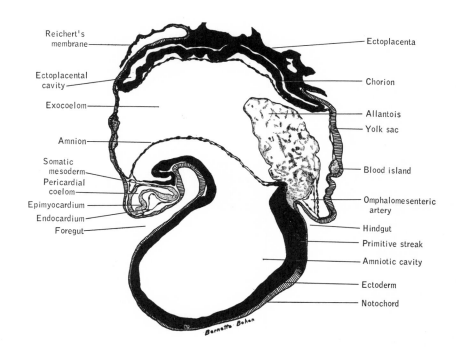

PARTLY DIAGRAMMATIC SAGITTAL SECTION OF EMBRYO of 7 days 18 hours (X100)

(From "The Biology of the Laboratory Mouse," 2nd Ed., Jackson Laboratory, Editor, Earl L. Green. Copyright © 1966. McGraw-Hill, Inc. Used by permission of McGraw-Hill Book Co.)

coelom. The outermost layer is ectoderm associated with somatic mesoderm, and the two together are called somatopleure. The somatopleure is continuous with the amnion. The innermost layer is endoderm, associated with splanchnic mesoderm, and the two together are called splanchnopleure. The intervening coelom is continuous with the exocoelom. The coelom is not divided into paired cavities in the mouse but extends beneath the foregut and head fold as the single pericardial cavity. The original shape of the coelom is that of an inverted U($\cap$), but, as the anterior intestinal portal moves posteriorly with the downgrowth of gut endoderm, the shape changes to an inverted V(Λ) and finally to an inverted Y (λ), with a single anteriorly directed tubular cavity as the stem of the inverted Y(λ).

The circulatory system derives from blood islands, aggregations of mesenchymal cells in the mesoderm of the splanchnopleure. Among these aggregations appear lacunae which join together to form a continuous blood vascular system. The contained cells give rise to some blood cells as early as 7 days gestation. At this time the heart develops, the splanchnic mesoderm of the pericardial cavity forming the epicardium (outer heart membrane) and the myocardium (muscles) of the heart wall. Between the splanchnic mesoderm and the endodermal floor of the foregut loose mesenchymal cells, probably of endodermal origin, form the endocardium (mesothelial lining of the heart). The endocardium forms at first a straight tube, but, as it grows within the confines of the pericardial cavity, it is coiled upon itself to form the various chambers of the heart. The heart is soon joined by the aortic arches which pass through the visceral arches. Anterior extensions of these vessels become the paired ventral and dorsal aortae. The ventral aortae proceed anteriorly into the head as the external carotid arteries and the dorsal aortae merge posteriorly into the single large vitelline or omphalomesenteric artery, leading to the yolk sac. Blood from the vitelline artery returns to the embryonic heart, (after discharging its waste and acquiring nutrition from the yolk sac) by way of paired vitelline or omphalomesenteric veins. Thus function begins as developmental (structural) changes continue. The rudimentary yolk sac is intimately associated with the placenta to absorb nutrition from the mother, to provide a channel for excretion, and to afford a membrane for protection. It eventually envelops the amnion and the exocoelom.

At $7\frac{1}{2}$ days gestation the amnion covers the dorsal surface of the embryo. Owing to the inversion of the germ layers, it eventually surrounds the embryo except at the umbilical cord. The embryo finally seems to float freely within the amniotic fluid, anchored only by the cord.

g. *Reichert's Membrane:* Besides the amnion and yolk sac, the mouse embryo has a third extraembryonic protective membrane called Reichert's membrane. This is found only in rodents. At $5\frac{1}{2}$ days the trophoblast surrounds the embryo except at the region of the ectoplacental cone and is in close contact with the uterine mucosa. On the inner surface of the trophoblast are a few scattered endoderm cells, which at $6\frac{1}{2}$ days compose an almost continuous sheet. Between the sheet and the trophoblast develops the thin, tough, homogeneous, noncellular, acidophilic Reichert's membrane. It is usually first seen at the ventral extremity of the egg cylinder. Since it expands with the enlargement of the embryonic mass during blastulation, it must be elastic. It has been suggested that it is a secretion of the related endoderm, which could explain its growth and expansion. It is definitely a protective covering for the embryo.

h. *Giant Cells:*   From 6 to about 14 days gestation excessively large cells, called giant cells, lie between Reichert's membrane and the decidua. Neither their origin nor their function is clear cut; some investigators believe that they support Reichert's membrane, and others attribute steroid-hormone production to them.   There is also recent evidence that they aid in the transformation of the trophoblast and are, therefore, necessary for proper implantation.

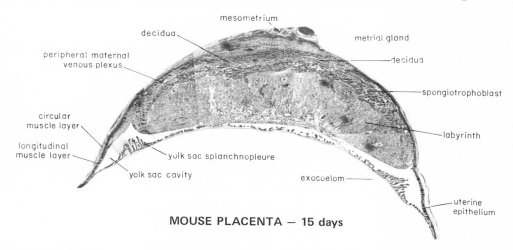

MOUSE PLACENTA — 15 days

It seems that they are under the control of the ovary, since ovariectomized or superovulated mice have difficulty or fail in the natural growth of the inner cell mass, the expansion of the blastocyst, and the transformation of the trophoblast requisite to implantation.   Isoantigens appear in significant quantity in the trophoblast by 4 days gestation and the maternal tolerance of an embryonic homograft may be due to an inert barrier of giant cells between the mother and the developing embryo.   They may therefore provide protection in the nature of an immune reaction.   They first appear between the ventral side of the embryo and the decidua and continue to enlarge for several days and move into the uterine cavity ventral to the embryo.   Other and more numerous giant cells appear at the sides of the ectoplacental cone, from which they are derived, and move posteriorly.   By 8 days these have protoplasmic processes which traverse the vascular area between the decidua and Reichert's membrane.   Still other giant cells, which are multinucleate, may be found in the decidua at 7 days.   These are known as synplasia.   There are also secondary giant cells, which, although conspicuous for their size, are not as large as the others.

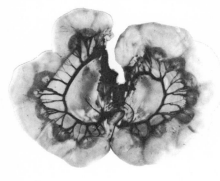

Paired gravid uteri of mouse at 18 days gestation showing the distribution of india ink injected into the uterine arteries and stopping at the maternal placenta. Since none of the ink particles are found in the embryo or embryonic placenta, there is no direct connection of the two circulatory systems.

Chapter  CHRONOLOGY OF DEVELOPMENT:
8-16 days

A. THE 8 DAY EMBRYO: The 8 day embryo can be identified by its 4 pairs of somites. The body is much coiled, like an extended letter S with the two ends curled in the same direction, and a deeply concave mid-region. Optic evaginations and otic (auditory) invaginations are present. Remnants of the primitive streak persist. In transverse section the neural plate and underlying endoderm are flattened, in anticipation of the reversal of the germ layers. The neural groove is still open throughout its length, but the anterior neural ectoderm is beginning to thicken and the anterior end of the groove (neuropore) to close. The foregut has thyroid and liver primordia. The midgut remains wide open, the allantois is fused with the chorion, and the yolk sac has begun to develop blood islands.

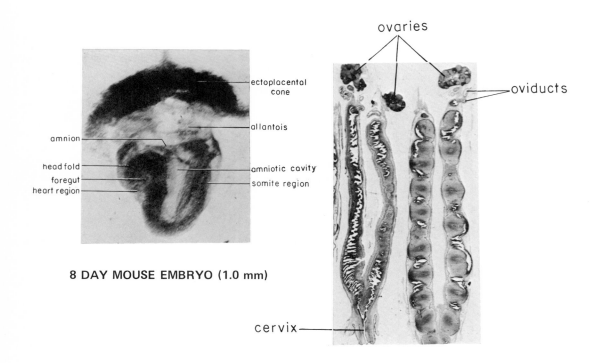

8 DAY MOUSE EMBRYO (1.0 mm)

NON-GRAVID AND GRAVID UTERI OF MOUSE (8 g.d.)

Growth of the foregut and hindgut initiates the reversal of the anterior-posterior relationships so that the embryo eventually acquires the C shape characteristic of most vertebrate embryos, with the open part of the C (the midgut) ventrally directed. Transverse sections show that the head end is turning clockwise while posterior regions are turning counterclockwise. The midgut remains connected with the yolk cavity but also rotates rapidly before the completion of the terminal twisting. It rolls to one side, taking with it the associated splanchnopleure, which fuses ventrally to almost close to the midgut by 8 3/4 days. The result is much as if one pushed upward against the convex midgut, making it concave. The embryo then turns its left side ventrally, leaving the placenta dorsal.

The coelom is partially closed off ventrally to the head process as the pericardial cavity, containing the tubular heart. Epi-, myo-, and endocardium are all present, as is the dorsal mesocardium. However, the mesocardium soon disappears. Folds in the endocardial tube, necessitated by the active proliferation of heart tissue, aid in the formation of the four-chambered heart. The first pair of aortic arches is also visible. Early forming blood islands and lacunae leading to vessels may be seen in the yolk sac.

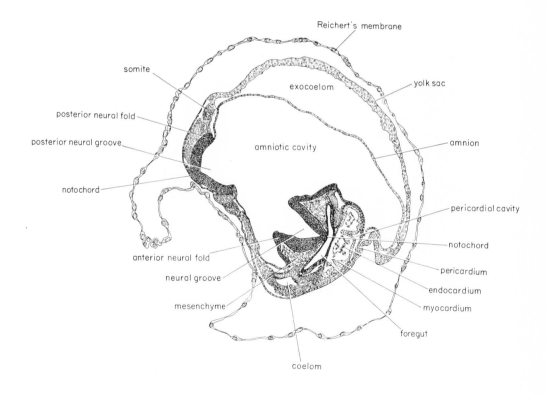

8 DAY MOUSE EMBRYO
(transverse section)

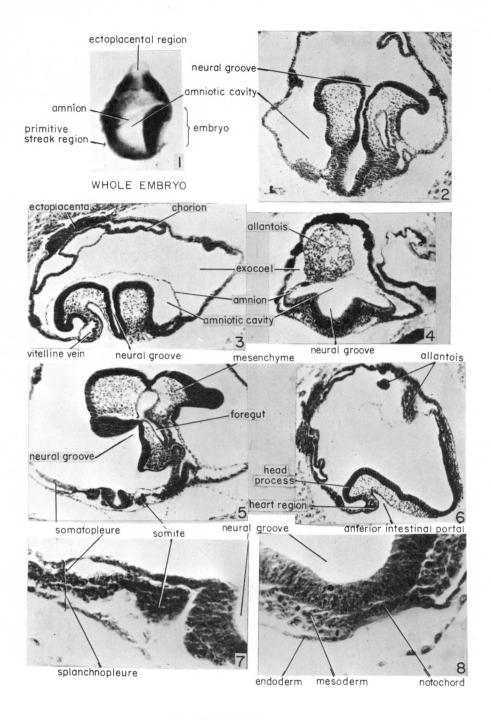

MOUSE EMBRYO — 8 days
(Photographs)

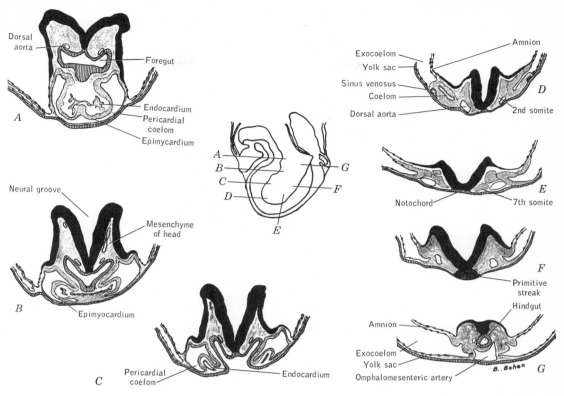

**SECTIONS TRANSVERSE TO NEURAL GROOVE
OF 8-DAY 1-HOUR, 7-SOMITE EMBRYO**

The location of each section is indicated on the key diagram.

(From "The Biology of The Laboratory Mouse", 2nd Ed., Jackson Laboratory, Editor, Earl L. Green. Copyright © 1966. McGraw-Hill, Inc. Used by permission of McGraw-Hill Book Co.)

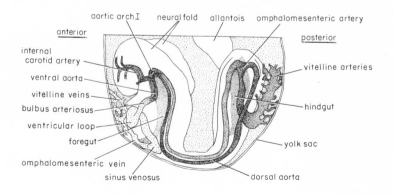

**CIRCULATORY SYSTEM OF
8 DAY MOUSE EMBRYO**

(Redrawn from Green '66, "Biology of the
Laboratory Mouse, McGraw-Hill, Inc.)

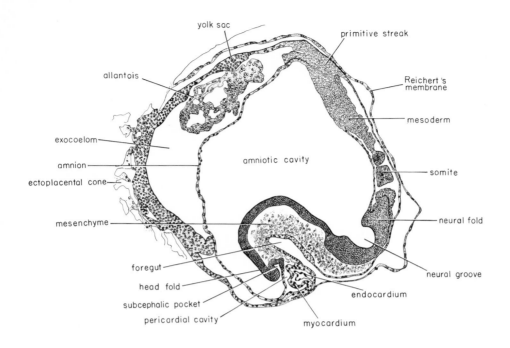

8 DAY MOUSE EMBRYO — HEAD PROCESS
(sagittal section)

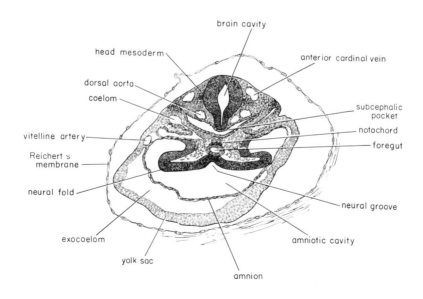

8 DAY MOUSE EMBRYO
(transverse section)

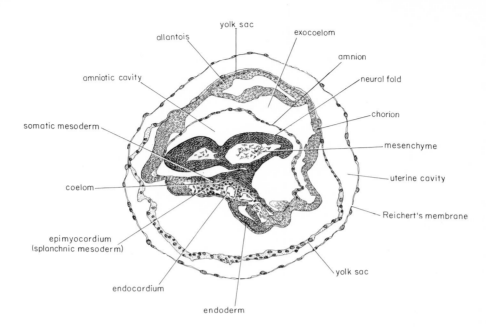

8 DAY MOUSE EMBRYO
(transverse section)

B. THE 8½ DAY EMBRYO: At $8\frac{1}{2}$ days gestation two major activities are under way in the embryo. One is the development of somites and of neuromeres, which indicate the metamerism or segmentation of the muscles, skeleton, brain and spinal cord. The other is the beginning of placentation. There is abundant mesenchyme, some of which has been organized into 8 to 12 somites; some early heart parts can be identified; blood islands are plentiful in the yolk sac, blood vessels begin to appear; the nephrogenic cord can be seen; the stomodeum is invaginating in the oral region; the first two pairs of visceral pouches are visible; the mid-gut is still slightly open but the intestinal portals are converging toward the mid-body region, thus closing off part of it. The amnion, which covers the embryo dorsally, forms lateral limiting sulci on either side of the body folds. The amniotic cavity is enlarging. Reichert's membrane is distinct and intact, completely separating the embryo and its extra-embryonic membranes from the maternal tissues. The untwisting of the embryo is not yet complete. It is like a corkscrew, with cephalization enlarging the anterior end and the posterior end coiled in the opposite direction.

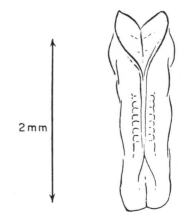

2 mm

DORSAL VIEW OF 8.5 DAY EMBRYO

(Theiler and Stevens 1960)

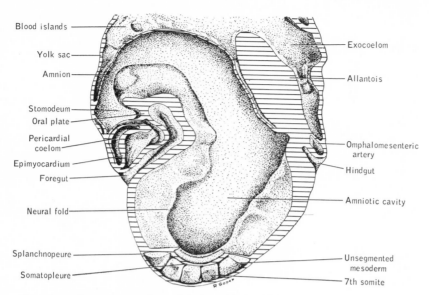

Drawing of reconstruction of 8-day 1-hour, 7-somite embryo. The recon-construction is cut in the midsagittal plane and only the right half shown except at the ventral extremity where the last 4 somites and part of the un-divided mesoderm of the left side are included. Cut areas are shown by horizontal shading.

(From "The Biology of The Laboratory Mouse," 2nd Ed., Jackson Laboratory, Editor, Earl L. Green. Copyright © 1966. McGraw-Hill, Inc. Used by permission of McGraw-Hill Book Co.)

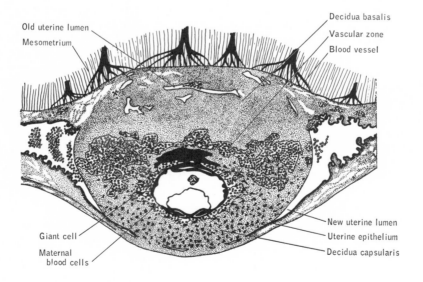

Longitudinal section (partly diagrammatic) of uterus at site of implantation of 8 day 6 hours, 5-somite embryo. Cut parallel to mesometrium.

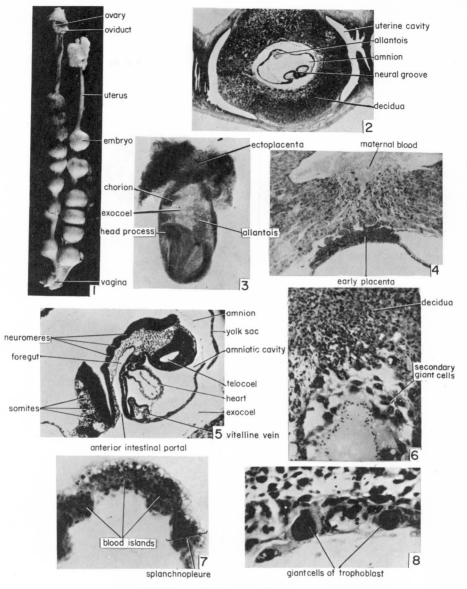

MOUSE EMBRYO — 8.5 days

Fig. 1 — Photograph of entire uterus of gravid female at 8.5 days gestation showing 14 sites of implantation of embryos.

Fig. 2 — Transverse section through entire decidua of 8.5 day embryo.

Fig. 3 — Embryo dissected out of the uterus with membranes intact.

Fig. 4 — Section through early placentation, showing both embryonic and maternal tissues.

Fig. 5 — Sagittal section showing cephalic flexures, head process, anterior intestinal portal, and transverse section of neural groove indicating a twist in the body at this level.

Fig. 6 — High power view of implantation site and area of invasion of maternal tissues, with secondary giant cells.

Fig. 7 — Blood islands in splanchnopleure.

Fig. 8 — Giant cells of trophoblast which probably are functional in invasion of the maternal tissues.

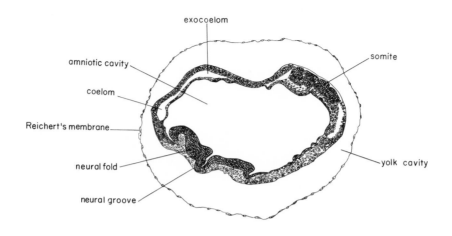

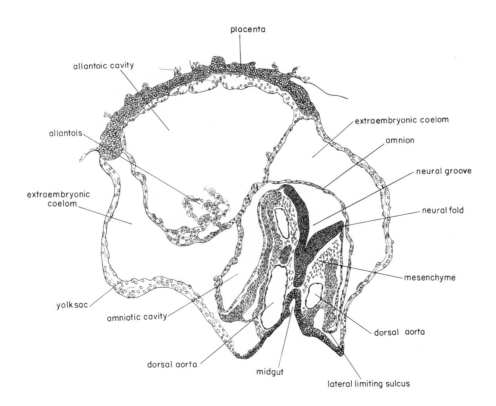

8.5 DAY MOUSE EMBRYO
(transverse section)

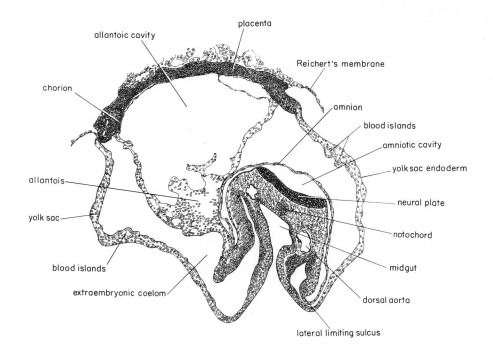

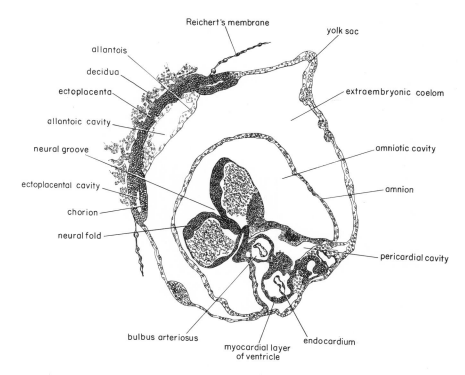

8.5 DAY MOUSE EMBRYO
(transverse section)

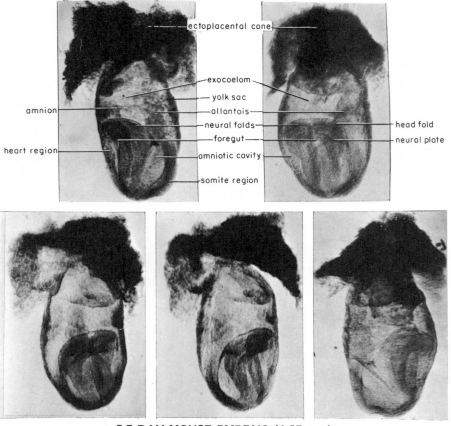

8.5 DAY MOUSE EMBRYO (1.25 mm)

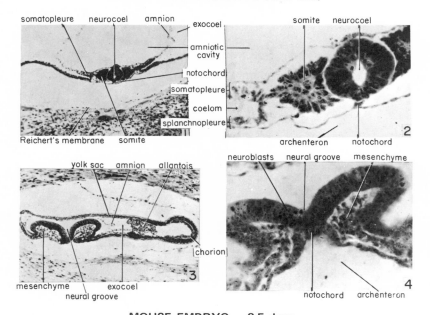

MOUSE EMBRYO — 8.5 days
(transverse sections)

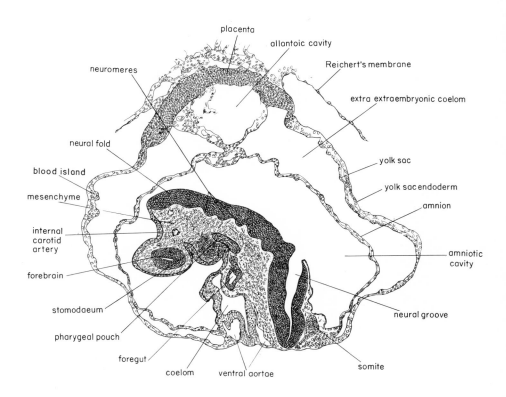

8.5 DAY MOUSE EMBRYO
(sagittal section)

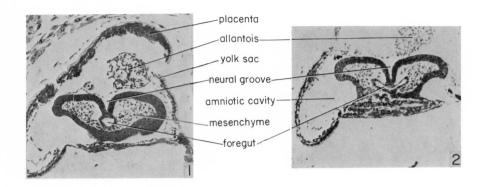

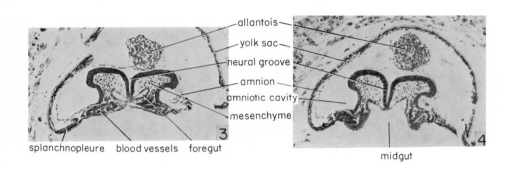

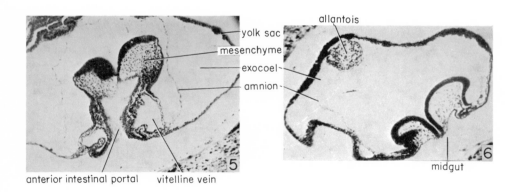

NEURULATION IN MOUSE EMBRYO — 8.5 days
(Photographs)

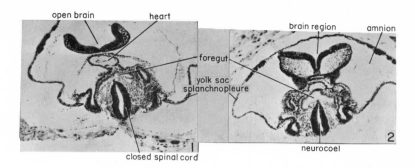

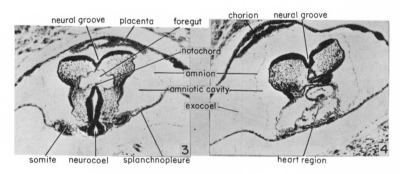

MOUSE EMBRYO — 8.5 days
(transverse sections showing evidence of cranial and
cervical flexures by proximity of brain and cord)

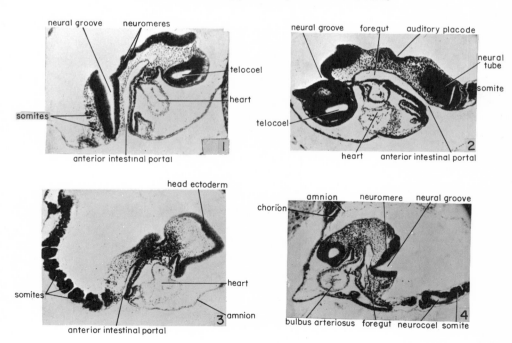

MOUSE EMBRYO — 8.5 days
(sagittal sections)

C. THE 9 DAY EMBRYO: Probably the most significant and involved changes in the embryo occur between $8\frac{1}{2}$ and 9 days, when organogenesis is greatly accelerated and the contour of the embryo is being altered simultaneously.   The most devastating congenital anomalies can be produced in embryos subjected at this time to various types of trauma.   These include stunting, edema, hydrocephaly and microcephaly, microphthalmia, degeneration of part of the neural tube, and related skeletal deformities.   On the other hand, this is about the earliest stage at which the embryo can be dissected out without injury. It is clearly a vertebrate and can be confused with a variety of other vertebrate embryos.   It has a distinct head, body, and tail, and the allantois protrudes from near the base of the hindgut.   It is almost completely enclosed in the amnion.

The 9 day embryo has 13 to 20 somites.   The neural tube is closed except for the posterior neuropore and the roof of the myelencephalon, and the entire nervous system is undergoing cellular differentiation.   Visceral arches I (mandibular) and II (hyoid) are present, as is Rathke's pocket; the large paired sacs may be seen on either side of the myelencephalon; the protruding allantois and heart can be identified and the forelimb buds are forming.

In sagittal section the 9 day mouse embryo resembles the 72 hour chick embryo, with the brain cavities indicated, all sense organ primordia (optic, otic and olfactory) apparent, the four chambered heart formed, the stomodeum broken through and Rathke's pocket formed.   The four chambered heart is now pulsating regularly.   The sinus venosus and the bulbus arteriosus can both be located; the paired dorsal aortae have fused into a single vessel, which extends into the tail fold after giving off the vitelline artery; segmental arteries

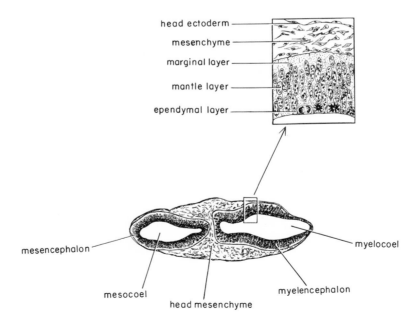

MOUSE EMBRYO — 9 g.d.
(transverse section)

may be seen to issue from all along the aorta, between the somites; and the external and internal carotids and cerebral arteries proceed anteriorly. The anterior and posterior cardinal veins are forming.

The embryo is still so twisted, particularly at the posterior end, that a transverse section may cut it at three levels. The placenta is developing rapidly with the decidua capsularis separating the embryo from the uterine lumen and the decidua basalis forming a widening junction between embryo and maternal tissues. Blood islands and capillaries are numerous in the yolk sac.

Brain and spinal cord sections show marginal, mantle and ependymal layers, with the ependymal layer particularly exhibiting many mitoses. The acousticofacial ganglion (cranial nerves II and VIII) is developing just anterior to the otic vesicle.

The heart and adnexa deserve special mention at this time, when the circulatory system begins to play a major role in development. Metabolic wastes must be removed, and nutritional elements must be collected and delivered to every part of the rapidly growing embryo. The heart is well developed and functional, with four chambers each lined with endocardium, consisting of myocardium, and surrounded by pericardium. These chambers form as function is initiated. The sinus venosus enters the right atrium, and at the same level the right ventricle opens into the bulbus arteriosus. Anteriorly, near the thyroid primordium in the floor of the pharynx, are the paired ventral aortae, which feed the aortic arches and then become the external carotid arteries. Lateral to the external carotid arteries are the anterior cardinal veins. As usual, the veins are thin-walled in comparison with the arteries. The ventricles are more posterior. Between the ventricles are the interventricular foramen, septum, and sulcus.

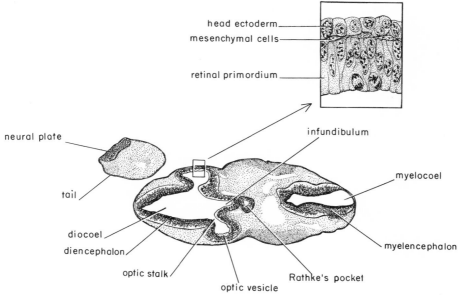

MOUSE EMBRYO — 9 g.d.
(transverse sections)

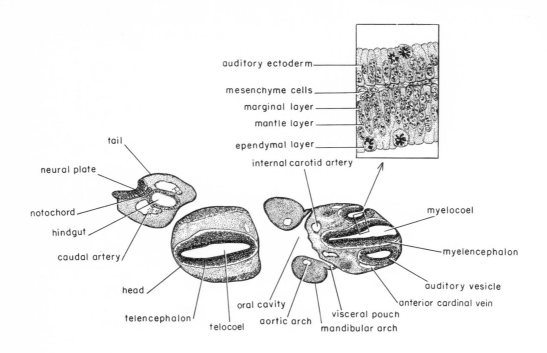

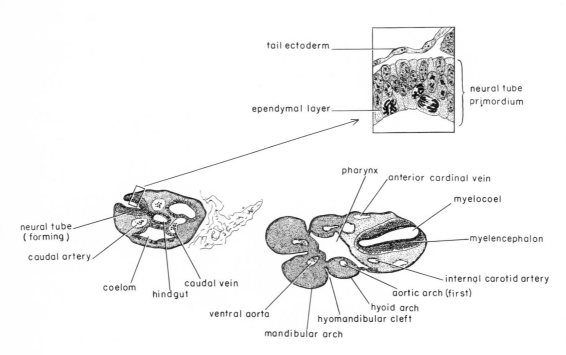

MOUSE EMBRYO — 9 g.d.
(transverse sections)

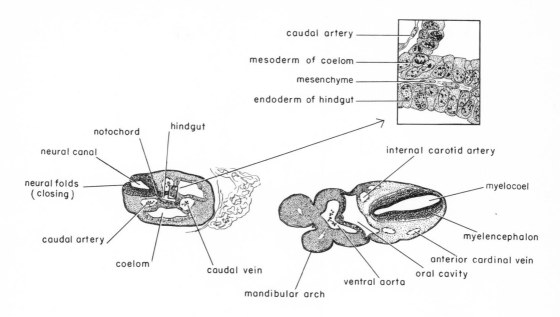

caudal artery
mesoderm of coelom
mesenchyme
endoderm of hindgut

notochord
hindgut
neural canal
neural folds (closing)
caudal artery
coelom
caudal vein

internal carotid artery
myelocoel
myelencephalon
anterior cardinal vein
oral cavity
ventral aorta
mandibular arch

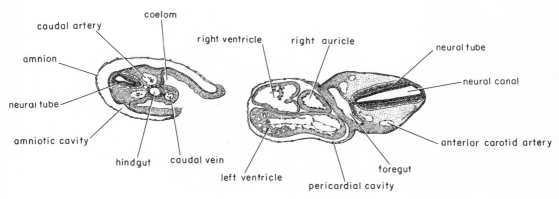

caudal artery
coelom
amnion
neural tube
amniotic cavity
hindgut
caudal vein

right ventricle
right auricle
neural tube
neural canal
anterior carotid artery
foregut
pericardial cavity
left ventricle

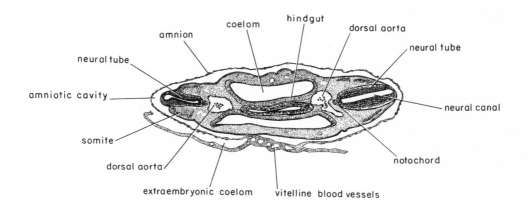

amnion
coelom
hindgut
dorsal aorta
neural tube
neural tube
amniotic cavity
neural canal
somite
dorsal aorta
extraembryonic coelom
vitelline blood vessels
notochord

MOUSE EMBRYO — 9 g.d.
(transverse sections)

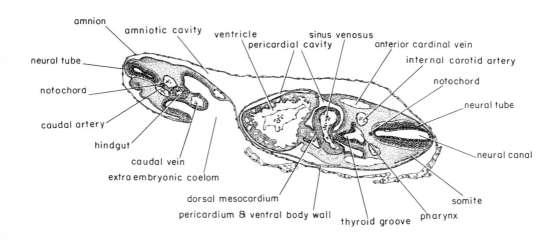

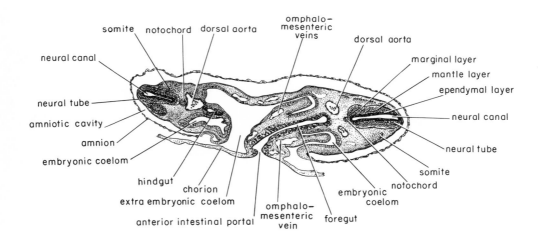

MOUSE EMBRYO — 9 g.d.
(transverse sections)

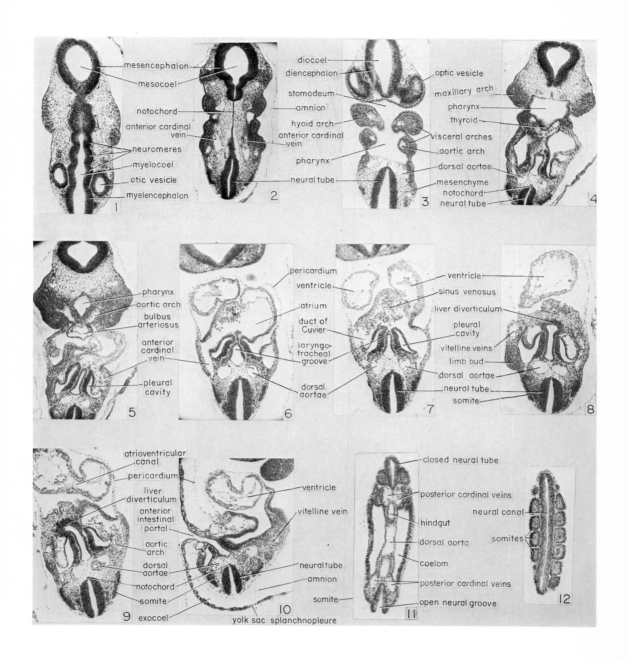

MOUSE EMBRYO — 9 days
(Photographs)

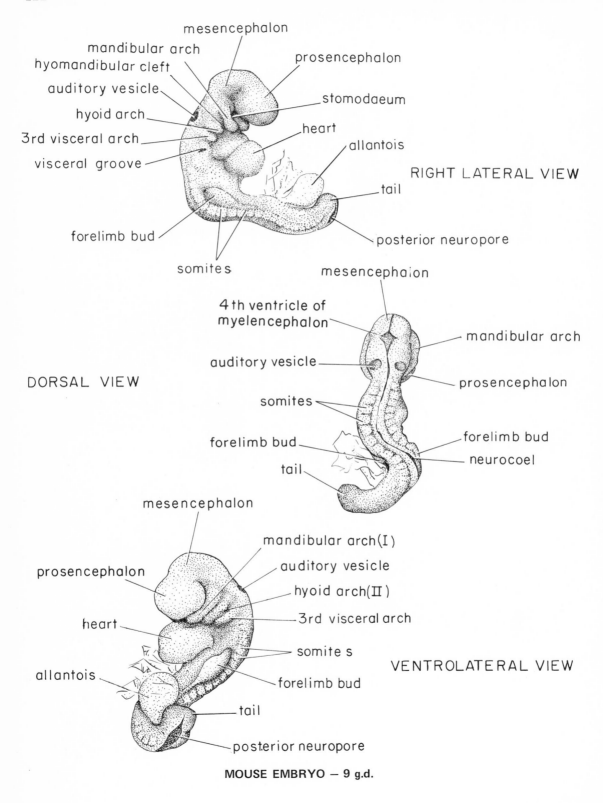

mesencephalon

mandibular arch
hyomandibular cleft
auditory vesicle
hyoid arch
3rd visceral arch
visceral groove

prosencephalon

stomodaeum

heart
allantois

RIGHT LATERAL VIEW

tail

forelimb bud

posterior neuropore

somites

mesencephalon

4th ventricle of
myelencephalon

auditory vesicle

DORSAL VIEW

somites

forelimb bud

tail

mandibular arch

prosencephalon

forelimb bud
neurocoel

mesencephalon

prosencephalon

heart

allantois

mandibular arch(I)
auditory vesicle
hyoid arch(II)
3rd visceral arch
somites

VENTROLATERAL VIEW

forelimb bud

tail

posterior neuropore

MOUSE EMBRYO — 9 g.d.

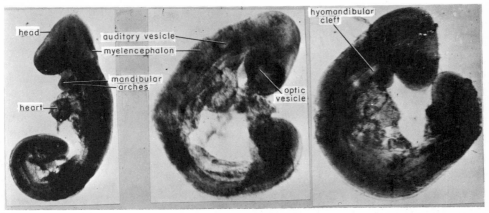

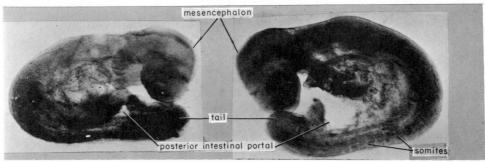

9.0 DAY MOUSE EMBRYO (2.0 mm)
(Photographs)

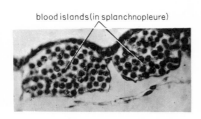

MOUSE EMBRYO — 9 days

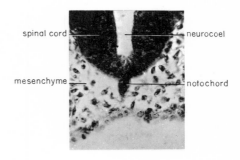

MOUSE EMBRYO — 9 days

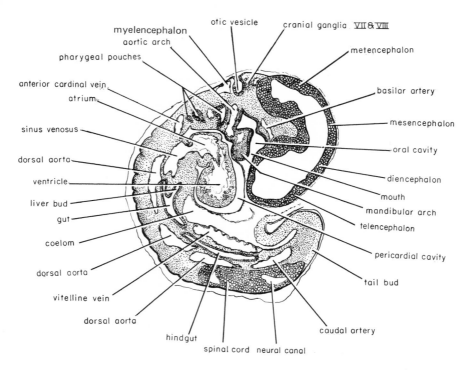

MOUSE EMBRYO — 9 days
(mid-sagittal)

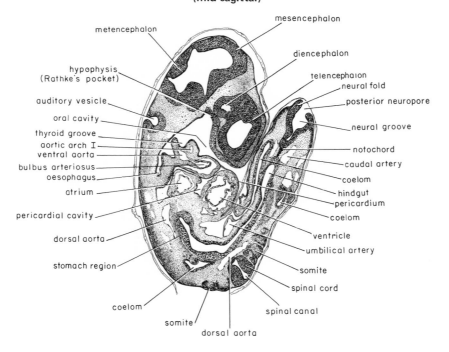

PARASAGITTAL SECTION OF 9 DAY MOUSE EMBRYO

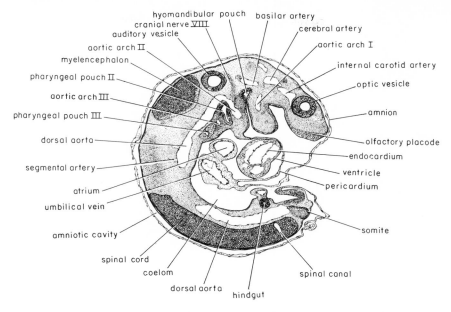

PARASAGITTAL SECTION OF 9 DAY MOUSE EMBRYO

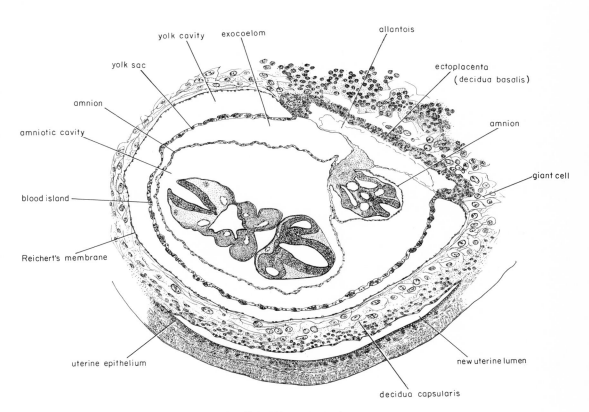

MOUSE EMBRYO — 9 days
(showing membranes)

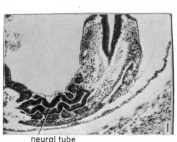

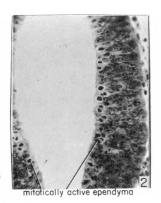

neural tube
(tortuous due to body flexures and torsions)

mitotically active ependyma

NEURAL TUBE OF MOUSE EMBRYO — 9 days

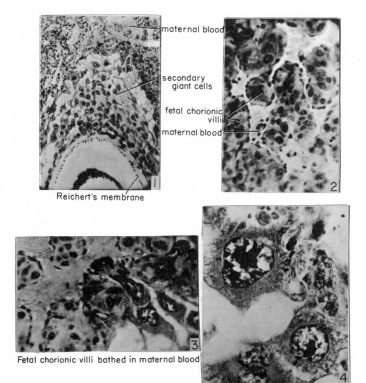

maternal blood

secondary
giant cells

fetal chorionic
villi

maternal blood

Reichert's membrane

Fetal chorionic villi bathed in maternal blood

Giant trophoblast cells

IMPLANTATION SITE — MOUSE EMBRYO 9 days

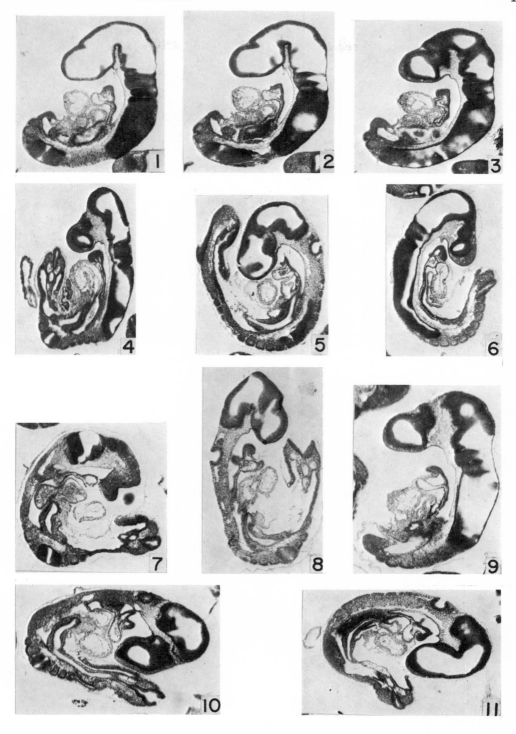

Photographs of Mid- and Para-sagittal sections of 9 day mouse embryo showing degree of cephalic flexures and the proximity of the head and tail. Note appearance of some of the major organ systems.

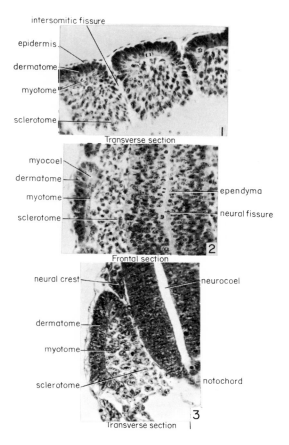

**STATE OF SOMITE FORMATION
IN 9 DAY MOUSE EMBRYO**

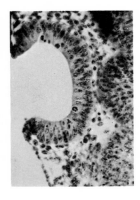

**OTIC VESICLE OF
MOUSE EMBRYO — 9 days
(showing active mitosis)**

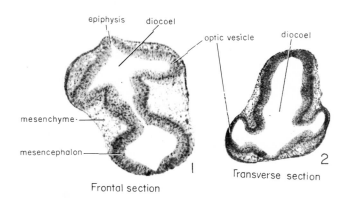

OPTIC VESICLES OF MOUSE EMBRYO — 9 days

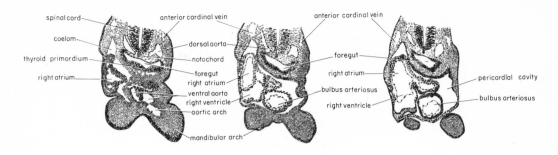

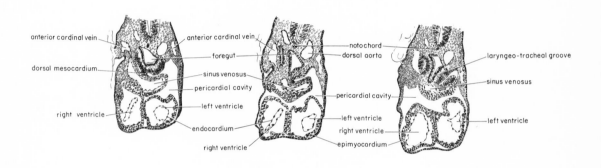

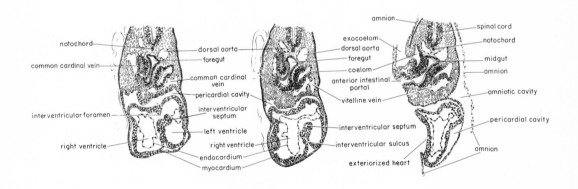

DEVELOPMENT OF THE MOUSE HEART AT 9 GESTATION DAYS
Serial X-Sections

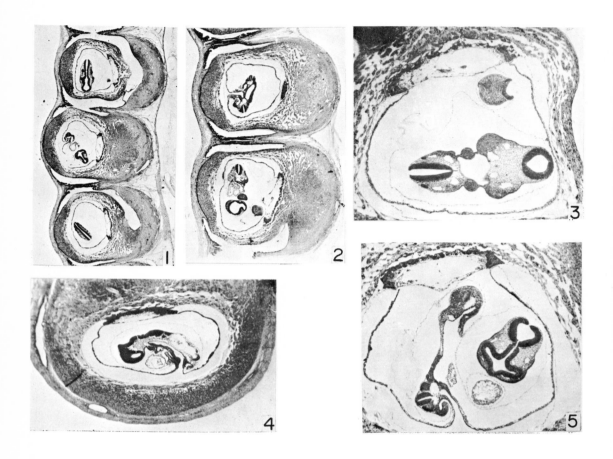

MOUSE EMBRYO — 9 days
(within the uterus at various magnifications)

Figs. 1, 2 — Longitudinal sections of gravid uterus of 9 day mouse gestation showing embryos in various transections and the occluded uterine cavity. Fig. 2 is at higher magnification than Fig. 1.

Fig. 4   — Still higher magnification of section of 9 day embryo in utero. Note anterior intestinal portal leading into foregut, and prominent heart beneath the head.

Figs. 3, 5 — Enlarged views of embryonic sections while in the uterus, showing relation to chorionic placenta. Note in Fig. 5 three separate sections through the central nervous system, indicating degree of flexion and torsion. Note also anterior intestinal portal.

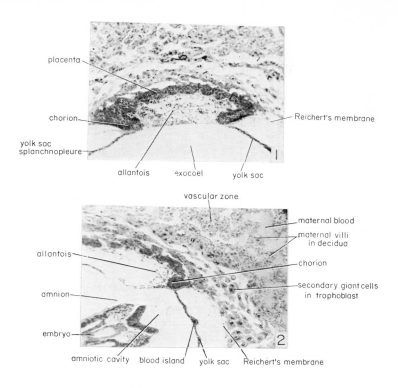

DEVELOPING PLACENTA OF MOUSE — 9 days

D. THE 9½ DAY EMBRYO: The mouse embryo is now embarked on developmental changes that are characteristic of all vertebrate embryos but
with rather minor variations.   However, since its development is telescoped
into such a brief period, the changes occur at accelerated rates compared to
those in many mammals.

Embryos at this stage may be dissected away from their membranes quite
easily and examined whole, with transmitted light. If they are fixed and cleared
in oil of wintergreen, their inner structures show up even better. Sections in
various planes are necessary to establish the extent of organ differentiation,
however.

The reversal of the original lordosis of the back now brings the telencephalon and tail into close approximation, with the dorsal side arched outward.
The shape might be called a kyphosis curve, a C with the ends somewhat overlapping. In frontal view the tail overlaps and is generally situated to the right
of the head. The head is far in advance of the rest of the body in development,
and 21 to 25 somites are apparent through the surface skin, gradually tapering
off toward the tail, with the more anterior ones always the further developed.
The posterior neuropore is closing.

The four major divisions of the brain are also apparent from the surface
since the brain vesicles are beginning to separate. Most prominent, of course,

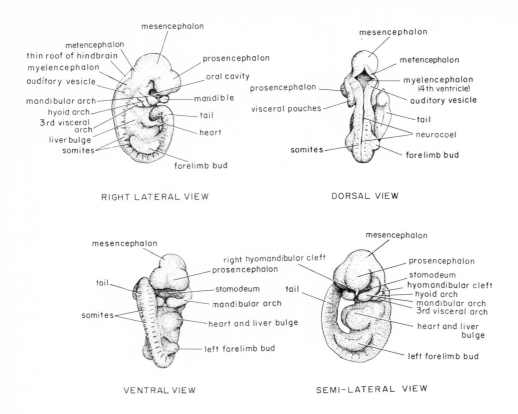

RIGHT LATERAL VIEW   DORSAL VIEW

VENTRAL VIEW   SEMI-LATERAL VIEW

MOUSE EMBRYO — 9.5 g.d.

are the two vesicles of the prosencephalon. The single mesencephalon is at the peak of the head, followed by the short metencephalon and finally the elongated myelencephalon. The last region is identified by the otic vesicles, which are now all but covered over. Crowded between the head and the tail are bulges of at least three pairs of visceral arches, the bulbous and exteriorized heart, and the liver. The forelimb buds show but, owing to cephalization, may appear to be placed almost at mid-body level.

In sections the brain cavities exhibit characteristic wall structures, thick in the dorsal walls of mesencephalon and the metencephalon and thin in the myelencephalon. Ventrally the infundibulum extends toward Rathke's pocket, and nearby are the paired optic vesicles as lateral projections. The spinal cord is well differentiated.

The primitive streak has disappeared by being incorporated into the embryo. The more anterior somites have dermatome, myotome, and some sclerotome but the myocoel is not visible unless in the most anterior ones. Much mesenchyme is scattered about between organs and blood vessels. The lateral thyroid diverticula appear, and just posteriorly the primordia of the pronephric ducts and tubules. The primordial germ cells are migrating via the mesentery toward their final residence in the gonads.

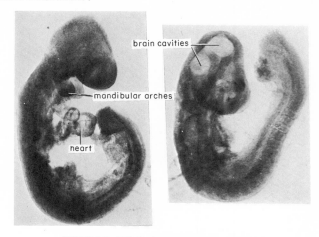

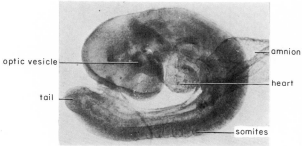

9.5 DAY MOUSE EMBRYO (2.25 mm)
(Photographs — Whole Embryos)

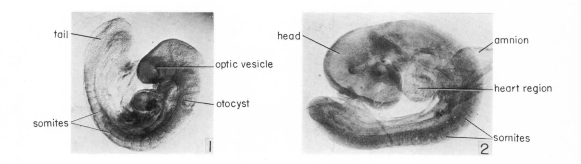

WHOLE MOUSE EMBRYO — 9.5 days
(showing approximation of head and tail)
(Photographs — Whole Embryos)

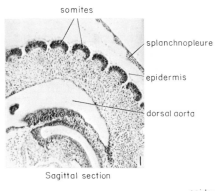

Sagittal section

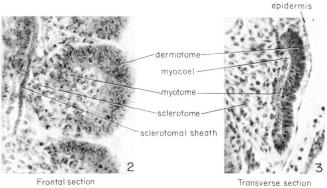

Frontal section   Transverse section

SOMITES OF MOUSE EMBRYO at 9.5 days

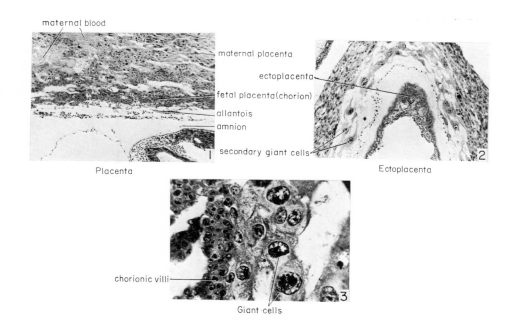

Placenta   Ectoplacenta

PLACENTAL RELATIONS IN MOUSE EMBRYO at 9.5 days
(Photographs)

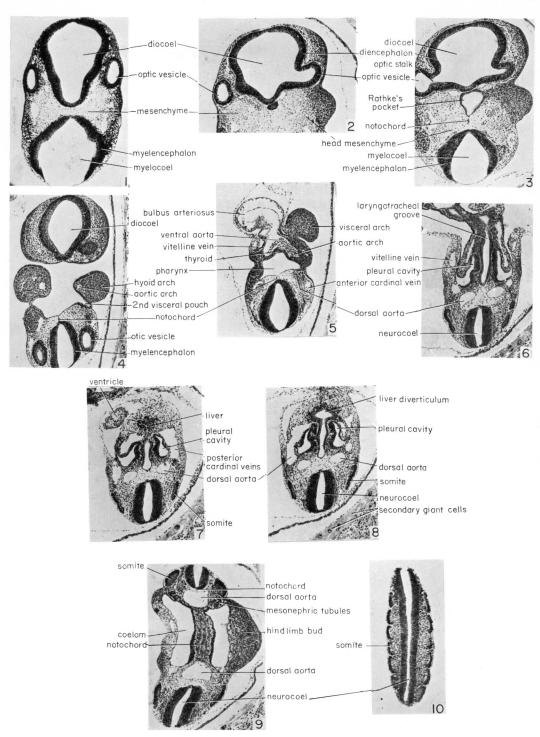

SECTIONS OF MOUSE EMBRYOS at 9.5 days
(Photographs)

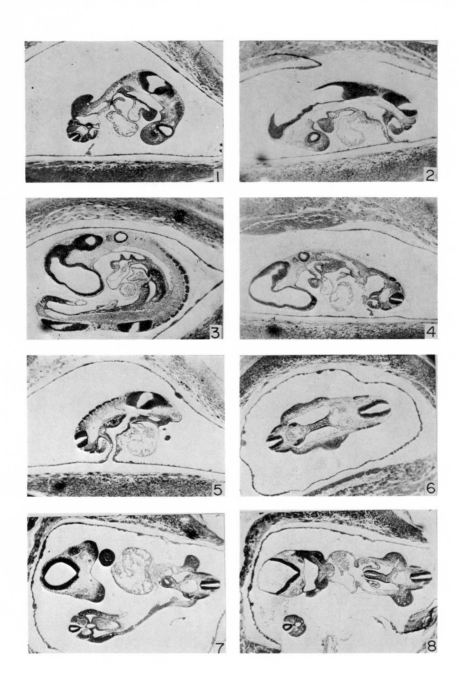

SECTIONS OF MOUSE EMBRYOS IN UTERUS at 9.5 days
(Photographs)

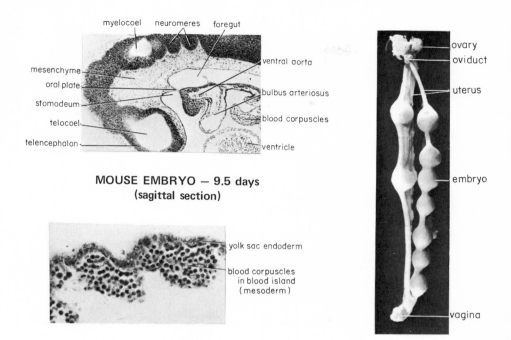

myelocoel neuromeres foregut

mesenchyme
oral plate
stomodeum
telocoel
telencephalon

ventral aorta
bulbus arteriosus
blood corpuscles
ventricle

MOUSE EMBRYO — 9.5 days
(sagittal section)

yolk sac endoderm

blood corpuscles
in blood island
(mesoderm)

YOLK SAC SPLANCHNOPLEURE
IN MOUSE EMBRYO — 9.5 days

ovary
oviduct
uterus

embryo

vagina

GRAVID UTERUS OF 9.5 day
PREGNANT MOUSE

The gut, by this time, is rather a simple tube, wider at both ends than in the middle. The primordia of the lungs, liver, and dorsal pancreas are small but discernible. Lateral to the anterior region of the gut is a thick epithelial-like plate of cells, temporarily well-defined, called the anterior splanchnic mesodermal plate (ASMP). The cytoplasm of the constituent cells is rather basophilic while the nuclei resemble those of the loose mesenchyme. It has been suggested that this transient, thick epithelium may have some growth and morphogenetic function, particularly in the development of the stomach, greater omentum, and spleen. Shortly after the embryo has turned on its axis the anterior gut and coelom close as far back as the primordium of the liver. Posterior to the ASMP the splanchnic mesoderm, which covers the wide anterior portion of the intestine, is several layers in thickness, composed of loosely arranged mesenchymal cells. More posteriorly the mesoderm is only one cell thick, formed in a plate-like arrangement. From the 16th intersegmental artery posteriorly the splanchnic mesoderm lateral to the gut, and also covering the aorta and the umbilical arteries, is organized into a compact epithelial plate which is thin but resembles the ASMP. The posterior boundary of the coelom is formed partly by the roots of the umbilical artery as they pass around the gut. The coelom may be seen to extend caudally and ventrally a short distance lateral to the umbilical roots, thus forming a pocket on each side. The vitelline vein enters the body from the left, a branch passing to the right on the ventral side of the gut, but both branches go directly to the heart through the newly

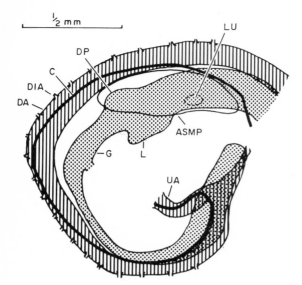

Parasagittal reconstruction of an early 9½ day mouse embryo showing the dorsal aorta and gut projected onto a parasagittal plane. The aorta is a single median structure except at the anterior and posterior ends, where it is double, with the gut lying in part between the two branches. ASMP, extent of anterior, dorsal, and posterior borders of the coelom; DA, dorsal aorta, DIA, dorsal intersegmentary artery; DP, dorsal pancreas; G, gut; L, liver; LU, lung bud; UA, umbilical artery. Embryo measured 2.4 mm.

(Courtesy Margaret C. Green, 1967 Developmental Biology 15:62-89, Academic Press.)

forming liver on either side of the gut. Shortly a new anastomosis forms between the left and right branches around the dorsal side of the gut and the central connection is lost. Thus, the vitelline vein passes dorsal to the gut from left to right and then into the liver. The anastomosis occurs just posterior to the dorsal pancreas, and anterior to the posterior end of the ASMP.

The embryonic-maternal relations should be examined at this time in an attempt to determine the area where the two sources of tissue interdigitate. The yolk sac marks the inner boundary of Reichert's membrane. Outside Reichert's membrane some scattered giant cells lie between the embryo and the decidua.

E. THE 10 DAY EMBRYO:
The 10 day mouse embryo is structurally comparable to the 96 hour chick embryo. It has 26 to 28 somites, measures about 3.8 mm from crown to rump in total length. If straightened out it might well be twice the crown-rump length, and is enlarging rapidly in almost all directions, changing from a slim and elongate shape to an almost bulbous one. This is due largely to expansion of the brain vesicles. Most obvious at this time is the further development and ventral curvature of the head region with the mesencephalon forming its main (and most anterior) bulge. The mid-body region is beginning to round out and incorporate its earlier bulges. The tail is still curled to the right side.

In cleared whole specimens many internal structures can be discerned, such as the visceral arches, the heart, the liver, and the rudimentary mesonephros. The otic vesicles are now closed to the outside. The olfactory discs are invaginating to pits, an internasal cleft is forming between them, and triangular cells of Cajal of the accessory olfactory bulb appear. The paired telencephalic vesicles continue to expand, but neither is as prominent as the median mesencephalon. The isthmus between the metencephalon and myelencephalon is deepened, and the roof of the latter is very thin.

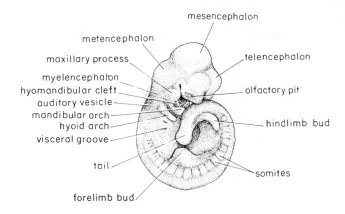

RIGHT LATERAL VIEW

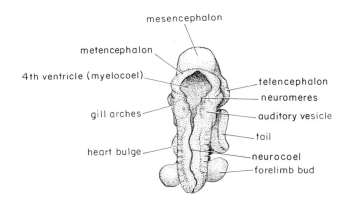

DORSAL VIEW

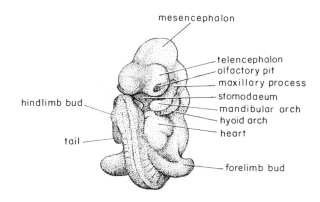

VENTROLATERAL VIEW

MOUSE EMBRYO — 10 g.d.

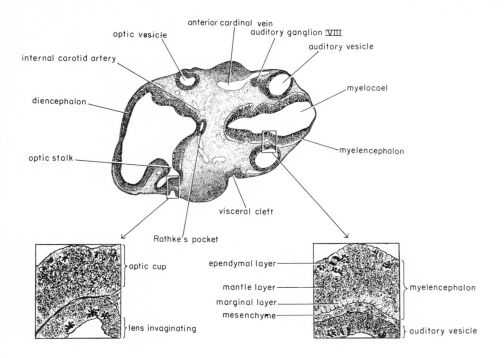

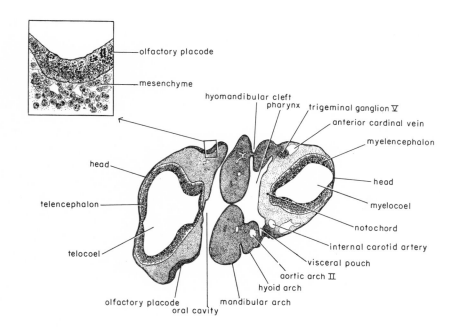

MOUSE EMBRYO — 10 gestation days
(transverse sections)

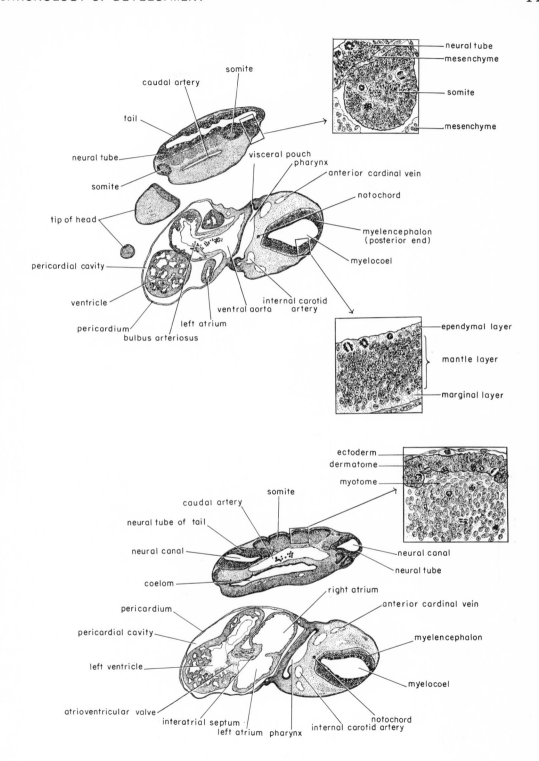

MOUSE EMBRYO — 10 g.d.

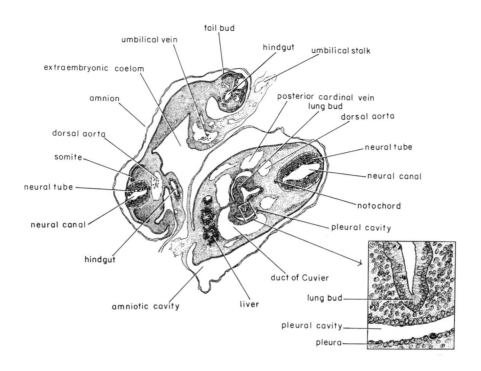

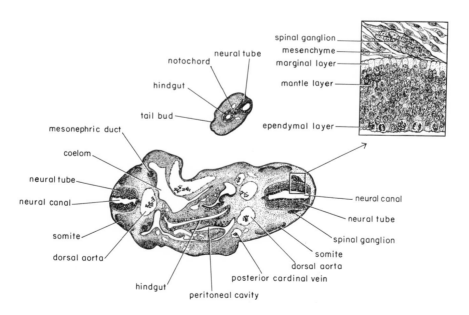

MOUSE EMBRYO — 10 g.d.

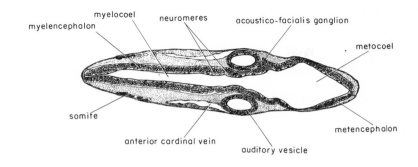

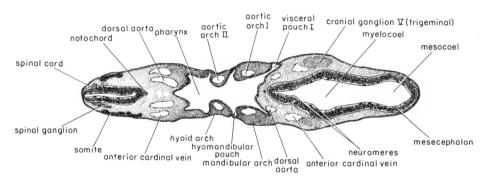

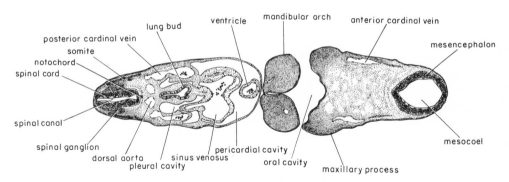

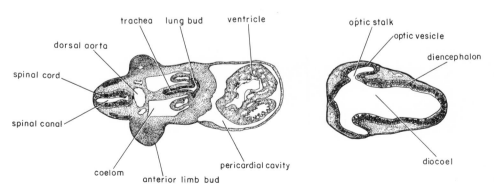

MOUSE EMBRYO — 10 g.d.
(Frontal Sections)

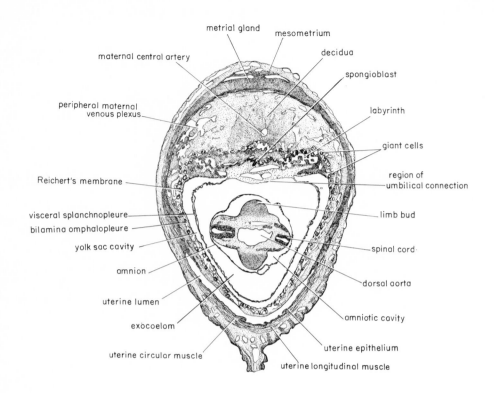

metrial gland   mesometrium

maternal central artery   decidua

spongioblast

peripheral maternal
venous plexus   labyrinth

giant cells

Reichert's membrane   region of
umbilical connection

visceral splanchnopleure   limb bud

bilamina omphalopleure

yolk sac cavity   spinal cord

amnion   dorsal aorta

uterine lumen

exocoelom   amniotic cavity

uterine circular muscle   uterine epithelium

uterine longitudinal muscle

PLACENTAL RELATIONS OF THE 10 DAY MOUSE EMBRYO

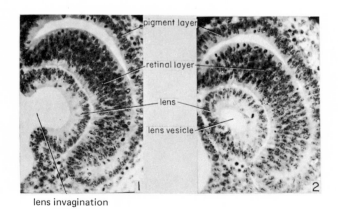

pigment layer

retinal layer

lens

lens vesicle

lens invagination

EYE DEVELOPMENT IN MOUSE EMBRYO at 10.0 days

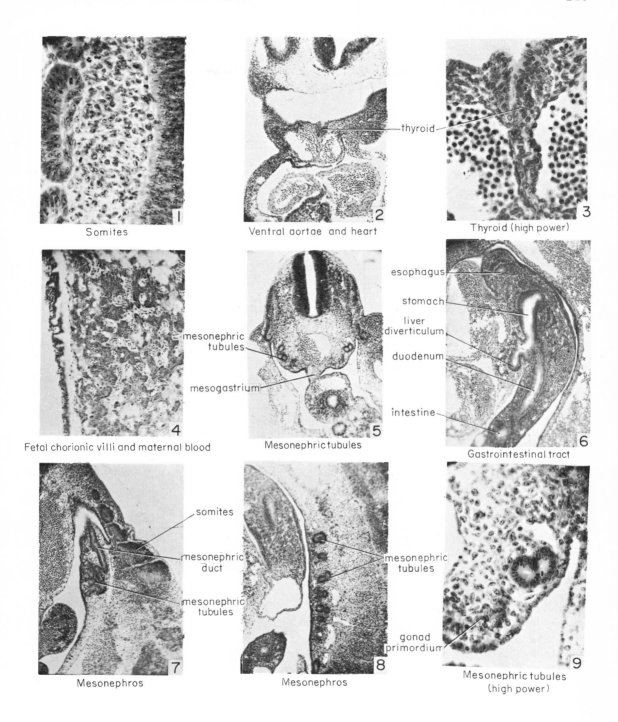

1 Somites

2 Ventral aortae and heart — thyroid

3 Thyroid (high power)

4 Fetal chorionic villi and maternal blood

5 Mesonephric tubules — mesonephric tubules, mesogastrium

6 Gastrointestinal tract — esophagus, stomach, liver diverticulum, duodenum, intestine

7 Mesonephros — somites, mesonephric duct, mesonephric tubules

8 Mesonephros — mesonephric tubules

9 Mesonephric tubules (high power) — gonad primordium

MOUSE EMBRYO at 10.0 days
(Photographs)

In sections visceral pouch III can be identified indicating that the visceral arches and pouches also develop in sequence from anterior toward posterior. The first three pairs of aortic arches are visible. The diverticulum has expanded and begins to bifurcate into primitive lung buds, later to form bronchi, joining the foregut at the laryngotracheal groove. The liver first appears. Although the oral (stomodeal) membrane has broken through at 9 days gestation the cloacal (proctodeal) membrane has just formed.

The heart is most important because it removes metabolic wastes from the newly formed and forming organs and brings requisite nutrition to them. It is therefore differentiated before the other organs and functions regularly with an ever-increasing volume of corpuscles and fluid. The corpuscles come from hematopoietic centers in the yolk sac splanchnopleure. Serial sections through the heart region at 10 days show not only the four chambers but myocardial development so well advanced that the atria can be easily distinguished from the ventricles, which appear to be filled with trabeculae. The endocardial cushion and interventricular septum are being completed, and a thick pericardial membrane encloses all. In more posterior sections the proximity and actual vascular relations of the liver and heart can be seen. At about mid-body level the pronephric ducts and tubules can be located. The paired pronephroi project as bulges into the coelom, connecting with it via the ciliated nephrostomes.

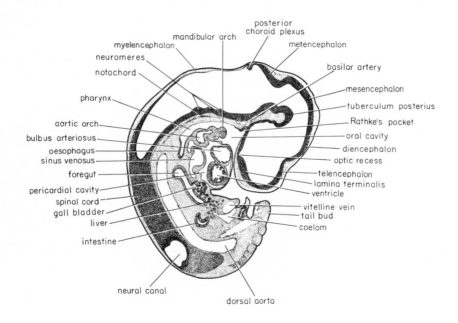

MOUSE EMBRYO — 10 days
(mid-sagittal)

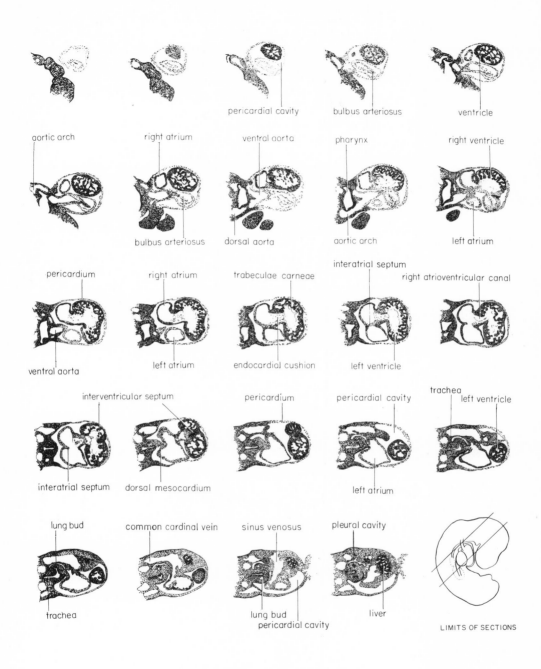

**DEVELOPMENT OF THE MOUSE HEART
AT 10 GESTATION DAYS
(Serial Sections)**

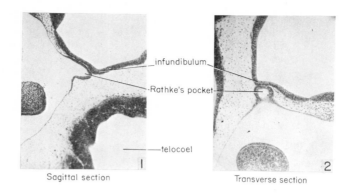

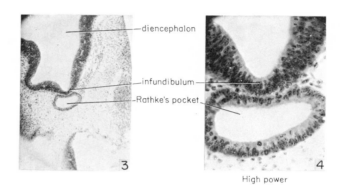

**PITUITARY GLAND DEVELOPMENT
IN MOUSE EMBRYO at 10.0 days**

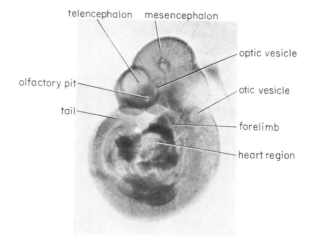

MOUSE EMBRYO at 10.0 days

F. THE 10½ DAY EMBRYO: At $10\frac{1}{2}$ days the embryo has 29 to 36 somites and measures 5.2 mm from crown to rump. Again, its total straightened length might be twice the crown-rump length. The forelimb buds are growing rapidly, the hindlimb buds make their appearance, and four visceral arches can be distinguished.

Sections show that the outer surface of each optic vesicle has invaginated to form an optic cup which is being pinched off from the cavity of the diencephalon to form an optic stalk. In each cup appears a lens placode, a thickening of the ectoderm. The lens placode may even be pinched off and contain a vesicle. The inner (retinal) layer of the double-layered optic cup becomes thick with neuroblasts, while the outer (pigmented) layer (closer to the brain) becomes thinner. Numerous mitoses are seen in each layer. The endolymphatic duct, a remnant of the opening of the otic vesicle leads ventro-mesially toward the vesicle, closely associated with a cluster of neuroblasts. These give rise to the acoustic nerve (cranial nerve VIII). Slightly anteriorly is the facial nerve, (cranial nerve VII). The olfactory pits have deepened.

The spinal ganglia are metameric and resemble superficially the cranial ganglia, which are actually quite different.

The dermatome of the anterior somites is very thick, and the myotome (lining the myocoel) is thickening. The somites appear to have moved away slightly from the midline leaving the spongy sclerotome behind. Overlying the somites is the integumentary ectoderm, which is very thin at this time.

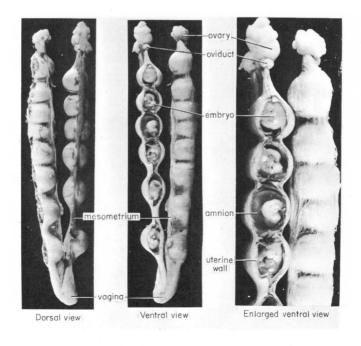

MOUSE EMBRYOS IN UTERUS at 10.5 days

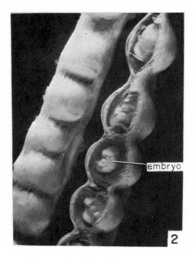

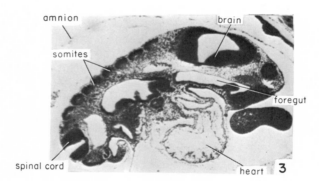

MOUSE EMBRYO AT 10.5 DAYS DEVELOPMENT

Fig. 1 — Paired uteri of gravid mouse at 10.5 days gestation, with embryos exposed in situ. Note ovaries above and vagina below, where bicornuate uteri converge.

Fig. 2 — Enlarged view of uterus showing (right) embryos in situ. Note various positions of embryo in muscular uterus.

Fig. 3 — Section of 10.5 day embryo in situ, showing much coiled position so that both brain and caudal neurocoel are shown in the same field.

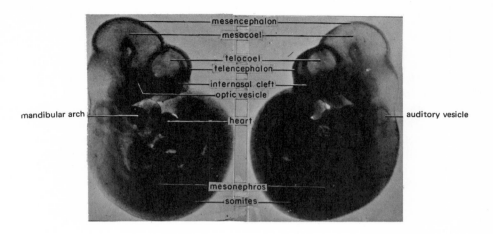

10.5 DAY MOUSE EMBRYO (4.75 mm)

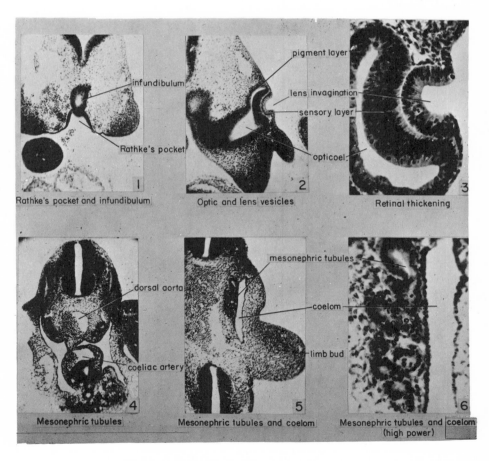

SECTIONS OF MOUSE EMBRYO at 10.5 days
(Photographs)

Sagittal sections show a wide open mouth, with no remains of the stomodeum and a trachea separate from and ventral to the foregut (esophagus).

By this time the gut has elongated and the region between the liver, pancreas, and lungs has grown enormously. The stomach is now clearly distinguished by a narrowing of its lumen both anterior and posterior to it. The dorsal mesentery of the stomach has enlarged toward the right side and forms a fold which will become the greater omentum. The space between this fold and the forming stomach becomes the omental bursa. The stomach now lies slightly to the left of the midline. The endodermal portion of the dorsal pancreas has enlarged and grown into the fold of the dorsal mesentery, extending caudally from the stomach on the left side. The endodermal portion of the ventral pancreas has begun to bud off from the gut just posterior to the liver, and the biliary ducts are enlarging as they grow into the liver. The anterior part of the ASMP has disappeared, but may still be seen in the vicinity of the stomach and pancreas. The intestine is somewhat elongated, and a loop is formed to the left.

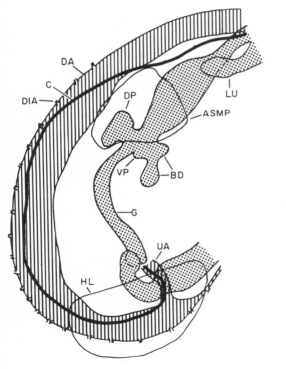

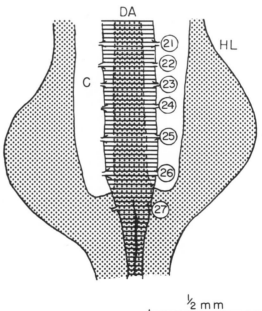

Parasagittal section reconstruction of 10½ day mouse embryo. C, border of coelom; DA, dorsal aorta; DIA, dorsal intersegmentary artery; DP, dorsal pancreas; G, gut; HL, hind limb bud; BD, biliary ducts; LU, lung; UA, umbilical artery; VP, ventral pancreas. Embryo measures 3.6 mm.

(Courtesy Dr. Margaret C. Green, 1967, Developmental Biology 15:62-89, Academic Press.)

Frontal section of 10½ day mouse embryo, reconstructed, to show structures related to the hind limb region projected onto a dorsal plane. C, coelom; DA, dorsal aorta; HL, hind limb bud. Numbers are intersegmental levels.

(Courtesy Dr. Margaret C. Green, 1967, Developmental Biology 15:62-89, Academic Press.)

The splanchnic mesoderm has increased in thickness, but appears to be loose mesenchyme covered by a single layer of epithelium without the plate-like structure seen earlier. It is probable that this splanchnic mesoderm interacts with the endoderm of the gut to promote its growth.

Already the liver seems to be establishing itself as a hematopoietic center, supplementing the vascular centers in the yolk sac splanchnopleure. Primary intestinal loops appear.

The heart has the interventricular septum, the septum primum, the atrioventricular canals and the right venous valve primordium. Paired aortic arches III, IV, and VI are formed. Lateral to the single large dorsal aorta, which is usually engorged with corpuscles, are the pronephroi. Although they never function they give rise to some genital structures. Frontal sections show the paired pronephric ducts, connected at their anterior ends with the pronephric tubules and at their posterior ends with the cloaca. The mesonephroi continue to develop.

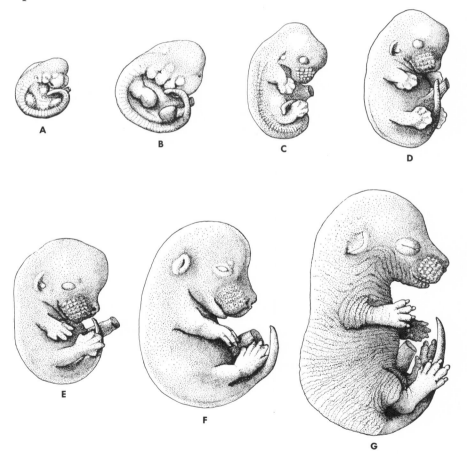

DIAGRAMS SHOWING DEVELOPMENT OF MOUSE EMBRYO
from 10½ to 16½ days

(From R. Rugh, "Vertebrate Embryology", Harcourt, Brace & World, Inc., New York, 1964.)

G. THE 11 DAY EMBRYO: The 11 day mouse embryo is comparable to the 30 day human embryo. It has 37 to 42 well defined somites and measures 6.2 mm from crown to rump. The body in general still shows kyphosis and cephalization - the head is about one-third the total body length - but is filling out. There is an umbilical hernia, which later recedes. The tail is still growing and much coiled, so that the olfactory pits, (now nasal chambers) are close to its base. The forelimb buds appear to be curved and have knoblike extremities. The hindlimbs are still buds. The eye parts are usually visible from the surface.

Brain differentiation continues, with the walls of the entire central nervous system actively proliferating neuroblasts which begin to occlude some of the neural cavities. The floor of the diencephalon may project as a sac. The epiphysis first appears as a median dorsal evagination from the diencephalon.

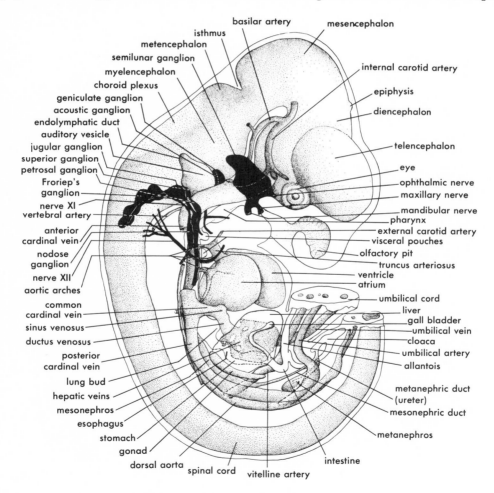

**RECONSTRUCTION OF MOUSE EMBRYO
AT 11 DAYS GESTATION**

(From R. Rugh, "Vertebrate Embryology", Harcourt, Brace & World, Inc., New York, 1964.)

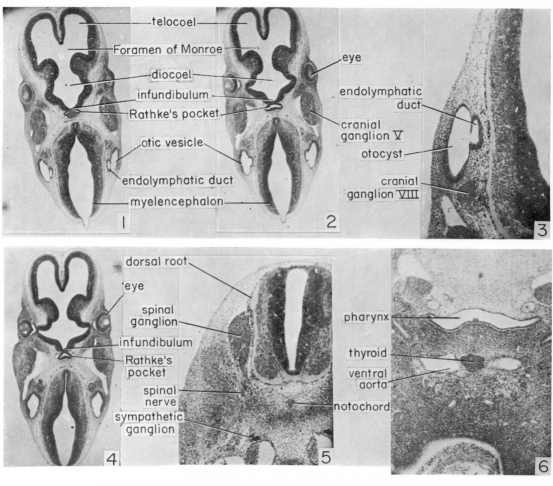

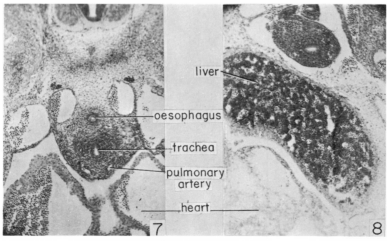

MOUSE EMBRYO SECTIONS at 11 days
(Photographs)

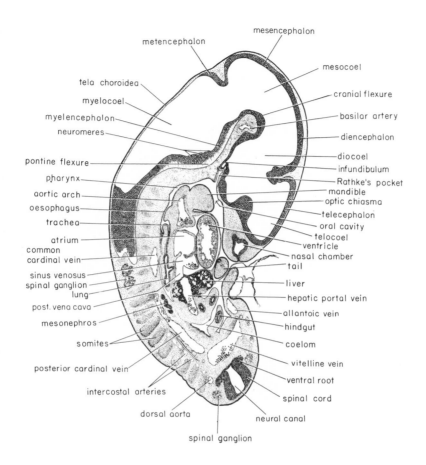

MOUSE EMBRYO — 11 days
(mid-sagittal)

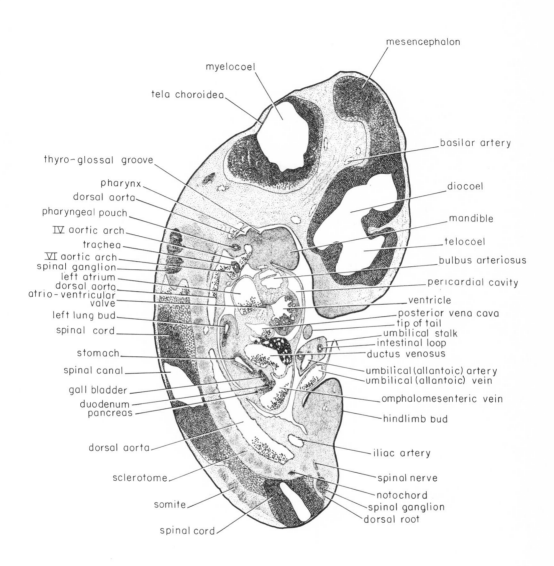

MOUSE EMBRYO — 11 days
(para-sagittal)

Rathke's pocket and the infundibulum are contiguous, but there is no cellular differentiation in them. In the roof of the myelencephalon is the thin and vascular posterior choroid plexus. The isthmus between the metencephalon and myelencephalon has further deepened. Owing to the extreme flexure of the brain around the tip of the notochord, a section can be cut that shows it apparently separating the diencephalon from the metencephalon. Lateral to the hindbrain cranial ganglia V to IX suddenly develop. The largest aggregation of neuroblasts is lateral to the pharynx, where the trigeminal (ganglion V) forms. Its branches issue to the ophthalmic, maxillary, and mandibular regions. A separate group of ganglia (X to XII) controls the visceral organs and is less compact. Tucked between these two areas of neuroblastic activity on each side is the enlarging otic vesicle, which has lost all connections with the outside. The epithelial lining of the semicircular canals first appears. The original invagination of ectoderm from the surface, now the lining of the endolymphatic duct, is elongated and joins a vestibular portion, which in turn joins a cochlear portion. Neither is at all differentiated. These may be identified as the ultimate saccule and utricle. Mitral cells arise in the olfactory bulbs, along with the triangular cells of Cajal in the accessory olfactory bulbs. Some superficial tufted (sensory) cells are also apparent. Olfactory nerves reach the telencephalon. The vomeronasal organ is visible. The spinal cord begins to display typical organization, with ventral horns and ependyma. There is as yet no sharp distinction between white matter and grey matter. The spinal ganglia are well formed, with both dorsal and ventral roots. Near the heart they give off sympathetic branches. At about heart level, a very small single cluster of cells beneath the spinal cord is the sole remnant of the notochord.

The thyroid diverticulum may still retain a very small tubular connection with the pharynx, which is lost during this day. Around the diverticulum are clusters of gland cells. These quickly aggregate into lobules and become highly vascular. The parathyroid, and thymus glands and the ultimobranchial bodies begin to form. The dorsal and ventral pancreatic rudiments are fusing.

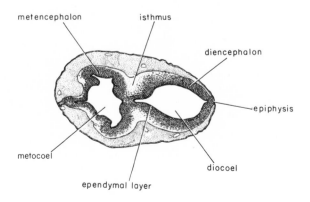

MOUSE EMBRYO — 11 gestation days
(transverse sections)

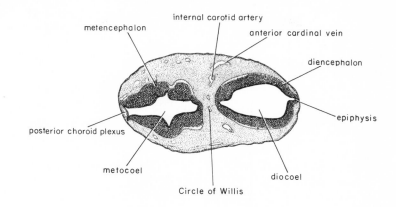

internal carotid artery

metencephalon

anterior cardinal vein

diencephalon

epiphysis

posterior choroid plexus

metocoel

diocoel

Circle of Willis

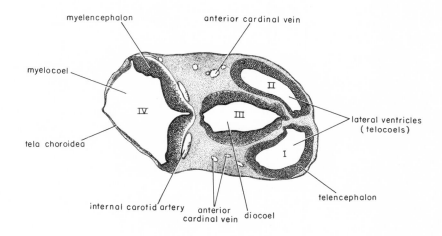

myelencephalon

anterior cardinal vein

myelocoel

II

IV

III

lateral ventricles (telocoels)

tela choroidea

I

internal carotid artery

anterior cardinal vein

diocoel

telencephalon

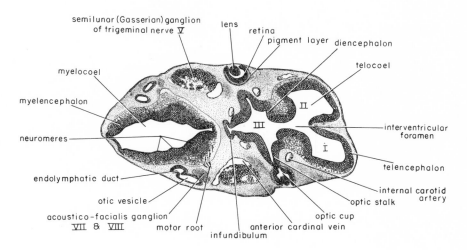

semilunar (Gasserian) ganglion of trigeminal nerve V

lens

retina

pigment layer

diencephalon

myelocoel

telocoel

myelencephalon

II

neuromeres

III

interventricular foramen

I

endolymphatic duct

telencephalon

otic vesicle

internal carotid artery

acoustico-facialis ganglion VII & VIII

motor root

infundibulum

anterior cardinal vein

optic cup

optic stalk

MOUSE EMBRYO — 11 g.d.
(transverse sections)

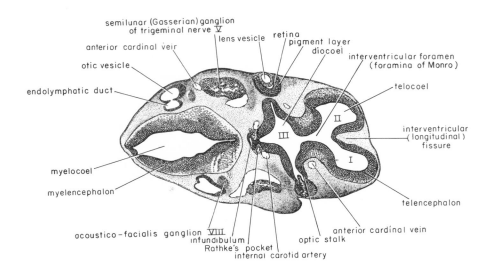

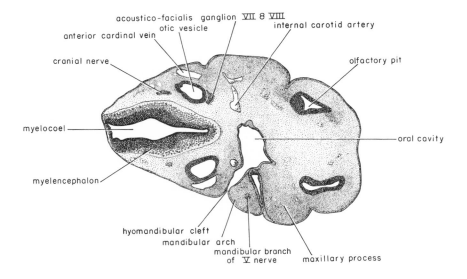

MOUSE EMBRYO — 11 g.d.
(transverse sections)

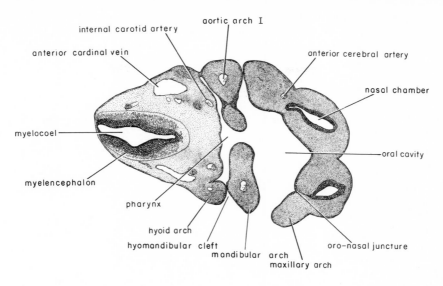

internal carotid artery

aortic arch I

anterior cardinal vein

anterior cerebral artery

nasal chamber

myelocoel

oral cavity

myelencephalon

pharynx

oro-nasal juncture

hyoid arch

hyomandibular cleft

mandibular arch

maxillary arch

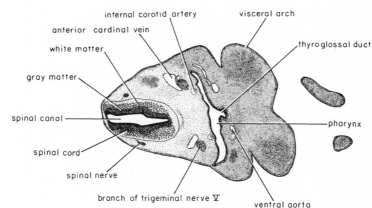

internal carotid artery

visceral arch

anterior cardinal vein

thyroglossal duct

white matter

gray matter

spinal canal

spinal cord

pharynx

spinal nerve

branch of trigeminal nerve V

ventral aorta

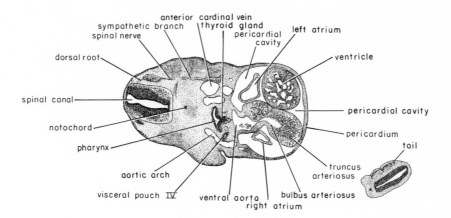

anterior cardinal vein

sympathetic branch

thyroid gland

spinal nerve

pericardial cavity

left atrium

dorsal root

ventricle

spinal canal

notochord

pericardial cavity

pharynx

pericardium

aortic arch

tail

visceral pouch IV

truncus arteriosus

ventral aorta

bulbus arteriosus

right atrium

MOUSE EMBRYO — 11 g.d.
(transverse sections)

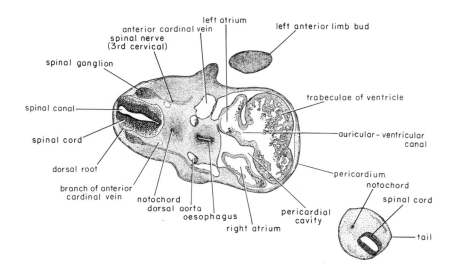

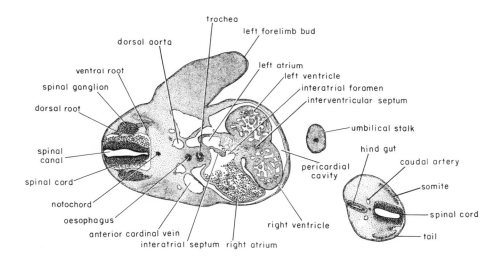

MOUSE EMBRYO — 11 g.d.
(transverse sections)

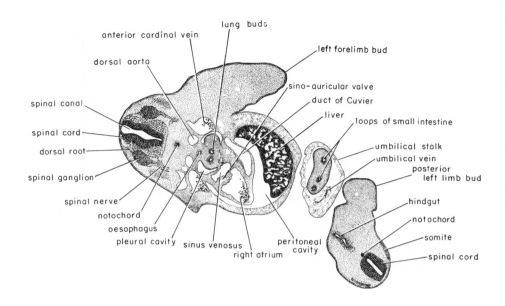

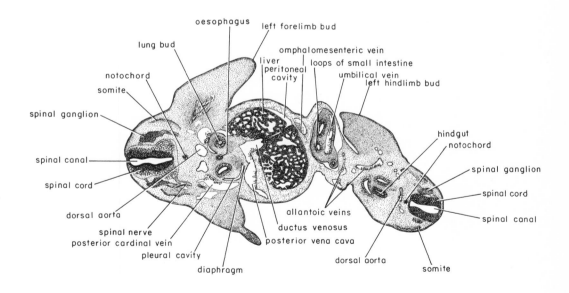

MOUSE EMBRYO — 11 g.d.
(transverse sections)

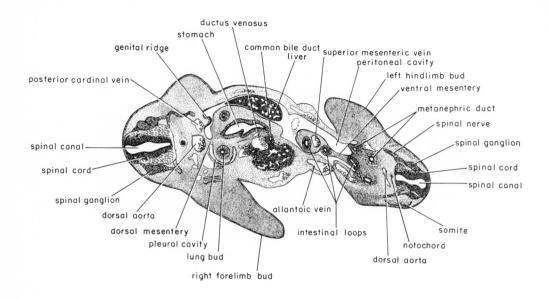

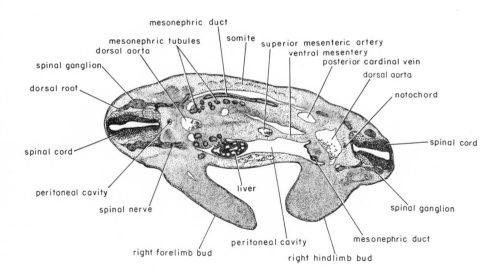

MOUSE EMBRYO — 11 g.d.
(transverse sections)

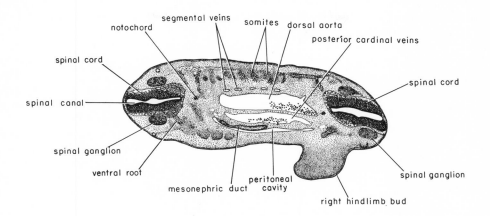

notochord
segmental veins
somites
dorsal aorta
posterior cardinal veins
spinal cord
spinal canal
spinal cord
spinal ganglion
ventral root
mesonephric duct
peritoneal cavity
right hindlimb bud
spinal ganglion

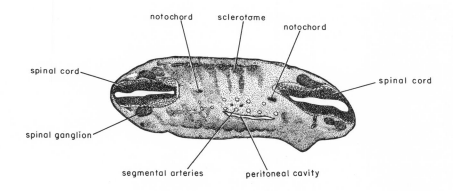

notochord
sclerotome
notochord
spinal cord
spinal cord
spinal ganglion
segmental arteries
peritoneal cavity

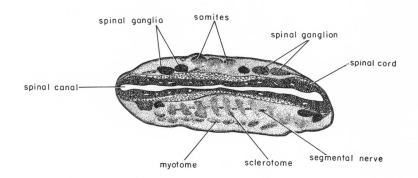

spinal ganglia
somites
spinal ganglion
spinal cord
spinal canal
myotome
sclerotome
segmental nerve

MOUSE EMBRYO — 11 g.d.
(transverse sections)

The thick columnar layer of cells comprising the anterior splanchnic mesodermal plate (ASMP) now may be seen over the pancreas and the posterior part of the stomach. It is in the process of disappearing except from the dorsal part of the mesenteric fold and the posterior part of the omental bursa on the side adjacent to the stomach.

The heart continues toward completion, with the interatrial foramen much constricted and the endocardial cushion fused. The ventricular walls are much thickened, whereas the atrial walls appear to be thinner and more expanded. The dorsal mesocardium, which was formed with the heart and supports it for some time, is still present at its extremities, but the ventral mesocardium has ruptured to give a single pericardial cavity. The diaphragm is a new development, separating the pericardial cavity from the peritoneal cavity. The pleural cavity (now cut off from the coelom) can be seen at about the level of the sinus venosus and diaphragm.

Internal carotid arteries and anterior cardinal veins are visible anteriorly. Since they are all thin-walled at this time, their positions rather than their structure distinguish them. The circle of Willis, which connects the internal carotid arteries with the basilar arteries around the forming pituitary gland, (Rathke's pocket and infundibulum combined) is also visible. More posteriorly are the paired lung buds, the right one of which is developing bronchial areas, the umbilicus, allantoic veins, and metanephric ducts. Numerous mesonephric tubules lie laterally near the peritoneal cavity, and posteriorly the mesonephric ducts lead to the urogenital sinus (cloaca). The subcardinal veins are forming ventrally to the mesonephroi. The most posterior sections, which are likely to be frontal rather than transverse because of the twisting of the body, clearly demonstrate the metameric arrangement of the somites and the spinal ganglia. Since many of the organ systems are longitudinally distributed, frontal sections are extremely instructive. They show the neural tube with its typical cellular differentiation; the relation of pharynx to trachea to lung buds; the descending aorta with its branching segmental arteries; and the paired excretory (mesonephric and metanephric) ducts.

It is quite obvious, as one examines the living or cleared whole specimen at 11 days or sections of it (in any of the three planes), that the embryo is now an intricate mosaic of interrelated developing organ systems, all integrated for the proper functioning of the organism as a whole. Time and place relationships must be adhered to, or else there will be defective form and, in consequence, defective function. The vast majority of embryos will conform to the necessary pattern and arrive at a state of independent existence at about the same time.

From this stage on, general descriptions will be provided at daily intervals through 16 days, and thereafter certain organ systems will be independently described to show how they originate and develop. The purpose of this organization is to impress upon the student that the embryo is not made up of separate and independent parts that can be fitted together at a certain time but that its development is continuous and involves all its organ systems, some of which appear early and others late. If the student is aware of this situation, we can finally study specific organ systems without the risk of separating, in his mind, the developmental histories of parts that must be related to the whole.

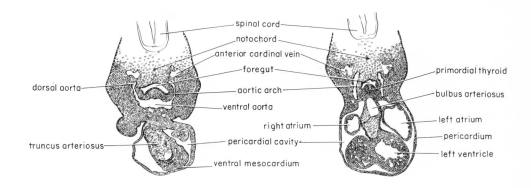

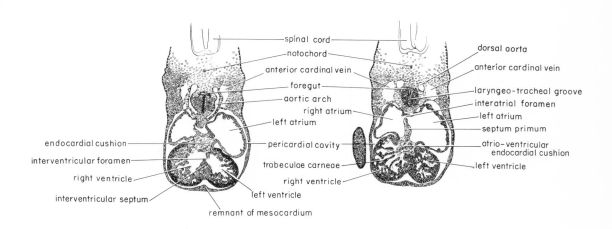

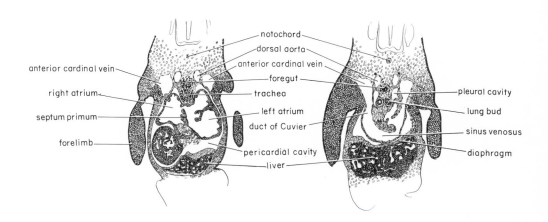

**DEVELOPMENT OF THE MOUSE HEART
AT 11 GESTATION DAYS**

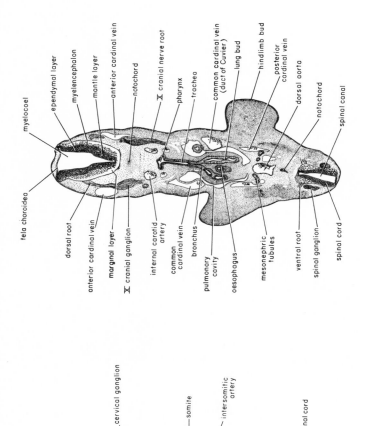

MOUSE EMBRYO – 11 gestation days
(frontal sections)

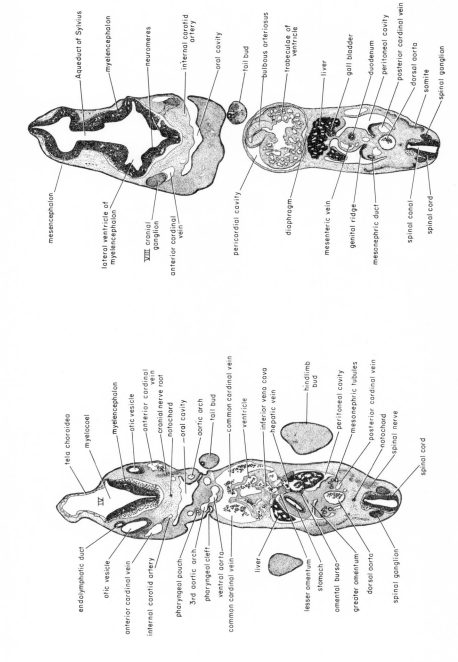

MOUSE EMBRYO – 11 gestation days
(frontal sections)

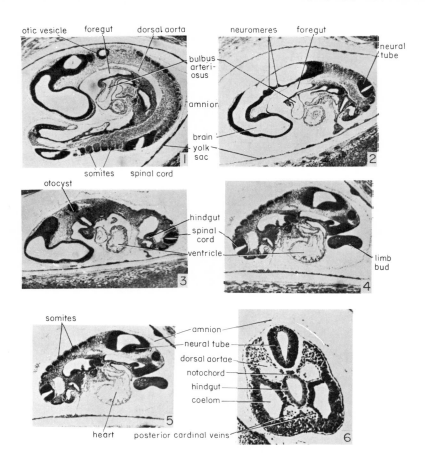

MOUSE EMBRYO IN UTERUS at 11.5 days
(Photographs of Random Sections)

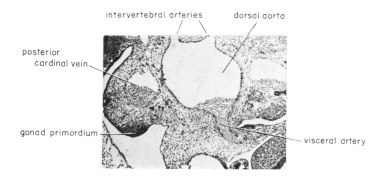

SECTION THROUGH 11.5 DAY MOUSE EMBRYO

Showing dorsal aorta with two dorsally-directed intervertebral arteries and a single ventrally-directed visceral
artery. Note also posterior cardinal vein in mesonephros.

H. THE 12 DAY EMBRYO:
The 12 day mouse embryo is comparable in development to the 36 day human embryo. It has from 43 to 48 somites and measures 7.2 mm from crown to rump. The body is still coiled upon itself, and the cranial and cervical flexures are advanced, but the back is beginning to straighten. All four limb buds are prominent, although the anterior pair is slightly better developed than the posterior pair. The extremities are flared out into plates with indications of digital divisions. This is a critical period for digit formation, from mesenchyme to precartilage.

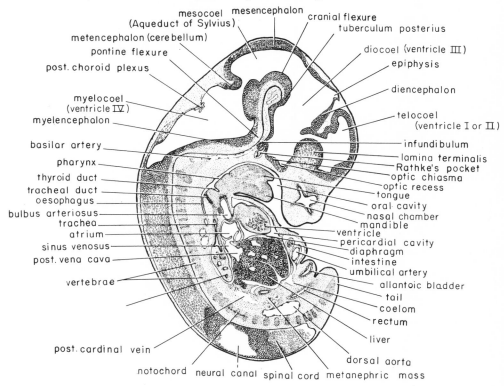

MOUSE EMBRYO — 12 days
(mid-sagittal)

The external ear and eye regions can be located. The vestibular and cochlear portions of the otic vesicles are much enlarged. In the narrow optic stalk behind each optic cup an artery may be seen. The lenses are now below the surface, and vitreous humor is forming behind them. A fibrous portion is differentiating posteriorly to the vesicle in each. The retinal layer of the optic cups is very thick, stretching the pigmented layer until it is much thinner than before. Short axon cells of Cajal arise in the olfactory bulbs.

Mid-sagittal sections show the brain convolutions to be extensive, involving thickenings and thinnings at the various levels. Eventually most of the vesicles will be obliterated with tissue. The roof of the mesencephalon is especially thick, as are the roofs of the telencephalic vesicles. The infundibulum seems to be encircling and incorporating Rathke's pocket just posterior to a prominent

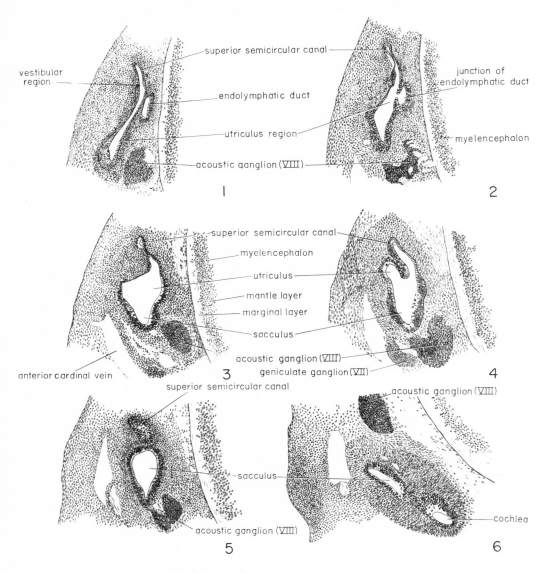

vestibular region

superior semicircular canal

endolymphatic duct

utriculus region

acoustic ganglion (VIII)

1

junction of endolymphatic duct

myelencephalon

2

superior semicircular canal

myelencephalon

utriculus

mantle layer

marginal layer

sacculus

acoustic ganglion (VIII)

geniculate ganglion (VII)

anterior cardinal vein

3

4

superior semicircular canal

acoustic ganglion (VIII)

sacculus

acoustic ganglion (VIII)

cochlea

5

6

MOUSE EAR DEVELOPMENT — 12 g.d.

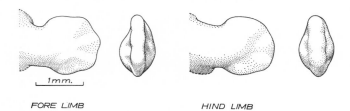

1mm.

FORE LIMB   *HIND LIMB*

**RIGHT FORE AND HIND LIMB OF 12 DAY
NORMAL MOUSE EMBRYO**

(Grüneberg 1961, 1963)

thickening in the floor of the telocoel, the lamina terminalis. Many neurons are present in the dorsal and ventral, cochlear, basal, optic, lateral, cuneate, and lateral reticular nuclei, indicating that neurodifferentiation has begun.

Mid-sagittal sections also show an open mouth, with a transverse groove in the mid-ventral floor marking the posterior limit of the tongue. Just posterior to this is the pharynx, in the mid-ventral floor of which are the remnant of the thyroid duct and then the tracheal duct, leading posteriorly to the trachea, the bronchi, and the lung buds. Parathyroid III and the thymus have separated from visceral pouch III. The liver, is a very large and highly vascular organ, surrounding a large posterior vena cava which joins the sinus venosus. More posteriorly are the fused dorsal and ventral pancreatic rudiments, and the slightly coiled intestine, leading to the origin (at hindgut level) of the allantois and the umbilical vessels that leave the body via the umbilical cord.

Slightly off-center sagittal (parasagittal) sections show the metameric and mesenchymal vertebrae, derived from sclerotome. These extend almost to the tip of the tail. Parasagittal sections also show the degeneration of the pronephric tubules (but not the pronephric ducts of the female), the gradual regression of the mesonephric tubules (but not the mesonephric ducts of the male), and the more posterior paired metanephric cell masses and short (urogenital sinuses) ducts (ureters) leading to the cloaca.

Aortic arches III and IV continue to enlarge, V is gone, and right VI is reduced. The ventricles of the heart appear to be almost occluded by the expanding trabeculae. The interventricular foramen persists as the interventricular septum grows cephalad. Sections of the liver may appear to be within the pericardial cavity, but more anterior or posterior sections show that the diaphragm separates the pleural and peritoneal cavities.

Transverse sections through the anterior end of the embryo show the nasal septum separating the paired nasal chambers; the thickened Jacobson's organ in each chamber; the posterior nares or nasal choanae, which connect the nasal chambers with the pharynx; and the laterally directed nasolacrimal ducts on either side of the obviously muscular tongue.

The surface of each thymus is covered by a basement membrane, which separates the gland from the surrounding mesenchyme. Some thymus cells are ciliated and appear to be derived from pharyngeal epithelium. They contain thin-walled vesicles.

At the level of the liver and intestinal loops are the mesonephric ducts and adjacent to them and bulging into the peritoneal cavity are the genital ridges. The vitelline vein may be seen at this time near the most posterior level of the liver, as a broad venous channel leading to the heart. Sex of the embryo can be determined from the initial arrangement of these cells. The ridges may be recognizable as testes with their epithelial cords, or as ovaries with their nests of ova. The proximity of the ridges and the ducts suggests their ultimate relationship in the male. The subcardinals anastomose to form the renal portal veins. Still further posteriorly the metanephric ducts, associated with the nearby but as yet undeveloped metanephroi, enter the cloaca.

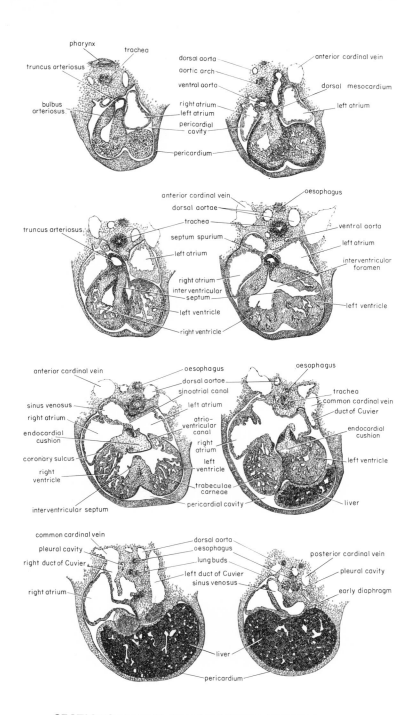

**SECTIONS OF THE 12 DAY MOUSE EMBRYO HEART
IN SEQUENCE**

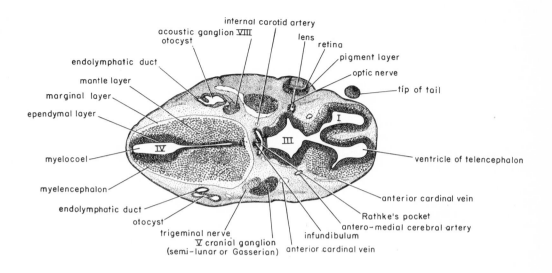

internal carotid artery

acoustic ganglion VIII
otocyst

lens
retina

endolymphatic duct

pigment layer

mantle layer

optic nerve

marginal layer

tip of tail

ependymal layer

I

IV

III

myelocoel

ventricle of telencephalon

myelencephalon

endolymphatic duct

anterior cardinal vein

otocyst

Rathke's pocket

antero-medial cerebral artery

trigeminal nerve
V cranial ganglion
(semi-lunar or Gasserian)

infundibulum

anterior cardinal vein

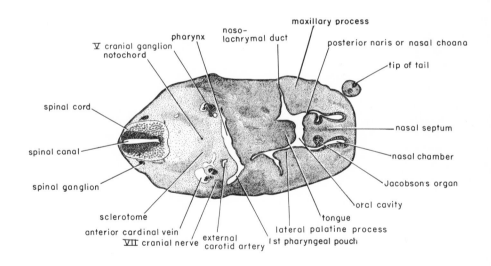

maxillary process

pharynx
naso-
lachrymal duct

V cranial ganglion
notochord

posterior naris or nasal choana

spinal cord

tip of tail

spinal canal

nasal septum

spinal ganglion

nasal chamber

Jacobson's organ

sclerotome

oral cavity

anterior cardinal vein
VII cranial nerve

tongue

external
carotid artery

lateral palatine process
1st pharyngeal pouch

MOUSE EMBRYO — 12 gestation days
(transverse sections)

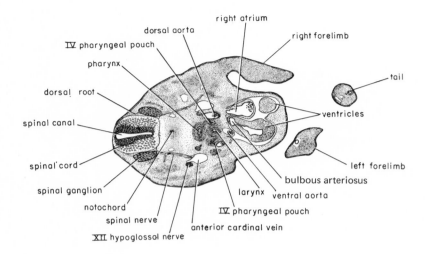

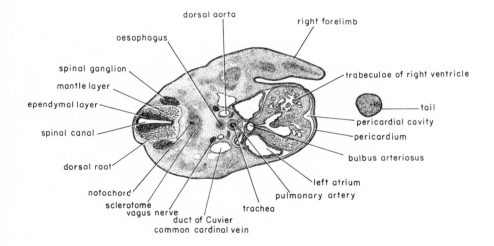

MOUSE EMBRYO — 12 g.d.
(transverse sections)

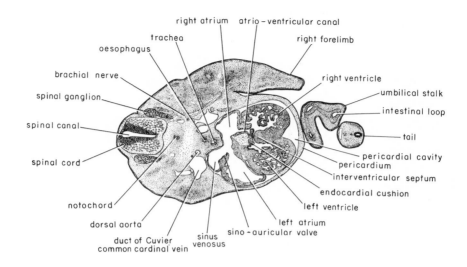

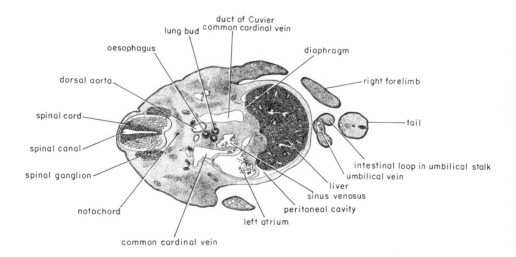

MOUSE EMBRYO — 12 g.d
(transverse sections)

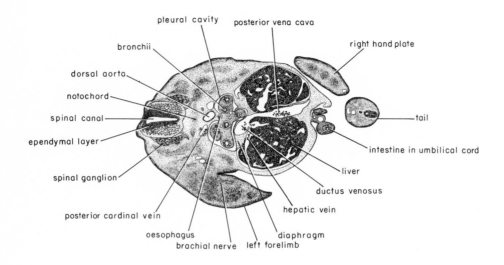

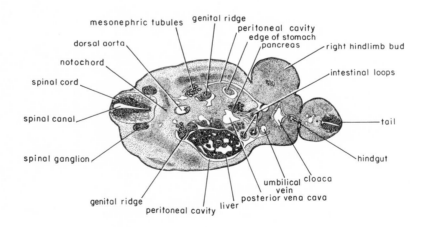

MOUSE EMBRYO — 12 g.d.
(transverse sections)

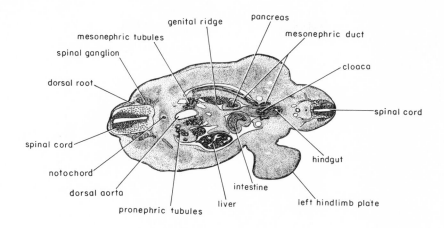

genital ridge
pancreas
mesonephric tubules
mesonephric duct
spinal ganglion
cloaca
dorsal root
spinal cord
spinal cord
hindgut
notochord
dorsal aorta
intestine
pronephric tubules
liver
left hindlimb plate

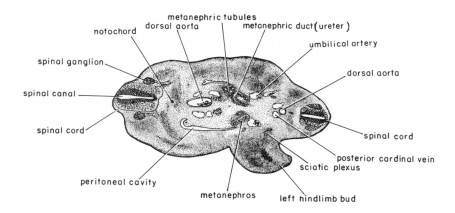

metanephric tubules
dorsal aorta
metanephric duct (ureter)
notochord
umbilical artery
spinal ganglion
dorsal aorta
spinal canal
spinal cord
spinal cord
posterior cardinal vein
peritoneal cavity
sciatic plexus
metanephros
left hindlimb bud

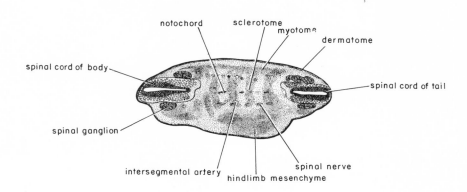

notochord
sclerotome
myotome
dermatome
spinal cord of body
spinal cord of tail
spinal ganglion
intersegmental artery
spinal nerve
hindlimb mesenchyme

MOUSE EMBRYO — 12 g.d.
(transverse sections)

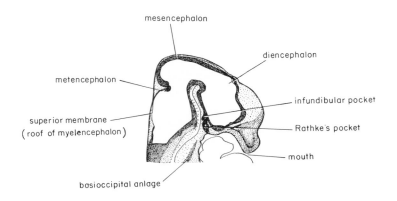

MOUSE HEAD at 12.5 g.d.
(sagittal section)

(Redrawn from Forsthoefel 1963)

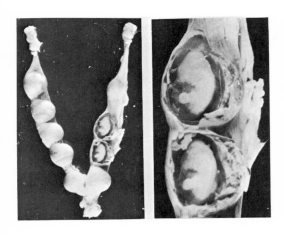

MOUSE EMBRYOS IN UTERUS
at 12.5 days

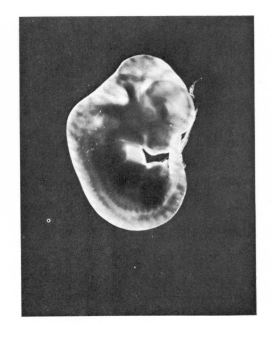

MOUSE EMBRYO at 12.5 days

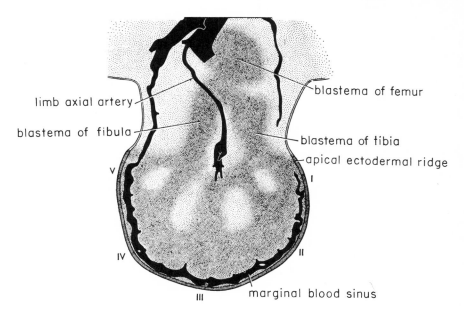

limb axial artery

blastema of fibula

blastema of femur

blastema of tibia

apical ectodermal ridge

marginal blood sinus

I----V, position of future digits

**RIGHT HIND LIMB OF 12.5 day
NORMAL MOUSE EMBRYO**

(Carter 1954, Grüneberg 1963)

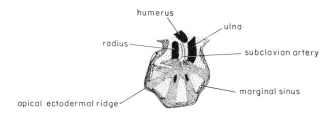

humerus

radius

ulna

subclavian artery

apical ectodermal ridge

marginal sinus

**MOUSE LEFT FORELIMB at 12.5 g.d.
(Reconstruction)**

(Redrawn from Forsthoefel 1959, 1963)

1 mm

**RIGHT FORE AND HIND LIMB OF 12.5 day
NORMAL MOUSE EMBRYO**

(From Grüneberg 1962)

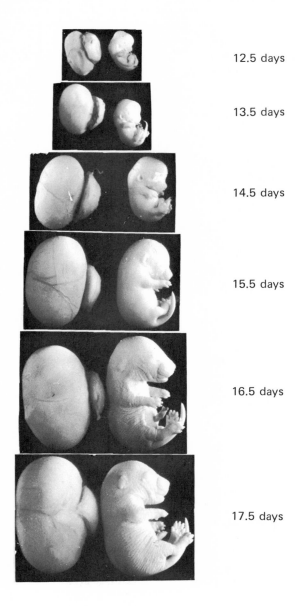

12.5 days

13.5 days

14.5 days

15.5 days

16.5 days

17.5 days

**MOUSE FETUS WITHIN ITS CHORIONIC VESICLE AND
LITTER MATE AFTER REMOVAL FROM ITS VESICLE
TO SHOW RELATIVE SIZES AND PLACENTAE.***

*Note: Capillaries on surface of vesicle and discoidal type of
attached placenta. The contained embryos are obviously
crowded with the approximation of head and tail.

I. THE 13 DAY EMBRYO: The 13 day mouse embryo is comparable to the 38 day human embryo. It has 52 to 60 somites and measures 9.4 mm from crown to rump. The head still comprises more than one-third of the total body volume. The back is straightening. The tip rather than the base of the tail now touches the side of the face, so that the tail seems to be shortening. Actually, since it has acquired all but the 5 most caudal somites, it has almost reached its maximum length. The somites still show through the integument, but the skin layers are differentiating. The hair follicles of the face (vibrissae) appear in rows. The external auditory meatus is circular and easily visible on each side of the head with a covering by the early pinna. The eyes appear on the surface as ovals but their inner structures cannot be seen. The limb buds have grown further, with differentiation of their extremities into early (mesenchymal) digits, although these are not distinct. There is chondrification of the ribs and the humerus. The umbilical hernia is receding into the body, and the mammary glands are cup-shaped.

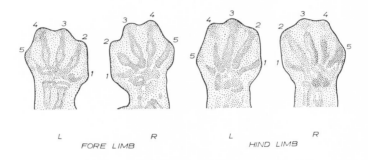

FEET OF NORMAL 13 DAY MOUSE EMBRYO
(Grüneberg 1961, 1963)

Mid-sagittal sections show further thickening of the brain walls, particularly in the laminia terminalis, dorsal thalamus, tuberculum posterius, roof of the mesencephalon, and floor of the myelencephalon. The first two ventricles (the telocoels) are expanding and will cover part of the diencephalon and third ventricle. The anterior choroid plexus has expanded laterally into the first two ventricles. The thin roof of the myelencephalon (the fourth ventricle) is much folded into the myelocoel, and becoming the vascular posterior choroid plexus. The spinal cord extends almost to the tip of the tail, and paired spinal ganglia extend to the level of somite 40. The eyes have lost their lens vesicles by the close apposition of lens epithelium to lens fibers, and behind the lenses vitreous humor is accumulating; it may be loosely cellular. Surrounding each eye is the early formation (mesenchyme) of the eye muscles (there is no evidence of cartilage or bone yet). Both above and below the eye, the folds will be the lids. The retina has further thickened (to about 10 times the thickness of the pigmented layer) but does not yet exhibit any indications of the various cell layers to be developed. There are nerve fibers in the optic stalks, and oculomotor nuclei are forming. Each ear, surrounded by mesenchyme and early cartilage, comprises a long endolymphatic duct connected laterally with the ampulla and mesially with the utricle, saccule, and elongated and coiled cochlea.

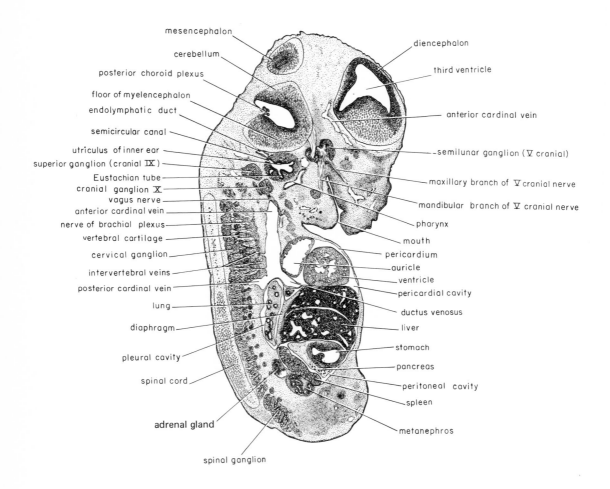

mesencephalon
cerebellum
posterior choroid plexus
floor of myelencephalon
endolymphatic duct
semicircular canal
utriculus of inner ear
superior ganglion (cranial IX)
Eustachian tube
cranial ganglion X
vagus nerve
anterior cardinal vein
nerve of brachial plexus
vertebral cartilage
cervical ganglion
intervertebral veins
posterior cardinal vein
lung
diaphragm
pleural cavity
spinal cord
adrenal gland
spinal ganglion

diencephalon
third ventricle
anterior cardinal vein
semilunar ganglion (V cranial)
maxillary branch of V cranial nerve
mandibular branch of V cranial nerve
pharynx
mouth
pericardium
auricle
ventricle
pericardial cavity
ductus venosus
liver
stomach
pancreas
peritoneal cavity
spleen
metanephros

MOUSE EMBRYO — 13 days
(para-sagittal)

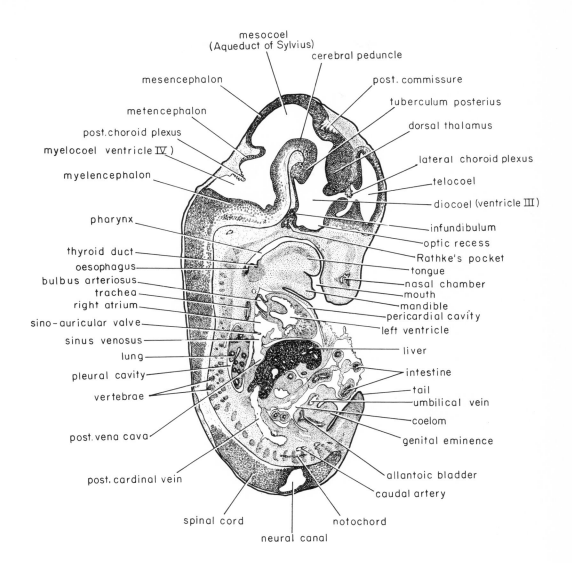

mesocoel
(Aqueduct of Sylvius)

cerebral peduncle

mesencephalon

post. commissure

metencephalon

tuberculum posterius

post. choroid plexus

dorsal thalamus

myelocoel ventricle IV)

lateral choroid plexus

myelencephalon

telocoel

diocoel (ventricle III)

pharynx

infundibulum

optic recess

thyroid duct

Rathke's pocket

oesophagus

tongue

bulbus arteriosus

nasal chamber

trachea

mouth

right atrium

mandible

sino-auricular valve

pericardial cavity

left ventricle

sinus venosus

liver

lung

intestine

pleural cavity

tail

vertebrae

umbilical vein

coelom

post. vena cava

genital eminence

post. cardinal vein

allantoic bladder

caudal artery

spinal cord

notochord

neural canal

MOUSE EMBRYO — 13 days
(mid-sagittal)

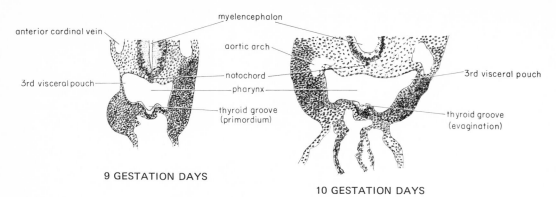

anterior cardinal vein

myelencephalon

aortic arch

notochord

pharynx

3rd visceral pouch

thyroid groove
(primordium)

3rd visceral pouch

3rd visceral pouch

thyroid groove
(evagination)

9 GESTATION DAYS

10 GESTATION DAYS

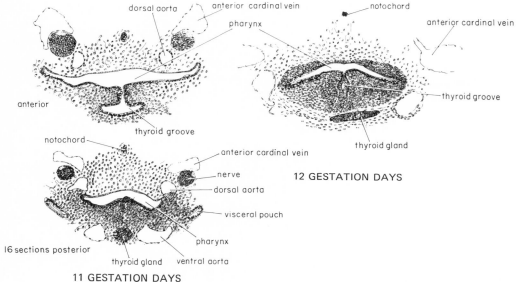

dorsal aorta

anterior cardinal vein

pharynx

notochord

anterior cardinal vein

anterior

thyroid groove

thyroid groove

thyroid gland

12 GESTATION DAYS

notochord

anterior cardinal vein

nerve

dorsal aorta

visceral pouch

16 sections posterior

pharynx

thyroid gland   ventral aorta

11 GESTATION DAYS

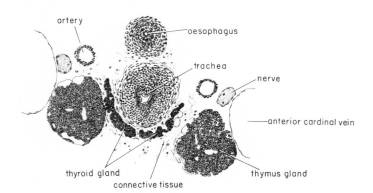

artery

oesophagus

trachea

nerve

anterior cardinal vein

thyroid gland

connective tissue

thymus gland

13 GESTATION DAYS

DEVELOPMENT OF THE THYROID GLAND IN THE MOUSE
X-Sections

The thyroid is a definitely lobular horseshoe shaped structure ventral to the trachea. Nearby are the paired thymus glands, adjacent to the anterior cardinal veins. Some thymus cells are differentiated into stromal elements with pseudopodia, which seem to encircle or engulf other cells. Some of these may be advance lymphopoietic cells. Between the thymus glands is loose connective tissue. Both the lungs and the liver have enlarged considerably, and the lungs show lobular development. The cells of the spleen may now be seen accumulating under the epithelium of the posterior part of the mesenteric fold. The anterior splanchnic mesodermal plate persists longest in the region of spleen development. The gut now appears more as it will in the adult, and the vitelline vein, passing dorsally from the umbilicus, loops around the duodenum on its path to the liver. The posterior vena cava arises from the right posterior cardinal vein but at this time the paired posterior cardinals are large, lying on either side of the dorsal aorta and deriving their venous blood from the more posterior regions of the developing embryo. Between 12 and 13 days a connection had been formed between the right posterior cardinal vein and channels in the liver which lead to the heart. Then the anterior portion of the right posterior cardinal vein (anterior to the junction with the left branch) decreased in size, as did the posterior portion of the left posterior cardinal so that by 14 days the venous drainage from the trunk caudal to the liver is largely through the remaining portions of both the posterior cardinals which have joined to form a single vessel, the posterior vena cava. The hepatic portion of the posterior vena cava is formed largely from the vitelline vein. The muscular primordia and the thickening of the submucosa of the esophagus are apparent, as are vacuoles in the stomach epithelium and beginning of intestinal villi. A genital eminence may be found just beneath the tail, closely associated with the origin of the allantois.

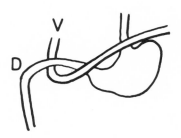

Diagrammatic representation of the relation of the vitelline vein to the duodenum in the 13½ day mouse embryo, ventral view. D, duodenum; V, vitelline vein.

(Courtesy Dr. Margaret C. Green, 1967, Developmental Biology 15:62-89, Academic Press.)

Dorsally many vertebral cartilages are seen, each separate from its neighbor and derived from the scleratome of two adjacent somites. Mesenchymal concentrations, particularly in the head, are precartilage masses. The aortic, pulmonary, and interventricular septa and the atrioventricular valves are complete, and the right dorsal aorta between aortic arches III and IV has disappeared. The segmental arteries and veins are well formed. Enucleated cells are only about 1% of the red blood cells. The metanephroi are prominent, but no vestiges of the pronephroi or mesonephroi remain except the ducts, which are present according to sex. A suprarenal (adrenal) gland is located just anterior to each metanephros. Cellular differentiation has progressed to the point that sex can be predicted with certainty. Serial sagittal sections are highly instructive particularly for following the various blood vessels, which are now numerous.

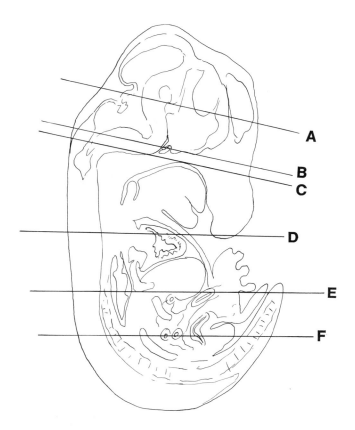

A

B
C

D

E

F

Guide lines represent positions of the following sections.

(Series from Rugh: "Vertebrate Embryology,"
Harcourt, Brace & World, 1964.)

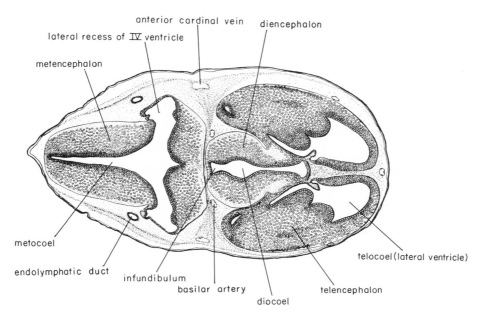

anterior cardinal vein

lateral recess of IV ventricle

diencephalon

metencephalon

metocoel

endolymphatic duct

infundibulum

basilar artery

diocoel

telencephalon

telocoel (lateral ventricle)

A

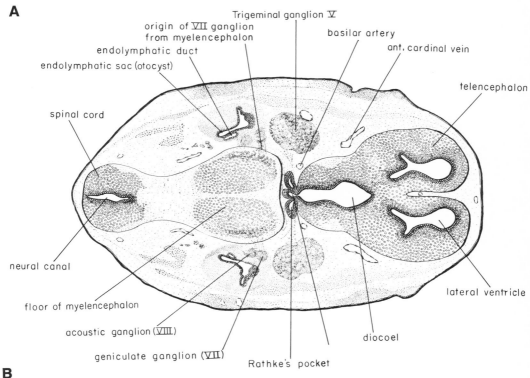

Trigeminal ganglion V

origin of VII ganglion
from myelencephalon

basilar artery

endolymphatic duct

ant. cardinal vein

endolymphatic sac (otocyst)

telencephalon

spinal cord

neural canal

floor of myelencephalon

acoustic ganglion (VIII)

geniculate ganglion (VII)

Rathke's pocket

diocoel

lateral ventricle

B

MOUSE EMBRYO — 13.5 g.d.
(transverse sections)

(From R. Rugh, "Vertebrate Embryology", Harcourt, Brace & World, Inc., New York, 1964.)

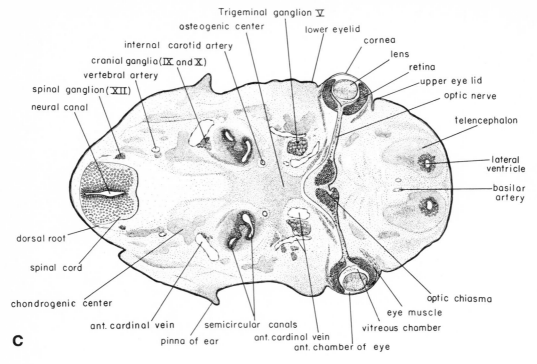

C

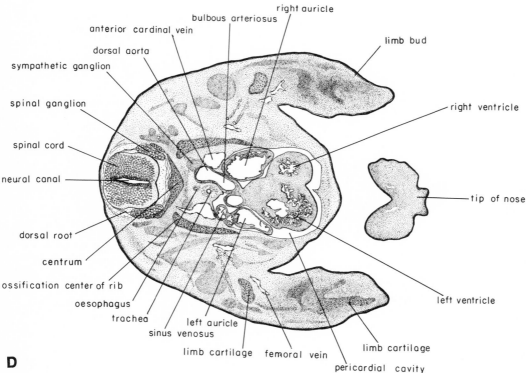

D

MOUSE EMBRYO — 13.5 g.d.
(transverse sections)

(From R. Rugh, "Vertebrate Embryology", Harcourt, Brace & World, Inc., New York, 1964.)

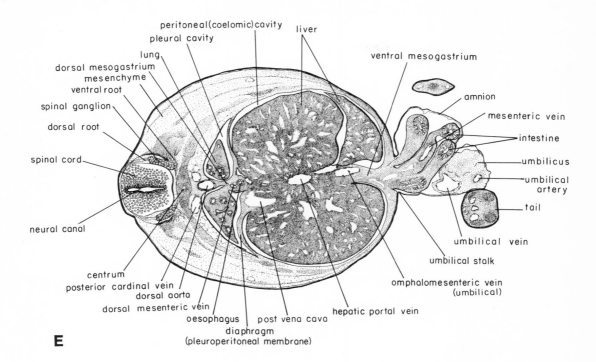

E

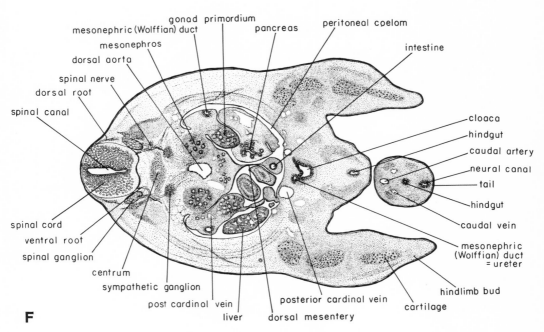

F

MOUSE EMBRYO — 13.5 g.d.
(transverse sections)

(From R. Rugh, "Vertebrate Embryology", Harcourt, Brace & World, Inc., New York, 1964.)

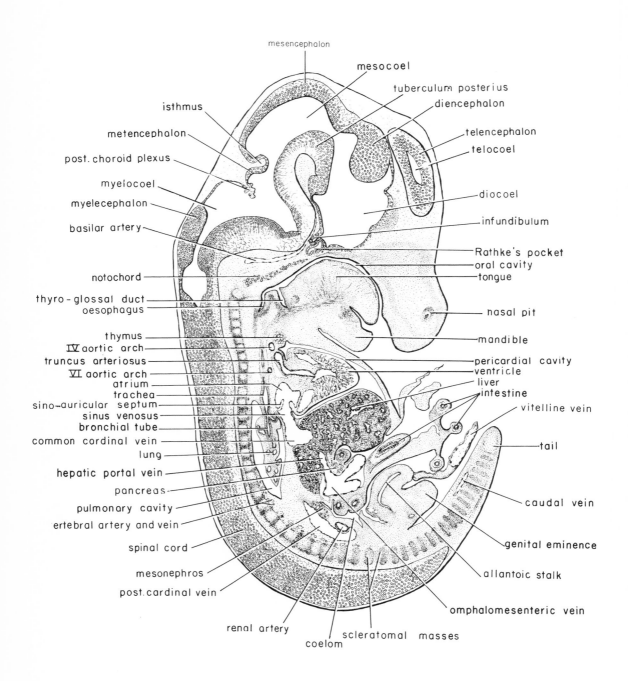

SAGITTAL SECTION OF MOUSE EMBRYO
(13.5 gestation days)

(From Rugh: "Vertebrate Embryology,"
Harcourt, Brace & World, 1964.)

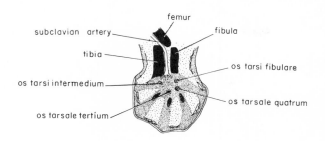

MOUSE LEFT HINDLIMB at 13.5 g.d.
(Reconstruction)
(Redrawn from Forsthoefel, 1959, 1963)

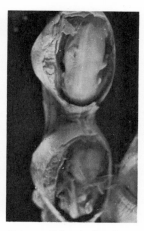

Dorsal View   Ventral View   Same Embryos Exposed   Enlarged View in Amnion

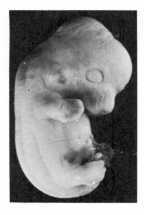

Embryo with Amnion Removed

MOUSE EMBRYOS IN UTERUS at 13.5 days

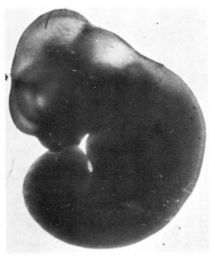

WHOLE MOUSE EMBRYO
at 13.5 days

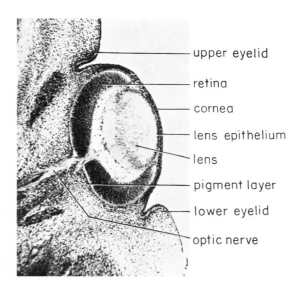

upper eyelid

retina

cornea

lens epithelium

lens

pigment layer

lower eyelid

optic nerve

MOUSE EMBRYONIC EYE
at 13.5 days

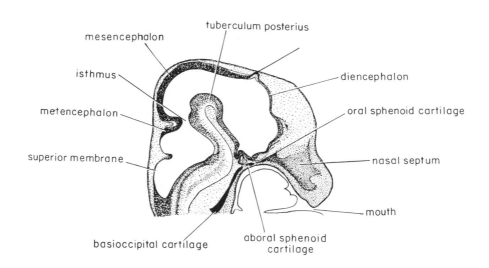

mesencephalon

tuberculum posterius

isthmus

diencephalon

metencephalon

oral sphenoid cartilage

superior membrane

nasal septum

mouth

basioccipital cartilage

aboral sphenoid cartilage

MOUSE HEAD at 13.5 g.d. (Sagittal section)
Showing early chondrification.
(Redrawn from Forsthoefel 1963)

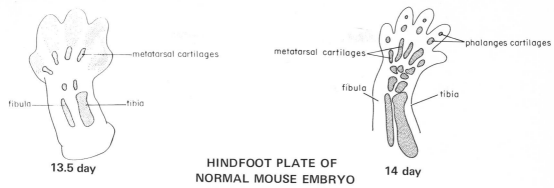

HINDFOOT PLATE OF NORMAL MOUSE EMBRYO

(Sisken & Gluecksohn — Waelsch 1959 Grüneberg 1963)

J. THE 14 DAY EMBRYO:

The 14 day mouse embryo compares well with the 6 weeks old human embryo. It has 61 to 62 somite pairs and measures $10\frac{1}{2}$ mm from crown to rump. By this time major congenital anomalies can no longer be produced by trauma or other insult to the fetus because most of the major organs have been laid down, and future development is largely a matter of refinement and cellular differentiation. The only systems that remain particularly vulnerable to trauma is the skeletal system, in which cartilage and then ossification centers begin to form at about 12 days, and the nervous system which is made up largely of differentiating neuroblasts. Radiation exposure of the 14 day embryo generally results in structural changes in the skeleton (stunting) and may affect the functioning of the nervous system. The first seven ribs are chondrified. The first cartilage is seen in the otic capsules. The region of the developing frontal bones and the zygomatic arch show ossification centers. We are therefore now describing a topographically complete embryo.

The main changes in contour occur in the head. The face assumes a pig or rodent-like shape, with a snout and forehead bulges. The back continues to straighten. The appendages look like paddles, with fanlike extremities having partially separated digits, each external auditory meatus is open, and partially covered by a single-scalloped pinna, and each eyeball is larger and more distinct than at 13 days, but still undistinguished from the surface and not yet covered by the lids. The external nares are open. The skin layers begin to appear with occasional concentration of cells that later give rise to hair follicles, like those already on the face. The facial hair shafts, roots and bulbs, and papillae are all recognizable. The cloacal membrane has ruptured to form the lining of the anal chamber.

The brain can be dissected out, and the major parts identified. There are paired telencephalic lobes (cerebral hemispheres) between which is the epiphysis (pineal). Posterior to them is the single, bulbous mesencephalon. The metencephalon (cerebellum) is laterally expanded and thick-walled but extends posteriorly only to the thin-walled posterior choroid plexus of the myelencephalon. The myelencephalon tapers into the spinal cord. Lateral or ventral views show the olfactory lobes, optic chiasma, and pituitary. The brain is about 6 mm in length. The skin of the face, in contrast with that over the body, does show vibrissae formation which begins at 13 days, and is actively developing at 14 days.

The pineal gland exhibits cellular differentiation. It grows into the head mesenchyme from the diencephalon, closely associated with a cerebral vessel. The pituitary, especially the anterior lobe (from the infundibulum) is glandular-looking, although it has no follicles or secretion yet. It somewhat surrounds the intermediate lobe. The sphenoid cartilage and sella turcica into which the pituitary grows are visible. A lens and its covering epithelium are now suspended in each optic cup and so the iris is formed, as well as an anterior chamber between lens and cornea. The fibrous structure of the lens continues to differentiate. The posterior wall of the optic cup is the much thicker retina, while nerve fibers may be seen passing in from the optic nerve to line the optic cup. The optic fibers connect with the brain. The ears have grown to six times the length of the otic vesicles at 9 days. Semicircular canals, ampulla, utricle, saccule, and a remnant of the endolymphatic sac are present in each one. The ear areas are invested with loose mesenchyme, which will develop into encapsulating otic cartilage.

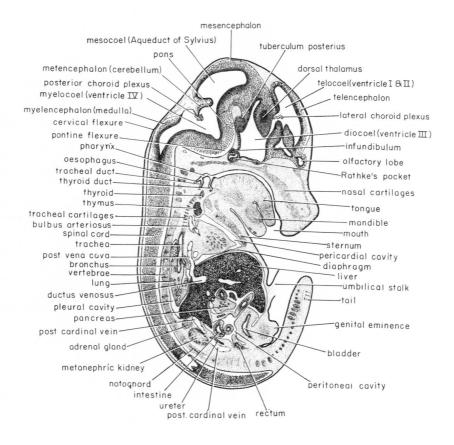

MOUSE EMBRYO — 14 days
(mid-sagittal)

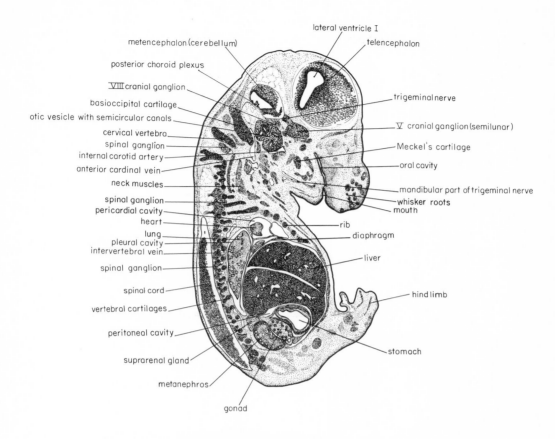

MOUSE EMBRYO — 14 days
(para-sagittal)

Transverse striated muscle fibers are apparent in the tongue, and the beginnings of the incisors with dental papillae, and outer and inner enamel, in the lateral oral epithelium closely associated with Meckel's cartilage and early ossification. The first molar bud is visible on each side. Salivary glands are supplied with secretory ducts.

The liver continues to grow and become more vascular, and the pancreas shows histological differentiation and vascularization. Posterior to the liver is the large and thick-walled stomach. Intestinal loops are plentiful, with their first villi.

The heart is essentially complete. The foramen ovale persists, and the aortic pulmonary semilunar valves appear. Aortic arch III branches into the lingual and carotid arteries. The left aortic arch IV (the systemic arch) receives the ductus arteriosus from left aortic arch VI, gives off the left subclavian and vertebral arteries, and continues as the dorsal aorta. The diaphragm is completed by the closing of the pleuroperitoneal canals. Enucleated cells

may constitute 25% of the red blood cells.   The mesonephroi are much reduced
except for the parts (ducts) giving rise to the epididymi in the male, and the
ureters open into the cloaca (urogenital sinus).   The oviducts (pronephric ducts)
cross over the ureters toward the pelvis, and the ovaries and testes become
quite vascular.   The metanephroi are paired, compact, masses of tubules and
ducts, close to the gonads and suprarenal glands.

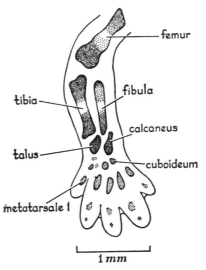

**CARTILAGINOUS SKELETON
OF LEFT HIND LIMB OF 14.5 day
NORMAL MOUSE EMBRYO**

(Searle 1963, Grüneberg 1963)

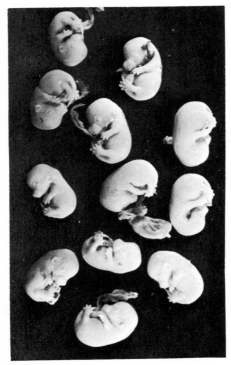

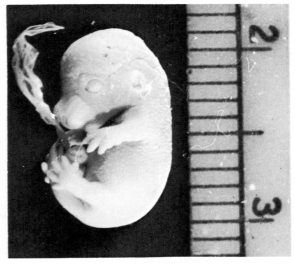

ENTIRE LITTER   SIZE IN MILLIMETERS

MOUSE EMBRYOS at 14.5 days

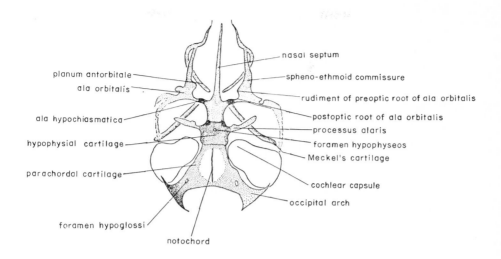

**DORSAL VIEW OF CHONDROCRANIUM OF
NORMAL 14.5 day MOUSE EMBRYO**

(Grüneberg 1953, 1963)

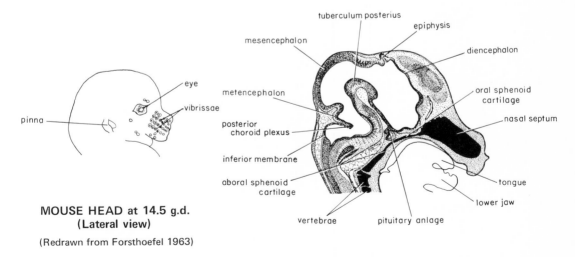

**MOUSE HEAD at 14.5 g.d.
(Lateral view)**

(Redrawn from Forsthoefel 1963)

**MOUSE HEAD at 14.5 g.d.
(Sagittal section)**

(Redrawn from Forsthoefel 1963)

K. THE 15 DAY EMBRYO: The 15 day mouse embryo corresponds in development to a 55 day human embryo. It has its full quota of 65 pairs of somites and measures about 12 mm, from crown to rump.

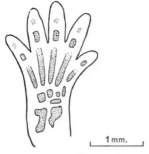

LEFT HINDFOOT OF 15 day NORMAL MOUSE EMBRYO

Methylene-blue preparations.

1mm.   (From Grüneberg 1956)

Superficially the head is gradually taking on the rodent shape. On each side the external auditory meatus is a clearcut pit with the pinna all but overlapping it from behind. The eyes are partially visible through the skin. The appendages are much longer and better developed than at 14 days, with the digits almost completely separated, having small extensions at their tips. The vibrissae on the face are easily recognized. Hair follicles are extensively distributed elsewhere over the body. The skin seems to be growing faster than the body, as it is greatly wrinkled. Since some of the intestinal loops still project into the umbilical cords the umbilical hernia remains. Owing to further straightening of the back, the tail seems shorter than before, curling between the hind legs toward the face but not touching it.

The brain appears as it did at 14 days except that each part is further enlarged and some are thickened. The cerebrum seems to be growing fastest. It is obvious that neuroblasts are proliferating rapidly to fill the cerebral vesicles and thus to produce a substantive brain. Trauma at this time can lead to cessation of this proliferation and hydrocephalus. The cerebellum is fused at the mid-line. The eyelids are advancing over the eyes but more significant is the development of inner and outer nuclear layers in the retina. The ears have become complicated ramifications of canals. The olfactory organs have not changed radically but have expanded, with the lining epithelium thickening. They are embedded in the nasal and ethmoid cartilages. The anterior, posterior, and intermediate lobes of the pituitary are present but are cytologically undifferentiated. An infundibular recess remains as does the lumen of Rathke's pocket between the anterior (pars distalis) and intermediate lobes. The pineal gland shows signs of glandular function. A stalk still connects it with the diencephalon.

Mid-body transverse sections show that the spinal cord is much like that of the adult. Marginal, mantle, and ependymal layers are easily distinguished. Thickest now is the mantle layer. The ependymal layer is crowded around the neural canal, full of mitoses. The spinal root ganglia are now well developed and the dorsal and ventral roots are properly associated with the cord. Below the cord is the remnant of the notochord, which is being surrounded and incorporated by the sclerotome of the centrum. The notochord generates from anterior to posterior, so that it is visible later in posterior sections rather than in anterior ones. The ribs are so well ossified that they compose a substantial rib cage, which gives the body a new rigidity.

The sternal cartilage is new, and cartilage is forming in the walls of the trachea. The thyroid is well advanced, and the thymus glands are enlarging rapidly, even faster than the thyroid. The liver appears to fill about half the body cavity. Among its cells is the gall bladder, and close to it the highly glandular pancreas. Many lymph gland cells appear to be definite lymphocyte precursors, and are small thymic lymphocytes. Stellate reticular cells, columnar cells in acinar formation and containing glycogen, and hypertrophied cells may be found. For the first time parenchymal blood vessels are seen. Nucleated cells constitute only about 5% of the red blood cells. Posteriorly, at the base of the tail, the urethra enters the bladder.

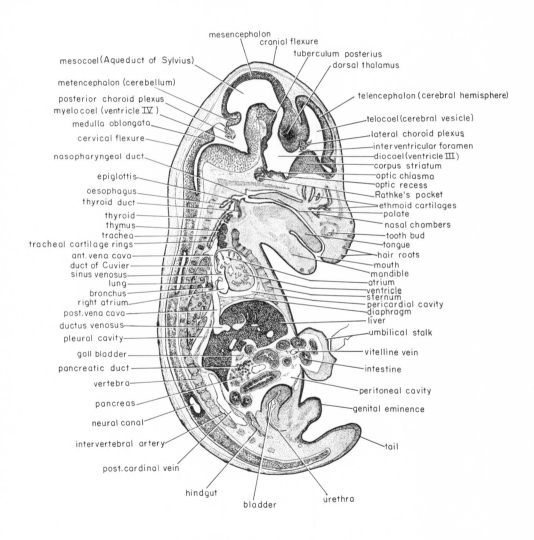

MOUSE EMBRYO — 15 days
(mid-sagittal)

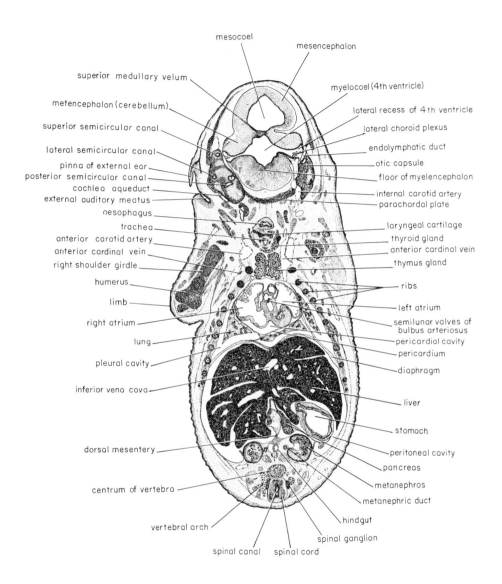

MOUSE EMBRYO — 15 days
(frontal section)

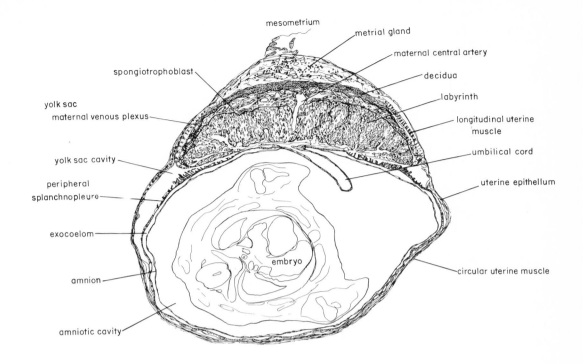

mesometrium

metrial gland

maternal central artery

spongiotrophoblast

decidua

labyrinth

yolk sac

maternal venous plexus

longitudinal uterine
muscle

yolk sac cavity

umbilical cord

peripheral
splanchnopleure

uterine epithellum

exocoelom

amnion

embryo

circular uterine muscle

amniotic cavity

MOUSE PLACENTA at 15 days

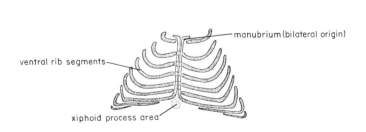

manubrium (bilateral origin)

ventral rib segments

xiphoid process area

**THORAX OF NORMAL 15 day
MOUSE EMBRYO**

(Grüneberg 1953, 1963)

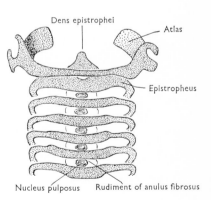

Dens epistrophei

Atlas

Epistropheus

Nucleus pulposus

Rudiment of anulus fibrosus

**VENTRAL VIEW OF CERVICAL
VERTEBRAE OF NORMAL
15 day MOUSE EMBRYO**

(Grüneberg 1953, 1963)

L. THE 16 DAY EMBRYO: The 16 day mouse embryo is comparable to the 10. 4-week human embryo. It measures about 15 mm from crown to rump, is recognizable as a mouse, and moves actively within the uterus. It is sufficiently straightened out that its fore- and hindlimbs no longer touch, and its skin is extensively wrinkled, with hair follicles. The eyelids have fused over the eyes and the pinnas cover the auditory meatuses.

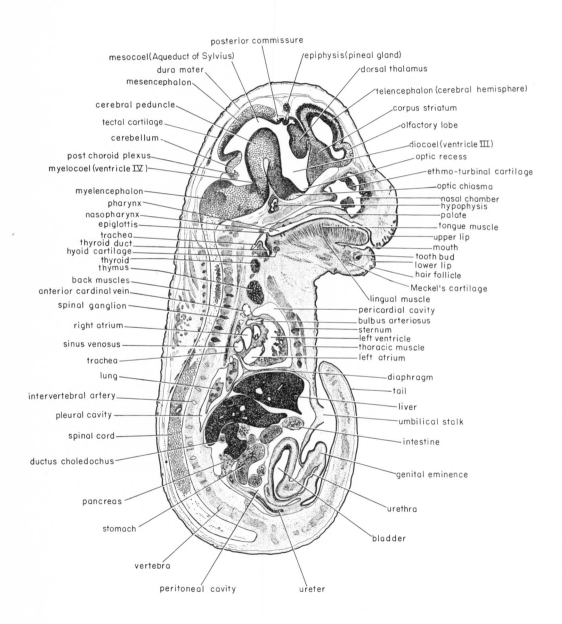

MOUSE EMBRYO — 16 days
(mid-sagittal)

Sagittal sections show that the pineal is almost entirely separated from the diencephalon, the cerebral peduncle is growing upward to fill the mesocoel, the corpora striata are extremely thick, and the corpus callosum is formed. The brain, except for the cerebellum, is completing its development. The nasal chambers are extensive.

The most apparent changes relate to the striated muscles and the skeleton, which are present throughout the embryo. Muscles of the tongue and back are most prominent, while the cranial, sternal, and vertebral regions exhibit many ossification centers. The laryngeal and tracheal cartilages are developing.

The thyroid is a bilobed, highly vascular organ with the parathyroids attached to it and the ultimobranchial bodies disappearing within its substance. The thymus is several times the size of the thyroid and is found just cephalad to the heart. The lungs have alveoli. Parasagittal sections show the metanephroi with well-formed glomeruli. The bladder is a large muscular chamber, closely associated with the ureters. Cartilage is changing to bone in the appendages, so that they look like fore- and hindlimbs, with integument folded at their bases like accordians awaiting their further growth. The hyaloid and retinal arteries enter the eyes with the optic nerves. Approximately 1% of the red blood cells remain nucleated, in the immature state.

The centrum is ossified. Except for further ossification, development of full musculature, and further growth of the brain and hematopoietic centers, the mouse is now essentially complete. From this point on, certain organ systems will be described as they develop, and independently of the adnexa or the embryo as a whole. Description will be given first of the changes observable externally and then of the histological changes.

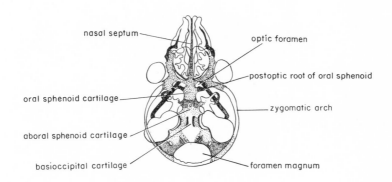

MOUSE CHONDROCRANIUM at 16.5 g.d.
(Ventral view)
(Redrawn from Forsthoefel 1963)

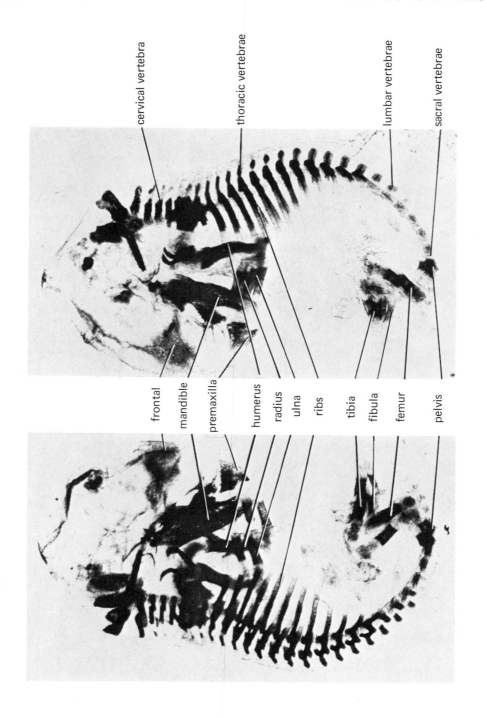

SKELETON OF MOUSE EMBRYO — 16.5 days

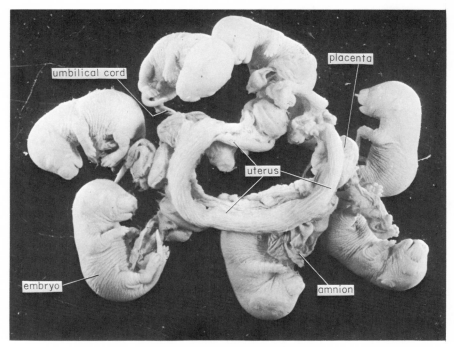

DORSAL VIEW

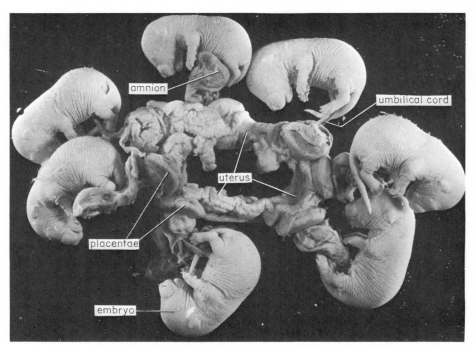

VENTRAL VIEW

MOUSE LITTER AT 16.5 gestation days

Chapter  ORGANOGENY

EXTERNAL CHANGES

BODY CONTOUR: The accompanying photograph shows a series of mouse embryos from 10 to 18 days gestation. Such a series demonstrate the chronological changes in general topography, emphasizing (1) change in body posture from a much-coiled C shape at 10 or 11 days to the late fetus of 16 days, when the back is much straightened; (2) change from a lobular head with pronounced visceral arches to an elongated head with snout and vibrissae and no superficial evidence of the arches; (3) the early appearance of the otic and the optic vesicles at 9 days, both to be partially covered by 15 days; (4) growth of the appendages, from appearance of the forelimbs at 9 days and that of the hindlimbs at 10 days to digital development at 16 days; (5) excessive wrinkling of the fast growing skin at 16 days in anticipation of the filling out of the next 3 days; (6) incorporation of the bulging visceral and umbilical areas of the early

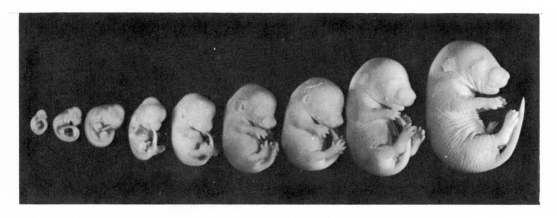

MOUSE EMBRYOS FROM 10 to 18 GESTATION DAYS

stages, into the slender abdomen of the newborn; (7) early growth of the tail, so long with its somites that it is coiled to the right of the head at 10 days, and the changes leading to a relatively short motile tail lacking any vestige of the somites and no longer touching the face. One cannot see, in these illustrations, the changes in skin texture and color. At times the skin is quite translucent and pink. The texture and color of the skin are often indications of the newborn's general health. Between 10 and 18 days gestation, the embryo increases in crown-rump length from an average of 4.08 to 20.31 mm and in weight from about 0.0061 to 1.087 grams.

A transient ectodermal ridge (VER) about 300 μ long arises on the ventral aspect of the tail tip, where the ectoderm is thickened and columnar rather than squamous. It gives a positive alkaline phosphatase reaction suggesting cell hypertrophy. The VER originates at about 9 days gestation from the cloacal membrane, where the ectoderm and endoderm meet. It reaches its maximum development at 10 days, is less obvious at 11 days, and disappears by 12 days. It is believed by some to be a stimulating organ for the production of paraxial mesoderm.

APPENDAGES: The most critical period for appendage development seems to be at 12 days, when there are many precartilage concentrations of mesenchyme. This corresponds to about 36 days for the human embryo, a time when the drug thalidomide administered to a pregnant woman, has its most devastating effect on human embryonic limbs. In the mouse the sclerotome makes no contribution to the skeleton of either girdle or limbs.

At 9 days no external evidence of forelimb primordia is visible but sections show that the ectoderm is thickening in the forelimb regions. A pseudostratified layer about four cells thick and about 7 somites long protrudes directly out from the somatopleure on each side. Mesenchyme accumulates within the budlike outgrowths, and by 10 days they have begun to bend in a ventral direction. The mesenchyme cells are covered first by a layer of cuboidal ectoderm and then by a layer of flattened squamous ectoderm. The cuboidal layer forms a well-defined apical ectodermal ridge along the ventrolateral margin of each bud. At least one more row of cells is added, and a blood vessel appears below the ridge. The segmental arteries may be used to locate specifically the forelimb buds. Often the right bud is slightly anterior to the left one. As the embryo grows, the buds grow anteroposteriorly, but they grow directly outward at a faster rate. Since they do not grow anteroposteriorly as rapidly as the crown-rump length increases, the number of somites related to a bud is gradually reduced to about 5. At 11 days the footplate begins to develop in each bud and blastema condensations appear for the scapula, humerus, and ulna. At 12 days the footplate is polygonal (pentagonal) and the ectoderm and marginal sinus are complete. The sinus empties through the postaxial and preaxial veins into the postaxial part of the limb. The blastemas for all five metacarpals may be seen, joined to the common carpal blastema, and there is some chondrification in the radius and metacarpals 2, 3, and 4. At 13 days the footplate is deeply indented, and the apical ectoderm has begun to regress. Nerves supply the first phalanges, muscles are present throughout the limbs and ossification has started in the humerus, radius, and ulna. At 14 days the phalanges are separated distally, and necrosis begins in the intervening webbing. The marginal sinus breaks up and no apical ectoderm remains. Muscles are well developed throughout. Chondrification occurs in all the first phalanges, as well as in the second phalanges of digits 2, 3, and 4 and, in the scapula, radius, and ulna. Capillary invasion indicates the impending transformation of perichondrium into periosteum. At 15 days the digits are entirely separate, and ossification is proceeding rapidly everywhere, with the scapula and humerus ahead of the radius and ulna. The shoulder and elbow joints are well advanced. By 16 days all skeletal parts are chondrified. Ossification is well advanced in the scapula and in the shafts of the humerus, radius, and ulna. By birth (19 days) all skeletal parts are ossified except the carpus and pollex. (Note from table on page 212 that forelimb development precedes that of the hindlimb by about one day.)

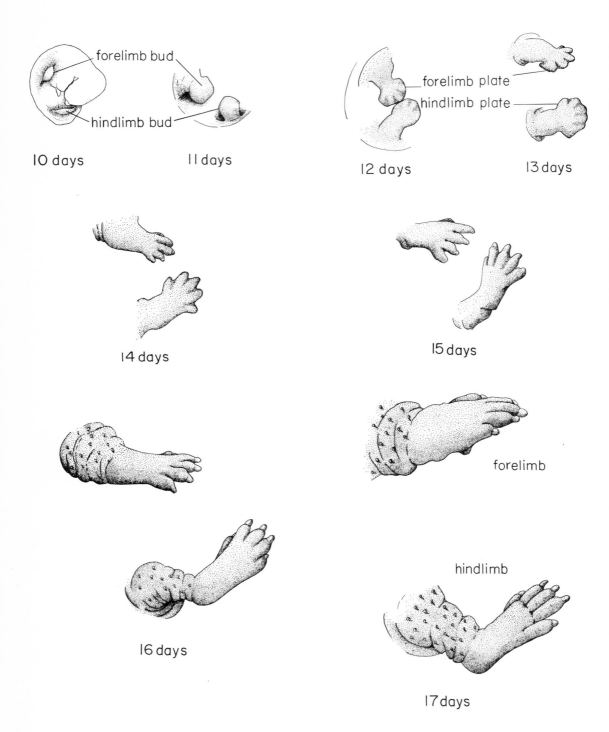

DEVELOPMENT OF APPENDAGES OF MOUSE EMBRYO

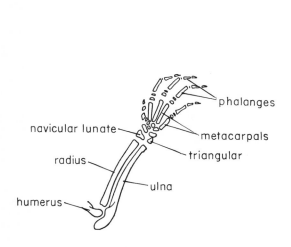

navicular lunate

phalanges

metacarpals

radius

triangular

humerus

ulna

**RIGHT FORE LIMB OF
NORMAL ADULT MOUSE**

(Freye 1954, Grüneberg 1963)

femur

fibula

tibia

calcaneous

talus

cuboideum

metatarsals

phalanges

**RIGHT HIND LIMB OF
NORMAL ADULT MOUSE**

(Searle 1963, Grüneberg 1963)

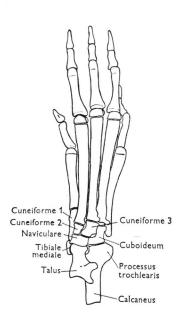

Cuneiforme 1

Cuneiforme 2

Cuneiforme 3

Naviculare

Tibiale
mediale

Cuboideum

Talus

Processus
trochlearis

Calcaneus

**RIGHT HIND FOOT OF
NORMAL ADULT MOUSE**

(Grüneberg 1956, 1963)

LIMB DEVELOPMENT*

AGE IN DAYS	FORELIMB	HINDLIMB
9	Limb buds as low ridges	
10	Limb buds/semicircular	Limb buds as low ridges
11	Separation into leg and circular footplate	Limb buds semicircular
12	Footplate pentagonal	Separation into leg and circular footplate
13	Footplate indented	Footplate pentagonal
14	Digits separated distally; still webbed proximally	Footplate deeply indented
15	Digits separated throughout, and very divergent; end phalanges beginning to show.	
16	Digits 2 to 5 nearly parallel and proximally webbed end phalanges clear, hindlimbs somewhat less advanced than forelimbs.	
17	Fingers and toes completely webbed as in newborn.	

* After Grüneberg, 1943 and 1963.

(Note: 15, 16, 17 day descriptions apply to both forelimb and hindlimb.)

The hindlimb buds appear at 10 days as crescent-shaped laterally directed projections largely mesenchyme. They lag behind the forelimbs in growth and differentiation, not exhibiting their characteristic elongation at 15 and 16 days. At 15 days cleared specimens show the tibia and fibula, and the tarsals have ossification centers. At the base of each appendage, the skin is folded, in preparation for further extension of the limb skeleton. Hair follicles are visible on the skin. The folds persist at 17 days but are partially flattened through stretching. The hindfeet are still webbed but have clawed digits.

SENSE ORGANS:[*] The large paired otic vesicles are apparent as early as 9 days. Anteriorly the paired telencephalic vesicles form bulges, just posterior to which the paired optic protuberances from the diencephalon arise at 10 days. At this time the first signs of olfactory pits also appear. Therefore, soon after the untwisting of the embryo, indications of sense organ development may be seen through the skin.

At 12 days the eyes are large oval swellings. Just posterior to them are the remnants of the otic vesicle openings, or endolymphatic ducts. During the next 3 days some eye parts become visible through the temporarily exposed cornea, only to be covered completely by the dorsal and ventral eyelids, which grow together by 16 days. The mouse is born blind because of this fusion of the eyelids.

The pinna, a double layered flat fold of skin, begins to grow forward over the external auditory meatus, on each side at 13 days. It almost completely covers the meatus by 17 days.

*External changes only. See page 245 for internal changes.

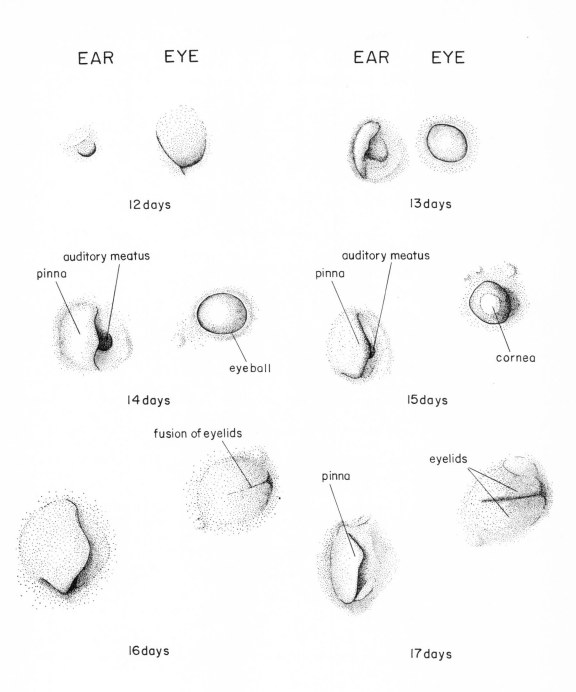

EXTERNAL VIEWS OF RIGHT EYE AND EAR
IN MOUSE EMBRYOS

The olfactory pit develops into external nares connected internally with ramifying tubes of the nasal chambers and ultimately with the pharynx just dorsal to the epiglottis. From the surface only facial changes around the external nares are evident.

SKIN, HAIR FOLLICLES, AND VIBRISSAE: Cup-shaped mammary welts may be seen at $10\frac{1}{2}$ days. The primary vibrissae are elevated on the face at 13 days. The earliest differentiation of the skin and related parts occurs at about 14 days, when occasional aggregations of cells, forerunners of the hair

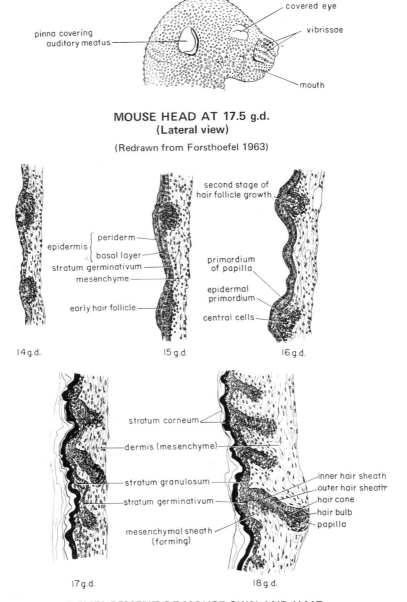

MOUSE HEAD AT 17.5 g.d.
(Lateral view)

(Redrawn from Forsthoefel 1963)

DEVELOPMENT OF MOUSE SKIN AND HAIR

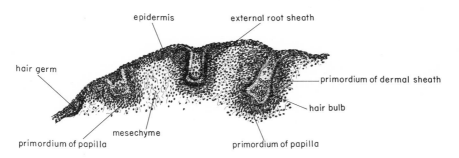

13 gestation days

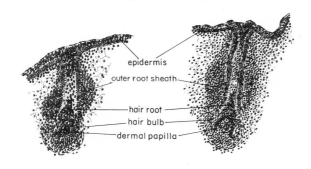

14 gestation days

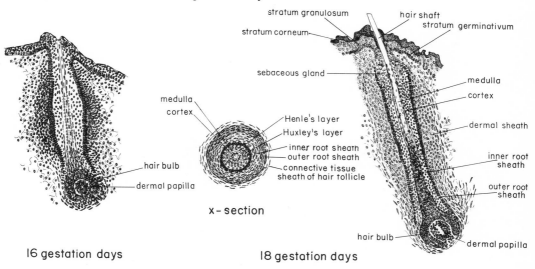

16 gestation days

18 gestation days

DEVELOPMENT OF MOUSE VIBRISSAE

follicles, appear in a single layer of ectoderm. At $14\frac{1}{2}$ days the vibrissae papillae are invaginated, and ectoderm (periderm) is proliferating in the external
nares. By 15 days a second skin layer, the stratum germanitivum, arises and
between it and the first layer a basal layer develops. Much loose mesenchyme
is present below these layers, when the hair germs are forming. At 16 days
the periderm is thick in the nares, on the eyelids and in the external meatuses;
the vibrissae are cornified and papillae for the body hair follicles are visible.
Some of these follicles are in the second stage of growth. For the first time the
stratum corneum appears below a sloughing off layer of superficial squamous
epithelium. The hair follicles differentiate rapidly and are abundant, but not
until 18 days do hair bulb, core, and inner and outer sheaths all project deeply
into the skin (dermis). The periderm of the nares sloughs off. By 19 days the
vibrissae can be charted easily on the face and jaws. All their layers are apparent in cross section at this time. At birth the surface layer of epidermis is
cornified, but hair has not yet emerged.

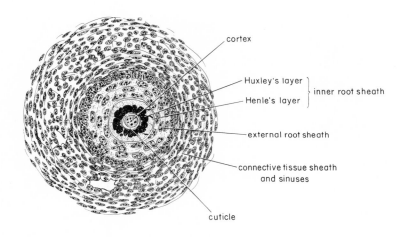

cortex

Huxley's layer
Henle's layer } inner root sheath

external root sheath

connective tissue sheath
and sinuses

cuticle

NEWBORN MOUSE VIBRISSA
(x-section under high power)

INTERNAL CHANGES

SKELETON: Chondrification centers may be seen first in sections as early as
11 days gestation. At $11\frac{1}{2}$ days there are blastema condensations for
the scapulna, humerus, and ulna, which begin to chondrify at $12\frac{1}{2}$ days. At this
time the blastemas for the radius and ulna are joined to the metacarpals by the
common carpal blastema. The interrelation of these various centers is an integral part of the developmental sequence. Nerves are also forming, some of
which reach the ends of the radius and ulna and vertebral condensation of mesenchyme is taking place. The precartilaginous nasal capsule, cartilaginous otic
capsule, and primordia of the otic ossicles appear by 14 days. Chondrification
is active, and many ossification centers are visible at $14\frac{1}{2}$ days and ossification
is widespread by 16 days.

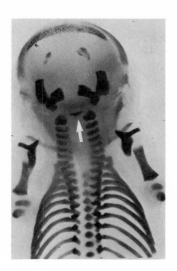 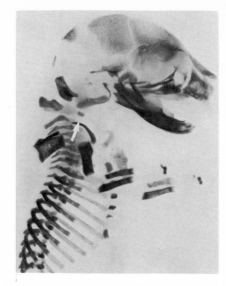

CFI mouse fetuses at 16 days gestation showing ossification center in the anterior arch of the atlas.

(Courtesy K. Hoshino, Congen. Anom. Japan 1967, Vol. 7:32–38.)

TIME OF ORIGIN OF VARIOUS ORGANS*

CFI MICE

ORGAN	GESTATION DAY	ORGAN	GESTATION DAY
Blood island	7+	Maxillary process	9
Foregut	7+	Forelimb bud	9
Heart mesoderm	7+	Lens placode	10
Head fold	7+	Nasal placode	10
Neural groove	8	Olfactory pit	10
Visceral arch I	8	Hindlimb bud	10
Neural tube anterior	9	Lens vesicle	11
Neural tube posterior	9	Lens fibers	11
Brain vesicle	9	Sclerotome	11
Eye cup	9	Eyelid	12
Otic vesicle	9		

* Data assembled from T. Ogawa 1967, Congenital Anomalies (Japan) 7:27-31.

GESTATIONAL AGE AND SOMITE NUMBER

GESTATIONAL AGE	SOMITE NUMBER
7 days	1 — 5
8 days	8 — 13
9 days	13 — 20
10 days	22 — 29
11 days	36 — 42
12 days	48 — 53
13 days	60+

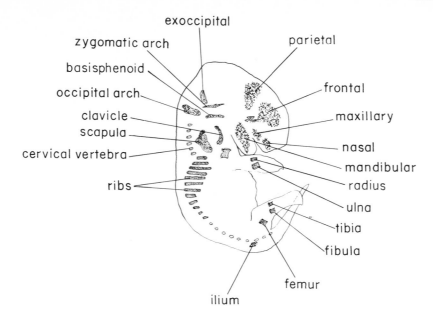

SKELETAL SYSTEM OF MOUSE at 15 g.d.
(showing ossification centers)

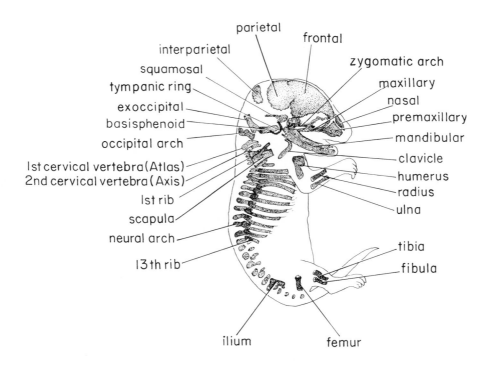

SKELETAL SYSTEM OF MOUSE at 16 g.d.

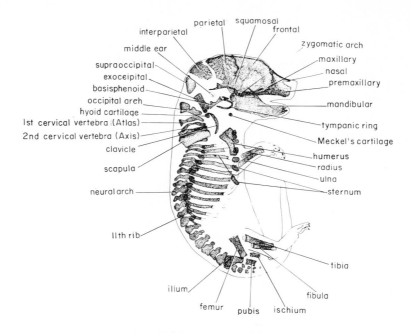

SKELETAL SYSTEM OF MOUSE at 17 g.d.

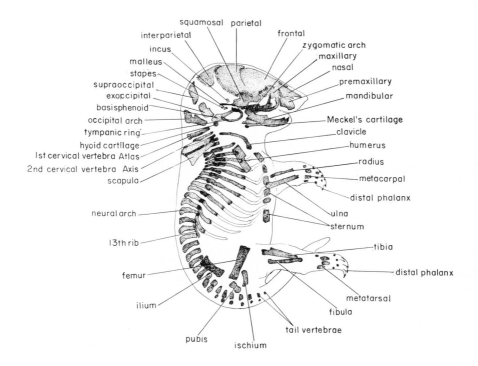

SKELETAL SYSTEM OF MOUSE at 18 g.d.

MOUSE FETUS FROM 15 to 18 days GESTATION
(showing extent of development of the skeleton)

(Spalteholz technique)

The chondrification centers themselves apparently are not targets of gene action. The osseous skeleton that develops from them tends to reflect conditions affecting the cartilaginous precursors. Therefore, most abnormalities of the skeleton can be traced to the cartilage and in turn to the membraneous blastema in which it arises. The mesenchymal stage is most vulnerable to environmental trauma. Trauma as early as $7\frac{1}{2}$ days may cause stunting, through damage to the mesenchyme, and hence to chrondrifications which affect the osteoblasts arising later in these centers.

The rib centers for the anterior (thoracic) regions appear early, by 12 days, and develop ahead of those for more posterior regions. Some of the membrane bones of the skull and jaw can be identified at this time. At 14 days frontal and zygomatic ossifications start to form. At 15 days the basic ossification centers are sufficiently developed that alizarin red S stains them specifically. Not only the appendage centers but also the cranial, pectoral, and pelvic centers can be recognized. The centras chondrify at 16 days. By 17 days the sternum is formed, the cranial cavity is almost encased, the tympanic rings can be identified, and the mandibular articulations at the zygomatic arches are established. At 18 days the appendage parts become stainable, and the bones contain hematopoietic marrow. The cranial parts have not yet fused but are expanding as the brain within enlarges. The scapulae are the largest bones in the body at this time.

The vertebrae originate from the sclerotomes. Each sclerotome consists of an anterior or cranial zone of low density and a posterior or caudal zone of high density, with a sharp demarcation line known as the sclerotomal fissure (fissure of von Ebner) between the two zones. The fissure does not reach the mid-line in the vicinity of the notochord, and it is soon invaded by cells from the more caudal zone. The somites are bounded by segmental blood vessels. The mesenchymal (sclerotomal) material for the vertebrae is bounded by sclerotomal fissures. The fissures separate this material into segments alternating with the myotomal and dermatomal portions of the somites, and so the vessels that were intersegmental with respect to the somites become midsegmental with respect to the vertebrae. The zones of lesser density chondrify to give rise to the centra of the vertebra, and the zones of higher density (perichordal discs) form the annuli fibrosi of the intervertebral discs.

The notochord is at first a cylindrical rod of cells of uniform consistency. As chondrification proceeds, it thins inside the centra but shows some swelling at the levels of the intervertebral discs. Eventually it is completely ossified, and only an acellular notochordal sheath remains in the vertebrae.

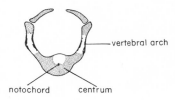

**TRANSVERSE SECTION THROUGH
A LUMBAR VERTEBRA OF
A 17 day MOUSE EMBRYO**

(Grüneberg 1950, 1963)

**LUMBAR REGION
OF A NORMAL
NEWBORN MOUSE**

Alizarin clearance preparations.

(From Grüneberg 1950)

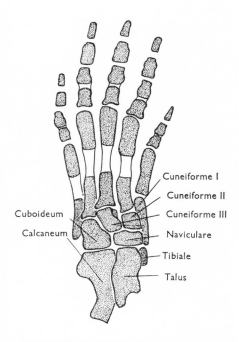

**EXTERNAL ASPECT OF LEFT
HIND FOOT OF NORMAL
NEWBORN MOUSE**

(Grüneberg 1953, 1963)

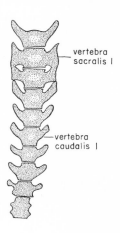

**VENTRAL VIEW OF SACRAL
AND UPPER CAUDAL
VERTEBRAE OF NORMAL
NEWBORN MOUSE**

(Grüneberg 1953, 1963)

CHONDRIFICATION AND OSSIFICATION CENTERS
IN SKELETAL DEVELOPMENT:CFI MICE*

BONES CRANIAL BONES	CHONDR. GESTATION DAYS	OSSIF.	BONES FACIAL BONES	CHONDR. GESTATION DAYS	OSSIF.
Basioccipital	13	14	Maxilla	—	—
Exoccipital	13	14	Lateral plate	—	15
Supraoccipital	16	16	Palatine process	—	15
Parietal	—	15	Zygomatic process	—	15
Interparietal	—	15	Premaxilla	—	—
Frontal	—	14	Median plate	—	15
Sphenoidal	—	—	Horizontal plate	—	15
Presphenoid body	17(?)	18	Perpendicular plate	—	16
Lateral process	13	15	Zygomatic	—	16
Inter pterygoid	13	14	Lacrimal	—	16
Alar process	14	15	Palatine	—	15
Squamosal	—	14	Nasal	14	16
Tympanic ring	—	16	Vomer	—	15
			Mandible body	—	13
			Coronoid process	—	16
			Condyloid process	—	15
			Angular process	—	16
			Hyoid process	14	17

TRUNK & GIRDLE BONES			BONES OF EXTREMITIES		
Clavicle	—	13	Humerus	13	14
Scapula	13	14	Radius	13	14
Ribs	13	14	Ulna	13	14
Sternebrae	15	16	Carpals	14	—
Ilium	13	15	Metacarpals	13	16
Ischium	14	16	Digits (forelimb)		
Pubis	14	16	Proximal	14	18
Vertebrae			Middle	14	18
Cervical arch	13	14	Distal	15	17
body	13	18	Femur	13	14
Thoracic arch	13	15	Tibia	13	14
body	13	15	Fibula	13	14
Lumbar arch	13	15	Tarsals	13	18
body	13	15	Metatarsals	13	16
Sacral arch	13	16	Digits (hindlimb)		
body	13	16	Proximal	14	18
Caudal arch	13	18	Middle	15	18
body	13	17	Distal	15	17

*Data assembled from K. Hoshino 1967, Congenital Anomalies (Japan) 7:32–38. (The data of this table do not coincide with data of the following table, derived 34 years earlier. Author)

APPEARANCE OF OSSIFICATION CENTERS IN THE MOUSE*

SKULL	Prenatal Time Day	Hr.	Postnatal Time Days	SKULL	Prenatal Time Day	Hr.	Postnatal Time Days
Alisphenoid	15	11		Orbitosphenoid	18	6	
Basihyal	17	1		Palatine	15	11	
Basioccipital	15	11		Parietal	15	11	
Basisphenoid	15	11		Periotic	17	1	
Ceratohyal			17	Premaxilla	15	11	
Epihyal			21	Presphenoid	18(17)	6	
Ethmoid			2(1)	Pterygoid	15	11	
Exoccipital	15	11		Squamosal	15	11	
Frontal	15	11		Stylohyal			20
Interparietal	15	11		Supraoccipital	15(17)	11	
Jugal	15	11		Thyrohyal			4
Lacrimal	17(16)	1		Tympanic	16		
Mandibular	15	11		Tympanohyal			21
Maxilla	15	11		Vomers	15	11	
Nasal	17(16)	1					

ANTERIOR APPENDAGES	Prenatal Time Day	Hr.	Postnatal Time Day	Hr.	POSTERIOR APPENDAGES Bone	Prenatal Time Day	Hr.	Postnatal Time Day	Hr.
Clavicle:					Ilium:				
Primary Center	15(14)	0			Primary center	15	11		
Sternal Ossicle			35		Iliac crest			14 weeks	
					Ischium:				
Scapula:					Primary center	17(16)	1		
Primary center	15	11			Pubis:				
Coracoid			5(2)	11	Primary center	17(16)	1		
Subcoracoid			8(7)		Pectineal eminence	17	1		
Acromion			35		Os Acetabulum			12 days	
					Femur:				
Humerus: :					Primary center	15	11		
Primary center	15	11			Greater trochanter			14(11)	
Greater tuberosity			5(4)	11	Lesser trochanter			14(11)	
Head			7(7)	10	Head			15(14)	
Capitellum			5(3)	11	Medial condyle			7	
Trochlea			5(3)	11	Lateral condyle			9	
Medial condyle			9(7)		Tibia:				
Lateral condyle			19(7)		Primary center	15	11		
					Distal epiphysis			9(6)	
Ulna:					Proximal epiphysis			18(7)	
Primary center	15	11			Greater tuberosity			18(16)	
Distal epiphysis			5(3)	11	Fibula:				
Proximal epiphysis			5(5)	11	Primary center	15	11		
					Distal epiphysis			7(6)	
Radius:					Proximal epiphysis			21(17)	
Primary center	15	11			Patella			18	
Distal epiphysis			5(3)	11	Fabella			18	
Proximal epiphysis			9(7)		Semilunar cartilage) medial			19(15)	
					) lateral			(18)	

* Adapted from M. L. Johnson, Am. Anat. 52 241-271 (1933). Dates in parenthesis are different, given by Z. T. Wirtschafter in "The Genesis of the Mouse Skeleton: A Laboratory Atlas." 1960, C. C. Thomas, Springfield, Illinois.

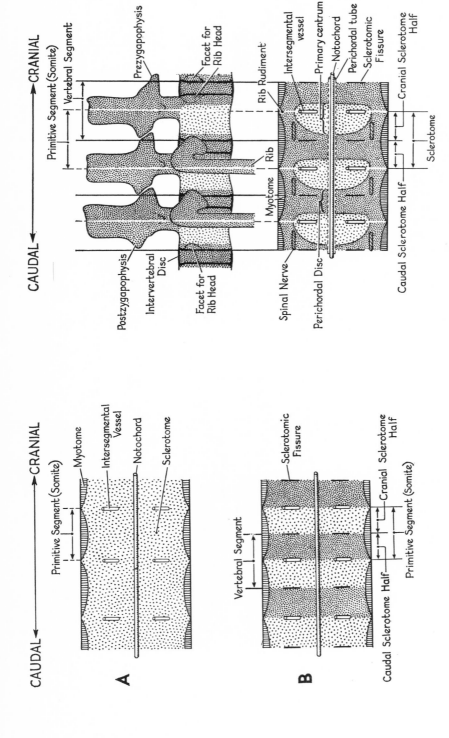

Diagrams illustrating the participation of the sclerotome-halves in the formation of the definitive vertebrae and intervertebral discs. In the upper half, vertebrae and ribs are shown as seen from the right side; in the lower half of the diagram, the sclerotomic origin of the various parts is shown in a frontal section.

(Sensenig 1949, Grüneberg 1963)

Diagrams (in the frontal plane) of two stages in the differentiation of the sclerotomes. A, sclerotomes of uniform tissue density. B, formation of the sclerotomic fissure (fissure of von Ebner) which separates anterior and posterior sclerotome halves of differing tissue density.

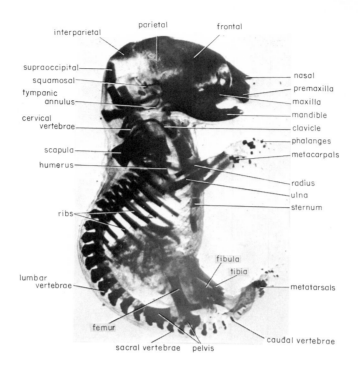

SKELETON OF MOUSE EMBRYO at 18.5 days

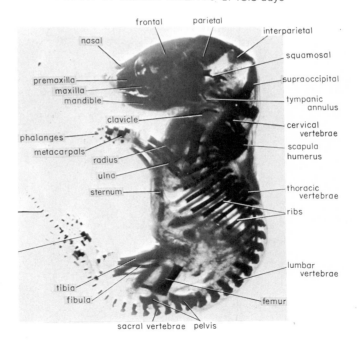

SKELETON OF MOUSE EMBRYO
Newborn

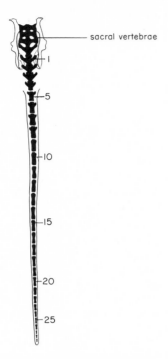

**SACRUM AND CAUDAL
VERTEBRA OF NORMAL
ADULT MOUSE**

(Grüneberg 1950, 1963)

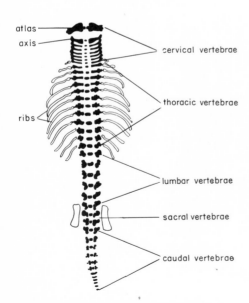

**AXIAL SKELETON OF NORMAL
NEWBORN MOUSE**

(Stevens & Mackensen 1958, Grüneberg 1963)

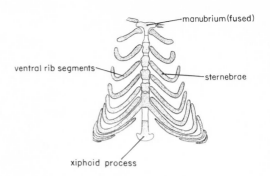

**THORAX OF NORMAL
NEWBORN MOUSE**

(Grüneberg 1953, 1963)

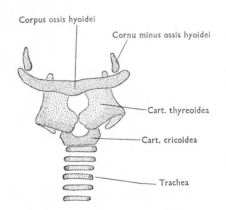

**VENTRAL VIEW OF LARYNX
OF A NORMAL 17 day
MOUSE EMBRYO**

(Grüneberg 1953, 1963)

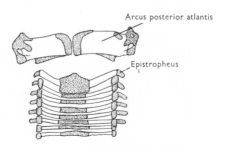

**DORSAL VIEW OF CERVICAL
REGION IN NORMAL
NEWBORN MOUSE**

(Grüneberg 1953, 1963)

TOOTH DEVELOPMENT: The embryonic and maternal genotypes are both relevant here. Prenatal (genetic and nutritional) factors are of prime importance, as is also lactation, in determining the growth and ultimate size of the teeth. Inadequate mesenchyme building material may result in failure to achieve a minimum level of growth and, therefore, in a lack of teeth. Lactation is genetically controlled, but can be influenced by the environment.

The mouse has a monophyodont dentition and a dental formula of: incisors 1/1; cuspids 0/0; premolars 0/0; and molars 3/3, making a total of 16. The first molars arise first, followed by the second and then the third, the latter at 4 to 6 days after birth. The first molars are the largest and the third the smallest. The development of the molars in the upper jaw lags behind those in the lower jaw by 12 to 24 hours, and the third molars may be missing in the first litter of any female.

Before gestation day 12 there is no indication of the differentiation of the dental lamina, which is the first of normal dental structures to appear. Molar development will be described in gestational sequence. *

Day 12: The first indication of odontogenesis is the stratification of the oral epithelium along the free margin of the jaws in the vicinity of the future dental arches. The dental lamina consists of 5 layers of cuboidal cells at the most. The remaining oral epithelium has one or two layers of cuboidal cells. There are numerous mitotic figures in both the oral ectoderm and the underlying mesoderm.

* Based upon studies by Dr. S. A. Cohn, 1957, Am. Jour. Anat. 101:295-320.

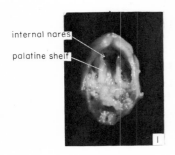
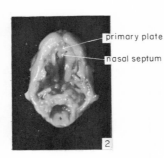
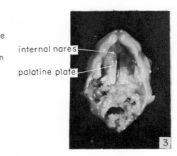

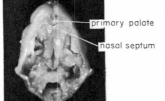

Fig. 1 — Normal palate, stage #1, inbred C57BL and A/Jax mice.
Fig. 2 — Normal palate, stage #3.
Fig. 3 — Normal palate, stage #4.
Fig. 4 — Normal palate, stage #6. The palatine shelves have already begun to fuse.

Courtesy G. Callas and B. F. Walker, 1963, Anat. Rec. 145:61-71. Chronological age of all four mice was between 14 days and 7 hours and 15 days and 6 hours, with staging based upon actual development of the palate.

PALATE DEVELOPMENT IN THE MOUSE

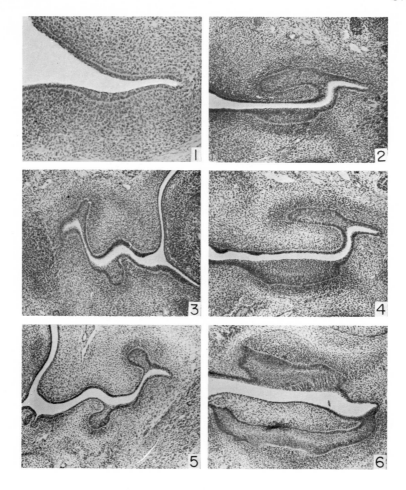

PRENATAL DEVELOPMENT OF MOUSE MOLARS — 12 to 15 days

Fig. 1 — Day 12.   Sagittal section.   Thickening of oral epithelium in region of lower jaw denotes beginning of dental lamina.

Fig. 2 — Day 13.   Sagittal section.   Note thickening of dental lamina in both jaws.   Adjacent mesenchyme cells stain darkly.

Fig. 3 — Day 13.   Frontal section of dental lamina.

Fig. 4 — Day 14.   Sagittal section.   Note the growth in length and thickness of the dental lamina as compared to Fig. 2.

Fig. 5 — Day]4.   Frontal section.   Tooth buds for upper and lower first molars are present.

Fig. 6 — Day 15.   Sagittal section.   Note the marked increase in length of the dental lamina.   The shallow invagination on its deep surface marks the site of the enamel organs of the first molars.

(Courtesy Dr. S. A. Cohn, Am. Jour. Anat. 101:295-320, 1957.)

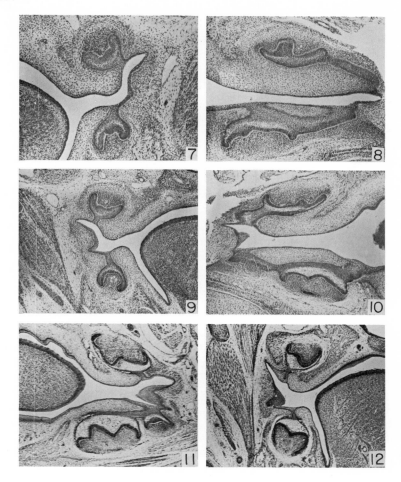

PRENATAL DEVELOPMENT OF MOUSE MOLARS — 15 to 18 days

Fig. 7 — Day 15. Frontal section. Cap stage of enamel organ of upper and lower first molars.

Fig. 8 — Day 16. Sagittal section. Enamel organs of the first molars can be seen on each dental lamina.

Fig. 9 — Day 16. Frontal section. Note the deepening of the invagination in the enamel organ of the lower first molar and the thinning out of its connection to the dental lamina.

Fig. 10 — Day 17. Sagittal section. Observe the increase in size of the enamel organs of the first molars. Note epithelial island in lower molar.

Fig. 11 — Day 18. Sagittal section. Enamel organs of the first molars are in the bell stage. Note the increase in stellate reticulum. The second lower molar is also visible.

Fig. 12 — Day 18. Frontal section. Enamel organs of the first molars are nearly separated from the dental lamina. Note how the outer enamel epithelium has thinned out.

(Courtesy Dr. S. A. Cohn, Am. Jour. Anat. 101:295-320, 1957.)

Day 13: Cell proliferation causes the thickening and elongation of the dental lamina. Growth in length parallels growth of the jaws. The dental lamina consists largely of cuboidal cells, while its basal layer consists of low columnar cells whose nuclei are more or less oriented toward the oral cavity. The relatively clear cytoplasm of these cells lies next to the underlying mesoderm. The originally cuboidal cells on the oral surface of the dental lamina are now more flattened.

Day 14: The length of the dental lamina is increased by anterior-posterior growth. Both upper and lower first molars now show enamel organs. A club-shaped tooth bud is formed by rapid cell proliferation on the basal surface of the dental lamina. Around the base of the bud are deeply staining mesodermal cells. Bone is beginning to form.

Day 15: The lengthening of the dental lamina continues. The tooth buds of the first molars show invaginations on their deep surfaces. This invagination is filled with deeply staining mesodermal cells which initiate the formation of the dental papilla and vascular elements. Between the central cells of the enamel organ a stellate reticulum appears, which defines an outer and inner enamel epithelium. The primordium of the dental sac may be seen as two or three layers of flattened mesenchymal cells surrounding the enamel organ.

Day 16: The size of the enamel organs of the first molars is now markedly increased by proliferation of cells from the inner and outer enamel epithelium. The intercellular spaces of the stellate reticulum is increased. The outer enamel epithelium is reduced to a thin layer of low columnar cells lying over a few layers of squamous cells. The inner enamel epithelium is but a single layer of columnar cells whose nuclei show no uniformity in position. These cells increase in height during proliferation. The future dentino-enamel junction is seen as a narrow eosinophilic zone between the inner enamel epithelium and the adjacent cells of the dental papilla. The expanding invagination of the enamel organ continues to be filled by the proliferation of cells of the dental papilla. The well-defined dental sac consists of several layers of flattened cells oriented closely around the enamel organ. Cells within the dental papilla and adjacent to the dental sac are bathed in increasing vascularity. The cell stalk connecting the enamel organ and the dental lamina becomes tenuous. Bone appears around the tooth germs of the first molars. Tooth buds of the second molars now make their appearance, to which the dental lamina extend posteriorly.

Day 17: There is accentuation of growth of the enamel organs of the first molars, especially in the cervical region, increasing the size of the pattern of the future crown. The stellate reticulum is also expanded, both by cell proliferation and enlargement of the interstices. The stratum intermedium first appears as a layer of flattened cells between the stellate reticulum and the inner enamel epithelium. An epithelial island is first visible, and will participate in root formation during post-natal development. There is cell proliferation in both the inner enamel epithelium and the dental papilla. Enamel organs of the second molars are now in the cap stage, similar to those of the first molars on day 15.

Day 18: The enamel organs of the first molars are now in the bell stage, beginning to form the pattern of the cusps and the outline of the future dentino-enamel junction. There are now no more than three layers of cuboidal cells in the outer enamel epithelium. Vascular sprouts and fibroblasts invade the outer enamel epithelium and the stellate reticulum. The inner enamel epithelial cells continue to proliferate, and capillaries of the dental papilla are seen. The connection between the enamel organ and the dental lamina is all but lost. The enamel organs of the second molars are comparable to those of the first molars on gestation day 16.

Days 19 and 20: The crown pattern of the enamel organs of the first molars is almost completed. Proliferation in the cervical region persists for some time after birth. Certain cells of the inner enamel epithelium are transformed into fully differentiated ameloblasts which more than double their height and their nuclei become oriented farthest from the future dentino-enamel junction. Ameloblast development begins at the high points which correspond to the growth centers on the cusps. Some of the cells of the inner enamel epithelium remain in the low columnar state, and may be seen extending along an entire margin of each cusp near its apex, invaginating pulpward to form one or more shallow depressions which disrupt the even contour of the future dentino-enamel junction, leaving the pulpal surface convex. The invagination appears to carry inward the cells of the stratum intermedium and stellate reticulum. Cells from the dental papilla differentiate on day 20 into odontoblasts, aligning themselves opposite the ameloblasts, and begin to form predentin. Odontoblasts differentiate next to the convex surface of the cord of undifferentiated cells of the inner enamel epithelium and a concavity of predentin forms along an entire margin of each cusp to be enamel-free during subsequent development. These changes occur in all molars. The squamous cells of the stratum intermedium become more cuboidal opposite ameloblasts undergoing differentiation but remain unchanged opposite the cord of undifferentiated cells. The second molars reach this stage of development by day 18, as the bony encapsulation of the first molars is almost completed and extends to the second molars.

TABLE 6

TABULAR SUMMARY OF MOLAR DEVELOPMENT IN THE MOUSE*

	MOLAR 1	MOLAR 2	MOLAR 3
Tooth bud appearance	Gestation day 14	Gestation day 16	Post-natal day 4 to 6
Initial dentinogenesis	Gestation day 20	Post-natal 2	Post-natal 10
Initial amelogenesis	Post-natal 1, 2	Post-natal 3, 4	Post-natal 11, 12
Eruption to oral cavity	Post-natal 16, 17	Post-natal 18, 19	Post-natal 28, 29
Functional occlusion	Post-natal 24	Post-natal 25	Post-natal 35
Cusps: upper/lower	3/5	3/4	3/3
Roots: upper/lower	3/2	3/2	3/1

* Modified from Cohn: Am. Jour. Anat. 101:295-320, 1957.

Photograph of wax plate reconstruction of normal upper incisor germs, epithelial and oral epithelium. Labial view.
(Courtesy P. A. Knudsen, Aarhus from Acta Odontologica 23:391—409, 1965)

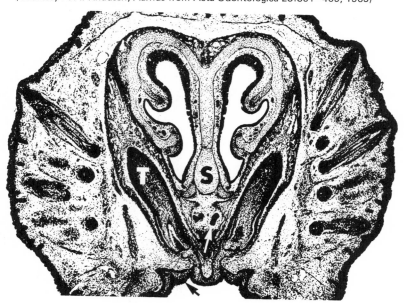

Normal mouse embryo. 18 days old. Frontal section. Upper incisor germs.
T = tooth germ
S = septal cartilage
White arrow = infraseptal nasal glands
Black arrow = oral epithelium
(H.E.).
(Courtesy P. A. Knudsen, Aarhus from Acta Odontologica 24:55—77, 1966)

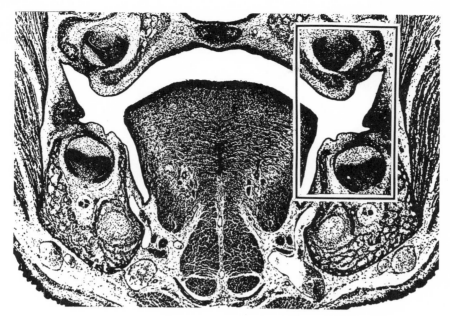

Normal mouse embryo. 18 days old. Frontal section. First molar germs in the upper and lower jaws. Note the position of the tooth germs and the size of the vestibule of the oral cavity (in the frame)
(Courtesy P. A. Knudsen, Aarhus from Acta Odontologica 24:55—77, 1966)

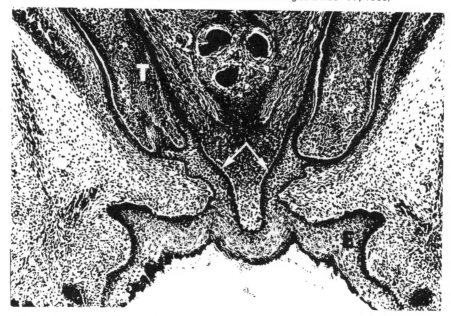

Normal mouse embryo. 18 days old. Epithelial laminae connecting the incisor germs and the oral epithelium. The portion near the tooth germ comprises stellate reticulum and outer dental epithelium, whilst the remainder has the same appearance as the epithelium in the oral cavity (arrows show the transition).
T = tooth germ
E = oral epithelium

(Courtesy P. A. Knudsen, Aarhus, from Acta Odontologica 23:71—89, 1965)

In summary, molar development in the mouse is not completed until about day 35 after birth. The number of cusps (upper/lower) for the three molars is: 3/5, 3/4, and 3/3 and the number of roots is 3/2, 3/2, and 3/1. The enamel-free areas typical of rodent molars are initiated before birth because of the failure of certain ameloblasts to undergo cyto-differentiation. The squamous cells of the stratum intermedium appear to be related to the cyto-differentiation of the ameloblasts under which condition they become cuboidal.

For completion of molar development during post-natal days 0-35 see the original reference. Dr. Cohn writes: "The mouse molar is an excellent and readily available source of didactic material of all periods of tooth development for use by students."

The incisor primordia arise at 13 days, just posteriorly to the lip furrow band. At 14 days the inner and outer enamel epithelia are differentiated, and nearby is Meckel's cartilage. Within each primordium is a stellate reticulum. By 15 days the dental papillae appear, as the inner and outer enamel epithelia are expanded, more particularly in the ventral incisors. By 16 days all of the aforementioned structures have proliferated, the surrounding mesenchyme is being organized into bone, and ameloblasts and odontoblasts ring the papillae. At 18 days the alveolar bone formation is prominent, incorporating the abundant surrounding mesenchyme. Complete differentiation of the distal and intermediate portions of the incisors depends upon association with the proximal portions. This results in complete and integrated parts for the upper and lower incisors in the mouse.

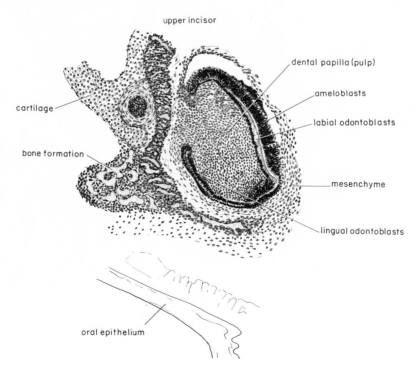

INCISOR DEVELOPMENT — MOUSE

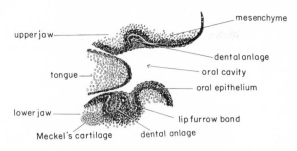

13 gestation days

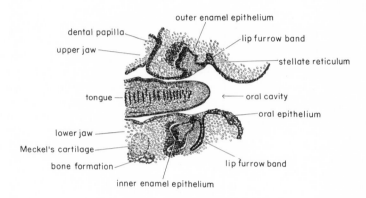

14 gestation days

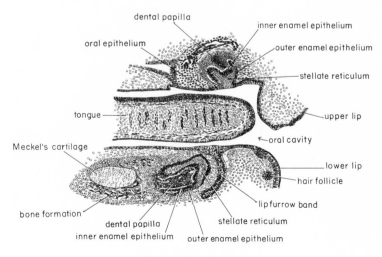

15 gestation days

INCISOR DEVELOPMENT — MOUSE

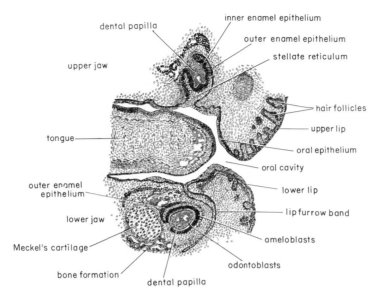

16 gestation days

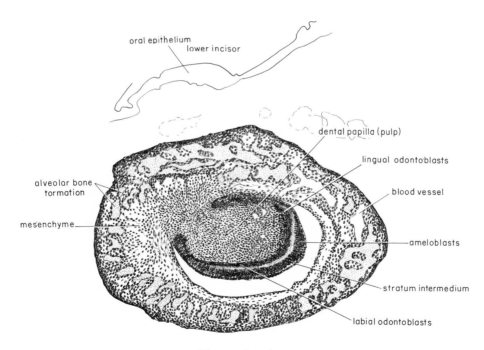

18 gestation days

INCISOR DEVELOPMENT — MOUSE

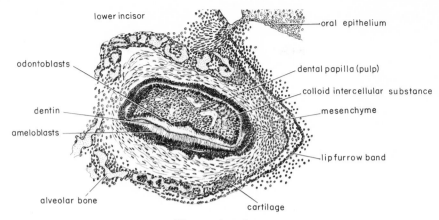

18 gestation days

INCISOR DEVELOPMENT — MOUSE

BRAIN: The central nervous system is the first system to develop and to differentiate, and one of the last to be completed. The cerebellum, for instance, is not entirely differentiated until some days after birth. Grossly, however the primary parts of the brain can be identified soon after the neural groove, neural plate, and head process stage at $7\frac{1}{2}$ days and by 14 days the brain is typically that of a mammal. Development is very rapid. At 7 3/4 days the neural plate has its limiting folds, and the otic disc and preotic transverse sulcus are visible. At 8 days the neural tube is closed in part, neural crests have spread ventrolaterally and cranial ganglia V, VII, VIII, IX, and X are apparent. At $8\frac{1}{2}$ days the anterior neuropore begins to close and the optic sulcus appears. Then the three primary brain vesicles and the cranial flexure form; the rhombencephalon acquires neuromeres; the cranial ganglia separate from the neural tube, and the trigeminal ganglion (V) becomes very large with an ophthalmic branch. At 9 days the otic vesicle is closed; Rathke's pocket can be seen; the roof of the rhombencephalon is thin; the neural crests are independent units; the lamina terminalis is present; the anterior neuropore is closed; and the posterior neuropore is closing. At $9\frac{1}{2}$ days the posterior neuropore closes, and at 10 days the telencephalic evaginations are evident. The brain is now subdivided into five major sections, the trigeminal ganglion has its three main branches (ophthalmic, maxillary, and mandibular), the cranial ganglia are distinct, and the acoustic (VIII) nerve is in direct contact with the otic vesicle. At $10\frac{1}{2}$ days the infundibulum is an outpocketing of the diencephalon, the lamina terminalis is well defined, the facial ganglion (VII) sends its nerve to the brain, the cervical spinal ganglia are metameric, and cranial nerves V to X all have established their connections with the brain.

At 11 days the infundibulum begins to pinch off from the diencephalon, the roof of the fourth ventricle is very thin, and the cervical flexure appears. The first cervical ganglion degenerates, and the second cervical ganglion is recognizable at the level of the sixth somite. The olfactory nerve (I) fibers reach to the telencephalon, on the underside of which are the short, anteriorly projecting olfactory bulbs, really extensions of the brain. The diencephalon is obscured from above, except for a slight portion on each side, by the large and bulbous single-lobed mesencephalon. In lateral view the diencephalon can be identified by the optic chiasma and infundibulum. The metencephalon (cerebellum) forms a transverse fold posterior to the mesencephalon, and just posterior to its center is the triangular and lucid (because it is so thin) roof of the myelencephalon, which tapers rapidly into the spinal cord. At $12\frac{1}{2}$ days the cerebellum is much thickened, the posterior choroid plexus is apparent in the roof of the myelencephalon, the pontine flexure is present, the telencephalic vesicles are enlarging, and the spinal ganglia are visible to about the level of somite 40. At 13 days oculomotor nuclei appear; the cerebral hemispheres partly cover the diencephalon; the anterior choroid plexi project into the first and second ventricles; and the corpora striata, epiphysis, optic thalamus, and foramen of Monro can be seen.

By 15 days gestation all these parts are further developed, especially by enlargement, but the basic relations remain unchanged. In lateral view the cerebellum is tucked among mesencephalon, myelencephalon, and spinal cord. Ventrally both the optic chiasma and infundibulum are clearly visible. The optic nerves to the brain are distinct, the foramen of Monro is reduced, there is a choroid plexus in the third ventricle, and the pontine flexure has straightened the body. At 17 days the olfactory nerve (I) and the optic nerve (II) emerge from telencephalon and diencephalon respectively, the cerebellum is enlarged but not yet folded; and the infundibulum persists. The greatest growth has occurred in the telencephalon which will give rise to the cerebral hemispheres.

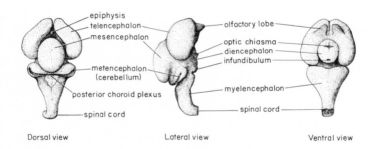

14 g.d. — 6 mm.

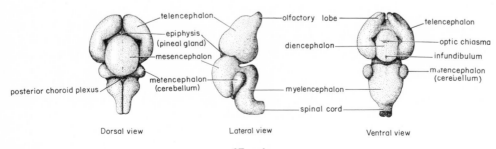

15 g.d.

MOUSE BRAIN

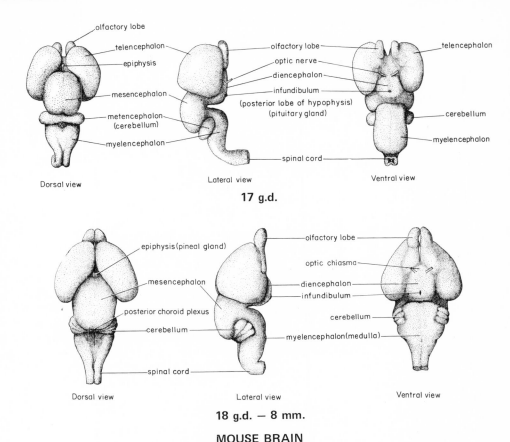

Dorsal view   Lateral view   Ventral view

17 g.d.

Dorsal view   Lateral view   Ventral view

18 g.d. — 8 mm.

MOUSE BRAIN

At 18 days the brain is essentially complete in general topography. The telencephalon is separated into two cerebral lobes, or hemispheres, the olfactory lobes are prominent, and the cerebellum is beginning its characteristic transverse folding. At 19 days it has both shallow and deep transverse folds; although it is not fully differentiated until some time after birth.

Through recent studies (Nimi et al '61) it is possible to describe in detail the development of one part of the brain, the diencephalon of the mouse.

The structural changes of the diencephalon from gestation day 10 onward can be divided principally into the development of the epithalamus, dorsal thalamus, ventral thalamus, and hypothalamus all by the ventricular sulci. Representative mid-transverse sections from this original source have been redrawn for reproduction here. These four zones can be distinguished from each other by the ventricular sulci or eminences as well as by other structural changes that appear during development (see opposite page).

There are three stages of nuclei development in the diencephalic wall. The second stage, from gestation day 13 to 15, shows differentiation of the various layers: germinal, mantle, and marginal. These layers increase in volume while they show cellular differentiation into distinct nuclear groups.

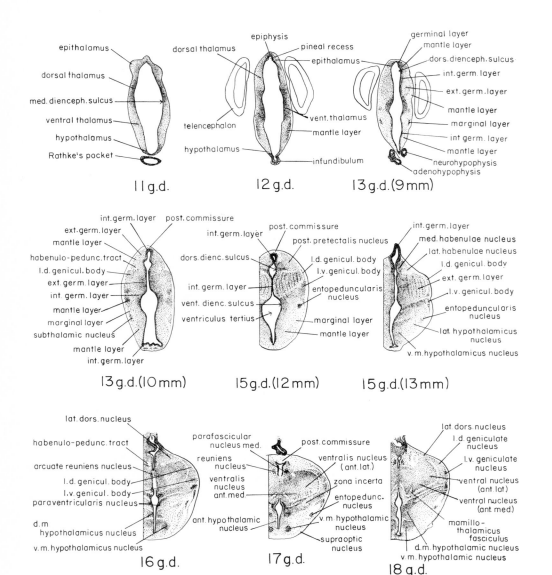

**ONTOGENETIC DEVELOPMENT OF THE
DIENCEPHALON OF THE MOUSE**

(Courtesy of Niimi, Harada, Kusada, and Kishi 1961.)

This differentiation seems to progress from caudal to cephalic levels of the diencephalon. During the third stage, from gestation day 16 until after birth, the orderly structure within the original three layers is lost in favor of differentiation into special central nervous system nuclei. The dorsal thalamus shows this differentiation last.

The *epithalamus* is large on gestation day 13, but decreases in size and at day 16 the median habenular nucleus arises from the external germinal layer, and the lateral habenular nucleus arises from the mantle layer. It appears that the pretectalis and posterior nuclei may arise from the mantle layer also, while the posterior commissure nucleus arises from the external germinal layer.

The *dorsal thalamus* is rather poorly developed at gestation days 11 and 12, but shortly increases in volume. By the 16th day the internal germinal layer differentiates into the median group of nuclei known as the reuniens arcuatus and reuniens medianus. The massa intermedia is formed by day 17 by the fusion of the internal germinal layer from both sides. During days 17 and 18 the external germinal layer differentiates into the anterior and mesial groups of nuclei. In the anterior group are the parataenialis and both the anterior dorsal and ventral nuclei, but the anterior medialis nucleus has not yet formed. The mesial group differentiates into the paramedianus, parafascicularis, laminaris, and median dorsal nuclei. From the mantle layer there develop the latero-dorsal geniculate body and on days 15 and 16 the median dorsal geniculate body. During days 16 to 18 the latero-dorsal and ventral nuclei are gradually developed within the mantle layer.

The *ventral thalamus* is well developed by 12 days gestation, but then it begins to decrease in volume. All of the nuclei of this ventral thalamus develop from the mantle layer. By days 15 and 16 there can be distinguished the reticular nucleus, the zona incerta, the latero-ventral geniculate body, and the median ventral geniculate body. Before this, on day 13, can be seen the massa cellularis reuniens thalami.

By 11 days gestation the *hypothalamus* is not well developed, but shortly increases in volume. By the 16th day the internal germinal layer differentiates into the periventricular group of nuclei; the preopticus, the hypothalamicus, the suprachiasmaticus, and the supraopticus nuclei. The mantle layer differentiates on days 15 and 16 into the mesial group of nuclei: the massa cellularis reuniens hypothalami, the median preopticus, the anterior hypothalamicus, the ventro-medial hypothalamicus, the dorso-medial hypothalamicus, the dorsal hypothalamicus, the posterior hypothalamicus, as well as nuclei for the mammillary body. The mammillary body includes the magnocellularis, parocellularis, intercalatus, supramamillaris, and the premamillaris dorsal and ventral nuclei. The anlage of the mamillary body is first seen on gestation day 13. Most of the paraventricular nucleus arises from the mantle layer. During days 15 and 16 the marginal layer differentiates into the lateral group of nuclei: the lateral preoptic, the lateral hypothalamicus, the mamilloinfundibularis, the subthalamicus, and the entopeduncularis nuclei.

In general, the development of the diencephalic nuclei of the mouse is quite similar to that of other vertebrates studied.

SPINAL CORD: The earliest indication of the spinal cord is the neural plate seen at $8\frac{1}{2}$ days. The posterior neuropore closes at 9 days. At 10 days the neural groove is closed into a tube in limited regions, forming a large neural canal and the relatively thick layer of surrounding neuroblasts. The neural tube extends temporarily into the tail but decreases in diameter and disappears there by 13 days. It occurs as a completed structure in the tail, not developing from neural plate as in the body. Neural crests appear in the body simultaneously with the closing of the neural tube. More laterally are the paired somites, the most anterior of which may show early differentiation. By 11 days the spinal cord has thickened by the proliferation of its cells, and the ependymal layer, ventral horns, spinal ganglia, and spinal nerves are visible. Abundant sclerotomal mesenchyme is distributed around the cord, except dorsally, and encloses the ventrally located remnant of the notochord. By 12 days the texture of the cord is quite typical in transverse sections with marginal white and more central gray mantle layers and an ependymal layer that is thicker dorsally than elsewhere. Spinal ganglia are prominent with both dorsal and ventral roots. Development proceeds with histological and cytological refinement of parts. Neuroblasts fill the expanding mantle layer, spinal arteries arise both dorsally and ventrally, the invading centra entirely obliterate the notochord and cartilaginous neural arches appear. The cord is depressed from the dorsal skin, and mesenchyme completely surrounds it. At 17 days it could satisfy the requirements of any adult vertebrate cord, even to the presence of sympathetic ganglia. The original neural tube persists as a very small subcentral hole surrounded by a thin layer of ependymal cells. At 18 days the spinal cord is structurally and functionally complete.

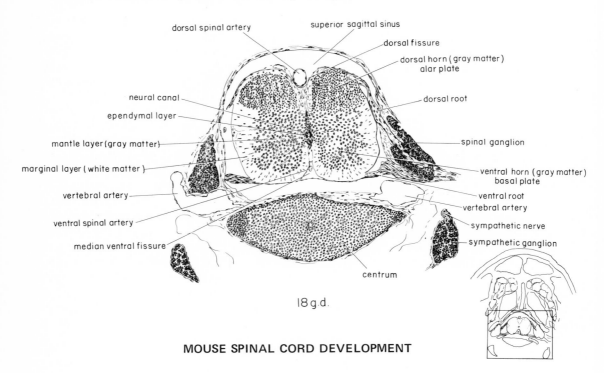

18 g.d.

MOUSE SPINAL CORD DEVELOPMENT

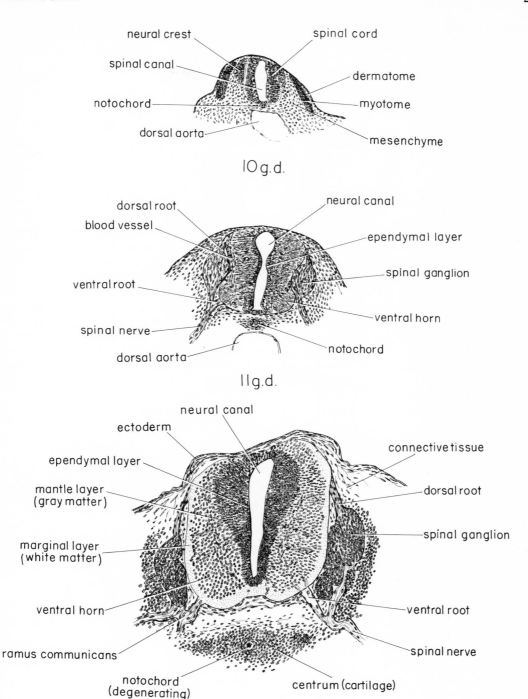

neural crest — spinal cord
spinal canal
notochord — dermatome
dorsal aorta — myotome
— mesenchyme

10 g.d.

dorsal root — neural canal
blood vessel — ependymal layer
ventral root — spinal ganglion
spinal nerve — ventral horn
dorsal aorta — notochord

11 g.d.

neural canal
ectoderm
ependymal layer — connective tissue
mantle layer (gray matter) — dorsal root
marginal layer (white matter) — spinal ganglion
ventral horn — ventral root
ramus communicans — spinal nerve
notochord (degenerating) — centrum (cartilage)

12 g.d.

MOUSE SPINAL CORD DEVELOPMENT

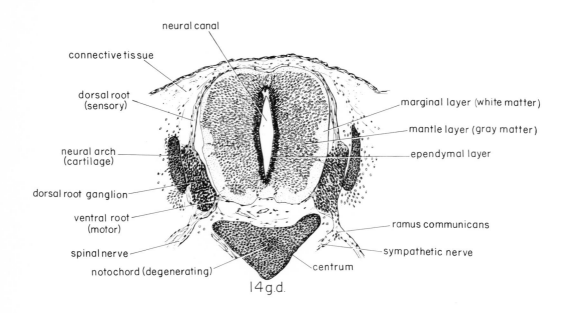

neural canal

connective tissue

dorsal root
(sensory)

neural arch
(cartilage)

dorsal root ganglion

ventral root
(motor)

spinal nerve

notochord (degenerating)

marginal layer (white matter)

mantle layer (gray matter)

ependymal layer

ramus communicans

sympathetic nerve

centrum

14 g.d.

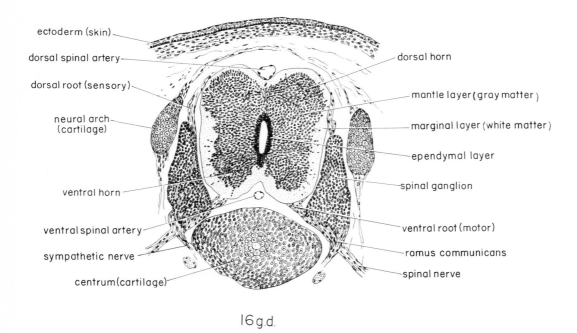

ectoderm (skin)

dorsal spinal artery

dorsal root (sensory)

neural arch
(cartilage)

ventral horn

ventral spinal artery

sympathetic nerve

centrum (cartilage)

dorsal horn

mantle layer (gray matter)

marginal layer (white matter)

ependymal layer

spinal ganglion

ventral root (motor)

ramus communicans

spinal nerve

16 g.d.

MOUSE SPINAL CORD DEVELOPMENT

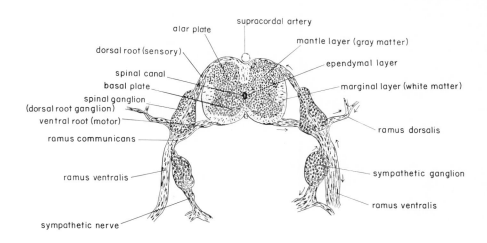

SPINAL CORD AND NERVES OF MOUSE
17 gestation days (transverse section)

SENSE ORGANS:

The Eyes (Optic Apparatus): At 8 days gestation the optic vesicles appear, the optic stalk and double-layered cup begin to close on day $9\frac{1}{2}$, the lens vesicle first invaginates on day 10. By day $10\frac{1}{2}$ the optic cup first comes into contact with the ectoderm of the head, the optic stalk shortens, the choroid fissure forms and the nervous layer of the retina is prominent. On day 11 the lens vesicle closes off from the head ectoderm. By $11\frac{1}{2}$ days the lens shows outer epithelial and inner fibrous parts, the inverted choroid fissure is deep, the hyaloid vessels and plexi are formed, the vitreous mesenchyme accumulates and the nervous layer of the retina is at least 4 times the thickness of the pigmented layer. Pigment appears in the retinal region and the posterior lens cells elongate. On day 12 the choroid fissure closes, and by $12\frac{1}{2}$ days the lens becomes separate from the epidermis and drops below the surface. Its fibrous part is expanding at this time. The vitreous humor forms and mesenchyme intercepts the lens and the epidermis. On day 13 lens fibers invade the lens vesicle, the primary lid fold begins to form, nerve fibers appear in the optic stalk, and the oculomotor nuclei form. By $13\frac{1}{2}$ days the lens expands vertically more than laterally, the anterior chamber of the eye forms, the nervous layer of the retina is at least 8 times as thick as the pigmented layer, the optic (II) nerves can be identified, the iris forms, and the upper eyelids and the ocular muscles arise.

By 14 days the lens epithelium, facing the anterior chamber, is cellular and becomes thinner as the lens enlarges. The posterior chamber contains scattered cells and the optic nerve (II) is clearly defined. The lower eyelid also forms, growing toward the upper eyelid, with which it will fuse to cover the eye before birth. By $14\frac{1}{2}$ days both corneal and scleral mesenchyme form around the eyeballs.

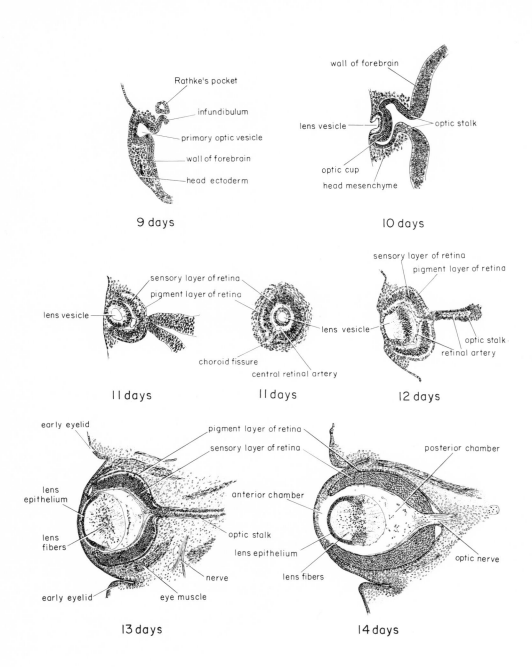

SECTIONS OF THE EYES OF THE EMBRYONIC MOUSE

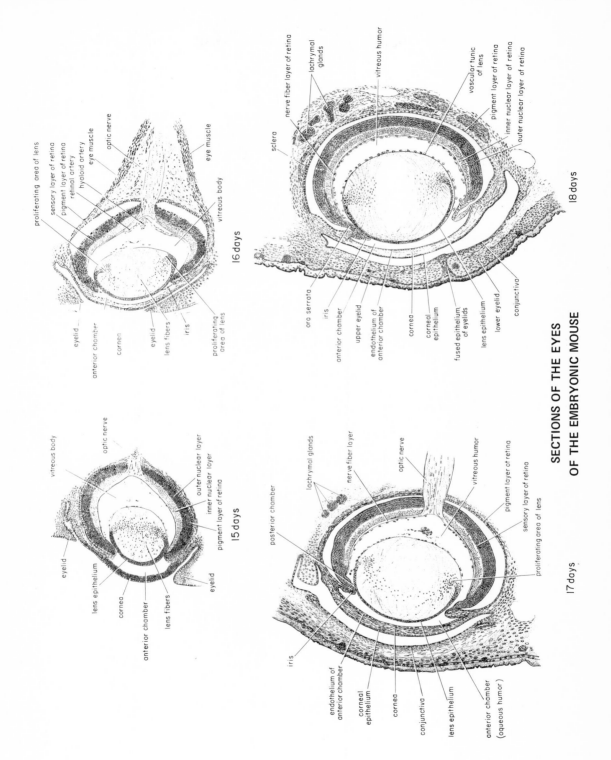

SECTIONS OF THE EYES OF THE EMBRYONIC MOUSE

16 days

18 days

15 days

17 days

By 15 days the retina begins to show cellular differentiation into the inner and outer nuclear layers, as the lens fibers further elongate and the optic nerve increases in diameter. The epidermis covering the lens begins to differentiate into the cornea. The pigmented layer is distinct but not yet highly pigmented. By 16 days the pigmented and retinal layers are separated, the iris forms, and the lens becomes elongate-oval in a dorso-ventral direction. The lens vesicle has disappeared except at the margins of the lens epithelium. The vitreous humor accumulates and a large blood vessel appears near the entrance of the hyaloid artery. The eyelids fuse, the cornea and sclera show stratified epithelia, and neuroblasts appear in the retina.

Day 17 sees the first appearance of the lachrymal glands in the mesenchyme near the eye, the iris is well advanced and the ora serrata can be identified. Beneath the closed eyelids there is differentiation of the layers into the endothelium of the anterior chamber, the cornea, and the outermost corneal epithelium. The innermost layer of the closed eyelids becomes the conjunctiva. The retina is further differentiated into its several layers (the mouse has no cones) and a nerve fiber layer lines the retina from the optic nerve. A ciliary ring is formed. By 18 days the eye is essentially complete, with a vascular tunic around the lens, the inner and outer nuclear layers of the retina clearly distinct, and the sclera encapsulating the eye. The cornea is about 3 times as thick as the sclera, and the iris is fully formed.

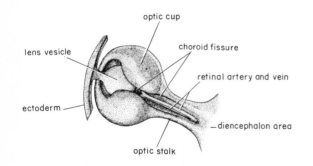

OPTIC VESICLE FROM VENTRAL SIDE SHOWING CHOROID FISSURE

SCHEMATIC DRAWING OF EYE

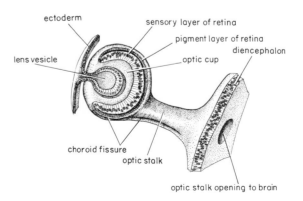

The Ears (Auditory Apparatus): At 8 days gestation the otic invaginations may be seen on the surface of the head, lateral to the myelencephalon, and by $8\frac{1}{2}$ days vesicles form. These vesicles deepen quickly and then close over at about 9 days. By 11 days the original endolymphatic cavities, which are mesio-dorsal, elongate mesio-ventrally to form the cochlear duct, and by $11\frac{1}{2}$ days mesenchyme extends around the otic capsules. The otic vesicles are compressed laterally and both the utricle and saccule portions are distinguishable. On day 12 the semicircular canals begin to form from the utricle and are lined with epithelium. By 13 days the semicircular canals are formed with their ampullae, the cochlea shows its first twist, and the ampullary branches of the auditory nerve (VIII) develop. The 3rd pair of visceral grooves become the external ear ducts. The otic capsule is pre-cartilaginous and the external auditory

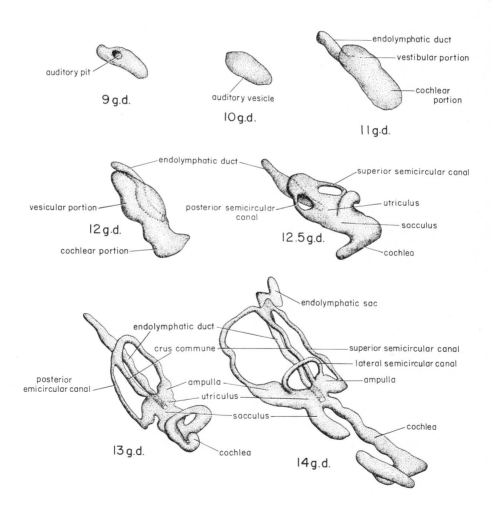

DEVELOPMENT OF THE MOUSE EAR
(graphic reconstruction)

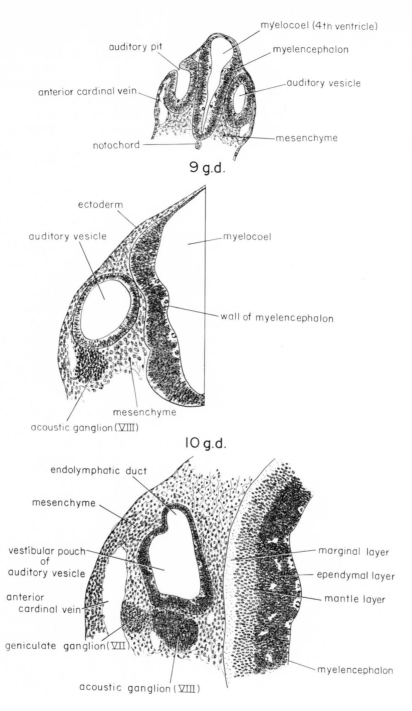

auditory pit

myelocoel (4th ventricle)

myelencephalon

anterior cardinal vein

auditory vesicle

notochord

mesenchyme

9 g.d.

ectoderm

auditory vesicle

myelocoel

wall of myelencephalon

mesenchyme

acoustic ganglion (VIII)

10 g.d.

endolymphatic duct

mesenchyme

vestibular pouch of auditory vesicle

anterior cardinal vein

geniculate ganglion (VII)

acoustic ganglion (VIII)

marginal layer

ependymal layer

mantle layer

myelencephalon

11 g.d.

MOUSE EAR DEVELOPMENT

(Sections)

neatus is partly covered by the pinna forming from the third visceral arch. The tympanic cavities form from the remnants of the first visceral clefts. True cartilage does not appear in the otic capsule until about day $14\frac{1}{2}$, the utrico-saccular duct is reduced, the cochlear duct is further twisted and the pinna almost completely overlaps the outer auditory meatus. By 16 days the endolymphatic duct has expanded, the cochlea has 1 3/4 turns, the otic capsule is extensively chondrified, and the meatus is filled with periderm and covered by the pinna. By 17 days the ear parts are essentially complete with tympanic cavity, auditory tube, nasopharyngeal ostium, cartilaginous ossicles in mesenchyme, and a plugged meatus. By 19 days the otic capsules are ossified, and the pinna seals over the meatus.

The Nose (Olfactory Apparatus): By gestation day $8\frac{1}{2}$ the olfactory placodes form, the olfactory vesicles develop by day $10\frac{1}{2}$ and olfactory pits by day 11. By day $11\frac{1}{2}$ deep olfactory pouches (vomeronasal organs) are formed while mitral cells originate in the olfactory epithelium and corresponding triangular (Cajal) cells of the accessory bulb appear, sometimes even earlier. A few superficial tufted cells begin to appear, but not many are seen until later (about day 18). By day 12 short axon cells of Cajal are found and continue to appear for about 6 days more. On the 11th day there is rapid proliferation of granule cells of both the olfactory and accessory bulbs, and this proliferation continues for several weeks after birth. By day 12 the olfactory pouches narrow to the tube-like vomeronasal organ and by day $12\frac{1}{2}$ olfactory (I) nerves form. By day $13\frac{1}{2}$ the bucconasal partition is ruptured and the nasal capsule and septum become pre-cartilaginous. By $14\frac{1}{2}$ days choanae are slit-like, there is a long vomeronasal organ, thick walled tubes in the nasal septum, and a nasolachrymal duct. By day 15 the palatine processes meet mesially, and the nasopalatine duct is separated from the posterior choanae. By day 16 the palate is completed, there is a long nasopharyngeal meatus, secondary choanae, and the nares are plugged temporarily. On day 17 lateral nasal mucous glands appear and the nares open on day 19.

THE ENDOCRINE ORGANS:

The Thyroid, Parathyroid, and Ultimobranchial Bodies: At $8\frac{1}{2}$ days gestation the first indication of the median thyroid thickening in the floor of the foregut occurs with a distinct primordium of evaginating endoderm appearing a few hours later. By 10 days the duct forms. There develop paired lateral thyroid diverticulae and by 11 days there remains only a strand of tissue where the original thyroid evagination had formed, connecting the thyroid with the pharynx. Portions of the laryngotracheal groove from which originated the thyroid duct may remain in the floor of the foregut. The parathyroid primordia from the dorsal part of the 3rd visceral pouch, and the ultimobranchial bodies from the epithelium of the 4th to the 6th visceral pouches, appear by this time. By 12 days, the thyroid diverticulae lose their cavities and become cellular aggregates, as the parathyroids and ultimobranchial bodies become detached. By 13 days the paired thyroid gland becomes lobular and forms a crescent shaped collar around the lower pharynx, comprising the thin isthmus which is ventral to the 3rd tracheal ring. The parathyroids are now attached to the thyroid and the regressing ultimobranchial bodies are embedded in the lateral wings of the thyroid substance. By 17 days there are numerous follicles in the bi-lobed thyroid well supplied with blood vessels, and this endocrine gland is encapsulated. Since the thyroid follicles begin to show colloid the follicle stimulating hormone (FSH) must be elaborated by the pituitary gland (hypophysis). Tracheal cartilage intercepts the thyroid and the trachea. By 15 days the beginning of organization of the parathyroids may be seen. These are all but surrounded by thyroid follicles, but easily distinguished from them. The non-glandular parathyroids are dorso-laterally located and are separated from the thyroid substance by a layer of connective tissue. (See page 186 for illustrations of earlier stages of thyroid development.)

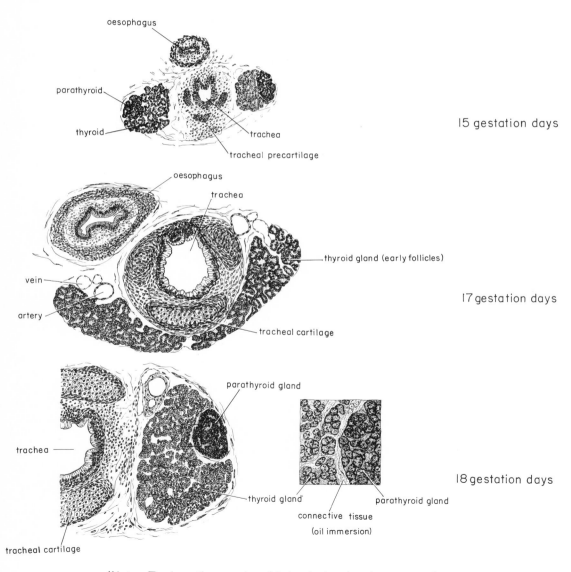

(Note: To show the parathyroid glands these sections were taken anterior to the isthmus which therefore does not show.)

*The Thymus**: At 12 days gestation the first indication of thymus development appears when the subscapular primordium is covered by a basement membrane separating the epithelial bud from the surrounding mesenchyme. It arises from the epithelium of the 3rd and 4th visceral pouches, hence its original lining is endodermal, as is that of the thyroid. The cells actually resemble those of the pharyngeal endodermal epithelium and carry cilia and microvilli on their free surfaces. The adjoining cells are connected by desmosomes, and within the plasma membranes of the cells are oval structures, honey-combed by thin walled tubes. Stellate mesenchymal cells of the branchial area become flattened and spindle-shaped as they are compressed by the outgrowing endodermal thymic bud, and differentiate to form a capsule of fibroblastic cells. Some of these appear to be elaborating collagen. The free surfaces of the outermost cells of the primitive thymic bud are covered by a fine fibrillar membrane which separates the endodermal cells from the surrounding mesenchyme. One of three prominent and large nuceoli are seen as fenestrated spheres in dense granular opaque substance of the cytoplasm of these cells, closely adherent to the nuclear membrane whose outer lamella is beaded with ribosomes. There is a paucity of organelles in the cytoplasm, except for some free ribosomes and small oval mitochondria. Cristae are few, short, and unoriented. Golgi are present but not significant. The vacuoles are large, round, have translucent matrices, and are reduced as development proceeds. The plasma membranes of contiguous cells are lined intermittently by desmosomes, and terminal bars attach them at the luminal surface. Large epitheloid cells may also be seen interspersed among the thymic cells at their periphery. These possibly degenerating cells have dark globular inclusions. The thymus as an endocrine organ appears to be proliferating much faster than is the nearby thyroid.

By 13 days some of the endodermal cords differentiate into stromal elements with pseudopodia which insinuate themselves between the adjacent cells and encircle others. These free cells differentiate along the divergent lines of lymphopoiesis. The thymus primordium is now well encapsulated by fibroblasts which have derived much connective tissue and extra-cellular collagenous material. There is no evidence yet of any lobule formation or vascularization in the thymic matrix. In the peripheral area there appear many mitoses, and there is an outermost double layer of cells just beneath the capsule, distinguishable from those within, which begins to show heterogenity. Some enlarged cells invade the thymic mass and cause the appearance of lacunae, which spaces are soon filled with smoother, and more rounded cells that probably are stem cells for lymphopoiesis. The lymphocyte precursors have rather opaque hyaloplasm, with increased ribosome population and polygonal aggregates. Granules of ribonucleoprotein and mitochondria are also evident. Cristae become more regular and numerous. There are membranous filaments which attach immature thymic lymphocytes to the circumscribing epithelial cells.

By 14 and 15 days the mouse thymus shows the most rapid histogenetic and organogenetic changes, assuming the structure of the adult and a position close to the pericardial cavity. The surface of the thymic primordium has become scalloped and undulating, and trabeculae begin to invade and divide the organ

---

* This description combines the excellent original study by Dr. F. T. Sanel, yet to be published, and our direct observations.

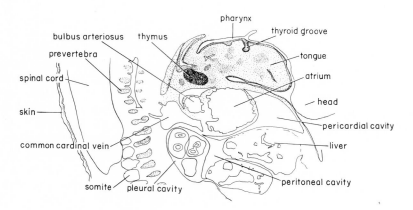

THYMUS at 12 g.d. (sagittal section)

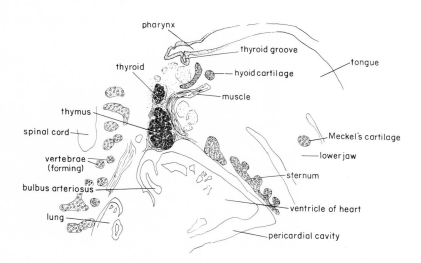

THYMUS at 14 g.d. (sagittal section)

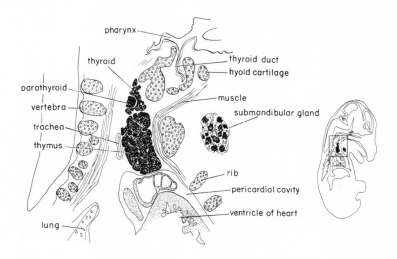

THYMUS at 15 g.d. (parasagittal section)

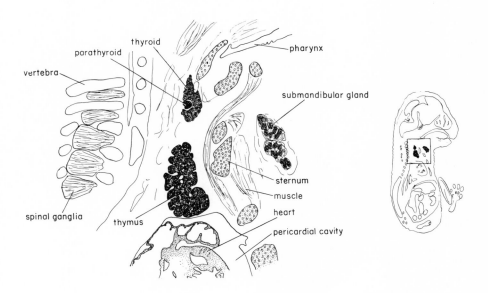

THYMUS at 16 g.d. (parasagittal section)

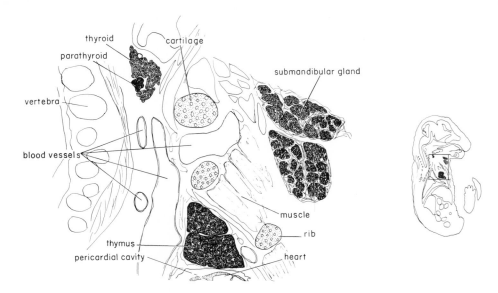

THYMUS at 17 g.d. (parasagittal section)

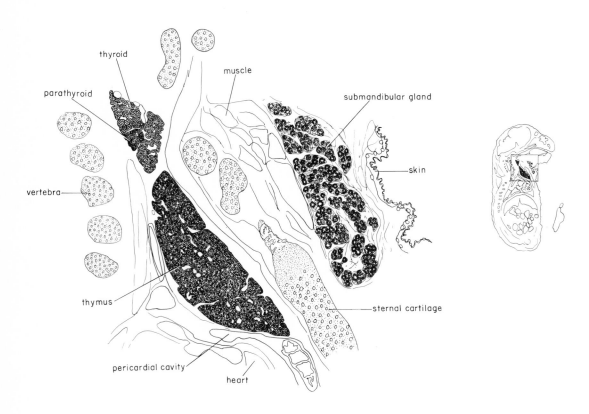

THYMUS at 18 g.d. (parasagittal section)

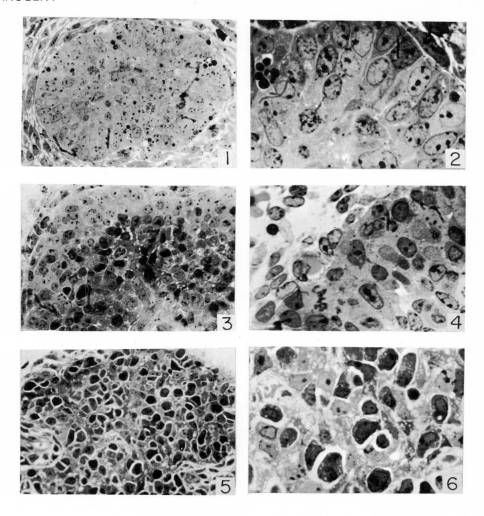

DEVELOPMENT OF MOUSE (C57 black) THYMUS GLAND

Fig. 1 — The mesenchymal cells of the branchial area are compressed by the out-growing endodermal bud. Notable are the numerous cells in mitosis, the pycnotic inclusions and the relative homogeneity of the cell population. (12 days)

Fig. 2 — The epithelium of the anlagé, predominantly columnar, is primitive and undifferentiated. In a few cells, slight condensation of nuclear chroma-tin and increasing basophilia are seen. (12 days)

Fig. 3 — The mesenchymal cells, now fibroblastic, encapsulate the still predomi-nately epithelial primordium. Transforming columnar cells in the sub-cortical area disrupt the endodermal cords. (13 days)

Fig. 4 — A slightly higher proportion of epithelial cells in division are seen in peripheral areas. Lymphoid precursors are sometimes identifiable. Note the erythroblast in the pericapsular space. (13 days)

Fig. 5 — Invasive septa are beginning to shape the anlagé into lobules. Stromal cells have developed long cytoplasmic processes that encircle the differ-entiating thymocytes. (14 days)

Fig. 6 — The vacuolated cytoplasm of the epithelial cells is characteristic of early stages. Many large lymphocytes are developing within the thymic reticulum. (14 days)

(Courtesy of F. T. Sanel)

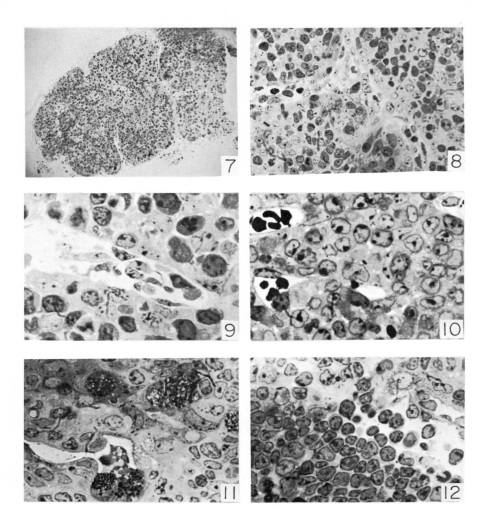

DEVELOPMENT OF MOUSE (C57 black) THYMUS GLAND

Fig. 7 — A low power view of a definitely lymphoid organ now recognizable as the thymus. Blood vessels are limited for the most part to the trabeculae although a rare capillary has penetrated the parenchyma. (15 days)

Fig. 8 — Some polarization of like cell species has occurred, but division into cortex and medulla is as yet not apparent. Note the similarity of the mononuclear cells within the blood vessels to those of the matrix. (15 days)

Fig. 9 — Cuboidal epithelium frequently underlies the capsule. Free lymphoid cells predominate in subcortical areas. (15 days)

Fig. 10 — Large ovate reticulo-epithelial cells form a compact stroma in the medulla and are numerous in this quite vascular region. (18 days)

Fig. 11 — Granule containing cells in the vicinity of the medullary blood vessels may be mast cells, although these did not stain metachromatically. Basophilic inclusions within stromal cells nearby are not uncommon. (19 days)

Fig. 12 — Thymic lymphocytes at various stages of development crowd into perivascular channels at the cortico-medullary junction and appear to be streaming into the systemic circulation via these pathways. (19 days)

(Courtesy of F. T. Sanel)

into lobules. Blood vessels (parenchymal) extend into the septa carrying ery-throid elements. Some lobules may even begin to show cortical and medullary differentiation. The thymic cells are rounded and basophilic, lodged within a reticulum or stroma the cells of which have cytoplasmic elongations often linked by desmosomes. It is within such a matrix that the early lymphoid cells divide and mature. The small lymphocytes measure from 12 to 18 microns and the nucleocytoplasmic ratio is now 2:1. Chromatin masses form an irregular ring around the inner wall of the nuclear membrane, and the nucleoli are less con-spicuous. Ribosomes are being concentrated. There is evidence that the epi-thelial cells are being transformed into stellate reticulo-epithelial cells with long processes buttressing the tissue. These are the cytoreticulum or skeleton of the gland. There are also columnar cells in the acinar formation containing aggregates of particulate glycogen; and hyperthrophied cells similar to those in the medullary zone of the adult thymus; all of epithelial origin.

At 16 to 19 days the largest proportion of thymocytes are medium sized, but there are also large thymocytes, and some small cells indigenous to the mature organ. There is no evidence at any time of a germinal center in the development of the thymus. The epithelial cell derivatives are more or less segregated into similar groups, the stromal cells with cytoplasmic prolonga-tions polarized in the cortical regions. Some cells are compressed into colum-nar or cuboidal shapes in an acinar configuration, often contiguous cells joined by desmosomes at the luminal surface of which are microvilli bearing hairy or bristle-like material, and conventional cilia. There is evidence of glycogen storage. The hypertrophied cells occasionally seen in the adult thymic medulla are first seen at 18 days. These cells may contain odd-shaped vacuoles, myelin figures, and flocculent material. By this time (18 days) the thymus has reached almost its natal size and is bounded by vertebrae, pericardium, and the sternal cartilage. There is some evidence that the thymic epithelial cells are secre-tory, even during the last phases of development. The capillary walls of the thymus contain fenestrae, thus supporting the contention that the gland has an endocrine function.

The Pituitary Gland: Rathke's pocket (hypophyseal pouch) is first defined on gestation day $8\frac{1}{2}$ but the infundibular evagination of the diencephalon, which is to be intimately associated with Rathke's pocket, does not occur until about day $11\frac{1}{2}$. Rathke's pocket becomes detached by 12 days and shows cellular pro-liferation ventro-mesially in the ultimate pars distalis (anterior lobe). By 14 days there is a solid hypophyseal stalk and the infundibulum becomes pinched off and connected only by an infundibular recess to the diencephalon. The lumen of the original Rathke's pocket is compressed. That portion of the roof of the original Rathke's pocket adjacent to the ectoderm of the infundibulum will be-come the pars intermedia, and below all will be the mesenchymal precursors of the sphenoid cartilage. The arachnoid space which partially encircles the de-veloping pituitary gland from below is the beginning of the sella turcica. Thus, by 14 days the pars distalis (anterior lobe) and intermedia can be identified and distinguished, and by 16 days the pars neuralis (posterior lobe) also develops. Thus all three of the major components of the pituitary gland are differentiating by 16 days gestation. The pars neuralis is really dorsal to the pars intermedia but does not extend quite as far anteriorly as does the more ventrally located pars distalis. By 17 days the pituitary gland seems to elaborate some of its normal secretions. By 18 days the cell aggregates of the anterior lobe become lobular and occlude the remnants of Rathke's pocket. Lumina are trapped in the anterior lobe cell proliferation, and by this time it is quite obvious that an endocrine gland is forming. The cell configurations of the three parts of the pituitary are quite distinct, the most glandular-looking portion being the anterior lobe. Its lining epithelium develops from brain ectoderm and Rathke's pocket ectoderm, but it is quickly surrounded by mesenchyme. While it is a single gland of three distinct functioning parts, the pituitary arises primarily through the cooperative development of ectoderm from two originally unrelated regions.

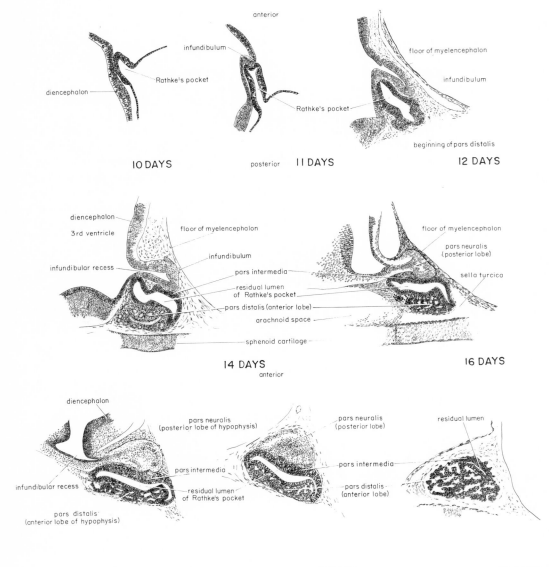

DEVELOPMENT OF PITUITARY GLAND — MOUSE
(Sagittal sections)

The Pineal Gland (Epiphysis): By $11\frac{1}{2}$ days there is the first indication of the epiphyseal evagination from the roof of the diencephalon. It occurs just posterior-dorsal to a line dividing the diencephalon from the telencephalon. By 12 days this becomes a distinct evaginating pocket which is pinched off from the forebrain by 13 days, and by 16 days takes on a lobular and glandular structure. A tubular connection from the 3rd ventricle (diocoel) persists as the pineal differentiates. At about 18 days it becomes highly glandular and the original tubular connection with the brain becomes the pineal stalk. It is surrounded by the pia mater.

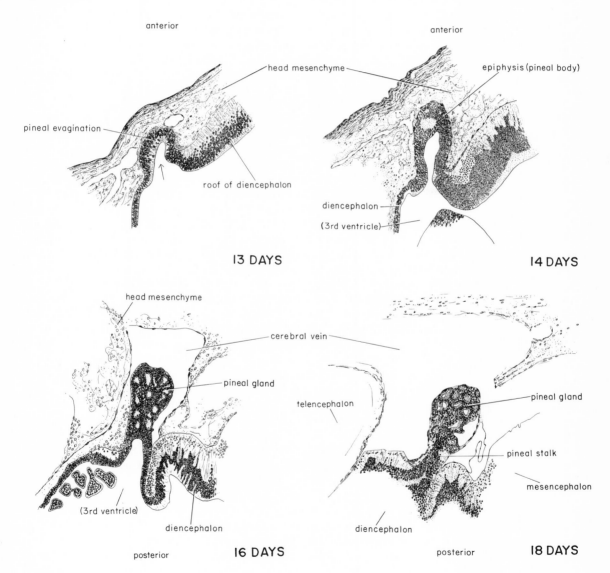

DEVELOPMENT OF PINEAL GLAND — MOUSE
(Sagittal sections)

The Adrenal Glands: On day 11 the adrenal blastemas are seen and the sympathetic neuroblasts to the adrenal cortex by $12\frac{1}{2}$ days. The consolidation of the cortex and medulla (but no capsule) occurs by 14 days; strands are found in the medulla and cells in nests, which begin to control glycogenesis, by 17 days. By 19 days or just before birth the adrenal medulla is distinguishable.

THE DIGESTIVE SYSTEM: The foregut forms as early as $7\frac{1}{2}$ days, the oral (stomodeal) membrane ruptures on day 8, the liver primordium forms and the yolk stalk becomes a narrow tube with differentiation of the hindgut at 9 days.   By $9\frac{1}{2}$ days the laryngotracheal groove, liver, and dorsal pancreas begin to form, the vitelline duct closes, and the cloaca develops. By 10 days the stomach begins to differentiate, the liver acquires trabeculae, the endoderm of the vitelline duct is resorbed and the proctodeal membrane is formed. At this time the 1st pharyngeal pouch reaches the outer head ectoderm, the 2nd forms the visceral groove, the 3rd touches the head ectoderm. By $10\frac{1}{2}$ days the ultimobranchial bodies form from the epithelium of visceral pouches 4 to 6; the stomach is well differentiated, both the duodenum and the hepato-pancreatic ducts are formed, the much enlarged dorsal pancreas has a duct, and the ventral pancreas can be identified. On day 11, the tongue primordium is developed, the trachea separates from the esophagus, the stomach changes its position to oblique, the liver becomes lobular, the cloacal cavity is divided into urogenital and rectal portions, the post anal gut regresses, and an umbilical hernia is first formed. By day 12, the dorsal and ventral pancreatic rudiments fuse, and the umbilical hernia begins to be incorporated into the intestinal loop. By 13 days, the dental lamina- appear as placodes, epithelial cords form the salivary glands, the distal end of the tongue is free, and the cloaca has a urogenital sinus and rectum. On day 14, the dental lamina grow deeply into gaps between the incisor and molar parts, the salivary glands have secretory buds, there is an enormous umbilical hernia, the pancreas develops islets and tubules and is well vascularized, and the proctodeal membrane begins to rupture. By day 15 the molar lamina have a trough-shaped rim, and the incisor germs are long. By day 16 the umbilical hernia is usually withdrawn. By day 17 the molar lamina with two concentrations of the enamel organ and papillary blastema are present; the upper and lower incisors lengthen; tall ameloblastic epithelia and papillae are vascular; liver glycogen is accumulating; the pancreas is compact with islets, ducts, acini and less connective tissue; the gut is withdrawn from the umbilicus. By day 18, the incisors are about to erupt with their dentine and enamel layers, the molars have transverse ridges, the intestinal derivatives become functionally active with secretory granules in the acini cells of the pancreas. Regarding the further development of the teeth, the post-natal sequence of eruption involves first the incisors, then the 1st, 2nd, and 3rd molars - a process which may take up to 5 weeks.

The Liver: At 9 days the liver diverticulum first forms, and proliferates cells rapidly beginning at $9\frac{1}{2}$ days gestation. Shortly thereafter epithelial cords appear in the liver primordia. Nearby is a dorsal pancreatic constriction and by $10\frac{1}{2}$ days the liver acquires large blood vessels which later become the vitelline veins. Beginning at 11 days, the ventral pancreatic rudiments appear and

---

* Tooth development is described in more detail under the heading of Skeleton.

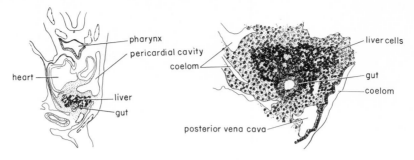

LIVER at 10 g.d.

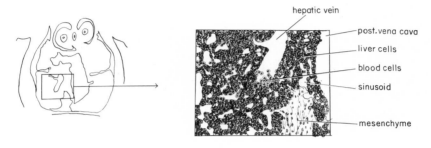

LIVER at 11 g.d.

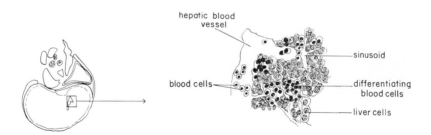

LIVER at 12 g.d.

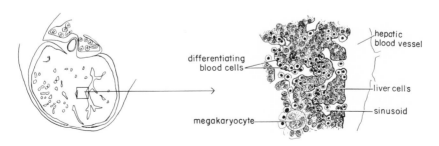

LIVER at 13 g.d.

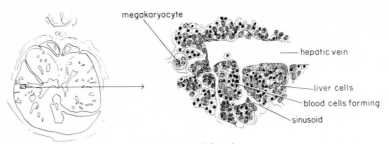

LIVER at 14 g.d.

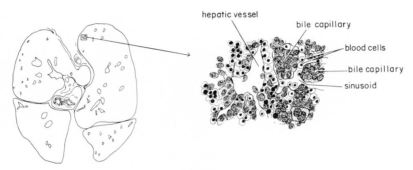

LIVER at 15 g.d.

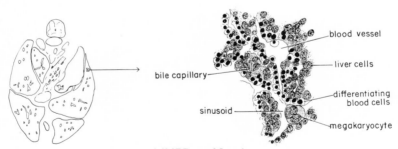

LIVER at 16 g.d.

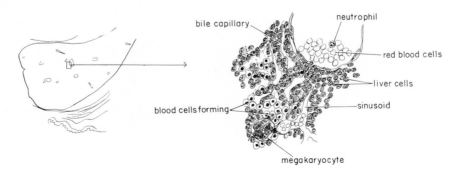

LIVER at 18 g.d.

soon thereafter the stomach expands. By $11\frac{1}{2}$ days the dorsal and ventral pancreatic rudiments fuse near the duodenum, and by $13\frac{1}{2}$ days vacuoles appear in the stomach epithelium suggesting its glandular function. It is not until day 16 that there is proliferation of the gastric glands.

In sections, liver cells may be identified as early as day 10, closely associated with the foregut and somewhat surrounded by trapped coelomic spaces. Close by is the large posterior vena cava. By day 11 the liver cells surround the hepatic vein, and are close to the posterior vena cava. Blood cells appear in the forming blood vessels, the liver mass is full of sinusoids and is invaded by mesenchyme. By day 12 there appear many early hematopoietic cells intermingled with the liver cells, some lying freely within the hepatic blood vessels. These include hemocytoblasts, myeloblasts, promyelocytes, metamyelocytes, polymorphonuclears, proerthythroblasts, basophilic erythroblasts, polychromatiophilic erythroblasts, and orthochromatic erythroblasts. The last three are found in substantial numbers while the others are less than 1%. By day 13 some megakaryocytes are present, indicating the hematopoietic function of the liver. There will also appear many nucleated red cells. By day 15 bile capillaries can be distinguished from blood capillaries since they are devoid of blood cells of any kind, and are lined with true liver cells. By 16 days all of these elements have increased in number and volume, with the quantity of differentiating blood cells appreciably increased. By 18 days the liver appears to be more hematopoietic than endocrine, with numerous sinusoids and blood cells in various stages of formation.

The Spleen: At 13 days, the primordium of the spleen, located just dorsal to the stomach and near the level of the gonad, may first be seen. It does not enlarge as rapidly as does the thymus, nor does it change its location. It may be found at 15 and 16 days approximately where it originated. It is suspended by the dorsal mesogastrium into the peritoneal cavity. By 17 days it is elongating and by 18 days is a long and slender organ tucked in between the metanephros, stomach, and outer body wall. It is not yet differentiated into the typical pulp areas.

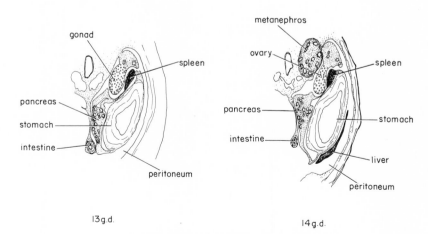

DEVELOPMENT OF THE SPLEEN
(Drawn to scale)

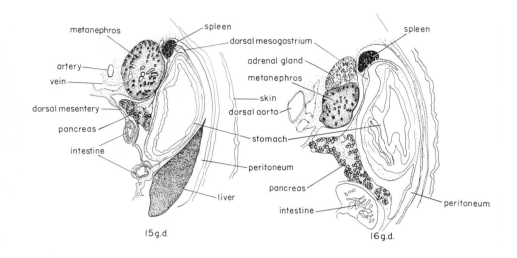

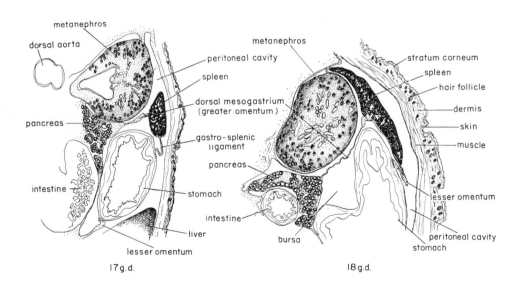

DEVELOPMENT OF THE SPLEEN

RESPIRATORY SYSTEM: By gestation day $8\frac{1}{2}$ the first pharyngeal pouch is formed; the second pouch and indications of the laryngo-tracheal groove appear on day $9\frac{1}{2}$; the third pouch develops by day 10 as the laryngo-tracheal groove extends into a pair of lung buds. At this time the trachea separates from the esophagus, the 4th and 6th pharyngeal pouches are formed, and larynx and trachea are distinguishable. On day $10\frac{1}{2}$, the right lung bud is slightly in advance of the left. By day 11, the larynx acquires arytenoid lateral swellings and the connection with the trachea is a slit, the upper part of the larynx is completely compressed, and bronchi are formed. By day $11\frac{1}{2}$, the pharyngeal pouches close off, there are arytenoid and epiglottis swellings, the tracheal-pharyngeal connection is very narrow, the bronchi have 2 or 3 buds, and the pleuro-peritoneal septa develop. On day $12\frac{1}{2}$, the cervical sinus closes, the trachea is occluded, the right bronchus has both secondary and tertiary buds (with fewer in the left) and the pleuro-peritoneal cavity persists. At 13 days, the epiglottis is separated from the arytenoid bodies by a transverse groove, the epiglottis grows separately from the lower larynx (which is occluded) the bronchial tree has many branches and buds, and the pleuro-peritoneal connection is narrowing. By $14\frac{1}{2}$ days, the larynx is enlarged, the bronchial tree branched further, and lungs are lobed and vascularized. There is a hyoid but no laryngeal or tracheal cartilage, and the diaphragm now separates the peritoneal and pleural cavities. By day 16, the epiglottis projects into the nasopharyngeal meatus, the laryngeal and tracheal cartilages appear, and the larynx acquires a ventricle with secondary grooves. By 17 days the epiglottis remains as a nasopharyngeal duct with pre-cartilage, the laryngeal ventricle expands, and the lung tissue differentiates. By day 19, just before birth, the cavity of the lower larynx and trachea becomes continuous with the ventricle of the upper part, the cartilaginous epiglottis at the root of the tongue is covered by the soft palate, the nares are open so the air passage to the lung is now complete and the lungs can become inflated with air. The mouse fetus can be delivered by caeserian section at this time.

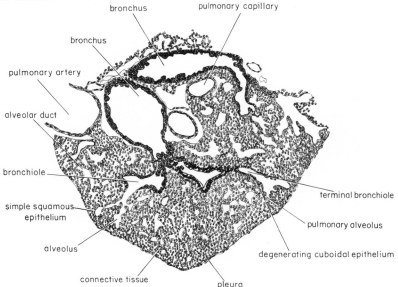

**DEVELOPING PULMONARY LOBULE
IN LUNG OF MOUSE at 17 g.d.**

CIRCULATORY SYSTEM: As early as 7 days there are paired cardiac mesenchymal primordia which are fusing. By $7\frac{1}{2}$ days there is a pleuroperitoneal cavity that is crescent-shaped, and endothelial cells between the endoderm and the splanchnic mesoderm. By 8 days, a tubular heart with the beginning of myocardial contractions appears; the tubular portion of the heart elongating and being bent into an S-shape, the atrial and bulbo-ventricular areas clearly defined with the latter contracting. By $8\frac{1}{2}$ days the first pair of aortic arches appear; and by 9 days aortic arch #2, cardiac veins, the sinus venosus, umbilical veins, the atrium, ventricular loop, arterial trunk all develop and the circulation is established. By $9\frac{1}{2}$ days, the first three aortic arches are prominent, and the interventricular sulcus is formed; aortic arch #1 begins to regress, #4 is forming, and by 10 days, paired heart chambers may be seen. At $10\frac{1}{2}$ days of the four pairs of aortic arches #1 and #2 regress as #3 and #4 enlarge and become well developed, #5 and #6 begin to form, the atrial septum appears as well as the atrio-ventricular canal. By day 11, aortic arch #7 (pulmonary) forms, the interventricular septum appears, the atrio-ventricular cushions and septa form, small pulmonary veins grow into the left atrium, aortic arch #5 regresses, common cardinal veins appear, and the hepatic vein collects blood from the vitelline and umbilical veins through the liver. The atrial septum is not complete at this time but the dorsal and ventral atrio-ventricular cushions form. Aortic arches #3 and #4 are very well developed and symmetrical, #5 disappears, #6 is asymmetrical with the right part narrowing, #7 is branching off of #6. By 12 days, the foramen ovale forms, the atrial septum is almost complete, the cervical sinus closes, the aortic trunk is partially divided into systemic and pulmonary stems, the internal carotids and pulmonaries enlarge, and the auricle forms. By $12\frac{1}{2}$ days, the heart and aortic trunk are longitudinally divided and the inferior cardinal veins are formed. Aortic arch #3 is symmetrical, #4 has only the left portion which is the large systemic arch with right #4 being small and leading to the vertebrae and subclavian arteries of the

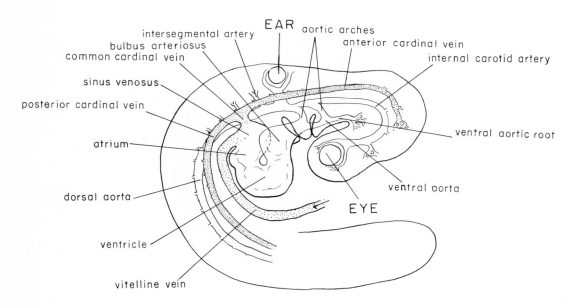

**DIAGRAM OF HEART AND CIRCULATORY SYSTEM OF RIGHT SIDE
9 DAY MOUSE EMBRYO**

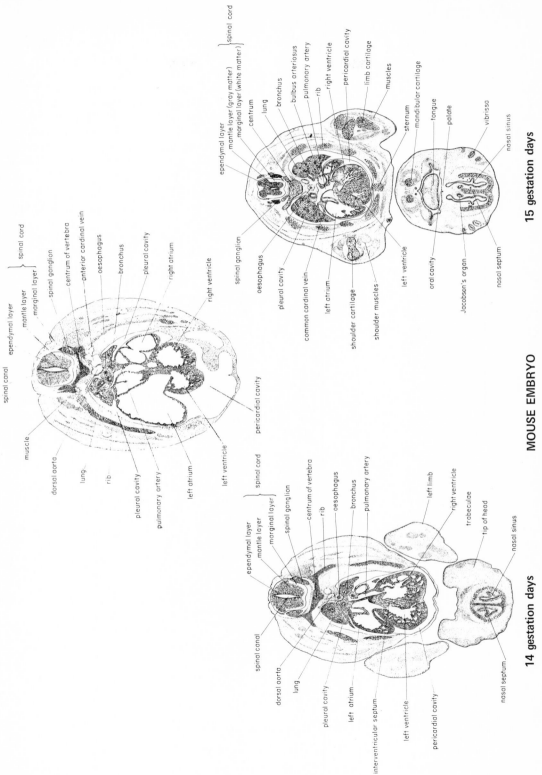

MOUSE EMBRYO

Transverse section through cardiac level

15 gestation days

14 gestation days

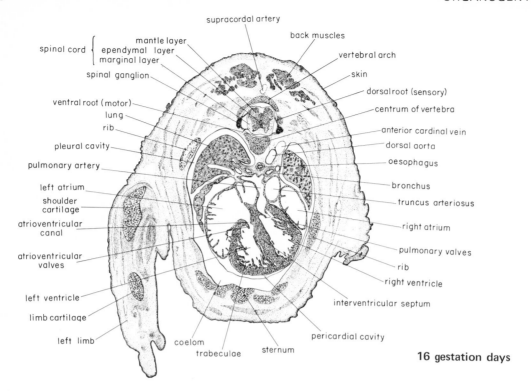

supracordal artery
back muscles
mantle layer
spinal cord { ependymal layer
marginal layer
spinal ganglion
ventral root (motor)
lung
rib
pleural cavity
pulmonary artery
left atrium
shoulder cartilage
atrioventricular canal
atrioventricular valves
left ventricle
limb cartilage
left limb
coelom
trabeculae
sternum

vertebral arch
skin
dorsal root (sensory)
centrum of vertebra
anterior cardinal vein
dorsal aorta
oesophagus
bronchus
truncus arteriosus
right atrium
pulmonary valves
rib
right ventricle
interventricular septum
pericardial cavity

16 gestation days

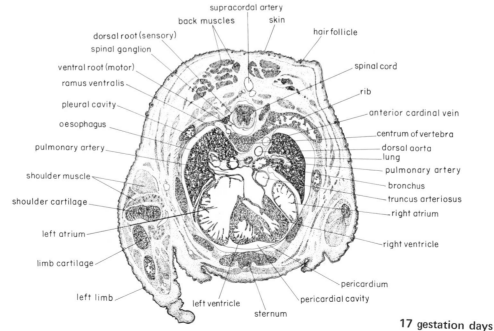

supracordal artery
back muscles
skin
dorsal root (sensory)
spinal ganglion
ventral root (motor)
ramus ventralis
pleural cavity
oesophagus
pulmonary artery
shoulder muscle
shoulder cartilage
left atrium
limb cartilage
left limb
left ventricle
sternum

hair follicle
spinal cord
rib
anterior cardinal vein
centrum of vertebra
dorsal aorta
lung
pulmonary artery
bronchus
truncus arteriosus
right atrium
right ventricle
pericardium
pericardial cavity

17 gestation days

MOUSE EMBRYO
Transverse section through cardiac level

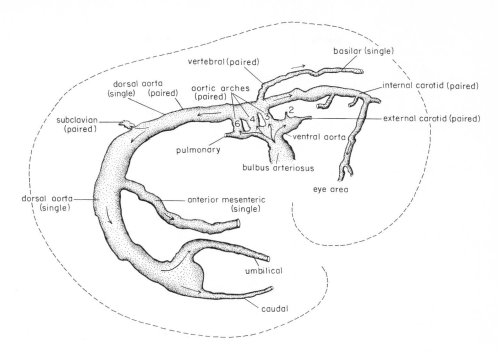

ARTERIES OF 11 DAY MOUSE EMBRYO OF RIGHT SIDE
(graphic reconstruction)

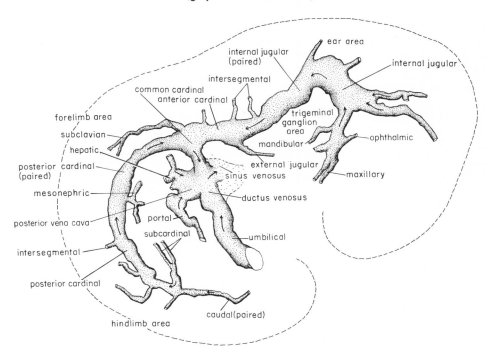

VEINS OF 11 DAY MOUSE EMBRYO OF RIGHT SIDE
(graphic reconstruction)

right side.   The left portion of #6 goes to the dorsal aorta and the right portion of #6 regresses except for connections with the pulmonary arteries. By 13 days, the dorsal aorta is reduced between aortic arches #3 and #4, the aortic trunks separate, the inferior vena cava collects blood from the renal, vitelline, and umbilical veins and includes the hepatic vein, the right inferior cardinal vein is interrupted and the left is reduced.   The aortic arch #3 is the only symmetric pair left, having lingual and carotid branches. By 14 days, the right portion of #4 loses its connection with the dorsal aorta and supplies the right subclavian and vertebral arteries.   The left portion of aortic arch #4 further enlarges as the systemic arch and receives a duct from #6 left. After giving off the left subclavian and vertebral arteries it becomes the descending aorta while the interatrial foramen persists.   By $14\frac{1}{2}$ days the fetal circulatory system is complete and functioning, with the large vitelline circuit in addition to the allantoic (umbilical) vessels.   At birth the vitelline and umbilical (allantoic) veins collapse and degenerate, the oval and interatrial foramina close, and the arterial duct (#6 left) regresses and disappears.

BLOOD OF THE MOUSE FETUS: Blood islands may be seen in the splanchnic mesoderm of the 7 and 8 day mouse embryo and are the only source of red cells for the embryo through day 11. This yolk sac hematopoeisis provides the primitive generation of erythrocytes which are exceptionally large nucleated cells.   They may have volumes some 4 or 5 times that of erythrocytes of the adult mouse, and may be compared with pre-erythrocytes and normoblasts of bone marrow.   During days 11 and 12 many may be seen in mitosis, but by day 14 their nuclei are more likely to be pycnotic.   After day 15 these cells tend to diminish rapidly.   Active hemopoiesis in liver, spleen and bone marrow occurs only after the circulation is established on day 9.   From day 12 through 16 the liver is almost exclusively the fetal hematopoietic organ, and may contain hematopoietic foci even after birth.   This is true to a lesser degree for the spleen and marrow, with the spleen showing erythropoiesis and myelopoiesis by day 15 and the bone marrow by day 16.   The spleen is the first site for myelopoiesis, followed by bone marrow myeloid hematopoiesis.   Within the liver at 15 days may be found some myoblasts, and neutrophilic and basophilic leukocytes.   The erythroid precursors are quite similar to those found in bone marrow, and are of several distinct sizes.   Hepatically derived erythrocytes are enucleated and measure about 8 microns in diameter, being slightly larger than the 6 micron erythrocytes of the adult. Lymphocytes are first seen in the developing thymus.   It is difficult to obtain sufficient fetal blood for proper analysis before day 17, so that the following data are from 15 males and 15 females of 17 days gestation.

Fetal mice were removed from the uterus and their amniotic sacs, and the mucous was removed from their noses to allow normal respiration.   The mice were kept alive without anesthesia for the few minutes required until the blood was collected.   It was usually difficult to obtain from a single mouse enough blood for the entire count, so that two litter-mate mice were used.   The hemoglobin, red cell count, and platelets were determined from one mouse while the white cell count and the differentials were taken from the other.   The data below are taken from 15 fetuses of each sex, so represent an average.   For comparison similar counts are given for adults of both sexes at 9 weeks of age, all of the same strain.

TABLE 7

BLOOD ANALYSIS OF FETAL AND ADULT MICE*

| | 17 DAY FETUSES | | 9 WEEK OLD ADULTS | |
	MALES (15)	FEMALES (15)	MALES (25)	FEMALES (25)
Hemoglobin	8.9	8.3	14.1	15.1
RBC (Erythrocytes)	3,438,666	3,244,000	9,140,800	9,700,300
WBC (Leukocytes)	1,720	1,533	10,520	9,976
Platelets:	453,333	454,000	1,361,600	1,342,000
Neutrophils:Segmented	21.9	25.1	27.1	23.1
Neutrophils:Stabophils	10.3	7.1	1.1	0.4
Neutrophils:Metamyelocytes	1.5	0.8	0.0	0.0
Neutrophils:Myelocytes	0.1	0.1	0.0	0.0
Eosinophils:	2.5	1.0	3.5	4.1
Eosinophils:Meta	0.5	0.0	0.0	0.0
Monocytes:	18.7	19.7	5.8	4.3
Monocytes:Young	0.9	1.1	0.0	0.0
Lymphocytes:	31.8	30.4	61.5	67.0
Lymphocytes:Young	2.1	2.4	0.2	0.1
Blasts:	0.5	0.8	0.0	0.0
Histiocytes:	0.3	0.1	0.0	0.0
Phagocytes:	0.4	0.7	0.0	0.0
Granular-Vacuolated Cells:	0.9	4.1	0.0	0.0
Early Type Ring Nuclear Cell:	5.3	4.6	0.04	0.1
Double Nucleated Lymphocytes:	0.1	0.1	0.5	0.5
Nucleated Erythrocytes:	48.6	53.7	0.0	0.0
Unidentifiable Cells:	2.0	0.4	0.0	0.0

* Blood analyses made by Csilla Somogyi.

Differential values are in percentages.

The blood was generally taken from the jugular vein which is always plainly visible through the thin and translucent skin. The mouse was held in the left hand, the index finger pushing its head back and the thumb on the lower body. The jugular vein was pierced with especially fine scissors. The three suction pipettes were prepared in advance, complete with rubber tubing which allowed single hand manipulation. A single drop of blood was found to be enough for the differential count smear, after which the fetuses were disposed of by over-anesthetization.

Due to the fragility of the blood cells, differential counts were difficult to make, many of the cells being damaged by the smearing process. This was especially true of day 16, the cells being younger. Generally two smears were counted on day 17 to get the 100 cells. The erythrocytes were partially of the fetal type, appearing larger in the smears. Much stippling, polychromatophilia, and nucleated erythrocytes were seen (see accompanying photographs).

Counts at birth (day 19) showed a marked increase in hemoglobin, ery-throcytes, a slight increase in the leukocytes, a great increase in neutrophils, a decrease in lymphocytes and, of course, a decrease in nucleated reds and the younger leukocyte forms.

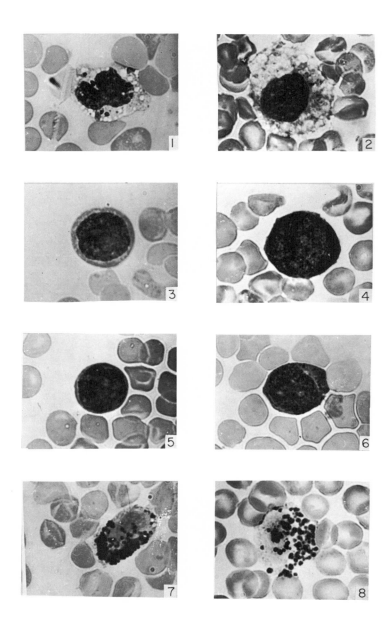

BLOOD TYPES OF THE 17 DAY FETAL MOUSE

Figs. 1, 2 — Granulated-vacuolated cells
Figs. 3 to 6 — Blasts: note dark cytoplasm and nucleoli
Figs. 7, 8 — Mast cells; tissue basophils

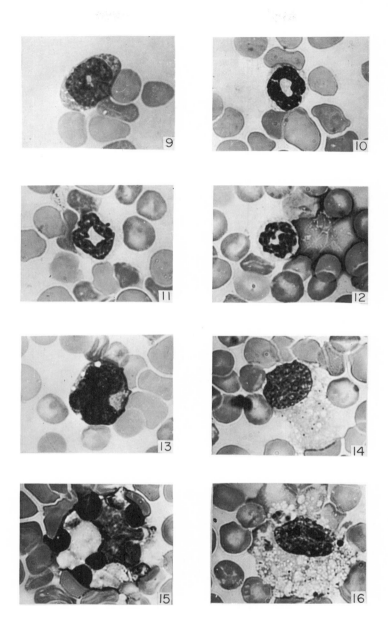

BLOOD TYPES OF THE 17 DAY FETAL MOUSE

Figs. 9 to 12 — Neutrophils; showing partial developmental
Fig. 13   —   Young monocyte with vacuoles
Fig. 14   —   Granular histiocyte, normally found only in adult bone marrow
Fig. 15   —   Phagocyte with inclusions
Fig. 16   —   Phagocytic histiocyte, not often found in mature blood

THE EXCRETORY SYSTEM: By 8 days, the nephrogenic cords appear, and by 10 days (in frontal sections) one may see the pronephric tubules and collecting pronephric ducts, suspended within the coelom. The tubules are enmeshed in mesenchyme, and by $10\frac{1}{2}$ days the nephric ducts make contact with the cloaca, and the mesonephroi begin to form tubules. By 11 days nephrotomes can be found, some with apparent nephrostomes opening into the coelom (peritoneal cavity). Each mesonephros consists of crowded nephric units not yet differentiated. The anterior tubules appear to be attached to nephric ducts, there are no renal corpuscles, and the metanephric urethral buds grow out from the posterior part of the nephric ducts. The cloaca begins to divide and some anterior nephrostomes may persist. By 12 days the transient mesonephric tubules will be seen forming and some will be degenerating, just dorsal to the gonad primordium. The pronephroi begin to degenerate but their ducts remain in the female as oviducts. The mesonephric (Wolffian) ducts can be seen, clearly lined with cuboidal epithelium and lying posterior to the tubules. They connect with the uro-genital sinus. The metanephroi will also be seen more posteriorly without any association with the mesonephroi. The metanephric ducts leading to the cloaca arise from the pelvis of each kidney with two branches (calyces) and are known as the future ureters. The cloaca is partially separated into the intestinal and uro-genital parts. Thus by 12 days the mouse embryo has portions of all three of its embryonic excretory systems. By $12\frac{1}{2}$ days the mesonephric tubules are scattered and only the anterior few connect with the mesonephric ducts. Posteriorly they are the vestigial renal corpuscles. The mesonephroi are shorter than the associated gonad primordia, and their ducts are short, and open into the urogenital portion of the cloaca. The external urethral papilla and perineum form. By 13 days there remain a few mesonephric tubules, and in the male each Wolffian (or mesonephric) duct is transformed into a vas

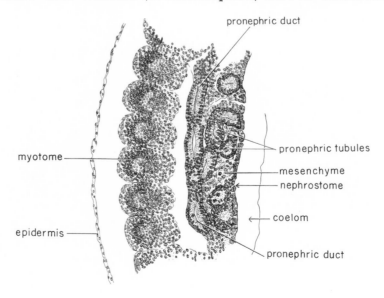

MOUSE EXCRETORY SYSTEM at 10 g.d.
(Sagittal section)

deferens. Each metanephros becomes highly tubular, and its ureter is a single, large tube clearly lined with cuboidal epithelium. By 13 days, the anterior and the cloacal membrane form as the metanephroi differentiate. By $13\frac{1}{2}$ days the mesonephroi regress, except for their anterior parts which become the epididymi of the male. The metanephroi move anteriorly behind the gonads and make contact with the adrenals, forming tubules and ampullae. The mesonephric and metanephric ducts open separately into the urogenital sinus. At 14 days the very close proximity of each metanephros and the gonad is obvious, and within the metanephros are collecting tubules and glomeruli with their Bowman's capsules. Thus relatively early in the development of the mouse, the true kidney is actively differentiating. Much of the kidney is mesenchyme and closely associated with it now is the adrenal gland. The ureters connect with the bladder and the cloacal membrane is beneath the urethral papilla. By 15 days the metanephros is encapsulated and its internal organization is that of a vertebrate kidney. By 16 days the two ureters can be seen expanding into the pelves of the kidneys and the medullary and cortical regions become distinguishable. The urogenital sinus and rectum are separated and the perineum develops further. By 17 and 18 days the kidney is fully differentiated and able to function, but excretion by the fetus continues to be primarily via the placenta.

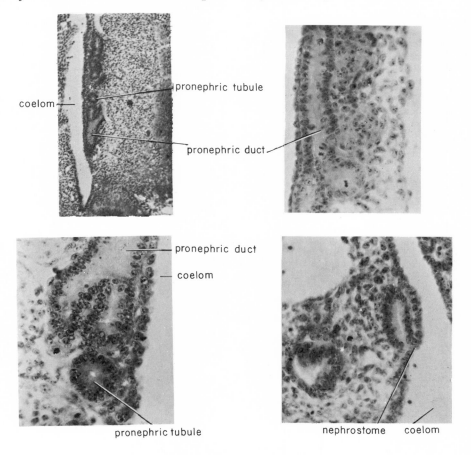

MOUSE PRONEPHRIC KIDNEY at 11 g.d.

(Photographs)

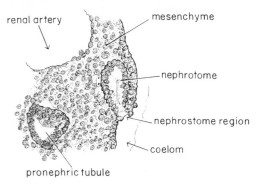

renal artery

mesenchyme

nephrotome

nephrostome region

coelom

pronephric tubule

EXCRETORY SYSTEM at 11 g.d.
under high power (x-section)

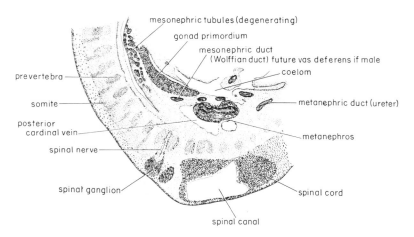

mesonephric tubules (degenerating)

gonad primordium

mesonephric duct
(Wolffian duct) future vas deferens if male

coelom

prevertebra

somite

metanephric duct (ureter)

posterior
cardinal vein

metanephros

spinal nerve

spinal ganglion

spinal cord

spinal canal

MOUSE EXCRETORY SYSTEM at 12 g.d.
(Sagittal section)

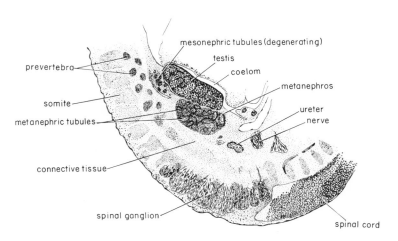

mesonephric tubules (degenerating)

testis

prevertebra

coelom

metanephros

somite

metanephric tubules

ureter
nerve

connective tissue

spinal ganglion

spinal cord

MOUSE EXCRETORY SYSTEM at 13 g.d.
(Sagittal section)

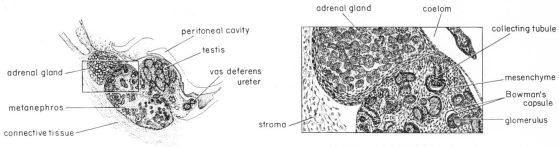

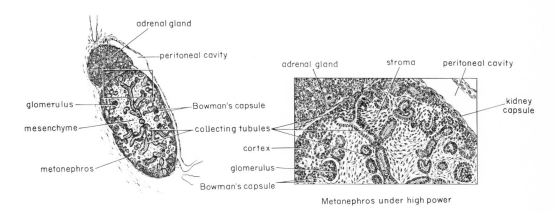

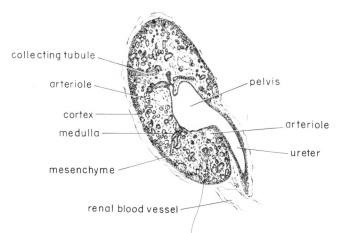

MOUSE EXCRETORY SYSTEM at 14 g.d.
(Sagittal section)

Metanephros under high power

MOUSE EXCRETORY SYSTEM at 15 g.d.
(Sagittal section)

Metanephros under high power

MOUSE EXCRETORY SYSTEM at 16 g.d.
(Sagittal section)
no mesonephros remaining

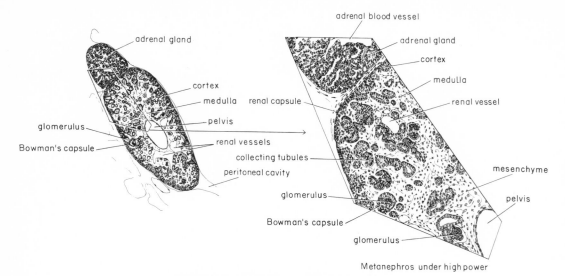

MOUSE EXCRETORY SYSTEM at 16 g.d.
(Sagittal section)

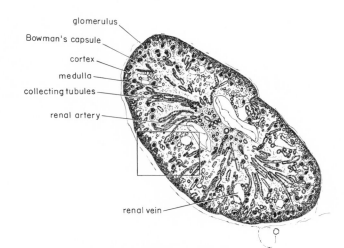

MOUSE EXCRETORY SYSTEM at 17 g.d.
(Sagittal section)

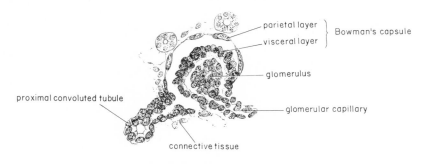

MOUSE EXCRETORY SYSTEM at 18 g.d.

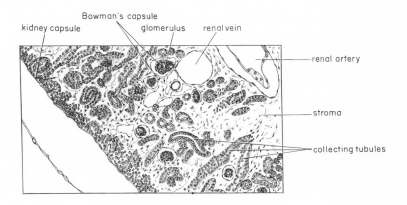

KIDNEY under high power

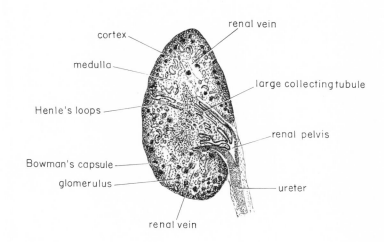

MOUSE KIDNEY at 18 g.d.
(x-section)

THE MUSCULAR SYSTEM: By as early as $5\frac{1}{2}$ to 6 days paired mesocardial primordia appear and cardial myoblasts by $7\frac{1}{2}$ days, with myocardial contractions as early as 8 days. By $7\frac{1}{2}$ days myotomes arise from somites in the cervical region and by 11 days myotomes appear with longitudinally directed myoblasts with ventral processes in some. By 13 days, the myoblasts show active proliferation and somite muscle fibrils can be found on day $14\frac{1}{2}$. Skeletal muscles become contractile, myosin synthesis is accelerated by day 15, and cross striated myofibrils are seen in the development of all of the musculature by 16 days. PAS - positive, diatase digestible material can be found uniformly distributed in the myo-tubes between days 15 and 16. Secondary fibers increase rapidly on days 17 and 18 but the diameter remains less than in the primary fibers in most muscles. Spindles may be seen developing in many muscles, containing 2 to 4 fibers. By 19 days the secondary fibers are well developed in most muscles, and both types of fibers are in the myotube stage. Another or tertiary fiber now appears, developing between the primary and secondary fibers. Muscle fibers are changing their shape to that found in the post-natal mouse. At birth some secondary fibers exceed the diameter of the primary fibers, the intercellular space is reduced, myotubes are still found even in tertiary fibers. The spindles usually consist of from three to five fibers. (See Wirsen & Larsson '64.)

THE GONADS:

The Testes: From 10 to 100 primordial germ cells may be found in the presumptive male mouse embryo in its yolk sac endoderm at $7\frac{1}{2}$ to 8 days gestation. These cells continue to undergo mitoses but while doing so they migrate via the gut mesentery and their own motility at about $8\frac{1}{2}$-9.0 days to reach the dorsal mesenteries and the left and right coelomic angles by 10 days. Immediately thereafter, by $10\frac{1}{2}$ days, the gonad primordia form close to the mesonephroi, in anticipation of the arrival of the migrating germ cells. At 11 days

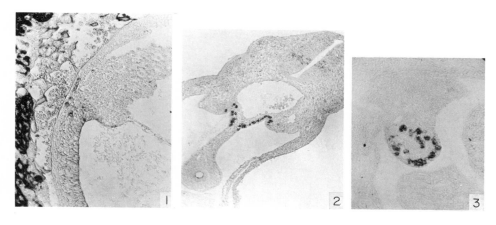

GERM CELL MIGRATION

Fig. 1 —   8 day mouse — stained for alkaline phosphatase
Fig. 2 — 10 day mouse — stained for alkaline phosphatase
Fig. 3 — 13 day mouse — stained for alkaline phosphatase

(from Mintz)

the gonad primordia are indistinguishable as to sex and all of the germ cells have reached their destination by $11\frac{1}{2}$ days. During transit their number increases to well over 5,000 cells, and these are believed to be the sole progenitors of the Type A stem cell spermatogonia of the adult testis. At 12 days the genital (germinal) ridge and newly arrived primordial germ cells appear as condensations of cells ventral to and apparently closely associated with the mesonephric masses. They project into the coelom and consist of blastemas containing all the primordial germ cells, often in the process of dividing. In both male and female the origins and migration of these primordial germ cells are identical, but now their organization and distribution begin to give the clue to the presumptive sex. In the males the primordial germ cells tend to become centrally located almost immediately. By 13 days the genital ridges enlarge considerably with interstitial tissue beginning to be distinguishable from the sex cords of the testis. At this time, the epithelium covering the genital ridge of the presumptive testis develops a slight photophatase-positive reaction. The genital ridge remains closely associated with the mesonephros and is surrounded by germinal epithelium. By 14 days each testis cord will show early spermatogenesis, particularly in the division of Type A spermatogonia. By $14\frac{1}{2}$ days gestation the interstitial tissue and the germinal epithelium are clearly defined. By 15 days the testis has prominent sex cords, each of which will become a seminiferous tubule as spermatogenesis begins. The cords now seem to contain rather uniform but indifferent cells, some of which are precursors of spermatogenetic cells and others of Sertoli cells. Gonocytes increase in size and in

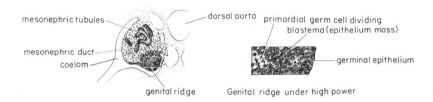

PREDIFFERENTIATED MOUSE GONAD at 12 g.d.

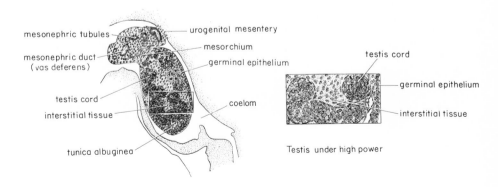

MOUSE TESTIS at 13 g.d.

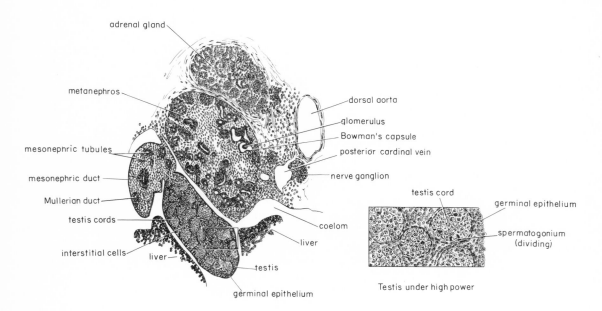

MOUSE TESTIS at 14 g.d.

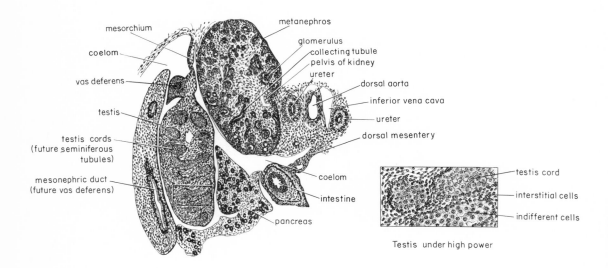

MOUSE TESTIS at 15 g.d.

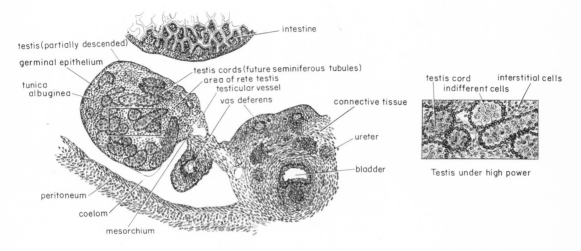

testis(partially descended)
germinal epithelium
tunica albuginea
testis cords(future seminiferous tubules)
area of rete testis
testicular vessel
vas deferens
intestine
connective tissue
ureter
bladder
peritoneum
coelom
mesorchium

testis cord   interstitial cells
indifferent cells

Testis under high power

MOUSE TESTIS at 16 g.d.

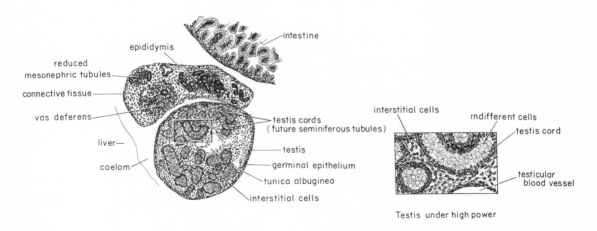

epididymis
reduced mesonephric tubules
connective tissue
vas deferens
liver
coelom
intestine
testis cords (future seminiferous tubules)
testis
germinal epithelium
tunica albuginea
interstitial cells

interstitial cells   indifferent cells   testis cord
testicular blood vessel

Testis under high power

MOUSE TESTIS at 17 g.d.

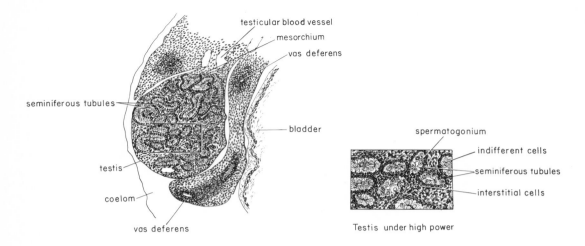

MOUSE TESTIS at 18 g.d.

their cytoplasmic inclusions, are centrally placed in the sex cords, and divide frequently in early fetal life. They divide in the fetal testis until day 16 or 17 when all divisions cease, to be resumed after birth. They continue maturation during the first post-natal weeks and become immature type A spermatogonia which then enlarge and initiate the cycle of spermatogenesis. The indifferent cells are mononucleate, continually divide, and after spermatogenesis begins, the remaining indifferent cells become Sertoli cells. Spermatogenesis in the mouse actively begins by 9 days after birth. Each vas deferens, and remnants of the associated Wolffian body may be seen close by the testes in sections of the fetus at this time. The Mullerian (pronephric) ducts persist in both sexes but function only in the female (as oviducts). The secondary sex characters begin differentiation, the males acquiring seminal vesicles and prostates with the regression of other and vestigial gonoducts by day 17. There is not much change during the next two days except in the enlargement of the seminiferous tubules, and vascularization of the tunica albuginea. Sex at birth can be determined by the distance between the anus and urethral papilla which is greater in the male than in the female.

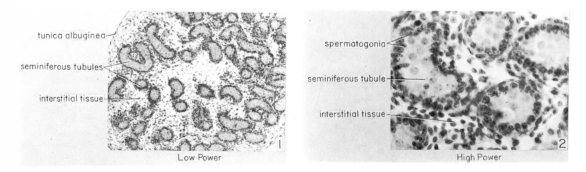

MOUSE TESTIS AT BIRTH

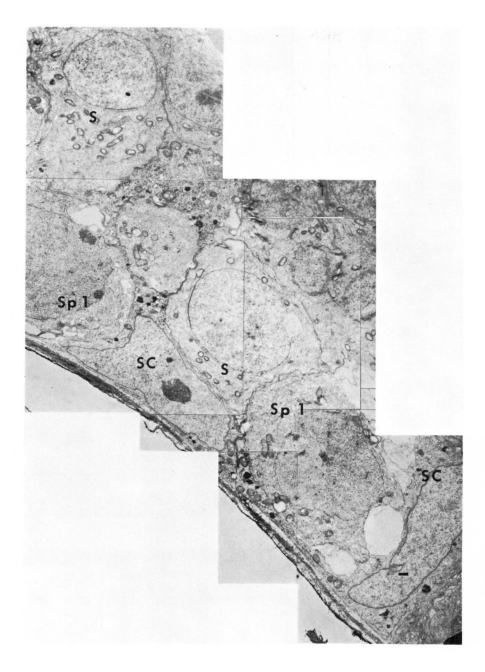

Electron microscope composite of peripheral portion of the seminiferous tubule of the mouse. The primary spermatocytes (Sp 1), adjacent to the external limiting membrane, are identified by the presence of synaptinemal complexes within the nuclei. They are embedded in the Sertoli cells (SC) and bounded centrally by the spermatids (S).

(Courtesy Dr. P. J. Gardner, from Gardner & Holyoke, Anat. Rec. 130:391-401, 1964.)

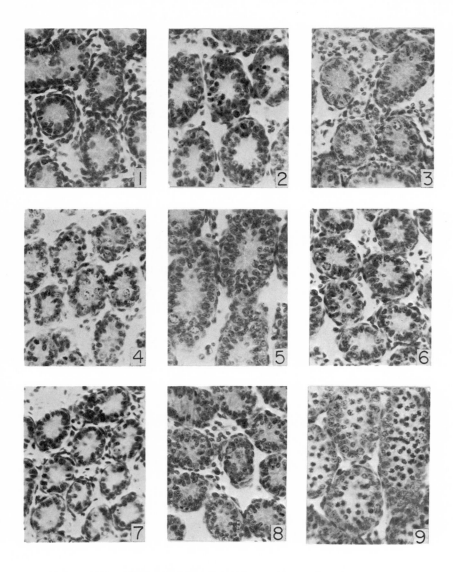

NEO-NATAL DEVELOPMENT OF MOUSE TESTIS

Fig. 1 — Section of testis of newborn mouse. Note small tubules, uniformity of spermatogenetic cells, and scattered interstitial tissue. No maturation.

Fig. 2 — Mouse testis at one day of age. Note beginning of lumen of seminiferous tubules.

Fig. 3 — Mouse testis at two days of age.

Fig. 4 — Mouse testis at 3 days of age.

Fig. 5 — Mouse testis at 4 days of age. Still no active differentiation of spermatogenetic cells.

Fig. 6 — Mouse testis at 6 days of age. Still relatively little interstitial tissue.

Fig. 7 — Mouse testis at 7 days of age.

Fig. 8 — Mouse testis at 8 days of age.

Fig. 9 — Mouse testis at 9 days of age and the beginning of active spermatogenesis. Note most cells with distinct chromosomes.

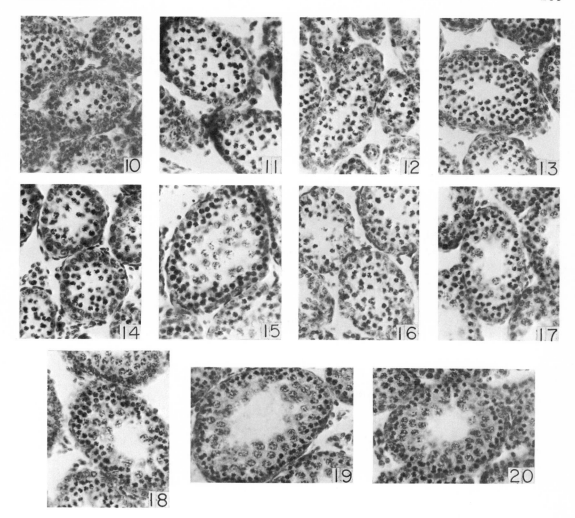

NEO-NATAL DEVELOPMENT OF MOUSE TESTIS

Fig. 10 — Mouse testis at 10 days of age. Note enlarging tubule with many cells in mitosis.

Fig. 11 — Further enlargement of tubules, and spermatogenetic cells rather scattered.

Fig. 12 — Mouse at 12 days of age, Sertoli cells first become obvious and most cells in spermatogonial stages.

Fig. 13 — Mouse testis at 13 days of age.

Fig. 14 — Mouse testis at 14 days of age.

Fig. 15 — Mouse testis at 15 days of age. Note many large primary spermatocytes loose within the seminiferous tubule, and spermatagonial stages at periphery.

Fig. 16 — Various stages of spermatogenesis seen at 16 days of age.

Fig. 17 — Secondary spermatocytes appear at about 17 days of age.

Fig. 18 — Spermatogonia and spermatocytes are seen at 18 days, and the tubule is much enlarged.

Figs. 19 & 20 — Still no spermatids or spermatozoa, but many primary and secondary spermatocytes and very much enlarged seminiferous tubules.

The Ovaries: The origin and migration of the primordial germ cells to their final site is the same in both sexes. In the female some 10 to 100 primordial germ cells arise at $7\frac{1}{2}$ to 8 days in the yolk sac splanchnopleure and migrate, via the gut mesentery, to the genital ridges during which process they increase manifold by mitosis. By day 13 the genital ridge is much enlarged by the aggregation of the migrating and mitotically active primordial germ cells, some of which will be in leptotene stage. The degenerating mesonephroi are nearby. The ostia are formed but the temporarily solid oviducts extend toward

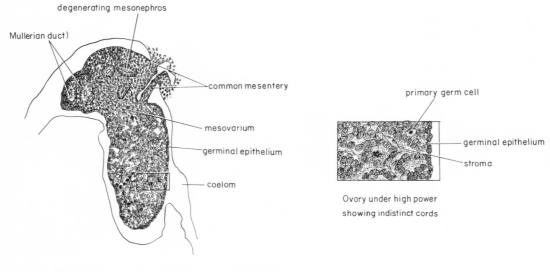

OVARY at 13 g.d.

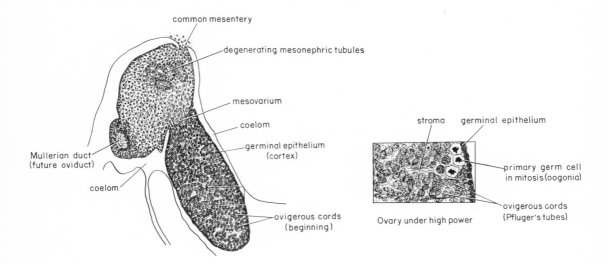

OVARY at 14 g.d.

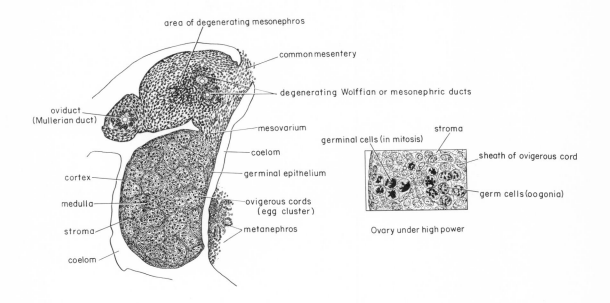

OVARY at 15 g.d.

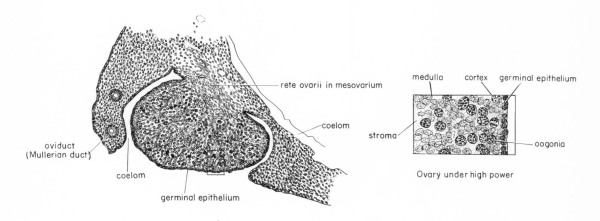

OVARY at 16 g.d.

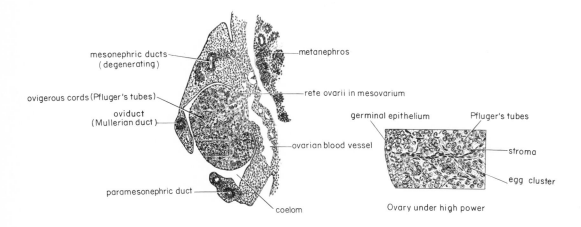

mesonephric ducts (degenerating)

metanephros

ovigerous cords (Pfluger's tubes)

rete ovarii in mesovarium

oviduct (Mullerian duct)

germinal epithelium

Pfluger's tubes

stroma

ovarian blood vessel

egg cluster

paramesonephric duct

coelom

Ovary under high power

OVARY at 17 g.d.

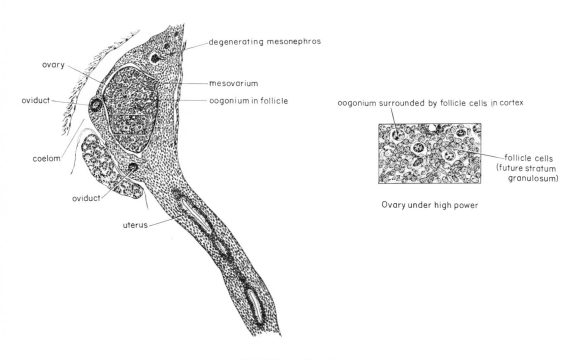

ovary

degenerating mesonephros

mesovarium

oviduct

oogonium in follicle

oogonium surrounded by follicle cells in cortex

coelom

follicle cells (future stratum granulosum)

oviduct

uterus

Ovary under high power

OVARY at 18 g.d.

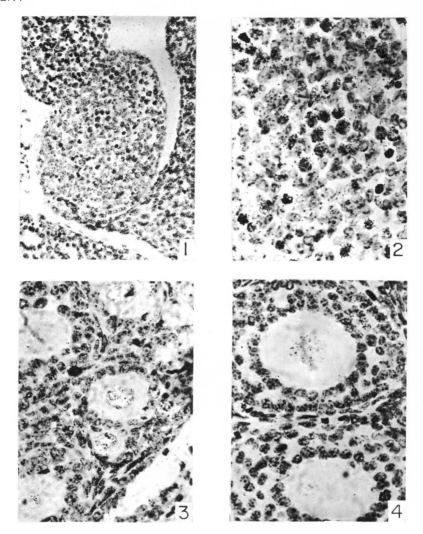

Fig. 1 — Ovary on 16th day of embryonic life.

Fig. 2 — 10 μCi tritiated thymidine was injected into the amniotic sac of a mouse embryo on the 15th day of pregnancy. The embryo was killed 24 hours later and an autoradiograph prepared of its ovary (Feulgen stain; K_2 liquid emulsion, Ilford; exposure 7 days). A group of labelled oöcytes in leptotene is seen in the center.

Fig. 3 — Tritiated thymidine injected on 14th day of embryonic life. The mouse was killed 7 days after birth. In the autoradiograph many labelled oöcytes are seen indicating that the oöcyte that synthesized its DNA on the 14th day of embryonic life persists in the post partum ovary.

Fig. 4 — Labelled oöcyte in a growing follicle of a 14 day old mouse. The radioactive DNA precursor had been injected on the 14th day of embryonic life.

(Courtesy Dr. Hannah Paters, Copenhagen, Denmark)

the cloaca. Germinal epithelium can be distinguished from the internal stroma (mesenchyme) and occasionally primary germ cells may be seen dividing. The early organization within the genital ridge is such that the germ cells are peripherally located in the presumptive ovary. At 14 days oögonia are in mitosis directly beneath the germinal epithelium. Stroma is abundant. The oviducts by-pass the nephric ducts to reach the pelvis and the urogenital sinus by 14 days. Soon (15 days) the oögonia appear in clusters, surrounded by a sheath of ovigerous cords, and loose mesenchymal stroma. By 16 days the cortex and medulla differentiate so that the presumptive sex of the female can be verified. Oögonia are abundant and many begin their maturation (synaptene) by day 16. By 17 days some will be in pachytene and others in diplotene and diakenesis. They cluster toward the cortex, as Pfluger's tubes, which are not really tubular at all. The females acquire their utero-vaginal canals. By 18 days follicle cells appear clustered around a selected oögonium (often in dictyate stage) that is destined to become an ovum. All presumptive female germ cells enter meiosis before birth, and there is no evidence of epithelial regeneration. Until recently the pre-natal preparation of mouse gametes was not clearly understood. It seems quite definite that such preparation is complex and crucial to the proper production of functional gametes during the later reproductive life of the mouse. Effects on these prenatal primordial germ cells may be mediated through their environment or through more complex and possibly unpredictable genetic factors. Some of these undetermined factors are the origin of the primordial germ cells in the yolk sac endoderm in the first place; the means of transit to the genital ridges, whether actively or passively; the factors which insure the synchronous onset of meiotic prophase in the oöcytes; the mechanism for meiotic pairing of allelomorphic chromosomes; and the relationship of the environment and genetic factors in gonad differentiation. The frequency in which ovo-testis combinations are found suggests that there is ontogenetically little difference in the production of sex dimorphism in the mouse. Finally, there is such rapid proliferation of the primordial germ cell during transit that the challenging question arises as to what controls the size of the ultimate gamete population. Thus there are many pages of normal embryology yet to be written.

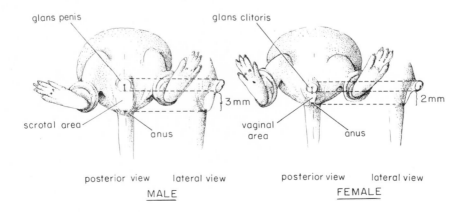

EXTERNAL GENITALIA OF THE NEW BORN MOUSE

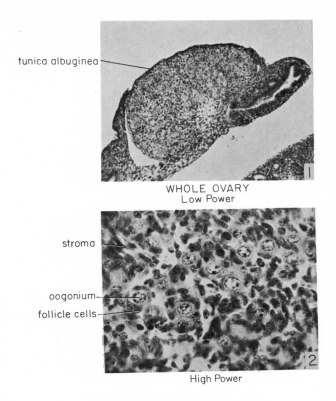

tunica albuginea

WHOLE OVARY
Low Power

stroma

oogonium

follicle cells

High Power

MOUSE OVARY AT BIRTH

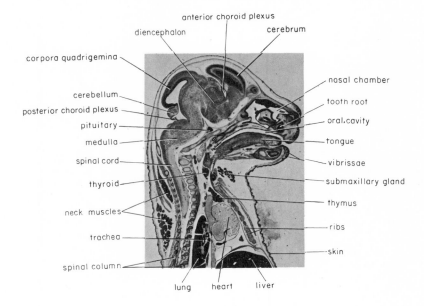

anterior choroid plexus

diencephalon   cerebrum

corpora quadrigemina

nasal chamber

cerebellum   tooth root

posterior choroid plexus   oral cavity

pituitary   tongue

medulla   vibrissae

spinal cord   submaxillary gland

thyroid   thymus

neck muscles   ribs

trachea   skin

spinal column

lung   heart   liver

HEAD AND CHEST OF MOUSE AT BIRTH
(Sagittal section)

Addenda

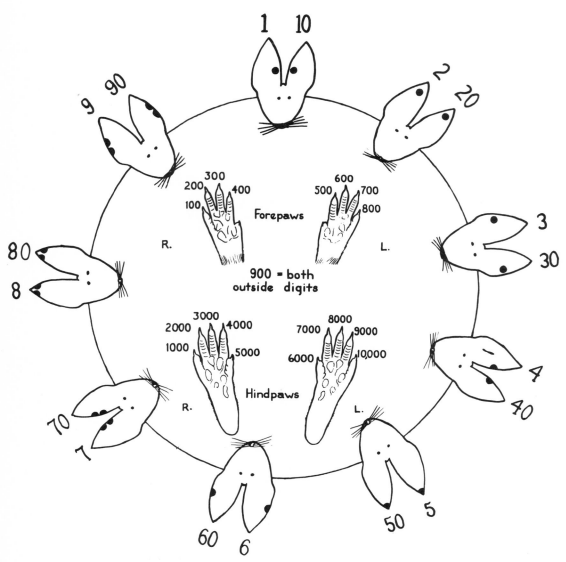

This plan shows how it is possible to mark permanently individual mice up to a total of 10,000. The black spots represent holes punched with an ear punch, and the toes are to be clipped. If this system is followed by all, and a mouse escapes its confines, it can be readily identified and returned to its proper place.

ANESTHESIA DOSAGES FOR ADULT MICE

Veterinarians Nembutal diluted to 10% with distilled water or saline may be injected intra-peritoneally for quick action or intra-muscularly for slower action. Duration about 1 hour.

WEIGHT OF MOUSE	CUBIC CENTIMETERS 10% SOLUTION	WEIGHT OF MOUSE	CUBIC CENTIMETERS 10% SOLUTION
10 grams	0.13	23 grams	0.30
11 ''	0.14	24 ''	0.31
12 ''	0.15	25 ''	0.32
13 ''	0.17	26 ''	0.34
14 ''	0.18	27 ''	0.35
15 ''	0.19	28 ''	0.36
16 ''	0.20	29 ''	0.38
17 ''	0.22	30 ''	0.39
18 ''	0.23	31 ''	0.40
19 ''	0.24	32 ''	0.42
20 ''	0.25	33 ''	0.43
21 ''	0.26	34 ''	0.44
22 ''	0.28	35 ''	0.46

COMPARATIVE AGES OF MOUSE AND HUMAN EMBRYOS*

MOUSE AGE, DAYS	HUMAN AGE, DAYS	MOUSE AGE, DAYS	HUMAN AGE, DAYS
0	1	8 4/5	24 1/3
1	2	9	25 1/2
2	3	9 1/2 − 9 2/3	26
4	4	10	27
5	5 − 6	10 1/2	28 1/2
5 1/2	7 − 8	11	30 3/4
6	9 − 10	11 1/2	33 1/2
6 1/2	11 − 13	12	36
7	14 − 17	12 1/3	36 1/2
7 1/2	18 − 20	13 − 13 1/2	38
8	20.5	14 1/2	47
8 1/3	21.0	15 1/2	65
8 1/2	22.0	16 1/2	84 1/2
8 2/3 − 8 3/4	23.0		

*In part from the author's "Vertebrate Embryology, The Dynamics of Development", Harcourt, Brace & World, Inc., 1964.

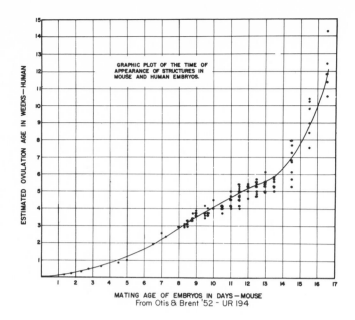

GRAPHIC PLOT OF THE TIME OF
APPEARANCE OF STRUCTURES IN
MOUSE AND HUMAN EMBRYOS.

ESTIMATED OVULATION AGE IN WEEKS—HUMAN

MATING AGE OF EMBRYOS IN DAYS—MOUSE
From Otis & Brent '52 - UR 194

9th day = 13 (9—17)
        Somites

28 days = 3.9 (4—5) mm

10th day = 25 (24—27)
        Somites

32 days = 7.3 (7—8) mm

11th day = 5.4 mm
        CR length

38 days = 10.0 (15—17) mm

12th day = 7.2 mm
        CR length

42 days = 13.0 (22—25) mm

COMPARISON OF MOUSE AND HUMAN EMBRYOS
(Courtesy Alden "Laboratory Atlas of the Mouse Embryo" and
Carnegie Institute of Washington)

EXTRAPOLATION TABLE FOR MOUSE TO RAT EMBRYONIC AGES

MOUSE	RAT	MOUSE	RAT
1	2	8.5 – 9.0	10.5
2	3.25	9.5	11
3	4	10	11.5
4	5	10.25	11.75
4.5	6	10.50	12.125
5	6.75	11	12.5
5.5	7.25	12	13
6.0	7.50	12.5	13.5
6.5	7.75	13.0	14.5
7	8.5	14.5	15.5
7.5	9	15	16
7.75	9.5	16 – 16.5	17 – 18
8	10	17 – 19	19 – 22
Post Partem: 1 to 20	1 to 16	Post Partem: 21+	17+

(These are based upon similarities in embryological development but cannot apply to every minute detail.)

RELATION OF MOUSE EMBRYONIC AGE TO SOMITE NUMBER
AND TO CROWN-RUMP LENGTH*

AGE, DAYS	SOMITES	LENGTH, MM.	AGE, DAYS	SOMITES	LENGTH, MM.
8	1 – 4		12½	49 – 51	8.9
8½	5 – 12	2	13	52 – 60	9.4
9	13 – 20	2.2	13½		9.8
9½	21 – 25	3.3	14½	61 – 64	11.2
10	26 – 28	3.8	15	65	
10½	29 – 36	5.2	15½		13.7
11	37 – 42	6.2	16½		16.1
12	43 – 48	7.2			

*From the author's "Vertebrate Embryology, The Dynamics of Development", Harcourt, Brace & World, Inc., 1964.

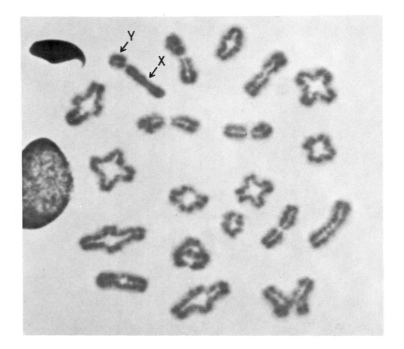

Bivalent chromosomes at late diakinesis in a primary spermatocyte
from a CBA mouse. The heteromorphic XY bivalent is easily recog-
nised. The chromosomes of seven autosomal bivalents are associated
by single terminal chiasmata. In eleven others there is a single sub-
terminal chiasma and in one bivalent, two diasmata. The appearance
differs from cell to cell due to variation in the number and positions
of chiasmata. Air-dried preparation.

(Courtesy Dr. C. E. Ford and Dr. E. P. Evans)

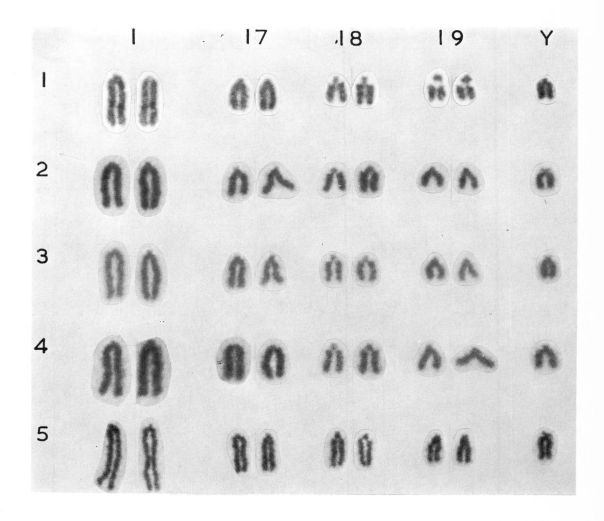

Selected chromosomes from five somatic cells of male CBA mice to demonstrate the distinctiveness of the two shortest pairs of autosomes (18 and 19) and the Y chromosome. Autosome "pairs" 1 and 17 were chosen arbitrarily to indicate the range in length of the remaining chromosomes. Air dried preparation of lymph node and spleen.
(Courtesy Dr. C. E. Ford, from TRANSPLANTATION 4:333, 1966)

WEIGHTS AND LENGTHS OF MOUSE EMBRYOS FROM 9½ GESTATION DAY TO 18½ GESTATION DAY AT HALF DAY INTERVALS

GESTATION AGE OF MOUSE EMBRYO: DAYS	TOTAL NUMBER OF YOUNG IN 5 LITTERS	AVERAGE WEIGHT IN GRAMS	RANGE IN INDIVIDUAL WEIGHTS: gms.	AVERAGE LENGTH IN mm.	RANGE OF INDIVIDUAL LENGTHS: mm.
9½	38	0.0027		2.8	2 – – – – 3.5
10	47	0.0051		3.5	2 – – – – 4.5
10½	42	0.015	0.01– – – – 0.025	4.34	3 – – – – 5
11	43	0.0195	0.01– – – – 0.025	5.1	3 – – – – 6.5
11½	53	0.029	0.02– – – – 0.04	6.1	4 – – – – 6.5
12	37	0.0417	0.02– – – – 0.06	7.0	5 – – – – 8
12½	39	0.0637	0.04– – – – 0.08	8.03	7 – – – – 9
13	44	0.0827	0.05– – – – 0.09	9.09	7 – – – – 9.5
13½	46	0.0961	0.035– – – – 0.014	9.31	6 – – – – 10.5
14	45	0.148	0.08– – – – 0.18	10.4	9.5 – – – – 11
14½	40	0.161	0.10– – – – 0.22	10.7	9.5 – – – – 11.5
15	34	0.256	0.23– – – – 0.32	12.51	11 – – – – 14
15½	36	0.317	0.16– – – – 0.43	13.31	11 – – – – 14.5
16	46	0.439	0.20– – – – 0.59	15.18	11 – – – – 17
16½	41	0.563	0.41– – – – 0.70	16.7	15 – – – – 18.5
17	46	0.661	0.33– – – – 0.93	17.39	14 – – – – 20
17½	45	0.910	0.79– – – – 1.08	19.83	18 – – – – 22
18	46	0.877	0.57– – – – 1.125	19.25	15 – – – – 24.5
18½	41	1.124	0.64– – – – 1.50	21.53	18 – – – – 25

Note: All data from Bouin-fixed embryos. To correct for live data add 24% to weights and 6.5% to lengths. (Data compiled by L. Skaredoff.)

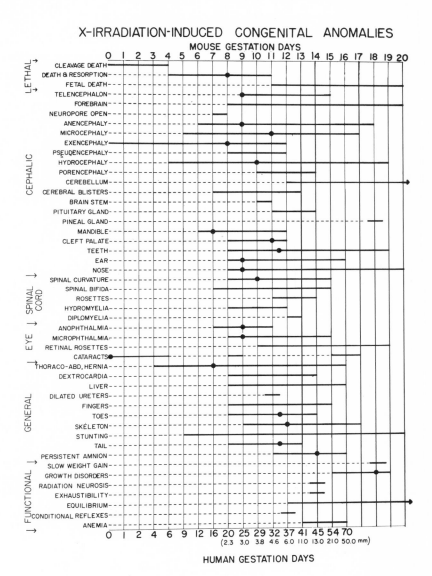

X-IRRADIATION-INDUCED CONGENITAL ANOMALIES

MOUSE GESTATION DAYS

This chart shows the mouse gestation days (above) and the time during development when various x-ray-induced abnormalities can be produced. It will be noted that the majority of these anomalies occur following irradiation on days 8, 9, and 10 when the major activity is organogenesis. The dot represents the period of greatest sensitivity, and the solid line the extent of sensitivity leading to a specific congenital anomaly. It will also be noted that by day 13 the organs have been so well formed (differentiated) that congenital anomalies are more difficult to produce.

(From Rugh 1964 Radiology 82:917)

COMPARISON OF DEVELOPMENT: MOUSE AND HUMAN*

STAGE OF DEVELOPMENT	MOUSE DAYS	MOUSE HOURS	MOUSE SOMITES	HUMAN
2 cells		24—38	0	24—36 hours
4 cells		38—50	0	36—48 ''
5—8 cells		50—64	0	48—72 ''
9—16 cells		60—70	0	72—96 ''
Blastula		74—82	0	4.5 days
Implantation	4	12	0	6+ ''
Proamniotic cavity	5		0	7 ''
Primitive streak	6	12	0	13.5 ''
Head process	7		0	18 ''
Allantois	7	6	0	16.5 ''
Foregut pocket	7	22	0	18 ''
First somites	7	18	2	18 ''
4 somites	8	8	4	19 ''
Right & left heart primordia	8	8	4	19 ''
1st pharyngeal pouch	8	8	4	19 ''
Hindgut pocket	8	1	7	18 ''
Mediam thyroid primordium	8	12	6	19 ''
Optic sulcus	8	13	9	21 ''
1st aortic arch	8	13	9	19 ''
Anterior cardinals	8	14	9—10	21 ''
10 somites	8	14	10	20 ''
Thyroid primordia	8	16	12	20 ''
Otic invagination	8	18	13	21 ''
Anterior neuropore closing	8	18	13	21 ''
Both 1st & 2nd pharyngeal pouches	8	19	14	21 ''
Liver diverticulum	8	20	14—15	22 ''
Dors, mesocardium disappears	8	21	15	22 ''
Nephrogenic cord	8	21	15	20 ''
Ant. neuropore open in prosencephalon only	8	21	15	22 ''
Deep otic invagination	8	22	16	23 ''
Ant. neuropore closed	9	1	18+	23 ''
Otic cyst closed	9	2	19	28 ''
Oral membrane perforate	9	2	19	25 ''
1st & 2nd aortic arches	9	4	20	23 ''
Dorsal aorta fuses	9	4	20	23 ''
Dorsal flexure disappears	9	0		26 ''
Post. cardinal channel	9	4	20	26 ''
Rathke's pocket	9	9	23	29 ''

* Adapted from data in "Equivalent ages in mouse and human embryos" by E. M. Otis and R. Brent, 1952, UR-194. Note: Mouse strains may differ as much as by 24 hours, and the human ages given are approximate and may be off by 1 week or more, particularly with the later stages.

STAGE OF DEVELOPMENT	MOUSE DAYS	MOUSE HOURS	MOUSE SOMITES	HUMAN
Anterior limb bud	9	9	23	26 days
Lat. thyroid diverticulum	9	12	24	23 ʼʼ
Proliferation of liver	9	12	24	22 ʼʼ
Post. neuropore closing	9	12	24	26 ʼʼ
Mesonephric tubules & duct	9	12	24	25 ʼʼ
Epithelial cords in liver	9	15	25	25 ʼʼ
Gall bladder separating	9	15	25	26 ʼʼ
Primary lung diverticulum	9	15	25	26 ʼʼ
Dors. pancreatic constriction	9	15	25	26 ʼʼ
Thickened lens disc	9	15	25	28 ʼʼ
Omental bursa	9	15	25	26 ʼʼ
3 pharyngeal pouches	9	15	25	24 ʼʼ
Endocardial cushions	9	18	26	25 ʼʼ
First 3 aortic arches	10	0	27	28 ʼʼ
Cerebral evagination	10	0	27	31 ʼʼ
Olfactory disc	10	0	27	28 ʼʼ
Vitelline veins in liver	10	12	28—36	25 ʼʼ
Rt. venous valve primordium	10	12	ʼʼ	30 ʼʼ
Posterior limb bud	10	12	ʼʼ	28 ʼʼ
Olfactory pit	10	12	ʼʼ	29 ʼʼ
Lens vesicle	10	12	ʼʼ	29 ʼʼ
Endolymphatic appendage	10	12	ʼʼ	29 ʼʼ
Aortic arches # 3, 4, 6	10	12	ʼʼ	
Primary intestinal loops	10	12	ʼʼ	29 ʼʼ
Interventricular septum	10	12	ʼʼ	29 ʼʼ
Mesonephric ducts to U.G. sinus	11	0	37—42	29 ʼʼ
Short uretric bud	11	0	ʼʼ	29 ʼʼ
Trachea separate	11	0	ʼʼ	29 ʼʼ
Thyroid remnant to pharynx	11	0	ʼʼ	29 ʼʼ
Lens vesicle closed	11	0	ʼʼ	31 ʼʼ
Ventral pancreatic rudiment	11	0	ʼʼ	31 ʼʼ
Cochlear duct	11	0	ʼʼ	33 ʼʼ
Endocardial cushion fused	11	0	ʼʼ	35 ʼʼ
Subcardinals formed	11	12	ʼʼ	30 ʼʼ
Cephalic umbil, veins atrophy	11	12		32 ʼʼ
Ant. limb curved	11	12		29 ʼʼ
Aortic-pulmonary septum	11	12		31 ʼʼ
Otic mesenchyme	11	12		
Expansion of stomach	11	12		31 ʼʼ
Hypophyseal evagination	11	12		33 ʼʼ
Pigment in retina	11	12		33 ʼʼ
Elongation post. lens cells	11	12		33 ʼʼ
Epiphyseal evagination	11	12		33 ʼʼ
Septum primum of heart	11	12		35 ʼʼ
Epithelium of semi-circ. canals	11	12		35 ʼʼ

STAGE OF DEVELOPMENT	MOUSE DAYS	MOUSE HOURS	MOUSE SOMITES	HUMAN
Fusion dors. & vent. pancreas	11	12		35 days
Bronchial areas of rt. lung	11	12		35 ʺ
No lumen in Rathke's pocket	11	12		42 ʺ
Pulmonary vein to left atrium	11	12		35–40 ʺ
Olfactory nerves to brain	11	12		42 ʺ
Vomeronasal organ	11	12		37 ʺ
Mesenchyme of ribs	12	0		31+ ʺ
Secondary bronchi	12	0		36+ ʺ
Choroid fissure closed	12	0		40 ʺ
Chondrification of neural process	12	0		37 ʺ
Semicircular canals formed	12	0		37 ʺ
Chondrification of centrum	12	0		37 ʺ
Periderm present	12	0		45 ʺ
Lens vesicle below surface	12	12		33 ʺ
Subcardinal anastomose	12	12		40 ʺ
Inf. vena cava enters heart	12	12		45 ʺ
Sup. & Inf. colliculus separate	12	12		37+ ʺ
Post. cardinals degenerate	12	12		45 ʺ
Epithelial cords in testis	12	12		45 ʺ
Choroid plexus in IV ventricle	12	12		49 ʺ
Mesenchyme in ocular muscles	12	12		49 ʺ
Rathke's pouch detached	12	12		50 ʺ
Rt. dors. aorta between III & IV disappears	13	0		45 ʺ
Aortic pulmonary septum complete	13	0		35 ʺ
Esophageal submucosa thickens	13	0		35+ ʺ
Atrio-ventricular valve	13	0		37+ ʺ
Lens fibers inside vesicle	13	0		45 ʺ
Otic capsule precartilaginous	13	0		45 ʺ
Inter. ventricular septum complete	13	0		47 ʺ
Primary lid fold	13	0		45 ʺ
Inner neuroblasts of retina	13	0		49 ʺ
Nerve fibers in optic stalk	13	0		49 ʺ
Chondrification of ribs	13	0		45 ʺ
Oculomotor nuclei	13	0		52 ʺ
Initiation of aortic & pulmonary semilunars	13	12		35+ ʺ
Vacuoles in stomach epithelium	13	12		45 ʺ
Interdigital notches in hand plate	13	12		37+ ʺ
Muscular primordia around esophagus	13	12		37 ʺ
Cartilage advanced in humerus	13	12		49 ʺ
Enucleate red cells 1%	13	12		51 ʺ
Skin layers differentiated	13	12		52 ʺ
Aortic pulmonary semilunars	14	12		37+ ʺ
First intestinal villi	14	12		52 ʺ
Cartilage in humerus	14	12		54 ʺ

STAGE OF DEVELOPMENT	MOUSE DAYS	MOUSE HOURS	MOUSE SOMITES	HUMAN
Ossification of frontal & zygomatic arch	14	12		60 days
Saccule & utricle separated	14	12		60 ''
1st cartilage in otic capsule	14	12		60 ''
1st 7 ribs chondrified	14	12		60+ ''
Rudimentary periotic cistern	14	12		60+ ''
Enucleate red cells 25%	14	12		60+ ''
Scala tympani forming	14	12		63+ ''
Continuous muscle fibrils	15	12		63+ ''
Cerebellum fused at mid-line	15	12		68+ ''
Ossification of humerus	15	12		70+ ''
Stratum granulosum	15	12		75+ ''
Nucleate cells 5%	15	12		70 ''
Rib ossification	15	12		80 ''
Perichondrium — otic capsule	16	12		80 ''
Corpus callosum	16	12		90 ''
Ossification of centrum	16	12		90 ''
Alveoli in lungs	16	12		90 ''
Nucleate cells 1%	16	12		95 ''
Proliferation of gastric glands	16	12		105 ''

TECHNIQUE FOR THE STUDY OF EMBRYONIC AND FETAL MOUSE CHROMOSOMES

This technique is a slight modification of that found in Ford and Woollam 1963, Stain Technol. 38:271 with some changes suggested by Dr. C. E. Ford (personal communication).

The pregnant female is injected intraperitoneally with 0.3 ml of 0.025% colchicine 1½ hours before intended sacrifice. This period can be lengthened to 4 hours and might present more figures. Up to about 12 days gestation the fetuses are small enough to be used entirely. After that the fetuses may be removed, decapitated, and the liver excised and used alone. Whether the whole fetus or the excised liver is used, it is placed in 5 ml of 0.1% colchicine in Hank's balanced salt solution and broken up by slow aspiration, using, of course, a separate pipette for each sample. After 1.25 to 1.5 hour in suspension the whole is centrifuged for 5 minutes at 400 rpm and the supernatant removed. Add 5 ml of 1% sodium citrate and let suspension stand 15 to 20 minutes (no longer or the cells will cytolyze). Centrifuge 2 to 3 minutes slowly, to avoid damage to the cells. Add carefully 1 to 2 ml of fresh methanol; acetic acid (3:1), cells gently shaken and fixed at 4°C, for 30 minutes. Centrifuge, remove supernatant, and add sufficient 45% acetic acid to make suspension for slides (about 0.5 ml for 6 slides). Place suspension by drops on slides at 54°C. on hotplate with 2 rows of 4 drops each. Each drop will form a series of concentric rings. When dry, stain in LAO* (lactic-acid orcein) for at least 30 minutes, wash off excess stain with 3 changes of 45% acetic acid and air dry the slides.

Since large aggregates of cells are a problem, a very fine pointed pipette should be used, preferably one made from a 2 mm bore glass tubing drawn out in a flame to a fine point.

Abnormalities may include: 2N + and 2 N− groups, fragmentation, stickiness and hence fusion of chromosomes, and grossly abnormal configurations. One must first become thoroughly acquainted with the normal compliment of 40 chromosomes, and identify as many pairs as possible before attempting to study anomalies.

*LAO (2 gm. synthetic orcein added to 50 ml glacial acetic acid, 42.5 ml of 85% lactic acid, and 7.5 ml of distilled water as per Welshons et al 1962, Stain Technol. 37:1-5).

TIME OF ORIGIN OF VARIOUS ORGAN PRIMORDIA IN THE MOUSE

ECTODERMAL DERIVATIVES:	GESTATION DAYS												
	7	8	9	10	11	12	13	14	15	16	17	18	19
NERVOUS SYSTEM:													
Neural folds		x											
Neural tube		x											
Neural crests			x										
Anterior neuropore		x											
Posterior neuropore		x											
BRAIN:													
Prosencephalon		x											
Mesencephalon		x											
Rhombencephalon		x											
Cephalic flexure		x											
Pontine flexure					x								
Telencephalon			x										
Olfactory lobes			x										
Lamina terminalis					x								
Diencephalon			x										
Optic vesicles			x										
Epiphysis					x								
Infundibulum			x										
Ant. choroid plexus								x					
Rathke's pocket			x										
Optic recess					x								
Mesencephalon:													
Cerebral peduncle							x						
Aqueduct of Sylvius					x								
Pons Varolli								x					
Isthmus				x									
Tuberculum posterius						x							
Metencephalon:			x										
Myelencephalon:			x										
Metatela (thin roof)				x									
Tela choroidea				x									
Post. choroid plexus						x							
NERVES:													
Cranial I				x									
Cranial II				x									
Cranial III							x						
Cranial IV					x								
Cranial V		x											
Cranial VI			x										
Cranial VII		x											
Cranial VIII		x											
Cranial IX		x											
Cranial X		x											
Cranial XI			x										
Cranial XII			x										

	GESTATION DAYS												
ECTODERMAL DERIVATIVES:	7	8	9	10	11	12	13	14	15	16	17	18	19
SPINAL CORD:													
Marginal layer					x								
Mantle layer					x								
Ependymal layer					x								
Dorsal sensory roots				x									
Ventral motor roots					x								
Dorsal root ganglia				x									
Spinal nerves					x								
SENSE ORGANS:													
EYE:													
Optic vesicle		x											
Optic cup			x										
Optic stalk			x										
Optic chiasma							x						
Retinal layer							x						
Pigmented layer							x						
Lens				x									
Choroid fissure				x									
Vitreous humor						x							
Lachrymal gland											x		
Cornea											x		
Conjunctiva											x		
Iris											x		
EAR:													
Auditory vesicle		x											
Auditory cup			x										
Endolymphatic duct				x									
Sacculus					x								
Utriculus					x								
Cochlea							x						
Semicircular canals							x						
Otic capsule										x			
Pinna							x						
NOSE (Olfactory Organ):													
Placode			x										
Nasal pit				x									
Nasal sinus						x							
Naso-lachrymal duct								x					
Posterior choanae									x				
Nasal septum								x					
Nasopharyngeal duct									x				
Vomeronasal organ						x							
Palate										x			
Nasopharyngeal meatus										x			
Lat. nasal mucous glands											x		
Nares open													x
TAIL BUD:				x									
FORELIMB BUD:			x										

	GESTATION DAYS												
ECTODERMAL DERIVATIVES:	7	8	9	10	11	12	13	14	15	16	17	18	19
HINDLIMB BUD:				x									
SKIN:													
Hair germ						x							
Vibrissae roots						x							
Periderm								x					
Stratum germanitivum									x				
Stratum corneum										x			
Mammary welts				x									
STOMODEUM:			x										
PROCTODEUM:				x									
ENDODERMAL DERIVATIVES:													
DIGESTIVE SYSTEM:													
Yolk sac	x												
Foregut (AIP)	x												
Hindgut (PIP)		x											
Oral cavity			x										
Palate						x							
Tongue					x								
Teeth								x					
Pharynx			x										
Pharyngeal pouches			x										
Thymus gland						x							
Thyroid gland			x										
Thyroid lobular						x							
Parathyroid gland					x								
Ultimobranchial body					x								
Salivary glands								x					
Larynx					x								
Esophagus					x								
Stomach					x								
Duodenum					x								
Pancreas					x								
Pancreatic duct					x								
Liver diverticulum			x										
Liver trabeculae					x								
Spleen							x						
Adrenal gland					x								
Small intestines					x								
Large intestines						x							
Umbilical hernia					x								
Umbilical hernia withdrawn										x			
Rectum							x						
Gall bladder					x								
Allantois	x												
Urinary bladder								x					
Cloaca			x										

					G E S T A T I O N		D A Y S						
ENDODERMAL DERIVATIVES:	7	8	9	10	11	12	13	14	15	16	17	18	19
RESPIRATORY SYSTEM:													
Laryngo-tracheal groove			x										
Trachea					x								
Epiglottis							x						
Bronchi					x								
Lung buds			x										
Bronchioles						x							
MESODERMAL DERIVATIVES:													
BODY CAVITIES & MESENTERIES													
Coelom (perit. cavity)		x											
Dorsal mesentery					x								
Ventral mesentery					x								
Dorsal mesocardium				x									
Ventral mesocardium					x								
Pericardial cavity		x											
Diaphragm								x					
Pleura cavity				x									
SKELETAL SYSTEM: (Chondrif.)													
Notochord (endodermal)	x												
Ribs - cartilage						x							
Ribs - bone							x						
Centrum (notochord)							x						
Basioccipital cartilage								x					
Nasal capsule								x					
Otic capsule								x					
Zygomatic arch											x		
Tracheal rings									x				
Sternum									x				
Shoulder girdle									x				
Scapula						x							
Humerus						x							
Radius						x							
Ulna						x							
Carpus						x							
Auditory ossicles											x		
Pre-vertebrae						x							
Meckel's cartilage								x					
Tooth development:													
Molar						x							
Dental lamina									x				
Molar enamel organ									x				
Incisors							x						
Enamel organ								x					
Ameloblasts											x		
Odontoblasts											x		

| | GESTATION DAYS | | | | | | | | | | | | |
MESODERMAL DERIVATIVES:	7	8	9	10	11	12	13	14	15	16	17	18	19
CIRCULATORY SYSTEM:													
Heart	x												
Heart trabeculae					x								
Atria		x											
Ventricle		x											
Atrio-ventricular canal				x									
Sinus venosus			x										
Sino-auricular valve													
Bulbus arteriosus			x										
Ductus venosus					x								
Truncus arteriosus					x								
Inter-atrial septum				x									
Atrio-ventricular valve					x								
Arteries:													
Ventral aorta		x											
Aortic arch I		x			0								
Aortic arch II			x		0								
Aortic arch III					x								
Aortic arch IV				x									
Aortic arch V					x	0							
Aortic arch VI					x								
Aortic arch VII (Pulmon.)					x								
Dorsal aorta		x											
Internal carotid artery		x											
Intersegmental arteries					x								
Intercostal arteries					x								
Circle of Willis					x								
Iliac arteries					x								
Allantoic (umbilical) art.					x								
Vitelline (omphalomesent.)		x											
Caudal artery			x										
Basilar artery			x										
Pulmonary artery							x						
Cerebral artery			x										
Blood Islands:		x											
Veins:													
Allantoic					x								
Anterior cardinal			x										
Common cardinal (d. Cuvieri)					x								
Posterior cardinal						x							
Hepatic					x								
Hepatic portal					x								
Pulmonary	x												
Umbilical			x										
Sinus venosus			x										
Inferior vena cava				x									
Intervertebral							x						
Vitelline				x									

MESODERMAL DERIVATIVES:	GESTATION DAYS												
	7	8	9	10	11	12	13	14	15	16	17	18	19
UROGENITAL SYSTEM:													
Genital papilla								x					
Male external organs													
Female external organs													
EXCRETORY SYSTEM:													
Nephrogenic cord		x											
Pronephros			x										
Pronephric duct				x									
Mesonephros				x									
Mesonephric duct					x								
Metanephros						x							
Urogenital sinus					x								
Rectum							x						
Cloacal membrane							x						
Ureter						x							
Urethra										x			
GENITAL SYSTEM:													
Genital ridge primordium				x									
Testis					x								
Seminiferous tubules							x						
Vas deferens					x								
Wolffian duct					x								
Ovaries (genital ridge)				x									
Follicles, early oögonia							x						
Oviducts (Müllerian)				x									
Uterus											x		
MUSCULAR SYSTEM:													
Somites		x											
Myotomes		x											
Dermatome		x											
Scleratome		x											
Myocardia	x												
Myocardial contractions		x											
Myoblasts							x						
Muscle fibrils								x					

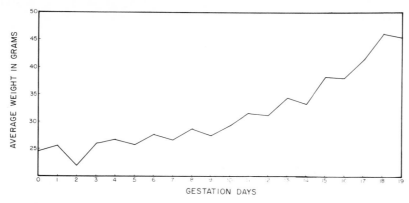

AVERAGE WEIGHT CHANGES DURING PREGNANCY IN MICE

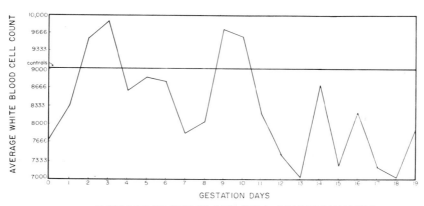

AVERAGE WHITE BLOOD CELL COUNT CHANGES
DURING PREGNANCY IN MICE

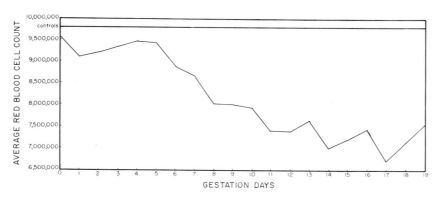

AVERAGE RED BLOOD CELL COUNT CHANGES
DURING PREGNANCY IN MICE

Glossary

ABORTION - Termination of pregnancy at a non-viable stage of the foetus.

ACHRONDROPLASTIC - Refers to miniature adult skeletal condition of some midgets.

ACIDOPHIL - Oxiphil; cell constituents stained with acid dyes, often used to designate an entire cell type. (*See* basophil.)

ACROBLAST - The association of idiosome and acrosome granule including the hypothetical acrosomic vacuole.

ACROSOME - A structure found in spermatids and spermatozoa arising from the acrosomic granule (which itself came from the idiosome of the Golgi body). Its shape is characteristic of the species and may be a rod, cone, or crescent, and there may also be an outer and inner zone. It stains well with PA-FA. It is not to be confused with the perforatorium. Functions in egg penetration.

ACROSOME PHASE - The period in spermiogenesis when the acrosome develops from the acrosomic granule, and the developing spermatid containing it takes the shape of the spermatozoa.

ACROSOME REACTION - Fusion of spermatozoon plasma membrane without a acrosome membrane opening the acrosome cavity and releasing the lytic agent hyaluronidase.

ACROSOMIC GRANULE - The single, round corpuscle which results from the fusion of the proacrosomic granules in the idiosome of young spermatids. (*Syn.*, das Korn, proacrosome, acrosomic bead, acrosome, archosome, mitosome, archoplasmic granule, idiospaerosome).

ACROSOMIC VACUOLE - Crescent-like space around the proacrosomic granules but may be a fixation artefact.

ACTIVATION - Stimulation of spermatozoon to accelerated activity, generally by chemical means (*e.g.*, fertilizin); process of initiating development in the egg; the liberation of naturally occurring evocators from an inactive combination.

ADAPTATION - Functional and correlative change, however brought about.

ADNEXA - Extra embryonic structures discarded before the adult condition is attained.

AER - Apical ectodermal ridge, the thickened outer margin of the mouse limb bud where the epidermis thickens for a short time at about 10.5 to 11.0 days gestation, before the mesenchyme condensations have begun to form for the digits. Disappears by day 13.

AFFINITY - Tendency of cells and tissues of the early embryo to cling together when removed from their normal environment. Equivalent to the cytarme of Roux.

AFTER-BIRTH - Extra-embryonic membranes which are delivered after the emergence of the fetus (mammal). Consists of placenta, amnion and yolk sac.

AGENESIS - Developmental failure of a primordium (*e.g.*, absence of arm or kidney).

AGGLUTINATION - Cluster formation; a spontaneously reversible reaction of spermatozoa to the fertilizin of egg-water. Active agent in zona pellucida.

AGGREGATION - Coming together of cells (*e.g.*, spermatozoa) without sticking, a non-reversible response comparable to chemotropism.

AGNATHUS - Absence of lower jaw.

AKINETIC - Without a kinetochore (*e.g.*, in a chromosome).

ALAR PLATE - Dorso-lateral wall of the myelencephaon, separated from the basal plate by the sulcus limitans.

ALBUGINEA OF TESTIS - The stroma of the primitive testis which forms a layer between the germinal epithelium and the seminiferous tubules.

ALECITHAL EGG - (*See* under EGG).

ALIMENTARY CASTRATION - Prolonged starvation.

ALLANTOIN - Nitrogenous portion of allantoic fluid.

ALLANTOIS - An extra embryonic sac-like extension of the hindgut of amniotes, having the dual function of excretion and respiration.

ALLELOMORPHS - Gene pairs; an allelomorph is one of two dissimilar genes which, on account of their corresponding position (locus) in corresponding (homolgous) chromosomes, are subject to alternative (Mendelian) inheritance in a diploid form. These genes may be identical (homozygous), or dissimilar (heterozygous), names similarly applied to chromosome or to individuals possessing such genes.

ALLO-HAPLOID - Androgenetic haploid.

ALLOMETRY - Study of the relative sizes of parts of animals at different absolute sizes, ages, weights, or chemical compositions. Term now used in place of heterogony by Huxley and Teissier (1936).

ALLOMORPHOSIS - The physical or chemical relation of parts of an organism at some early stage to either the whole or part of a later stage, (e.g., the egg size compared with the adult size or weight).

ALLO-POLYPLOID - Polyploid species hybrid.

AMBOCEPTOR - A synonym used for fertilizin in suggesting its double combination with the sperm and egg receptors in the process of fertilization. This double receptor may also receive blood inhibitors, or anti-fertilizin.

AMELOBLASTS - Cells which secrete the enamel cap of the (mammalian) tooth.

AMELUS - Failure of the extremities to develop, remaining as mere stubs.

AMNIOCARDIAC VESICLES - Paired primordia of the parietal cavity which appear in the mesoblast lateral to the head fold of the embryo, and grow beneath the foregut to give rise to the pericardial cavity. Named because of embryonic relation to both amnion and pericardium.

AMNION - Thin, double muscular membrane enclosing the embryos of some invertebrates and of reptiles, birds, and mammals. It is derived from the somatopleure in vertebrates, is filled with fluid which acts as a protective jacket.

AMNIOTIC BANDS - Fibrous bands from the amnion to the embryo due to local necrosis of foetal tissues.

AMNIOTIC RAPHÉ - Point of junction of the amniotic folds as they encircle the embryo, synonymous with sero-amniotic or chorioamniotic junction.

AMPHIMIXIS - Mixing of germinal substances accomplished during fertilization.

ANALOGOUS - Structures said to have the same function but different embryological and/or evolutionary origin. Opposed to homologous.

ANAL PLATE - A thickening and invagination of mid-ventral ectoderm just posterior to the primitive streak which meets evaginating endoderm of the hindgut, later to be perforated as the proctodeum (anus). Syn., cloacal membrane.

ANAPHASE - Phase of mitosis when the paired chromosomes are separating at the equatorial plate and begin to move toward the ends of the spindle.

ANASTOMOSIS - Joining together as of blood vessels and nerves, generally forming a network.

ANDROGAMONES - The anti-fertilizins of Lillie, so named by Hartmann. An acidic protein of low molecular weight.

ANDROGENESIS - Development of the egg with paternal. (sperm) chromosomes only, accomplished by removing the egg nucleus after activation by the spermatozoon but before syngamy (Wilson, 1925). May also be accomplished by irradiation damage of egg nucleus. Non-participation of the female pronucleus in fertilization and development.

ANESTRUS - The quiescent period which follows estrus in the reproductive cycle of the female mammal.

ANEUGAMY - Abnormal ploidy of one or both pronuclei. Fertilization involving a diploid pronucleus in addition to a normal haploid pronucleus.

ANEUPLOIDY - Deviation from normal diploidy but involving partial sets of chromosomes.

ANEUPLOIDY, MULTIFORM - Complex chromosomal mosaics, possibly the result of multipolar mitoses.

ANEUROGENIC - Used in relation to organs developed without proper components of the central nervous system (*e.g.*, limb buds in embryos without spinal cords).

ANGENESIS - Regeneration of tissues.

ANGIOBLAST - Migratory mesenchyme cell associated with formation of vascular endothelium.

ANLAGÉ - A rudiment; a group of cells which indicate a prospective development into a part or organ. *Syn.*, ebauché or primordium.

ANIMALIZATION - Changing by physical or chemical means the presumptive fate of embryonic areas which normally would have become endodermal. *Syn.*, ectodermization, or animalisierung of Lindahl.

ANORMOGENESE - A course of development which deviates in a typical manner from the normal.

ANTERIOR - Toward the head; head end. *Syn.*, cephalic, cranial, rostral.

ANTERIOR INTESTINAL PORTAL - The entrance from the yolk sac into the foregut.

ANTIFERTILIZIN - A sperm substance identified as an acidic protein, found on the surface of the spermatozoon derived from the plasma membrane and combines with fertilizin of great specificity to bring about attachment of the gametes.

ANURY - Tailless mice, homozygous TT, lacking the posterior portion of the body completely, generally die by 10.5 gestation days because of failure to make vascular connection with the mother. May involve anus, urethra, and genital papilla.

ANUS - The posterior opening of the digestive tract, temporarily closed over by the proctodeal membrane.

AORTIC ARCH - Blood vessel which connects the dorsal and ventral aortae by way of the visceral arch.

AORTIC BULB - Embryonic bulge of truncus arteriosus where it swings toward the midline to give rise to the aortic arches.

APICAL REGION (or apex) - Region of head, head cap, or nucleus of the spermatozoon facing the basement membrane of the seminiferous tubule during spermatid maturation. First point of entrance into the ovum.

APROSOMUS - Featureless face due to the arrest of development, the skin covering is normal but lacking in eyes, nose, and mouth.

AQUEDUCT OF SYLVIUS - Ventricle of the mesencephalon (mesocoel) becomes the aqueduct of Sylvius, connecting with the cavities of the optic lobes. *Syn.*, iter.

AQUEOUS HUMOR - Fluid which fills the anterior and posterior chambers of the eye between the lens, probably derived from mesoderm.

ARCHENCEPHALON - Anterior portion of the brain which gives rise to the telencephalon and the diencephalon; pre-chordal brain.

ARCHIPLASM - Specific material which gives rise to the asters and spindle.

ARCUALIA - Small blocks of sclerotomal connective tissue involved in the formation of vertebrae.

AREA - A morphogenetic cell group representing one of the constituent regions of a fate-map, generally of a blastula stage or later.

AREAL - First an invisible, then a sharply differentiated region of the blastema, out of which develops a primitive organ; the organ arising from the blastema through segregation, (organogenetisches or Lehmann).

ARRHENOKARYOTIC - Refers to a blastomere of the normally fertilized egg where there has been a separation of the nuclear components; or in cases of dispermy, where the haploid chromosomes from the single sperm are isolated in the blastomere.

ARRHENOTOKY - Parthenogenetic production of males, exclusively.

ASTER - The "star-shaped structure" surrounding the centrosome, lines radiating in all directions from the centrosome during mitosis.

ASTOMUS - Complete lack or atresia of the mouth.

ASTRAL RAYS - Lines which make up the aster.

ASTROCYTES - Stellate shaped cells arising from the spongioblasts of the mantle layer, classified under the more general term of neuroglia.

ASYNTAXIA DORSALIS - Failure of the neural tube to close.

ATELIOTIC - Arrested development of the skeleton due to non-union of the epiphyses, characteristic of some dwarfs.

ATOKUS - Without offspring.

ATTACHMENT POINT - Point of chromosome to which the spindle fibre is attached and therefore the portion of the chromosome nearest the centrosome in anaphase. *Syn.*, centromere, chromocenter, kinetochore.

ATTRACTION SPHERE - (*See* CENTROSPHERE).

AURICLE - Thin walled chamber(s) of the heart which receives blood from the sinus venosus and delivers it to the ventricle on the same side.

AUTOGAMY - Self-fertilization.

AUTOSOME - Any chromosome except the so-called sex (X or Y) chromosomes.

AUXESIS - Growth by cell expansion but without cell division.

AUXOCYTE - Pre-meitoic germ cell. *Syn.*, primary cyte, meiocyte.

AXENIC - Germ free animal (*Syn.*, gnotobiotic).

AXIAL FILAMENT - The central fibre in the tail of a spermatozoon.

AXIAL MESODERM - That portion of the epimeric mesoderm nearest the notochord. *Syn.*, vertebral plate.

AXIS OF THE EMBRYO - A line representing the antero-posterior axis of the future embryo.

BÄHNUNG - Competence or labile determination.

BALFOUR'S LAW - The intervals between cleavages are longer the more yolk a cell contains in proportion to its protoplasm. "The velocity of segmentation in any part of the ovum is, roughly speaking, proportional to the concentration of the protoplasm there; and the size of the segments is inversely proportional to the concentration of the protoplasm." (Balfour - "Comparative Embryology).

BASAL PLATE - Ventro-lateral wall of myelencephalon, separated from dorso-lateral alar plate by the sulcus limitans.

BASAL ZONE - A region below the stratum spongiosum forming a strip which is contiguous with the myometrium and contains fundic cells of the compact zone, polygonal elements termed decidual cells.

BASOPHIL - Cell constituents having an affinity for basic dyes, often used as an adjective for an entire cell. (*See* acidophil.)

BIO-ELECTRIC CURRENT - An electrical potential characteristic of life, disappearing upon death, associated with activities of muscle, nerve, secretion, and early embryos.

BIOGENETIC LAW - Ontogeny is a recapitulation of the early development of ancestral phylogeny. Embryos of higher forms resemble the embryos of lower forms in certain respects but they are never like the adults of the lower (or ancestral) forms. Not to be confused with the recapitulation theory.

BIOLOGICAL INTEGRATION - Correlation of parts through neural or humoral (or both) influences, acquired during development.

BIOLOGICAL MEMORY - Ontogenetic unfolding of anlagen phyletically accumulated.

BIOLOGICAL ORDER - Fundamental basis of experimental studies, the conformity of biological processes to causal postulates.

BIORGAN - An organ in the physiological rather than the morphological sense.

BIOTONUS - The ratio between assimilation and dissimilation. A/D ratio.

BLASTEMA - An indifferent group of cells about to be organized into definite tissues, kept together by the ectoplasmic matrix of the constituent cells. Considered to be primitive, embryonic, relatively undifferentiated regenerating cell masses. Thought by some to be produced by reserve cells which were arrested during earlier embryonic development.

BLASTOCOEL - Cavity of the blastula. *Syn.*, segmentation of subgerminal cavity.

BLASTOCYST - Mammalian blastula, containing large blastocoel. *Syn.*, blastodermic vesicle.

BLASTOCYT, ACTIVE - Blastocysts on day 4 of the mouse, in normal pregnancy, ready to implant, differing from dormant blastocysts in regard to size, mitotic activity, and fine structure. Can be rendered dormant if transplanted into dormant uterus.

BLASTOCYST, DORMANT - Blastocysts during delayed implantation are slightly larger than normal size. Development and mitotic activity may cease, but such a blastocyst can become active under oestrogen treatment. Chronologically they are older than active blastocysts.

BLASTODERM - "Because the embryo chooses this as its seat and its domicile, contributing much to its configuration out of its own substance, therefore, in the future, we shall call it blastoderm." (Plander, 1817). An embryo composed of a single germ layer.

BLASTODERMIC VESICLE - (*See* Blastocyst).

BLASTOMERE - One of the cells of the early cleavage of an egg. When there is a disparity in size the smaller blastomere is a micromere; the intermediate one is a mesomere; and the larger one is a macromere, but all are blastomeres.

BLASTOTOMY - Separation of cells or groups of cells of the blastula, by any means.

BLASTULA - A stage in embryonic development between the appearance of distinct blastomeres and the end of cleavage (*i.e.*, the beginning of gastrulation); a stage generally possessing a primary embryonic cavity or vesicle known as the blastocoel; invariably monodermic, although the roof may be multi-layered.

BLOOD ISLANDS - Pre-vascular groups of mesodermal cells found in the splanchnopleure, from which arise the blood vessels and compuscles. Largely entra-embryonic.

BOWMAN'S CAPSULE - Double walled glomerular cup associated with uriniferous tubule.

BRACHYPODISM - bp in mouse linkage group 5, reduces the length of the hands and feet so that the mice are incapable of jumping. Metacarpals and metatarsals are shortened, each digit lacks a phalanx. All long bones are shortened, somewhat less than in appendages.

BRACHYURY - Short tailed condition in mice, semi-dominant, heterozygotes have shortened tails of variable length. The spinal column, ribs and sternum may be affected, the notochord is involved, as are most parts posterior to the 6th thoracic vertebra.

BRADYAUXESIS - Negative heterogony, the part grows more slowly than the whole.

BRADYGENESIS - Lengthening of certain stages in development.

BRANCHIAL - Having to do with respiration (*e.g.*, branchial vessel in gill). (*See* visceral).

BRANCHIOMERY - Type of metamerism exemplified in the visceral arches.

BRYSHTHALMIA - Eyes that are too large, may be due to oversized lenses.

BUD - An undeveloped branch, generally an anlagé of appendage (*e.g.*, limb or wing bud).

BUDDING - Reproductive process by which a small secondary part is produced from the parent organism, and which gradually grows to independence.

BULBUS ARTERIOSUS - The most anterior division of the early, tubular, embryonic heart which leads from the ventricle to the truncus arteriosus.

BURSA FABRICII - Endodermal cavity derived from the posterior portion of the embryonic cloaca and communicating with the dorsal part of the proctodeum at the level of the urodeal membrane.

CACOGENESIS - Inability to hybridize; means "bad descent" (kakogenesis).

CAENOGENETIC - Term for new stages in ontogeny which have been intercalated as an adaptation to some inevitable condition which the mode of life of the young animal imposed.

CANALS OF GÄRTNER - Remnants of mesonephric ducts in the broad ligament close to the uterus and vagina.

CAPACITATION - Physiological conditioning of sperm in the female genital tract, allowing the release of their hyaluronidase. A necessary maturing of the spermatozoon before it can penetrate the zona pellucida as well as the cumulus cells.

CAP PHASE - Period of spermiogenesis during which the head cap develops from the acrosomic granule.

CARCINOGEN - A chemical substance which is capable of causing living cells to become cancer-like in growth and behavior.

CARDINAL VEINS - Anterior, posterior, and sub-cardinal veins; anterior veins receive blood from the head, including the first three segmental veins; posterior receive blood from all pairs of trunk segmental veins and veins of the Wolffian bodies; paired sub-cardinals enlarge, fuse, left half degenerates, and the balance fuses with the developing inferior (posterior) vena cava.

CARYOLYSIS - Solution or dissolution of the nucleus.

CARYORHEXIS - Breaking up of the nucleus, or its rupture. (*Syn.*, Karyorhexis).

CAUDAL REGION - Region of sperm head near insertion of tail; side of cell on the lumen side of seminiferous epithelium in case of spermatid; in general, means region opposite the head or apex.

CAUDAL TUBE - In spermiogenesis the intracytoplasmic membrane which forms a collar around the insertion of the tail on the nucleus during the acrosome phase; is lightly stained with hematoxylin.

CAVAL FOLD - The inferior vena cava develops in the lateral of the two plicae mesogastrica which is known as the caval fold.

CELL - Protoplasmic territory under the control of a single nucleus, whether or not the territory is bounded by a discrete membrane. By this definition a syncitium is made up of many cells with physiological rather than morphological boundaries.

CELL CHAIN THEORY - Theory of neurogenesis wherein the peripheral nerve is of pluricellular origin; opposed to the outgrowth theory.

CELL-CONE - A sub-system of an ordered class of cells; a single cell (other than a zygote) and all cells derived from it in a division hierarchy.

CELL THEORY - The body of any living organism is either a structural and functional unit or is composed of a nucleus and its sphere of influence, whether or not that sphere is bounded by a morphological entity. "Omnis cellula e cellula." Virchow

CEMENTOBLASTS - Cement forming cells of tooth.

CENTRAL CANAL - (*See* NEUROCOEL)

CENTRIOLAR APPARATUS - Structure(s) derived from centrioles; ring centrioles, axial formations in neck, middle piece, and tail of spermatozoon.

CENTRIOLE - The granular core of the centrosome, the radiating area comprising the centrosphere. Appears within the centrosome during mitosis.

CENTROMERE - An element of the chromosome thread where it attaches to the spindle, free of DNA.

CENTROSOME - The dynamic center involved in mitosis, including the central granule (centriole) and the surrounding sphere of rays (centrosphere). It is the center of the aster which outlasts the astral rays. Double centrosome called diplosome.

CENTROSPHERE - The rayed portion of the centrosome; the structure in the spermatid which gives rise to the acrosome. *Syn.*, Spermatosphere, idiosome; also attraction sphere.

CEPHALIC FLEXURE - Ventral bending of the embryonic head at the level of the mid- and hindbrain.

CEPHALO-THORACOPAGUS - Fusion of the head and chest regions in conjoined twins.

CEREBRAL FLEXURE - Flexures of the head region, including the cranial, pontine, and the cervical flexures.

CEREBRAL PEDUNCLES - Longitudinal tracts in the floor of the mesencephalon.

CERVICAL CYST - Imperfect occlusion of a branchial (2nd) cleft. *Syn.*, branchial cyst.

CERVICAL FISTULA - Incomplete closure of the branchial cleft.

CERVICAL SINUS - Depression between the third and fourth oral clefts and the body.

CHALONES - Internal secretions with depressing effects, opposed to hormones.

CHEMO-NEUROTROPISM - Chemical attraction of degenerating nerve upon regenerating nerve fibers. The chemical nature of nerve orientation (growth and connections) depending upon diffusing substances which seem to attract nerve fibers.

CHIMERA - Compound embryo derived by grafting together major portions of two embryos, generally of different species, exchange of parts too great to be called a transplant. From Greek mythology: forepart a lion, middle a goat, and hindpart a dragon.

CHOANA - The opening of the internal nares into the oral cavity, primitively in the anterior part of the mouth but secondarily moved posteriorly by growth of the palatine process.

CHONDRIFICATION - The process of forming cartilage, by the secretion of an homogeneous matrix between the more primitive mesoderm cells.

CHONDRIN - Chemical substances in cartilage matrix which makes it increasingly susceptible to basic stains.

CHONDROCRANIUM - That portion of the floor of the skull which is originally cartilaginous, and is later displaced by the basal bones of the skull.

CHORDA DORSALIS - *Syn.*, notochord.

CHORION - An extra-embryonic membrane which develops from the somatopleure as a corollary of the amnion, and which encloses both the amnion and the allantois; consists of inner mesoderm and outer ectoderm. *Syn.*, serosa, false amnion.

CHORION FRONDOSUM - That portion of the mammalian chorion which forms the placenta and adheres to the decidua basalis. Its villi are long, branched, and profuse.

CHORIONIC VILLI - Primary villi are tongue-like and penetrate and erode the endometrium, secondary villi are mesodermal invasions of the primary villi. Embryonic blood vessels develop in this mesoderm and become the tertiary or definitive placental villi.

CHORION LAEVE - That portion of the mammalian chorion except the chorion frondosum.

CHOROID COAT - A mesenchymatous and sometimes pigmented coat within the sclerotic coat but surrounding the (pigmented layer of the) eye in vertebrate embryos.

CHOROID FISSURE - An inverted groove in the optic stalk whose lips later close around blood vessels and nerves that enter the eyeball.

CHOROID KNOT - A thickened region of the fused lips of the choroid fissure, near the pupil from which arise the cells of the iris.

CHOROID PLEXUS - Vascular folds of the thin roof of the telencephalon, diencephalon and myelencephalon, into their respective cavities.

CHROMAFFIN TISSUE - Tissue of the developing adrenal gland which exhibits characteristic reactions with chromic acid salts.

CHROMATID - Longitudinal half of an anaphase, interphase, or prophase chromosome at mitosis. One of four strands (in meiosis) involved in crossing over and visible after pachytene. Becomes a chromosome at metaphase of the second (usually the reduction) division.

CHROMATID BREAKS - The artificial transverse severance of one or both threads after the chromosome has divided longitudinally. When breakage of both threads occurs at the same time this is called isochromatid break.

CHROMATIN - Deeply staining substance of the nuclear network and the chromosomes, consisting of nuclein; gives Feulgen reaction and stains with basic dyes.

CHROMATOBLASTS - Potential pigment cells which, upon proper extrinsic stimulation, will exhibit pigmentation.

CHROMATOID BODY - An irregular structure found in the cytoplasm of the spermatocyte and spermatid, intensely stained with iron hematoxylin.

CHROMATOPHORE - Pigment bearing cell frequently capable of changing size, shape, and color; responsible for superficial color changes in many animals under the influence of the sympathetic nervous system and/or the neuro-humors.

CHROMIDIA - Extra-nuclear granules of chromatin.

CHROMOMERE - Unit of chromosome recognized as a chromatin granule.

CHROMONEMA - Optically single thread within the chromosome, a purely descriptive term without functional implications.

CHROMONUCLEIC ACID - One of the two types of nucleic acid detected in chromatin only. *Syn.*, desoxyribose nucleoprotein, thymonucleic acid. (See plasmonucleic acid.)

CHROMOSOME - The chromatic or deeply staining bodies derived from nuclear network, which are conspicuous during mitotic cell division and which are represented in all of the somatic cells of an organism in a number characteristic for the species; bearers of the genes, distinct for high content of DNA.

CHROMOSOME ABERRATION - An irregularity in the constitution or the number of chromosomes which may produce modifications in the normal course of development.

CHROMOSOME, ACENTRIC - Chromosome without a centromere.

CHROMOSOME BREAKS - Artificial transverse severance of a chromosome before its natural (longitudinal) division into the chromatid threads.

CHROMOSOME DELETION - Loss of an acentric segment of a chromosome.

CHROMOSOME, DICENTRIC - Chromosome with two centromeres.

CHROMOSOME DUPLICATION - The occurrence of a segment twice in the same chromosome.

CHROMOSOME EXCHANGE, INTERCHANGE, OR INTRACHANGE - If two different chromosomes are broken, illegitimate union between the four broken ends leads to interchange. If each new chromosome contains a centromere (symmetrical interchange) there is no mechanical disadvantage attaching to the new formation. If new chromosome has both centromeres (asymmetrical interchange) the acentric fragment is likely to be lost while the dicentric chromosome may have mechanical difficulties in the later stages of division. Interchanges may occur when one chromosome is broken in two places and the fragments rejoin in a manner differing from the original alignments.

CHROMOSOME, HOMOLOGOUS - Similar to allelomorphic chromosomes.

CHROMOSOME INVERSION - The presence in a chromosome of a segment whose parts are in reverse linear order to that which is normal for that chromosome.

CHROMOSOMES, SEX - In many organisms sex is determined by a special chromosomal mechanism. In man and the fruit fly Drosophila, an embryo destined to develop into a male will have two chromosomes of the "sex" pair as distinguishable, known as an "X" and a "Y" chromosome. The "Y" is contributed by the spermatozoon, but half of the sperm carry "X" chromosomes. When an "X" bearing sperm fertilizes an ovum, it then becomes an embryo with "XX" which will become a female. This seems to be true also for the mouse. In birds, moths, and butterflies, the female has the dissimilar pair of sex chromosomes.

CHROMOSOME STRUCTURAL CHANGE - Any alteration in the order or arrangement of the component particles of one or more chromosomes. May be gross or minute. May include inversions, duplications, deficiencies involving small portions of any chromosome.

CHROMOSOME TRANSLOCATION - The change in position of a segment of a chromosome either to a different chromosome or to another part of the same chromosome.

CHROMOPHOBE - Cells whose constituents are non-stainable; no affinity for dyes.

CILIARY PROCESS - Supporting and contractile elements of the iris which originate from the lenticular zone.

CIRCLE OF WILLIS - An arterial circle formed by anastomoses between the internal carotids and the basilar artery; surrounds the pituitary gland.

CIRCULATORY ARCS - Intra-embryonic; vitelline; allantoic circulatory channels, each involving afferent and efferent tracts and interpolated capillary bed.

CLEAVAGE - The mitotic division of an egg resulting in blastomeres. *Syn.*, segmentation.

CLEAVAGE, IMMEDIATE - Sometimes the second polar body is as large as the maturing egg and may be fertilizable, giving rise to a mosaic individual if fertilized by another spermatozoon.

CLEAVAGE NUCLEUS - The nucleus which controls cleavage. This may be the syngamic nucleus of normal fertilization; the egg nucleus of parthenogenetic or gynogenetic eggs; or the sperm nucleus of androgenetic development.

CLEAVAGE PATH - Path taken by the syngamic nucleus to the position awaiting the first division.

CLITORIS - The small conical structure of the female mammal which is comparable both in position and in embryological origin to the penis of the male.

CLOACAL MEMBRANE - The endoderm of the large terminal cavity of the hindgut which fuses with the superficial ectoderm at the base of the tail to form a membrane that closes the cloaca to the outside, later to rupture as the anus. (*See* ANAL PLATE).

COCHLEA - Portion of the original otic vesicle associated with sense of hearing; supplied by vestibular ganglion of eighth cranial nerve, having to do with equilibration.

COELOM - Mesodermal body cavity of chordates, from the walls of which develop the gonads. It is subdivided in higher forms into pericardial, pleural, and peritoneal cavities. Extended as the exocoel or extra embryonic body cavity.

COENOBLAST - The layer which will give rise to the endoderm and mesoderm (obsolete).

COITUS - The sexual act of insertion of the male penis into the vagina of the female and the ejaculation of semen from the penis, sometimes resulting in fertilization.

COLLECTING TUBULE - Portion of nephric tubule system leading to the nephric duct (Wolffian, etc.); term also used to refer to tubules which conduct spermatozoa from the seminiferous tubule to the vasa efferentia, within the testis.

COLLICULI, INFERIOR - Posterior pair of thickenings of dorso-lateral walls of mesencephalon (two or four; corpora bigemina or quadrigemina) containing synaptic centers for auditory reflexes (mammal).

COLLICULI, SUPERIOR - Anterior pair of thickening of dorso-lateral walls of mesencephalon (two or four; corpora bigemina or quadrigemina) containing synaptic centers for visual reflexes in mammals. *Syn.*, optic lobes.

COLLOID - Dispersed substance whose particles are not smaller than 1μ nor larger than 100μ approximately. Physical state of protoplasm.

COMMISSURE, ANTERIOR - Axis cylinders, of spinal cord neuroblasts, which originate in the mantle layer, grow ventrally and cross over to the opposite side of the cord. Refers also to the fibers connecting the cerebral hemispheres, developing in the torus transversus of the lamina terminalis.

COMMISSURE, INFERIOR - Floor of the diencephalon between the mammillary tubercles.

COMMISSURE, POSTERIOR - Roof of the brain between the anterior limit of the mesencephalon and the synencephalon of the forebrain.

COMMISSURE, TROCHLEARIS - Region of the dorsal isthmus, the roof between the metencephalon and the mesencephalon.

COMPETENCE - State of reactivity, of disequilibrium in a complex system of reactants. Possessing labile determination or having reaction possibility. Competencies may appear simultaneously or in sequence within a given area, some to disappear later even without function. Embryonic competence seems to be lost in all adult tissues but may be reclaimed in a blastema. It is a name for the state of the cell area at or before the time when irritability is resolved and a developmental path is chosen. The word supercedes the older words of "potence", "potency", or "potentiality".

CONES OF GROWTH - The enlarged outgrowth of the neuroblast forms the axis cylinder or axone of the nerve fiber and is termed the cone of growth because the growth processes by which the axone increases in length are supposed to be located there.

CONGENITAL - An adjective which refers to (abnormal) conditions acquired during embryonic or fetal life, to be contrasted with genetic and post-natal acquired characters.

COPULATION PATH - The second portion of sperm migration path through the egg toward the egg nucleus, when there is any deviation from the entrance or penetration path; the path of the spermatozoon which results in syngamy.

CORDS, MEDULLARY - Structures which give rise to the urogenital connections and take part in the formation of the seminiferous tubules, and are derived from the blastema of the mesonephric cords.

CORDS, SEX - Strands of somatic cells and primordial germ cells growing from the cortex toward the medulla of the gonad primordium. Best seen in early phases of testes development.

CORNEA - Transparent head ectoderm plus underlying mesenchyme forms a layer directly over the eye.

CORONA RADIATA - Layer of follicle cells which immediately surround the egg of the mammal, and which cells are elongated and acquire intercellular canals radiating outwardly from the egg to the surrounding theca. *Syn.*, follicular epithelium.

CORPORA QUADRIGEMINA - Two pairs of rounded elevations arising from the dorso-lateral thickened walls of the mesencephalon associated with centers of hearing and vision.

CORPUS ALBICANS - Scar tissue over the point of rupture of an ovarian follicle following absorption of the corpus luteum.

CORPUS HAEMORRHAGICUM - Blood clot found in recently ruptured ovarian follicle.

CORPUS LUTEUM - A yellow granular substance derived from the zona granulosa found in the empty follicular vesicle after ovulation in mammals; endocrine function relative to gestation and ovulation. Substance called lutein.

CORPUS STRIATUM - Center of coordination of certain complex muscular activities, derived from the mantle layer of the ventro-lateral walls of the mammalian telencephalon.

CORPUS VITREUM - (*See* VITREOUS HUMOR).

COWPER'S GLANDS - Derivatives of the urethral epithelium, adjacent to the prostate, providing fluid for spermatozoa. *Syn.*, bulbo-urethral glands.

CRANIAL - Relative to the head; "craniad" means toward the head. *Syn.*, rostral, cephalad.

CRANIAL FLEXURE - Forward bending of the forebrain with the angle of the bend occuring transversely at the level of the midbrain. (*See* CEPHALIC FLEXURES).

CRANIOPAGUS - Cranial union in conjoined twins.

CRANIOSCHISIS - Open-roofed skull associated with undeveloped brain.

CREST, NEURAL - Paired cell masses derived from ectoderm cells along the edge of the former neural plate, and wedged into the space between the dorso-lateral wall of the closed neural tube and the integument. Gives rise to spinal ganglia after segmentation.

CREST SEGMENT - The original neural crests which become divided into segments, with the aid of the somites, from which develop the spinal and possibly also some cranial ganglia.

CROSS-FERTILIZATION - Union of gametes produced by different individuals which, if they are of different species, may produce hybrids with variable viability.

CROSSING OVER - Mutual exchange of portions of allelomorphic pairs of chromosomes during the process of synapsis in maturation.

CRYPORCHISM - An exceptional condition in which the testes of the male mammal fail to descend into the scrotum, usually causing sterility because of the body heat.

CRYPTS - Depressions found in the uterine wall for the reception of chorionic cotyledons.

CUMULUS OÖPHROUS - The aggregation of cells which immediately surrounded the mammalian egg within its Graafian follicle.

CUSHION SEPTUM - Two endothelial thickenings arise within the auricular canal and grow together to form a partition known as the cushion septum of the heart.

CUTIS PLATE - (*See* DERMATOME).

CYANOSIS - Mixing of arterial and venous blood in the newborn due to the failure of the ductus Botalli and the incompletely formed interauricular canal, resulting in "blue babies" of high mortality. Bluing of the skin as a result of a circulatory defect.

CYCLE OF SEMINIFEROUS EPITHELIUM - Successive cellular changes which appear in any area of a seminiferous tubule, consisting of 14 stages in the rat, each consisting of typical cell associations.   A cycle comprises the period between which two appearances of the same cell association occurs in the same area.

CYCLE, SEXUAL - Cyclic breeding activity, most evident in the female, associated with definite changes in the genital and endocrine systems.

CYCLOPIA - Failure of the eyes to separate; median fusion of the eyes which may be due to suppression of the rostral block of tissue which ordinarily separates the eyes.

CYSTIC DUCT - Narrow proximal portion of embryonic bile duct leading from the gall bladder to the common bile duct.

CYTASTERS - Asters arising independently of the nucleus in the cytoplasm.   May contain centrosomes, and achromatic figure with attraction sphere and astral rays and may divide and even cause the cytoplasm around them to divide.   Activity and structure unrelated to chromosomal material.

CYTE - A suffix meaning "cell" as oö-cyte (egg forming cell), spermato-cyte (sperm forming cell), or osteo-cyte (bone forming cell).

CYTOCHROME - An oxidizable pigment found in nearly all cells exhibiting definite spectral bands in reduced form, discovered by Keilin (1925).   Insoluble in water, poisoned by HCN, CO_2, and H_2S.

CYTOLEOSIS - Process by which a cell, already irreversibly differentiated, proceeds to its final specialization.

CYTOLISTHESIS - Tendency of embryonic cells to aggregate and to fill up disruptions of their union even in the absence of a common surface membrane, due to surface tension and selective adhesiveness (Roux, 1894). Moving of cells over one another by sliding, rotation, or both processes.

CYTOLOGY - The study of cells.

CYTOLYSIS - Breakdown of the cell, indicated by dispersal of formed components.

CYTOPLASM - The material of the cell exclusive of the nucleus; protoplasm apart from nucleoplasm.

CYTOSOME - Cytoplasmic mass exclusive of the nucleus.

CYTOTROPISM - Inevitable movement of a cell in response to external forces.

DECIDUA - The portion of the uterine wall cast off at the time of parturition.

DECIDUA BASALIS - That portion of the uterine wall to which the placenta is attached. *Syn.*, decidua serotina.

DECIDUA CAPSULARIS - The portion of the uterine mucosa and epithelium which covers the mammalian blastocyst opposite the placenta. *Syn.*, decidua reflexa.

DECIDUA VERA - The portion of the uterine wall aside from that associated with either the decidua basalis or the decidua capsularis, but which will eventually be in contact with the decidua capsularis with the expansion of the embryo.

DECIDUAL REACTION - The tissue changes which occur following the burrowing of the fertilized egg into the endometrium of the uterus.

DECIDUATE - The type of placentation which is characterized by the destruction of material (uterine) tissue, and hemorrhage at parturition.   True placenta.

DELAMINATION - A separation (of cell layers) by splitting, a process in mesoderm formation.

DENTAL PAPILLA - The mesenchymal portion of the tooth primoridium.

DENTAL RIDGE - A plate of cells which grows into the future gums from the lining of the mouth of the embryo, giving rise to the enamel-forming cells of the tooth,

DENTINE - The main portion of the tooth derived from mesoderm.

DERMAL BONES - Bony plates which originate in the dermis and cover the cartilaginous skull.

DERMATOME - The outer unthickened wall of the somite which gives rise to the dermis. *Syn.*, cutis plate.

DERMIS - The deeper layers of the skin entirely derived from mesoderm (dermatome).

DERMOCRANIUM - The portion of the skul which does not go through an intermediate cartilaginous stage in development. Syn. , membrano-cranium.

DETERMINATION - Process of development indicated when a tissue, whether treated as an isolate or a transplant, still develops in the originally predicted manner.

DETERMINATION OF SEX - Method by which the sex of the unborn is revealed. Not to be confused with sex determination which is generally achieved at the time of fertilization.

DEUTOPLASM - Yolk or secondary food substance of the egg cytoplasm, non-living.

DEVELOPMENT - Gradual transformation of dependent differentiation into self-differentiation; transformation of invisible multiplicity into a visible mosaic, elaboration of components in successive spatial hierarchies.

DIAKENISIS - A stage in maturation when the double chromosomal threads fuse to form the haploid number, generally in curious shapes, and then line up for the first two maturational divisions. The nuclear membrane is still present.

DIAPHRAGM - (See SEPTUM TRANSVERSUM).

DICHIRUS - Partial duplication of digits in hand or foot, possibly inherited. A type of polydactyly.

DIENCEPHALON - The portion of the forebrain posterior to the telencephalon, including the second and third neuromeres.

DIESTRUS - Short period of quiescence immediately following estrus in the mammalian sexual cycle.

DIFFERENTIATING CENTER - Area responsible for the localization and determination of various regions of the embryo, resulting in harmonious proportioning of parts.

DIFFERENTIATION - Acquisition of specialized features which distinguish areas from each other; progressive increase in complexity and organization, visible and invisible; elaboration of diversity through determination leading to histogenesis; production of morphogenetic heterogeneity. Syn. , differenzierung.

DIFFERENTIATION, CELLULAR - The process which results in specialization of a cell as measured by its distinctive, actual, and potential functions.

DIFFERENTIATION, CORPORATIVE - Differentiation resulting from the physiological functioning of parts.

DIFFERENTIATION, DEPENDENT - All differentiation that is not self-differentiation; the development of parts of the organism under mutual influences, such influences being activating, limiting, or inhibiting. Inability of parts of the organism to develop independently of other parts. Such a period in ontogeny always precedes that of irreversible determination. "Experimental embryology is a study of the differentiations which are dependent, causally effected. " (Roux, 1912). Syn. , correlative differentiation, Abhangige Differenzierung, Différentiation provoqueé.

DIFFERENTIATION, FUNCTIONAL - Differentiation of tissues resulting from forces associated with functions (stresses and strains) which they are performing.

DIFFERENTIATION, POTENCY - The total repertoire of differentiations, cytological and histological, available to a given cell. Wider significance than prospective fate.

DIFFERENTIATION, SELF - The perseverance in a definite course of development of a part of an embryo, regardless of its altered surroundings. Syn. , différentiation spontanée.

DIFFUSE PLACENTA - Placenta in which the individual villi are scattered over the intercotyledonary areas (e.g. , Giraffe).

DIKINETIC - Dicentric, having two kinetochores.

DIMEGALY - Possessing spermatozoa or ova of two sizes.

DIOCOEL - The cavity of the diencephalon, the ultimate third ventricle.

DIPHYGENIC - Having two types of development.

DIPLICHROMOSOME - Two identical chromosomes, held together at the kinetochore and originated by doubling of chromosomes without separation of daughter chromosomes.

DIPLOID - Normal number of chromosomes double the gametic or haploid; complete set of paired chromosomes as in the fertilized egg or somatic cell.

DIPLOTENE - The stage in maturation following the pachytene when the chromosomes again appear double and do not converge toward the centrosome. Sometimes refers to split individual chromosomes.

DIPYGUS - (*See* duplicatus inferior).

DISCOIDAL PLACENTA - Placenta developing on only one side of the blastocyst (*e.g.*, Rodents) in the general shape of a button or disc. Opposed to zonary placenta.

DISCUS PROLIGERUS - The oöcyte of the mammal is attached to the inner wall of the follicle by its neck which, along with the cells surrounding the ovum, are together known as the discus proligerus.

DISTAL - Farther from any point of reference, away from the main body mass.

DIVERTICULUM - The blind outpocketing of a tubular structure (*e.g.*, liver or thyroid anlagé).

DIVISION HIERARCHY - "Four dimensional array of cells of which one and only one member (the zygote) is before all other members in time, and is the only one to which every other term stands in a relation which is some power of D (*i.e.*, the relation is Dpa)." (Bertelanffy & Woodger, 1933).

DNA - A double helix consisting of two polynucleotide chains linked by pairs of purine and pyrimidine bases. Genetic information is coded in the order in which these bases are dispoded. There are two functions: self-replicating and heterocatalytic.

DOMINANCE - A relationship between two allelomorphic genes in a heterozygote. It may be complete or incomplete, in the latter case a heterozygote could be distinguished from a homozygote dominant.

DOMINANT - When (A) of a gene pair (A + a) in a heterozygote produces a phenotype resembling that of the homozygote (AA), "A" is regarded as dominant over "a". The alternative is recessive ("a" recessive to "A").

DOPA - 3:4:dioxyphenylalanin, an intermediate oxidation product of tyrosine and one that appears as a precursor of melanin pigment.

DORSAL ROOT GANGLION - The aggregation of neuroblasts which are derived from the neural crests and which send their processes into the dorsal horns of the spinal cord.

DORSAL THICKENING - The roof of the mesencephalon which gives rise to the optic lobes.

DUCT - (*See* ducts under specific names).

DUCTUS ARTERIOSUS - (*See* DUCTUS BOTALLI).

DUCTUS BOTALLI - The dorsal portion of the sixth pair of aortic arches which normally becomes occluded after birth, the remainder of the arch giving rise to the pulmonary arteries. *Syn.*, ductus arteriosus.

DUCTUS CHOLEDOCHUS - Common chamber associated with the duodenum into which the three pancreatic ducts, the hepatoenteric duct and the cystic duct (from the gall bladder) all empty, prior to their developing separate openings into the gut.

DUCTUS COCHLEARIS - The connection between the lagena and the utricle.

DUCTUS CUVIERI - Union of all somatic veins which empty directly into the heart, specifically the vein which unites the common cardinals and the sinus venosus. Sometimes regarded as synonymous with common cardinal.

DUCTUS CYSTO ENTERICUS - The original caudal duct which is derived principally from the right lobe of the liver.

DUCTUS ENDOLYMPHATICUS - The dorsal portion of the original otic vessels which has lost all connection with the epidermis, and which is partially constricted from the region which will form the semi-circular canals.

DUCTUS HEPATO-ENTERICUS - The original cephalic duct which is derived principally from the left lobe of the liver.

DUCTUS VENOSUS - The anastomising sinusoids of the umbilical blood stream form a major channel through the substance of the mammalian liver, to receive blood from the left and right hepatic (omphalomesenteric) veins as it leaves the liver to join the posterior vena cava and then enter the right auricle.

DUODENUM - Portion of the embryonic gut associated with the outgrowths of the pancreas and the liver (bile) ducts.

DUPLICITAS INFERIOR - Conjoined twins fused anteriorly, having two rumps. *Syn.*, dipygus.

DYADS - Aggregations of chromosomes consisting of two rather than four (tetrad) parts, term used to describe condition during maturation process.

DYSTELEOLOGY - Apparent lack of purpose in organic processes or structures although they may ultimately be shown to be teleological.

ECTODERM - Primary germ layer from which are derived the skin and all of its derivatives, the nervous system and sense organs and parts of the mouth and anus.

ECTRODACTYLY - Absence of hallux and sometimes one or two adjacent digits (*Syn.*, oligodactylism).

EDEMA - General puffiness or swelling of parts due to the accumulation of fluid in the tissues.

EFFERENT DUCTULES - Some mesonephric tubules adjacent to the testes which, together with a portion of the mesonephric duct, become the epididymis.

EGG MEMBRANES - Includes all egg coverings such as vitelline membrane, chorion, and the teritary coverings.

EGG RECEPTOR - Part of Lillie's scheme picturing parts that go into the fertilization reaction involving fertilizin. Egg receptor plus amboceptor plus sperm receptor gives fertilization.

EJACULATION - The forcible emission of mature spermatozoa from the body of the male.

EJACULATORY DUCT - The short portion of the mesonephric duct between the seminal vesicles and the urethra.

ELECTRODYNAMIC THEORY OF DEVELOPMENT - Theory that cell mitoses establish a definite differential potential capable of orienting growing nerve roots (axis cylinders) and thereby directing them (*e.g.*, toward the brain).

EMANCIPATION - Dynamic segregation from "autonomisation" establishment of local autonomy within embryonic areas.

EMBRYO - Any stage in the ontogeny of the fertilized egg, generally limited to the period prior to independent food-getting. The stage between the second week and the second month of the human embryo, or between about 4.5 and 15 days for the mouse. (*See* Fetus).

EMBRYOMA - (*See* teratoma).

EMBRYONIC DISC - The portion of the early mammalian embryo where the ectoderm and endoderm are in close contact with each other.

EMBRYONIC FIELD - Region of formative processes within the embryo, larger than the area of ultimate realization of structures concerned.

EMBRYONIC KNOB - The inner, trophoblastic, cell mass of the mammalian embryo (ectodermal).

EMBRYOTHROPH - The materials obtained when the tissues are broken down by the mammalian embryo, prior to the establishment of the placental circulation.

EMBRYOTROPHY - The means or the actual nourishment of the embryo.

ENCAPSIS - Superordinate system within the embryo. Processes may be purposeful for a subordinate system and yet destroy another system to which it itself is subordinate. These relations are called encapsis.

ENAMEL ORGAN - The ectodermal portion of the tooth anlage.

ENDOCARDIAL CUSHION OF ATRIO-VENTRICULAR CANAL - A median partition dividing the atrium into right and left channels.

ENDOCARDIUM - Delicate endothelial tissue forming the lining of the heart.

ENDOCHRONDRAL BONE - Bone pre-formed in cartilage. *Syn.*, cartilage bone.

ENDODERM - The outermost layer of the didermic mouse gastrula or trophoblast and the germ layer from which are derived the lining of the digestive tract and all of its derivatives.

ENCOLYMPHATIC DUCT - (*See* DUCTUS ENDOLYMPHATICUS).

ENDOLYMPHATIC SAC - (*See* SACCUSS ENDOLYMPHATICUS).

ENDOMETRIUM - (*See* UTERINE MUCOSA).

ENTERON - The definitive gut of the embryo, always lined with endoderm.

ENTYPY - A method of amnion formation in the mammal in which the trophoblast above the embryonic knob is never interrupted; a method of gastrulation (rodents) wherein the endoderm comes to lie externally to the amniotic ectoderm.

EPENDYMAL CELLS - Narrow zone of non-nervous and ciliated cells which surround the central canal (neurocoel), from the outer ends of which branching processes extend to the periphery, such processes forming a framework for other cellular elements in the spinal cord and brain.

EPICARDIUM - Outer thin layer covering the myo-cardium; originally part of the epi-myocardium.

EPIDERMIS - The ectodermal portion of the skin including the cutaneous glands, hair, feathers, nails, hoofs, and some types of horns and scales in various vertebrates.

EPIDIDYMIS - A tubular portion of the male genital system, derived from the anterior part of the Wolffian body, which conducts sperm from the testis to penis.

EPIGAMIC - Tending to attract the opposite sex.

EPIGENESIS - Developing of systems starting with primitive, homogeneous, lowly organized condition and achieving great diversification. Term coined by Harvey, the antithesis of preformation.

EPIGENETIC CRISIS - Change in speed (rate of development) or in direction of a part, rendering it more vulnerable to environmental variables. May be confused with "critical period", a developmental process with interactions. May be correlated with increase in nitrogen synthesis in cells of a specific area.

EPIMERE - The most dorsal mesoderm, that lying on either side of the nerve and notochord, which gives rise to the somites. *Syn.*, axial mesoderm.

EPIMORPHOSIS - Proliferation of material precedes the development of new parts.

EPIPHYSIS - An evagination of the anterior diencephalon of vertebrates which becomes separated from the brain as the pineal (endocrine) gland of the adult.

EPIPLOIC FORAMEN - Opening from the peritoneal cavity into the omental bursa, formed with change in position of the stomach. *Syn.*, foramen of Winslow.

EPITHELIUM - A thin covering layer of cells, may be ectodermal, endodermal, or mesodermal.

EPÖOPHORON - The anterior portion of the mesonephros rudimentary in the female but becoming the epididymis in the male bird and mammal.

EQUATIONAL MATURATION DIVISION - The maturational divisions in which there is no (qualitative) reduction in the chromosomal complex, similar in results to mitosis.

EQUATORIAL PLATE - The lateral view of the chromosomes, lined up on the mitotic spindle, prior to any anaphase movement.

ERGASTOPLASM - Basophilic parts of the cytoplasm, mitochondria of cytologists.

ESTRIN - An hormone found in the mammalian ovarian follicle.

ESTROGEN - Secretion product of the ovary which controls estrus and endometrial growth.

ESTROUS CYCLE - The periodic series of changes which occur in the mammalian uterus, related to the preparation of the uterus for implantation of the ovum, and to repair.

ESTRUS - Period of the reproductive cycle of the mammal when the uterus is prepared for implantation of the ovum.

EUCHROMATIN - The part of the regular chromatic structure of the nucleus which is rich in thymonucleic acid, and presumably the genes, alternating (in the chromosomes) with achromatic regions. It is in the form of discs, and takes methyl green stain.

EUPLOIDY - Deviation from the normal diploid condition but involving complete sets of chromosomes.

EUSTACHIAN TUBE - Vestige of the endodermal portion of the hyomandibular pouch connecting middle ear and pharyngeal cavity, lined with endoderm.

EVAGINATION - The growth from any surface outward.

EXOCOEL - The cavity within mesoderm beyond the limits of the embryo, continuous with the coelom. *Syn.*, extra embryonic body cavity; coelom; seroamniotic cavity.

EXOGENOUS - Originating from without the organism.

"EX OVO OMNIA" - All life comes from the egg (Harvey, 1657).

EXTRA EMBRYONIC - Refers to structures apart from the embryonic body, such as the membranes.

FACTOR - The hypothetical determinant of a character in respect of which an organism may show alternative (Mendelian) inheritance.

F_1, F_2 - First and second filial generation.

FALCIFORM LIGAMENT - Portion of the original ventral mesentery between the liver and the ventral body wall, supporting the liver.

FALLOPIAN TUBES - The oviducts of the mammal.

FALSE AMNIOTIC CAVITY - A temporary cavity arising in the dorsal trophoblast of the mammalian embryo, having no connection with the true amniotic cavity.

FERTILIZATION - Activation of the egg by a spermatozoön and syngamy of the two pronuclei; union of male and female gamete nuclei; amphimixis.

FERTILIZATION, PARTIAL - Male pronucleus fails to meet the female pronucleus, and eventually unites with a blastomere nucleus of the 2 or 4 cell stage.

FERTILIZATION, SOMATIC - Sperm penetration of cells of the female genital tract, even without syngamy. May be confused with phagocytosis.

FERTILIZATION MEMBRANE - A non-living membrane seen to be distinct from the egg shortly after fertilization, very probably the vitelline membrane elevated off of the egg (or from which the egg has shrunken away by exosmosis).

FERTILIZIN - A substance in the jelly coat of the egg, a glyco-protein with a molecular weight of 82,000 or more. In solution it is multivalent, the molecules being capable of linking together several spermatozoa. Functions to attract homologous spermatozoa to the jelly coat surface, a necessary preliminary to fertilization. May also be a component of the plasma membrane of the egg.

FETUS - Embryo after it has attained definite characteristics of the species; the embryo of the mammal when it has attained sufficient development to survive independently of the mother, about 17 days for the mouse.

FETUS PAPYRACEUS - Compressed fetus, abnormal: "paper-doll fetus".

FEULGEN REACTION - Schiff's aldehyde test accomplished by hydrolysis of thymonucleic acid to yield the aldehyde which reacts with fuchsin given a brilliant violet or pink color, a specific test for the thymonucleic acid of chromosomes.

FIBRILLATION - Process of formation of (collagenous) fibers by the aggregation of ultramicrons whose axes are nearly parallel. May be the method of axis formation in limb rudiments.

FIELD - Mosaic of spatio-temporal activities within the developing organism constitute fields; areas of instability with positional relations to the whole organism, with which specific differentiations are about to take place (*e.g.*, heart or limb fields). Dynamic system of interrelated parts in perfect equilibrium in the undifferentiated organism. Not a definite circumscribed area (like a stone in a mosaic) but a center of differentiation with intensity diminishing with the distance from the center, and with different fields overlapping. A system of patterned conditions in a self-sustaining configuration. Has a material substratum which may be reduced without fundamentally altering the original field pattern. Field is both heteroaxial and heteropolar. "Morphe concept" of Gurwitsch (1914).

FIELD, MORPHOGENETIC - Embryonic area out of which specific structures will develop; fields which determine the development of form in a unitary structure.

FIELD ORGAN - Area in which a specific organ of the embryo will develop (*e.g.*, eye field.

FLEXURE - Refers to a bending such as the cranial, cervical and pontine flexures. Also dorsal and lumbo-sacral flexures of the pig.

FOLLICLE - A cellular sac within which the egg generally goes through the maturation stages from oögonium to ovum; made up of follicle cells, theca interna and externa.

FOLLICLE, GRAAFIAN - The follicle of the mammalian ovary, including a double-layered capsule; the membrana granulosa, discus proligerus, corona radiata, and follicular fluid.

FONTANELLES - The area on top of the fetus's skull that is not completely covered by bones, the so-called "soft spot" on the newborn child's head.

FORAMEN - (*See* under specific names as INTERATRIAL, EPIPLOIC, MUNRO, etc.)

FORAMEN OVALE - An opening between the embryonic auricular chambers of the heart.

FOREBRAIN - The most anterior of the first three primary brain vesicles, associated with the lateral opticoels. *Syn.*, prosencephalon.

FOREGUT - The more anterior portion of the enteric canal, the first to appear, aided by the development of the head fold. Its margin is the anterior intestinal portal.

FREEMARTIN - Mammalian intersex due to masculinization of a female by its male partner when the foetal circulations are continuous and the sex hormones are intermingled, as in parabiosis.

FRONTAL - A plane at right angles to both the transverse and sagittal, dividing the dorsal from the ventral. *Syn.*, coronal.

FURCHUNG - Division of the egg cell into blastomeres by mitosis.

GAMETE - A differentiated (mature) germ cell, capable of functioning in fertilization. (*e.g.*, spermatozoön, ovum) *Syn.*, germ cell.

GAMETOGENESIS - The process of developing and maturing germ cells.

GANGLION, ACOUSTIC - Eighth (VIII) cranial ganglion from which the fibres of the eighth cranial nerve arise, purely sensory. Ganglion later divides into vestibular and spiral ganglia.

GANGLION, ACUSTICO-FACIALIS - Early undifferentiated association of the 7th and 8th cranial ganglia.

GANGLION, GASSERIAN - The fifth (V) cranial ganglion, carrying both sensory and motor fibres. *Syn.*, trigeminal ganglion, semilunar ganglion. (*See* Trigeminal ganglion.)

GANGLION, GENICULATE - The ganglion at the root of the facial (VII) cranial nerve, carrying both sensory and motor fibres. Later divides into vestibular and spiral ganglia.

GANGLION, NODOSAL - Ganglion associated with the vagus (X) cranial nerve which carries afferent fibres to pharynx, larynx, trachea, oesophagus, thoracic and abdominal viscera.

GANGLION, PETROSAL - Ganglion associated with the glossopharyngeal (IX) cranial nerve, more peripheral than the superior ganglion carrying sensory fibres from pharynx and root of tongue. From myelencephalon.

GARTNER'S CANAL - Remains of the mesonephric duct in female mammals.

GASSERIAN GANGLION - The fifth cranial or trigeminal ganglion, derived from the hindbrain.

GASTRO-HEPATIC OMENTUM - Portion of the ventral mesentery between the liver and the stomach which persists. *Syn.*, ventral mesogastrium.

GASTROCOEL - Major cavity formed during the process of gastrulation. *Syn.*, archenteron.

GASTROSCHISIS - Improper closure of the body wall along the mid-ventral line, persistent externalized viscera.

GASTRULA - The didermic or double-layered embryo. The two layers are ectoderm and endoderm with only positional significance when first formed. In the mouse the endoderm is at first external to ectoderm.

GASTRULATION - Dynamic processes involving cell movements which change the embryo from a monodermic to a di- or tri-dermic form, generally involving inward movement of cells to form the enteric endoderm. Process varies in detail in different forms, but may include epiboly, concrescence, confluence, involution, invagination, extension, convergence - all of which are descriptive terms for morphogenetic movements.

GEL - A system in which there is a reduction in the amount of solvent relative to the amount of solid substance, thereby causing the whole to become viscous (*e.g.*, asters).

GENE - Self-producing molecule transmitted by the chromosome which determines the development of the characters of the individual, some of which may be solely embryonic.

GENES, LINKED - Genes showing the tendency to assort in parental combinations in a heterozygote instead of assorting independently (*See* linkage).

GENETIC LIMITATION - Each cell must react exclusively in accordance with the standards of the species which it represents.

GENITAL - Refers to the reproductive organs or processes, or both.

GENITAL DUCTS - Any ducts which convey gametes from their point of origin to the region of insemination. *e.g.*, collecting tubules, vas deferens, vas efferens, epididymis, seminal vesicle, oviduct (Fallopian tub) uterus, etc. *Syn.*, gonoduct.

GENITAL RIDGE - Initial elevation for the development of the external genitalia; paired mesodermal thickenings between the meso-nephros and the dorsal mesentery of all vertebrates, which are the gonad primordia.

GENITAL TUBERCLE - The ridge at the base of the phallus, also the primordium of the mammalian labioscrotal swellings, primordium of either penis or clitoris.

GENITALIA - Refers to the sexual organs, external or internal.

GENOME - Haploid gene complex; minimum (haploid) number of chromosomes with their genes derived from a gamete.

GENOTYPE - The actual genetic make-up of an individual, regardless of its appearance (opposed to phenotype).

GERM - The egg throughout its development, or at any stage.

GERM CELL - A cell capable of sharing in the reproductive process, in contrast with the somatic cell. (*e.g.*, spermatozoön or ovum.) *Syn.*, gamete.

GERM LAYER - A more-or-less artificial spatial and histogenic distinction of cell groups beginning in the gastrula stage, consisting of ectoderm, endoderm and mesodermal layers. No permanent or clear cut distinctions, as shown by transplantation experiments.

GERM PLASM - The hereditary material, generally referring specifically to the genotype. Opposed to somatoplasm.

GERMINAL EPITHELIUM - The peritoneal epithelium out of which the reproductive cells of both the male and female develop. *Syn.*, germinal ridges, gonadal ridges.

GERMINAL SPOT - *Syn.*, nucleolus of ovum.

GERMINAL VESICLE - The pre-maturation nucleus of the egg.

GESTALTEN - A system of configurations consisting of a ladder of levels; electron, atom, molecule, cell, tissue, organ, and organism, each one of which exhibits specifically new modes of action that cannot be understood as mere additive phenomena of the previous levels. With each higher level new concepts become necessary. The parts of a cell cannot exist independently, hence the cell is more than a mere aggregation of its parts, it is a patterned whole. Coherent unit reaching a final configuration in space. Gestaltung means formation.

GESTATION - Period of carrying the young within the uterus, 19 to 21 days in the various strains of mice.

GIANT CELLS (in placenta) - Contiguous with the spongiotrophoblasts; nuclei invaginated in many places and the recesses contain cytoplasm. Cytoplasm complex, vacuoles and membranes have general appearance of phagocytes. Contains mucopolysaccharides, are fibrous, and sometimes seem to be continuous with Reichert's membrane. Surface is often in direct contact with maternal blood.

GLIA CELLS - Small rounded supporting cells of the spinal cord, derived from the germinal cells of the neural ectoderm.

GLOMERULUS - An aggregation of capillaries associated with the branches of dorsal aorta but lying within the substance of the functional kidney; function is excretory.

GLOMUS - The vascular aggregations within the head kidney or pronephros, never to become a glomerulus.

GLOTTIS - The opening between the pharynx and the larynx.

GNOTOBIOTIC - Animal that is germ free (*Syn.*, axemic).

GOLGI APPARATUS - May be a dense reticular mass of argentophilic or osmiophilic bodies, enclosing argentophobic or osmiophogic inclusions, disposed near the nucleus and often around the centrosome. May also be scattered in small bodies, associated with ribosomes, vesicles, and vacuoles in electron micrographs.

GONAD - The organ within which germ cells are produced and generally matured, (*e.g.* ovary or testis.) *Syn.*, sex or germ gland.

GONIUM - Suffix referring to a stage in the maturation of a germ cell prior to any maturation divisions. *e.g.*, spermatogonium, or oögonium.

GONODUCT - (*See* GENITAL DUCTS).

GONOSOMIC MOSAIC - Individual that may be phenotypically normal, karyotypically normal in tissues examined, but imbalanced in the reproductive cells and meiosis.

GRAAFIAN FOLLICLE - (*See* FOLLICLE, GRAAFIAN).

GRADIENT - Gradual variation of developmental forces along an axis; scaled regions of preference. (*See* AXIS).

GRANULES, CORTICAL - Granules 0.1 to 0.5 microns in diameter, in the egg surface, which disappear upon fertilization. May release a membrane-modifying agent, with progressive changes in the zona pellucida.

GRANULOSA - The layer of follicle cells which surround the mammalian ovum, so called because of their granular appearance when crowded.

GROWTH - Cell proliferation; a developmental (synthetic) increase in total mass of protoplasm at the expense of raw materials; an embryonic process generally following differentiation (*See* heterogony).

GROWTH, ACCRETIONARY - Growth involving increase in non-living structural matter.

GROWTH, AUXETIC - Growth involving increase in cell size alone.

GROWTH, ISOGONIC - Similar rates of growth in different regions of the embryo.

GROWTH, MULTIPLICATIVE - Growth involving increase in the number of nuclei and of cells. *Syn.*, meristic growth.

GROWTH, PARTITION COEFFICIENTS OF - Inherent growth rates (*e.g.*, in limb rudiments) involving changes in proportions.

GROWTH COEFFICIENT - Growth rate of a part relative to the growth rate of the whole (organism) depending on factors inherent in the tissues concerned.

GROWTH POTENTIALS - Capabilities or predispositions for growth.

GROWTH REGULATION - A substance (R) postulated by Harrison, distinct from nutritional factors, present in the circulating medium of the organism, which controls growth.

GUBERNACULUM - The fibrous cord which draws the testis down into the scrotum of the male mammal just before birth.

GYNOGAMONES - Highly acidic, polysaccharide containing protein of low nitrogen content, and elongate, gel-forming molecular structure. Possibly the fertilizins of Lillie, but so named by Hartmann.

GYNOGENESIS - Development of an egg with the egg nucleus alone. This may be brought about by rendering the sperm nucleus functionless for syngamy by irradiation or other means, or by surgical removal. Opposed to androgenesis.

HAEMOTROPHE - The nutritive substances supplied to the embryo from the maternal blood stream.

HAPLOID - Having a single complete set of chromosomes, none of which appear in pairs, the condition in the gametic nucleus. Opposed to diploid, or twice the haploid, where the chromosomes appear as pairs (*e.g.*, as in somatic cells).

HARDERIAN GLAND - A solid ingrowth of ectodermal cells of the conjunctival sac appearing at the innermost angle of the nictitating membrane.

HEAD CAP - Thin membrane arising from the acrosomic granule and extending over a large portion of the nuclear surface of the mature spermatozoon; staining with PA-PSA.

HEAD OF SPERMATOZOÖN - Nucleus, head, cap, and acrosome in spermatids at the acrosome and maturation phases, and in spermatozoa.

HEAT, PERIOD OF - Period of strong mating impulse in some female mammals. *Syn.*, estrus.

HEMIKARYOTIC - Haploid. In merogony, hemikaryotic, arrhenokaryotic, androgenetic or in artificial parthenogenesis, hemikaryotic, thelykaryotic, gynogenetic.

HEMIMELIA - Reduction or absence of one bone of a normal pair such as radius-ulna, tibia-fibula; the entire limb and girdle may be involved. Some evidence as genetic dominant, may be lethal.

HEMIMELUS - Failure of distal portion of appendages to develop.

HEMIPLACENTA - The chorion, the yolk sac, and generally the allantois which together serve as an organ of nutritional supply to the uterine young of marsupials.

HEMIZYGOTE - A diploid organism in which one chromosome is present only once, as in the case of the sex ("X") chromosome in the male of many species.

HEMOTROPHE - Nutritive materials absorbed by the placenta or fetal membranes directly from the circulation of maternal flood. Type of nutrition found in hemochorial placentas.

HEPATIC PORTAL VEINS- Remnants of the posterior portions of the left vitelline or omphalomesenteric vein, supplied with blood mainly from the placenta but also from veins of the alimentary canal and connected with the hepatic veins only through sinuses within the liver. Function eventually assumed by the mesenteric vein.

HEPATIC SINUSOIDS - Maze of dilated and irregular capillaries between the loosely packed framework of hepatic tubules.

HEPATIC VEINS - Veins from the liver to the heart, originating as the anterior portions of the vitelline or the omphalomesenteric veins.

HERMAPHRODITE - An individual capable of producing both spermatozoa and ova.

HERTWIG'S LAW - The nucleus tends to place itself in the center of its sphere of activity; the longitudinal axis of the mitotic spindle tends to lie in the longitudinal axis of the yolk-free cytoplasm of the cell.

HETEROCHROMATIN - Part of the chromatic structure which seems to be related to the formation of the nucleolus. Takes a violet stain after methyl green but is digested away by ribonuclease. Probably represents both thymo- and ribo-nucleic acids.

HETEROPLASIA - Development of a tissue from one of a different kind.

HETEROPLOIDY - Any deviation from the normal diploid number of chromosomes.

HETEROPYCNOSIS - Character of X and Y chromosomes before the first meiotic division in spermatogenesis; X and Y have end-to-end association in synapsis; heteropycnotic X may be genetically inactive.

HETEROZYGOUS - Condition where the zygote is composed of gametes bearing allelomorphic genes. Opposed to homozygous.

HINDBRAIN - The most posterior of the three original brain divisions, the first neuromere of which is larger than the succeeding neuromeres, there being a total of five. *Syn.*, rhombencephalon.

HINDGUT - Portion of embryonic gut just posterior to the posterior intestinal portal. Level of origin of the rectum, cloaca, post-anal gut, allantois, and caudal portions of the uro-genital systems.

HISTOGENESIS - The appearance, during embryonic development, of histological differentiation; the development of tissue differentiation.

HISTOLYSIS - The destruction of tissues.

HISTOTELEOSIS - Process by which a cell-line, already irreversibly differentiated, proceeds to its final histological specialization.

HISTOTROPHE - The nutritive substances supplied to the embryos of viviparous forms from sources other than the maternal blood stream (*e.g.*, from uterine glands). Secretion and degradation product of the endometrium as well as extravasated maternal blood, which undergo absorption. Found in epitheliochorial placental types.

HOMOIOTHERMAL - Refers to condition where the temperature of the body of the organism is under the control of an internal mechanism; the body temperature is regulated under any environmental conditions. Opposed to poikilothermal. *Syn.*, warm blooded (animals).

HOMOLOGOUS - Organs having the same embryonic development and/or evolutionary origin, but not necessarily the same function.

HOMOLOGY - Similarity in structure based upon similar embryonic origin.

HOMOZYGOUS - Condition where the zygote is composed of gametes bearing identical rather than allelomorphic genes.

HORIZONTAL - An unsatisfactory term sometimes used synonymously with frontal, longitudinal, and even sagittal plane or section. Actually means across the lines of gravitational force.

HORMONE - A secretion of a ductless gland which can stimulate or inhibit the activity of a distant part of the biological system already formed.

HUMORAL SYSTEM - Body fluids carrying specific chemical substances which may circulate in formed channels (blood vessels or lymphatics) or diffuse freely in the body cavities or tissue spaces, (*e.g.*, neurohumors of Parker which act on the pigmentary system).

HYALOPLASM - Ground substance of the cell apart from the contained bodies.

HYALURONIDASE - Enzyme from plasma membrane of the sperm, derived from spermatogenic epithelium, and aid to penetrating cumulus oöphorus. When sperm die they release their quanta of this enzyme, but living sperm cannot release it until they have undergone physiological conditioning known as capacitation.

HYBRID - A successful cross between different species, although organism may be sterile (*e.g.*, mule).

HYBRIDIZATION - Fertilization of an egg by sperm of a different species.

HYDROCEPHALUS, CONGENITAL - Generalized disturbance of the membranous skeleton (recessive and lethal at birth), due to a shortening of the chondrocranium. Affects the entire skeleton because the cartilage is abnormal, or delayed in development.

HYDRODYNAMICS - Process by which the detailed architecture of the blood vessels is derived, such details as size, angles or branching, courses to be followed, etc. The internal water pressure may be the cause of specific developmental procedure.

HYMEN - A membrane of varying thickness in different individuals which closes the lower portion of the vagina, and is generally ruptured during the initial coitus. The mouse vagina is generally covered through weaning period.

HYOID ARCH - The mesodermal mass between the hyomandibular and the first branchial cleft, or between the first and second visceral pouches or clefts which gives rise to parts of the hyoid apparatus. *Syn.*, second visceral arch.

HYOMANDIBULAR - Refers to the pouch, cleft, or slit between the mandibular and the hyoid arches.

HYPERINNERVATION - Supplying an organ with more than a single (normal) nerve fiber.

HYPERPLASIA - Overgrowth; abnormal or unusual increase in elements composing a part.

HYPERTROPHY - Increase in size due to increase in demands upon the part concerned.

HYPERTROPHY, COMPENSATORY - Increase in size of part or a whole organ due to loss or removal of part or the whole of an organ (generally hypertrophy in one member of the pair of organs).

HYPOMERE - The most ventral segment of mesoderm out of which develop the somatopleure, splanchnopleure, and coelom. *Syn.*, lateral plate mesoderm.

HYPOMORPHIC - Cells or tissues which are subordinate to formative processes.

HYPOMORPHOSIS - Harmonious underdevelopment.

HYPOPHYSIS - An ectodermally derived structure arising anterior to the stomodeum and growing inwardly toward the infundibulum to give rise to the anterior and intermediate parts of the pituitary gland. *Syn.*, Rathke's pocket.

HYPOPLASIA - Undergrowth or deficiency in the elements composing a part.

HYPOTHALAMUS - Ventral portion of lateral thickening of diencephalon, not clearly distinguishable from the mesothalamic portion of the optic thalamus.

HYPOTHESIS - A complemental supposition; a presumption based on fragmentary but suggestive data offered to bridge a gap in incomplete knowledge of the facts. May even be offered as an explanation of facts unproven, to be used as a basis of expectations to be subject to verification or disproof.

HYSTEROTELY - Formation of a structure is relatively delayed.

IDIOZOME - The material out of which the acrosome is formed during the metamorphosis of spermatid to spermatozoön.

IMPLANTATION - The process of adding, superimposing, or placing a graft within a host without removal of any part of the host; the attachment of the mammalian blastocyst.

IMPLANTATION, DELAYED - Implantation of blastocyst may be delayed in females that are suckling a previous litter. Can also be induced in pregnant, non-suckling mice if they have been ovariectomized after the current ovulation, and are given daily injections of progesterone. Estrogens terminate the delay and implantation follows.

INDECIDUATE PLACENTA - The type of placenta in which each villus simply fits into a crypt, as a plug fits into a socket, from which it is withdrawn at birth without serious hemorrhage or destruction of maternal tissues. *Syn.*, nondeciduate.

INDUCTION - Causing cells to form an embryonic structure which neither the inductor nor the reacting cells would form if not combined; the calling forth of a morphogenetic functional state in a competent blastema as a result of contact. In contrast with evocation, induction is successive, and purposeful in the sense that one structure leads to another. Sometimes loosely used to include evocator influences from non-living materials. Originally meant diversion of development from epidermis toward medullary plate.

INFUNDIBULUM OF THE BRAIN - Funnel-like evagination of the floor of the diencephalon which, along with the hypophysis, will give rise to the pituitary gland of the adult.

INFUNDIBULUM OF THE OVIDUCT - (*See* OSTIUM ABDOMINALE).

INGUINAL CANAL - The canal connecting the body or abdominal cavity with the scrotum in the male, through which the testes may descend just before birth.

INHIBITION, CONTACT - When two normal tissues meet, as in a culture, their forward movement ceases and they form a stable region of attachment at their surfaces of contact.

INNER CELL MASS - The spherical cells on the inner side of the mammalian blastocyst.

INSEMINATION - The process of impregnation; to fertilize.

INSTINCT - "The overt behavior of the organism as a whole" . . . . . which is in physiological condition to act according to its genetically determined neuromuscular structure when adequate internal and external stimuli act upon it." (Hartmann, 1942, Psychosomatic Med. 4:206.)

INTERATRIAL FORAMEN - (*See* FORAMEN OVALE).

INTERAURICULAR SEPTUM - A longitudinal sheet of (mesodermal) tissue which grows ventrally from the roof of the auricular chamber to divide it into right and left halves.

INTERKINESIS - Resting stage between mitotic divisions.

INTERMEDIATE CELL MASS - The narrow strip of mesoderm which, for a time, joins the dorsal epimere with the ventral hypomere, being made up of a dorsal portion continuous with the dorsal wall of the somite and the somatic mesoderm and a ventral portion continuous with the ventral wall of the somite and the splanchnic mesoderm. Source of origin of the excretory system. *Syn.*, nephrotome or middle plate.

INTERNAL LIMITING MEMBRANE - A membrane which develops on the innermost surface of the inner wall of the optic cup.

INTERSEX - An individual without sufficient sexual differentiation to diagnose as male or female.

INTERSTITIAL CELLS - Specialized cells between the seminiferous tubules of the testes, produce hormones.

INTERSTITIAL TISSUE OF TESTIS - Cell aggregates between the seminiferous tubules of the testis which elaborate a male sex hormone.

INTERVENTRICULAR SEPTUM - A partition growing anteriorly from the apex of the ventricle, which extends from the auricle to the bulbus arteriosus and divides the ventricle.

INTERVERTEBRAL FISSURE - A cleft between the caudal and cephalic divisions of the sclerotome.

INTERZONAL FIBRE - Portion of the spindle fibres located between chromosome groups in the anaphase and telophase stages.

INTESTINAL PORTAL - An opening from the midgut into either the anterior or posterior levels of the formed gut.

INVAGINATION - Movement by in-sinking of the egg surface and forward migration involving displacement of inner materials. The folding or impushing of a layer of cells into a preformed cavity as one of the methods of gastrulation. Not to be confused with involution.

INVOLUTION - Rotation of a sheet of cells upon itself; movement directed toward the interior of an egg; the rolling inward or turning in of cells over a rim. One of the movements of gastrulation. *Syn.*, embolic invagination; einrollung, or umschlag.

IRIS - The narrow zone bounding the pupil of the eye in which two layers of the optic cup become blended so that the pigment from the outer layer invades the material of the inner layer, giving the eye a specific color by variable reflection.

ISAUXESIS - Relative growth comparisons in which the rate of the part is the same as that of the whole. (*Syn.*, isogony.).

ISO-AGGLUTININ - (*Syn.*, for fertilizin.)

ISOGONY - Proportionate growth of parts so that growth coefficient is unity and there are constant relative size differences. Equivalent relative growth rate.

ISO-HISTOGENIC - Uniform with regard to the histologically compatible factors.

ISOMETRY - Study of relative sizes of parts of animals of the same age.

ISOPYCNOSIS - Condition characteristic of all chromosomes of the male, including the X. In females only one X is isopycnotic with the autosomes, the others are heteropycnotic hence the females often react as heterozygotes with regard to the X chromosome.

ISOTROPIC - Synonym for pluripotent.

ISOTROPY - Originally used to mean absence of predetermined axes within the egg; now means condition of egg where any part can give rise to any part of the embryo (*e.g.*, equivalence of all parts of the egg protoplasm).

ITER - (*See* AQUEDUCT OF SYLVIUS).

JACOBSON'S ORGAN - Ventro-medial evaginations from the olfactory pits which later become the glandular and sensitive olfactory epithelia.

JANICEPS - Janus monster, face to face union of conjoined twins.

JANUS EMBRYO - Double monster with faces turned in opposite directions. *Syn.*, duplicatas cruciata typica.

JUGULAR VEINS - Veins which bring blood from the head; the superior or internal jugular being the anterior cardinal veins and the inferior jugular veins growing toward the lower jaw and mouth from the base of each ductus Curieri.

KARYOPLASM - Protoplasm within the confines of the nucleus.

KERN-PLASMA RELATION - Ratio of the amount of nuclear and of cytoplasmic materials present in the cell. It seems to be a function of cleavage to restore the kern-plasma relation from the unbalanced condition of the ovum (with its excessive yolk and cytoplasm) to that of the somatic cell.

KINETOCHORE - Spindle fiber attachment region. *Syn.*, centromere.

LABIA - Latin for "lips", referring to the lateral folds of skin around the orifice of the vagina, possibly homologous to the scrotum.

LABIO-SCROTAL SWELLINGS - The primordia of the labia majora (female) or of part of the scrotum (male) in mammals. Mound-like swellings on either side of the genital tubercle that give rise to the labia of the female and scrotum of the male.

LACHRYMAL GROOVE - A shallow groove between the lateral nasal and the maxillary processes.

LACUNA - Literally a "little lake", referring to the numerous gaps in the mammalian trophoderm into which maternal blood is emptied when the vessels are destroyed.

LAMINA TERMINALIS - The point of suture of the anterior neural folds (*i. e.*, the anterior neuropore) where they are finally separated from the head ectoderm, consisting of a median ventral thickening at the anterior limit of the telencephalon from the anterior side of the optic recess to the beginning of the velum transversum and including the anterior commissure of the torus transversus.

LANGHANS CELLS - Found in the secondary and tertiary chorionic villi, closely opposed on their outer surfaces to the syncitium and their basal surfaces to the basement membrane. Chromophobic or slightly basophilic, meager endoplasmic reticulum (ergastoplasm), contain glycogen early in gestation, no lipids and few mitochondira.

LANUGO - The fine hairy covering of the fetal mammal.

LARYNGO-TRACHEAL GROOVE - A transverse narrowing of the post-branchial region of the embryonic pharynx with consequent formation of a groove which lead posteriorly to the lung primordia.

LARYNX - The anterior part of the original laryngo-tracheal groove which becomes a tube opening into the pharynx by way of the glottis.

LATERAL - Either the right (dextral) or left (sinistral) side; Lateral means toward the side.

LATERAL AMNIOTIC FOLDS - Folds of the amnion extending up over the sides of the embryo, developing as corollaries to, or in consequence of, the head and tail amniotic folds.

LATERAL LIMITING SULCUS - (*See* LIMITING SULCUS).

LATERAL MESOCARDIUM - Septum posterior to the heart extending from the base of each vitelline vein obliquely upward to the dorso-lateral body wall, representing one of the three parts of the septum transversum.

LATERAL MESODERM - (*See* LATERAL PLATE MESODERM).

LATERAL NEURAL FOLDS - (*See* MEDULLARY FOLDS).

LATERAL PLATES OR LATERAL PLATE MESODERM - The lateral mesoblast within which the body cavity (coelom and exocoel) arises. *Syn.*, lateral mesoderm.

LATERAL VENTRICLES OF THE BRAIN - The thick-walled and laterally compressed cavity of the prosencephalon which opens into the third ventricle by way of the foramin of Monro; the walls will become the cerebral hemispheres.

LECITHIN - Organismic fat which is phosphorized in the form of phosphatides.

LENS - A thickening in the head ectoderm opposite the optic cup which becomes a placode; invaginates to acquire a vesicle; and then pinches off into the space of the optic cup as a lens. Inner surface convex; substance fibrous.

LENS PLACODE - The early thickened ectodermal primordium of the lens.

LENTICULAR ZONE - The portion around the rim of the optic cup adjacent to the pupil, separated from the retinal zone in later development by the ora serrata.

LEPTOTENE - A stage in maturation which follows the last gonial division and is prior to the synaptene stage, structurally similar to the resting cell stage. The chromatin material is in the form of a spireme. The term means thin, diffuse.

LESSER PERITONEAL CAVITY - The growth of the liver to the right mesonephros and finally to the portal vein cuts off a portion of the peritoneal cavity giving rise later to the greater and lesser omental spaces on either side of the coeliac fold. *Syn.*, bursa omenti (major and minor).

LIMB BUDS - Swellings on the sides of vertebrate embryos which will eventually give rise to the appendages.

LINKAGE - Exists between two factors when they do not assort independently of one another in a double heterozygote; measured among gametes by frequency of recombination by crossing over.

LIPIDS - Fats and fatty substances such as oil and yolk (lecithin) found in eggs. E. g. cholesterol, ergosterol.

LIPIN - Fats and fatty substances such as oil and yolk (*e.g.*, lecithin) in eggs, important as water holding device in cells as well as insuring cell immiscibility with surrounding media. (*e.g.*, cholesterol, ergosterol).

LIPOGENESIS - Omission of certain stages in ontogeny.

LIPOPHORES - Pigmented cells in the dermis and epidermis, derived from neural crests and characterized by having diffuse yellow (lipochrome) pigment in solution.

LIPOSOMES - Droplets of yellow oil which may be formed by the coalescence of droplets of broken down lipochondria.

LIQUOR FOLLICULI - The fluid of the mammalian Graäfian follicle into which the matured ovum is freed when the discus proligerus is broken, finally to be liberated from the ovary at the time of ovulation. Contains hormones.

LITHOPEDION - Mummified or calcified fetuses; "stone-child".

LOBSTER CLAW - Missing digits in hands or feet, or split hand or foot; probably inherited.

LOCULUS - A local enlargement of the uterus which contains an embryo and its assocciated membranes.

LUMBO-SACRAL FLEXURE - The most posterior of the four flexures of the embryo.

LUTEIN - The yellow colored material contained in the cells which fill the empty mammalian Graäfian follicles. (*See* CORPUS LUTEUM).

MACROMERE - Larger of blastomeres where there is a conspicuous size difference.

MACROSOMIA - Gigantism, enlarged skeleton due to disturbed function of the pituitary and possibly also the thyroid glands.

MACROSTOMUS - Failure of the primitive mouth slit to reduce normally.

MALFORMATION, CONGENITAL - Abnormality at birth attributed to faulty development; may have a genetic basis but more frequently extrinsic trauma.

MALPIGHIAN BODY - A unit of the functional kidney including Bowman's capsule and the glomerulus. *Syn.*, renal corpuscle, Malphighian corpuscle.

MAMMARY GLANDS - Multiple milk glands of the typical mammal, derived from the milk ridges.

MANDIBULAR ARCH - The rudiment of the lower jaw or mandible, mesodermal, and anterior to the first or hyomandibular pouch. Gives rise to the palato-quadrate and to Meckel's cartilage.

MANDIBULAR GLANDS - Series of solid ingrowths of the oral mucosa extending on both sides of the base of the tongue to near the mandibular symphysis.

MANTLE FIBRES - Those fibres of the mitotic spindle which attach the chromosome to the centrosomes.

MANTLE LAYER OF THE CORD - Layer of the developing spinal cord with densely packed nuclei, slightly peripheral to the germinal cells from which they are derived. Includes the elongated cells of the ependyma.

MARGINAL LAYER OF THE CORD - Layer of the spinal cord peripheral to the mantle layer, practically devoid of nuclei.

MASSA INTERMEDIA - Fusion of thick lateral walls of diencephalon across the third ventricle.

MATERNAL PLACENTA - Uterine mucosal portions of the typical mammalian placenta.

MATRIX - Ground substance surrounding the chromonemata, usually less chromatic and making up the body of the chromosome. *Syn.*, kalymma or hyalonema.

MATRIX, INTERCELLULAR - The cytoplasmic wall substance of cells in a whole blastema which forms an integrated foam structure and because of its continuity, shows a very definite syncitial character.

MATROCLINUS - Tendency to resemble the mother, may occur in either male or female offspring hence is neither sex linked nor sex limited.

MATURATION - The process of transforming a primordial germ cell (spermatogonium or öogonium) into a functionally mature germ cell, the process involving two special divisions, one of which is always meiotic or reductional.

MATURATION PHASE - Sometimes used to designate the last period of spermiogenesis, leading to the release of free spermatozoa. This period begins when a new crop of spermatids arises from secondary spermatocytes in the same region of the seminiferous tubule.

MEATUS VENOSUS - The junction of the primitive omphalomesenteric veins posterior to the sinus venosus, around which develops the substance of the liver. Later it will also receive the left umbilical vein.

MECKEL'S CARTILAGE - The core of the lower jaw derived from the ventral part of the cartilaginous mandibular arch.

MECOMIUM - A green, pasty-like mass of necrotic cells, mucous and bile which accumulate in the digestive tract of the fetus.

MEDIAN PLANE - "Middle" plane (of the embryo). May be median sagittal or median frontal.

MEDULLA OBLONGATA - That portion of the adult brain derived from myelencephalon.

MEDULLARY - (See terms under NEURAL, such as canal, groove, plate, substance, tissue, tube.)

MEDULLARY CORDS - That portion of the suprarenal glands which is derived from the sympathetic nervous system; central cords. Also that portion of the embryonic gonad presumably derived from pre-migratory germ cells upon reaching the genital ridge.

MEIOSIS - A process of nuclear division found in the maturation of germ cells, involving a separation of members of pairs of chromosomes. Syn., reductional division.

MELANOKINS - Stimuli which act upon melanophores, such as temperature, humidity, light, hormones, and certain pharmacological agents.

MELANOPHORE, ADEPIDERMAL - Dermal melanophore.

MELANOPHORES - Cell with brown or black (melanin) pigment granules or rods, found in every class of vertebrates. Derived from the neural crests and migrating throughout the body.

MEMBRANA GRANULOSA - The layers of follicle cells which bound the mammalian follicular cavity.

MEMBRANA REUNIENS - A membrance which extends dorsally from the neural arches around the upper part of the neural tube; the line of later chondrification.

MEMBRANE, FERTILIZATION - A membrane representing either the elevated vitelline membrane or a newly formed membrane found at the surface of an egg immediately upon fertilization or following artificial parthenogenetic stimulation (activation); generally considered an adequate criterion of successful activation of the egg. First seen by Fol (1876) on the starfish egg.

MEMBRANE BONE - Bone developed in regions occupied by connective tissue, not cartilage.

MEMBRANE VITELLINE - (See VITELLINE MEMBRANE).

MEMBRANES - (See EGG MEMBRANES).

MEMBRANOUS LABYRINTH - The parts of the internal ear, lined with ectodermal epithelium and filled with endolymphatic fluid; including the ductus endolymphaticus, the pars superior labyrinthii, and the part inferiro labyrinthii.

MENSTRUATION - Process in Primates caused by decrease in secretion of estrogen and progestone, involving loss of endometrium and some hemorrhage; indication that implantation did not take place.

MEROMORPHOSIS - The new part regenerated is less than the part removed.

MESENCEPHALON - The section of the primary brain between the posterior level of the prosencephalon and an imaginary line drawn from the tuberculum posterius to a point just posterior to the dorsal thickening. Gives rise to the optic lobes, crura cerebri, and the aqueduct of Sylvius. *Syn.*, midbrain.

MESENCHYME - The form of embryonic mesoderm or mesoblast in which migrating cells unite secondarily to form a syncitium or network having nuclei in thickened nodes between intercellular space filled with fluid.

MESENTERY - Sheet of (mesoderm) tissue generally supporting organ systems. (*e.g.*, mesorchium, mesocardium).

MESIAL - *Syn.*, median, medial, middle.

MESOCARDIUM - The mesentery of the heart; may be dorsal, ventral, or lateral. *See* under LATERAL MESOCARDIA.

MESOCOLON - That portion of the embryonic dorsal mesentery which supports the colon.

MESODERM - The third primary germ layer developed in point of time, may be derived from endoderm in some forms and from ectoderm in others. *See* other terms such as MESOBLAST, MESENCHYME, LATERAL PLATE MESODERM, EPIMERE, MESOMERE, HYPOMERE, GASTRAL, PERISTOMIAL, AXIAL, etc.

MESOMERE - Cells of intermediate size when there are cells of various sizes (macromeres being the largest and micromeres the smallest, respectively). Also used as synonym for intermediate cell mass which gives rise to the nephric system.

MESOMETRIUM - Attachment of the uterus to be the coelomic wall.

MESONEPHRIC DUCT - The duct which grows posteriorly from the mesonephros to the cloaca and later becomes vas deferens. (*Syn.*, Wolffian duct).

MESONEPHRIC TUBULES - Primary, secondary, and sometimes tertiary tubules developing in the Wolffian body, functioning in the mammal.

MESONEPHROS - The Wolffian body, or intermediate kidney, functional as kidney in the embryonic mammal. (*See* EPIDIDYMIS. VASA EFFERENTIA).

MESORCHIUM - Mesentery (mesodermal) whiich surrounds and supports the testis to the body wall.

MESOTHELIUM - Epithelial layers or membranes of mesodermal origin.

MESOVARIUM - Mesentery (mesodermal) which suspends the ovary from the dorsal body wall.

METAMERISM - Serial segmentation, as seen in the nervous, muscular and circulatory systems.

METAMORPHOSIS - Change in structure without retention of original form, as in the change from spermatid to spermatozoön.

METANEPHRIC DIVERTICULUM - Bud-like outgrowth of the mesonephric duct just anterior to its juncture with the cloaca.

METANEPHROS - The permanent kidney of mammals, derived from the nephrogenous tissue of the most posterior somite level (renal corpuscles and secreting tubules) and from a diverticulum of the posterior somite level (renal corpuscles and secreting tubules) and from a diverticulum of the posterior portion of the Wolffian duct (collecting tubules and definitive ureter).

METAPHASE - Stage in mitosis when the paired chromosomes are lined up on the equatorial plate midway between the amphiasters, supported by the mitotic spindle, prior to any anaphase movement.

METAPLASIA - Permanent and irreversible change in both type and character of cells; transformation of potencies of an embryonic tissue into several directions, generally an indication of a pathological condition (*e.g.*, bone formation in the lung). It is thought that some differentiated tissue may become undifferentiated and then undergo a new differentiation in a different direction.

METATELA - Thin roof of 4th ventricle of the brain.

METENCEPHALON - The anterior part of the hindbrain (rhombencephalon) which gives rise to the cerebellum and the pons of the adult brain, separated from the mesencephalon by the isthmus, and including neuromere #6.

METESTRUS - Short period of regressive changes in the uterine mucosa in which the evidence of fruitless preparation for pregnancy disappear. *Syn.*, postestrus.

MICROCEPHALUS - Small or pin-headed; a condition due to the arrested development of the cranium and the brain, accompanied by reduced mentality.

MICROGNATHUS - Retarding of lower jaw in the new born.

MICROMERE - Smaller of the cells when there is variation in the size of blastomeres.

MICROMETRY - Measurement of a microscopic object, using an ocular micrometer.

MICROPHTHALMIA - Eyes that are too small, often due to undersized lenses.

MICROSOMIA - Dwarfism, reduced skeleton, due possibly to disturbed function of the pituitary and thyroid glands.

MICROSTOMUS - Small mouth; excessive closure of the mouth.

MICROSURGERY - Procedures described by Spemann, Chambers, Harrison, and others, where steel and glass instruments of microscopic dimensions are used to operate on small embryos.

MIDBRAIN - (See MESENCEPHALON).

MIDDLE PIECE - The region of the tail in immature or free spermatozoa which is located between the base of the neck and the ring centriole and in which a spiral-like structure of mitochondrial origin may be found.

MIDDLE PIECE BODY - A cytoplasmic remnant attached to the neck region in the maturing spermatids immediately before their release into the lumin of the seminiferous tubule as spermatozoa. This remnant is no longer visible in the spermatozoa found in the epididymis.

MIDGUT - That portion of the archenteron which will give rise to the intestines and to the yolk stalk; bounded in the early embryo by the anterior and the posterior intestinal portals.

MILIEU - Term used to include all of the physico-chemical and biological factors surrounding a living system (e.g., external or internal milieu).

MILK-RIDGE - A band of tissue between the somites (dorsally) and the level of the heart, liver, and mesonephros (ventrally) in the embryo, which gives rise to the mammary glands.

MITOCHONDRIA - Small, permanent cytoplasmic granules which stain with Janus Green B, Janus Red, Janus Blue, Janus Black 1, Rhodamin B, Diethylsafranin, dilute methylene blue, and which have powers of growth and division and are probably lipoid in nature, and may contain proteins, nucleic acids, and even enzymes. Syn., plastens.

MITOSIS - The process of cell division in somatic cells as distinct from germ cells, in which each of the daughter cells is provided with a set of chromosomes similar to one another and to that possessed by the parent cell; consists of prophase, metaphase, anaphase, and telophase.

MITOTIC INDEX - The number of cells, in each thousand, which are in active mitosis at any one time and place in an organism; the percentage of actively dividing cells.

MONOSPERMY - Fertilization accomplished by only one sperm. Opposed to polyspermy.

MONRO, FORAMINA OF - Tubular connections between the single third and the paired lateral ventricles of the forebrain.

MONSTER, AUTOSITE-PARASITE - Double embryos with great size discrepancy so that the smaller one bears a parasitic relationship to the larger; variously produced.

MONSTER, DICEPHALUS - Double-headed abnormality, produced by any means.

MONSTER, ISCHIOPAGUS - Double embryos, widely separated except at the tail; produced by any means.

MORPHOGENESIS - All of the topogenetic processes which result in structure formation; the origin of characteristic structure (form) in an organ or in an organism compounded of organs.

MORPHOGENETIC MOVEMENTS - Cell or cell area movements concerned with the formation of germ layer (e.g., during gastrulation) or of organ primordia. Syn., Gestaltungsbewegungen.

MORULA - A spherical mass of cells, as yet without segmentation cavity.

MOVEMENT, FORMATIVE - Localized changes in cell areas resulting in the formation of specifically recognizable embryonic regions.

MOVEMENT, HOMOLOGOUS - Movement of homologous muscles in transplanted limbs, the synchronous contraction of muscles.

MÜLLERIAN DUCT - (*See* OVIDUCT).

MUTATION - The inception of a heritable change, of rare occurrence; usually deterimental, but a few may be beneficial.

MYELENCEPHALIC TELA - The thin roof of the myelencephalon. *Syn.*, metatela.

MYELENCEPHALON - The posterior portion of the hindbrain (rhombencephalon) which has a thin roof that becomes the choroid plexus of the fourth ventricle and thick ventral and ventro-lateral walls which give rise to the medulla oblongata. The cranial ganglia 5 to 12 inclusive are associated with this portion of the brain.

MYELOBLASTS - Muscle forming (embryonic) cells.

MYELOCOEL - Cavity of the myelencephalon; fourth ventricle.

MYOBLASTS - Formative cells within the myotome or muscle plate which will give rise to the true striated muscles of the adult.

MYOCARDIUM - The muscular part of the heart arising from the splanchnic mesoblast.

MYOCOEL - Temporary cavities within the myotomes which may have been connected with the coelom.

MYOMATA - Benign tumor, derived from muscle fibers.

MYOTOME - The thickened primordium of the muscle found in each somite. *Syn.*, muscle plate.

NACHBARSCHAFT - Morphogenetic effects produced by contact with other tissues or structures of a developing organ; contiguity effects.

NARES, EXTERNAL - The external openings of the tubes which are connected with the olfactory vesicles.

NARES, INTERNAL - The openings of the tubular organ from the olfactory placodes into the anterior part of the pharynx.

NASAL CHOANAE - Openings of the olfactory chambers into the mouth.

NASAL PIT - (*See* OLFACTORY PIT).

NASO-FRONTAL PROCESS - A median projection overhanging the mouth and separating the olfactory pits.

NASO-LACRYMAL GROOVE - Groove between junction of naso-lateral and maxillary processes, extending to the mesial angle of the eye. Portion becomes tear (naso-lacrymal) duct which drains fluid from conjunctival sac into the nose.

NASO-LATERAL PROCESS - Lateral elevation dorsal to nasal (olfactory) pit.

NASO-OPTIC FURROW - *Syn.*, naso-lacrymal groove.

NEBENKERN - Cytological structure near the nucleus of the early spermatid.

NECK - Small space between the base of the nucleus and the middle piece in maturing spermatid and spermatozoön. Only the axis filament of the tail is visible there in most species.

NECROHORMONES - The chemical substances produced by degenerating nuclei which cause the premature and incomplete divisions of oöcytes in sexually mature mammals.

NECROSIS - Local death of a cell or group of cells, not the whole body.

NEIGHBORWISE - The reaction of a transplant appropriate to its new environment, indicating its plasticity, pluripotency, or lack of determination. *Syn.*, Artsgemäss.

NEMAMERE - One of the physical units composing a gene-string or genonema, which carries the genes. May be composed of several genes, or a single gene may extend over several nemameres. Governs biophysical reactions of the gene-string.

NEOPLASM - A new growth, generally a tumor. Histologically and structurally an atypical new formation.

NEPHROCOEL - The cavity, found in the nephrotome or intermediate cell mass, which temporarily joins the myocoel and the coelom.

NEPHROGENIC CORD - Continuous band of intermediate mesoderm (mesomere) without apparent segmentation, prior to budding off of mesonephric tubules.

NEPHROGENIC TISSUE - The intermediate cell mass, mesomere, or nephrotome which will give rise to the excretory system.

NEPHROSTOME - The funnel-shaped opening of kidney tubules into the coelom; the outer tubules of the mesonephric kidney acquire ciliated nephrostomal openings from the coelom and shift their connections to the renal portal sinus.

NEPHROTOME - The intermediate cell mass.

NEPHROTOMIC PLATE - *Syn.*, intermediate mesoderm, mesomere.

NERVE, ABDUCENS - Sixth (VI) cranial nerve arising from the basal plate of the myelencephalon which controls the external rectus muscles of the eye.

NERVE, ACCESSORY - Eleventh (XI) cranial nerve, motor, its fibers arising from posterior myelencephalon and first six segments of the spinal cord.

NERVE, AUDITORY - Eighth (VIII) cranial nerve, purely sensory, arising from acoustic ganglion and associated with the geniculate ganglion of the seventh nerve.

NERVE, FACIAL - Seventh (VII) cranial nerve, both sensory and motor related to taste buds and facial muscles. Arises from plate of myelencephalon.

NERVE, GLOSSOPHARYNGEAL - Ninth (IX) cranial nerve, somatic motor, arising superior and petrossal ganglia.

NERVE, HYPOGLOSSAL - Twelfth (XII) cranial nerve, somatic motor, arising from posterior myelencephalon and extending to the muscles of the tongue.

NERVE, OCULOMOTOR - The third cranial nerve which arises from neuroblasts in the ventral zone of the midbrain near the median line.

NERVE, OLFACTORY - First (I) cranial nerve, sensory, without ganglion and with non-medullated fibers, which arise from the epithelial linings of the olfactory pits and have synaptic connections in olfactory bulbs with nerves to brain.

NERVE, OPTIC - Second (II) cranial nerve, sensory, nerves arise from neuroblasts of sensory layer of retina, pass through choroid fissure to enter brain at diencephalic floor. In contrast with other cranial nerves these intersect so that each eye has connections with both sides of the brain (optic chiasma).

NERVE, VAGUS - A tenth (X) cranial nerve, mixed, arising from the myelencephalon and associated with jugular ganglion.

NERVES, CRANIAL, PERIPHERAL, SPINAL - Designated purely with respect to morphological position.

NEURAL ARCH - The ossified cartilages which extend dorsally from ten centrum around the nerve cord, involving both the caudal and the cephalic sclerotomes. The cephalic arch of one sclerotome fuses with the caudal of the next to form a single arch which corresponds to a vertebra. *Syn.*, vertebral arch.

NEURAL CANAL - (*See* NEUROCOEL and NEURAL TUBE).

NEURAL CREST - A continuous cord of ectodermally derived cells lying on each side in the angle between the neural tube and the body ectoderm separated from the ectoderm at the time of closure of the neural tube and extending from the extreme anterior to the posterior end of the embryo; material out of which the spinal and possibly some of the cranial ganglia develop, and related to the development of the sympathetic ganglia and parts of the adrenal gland by cell migration.

NEURAL FOLD - Elevation of ectoderm on either side of the thickened and depressing medullary plate; folds which close dorsally to form the neural tube. *Syn.*, medullary folds.

NEURAL GROOVE - The sinking in of the center of the medullary plate to form a longitudinal groove, later to be incorporated within the neural tube (spinal cord) as the central canal. *Syn.*, medullary groove.

NEURAL PLATE - Thickened broad strip of ectoderm along the future dorsal side of all vertebrate embryos, later to give rise to central nervous system. *Syn.*, medullary plate.

NEURAL TUBE - The tube formed by the dorsal fusion of the neural folds, the rudiment of the nerve or spinal cord.

NEUROBIOTAXIS - Concentration of nervous tissue takes place in the region of greatest stimulation.

NEUROBLASTS - Primitive or formative nerve cells, probably derived (along with epithelial and glia cells) from the germinal cells of the neural tube.

NEUROCOEL - The cavity of the neural tube, formed simultaneously with the closure of the neural folds. *Syn.*, central canal, neural canal.

NEUROCRANIUM - The dorsal portion of the skull associated with the brain and sense organs.

NEUROGEN - An evocator which causes neural induction in vertebrates. May include the organizer, chemical substances, carcinogens, estrogens, etc.

NEUROGENESIS, MECHANICAL HYPOTHESIS OF - Mechanical tension of plasm medium in any definite direction is said to orient and aggregate the fibrin micellae in a corresponding direction.

NEUROGLIA - (*See* GLIA CELLS).

NEUROHUMORS - Hormone-like chemical substance produced by nervous tissue, particularly the ends of developing nerves which consequently act as stimulating agents.

NEUROMERE - Apparent metamerism of the embryonic brain, the divisions being prosencephalon-3, mesencephalon-2, and rhombencephalon-6.

NEUROPORE - A temporary opening into the neural canal due to a lag in the fusion of the neural folds at the anterior extremity; in the vicinity of the epiphysis.

NEURULA - Stage in embryonic development which follows gastrulation and during which the neural axis is formed and histogenesis proceeds rapidly. The notochord and neural plate are already differentiated, and the basic vertebrate pattern is indicated.

NON-DECIDUOUS PLACENTA - *See* INDECIDUATE PLACENTA.

NORMALIZING - Formative action anchored in the organization associated with the determination of development, not super-material entelechy but an integral part of the organism itself. Integrating and balancing tendencies.

NOTOCHORD - Rod of vacuolated cells representing the axis of all vertebrates, found beneath the neural tube and dorsal to the archenteron. Origin variable or doubtful, in most cases thought to be derived from or simultaneously with the endoderm.

NOTOCHORDAL CANAL - An exaggerated primitive pit in some mammals which extends into the head process. May be homologous to neurenteric canal.

NOTOCHORDAL SHEATH - Double mesodermal sheath around the notochord consisting of an outer elastic sheath developed from superficial chorda cells and an inner secondary or fibrous sheath from chorda epithelium.

NUCLEOFUGAL - Refers to outgrowth in two or more directions from the nuclear region as a center, such as in the formation of myelin around a nerve fiber, starting at the sheath cell nucleus as a center and growing in two directions.

NUCLEOLONEME - Filamentous parts of the nucleolus, the other being amorphous.

NUCLEOLUS - An oval constituent of the nucleus which fades and disappears just before mitosis as the chromosomes condense and reappear after mitosis when the chromosomes resume their extended state.

NUCLEOPLASM - The gel-like and fluid plasm of the nucleus which is largely protein and some ribonucleic acid (RNA).

NUCLEUS, DEITER'S - Synaptic center at the boundary between the myelencephalon and the metencephalon, where sensory neurones of semicircular canals lead.

NUCLEUS, RED - Synaptic center of the mid-brain which acts as a coordinating pathway for synergic type of muscular control.

ODONTOBLASTS - Dentine forming embryonic cells; columnar shaped outer cells of the mammalian dental papilla.

OEDEMA - Excessive accumulation of water (lymph) in the tissues and cavities of the body; may be subcutaneous and/or intracellular. Due to a block in drainage channels and generally associated with cardiac inefficiency. (EDEMA).

OESOPHAGUS - Elongated portion of the foregut between the future glottis and the opening of the bile duct.

OLFACTORY CAPSULE - The extreme anterior ends of the skull trabeculae which form the cartilaginous capsules around the olfactory organs.

OLFACTORY LOBES - The anterior extremities of the telencephalic cerebral lobes, partially constricted, associated with the first pair of cranial nerves.

OLFACTORY PIT - Depressions within the olfactory placodes which will become the olfactory organs (external nares).

OLFACTORY PLACODE - The thickened ectoderm lateral to the stomodeal region primordia of the olfactory pits.

OLIGODACTYLY - Condition in which the fingers or toes are congenitally fewer than normal.

OLIGOSYNDACTYLISM - Numerical reduction of digits by fusion (syndactylism) or elimination or loss of a digit (oligodactylism). A semi-dominant condition in the mouse with manifestations on all four appendages. If homozygous, it dies in utero.

OMENTAL BURSA - Pouch formed in the dorsal mesogastrium as the embryonic stomach changes its position.

OMENTUM - *Syn.*, mesogastrium; gastro-hepatic omentum. Dorsal membrane which supports the gut.

"OMNE VIVUM E VIVO" - All life is derived from pre-existing life (Pasteur).

OMPHALOMESENTERIC VEINS - The vitelline veins as they enter the body at the level of the anterior intestinal portal; united posterior to the sinus venosus as the meatus venosus. Venous rings join these vessels dorsal to the gut to become a single curved vessel emptying through the liver into the meatus venosus. The vitelline vein is continuous with the omphalomesenterics, and is therefore extra-embryonic.

ONTOGENY - Developmental history of an organism; the sequence of stages in the early development of an organism.

OÖCYTE - The presumptive egg cell after the initiation of the growth phase of maturation. *Syn.*, ovocyte.

OÖGENESIS - The process of maturation of the ovum; transformation of the oögonium to the mature ovum. *Syn.*, ovogenesis.

OÖGONIA - The multiplication (mitotic) stage prior to maturation of the presumptive egg cell (ovum), found most frequently in the peripheral germinal epithelium.

OÖPLASM - Cytoplasmic substances connected with building rather than reserve materials utilized in the developmental process.

OPTIC CHIASMA - Thickening in the forebrain ventral to the infundibulum, found as a bunch of optic nerve fibres in the future diencephalon.

OPTIC CUP - Invagination of the outer wall of the primary optic vesicle to form a secondary optic vesicle made up of two layers; a thick internal or retinal layer continuous at the pupil and the choroid fissure, and a thin external layer which is pigmented. The cavity of the cup becomes the future posterior chamber of the eye.

OPTIC LOBES - The thickened, evaginated, dorso-lateral walls of the mesencephalon. (*See* COLLICULI, SUPERIOR).

OPTIC RECESS - A depression in the forebrain anterior to the optic chiasma which leads to the optic stalks.

OPTIC STALK - The attachement of the optic vesicle to the forebrain, at first a tubular connection between the optic vesicle and the diencephalon. The lumen is later obliterated by the development of optic nerve fibres.

OPTIC THALAMI - The thickened lateral walls of the diencephalon.

OPTIC VESICLE - Evaginations of forebrain ectoderm to form the primary optic vesicles which in turn invaginate to form the secondary optic vesicles or optic cups of the eyes.

OPTICOEL - The cavity of the primary optic cup.

OPTICO-OCULAR APPARATUS - Includes all the structures related to the eye: optic vesicles, optic stalks, and primary optic chiasma, which develop from the simple median anlagé precociously found in the medullary plate.

ORA SERRATA - The line of separation between the retinal and lenticular zones of the eye cup.

ORAL PLATE - Fused stomodeal ectoderm and pharyngeal endoderm to form the oral membrane. Breaks through to form the mouth. Syn., pharyngeal membrane, oral membrane, stomodeal plate.

ORGANIZATION - Indicated by the inter-dependence of parts and the whole. "When elements of a certain degree of complexity become organized into an entity belonging to higher level of organization," says Waddington, "we must suppose that the coherence of the higher level depends on properties which the isolated elements indeed possessed but which could not be exhibited until the elements entered into certain relations with one another." Relations beyond mere chemical equations; bordering on the philosophical idea. Process of differentiation or specialization which takes place according to a definite pattern in space and time, not chaotically in the direction of haphazard distribution (See Gestalten).

ORGANOGENESIS - Emancipation of parts from the whole; appearance or origin of morphological differentiation.

OSSEIN FIBRES - Organic fibres in bone which give it strength and resilience.

OSSIFICATION - The process of bone formation, occurring extensively in the embryo but persisting throughout life, balanced by simultaneous degeneration of bone; occurs in or around cartilage or in membranous form in looser connective tissue.

OSTEOBLASTS - Mesenchymal cells which actively secrete a calcareous material in the formation of bone; bone-forming cells.

OSTEOCLASTS - Bone destroying cells; cells which appear in and tend to destroy formed bone; constantly active, even in the embryo.

OSTIUM ABDOMINALE TUBAE - The most anterior, fimbriated end of the oviduct in female vertebrates; the point of entrance of the ovulated egg into the oviduct. Syn., infundibulum of the oviduct. (See TUBAL RIDGE).

OTIC VESICLE - Syn., auditory vesicle; otocyst.

OTOCEPHALY - Tendency to fusion or approximation of ears, accompanying cyclopia.

OTOCYST - The original auditory vesicle appearing at the level of the rhombencephalon, forming first as a placode. Syn., auditory vesicle.

OTOLITH - Granular concretion found within the (embryonic) ear.

OUTGROWTH NEURONE THEORY - The cells found along the course of a nerve fiber, the fiber developing as a protoplasmic outgrowth (extension) from a single ganglion cell.

OVARY - Sex gland in which ova are produced, characteristic of the female.

OVIDUCTS - The paired Müllerian ducts in both males and females, which generally degenerate in the males.

OVIGEROUS CORDS - Columns or strands of tissue which divide the germinal epithelium of the primordium of the ovary, carrying primordial germ cells with them and later breaking up into nexts of cells each of which contains an oögonium. Syn., egg tubes or cords of Pflüger (mammal).

OVIPOSITION - The process of laying eggs.

OVOGENESIS - (See OÖGENESIS).

OVOGONIA - (See OÖGONIA).

OVOPHILE - Presumed receptor portion of amboceptor suitable to receive the egg receptor, anti-fertilizin, or blood inhibors, in the fertilizin reaction (Lillie).

OVULATION - The release of eggs from the ovary, not necessarily from the body.

OVUM - Latin for egg.

PACHYTENE - Stage in maturation when the allelomorphic pairs of chromosomes are fused (telosynapsis or parasynapsis) so as to appear haploid, during which process crossing over may occur; stage just prior to diplotene. Syn., diplonema. The term means "thick" or "condensed".

PALATINE GLANDS - Oral glands anterior, lateral, and posterior to the choanae.

PALATO-QUADRATE - True ossified bone developing from the proximal parts of the first three visceral arches, a portion of which gives rise to the annulus tympanicus.

PALLIUM – Outer, thickened walls of the telencephalic vesicles which will give rise to the cerebral hemisphere; dorsal and posterior to the sulcus rhinalis.

PANCREAS – Digestive and endocrine glands arising as single dorsal and paired ventral primordia in the vicinity of the liver.

PAPILLARY MUSCLES – Muscles which arise from trabeculae carneae in the heart and later, in conjunction with the tendenous cords, control the heart valves.

PARABIOSIS – Lateral fusion of embryos by injuring their mirror surfaces and approximating them so that they grow together (*See* telobiosis).

PARAPHYSIS – A pouch-like evagination of the telencephalon median.

PARASYNAPSIS – Lateral fusion, term applied to chromosomes of maturation stages in pachytene or to experimental fusion of embryos. (*See* TELOSYNAPSIS).

PARATHYROIDS – Endocrine glands derived from endoderm of the third and fourth pairs of visceral pouches and which control calcium metabolism.

PARENCEPHALON – The anterior (ventral) portion of the diencephalon, separated from the synencephalon by the epiphysis.

PARIETAL CAVITY – (*See* PERICARDIAL CAVITY).

PARIETAL RECESS – Passage between the pericardial and periotoneal cavities of embryos.

PARTHENOGENESIS – Development of the egg without benefit of spermatozoa; development stimulated by artificial means.

PARTHENOGENESIS, ARTIFICIAL – Activation of an egg by chemical or physical means (*e.g.*, butyric acid, hypertonic solutions, irradiation, needle prick, etc.)

PARTITION-COEFFICIENT – The factor which determines the size of any part at any time by parcelling out materials; relative capacity for various parts of the embryo to absorb food from a common supply at different times. Such coefficients are expressions of intrinsic growth potentials, so balanced in normal development that no single structure can monopolize the nutriment to the detriment of other structures.

PATROCLINUS – Paternal influence where the F_1 tend to resemble their fathers more than their mothers.

PENETRANCE – A genetic term referring to the degree or percentage of genotypically abnormal.

PENIS – Elongated genital tubercle, enclosed in genital folds (prepuce) and associated with genital swellings (scrotal pouches) in male; organ of transfer of genital products from the testes of the male to the vaginal cavity of the female. *Syn.*, Phallus.

PERFORATORIUM – A structure lying between the acrosome and the nucleus of the sperm head, presumably derived from the nucleus.

PERIAXIAL CORDS – The primordia of the trigeminus and acustico-facialis ganglia and later mark the paths of the trigeminal and facial nerves. Distinguished as more deeply stained and concentrated masses than mesenchyme just posterior to the optic vesicles.

PERICARDIAL CAVITY – The cavity or membranous sac which encloses the heart, representing a cephalic portion of the coelom of the original amnio-cardiac vesicles within the embryonic body, bounded by the proamnion and posteriorly by the omphalomesenteric veins. *Syn.*, parietal cavity.

PERICARDIUM – The thin mesodermal membrane which encloses the pericardial cavity and heart

PERICHONDRIUM – Mesenchymal layer immediately around forming cartilage.

PERIOSTEUM – Mesenchymal layer, often originally perichondrium, which will be found immediately around forming bone.

PERITONEAL CAVITY – The body cavity (coelom) separated from the pleural cavity by the pleuro-peritoneal septum, including the septum transversum.

PERITONEUM – Coelomic mesothelium of the abdominal region reinforced by connective tissue.

PERIVEITELLINE SPACE – The space between the vitelline (fertilization) membrane and the contained egg, generally filled with a fluid. It is the space between the zona radiata and the egg.

PERIVITELLINE MEMBRANE - (*See* VITELLINE MEMBRANE).

PFLUGER, CORDS OF - The ovigerous layer which grows into the stroma of the ovary as ovigerous cords, carrying primitive ova with them.

PFLUGER'S LAW - The dividing nucleus elongates in the direction of the least resistance.

pH - Method of stating the measure of the hydrogen ion concentration, expressed as the log of the reciprocal of the hydrogen ion concentration in gram-mols per liter. The negative value of the power of 10 equivalent to the concentration of hydrogen ions in gram-molecules per liter. The neutral solution (neither acidic nor basic) has a pH value of 7: pH values less than 7 are acid and those more than 7 are alkaline.

PHAGOCYTOSIS - Process of engulfment of solid particles, generally by specific types of (white) cells known as phagocytes.

PHALLUS - *Syn.*, penis.

PHENOTYPE - The outward appearance of an organism regardless of its genetic make-up, opposed to genotype.

PHEROMONES - Substances produced by animals which elicit responses in other members of the same species. Female mice produce a pheromone which inhibits estrous cycles in other females. Male mice produce a pheromone which induces early puberty in females and more frequent estrus. In sequence they synchronize estrus in mice groups.

PHOCOMELIA - Failure of proximal portion of appendages to develop, distal parts may be normal. Disproportionate shortening of the limbs (micromelia) which may be associated with an otherwise normal axial skeleton, sometimes due to a single recessive gene but may also be caused by drugs (thalidomide). Homozygotes die soon after birth because of extensive median cleft palate which interferes with respiration and sucking.

PHYLOGENY - Series of stages in the history of the race; the origin of phyla.

PIGMENT LAYER OF OPTIC CUP - Thin outer wall of the primary optic cup, posterior to the retina, which never fuses with the rods of the retina.

PINEAL - (*See* EPIPHYSIS).

PINOCYTOSIS - Process of engulfment of water and solutes.

PITUITARY - (*See* HYPOPHYSIS).

PLACENTA - An extra embryonic vascular structure of placental mammals, which serves as an organ of nutritive and respiratory exchange between the fetus and the mother. Basically consists of uterine vascular endothelium, uterine stroma, uterine epithelium, fetal trophoblast, fetal stroma, and fetal capillary endothelium. When all of these structures are present it is known as an epitheliochorial placenta, found in pig and mare.

PLACENTA, ENDOTHELIOCHORIAL - There is loss of maternal connective tissue in addition to the maternal uterine epithelium. Found in carnivores, sloths, insectivores, and bats.

PLACENTA, EPITHELIOCHORIAL - Simple apposition of chorion to the endometrial epithelium without erosion, all membranes present (Cetacea, lemurs, mare, and pig).

PLACENTA, HEMOCHORIAL - Type in which there is ultimate loss of maternal endothelium with erosion of the uterine wall; the trophoblast is bathed directly by circulating maternal blood. Found in rodents, anthropoids, and man.

PLACENTA, HEMOENDOTHELIAL - The placental barrier becomes reduced to a layer of endothelium and a very thin plasmodium, the latter absent in some places.

PLACENTA, SYNDESMOCHORIAL - The uterine epithelium disappears through invasive activity of the trophoblast in cow and sheep.

PLACENTA, YOLK-SAC - Chorio-vitelline, found in mouse, in addition to hemochorial placenta, which engages actively throughout gestation in the absorption of transudate and secretion representing histiotrophe derived from the endometrium. A combination of advanced (hemochorial) and primitive (yolk sac) placentas. Main mediator of antibodies and glucose (mouse).

PLACODE - Plate or button-like thickening of ectoderm from which will arise sensory or nervous structures (*e.g.*, olfactory placode).

PLANE - (*See* "section".)

PLASMODESMATA - Protoplasmic bridges claimed to be the means of nerve fiber growth; plasmodesmata supposedly incorporated into the substance of the axone during its origin.

PLASMONUCLEIC ACID - One of the two types of nucleic acid, this one occuring in the cytoplasm, in the plasmosome (nucleolus), and possibly in minute quantities in the chromatin.

PLASMOSOME - A true nucleolus (*See* NUCLEOLUS).

PLASMOTROPHODERM - Outer layer of syncytial cells of the trophoderm following implantation. *Syn.*, syncytiotrophoderm.

PLASTENS - (*See* mitochondria.)

PLEIOTROPISM - Multiple effects of a single gene due to effects upon metabolism.

PLEURA - Membrane enclosing the cavity surrounding the lungs, consisting of splanchnic mesoderm.

PLEURAL CAVITY - The portion of the coelomic cavity separated ventrally by the septum transversum (pleuro-peritoneal septum) from the peritoneal cavity, and one into which the primary lung buds grow.

PLEXUS, CHOROID - Vascular folds in the roof of the prosencephalon, diencephalon, and rhombencephalon.

POLAR BODY - Relatively minute, discarded nucleus of the maturing oöcyte (generally three). *Syn.*, polocytes.

POLYANDROUS SYNGAMY (polyandry) - Development of two or more small pronuclei leading to the union of these with the female pronucleus.

POLYANDRY - Presence of one female and two male pronuclei in fertilization, arising from polyspermy. May be more common when coitus occurs late in estrus. Opposed to polygyny.

POLYDACTYLY - Extra digits in hands or feet; probably inherited.

POLYEMBRYONY - Natural isolation of blastomeres leading to the production of multiple embryos; development of several embryos from a single zygote.

POLYESTROUS CYCLE - Reproductive cycles which occur at least several times a year.

POLYESTRUS - Mammals which have more than a single estrus cycle in one year.

POLYGYNY - Failure of emission of first or second polar body with the result that the pronucleus unites with two female pronuclei. Opposed to polyandry.

POLYHYDRAMNIOS - Condition where the amniotic fluid exceeds the normal

POLYMEGALY - Several sizes, as for ova or sperm from one strain.

POLYPLOID - Possessing a multiple number of chromosomes, such as triploid (3 times the haploid number) tetraploid (4 times the haploid), etc. Always more than the normal diploid number of the type zygote.

POLYPLOIDOGEN - A chemical substance which brings about the polyploid condition, usually by inhibiting certain phases of nuclear division.

POLYSPERMY - Insemination of an egg with more than a single sperm, although but a single sperm nucleus is functional, in syngamy.

PONS VAROLII - The thickened floor and ventro-lateral zones of the metencephalon.

PONTINE FLEXURE - Cephalic flexure indicated by a ventral bulge in the floor of the myelencephalon.

POST-ANAL GUT - A posteriorly projecting blind pocket of the hindgut; that portion of the hindgut posterior to the anal plate or proctodeal plate. *Syn.*, post-cloacal gut.

POSTERIOR INTESTINAL PORTAL - Opening from the unformed midgut into the formed hindgut.

POSTERIOR TUBERCLE - (*See* TUBERCULUM POSTERIUS).

POSTESTRUS - Short period of regressive changes in the uterine mucosa following fruitless preparation for pregnancy.

POST-REDUCTION - Maturation in which the equational and reductional divisions occur in that order.

POTENCY - Ability to develop embryologically; capacity for completing destiny; ability to perform an action: "future development verbally transformed to an earlier stage" (Waddington). The test of potency is actual realization in development. It is an explanatory rather than a descriptive term for developmental possibility. A piece of an embryo has the possibility of a certain fate before determination, and the power to pursue it afterwards.

POTENCY, PROSPECTIVE - The sum total of developmental possibilities, the full range of developmental performance of which a given area (or germ) is capable. Somehow more than, and inclusive of, prospective fate and prospective value. Connotes possibility, not power. Not to be confused with competence.

PREFORMATION - Theory that the adult is represented in miniature within the egg or sperm, and that development is simply enlargement.

PREGNANCY - Condition of actually bearing an embryo of fetus within the uterus or Fallopian tubes.

PRE-MIGRATORY GERM CELL - Yolk laden cells of splanchnopleuric origin which migrate by way of blood vessels to the gonad primordia. Believed by some to be the precursors of gonad stroma and/or functional germ cells.

PRENATAL - Term used to refer to any stage in the development of the mammalian prior to delivery at birth, to distinguish from neo-natal or post-natal.

PRE-ORAL GUT - The extension of the pharynx anterior to the oral plate and behind the hypophysis, which flattens out and finally disappears. *Syn.*, Seessel's pocket.

PRE-REDUCTION - Maturation in which the reductional and equational divisions occur in that order.

PRIMARY OÖCYTE - The termination of the growth phase in the maturation of the ovum from the oögonial stage, prior to any maturational divisions.

PRIMARY SPERMATOCYTE - Stage in spermatogenesis whose division results in secondary spermatocytes; stage beginning with growth of the spermatogonia.

PRIMORDIAL GERM CELLS - The diploid cells which are destined to become germ cells. *Syn.*, primitive germ cells. *e.g.*, oögonia and spermatogonia.

PRIMORDIUM - The beginning or earliest discernible indication of an organ. *Syn.*, rudiment, anlagé.

PROACROSOMIC GRANULES - Small corpuscles appearing in the idiosome of the young spermatids soon after the beginning of spermiogenesis; stain purple with PA-PSA.

PROCESSUS VAGINALIS - Peritoneal recess into scrotal pouch.

PROCTODEUM - An ectodermal pit in the region of the future cloaca which invaginates to fuse with hindgut endoderm to form the anal or proctodeal plate, later to rupture and form the anus.

PROESTRUS - Period of active preparation of the uterine mucosa (endometrium) leading to estrus.

PROGESTERONE - Endocrine secretion from the corpus luteum which causes the thickening of the endometrium.

PROGESTIN - A hormone from the corpus luteum found in all Placentalia.

PRONEPHRIC CAPSULE - Mesodermal connective tissue covering of the pronephric masses derived from adjacent myotomes and somatic mesoderm.

PRONEPHRIC CHAMBER - A portion of the coelomic cavity open anteriorly and posteriorly but closed ventrally by the development of the lungs.

PRONEPHRIC DUCT - The outer portion of the pronephric nephrotomes which develops a lumen connected posteriorly with the mesonephric or Wolffian duct. *Syn.*, segmental duct.

PRONEPHRIC TUBULES - The lateral outgrowths of the most anterior nephrotomal masses which acquire cavities connected with the pronephric duct. Possibly become infundibulum of oviduct.

PRONEPHROS - The embryonic kidney of all vertebrates and consisting of as many primitive tubules as somites concerned; completely lost in all adult vertebrates except a few bony fish. *Syn.*, head kidney.

PRONUCLEI OF MOUSE - Nucleoli of pronucleus of mouse are devoid of RNA; may arise from the metamorphic head of the sperm, the nuclear membrane, or within the nuclear membrane. The nucleo-cytoplasmic ratio (N/C at this stage is relatively 1/30 and cleavage restores the somatic ratio of 1/7).

PRONUCLEUS - Either of the gametic nuclei in the egg after fertilization and before syngamy; female pronucleus is the mature egg nucleus after the elimination of the polar bodies, distinct from the germinal vesicle which is the pre-maturation nucleus.

PROPHASE - The first stage in the mitotic cycle when the spireme is broken up into definite chromosomes, prior to lining up on the metaphase (equatorial) plate.

PROSENCEPHALON - (*See* FOREBRAIN).

PROSOCOEL - Cavity of the prosencephalon.

PROSPECTIVE SIGNIFICANCE - The normal fate of any part of an embryo at the beginning of development. *Syn.*, prospective Bedeutung, Potentialite reele.

PROSTATE GLAND - Sex gland derived from the urethral epithelium surrounding the urethra near the neck of the bladder; secretes fluid for transport and activation of spermatozoa in mammal.

PROSIMAL - Nearer the point of reference, toward the main body mass.

PUPIL - The opening into the secondary optic vesicle, occluded in part by the lens, and regulated in diameter by the ciliary muscles of the iris.

PYCNOSIS - Increase in density of the nucleus (or the cytoplasm) which may be hyperchromatic. Pycnotic cells in the central nervous system are called chromophile cells. Such cells have an increased affinity for haematoxylin and methylene blue.

PYGOPAGUS - Rump union in conjoined twins.

RACHISCHISIS - Cleft spine, due to failure to close completely.

RAMUS-COMMUNICANS - The connection between the sympathetic ganglion and the spinal nerve, as numerous as the ganglia in any vertebrate; probably originating from the crest cells. Ramus means branch.

RATHKE'S POCKET - The tubular ectodermal hypophysis of the chick (*See* HYPOPHYSIS).

RAUBER'S CELLS - The remnant of the trophoblast at the point of junction with the embryonic knob.

RECAPITULATION THEORY - Theory that embryonic development reviews the major steps in evolutionary history (*See* qualifications under BIOGENETIC LAW).

RECESSIVE - Opposite of dominant, refers to gene which can be masked in the phenotype by the presence of its allelomorph.

RECTUM - Narrowed posterior portion of the hindgut, lined with thickened endodermal epithelium, which opens directly into the cloaca.

REDUCTIONAL MATURATION DIVISION - One of the two important divisions in the maturation of gametes which results in the separation of allelomorphic (homologous) pairs of chromosomes so that the resulting cells are invariably haploid. *Syn.*, meiotic division, disjunctional division. Opposed to equational division.

REFERTILIZATION - By injecting versene solutions into the Fallopian tube of rodents after the normal time of sperm penetration, a secondary penetration may occur but generally fails to form a pronucleus and degenerates.

REGENERATION - Repair or replacement of lost part or parts by growth and differentiation past the phase of primordial development. The vast organizing potencies of the different regions of the early embryo are lost after the completion of development and there remain only certain regions of the body which are said to be capable of regeneration. Regenerative powers are more extensive among embryos and adults of phyletically low forms.

REICHERT'S MEMBRANE - A thin, pink-staining non-cellular membrane between the distal endoderm and the trophectoderm, appearing just at 6.5 days gestation. It is continuous over the entire inner surface of the traphectoderm, but is probably derived from the distal endoderm. Its function is to maintain the separation of maternal and fetal tissues.

REGIONS, PRESUMPTIVE - Regions of the blastula which, by previous experimentation, have been demonstrated to develop in certain specific directions under normal entogenetic influences.

REGULATION - A reorganization toward the whole; the power of pre-gastrula embryos to utilize materials remaining, after partial excision, to bring about normal conditions; more flexible power than regeneration.

RENAL CORPUSCLES - Derivatives of the intermediate cell-mass, located adjacent to the median face of Wolffian body. *Syn.*, Malpighian body.

RENAL PORTAL SYSTEM - The venous system which carries blood to the kidneys, involving the lateral portions of the caval veins, (really parts of the posterior cardinals) the iliacs, and the dorso-lumbars.

RESIDUAL BODY - A large and irregular portion of the cytoplasm which is shed off just before the release of the maturing spermatids as spermatozoa. Usually it is poorly staining cytoplasm surrounding a mass stained with iron hematoxylin which may represent an accumulation of granules previously identified in the cytoplasmic body.

RESTITUTION - The rejoining of broken chromosome threads to produce a structure superficially indistinguishable from a normal chromosome.

RETE CORDS - Strands of epithelial cells, containing many primordial germ cells which connect with the seminiferous tubules and later become the vasa efferentia, in the bird. *Syn.*, rete testis.

RETINAL ZONE - Ectodermal derivatives of the optic cup consisting of the internal limiting membrane, retinal and lenticular zones, and outer pigmented layer. The retina proper includes portions from internal limiting membrane to the rods and cones inclusive. (No cones in the mouse).

RHINENCEPHALON - Most primitive part of the telencephalon, concerned with the olfactory sense and including the olfactory bulb, olfactory tract, and pyriform lobe.

RHOMBENCEPHALON - (*See* HINDBRAIN).

RHOMBOIDAL SINUS - (*See* SINUS RHOMBOIDALIS).

RIBOSOME - Cytoplasmic bodies consisting largely of RNA and protein and responsible for the basophilia of the cytoplasm.

RNA, MESSENGER - Template RNA, unstable, M.W. 500,000 including 1500 nucleotides, carries the transcription of that part of DNA which is concerned with the structure of proteins, each nolecule of which directs the synthesis of 10 to 20 molecules of protein, and can be associated with as many as 5 ribosomes.

RNA, RIBOSOMAL - Stable, M.W. 550,000 or 1,100,000 equalling 1650 or 3300 nucleotides, the major portion of RNA found in most cells, composed of 2 basic units, functions in protein synthesis but are non-specific with regard to type of protein synthesized.

RNA, TRANSFER - Soluble RNA M.W. 24,000 equalling 74 nucleotides, stable (double helical structure). For each amino acid there is a specific enzyme and one or more specific transfer RNA's. Function is to align amino acids in correct sequence in polypeptide chains.

RUNT DISEASE - Results from cellular homografts containing relatively large proportions of immunilogically competent cells injected into genetically foreign hosts that are unable to reject them promptly. Injected cells persist, proliferate, colonize, and often kill the host. Development is retarded, there is diarrhea, hyperplasia of lymphoid tissues and organs, especially the spleen, with hepatomegaly, effects on blood, marrow, and skin.

SACCULE - The outer and ventral portion of the inner ear from which is derived the cochlea. Associated with the VIII auditory nerve. *Syn.*, sacculus.

SACCUS ENDOLYMPHATICUS - The original endolymphatic duct, closed off from the exterior, which grows up over the myelencephalon to join the other sac and form a vascular covering of the brain.

SACCUS VAGINALIS - Scrotal pouch, peritoneal pocket in scrotal pouch.

SACH'S LAW - All cells tend to divide into equal parts and each new plane of division tends to intersect the preceding one at right angles.

SAGITTAL - A mesial plane, or any plane parallel to it, dividing the right parts of the body from the left. Right angles to both the frontal and transverse planes.

SCLEROTIC COAT - A tough mesenchymatous and partially cartilaginous coat outside of the choroid coat of the vertebrate eye. *Syn.*, sclera.

SCLEROTOME - Loose mesenchymal cells proliferated off from the inner and ventral edges of the myotomes which contributes to the formation of the axial skeleton. Three parts are distinguished; the narrow undivided perichordal part; the dense aggregations of caudolateral cells; and the cephalic portion, all of which contribute to the axial skeleton.

SCROTUM or SCROTAL SAC - A single or subdivided chamber, external to the body proper, within which the testes are retained, the internal body temperature being too high for survival of the spermatozoa.

SECONDARY OÖCYTE - The stage in oögenesis between primary oöcyte and ovum, may be either haploid or diploid, depending upon species considered and which maturation division occurs first.

SECONDARY SPERMATOCYTE - The stage in spermatogenesis whose next division results in haploid spermatids, these spermatocytes being either haploid or diploid depending upon species considered. (*See* POST and PRE-REDUCTION DIVISIONS).

SECRETORY TUBULE - The portion of the kidney tubule actually involved in excretory process.

SECTION - Generally a slice of an embryo, often of microscopic dimensions, taken in any one of the various planes such as frontal, transverse, or sagittal. (*See* SERIAL SECTIONS.)

SECTION, CROSS - Cut made at right angles to the long axis of the embryo. *Syn.*, transverse section.

SECTION, FRONTAL - Cut made parallel to the longitudinal axis of the embryo and separating the more dorsal from the more ventral.

SECTION, SAGITTAL - Cut made parallel to the longitudinal axis of the embryo but separating the right from the left portions. Term often confused with "median" or "longitudinal" which really mean no more than "axial," hence could also be "frontal".

SECTIONS, SERIAL - Thin (microscopic) slices of an embryo laid on the slide in sequence (generally from left to right, as one reads) so that the beginning of the embryo is at one side (left) and the end of the embryo at the opposite side (right) of the slide.

SEGMENTATION - Term used synonymously with cleavage. Also means serial repetition of embryonic rudiments (structural patterns) in successive levels of regular spacing, as in the case of somites, and spinal nerves. *Syn.*, cleavage.

SEGMENTATION CAVITY - The cavity of the blastula; *Syn.*, subgerminal cavity, blastocoel.

SEGREGATION, EMBRYONIC - Progressive restriction of original potencies in the embryo; the process of step by step repartitioning of the originally homogeneous zygote into the separate parts of the presumptive embryo.

SEMEN - Mixture of secretions from the bulbo-urethral glands (Cowper's glands), prostate gland, seminal vesicles and the suspended spermatozoa. Composite ejaculate of male during coitus which contains spermatozoa and hyaluronidase which liquefies the matrix of the cumulus oöphorus surrounding the ovulated eggs in the ampulla of the oviduct. The enzyme is derived from the spermatogenetic epithelium, not from the accessory organs, but semen does include secretions from male accessory organs.

SEMICIRCULAR CANALS - Tubular derivatives of the utricle lined with ectoderm from the otocyst, which constitute the accessory balancing mechanisms.

SEMI-LUNAR VALVES - Cup-like pockets within the aortic and pulmonary divisions of the bulbus, which prevent the back flow of blood.

SEMINAL VESICLE - Glandular dilatation of the distal end of the ductus deferens where spermatozoa are temporarily collected prior to ejaculation.

SEMINATION - The act of fertilizing, by the discharge of spermatozoa.

SEMINIFEROUS TUBULE - Tubular divisions of the testis derived from sexual (rete) cords, covered by a connective tissue theca and containing supporting (Sertoli) cells and (all) stages of spermatogenesis.

SEMIPLACENTA - Type of placenta in which the uterine mucosa and the chorion do not actually grow together so that there is no tearing at birth. *Syn.*, contact placenta.

SENESCENCE - The progressive loss of growth power; old age.

SENSORY LOAD - Determined by the number of receptor organs associated with a specific nerve.

SEPTUM - A partition.

SEPTUM SPURIUM - An embryonic partition or ridge which soon undergoes retrogression, but which is a prolongation of the dorsal wall of the atrium from one of the valvulae venosae, that effectively guards the sinus orifice against the backflow of blood to the heart. *Syn.*, false septum.

SEPTUM TRANSVERSUM - A partition which separates the peritoneal and pericardial cavities composed of three parts: a median mass made up of the liver, sinus and ductus venosus, and the dorsal and ventral ligaments; the lateral mesocardia; and also the lateral closing fold which extends from the mesocardia to the ventrolateral body wall. Beginning of diaphragm.

SERIAL SECTIONS - Thin (often of microscopic dimensions) sections of embryos which are mounted on slides in the order of their removal from the embryo, so that a study in sequence will provide an understanding of all organ systems from one region of the embryo to the other.

SEROSA - *Syn.*, chorion.

SERTOLI CELL - Derivative of the sexual cords of the testis, found within the seminiferous tubule and functionally similar to the follicle cell in the ovary in that it is the nutritive, supporting, or nurse cell of the maturing spermatozoa. The heads of adult spermatozoa may be seen embedded in the cytoplasm of Sertoli cells.

SEX, HETERODYNAMIC - The sex in which the gametes are of two kinds with respect to the possession of specific sex influencing chromosomes, such as the X-chromosome in Drosophila. The frog, mouse, and human male are presumably heterogametic.

SEX CELL CORD - Division of the sex-cell ridge or gonad primordium, not to be confused with sexual (rete) cords.

SEX CHROMATIN - Generally refers to the X chromosome; the maximum number of sex chromatin masses is 1 less than the number of X chromosomes. One chromosome is consistently isopycnotic and the others are all heteropycnotic. It replicates later and faster than the other chromosomes, probably because its constituent chromonemata must uncoil before DNA synthesis can take place. These are never seen in embryonic cells before the blastocyst stage, at the time of implantation.

SEX DETERMINATION - Generally means either the conditions of fertilization which determine the ultimate sex of the embryo, or the predetermination of sex by experimental means.

SEX LINKED - Genes borne on a sex chromosome and therefore conditioned in their heredity by the distribution of the sex chromosomes.

SEXUAL CORDS - Derivatives of the germinal epithelium from which they become separated and give rise to the bulk of the gonads of both sexes.

SEXUAL CORDS OF THE OVARY - Sex cords of the originally indifferent gonad primordium which form only the cords of the medulla of the ovary, the functional follicles coming from the germinal epithelium.

SEXUAL CORDS OF THE TESTIS - Sex cords of the originally indifferent gonad primordium which give rise to the seminiferous tubules of the testis, forming a rather solid mesenchymatous reticulum when cavities begin to appear lined with spermatogonia (from primordial germ cells) and Sertoli (from peritoneal cells), the whole constituting the seminiferous tubules.

SEXUAL CYCLE - Periodic sequence of changes in the uterine mucosa of the female placenta. Mammals, apart from pregnancy, include uterine changes as follows:
   Diestrus - period of quiescence, if short.
   Anestrus - period of quiescence, if long.
   Proestrus - period of construction, destruction, and some repair.
   Estrus - period of repair.

SHEATH, MYELIN - Myelin covering of axones in the so-called white matter of the spinal cord.

SINUS RHOMBOIDALIS - The region of the receding primitive streak around which the posterior ends of the neural folds are diverted in the chick embryo.

SINUS VENOSUS - The point of fusion of vitelline veins of the embryo or the most posterior of the original four chambers of the heart; bilaterally symmetrical and related to the ducts of Cuvieri and the ductus venosus to 45 hours; right horn elongated and left reduced with shifting of sino-auricular aperture and has the shape of horseshoe between atrium and the septum transversum. The most anterior part involved in formation of right auricle.

SITUS INVERSUS - An inversion of the bilateral symmetry; reversal of right and left symmetry.

SITUS INVERSUS VISCERUM - Twisting of the digestive tract and sometimes the heart, occurring naturally (rarely) or as a result of shifting of embryonic parts.

SKELETOGENOUS SHEATH - Sclerotomal cells which first form a continuous layer around both the notochord and nerve cord.

SKIN - (See DERMIS and EPIDERMIS). *Syn.*, integument.

SOMATIC - Relating to body in contrast with germinal cells; or relating to the outer body in contrast to inner splanchnic mesoderm.

SOMATIC DOUBLING - Doubling of the initial number of chromosomes with which the egg begins development, occurring (probably in most cases) at the first or early mitotic divisions (cleavages) of the egg, after fertilization.

SOMATIC UMBILICUS - A short, thick hollow stalk which connects the chick embryo with the underlying yolk-sac and the extra-embryonic membranes, composed of ectoderm and somatic mesoderm continuous with the amnion.

SOMATOBLAST - Blastomeres with specific germ layer predisposition, *i.e.*, ectodermal somatoblasts.

SOMATOPLEURE - The layer of somatic mesoderm and closely associated ectoderm, the extension of which (from the body wall) gives rise to both the amnion and chorion.

SOMITE - Blocks of paraxial mesoblast metamerically separated by transverse clefts, derived from enterocoelic or gastral mesoderm and giving rise to the dermatome, myotome, and sclerotome.

SPERM - The germ cell characteristically produced by the male. *Syn.*, spermatozoön, sperm cell, male gamete, spermatosome.

SPERM RECEPTOR - Chemical associated with the spermatozoa, reacting with fertilizin (amboceptor) in Lilli's side chain hyopthesis of the fertilizin reaction.

SPERMATELEOSIS - Metamorphic changes from spermatid to spermatozoon.

SPERMATID - The products of the second maturation division in spermatogenesis, the spermatids having certain cytological characteristics and being invariably haploid; cells which go through a metamorphosis into functionally mature spermatozoa.

SPERMATOCYTE - Stages in spermatogenesis between the time the primordial germ cell (spermatogonium) begins to grow, without division, until after the divisions which results in spermatids. (*See* PRIMARY and SECONDARY SPERMATOCYTES).

SPERMATOGENESIS - The entire process which results in the maturation of the spermatozoön.

SPERMATOGONIA: TYPE A - Cells with ovoid and pale nucleus, with thin nuclear membrane and fine chromatin granules; one large chromatin granule may also be found present at all stages of spermatogenetic cycle.

SPERMATOGONIA: INTERMEDIATE TYPE - Cells appearing near the end of initial stage (I) at which time they can still be confused with Type A cells, but they gradually take on the appearance of Type B cells as follows: Nuclear membrane thickens, nuclear contents darken; a few chromatin flakes appear close to the nuclear membrane and the nucleus progressively changes in shape from ovoid to round.

SPERMATOGONIA: TYPE B - Cells with a spherical and dark nucleus, coarse chromatin granules attached to the nuclear membrane; cells resulting from the division of the intermediate cell type spermatogonia and which ultimately produce primary spermatocytes.

SPERMATOGONIUM - The primordial germ cell of the male gonad, indistinguishable from somatic cells, both of which are diploid; stage prior to maturation when the presumptive spermatozoön undergoes rapid multiplication by mitosis.

SPERMATOSPHERE - (*See* IDIOZOME).

SPERMOPHILE GROUP - Portion of the amboceptor in Lillie's fertilizin hypothesis into which sperm receptors fit in the fertilization reaction.

SPINA BIFIDA - Split tail caused by a variety of abnormal environmental conditions any of which may prevent the proper gastrulation and neurulation which lead to this split-tailed condition.

SPINAL CORD - That portion of the central nervous system, excluding the brain, which is derived from the epithelial and neural ectoderm of the original blastula, consisting of ependyma, glia, neuroblasts and their derivatives and connecting cells.

SPINDLE - A group of fibres between the centrosomes during mitosis, to which the chromosomes are attached and by means of which (mantle fibre portion) the chromosomes are drawn to their respective poles.

SPINOUS PROCESS - Prolongation of neural processes fused dorsally to the neural canal; becomes dorsal spine of vertebra.

SPIREME - A continous chromatin thread characteristic of the so-called resting cell nucleus. Existence questioned by current cytoplogists.

SPLANCHNIC - Refers to the viscera, opposed to somatic or body.

SPLANCHNIC MESODERM - The visceral mesoderm, or that nearest the embryonic axis in the lateral plate.

SPLANCHNOCOEL - That portion of the enterocoel which lies between the somatic and splanchnic mesoderm within the body. *Syn.*, coelom.

SPLANCHNOCRANIUM - That portion of the skull which is preformed in cartilage and which arises from the first three pair of visceral arches. Opposed to neurocranium.

SPLANCHOPLEURE - The layer of endoderm and inner mesoderm (splanchnic) within which develop the numerous blood vessels of the area vasculosa and later the yolk-sac septa; the layers within the body which give rise to the lining and to the musculature of the alimentary canal.

SPLEEN - This organ arises as a proliferation from the peritoneum covering the left side of the dorsal mesentery just anterior to the pancreas.

SPONGIOBLASTS - Cells of the mantle layer of the developing spinal cord destined to form merely supporting tissue.

SPONGIOSA - The glandular layer of the uterus adjacent to the muscularis to which the trophoderm is attached the other portion of the uterine mucosa being the compacta.

STEM CELL RENEWAL - Phenomenon suggesting that a small number of spermatagonia undergo only one or two mitoses and then return to their original stem cell state; possibly later to undergo spermatogenetic mitosis.

STERILITY - Inability to breed. Condition may be temporary or permanent.

STOMODEUM - Ectodermal invagination (pit) which fuses with the pharyngeal endoderm to form the oral plate, which later ruptures to form the margins of the mouth cavity. The stomodeal portion of the mouth lining is therefore ectodermal.

STRATUM COMPACTUM - Outer cellular portion of the endometrium surrounding the blastocyst, subjacent to the junctional zone.

STRATUM GRANULOSUM - Layer of follicle cells surrounding the mammalian ovum.

STRATUM SPONGIOSUM - Deeper glandular part of the endometrium surrounding the blastocyst, with many secreting glands. Extends to the basal zone.

STROMA - The mesodermally derived, medullary, supporting tissues of an organ.

SUB-CARDINAL VEINS - Embryonic veins ventral to the nephric tissue the posterior portions of which fuse to contribute to the formation of the inferior vena cava.

SUB-CLAVIAN VEINS - These arise primitively as branches of the posterior cardinals.

SUBSTANTIA PROPRIA - Mesenchyme of the cornea continuous with the sclera.

SUBSTRATE - The substance which is acted upon by an enzyme.

SUB-ZONAL LAYER - The morula lies within a sub-zonal layer of cells later called the trophoblast.

SULCUS LIMITANS - Longitudinal groove between the dorsal alar plate and the ventral basal plate best seen at the level of the myelencephalon; and mark for locating the nuclei and fibre tracts.

SUPERNUMERARY NUCLEI - Nuclei of excess spermatozoa which invade the egg at fertilization, many of which cause accessory cleavages and then degenerate.

SUSTENTACULAR CELL - A cell which provides nourishment for another, such as the Sertoli or follicle cells of the gonads.

SYLVIUS, AQUEDUCT OF - (*See* AQUEDUCT OF SYLVIUS).

SYMPATHETIC SYSTEM - Originating either from mesenchymal element arising in situ or, more probably, from ectodermal elements emanating from the neural crests; to organize as a chain of ganglia near the dorsal aorata and controlling the involuntary (visceral) musculature.

SYMPODIA - Fusion, to varying degrees, of the legs (*e.g.*, mermaid or siren condition).

SYNAPSIS - Union, such as the lateral (parasynapsis) or terminal (telosynapsis) union of embryos; or pairing of homologous chromosomes.

SYNAPTENE STAGE - The stage in maturation between the leptotone and the synezesis (contraction) stage wherein the chromatin is in the form of long threads, intertwined in homologous pairs. *Syn.*, zygotene of amphitene.

SYNCYTIAL TROPHODERM - Layer of trophodermal cells of the embryo outside of but probably derived from the cell layer of Langhans.

SYNCTIUM - Propagation of nuclei with cytoplasmic growth but without cytoplasmic division so that there results a mass of protoplasm with many and scattered nuclei but with inadequate cell boundaries.

SYNDACTYLY - Either bony fusion or fleshy webbing of the digits, generally the second and their digits being involved. Probably inherited.

SYNENCEPHALON - The third or most posterior of the three primary divisions of the forebrain which gives rise to the posterior portion of the diencephalon. (The other divisions are parencephalon and telencephalon.)

SYNERESIS - A segregation of the colloidal phases, a corollary of ageing.

SYNEZESIS - The stage in maturation between synaptene and pachytene when the chrommatin threads are short and thick and the ends away from the centrosome are tangled.

SYNGAMY - Specifically the fusion of the gamete pronuclei, but also the union of gametes at fertilization. *Syn.*, zygotogenesis, fertilization.

SYNOPHTHALMIA - Fusion of the eyes as in cyclopia.

SYNTONIC FACTOR - Some regulating force which enables a particular cell to live harmoniously with other cells of the same type so that an organ will develop, not found in tissue cultures of cells isolated prior to differentiation, present during organogenesis.

SYNTONY - Indwelling integration of parts; a natural force within and between cells developing from the specific organization of living matter.

TAIL FOLD - A sulcus begins to develop beneath the posterior end of the embryo, giving rise to a tail fold similar to the head fold except that from the beginning it is made up of ectoderm and somatic mesoderm. The tail fold often appears prior to the head fold and is longer. *Syn.*, amniotic tail fold.

TELA CHORIOIDEA - *Syn.*, Thin roof of third and fourth brain ventricles.

TELENCEPHALON - The portion of the forebrain (ventricle) anterior to a plane which includes the posterior side of the choroid plexus and the anterior side of the optic recess or the portion of the forebrain ventral to a plane passing from the posterior wall ventral to the optic recess to the anterior wall in the center of the velum transversum. Gives rise to torus transversus (anterior commissure), cerebral hemispheres, corpora striata, paraphysis, anterior choroid plexus, olfactory lobes, lateral ventricles and part of the foramina of Monro.

TELOBIOSIS - Fusion of embryos end-to-end. (*See* Parabiosis).

TELOCOEL - Cavity of the telencephalon.

TELOPHASE - Last phase in mitosis when the respective chromosome groups have reached their respective astral centers and are beginning to re-form a resting cell nucleus, the stage often accompanied by the beginning of cytoplasmic division.

TELOSYNAPSIS - End-to-end fusion of chromosomes. (*See* PARASYNAPSIS).

TERATOGENETIC - Abnormality producing.

TERATOLOGY - Study of the causes of monster and abnormality formation.

TERATOMA - Structure which results from random differentiations; malignant assembly of tissues, often well differentiated histologically, generally embedded in an otherwise healthy organ. Some use term embryoma to refer to embryological differentiation and teratoma to mean both histological and morphological differentiation of the abnormal growth.

TESTES - Sex organs of the male in which spermatagonia are produced and matured, a distinguishing primary sex character of the male.

TETRADS - Paired (homologous) chromosomes which have become duplicated longitudinally in anticipation of the meiotic (reductional) division. When viewed from one end will appear as a group of four chromosomes, hence a tetrad.

THALAMUS - Dorso-lateral wall of the diencephalon which becomes thickened by the development of fibers passing from the cord to the more posterior parts of the cerebral hemispheres.

THECA - Connective tissue covering, generally refers to covering of ovarian follicle.

THECA EXTERNA - The outermost of the coverings of the ovarian follicle, rather loose connective tissue with abundant blood supply. Continuous with ovarian stroma.

THECA FOLLICULI - Refers to membraneous and cellular coverings of the ovum within the ovary.

THECA INTERNA - The layer of connective tissue consisting of closely packed fibres, possibly some of smooth muscle, immediately external to the ovarian follicle of birds and mammals. Less vascular and more compact than theca externa.

THORACO-GASTROSCHISIS - Failure of the body wall to close along the med-ventral line, including the thoracic region.

THORACOPAGUS - Thoracic union of conjoined twins.

THYMUS - Derivatives of first pair of branchial pouches of the embryo which separate from the pouches and migrate to a position directly anterior to the heart. Known as gland of adolescence because it recedes upon attaining sexual maturity. Endocrine function.

THYROGLOSSAL DUCT - A temporary tubular connection between the thyroid anlage' and the pharynx near the base of the tongue.

THYROID BODY or GLAND - Originates as an endodermal thickening in the floor of the pharynx between the second pair of visceral arches; evaginates to form a vesicle temporarily connected with the gut by the thyroglossal duct; separates from gut becomes divided and migrates to junction of subclavian and common carotid arteries. Somewhat similar history in all vertebrate embryos. Endocrine function.

TOPOGENESIS - All of the processes of movement which result in structure formation.

TOLERANCE, ACTIVELY ACQUIRED - If mammals, birds and amphibia are exposed to living homologous tissue cells at an early stage in development (before their immunological response faculty has become functionally mature), a partial or complete specific central failure of the mechanism of immunological response is indiced.

TONGUE - Solid mesodermal mass, covered with endoderm, derived by cell proliferation from the floor of the pharynx.

TONSILS - Lymphatic structures derived from the endoderm and mesoderm of the second pair of visceral pouches.

TOOTH GERMS - Conical bands of tissue which develop in the oral cavity of mammals, generally a single one for each of the temporary and permanent teeth.

TORSION - The twisting of the embryo so that it lies on its side.

TORUS TRANSVERSUS - Thickening in the median ventro-anterior wall of the lamina terminalis of the telencephalon, just exterior to the optic recess, representing the rudiment of the anterior commissure.

TOTIPOTENCY - Related to theory that the isolated blastomere is capable of producing a complete organism. Roux (1912) included several faculties such as (1) for self-differentiation; (2) for influencing differentiation or induction of other parts; (3) for specific reaction to differentiating influences as in dependent differentiation.

TRACHEA - That portion of the respiratory tract between the larynx and the lung buds, lined with endoderm, probably derived from the posterior portion of the original laryngo-traxheal groove.

TRACHEAL GROOVE - (*See* LARYNGO-TRACHEAL GROOVE).

TRANSLOCATION, RECIPROCAL - A balanced change in the chromosomes, segmental rearrangements of chromosomes.

TRANSVERSE - A plane (or section) which divides the anterior-posterior axis at right angles, separating the more anterior from the more posterior. *Syn.*, cross section, but this synonym is not generally satisfactory.

TRANSVERSE NEURAL FOLD - The continuation of the lateral neural folds (ridge) of the early frog embryo around the anterior and (*i.e.*, region of face), the region of the temporary anterior neuropore. *Syn.*, transverse medullary fold or ridge.

TRIASTER - Abnormal mitotic figure possessing three asters generally causing irregular distribution of chromosomes and abnormal cleavages. Other multiple aster conditions noted, (*e.g.* tetraster, etc.)

TRIGEMINAL GANGLION - Cranial (V) ganglia which consist of motor and sensory portions and arise from the most anterior crest segments in conjunction with cells from the inner (ganglionic) portion of the corresponding placode. Give rise to ophthalmic, mandibular, and maxillary branches; associated with the myelencephalon at the level of the greatest width of the 4th ventricle.

TRITOGENY - One-third of a fragment. (*See* merogony).

TROCHLEARIS NERVE - Cranial (IV) motor nerves arise from the dorsal surface of the brain near the isthmus, coming from medullary neuroblasts and innervating the superior oblique muscles of the eye.

TROPHECTODERM - Region of continuity of ectoderm and outer layer of trophoblast; extra-embryonic ectoderm following germ layer differentiation.

TROPHIC - The action of the nervous system in the absence of which the muscle tonus fails and in consequence, regeneration is impossible.

TROPHOBLAST - Thin layer of cells which constitute the wall of the mammalian blastocyste; outer layer of blastocyst prior to differentiation of the primary germ layers. The cellular parenchyma of the chorion and placenta, cells generally with large nuclei. Chords of the tropho-blast grow out from the initially smooth surface of chorion to penetrate and erode the endometrium to give rise to the primary chorionic villi. May produce steroid hormones, chorionic gonadotrophins, and other hormones. Mediates the metabolic exchange between mother and fetus.

TROPHOBLASTIC CELL COLUMNS - Distal ends of chorionic and placental villi; continue to grow in the form of columns of cytotrophoblast preceding the differentiation of the mesoderm in them.

TROPHOBLASTIC SHELL - (Peripheral cytotrophoblast). During the first phases of gestation the cytotrophoblast and trophoblastic shell produce proteolytic and cytolytic substances which are capable of attacking the endometrium.

TROPHOBLASTIC VILLI - Finger-like projections of chorionic mesoderm comprising the trophoderm of mammalian embryos.

TROPHOCHROMATIN - Nutritive chromatin of the nucleus.

TROPHODERM - Trophectoderm reinforced by a layer of somatic mesoderm. *Syn.*, extra-embryonic somatopleure, serosa.

TRUE KNOT - Slipping of the fetus through a looped umbilical cord to produce a true knot, distinguished from looped blood-vessels which cause external bulgings called false knots.

TRUE PLACENTA - A placenta in which the chorion and uterine mucusa are intimately associated, in contrast with the primitive contact type. *Syn.*, burrowing placenta.

TRUNCUS ARTERIOSUS - Anterior continuation of the bulbus arteriosus beneath the foregut, divided in antero-posterior direction by a septum which is continuous through the bulbus to the ventricle; gives off the external carotids to the mandibular arches and the second, third, and fourth aortic arches which join the dorsal aorata. *Syn.*, ventral aorta.

TUBAL FISSURE - Longitudinal slit in the roof of the pharynx which connects the median chamber of the tubo-tympanic cavity with the oral cavity.

TUBAL RIDGE - The primordia of the Müllerian ducts or oviducts arising in the embryo lateral to each mesonephros and adjacent to the respective Wolffian duct, the anterior ends of which (in the female) become the ostia abdominalia tubae.

TUBERCULUM POSTERIUS - A thickening in the floor of the brain at the region of the anterior end of the notochord, representing the posterior margin of the diencephalon.

TUBO-TYMPANIC CAVITY - Remnants of the dorsal parts of the first pair of visceral (hyomandibular) pouches and the lateral walls of the pharynx, connecting the pharynx and the middle ear, represented by the Eustachian tube of the adult bird or mammal.

TUBULES - (*See* under specific names such as COLLECTING, MESONEPHRIC, PRONEPHRIC, SEMINIFEROUS.)

TUNICA ALBUGINEA - (*See* ALBUGINEA OF TESTIS).

TWINS, IDENTICAL - True twins, from a single egg and having common membranes and umbilicus.

TWINS, ORDINARY - Pleural pregnancy resulting from the fertilization of separate ova simultaneously liberated from individual follicles. Separate development, implantation, decidua capsularis, and fetal membranes.

TYMPANIC CAVITY - Cavity of the middle ear, a vestige of the hyomandibular pouch. (*See* TUBO-TYMPANIC CAVITY).

TYMPANIC MEMBRANE - Membrane made up of ectoderm, mesenchyme, and endoderm which separates the tympanic cavity from the exterior. *Syn.*, ear drum.

ULTIMOBRANCHIAL BODY - (*See* POSTBRANCHIAL BODY).

UMBILICAL ARTERIES - Branches of the sciatic arteries of the embryo, the right member being the smaller; carry blood to the allantois.

UMBILICAL VEINS - At first paired veins in the lateral body wall of the embryo which bring blood from the allantois and join the ducts of Cuvier, right vein disappearing and the left changing its connection to join the anterior half of the ductus venosus. Only the proximal portion persists as a vein in the ventral body wall.

UMBILICUS - The stalk-like connection between the embryo and all extra-embryonic structures, including the somatic stalk, allantoic stalk plus its arteries and veins, and the yolk stalk with its arteries and veins.

UMBILICUS, SOMATIC - (*See* SOMATIC UMBILICUS.)

UMBILICUS, YOLK SAC - (*See* YOLK-SAC UMBILICUS.)

URACHUS - The canal which connects the allantois and the urinary bladder in embryos.

URETER - Diverticulum from the posterior end of the Wolffian (mesonephric) duct appearing in the embryo; functioning as an excretory duct of the adult.

URETHRA - Single duct of the male mammal which discharges urine and also through which semen is liberated from the male genital tract into the genital tract of the female during coitus; mesodermal.

URINARY BLADDER - An endodermally lined vesicle derived from the hindgut, homologous to the allantois of the chick, connected with ureters.

URINIFEROUS TUBULE - Functional kidney tubule of both mesonephros and metanephros.

UROGENITAL SYSTEM - The entire excretory and reproductive systems, some embryonic parts of which degenerate before birth of mammals. Shows various degrees of common origin and ultimate function. (*See* specific excretory and reproductive components.)

UTERINE GLANDS - Glands within the uterine mucosa which secrete fat, proteids, and glycogen, a source of embryonic nutrition.

UTERINE MILK - A viscid fluid secreted by the uterine mucosa consisting of fats, proteids, and glycogen, a source of embryonic nutrition.

UTERINE MUCOSA - Mucosal lining of the uterus which shows cyclic changes associated with reproductive activity. *Syn.*, endometrium.

UTERUS - Thick walled muscular structure of the female sexual system which is lined with highly secretory endometrium, and serves as an implantation site for the developing mammal (traditionally called the womb).

UTERUS, ACTIVE (OR SENSITIVE) - Uteri on days 4 to 5 of normal pregnancy when implantation is the normal event. Endocrinologically attuned to implantation, competent to produce a decidua as a result of blastocyst stimulation.

UTERUS, DORMANT - The uterus of delayed implantation, can be made active by oestrogen stimulation. Will inhibit maturation of transplanted trophoblast, but does not interfere with shedding of the zona pellucida. Zona shedding is age dependent, following trophoblast maturation.

UTRICLE - A vesicle, generally referring to the superior portion of the otocyst which gives rise to the various semicircular canals of the ear, and into which these canals open. Lined with ectoderm.

VAGINA - The cavity of the female mammal possessing, at its external boundaries, a homologue of the male penis called the clitoris.

VALVES, SEMI-LUNAR - (*See* SEMI-LUNAR VALVES).

VASA DEFERENTIA - Mesonephric or Wolffian ducts which persist as the male gonoducts of the mammal, connecting with the testes through the vasa efferentia and epididymis and functioning as sperm ducts after the degeneration of the embryonic mesonephros and the development of the gonads. *Syn.*, vas deferens.

VASA EFFERENTIA - Derivatives of the anterior half of the mesonephric or Wolffian body which become the epididymis. *Syn.*, vas efferens.

VEIN - (*See* under specific names).

VELUM TRANSVERSUM - Depressed roof of the telencephalon just anterior to the lamina terminalis, which later becomes much folded and vascular as the anterior roof of the third ventricle. The division point between the tel-and diencephalon.

VENA CAVA ANTERIOR - Junction of inferior jugular (anterior cardinal) and (in the chick) the subclavian and vertebral veins which empty into the ductus Cuvieri, and later the right auricle. *Syn.*, superior vena cava, or superior caval veins.

VENA CAVA POSTERIOR - The single median ventral vein which represents the remnant of the anterior right cardinal and which later receives the hepatic vein prior to joining the ductus Cuvieri, and later joins the right auricle directly.

VENTRAL - Belly surface. Ventrad means toward the belly surface.

VENTRAL LIGAMENT OF LIVER - *Syn.*, falciform ligament.

VENTRAL MESENTERY - Double layer of splanchnic mesoblasts which connects the alimentary canal with the extra-embryonic splanchnopleure in the embryo; in the region of the hindgut includes both somatic and splanchnic mesoderm as a thick mass of mesoblast which binds the hindgut to the somatopleure. In the region of the fore- and midgut of the later embryo this includes the meatus venosus and the liver material.

VENTRICLE III - Main cavity (diocoel) of the forebrain, related to paired lateral ventricles or telocoesls, by way of the foramina of Monro.

VENTRICLE IV - Main cavity of the hindbrain (rhombencephalon) connected anteriorly with the aqueduct of Sylvius and posteriorly with the neural canal and extending through both the metencephalon and myelencephalon, having as a roof the vascular posterior choroid plexus.

VENTRICLE, LATERAL - (*See* LATERAL VENTRICLES OF THE BRAIN).

VENTRICLE OF THE HEART - Double and very muscular chamber of the heart developing from the anterior myocardium, subdivided by septa and provided with valves; connected with bulbus arteriosus anteriorly.

VER - Ventral ectodermal ridge in the (mouse embryo) tail tip which is thickened or columnar rather than of pavement variety which covers the tail elsewhere. It extends about 300 microns from the tail tip craniad and resembles the apical ectodermal ridge of limb buds; gives positive alkaline phosphatase reaction which is a sign of functional hypertrophy of the cells. Has something to do with the outgrowth of the tail and is not peculiar to the mouse. Seen from 9 to 11 days, gone by 12 days.

VERNIX CAAEORA - A cheese-like material which sometimes covers the skin of the fetus, and is derived from dead cells and fat.

VERTEBRA - Derivatives of the sclerotome which surround the nerve cord and notochord, and finally incorporate the notochord by chondrification and ossification (centrum).

VERTEBRAL ARCH - (*See* NEURAL ARCH).

VERTEBRAL PLATE - (*See* AXIAL MESODERM).   *Syn.*, segmental plate.

VESICLE - (*See* under specific names).

VESICLE, GERMINAL - Nucleus of the egg while it is a distinct entity and before the elimination of either of the polar bodies.

VESTIBULE - A shallow basin into which the vagina and the urethra of the female mammal open.

VILLUS - A finger-like projection, such as the chorionic villus which is a projection of the mammalian chorion into folds of the uterine mucosa.

VISCERAL - Pertaining to the viscera.

VISCERAL ARCHES - Generally six pairs of mesodermal masses between the visceral pouches and lateral to the pharynx of all vertebrate embryos, including the mandibular, hyoid, and four branchial arches. Each arch is bounded by the endoderm on the pharyngeal side and ectoderm on the outside.

VISCERAL FURROW - Ectodermal invaginations which may meet endodermal pharyngeal evaginations to form visceral clefts. Syn., visceral groove.

VISCERAL GROOVE - (*See* VISCERAL FURROW).

VISCERAL MESODERM - (*See* SPLANCHNIC MESODERM and SPLANCHNOPLEURE).

VISCERAL PLEXUS - An aggregation of sympathetic neurones which control the viscera, having migrated posteriorly from the 10th (vagus) cranial ganglia.

VISCERAL POUCH - Endodermal evagination of the pharynx which, if they meet the corresponding visceral furrow, often breaks through to form the visceral cleft. *Syn.*, pharyngeal pouch.

VITALISM - A philosophical approach to biological phenomena which bases its proof on the present inability of scientists to explain all the phenomena of development. Idea that biological activities are directed by forces neither physical nor chemical, but which must be supra-scientific or super-natural. Effective guidance in development by some non-material agency (*See* mechanism).

VITELLIN - Egg-yolk phospho-protein.

VITELLINE - Adj., pertains to yolk, vein, or membrane.

VITELLINE ARTERY - Paired omphalomesenteric vessels which later fuse (as the dorsal mesentery forms) to go out through the umbilical stalk to the yolk as the vitelline (yolk) arteries, originating from the dorsal aorta.

VITELLINE MEMBRANE - The cytoplasm and yolk of the mouse egg is limited by a plasma or permeability membrane which is generally called the vitelline membrane, but is not to be confused with the membrane of the same name among invertebrates. During maturation of the oocyte this membrane becomes thrown into microvilli, some of which interdigitate with the surrounding follicle cells. As the zona pellucida is formed these microvilli seem to extend through the pellucida while follicle cell processes extend also through the pellucid area toward the vitellus. Its function, aside from being the plasma membrane of the ovum, is to aid in the engulfment of the invading spermatozoon.

VITELLINE SUBSTANCE - Yolk.

VITELLINE VEIN - (*See* OMPHALOMESENTERIC VEIN).

VITREOUS HUMOR - The rather viscous fluid of the eye chamber posterior to the lens, formed by cells budded from the retinal wall and from the inner side of the lens, hence ectodermal and probably also mesenchymal in origin. (*See* AQUEOUS HUMOR.)

VIVIPAROUS - Animals which bring forth young in advanced state of development, more advanced than eggs.

WAVE OF SEMINIFEROUS EPITHELIUM - Complete series of the successive cell associations found along a seminiferous tubule; the length of the wave being the distance between two successive, identical cell associations. The sequence of pictures along a wave is similar in sequence of events taking place in one given area during a cycle of the seminiferous epithelium.

WEBER'S LAW - The degree of sensitivity to a stimulus in any reacting system is not constant but depends, not alone on the nature of the stimulus, but upon the period of life and the strength of an already existing stimulus. A stimulus therefore represents a change, but a reacting system takes into account any pre-existing stimulus upon which this change is built. Theory that equal relative differences between stimuli of the same kind are equally perceptible.

WOLFFIAN BODY - (*See* MESONEPHROS).

WOLFFIAN DUCT - (*See* MESONEPHRIC DUCT, URINOGENITAL DUCT AND VAS DEFERENS).

WOLF SNOUT - Projecting of the premaxilla beyond the surface of the face, accompanying double (hare) lip and sometimes a cleft palate.

XANTHOLEUCOPHORE - Crystals and soluble yellow pigment; cells bearing such.

XANTHOPHORES - Yellow pigment in solution; cells bearing this yellow pigment.

X-CHROMOSOME - Female identifying chromosome when diploid (paired) but contains many genes unrelated to sex determination. In the female the two X chromosomes are different, one being isopycnotic and the other heteropycnotic.

XIPHOPAGUS - Xiphoid fusion of conjoined twins; sometimes the skin alone.

Y-CHROMOSOME - Short chromosome easily distinguished from autosomes and acrocentric. Presence with X chromosome typical for the male.

YOLK - Highly nutritious food (metaplasm) consisting of non-nucleated spheres and globules of fatty material found in all except alecithal eggs. *Syn.*, lecithin.

YOLK SAC - Extra-embryonic splanchnopleure.

ZONA PELLUCIDA - Transparent, non-cellular, secreted layer immediately surrounding the ovum, corresponding to the vitelline membranes of lower forms.

ZONA RADIATA - Zona pellucida which exhibits radial striations, not be confused with the corona radiata. *Syn.*, zona pellucida of the mammalian egg.

ZONA REACTION - A change occurs in the zona pellucida which renders it impermeable to further penetrations by active spermatozoa. The other mechanism of the prevention of polyspermy being a change involving the dissolution of the cortical granules of the ovum.

ZYGOTE - The diploid cell formed by the union of two gametes. *Syn.*, fertilized egg.

References

Adams, D. H.   1953.   "Some studies on liver catalase in embryonic and immature chickens and mice." Brit. Jour. Cancer. 7:501-508.

Adams, F. W., and H. H. Hillemann.   1950.   "Morphogenesis of the vitelline and allantoic placentae of the golden hamster." Anat. Rec. 108:363-383.

Ader, R., and P. M. Conklin.   "Handling of pregnant rats: Effect on emotionality of their offspring." Science. 142:411-412.

Agduhr, E.   1927.   "Studies on the structure and development of the bursa ovariea and the tuba uterina in the mouse." Acta Zool. Stockholm. 8:1-133.

Alden, R. H.   1948.   "Implantation of the rat egg.   III.   Origin and development of primary trophoblast giant cells. Am. J. Anat. 83:143-181.

Alfert, M.   1950.   "A cytochemical study of oögenesis and cleavage in the mouse." J. Cell. & Comp. Physiol. 36:381-409.

Allen, E.   1922.   "The estrous cycle of the mouse." Am. J. Anat. 30:297-371.

————.   1923.   "Ovogenesis during sexual maturity." Am. J. Anat. 31:439-470.

————, and E. A. Doisy.   1923.   An ovarian hormone: preliminary report on its localization, extraction and partial purification and action in test animals.   J. Am. Med. Assn. 81:819-821.

Allen, Ezra, and E. C. McDowell.   1940.   "Variations in mouse embryos of 8 days gestation." Anat. Rec. 77:165-171.

Allen, J. M.   1958.   "A chemical and histochemical study of aliesterase in the adrenal gland of the developing mouse." Anat. Rec. 132:195-207.

Amoroso, E. C., and A. S. Parkes.   1947.   "Effects on embryonic development of x-irradiation of rabbit spermatozoa in vitro." Proc. Royal Soc. London B. 134:57-78.

Angevine, L. B., Jr., and R. L. Sidman.   1961.   "Autoradiographic study of cell migration during histogenesis of cerebral cortex in the mouse." Nature (Lond.). 192:766-768.

————.   1962.   "Autoradiographic study of histogenesis in the cerebral cortex of the mouse." (Abstr.) Anat. Rec. 142:210.

Arey, L. B.   1965.   "Developmental Anatomy." W. B. Saunders Co., 695 pps.

Asayama, S., and M. Furusawa.   1960.   "Culture in vitro of prospective gonads and gonad primordia of mouse embryo." Dolutsugoho Zosshi (Zool.-Soc.-Japan) 69:280.

Asscher, A. W., and C. J. Turner.   1955.   Vaginal sulphhydryl and disulphide groups during the oestrous cycle of the mouse. Nature (Lond.). 175:900-901.

Atkinson, W. B., and C. W. Hooker.   1945.   The day to day level of estrogen throughout pregnancy and pseudopregnancy in the mouse. Anat. Rec. 93:75-89.

Atlas, M., and V. P. Bond.   1965.   "The cell generation cycle of the eleven-day mouse embryo." J. Cell. Biol. 26:19-24.

Auerbach, R.   1954.   "Analysis of the developmental effects of a lethal mutation in the house mouse." J. Exp. Zool. 127:305-330.

————.   1960.   "Morphogenetic interactions in the development of the mouse thymus gland." Developmental Biol. 2:271-284.

————.   1961.   "Genetic control of thymus lymphoid differentiation." Proc. Nat. Acad. Sci. 47:1175-1181.

————.   1961.   "Experimental analysis of the origin cell types in the development of the mouse thymus." Developmental Biol. 3:336-354.

---

* This reference list cannot be complete, but is nearly so. The author invites readers to apprise him of any appropriate and unlisted references. No apology is offered for the inclusion of some few references on the rat or related forms where comparable references on the mouse are not available. For late references, see special listing starting on page 407.

Auerbach, R. 1963. "Developmental studies of mouse thymus and spleen." N. C. I. Monograph. 11:23.

———. 1964. "On the function of the embryonic thymus." Wistar Inst. Sympos. Monograph. 2:1-8.

———. 1964. "Experimental analysis of mouse thymus and spleen morphogenesis" (R. A. Good & A. E. Gabrielsen ed.) "The thymus in immunobiology." Hoeber, N.Y. p. 95-111.

Austin, C. R. 1948. "Number of sperms required for fertilization." Nature (Lond.). 162:534-535.

———. 1948. "Functions of hyaluronidase." Nature (Lond.). 162:63-64.

———. 1949. "The fragmentation of eggs following induced ovulation in immature rats." J. Endocrinology. 6:104-111.

———. 1951. "Observations on the penetration of the sperm into the mammalian egg." Austr. J. Sci. Res. B. 4:581-596.

———. 1951. "Activation and the correlation between male and female elements in fertilization." Nature (Lond.). 168:558-559.

———. 1952. "The capacitation of the mammalian sperm." Nature (Lond.). 170:326.

———. 1955. "Polyspermy after induced hypothermia in rats." Nature (Lond.). 175: 1038.

———. 1957. "Fate of spermatozoa in the uterus of the mouse and rat." J. Endocrin. 14:335-342.

———. 1959. "Entry of spermatozoa into the Fallopian tube mucosa." Nature (Lond.). 183:908.

———. 1959. "The role of fertilization." Perspectives Biol. Med. 3:44.

———. 1960. "Fate of spermatozoa in the female genital tract." J. Reprod. Fert. 1:151.

———. 1960. "Capacitation and the release of hyaluronidase from spermatozoon." J. Reprod. Fert. 3:310-311.

———. 1960. "Anomalies of fertilization leading to triploidy." J. C. C. P. 56 Suppl. p. 1-16.

———. 1961. "Sex chromatin in embryonic and fetal tissue." Acta Cytol. 6:61-68.

———. 1961. "Early reactions of the rodent egg to spermatozoon penetration." J. Exp. Biol. 33:358-365, June.

———. 1961. "Significance of sperm capacitation." Proc. IV. Cong. Am. Reprod., Hague.

———. 1961. "The mammalian egg." Blackwell Scientific Pub., Oxford.

———. 1963. "Fertilization and transport of the ovum." in "Conference on Physiological Mechanisms Concerned with Conception," pp. 285-320. Pergamon Press.

———. 1965. "Fertilization." 145 pps. Prentice-Hall, Englewood, N.J.

———. 1965. "Ultrastructural changes in the egg during fertilization and the imitation of cleavage" (G. E. W. Wolstenholme and M. O'Connor, eds.) "Preimplantation Stages of Pregnancy" pps. 3-28. Little, Brown & Co., Boston.

———, and M. W. H. Bishop. 1957. "Fertilization in mammals." Biol. Rev. 32:296.

———. 1958. "Capacitation of mammalian spermatozoon." Nature (Lond.). 181:851

———. 1958. "Some features of the acrosome and perforatorium in mammalian spermatozoon." Proc. Royal Soc. (Lond.). B. 149:241-248.

———. 1958. "Role of the rodent acrosome and perforatorium in fertilization." Proc. Royal Soc. (Lond.). B. 149:241-248.

Austin, C. R., and A. W. H. Braden. 1953. "An investigation of polyspermy in the rat and rabbit." Austr. J. Biol. Sci. 6:674-692.

———. 1953. "Polyspermy in mammals." Nature (Lond.). 172:82-3.

———. 1953. "The distribution of nucleic acid in rat eggs in fertilization and early segmentation." Austr. J. Biol. Sci. 6:324-333.

———. 1954. "Anomalies in rat, mouse, and rabbit eggs." Austr. J. Biol. Sci. 7: 537-542.

———. 1955. "Observation on nuclear size and form in living rat and mouse eggs." Exp. Cell. Res. 8:163-172.

Austin, C. R., and A. W. H. Braden. "Early reactions of the rodent egg to spermato-
     zoon penetration." J. Exp. Biol. 33:358-365.
Austin, C. R., and H. M. Bruce. 1956. "Effect of continuous oestrogen administration
     on oestrous ovulation and fertilization in rat and mice." J. Endocrin. 13:376.
Austin, C. R., and J. Similis. 1948. "Phase-contrast microscopy in the study of fer-
     tilization and early development of the rat egg." J. Roy. Microscop. Soc.
     68:13-19.
Averill, R. L. W., C. E. Adams, and L. E. Rawson. 1955. "Transfer of mammalian
     ova between species." Nature (Lond.). 176:167.
Bacisch, P., and G. M. Wyburn. 1945. "Parthenogenesis of atretic ova in the rodent
     ovary." J. Anat. (Lond.) 79:177-179.
Backman, G. 1939. Das Wachstum der weissen Maus. Lunds Univ. Arsskr. Ard. Z.
     35 (12):1-26.
Badtke, G., and K. H. Degenhardt. 1963. "Uber die Enstehung kombinierter mis bil-
     dungen der Linse und der Hornkaut in den Augen Neugeborener des embryo-
     nalen Linsenblaschens vom Oberflackenektoderm." Klin. Monat. Augenheild.
     142:62-89.
Bader, R. S. 1965. "Fluctuating asymmetry in the dentition of the house mouse."
     Growth. 29:291-300.
Ball, W. D. 1963. "A quantitative assessment of mouse thymus differentiation." Exp.
     Cell. Res. 31:82-88.
_____, and R. Auerbach. 1960. "In vitro formation of lymphocytes from embryonic
     thymus." Exp. Cell. Res. 20:245.
Ball, Z. B., R. H. Barnes, and Mr. B. Visscher. 1947. "The effects of dietary caloric
     restriction on maturity and senescence, with particular reference to fertility
     and longevity. "Am. J. Physiol. 150:511-519.
Balmain, J. H., J. D. Biggers, and P. J. Claringbold. 1956. "Glycogen, wet weight
     and dry weight changes in the vagina of the mouse." Austr. J. Biol. Sci. 9:
     147-158.
Barnett, S. A. 1962. "Total breeding capacity of mice at two temperatures." J. Re-
     prod. Fert. 4:327-335.
_____, and E. M. Coleman. 1959. "The effect of low environmental temperature on
     the reproductive cycle of female mice." J. Endocrin. 19:232-240.
Barnett. S. A., and M. J. Little. 1965. "Maternal performance in mice at -3°C: food
     consumption and fertility." Proc. Royal Soc. (Lond.) B. 162:492-501.
Barraclough, C. A. 1955. "Influence of age on the response of preweaning female mice
     to testosterone propionate." Am. J. Anat. 97:493-521.
Barrowman, J., and M. Craig. 1961. "Haemoglobins in foetal C57 B1/6 mice." Nature
     (Lond.). 189:409-410.
_____. 1961. "Haemoglobins of foetal CBA mice." Nature (Lond.). 190:818-819.
Bateman, N. 1954. "The measurement of milk production of mice through preweaning
     growth of suckling young." Physiol. Zool. 27:163-173.
_____. 1954. "Bone growth: a study of the gray lethal and microthalmic mutants in
     the mouse." J. Anat. 88:212-262.
_____. 1960. "Selective fertilization at the locus T of the mouse." Genet. Res.
     Cambridge. 1:226.
Beatty, R. A. 1951. "Transplantation of mouse eggs." Nature (Lond.). 168:995.
_____. 1951. "Heteroploidy in mammals." Animal Breed. (Abstr.) 19:283-292.
_____. 1953. "Haploid rodent eggs." Proc. 9th Int. Cong. Genetics Bellogio-Caryo-
     logia. 6:784.
_____. 1957. "Parthenogenesis and polyploidy in mammalian development." 132 pps.
     Cambridge U. Press.
Beatty, R. A., and M. Fischberg. 1949. "Spontaneous and induced triploidy in pre-
     implantation mouse eggs." Nature (Lond.). 163:807-808.
_____. 1951. "Heteroploidy in mammals. I. Spontaneous heteroploidy in pre-
     implantation mouse eggs." J. Genet. 50:345-359.

Beatty, R. A., and M. Fischberg. 1951. "Cell number in haploid, diploid and polyploid mouse embryos." J. Exp. Biol. 28:541-552.

_____. 1952. "Heteroploidy in mammals. III. Induction of tetraploidy in pre-implantation mouse eggs." J. Genet. 50:471-479.

Beatty, R. A., and K. N. Sharma. 1960. "Genetics of gametes. III. Strain differences in spermatozoa from eight inbred strains of mice." Proc. Royal Soc. (Edinb.) B. 68:27-53.

Bennett, D. 1956. "Developmental analysis of a mutation in the pleiotropic effects in the mouse." J. Morphol. 98:199-234.

_____. 1964. "Abnormalties associated with a chromosome region in the mouse. II. Embryological effects of lethal alleles in the T-region." Science. 144:263-267.

_____, S. Badenhausen, and L. C. Dunn. 1959. "The embryological effects of four lethal t-alleles in the mouse, which affect the neural tube and skeleton." J. Morphol. 105:105-143.

Bennett, D., and L. C. Dunn. 1958. "Effects on embryonic development of a group of genetically similar lethal alleles derived from different populations of wild house mice." J. Morphol. 103:135-157.

Beaumont, H. M., and A. M. Mandl. 1963. "A quantitative study of primordiol germ cells in the male rat." J. Emb. Exp. Morphol. 11:715-740.

Ben-or, Sarah. 1963. "Morphological and functional development of the ovary of the mouse." J. Emb. Exp. Morphol. 11:1-11.

Berry, R. J. 1960. "Genetical studies on the skeleton of the mouse." Genet. Res. Cambridge.

Biancifiori, C., and F. Caschera. 1963. "The effect of olfactory lobectomy and induced pseudopregnancy on the incidence of methylcholanthrene-induced mammary and ovarian tumors in C3Hb mice. Brit. Jour. Cancer. 17:116-118.

Bierwolf, D. 1958. "Die Embryogenese des Hydrocephalus und der Kleinhirnmiss biklungen bein Dreherstamm der Hausmans." Morphol. Jahrb. 99:542-612.

Biggers, D. 1964. "The biology of cells and tissues in culture." Ed. G. N. Willmer Academic Press.

Biggers, J. D. 1953. "The carbohydrate components of the vagina of the normal and ovariectomized mouse during oestrogenic stimulation." J. Anat. 87327-336.

_____, M. R. Ashoub, A. McLaren, and D. Michie. 1958. "The growth and development of mice in three climatic environments. J. Exp. Biol. 35:144-155.

_____, and R. L. Brinster. 1964-5. "Biometrical problems in the study of early mammalian embryos in vitro." J. Exp. Zool. 158:39-47.

_____, and R. N. Curnow, C. A. Finn, and A. McLaren. 1963. "Regulation of the gestation period in mice." J. Reprod. Fert. 6:125-138.

_____, and C. A. Finn, and A. McLaren. 1961. "Long term reproductive performance of female mice." J. Reprod. Fert. 3:303 & 3:313.

_____. 1962. "Long term reproductive performance of female mice. II. Variation of litter size with parity." J. Reprod. Fert. 3:315-330.

Biggers, J. D., A. B. L. Gwatkin, and R. L. Brinster. 1962. "Development of mouse embryo in organ cultures of Fallopian tubes on a chemically defined medium." Nature (Lond.). 194:747-749.

_____, and A. McLaren. 1958. "Test tube animals - the culture and transfer of early mammalian embryos." Discovery. p. 423.

_____, B. Morre, B. Dianne, and D. G. Whittingham. 1965. "Development of mouse embryos in vivo after cultivation from two-cell ova to blastocysts in vitro." Nature (Lond.). 206:734-735.

_____, and L. M. Rinaldini. 1957. "The study of growth factors in time culture." Symp. Soc. Exp. Biol. XI. p. 264297.

Bishop, D. H., and J. H. Leathem. 1946. "Response of prepuberal male mice to equine gonadotropin. Anat. Rec. 95:313-319.

_____. 1948. "Effect of equine gonadotrophin on prepuberal male mice. Exp. Med. Surg. 6:28-30.

Bishop, D. W. , and A. Tyler. 1956. "Fertilizin in mammalian eggs. " J. Exp. Zool. 132:575-595.

Bishop, M. W. H. , and C. R. Austin. 1957. "Mammalian spermotozoa. " Endeavor. 16:137.

———, and A. Walter. 1960. "Spermatogenesis and the structure of mammalian spermatozoa. " Marshall's Physiology of Reproduction 3rd ed. vol. 1 pt. 2 p. 1, A. S. Parkes Ed. Longman Green & Co. , Publishers, London.

Bittner, J. J. 1936. "Differences observed in an inbred albino strain of mice following a change in diet. I. Litter size. " Jackson Mem. Lab. Nutr. Bull. 1:3-9.

———. 1936. "Differences observed in an albino strain of mice following a change in diet. II. Mortality. " Jackson Mem. Lab. Nutr. Bull. 2:3-11.

Blandau, R. J. 1961. "Biology of eggs and implantation from "Sex and Internal Secretions. " Ed. W. C. Young, Pub. Williams & Wilkins, Baltimore.

Blandau, Richard J. 1965. "Observations on the migration of living primordial germ cells in the mouse. " Anat. Rec.

Blandau, R. , L. Jensen, and R. Rumery. 1958. "Determination of the pH values of the reproductive tract fluids of the rat during heat. " Fert. & Steril. 9:207-224.

Blandau, R. J. , and D. L. Odor. 1949. "The total number of spermatozoa reaching various segments of the reproductive tract in the female albino rat at intervals after insemination. Anat. Rec. 103:93-109.

———. 1952. "Observations on sperm penetration into the oöplasm and change in the cytoplasmic components of the fertilizing spermatozoon in rat ova. " Fert. & Steril. 3:13-26.

Blandau, R. J. , and R. F. Rumery. 1964. "The relationship of swimming movement of epididymal spermatozoa to their fertilizing capacity. " Fert. & Steril. 15:571-579.

———, E. Warrick, and R. E. Rumery. 1965. "In vitro cultivation of fetal mouse ovaries. " Fert. & Steril. 16:705-715.

———, B. J. White, and R. E. Rumery. 1962. "In vitro observations on the movements of the primordial germ cells of the mouse. " Anat. Rec. 142:297.

———. 1963. "Observations on the movements of the living primordial germ cells in the mouse. " Fert. & Steril. 14:482-489.

Bloch, S. 1939. "Contributions to research on the female sex hormones. The implantation of the mouse egg. " J. Endocrin. 1:399-408.

———. 1958. "Beobachtungen uber Falle von fruh zeitiger Trachtigheit der Albino-Maus. Experientia. 14:141-142.

Bluhm, A. 1932. "Uber einen Fall von beeinflussung des geschlechtsverhaltnisses der Albino-Hausmaus durch behandlung des weibchens. " Z. ind. Abst. in Vereb. 62:88-89.

Bodermann, E. 1935. "A case of uniovular twins in the mouse. " Anat. Rec. 62:291-294.

Boell, E. 1948. "Respiratory metabolism of the mammalian egg. " J. Exp. Zool. 109-267.

Bogart, R. , R. W. Mason, H. Nicholson, and H. Krueger. 1958. "Genetic aspects of fertility in mice. " Int. J. Fert. 3:86-104.

Bomsel-Helmreich, O. 1965. "Heteroploidy and embryonic death" in "Preimplantation Stages in Pregnancy. " G. E. W. Wolstenholme & M. O'Connor, eds. p. 246-269, Little, Brown & Co. , Boston.

Bonnevie, K. 1950. "New facts on mesoderm formation and proamnion derivatives in the normal mouse embryo. " J. Morphol. 86:495-545.

———, and A. Brodal. 1946. "Hereditary hydrocephalus in the house mouse. IV. The development of the cerebullar anomalies during foetal life with notes on the normal development of the mouse cerebellum. " Norske Videns. -Akad. I. Oslo I. Mat. Natur. Klasse no. 4.

Boot, L. M. , and O. Muhlboch. 1953. "Transplantation of ova in mice. " Acta Physiol. pharm-neerl.

Boot, L. M., and O. Muhlboch. 1957. "The ovarian function in old mice. Acta Physiol. Pharmacol. Neer. 3:463.

Borghese, E., and A. Cassini. 1963. "Cleavage of mouse eggs" in "Cinemicrography in Cell Biology." p. 263, Ed. E. Rose, Academic Press, N.Y.

Borum, K. 1961. "Oögenesis in the mouse: a study of the meiotic prophase." Exp. Cell. Res. 24:495-507.

Bosshardt, K. K., W. J. Paul, K. E. O'Doherty, and R. H. Barnes. 1949. "Mouse growth assay procedures for the 'animal protein factor'." J. Nutr. 37:1.

Boving, B. G. 1954. "Blastocyst-uterine relationships." Cold Spring Harbor Symp. Quant. Biol. 19:9.

——————. 1959. "The biology of the trophoblast." Am. N.Y. Acad. Sci. 80:21-43.

——————. 1960. "Implantation." Am. N.Y. Acad. Sci. 75:700-725.

——————. 1960. "Invasion mechanisms in implantation." Anat. Rec. 136:p. 168.

——————. 1963. "Implantation mechanisms" in "Mechanisms concerned with conception." E. G. Hartman. ed. Pergamon Press.

Bowman, J. C., and D. S. Falconer. 1960. "Inbreeding depression and heterosis of litter size in mice." Genet. Res. 1:262-274.

——————, and R. C. Roberts. 1958. "Embryonic mortality in relation to ovulation rate in the house mouse." J. Exp. Biol. 35:138.

Boyd, J. D., and W. J. Hamilton. 1952. "Cleavage, early development and implantation of the egg" pps. 1-126 (A. S. Parkes ed.) "Marshall's physiology of reproduction," 3rd ed. vol. 2. Longman, Green, London.

Boyer, C. C. 1953. "Chronology of development for the golden hamster. J. Morphol. 92:1.

Bracish, P., and G. W. Wyburn. 1945. "Parthenogenesis of atretic ova in the rodent ovary." J. Anat. (Lond.) 79:177.

Bradbury, J. T., and R. G. Bunge. 1958. "Oöcytes in seminiferous tubules." Fert. & Steril. 9:18-25.

Braden, A. W. H. 1953. "The distribution of nucleic acid in rat eggs in fertilization and early segmentation." Austr. J. Biol. Sci. 6:665-673.

——————. 1954. "Reactions of unfertilized mouse eggs to some experimental stimuli." Exp. Cell. Res. 7:277-280.

——————. 1954. "The fertile life of mouse and rat eggs." Science 120:361.

——————. 1957. "The relationship between the diurnal light cycle and the time of ovulation in mice." J. Exp. Biol. 34:177-188.

——————. 1957. "Variation between trains in the incidence of various abnormalties of egg maturation and fertilization in the mouse." J. Genet. 55:476-486.

——————. 1957. "Differences between inbred strains of mice in the morphology of the gametes." Anat. Rec. 127:270-271.

——————. 1958. "Variation between strains of mice in phenomena associated with sperm penetration and fertilization." Genetics. 56:37-47.

——————. 1958. "Influence of time of mating on the segregation rates of alleles of the T locus in the house mouse." Nature (Lond.). 181:786-787.

——————. 1959. "Strain differences in the morphology of the gametes of the mouse." Austr. J. Biol. Sci. 12:65-71.

——————. 1959. "Are nongenetic defects of the gametes important in the etiology of prenatal mortality?" Fert. & Steril. 10:285-298.

——————. 1959. "Spermatozoa penetration and fertilization in the mouse." Proc. Int. Symp. Exp. Biol. Spollanzani, Paira, May.

——————. 1960. "Genetic influences on the morphology and function of the gametes" in "Mammalian genetics and reproduction." J. Cell & Comp. Physiol. 56: (Suppl. 1) 17-29.

——————. 1962. "Spermatozoon penetration and fertilization in the mouse." Symp. Genet. Biol. Ital. 9:1-8.

——————, and C. R. Austin. 1954. "The fertile life of mouse and rat eggs." Science. 120:361.

Braden, A. W. H., and C. R. Austin. 1954. "Fertilization of the mouse eggs and the effect of delayed coitus and of hot-shock treatment." Austr. J. Biol. Sci. 7: 552-565.

———. 1954. "The number of sperms about the eggs in mammals and its significance for normal fertilization." Austr. J. Biol. Sci. 7:543-551.

Braden, A. W. H., C. R. Austin, and H. A. David. 1954. "The reaction of the zona pellucida to sperm penetration." Austr. J. Biol. Sci. 7:391-409.

———, and S. Gluecksohn-Waelsch. 1958. "Further studies of the effects of the T locus in the house mouse on male fertility." J. Exp. Zool. 138:431-452.

Brambell, F. W. R. 1927. "The development and morphology of the gonads of the mouse. I. The morphogenesis of the indifferent gonad and the ovary." Proc. Royal Soc. (Lond.) B. 101:391-409; 102:206-222; 103:258-272.

———. 1928. "The development and morphology of the gonads of the mouse. III. The growth of the follicles." Proc. Royal Soc. (Lond.) B. 103:258-272.

———. 1937. "The influence of lactation on the implantation of the mammalian embryo." Am. J. Obstet. & Gynec. 33:942-953.

———. 1948. "Prenatal mortality in mammals." Biol. Rev. 23:370-407.

———, and A. S. Parkes. 1927. "The normal ovarian cycle in relation to oestrus production." Quart. J. Exp. Physiol. 18:185-198.

Brinster, R. L. 1963. "A method for in vitro cultivation of mouse ova from two cell to blastocyst." Exp. Cell. Res. 32:205-208.

———. 1964. "Possible energy sources for the development of the early mouse embryo." Jour. Cell Biol. 23:14A.

———. 1965. "Studies on the development of mouse embryos in vitro. I. The effect of osmolarity and hydrogen ion concentration." J. Exp. Zool. 158:49-57.

———. 1965. "Studies on the development of mouse embryos in vitro. II. The effect of energy source." J. Exp. Zool. 158:59-68.

———. 1965. "Studies on the development of mouse embryos in vitro. III. The effect of fixed nitrogen source." J. Exp. Zool. 158:69-77.

———. 1965. "Lactate dehydrogenase activity in the pre-implanted mouse embryos." Biochem. Biophys. Acta. 110:439-441.

———. 1965. "Studies of the development of mouse embryos in vitro: energy metabolism" in "Preimplantation Stages in Pregnancy." G. E. W. Wolstenholme & M. O'Connor, eds. p. 60-81, Little, Brown & Co., Boston.

———. 1966. "Glucose 6-phosphate-dehydrogenase activity in the preimplantation mouse embryo." Biochem. J. 101:161-163.

———, and J. D. Biggers. 1965. "In vitro fertilization of mouse ova within the explanted Fallopian tube." J. Reprod. Fert. 10:277-279.

Briody, B. A. 1959. "Response of mice to ectomelia and vaccinia virus." Bact. Rev. 23:61.

Briones, H., and R. A. Beatty. 1954. "Interspecific transfers of rodent eggs." J. Exp. Zool. 125:99.

Bruce, H. M. 1954. "Feeding and breeding of laboratory animals. XIV. Size of breeding group and production of mice." J. Hyg. 52:60-66.

———. 1959. "An exteroceptive block to pregnancy in the mouse." Nature (Lond.). 184:105.

———. 1960. "Further observations on pregnancy block in mice caused by the proximity of strange males." J. Reprod. Fert. 1:311-312.

———. 1960. "A block to pregnancy in the mouse caused by proximity of strange males." J. Reprod. Fert. 1:96-103.

———. 1961. "An olfactory block to pregnancy in mice. Part I. Characteristics of the block." Proc. 4th Congr. Anim. Reprod. (The Hague). 159-162.

———. 1965. "Effect of castration on the reproductive phenomena of male mice." J. Reprod. Fert. 10:141-143.

———, and J. East. 1956. "Number and viability of young from pregnancies concurrent with lactation in the mouse. J. Endocrin. 14:19-27.

Bruce, H. M., and D. M. V. Parrott. 1960. "Role of olfactory sense in pregnancy block by strange males." Science. 131:1526.

Brumby, P. J. 1960. "The influence of maternal environment on growth in mice." Heredity. 14:1-18.

Bryson, D. L. 1964. "Development of mouse eggs in diffusion chambers." Science. 144:1351-1353.

Bryson, V. 1944. "Spermatogenesis and fertility in Mus musculus as affected by factors at the T-locus." J. Morphol. 74:131-187.

_____. 1945. "Development of the sternum in screw tail mice." Anat. Rec. 91:119-141.

Bullough, W. S. 1942. "Oögenesis and its relation to the oestrous cycle in the adult mouse." J. Endocrin. 3:141-149.

_____. 1946. "Mitotic activity in the adult female mouse. A study of its relation to the oestrous cycle in normal and abnormal conditions." Philos. Trans. Royal Soc. (Lond.) B. 231:451-576.

_____, and H. F. Gibbs. 1941. "Oögenesis in adult mice and starlings." Nature (Lond.). 148:439-440.

Bulmer, D., and A. D. Dickson. 1960. "Observations on carbohydrate materials in the rat placenta." J. Anat. 94:46-58.

Burckhart, G. 1901. "Die Implantation des Eies der maus in die Uterusochleimhaut und die Umbildung derselben zur Decidua." Arch. Mikroscop. Anat. 57:528-569.

Burdick, H. O., B. B. Emmerson, and R. Whitney. 1940. "Effects of testosterone proprionate on pregnancy and on passage of ova through the oviducts of mice." Endocrin. 26:1081-1086.

_____, and G. Pincus. 1935. "The effect of oestrin injections upon the developing ova of mice and rabbits." Am. J. Physiol. 111:201-208.

_____, and R. Whitney. 1937. "Acceleration of the rate of passage of fertilized ova through the Fallopian tubes of mice by massive injections of an estrogenic substance." Endocrin. 21:637.

_____, R. Whitney, and B. Emerson. 1942. "Observations on the transport of tubal ova." Endocrin. 31:100-108.

_____, R. Whitney, and G. Pincus. 1937. "The fate of mouse ova tube-locked by injections of oestrogenic substances." Anat. Rec. 67:513-519.

Burns, E. L., M. Maskop, V. Suntzeff, and L. Loeb. 1936. "On the relation between the incidence of mammary cancer and the nature of the sexual cycle in various strains of mice." Am. J. Cancer. 26:56-68.

Burrows, H. 1935. "Pathological conditions induced by oestrogenic compounds in the coagulating gland and prostate of the mouse." Am. J. Cancer. 23:490-512.

Burstone, M. S. 1950. "The effect of radioactive phosphorus upon the development of the teeth and mandibular joint of the mouse." J. Am. Dental Assn. 41:1-18.

Calarco, Patricia G. 1965. "The histology and fine structure of the murine yolk sac." (Abstr.) Am. Zool. 5:224.

_____, and Frank H. Moyer. 1966. (Univ. Illinois, Urbana) "Structural changes in the murine yolk sac during gestation: cytochemical and electron microscope observations." J. Morphol. 119:341-356.

Callas, G., and B. E. Walker. 1963. "Palate morphogenesis in mouse embryos after X-irradiation." Anat. Rec. 145:61-68.

Carsner, C. L., and E. G. Rennels. 1960. "Primary site of gene action in anterior pituitary dwarf mice." Science. 131:829.

Carter, T. C. 1954. "The genetics of luxate mice. IV. Embryology." J. Genet. 52:1-35.

_____. 1959. "Embryology of the Little and Bagg X-rayed mouse stock." J. Genet. 56:401-435.

_____, M. F. Lyon, and R. Y. S. Phillips. 1955. "Gene-tagged chromosome translocations in eleven stocks of mice." J. Genet. 53:155-166.

Castle, W. E., W. H. Gates, S. C. Reed, and G. D. Snell. 1936. "Identical twins in a mouse cross." Science. 84:581.

Cattanach, B. M., and R. G. Edwards. 1958. "The effects of triethylenemelamine on the fertility of male mice." Proc. Royal Soc. (Edin.). 67:54.

Center, E. M. 1955. "Postaxial polydactyly in the mouse." J. Heredity. 46:144-148.

Cerey, K., J. Elis, and H. Raskova. 1965. "Studies on 6-azuridine and 6-azactidine. VI. Influence of 6-azactidine on prenatal development in mice." Biochem. Pharmacol. 14:1549-1556.

Cerruti, R. A., and W. R. Lyons. 1960. "Mammogenic activities of the mid-gestation mouse placenta." Endocrin. 67:884.

Chai, C. K. "Life span in inbred and hybrid mice." J. Heredity. 50:203-208.

———. 1966. "Characteristics in inbred mouse populations plateaued by directional selection." Genetics. 54:743-753.

Chandhuri, A. C. 1928. "The effect of the injection of alcohol into the male mouse upon the secondary sex ratio among the offspring." Brit. Jour. Exp. Biol. 5:185-186.

Chang, M. C. 1950. "Cleavage of unfertilized ova in immature ferrets." Anat. Rec. 108:31-44.

———. 1951. "Fertilizing capacity of spermatozoa deposited into the Fallopian tubes." Nature (Lond.). 168-697.

———, and D. M. Hunt. 1962. "Morphological changes of sperm head in the oöplasm of mouse, rat, hamster, and rabbit." Anat. Rec. 142:417-426.

Chang, T. K. 1939. "The development of polydactylism in a special strain of Mus musculus." Peking Nat. Hist. Bull. 14:119-132.

———. 1940. "Cellular inclusions and phagocytosis in normal development of mouse embryos." Peking Nat. Hist. Bull. 14 part 3.

Chapekar, T. N., G. V. Nayak, and K. J. Ranadive. 1966. "Studies on the functional activity of organically cultured mouse ovary." J. Emb. Ex. Morphol. 15:133-141.

Chardard-Ramboult. 1949. "Development de la glande thyroide chez la souris pendant la vie intra-uterine." Compt. Rend. Soc. Biol. 143:40-41.

Charlton, H. H. 1917. "The fate of unfertilized egg in the white mouse." Biol. Bull. 33:321-333.

Chase, E. B. 1941. "Studies on an anophthalmic strain of mice. II. Effect of congenital eyelessness on reproductive phenomena. Anat. Rec. 80:33-36.

Chase, H. B. 1951. "Inheritance of polydactyly in the mouse." Genetics. 36:697-710.

———. 1954. "Growth of hair." Phys. Rev. 34:113-126.

———. 1958. "The behaviour of pigment cells and epithelial cells in the hair follicle" in "The biology of hair growth." Chap. I. Academic Press, N.Y.

———, and E. Chase. 1941. "Studies on an anophthalmic strain of mice. I. Embryology of the eye region." J. Morphol. 68:279-301.

———, H. Ranch, and V. W. Smith. 1951. "Critical stages of hair development and pigmentation in the mouse." Physiol. Zool. 24:1-8.

Chesley, P. 1935. "Development of the short-tailed mutant in the house mouse." J. Exp. Zool. 70:429-459.

Chiquoine, A. 1954. "The identification, origin, and migration of the primordial germ cells in the mouse embryo." Anat. Rec. 118:135-146.

Chiquoine, A. D. 1958. "The distribution of polysaccharides during gastrulation and embryogenesis in the mouse embryo." Anat. Rec. 129:495-516.

———. 1959. "Electron microscopic observations on the developmental cytology of the mammalian ovum." Anat. Rec. 133:258.

———. 1960. "The development of the zona pellucida of the mammalian ovum." Am. J. Anat. 106:149.

Christian, J. J. 1964. "Effect of chronic ACTH treatment on maturation of intact female mice." Endocrin. 74:669-679.

———, and C. D. Lemunyan. 1958. "Adverse effects of crowding on lactation and reproduction of mice and two generations of their progeny." Endocrin. 63:517-529.

Christy, N. P., M. Dickie, and G. W. Woolley. 1950. "Estrus and mating in gonadectomized female mice with adrenal cortical abnormalities. Endocrin. 47: 129-130.

Clark, S. L. 1959. "The ingestion of proteins and colloidal material by columnar absorptive cells of the small intestine in suckling rats and mice." J. Biophys. Biochem. Cytol. 5:41-50.

Clauberg, C. 1931. "Genitalcyclus and Schwangershoft bei der weissen Maus. Dauer de Genital cyclus." Arch. Gynech. 147:549-596.

Clermont, Y., and E. Bustos. 1966. "Identification of five classes of type A spermatogonia in rat seminiferous tubules mounted 'in toto'." Anat. Rec. 154:332.

_____, and C. P. Leblond. 1953. "Renewal of spermatogonia in the rat." Am. J. Anat. 93:475-501.

_____, and C. Huckins. 1961. "Microscopic anatomy of the sex cords and seminiferous tubules in growing and adult albino rats." Am. J. Anat. 108:79-97.

_____, and B. Perey. 1957. "Quantitative study of the cell population of the seminiferous tubule in immature rats." Am. J. Anat. 100:241-267.

Cohen, A. I. 1961. "Electron microscopic observations of the developing mouse eye. I. Basement membranes during early development and lens formation." Develop. Biol. 3:297-316.

Cohn, S. A. 1957. "Development of the molar teeth in the albino mouse." Am. J. Anat. 101:295-320.

_____. 1966. "Lack of effect of acute neonatal anoxia on development of molar teeth of mice." Anat. Rec. 154:333.

Cole, H. A. 1933. "The mammary gland of the mouse during the estrous cycle, pregnancy and lactation." Proc. Royal Soc. (Lond.) B. 114:136-160.

Cole, R. J., and J. Paul. 1965. "Preimplantation stages of pregnancy." Ciba Foundation Symposium ed. G. E. W. Wolstenholme & M. O'Connor, p. 86 - Churchill, Ltd., London.

Coleman, D. L. 1966. "Purification and properties of δ-aminolevulinate dehydratase from tissues of two strains of mice." J. Biol. Chem. 241:5511-5517.

Connell, R. S. 1966. "Nucleoside phosphatases of the rat chorioallantoic placenta with increasing gestational age: electron microscope study." Anat. Rec. 154:334.

Cook, M. J. 1965. "The anatomy of the laboratory mouse." Academic Press, N.Y. 143 pps.

Cooper, George W. 1965. "Induction of somite chondrogenesis by cartilage and notochord: a correlation between inductive activity and specific stages of cytodifferentiation." Dev. Biol. 12:185-212.

Coppenger, C. J. 1964. "Effects of prenatal chronic gamma irradiation on the prenatal and postnatal development of the albino rat." Thesis, College Station, Tex., Agricultural and Mechanical Univ., 125 p.

Cox. D. F., J. E. Legates, and C. C. Cockerham. 1959. "Maternal influence on body weight." J. Animal Sci. 18:519-527.

Cox, F. K. 1926. "The chromosomes of the house mouse." J. Morphol. & Physiol. 43:45-54.

Crabtree, C. 1940. "Sex difference in the structure of Bowman's capsule in the mouse." Science. 91:299.

Craig, M. L., and F. S. Russell. 1963. "Electrophoretic patterns of hemoglobin from fetal mice of different inbred strains." Science. 142:398-399.

_____. 1964. "A developmental change in hemoglobins correlated with an embryonic red cell population in the mouse." Develop. Biol. 10:191-201.

Cranston, E. M. 1945. "The effect of lithospermum ruderale on the estrous cycle of mice." J. Pharmacol. Exp. Therap. 83:130-142.

Crelin, E. S., and J. Levin. 1955. "The prepuberal public symphsis and uterus in the mouse: their response to estrogen and relaxin." Endocrin. 57:730-747.

Crew, A. E., and P. Ch. Koller. "The sex incidence of chiasma frequency and genetical crossing over in the mouse." J. Genet. 26:359-383.

Crew, F. A. E., and L. Mirshaia. 1930. "Mating during pregnancy in the mouse."
     Nature (Lond.). 125: 564.

———. 1930. "The lactation interval in the mouse." Quart. J. Exp. Physiol. 20:105-
     110.

———. 1930. "On the effect of removal of the litter upon the reproductive rate of the
     female mouse." Quart. J. Exp. Physiol. 20:263-266.

Crippa, M. 1964. "The mouse karyotype in somatic cells cultured *in vitro*." Chromo-
     soma. 15:301-311.

Crisp, T. M. 1965. "Observations on the fine structure of lutein cells in mice." Anat.
     Rec.

Curry, G. A. 1959. "Genetical and developmental studies on droopy-eared mice." J.
     Emb. Exp. Morphol. 7:39-65.

Cutright, P. R. 1952. "Spermatogenesis in the mouse." J. Morphol. 54:197-220.

Dagg, C. P. 1960. "Sensitive stages for the production of developmental abnormalties
     in mice with 5-flurourocil." Am. J. Anat. 106:89-96.

———. 1963. "The interaction of environmental stimuli and inherited susceptibility to
     congenital deformity." Am. Zool. 3:223-233.

Dagg, C. P., *et al.* 1966. "Polygenic control of the teratogenicity of 5-fluorouracil in
     mice." Genetics. 53:1101-1117.

Dagg, Charles P. 1966. (Jackson Lab., Bar Harbor) "Teratogenesis," pp. 309-328. In
     E. L. Green (ed.) Biol. Lab. Mouse, 2nd ed. N. Y., McGraw-Hill.

Dalcq, A. M. 1955. "Processes of synthesis during early development of rodent's eggs
     and embryo." Studies on Fertility. 7:113.

———. 1956. "Effects du reactif de Schiff sur les oeufs en segmentation du rat et de
     la souris." Exp. Cell. Res. 10:99-119.

Dalcq, A., and J. Pasteels. 1955. "Determination photo metrique de la Teneur rela-
     tive en DNA des noyaux dans le oeufs en segmentation du rat et de la souris."
     Exp. Cell. Res. Suppl. 3:72-97.

Danforth, C. H. 1930. "Developmental anomalies in a special strain of mice." Am. J.
     Anat. 45:275-288.

———, and S. B. de Aberle. 1927. "Distribution of foetuses in the uteri of mice."
     Anat. Rec. 35:33.

———. 1927. "The functional interrelation of certain genes in the development of the
     mouse." Genetics. 12:340-347.

———. 1928. "The functional interrelation of the ovaries as indicated by the distribu-
     tion of foetuses in mouse uteri." Am. J. Anat. 41:65-74.

Daniel, J. F. 1910. "Observations on the period of gestation in white mice." J. Exp.
     Zool. 9:865-870.

Daoust, R., and Y. Clermont. 1955. "Distribution of nucleic acid in germ cells during
     the cycle of the seminiferous epithelium in the rat." Am. J. Anat. 96:255-
     279.

Davenport, C. B. 1925. "Regeneration of ovaries in mice." J. Exp. Zool. 42:1-ll.

Dawson, A. B. 1935. "The influence of hereditary dwarfism in the differentiation of the
     skeleton of the mouse." Anat. Rec. 61:485-493.

DeAberle, S. B. 1927. "A study of the hereditary anemia of mice." Am. J. Anat. 40:
     219-247.

Deane, H. W., B. L. Rubin, E. C. Driks, B. L. Lobel, and G. Peipsner. 1962.
     "Trophoblastic giant cells in placentas of rats and mice and their probable
     role in steroid-hormone production." Endocrin. 70:407-419.

Deanesly, R. 1930. "The corpora lutea of the mouse, with special reference to fat ac-
     cumulation during the oestrous cycle." Proc. Royal Soc. (Lond.) B. 106:
     578-595.

———. 1930. "The development and vascularization of the corpus luteum in the mouse
     and rabbit." Proc. Royal Soc. (Lond.) B. 107:60-76.

———, and A. S. Parkes. 1933. "Size changes in the seminal vesicles of mouse dur-
     ing development and after castration." J. Physiol. 78:442-450.

DeFeo, V. 1965. "Temporal aspect of the distribution of ova, in the rat uterus." Anat. Rec. 151:392.

DeFries, J. C. 1964. "Prenatal maternal stress in mice." J. Heredity. 55:289-295.

————. 1965. "Blocking of pregnancy in mice as a function of stress." Psychol. Rep. 17:96-98.

De Haan, R. L., and H. Ursprung, eds. 1965. "Organogenesis." Holt, Rinehart & Winston, 814 pps.

De Long, B. R., and R. L. Sidman. 1962. "Effects of eye removal at birth on histogenesis of the mouse superior colliculus: an autoradiographic analysis with tritiated thymidine." J. Comp. Neur. 118:205-224.

Deno, R. A. 1937. "Uterine macrophages in the mouse and their relation to involution." Am. J. Anat. 60:433-471.

Deol, M. S. 1962. "Genetical Studies on the skeleton of the mouse. XXVIII. Tail-short." Proc. Royal Soc. (Lond.) B. 155:78-95.

————. 1963. "The development of the inner ear in mice homozygous for shaker-with-syndactylism." J. Emb. Exp. Morphol. 11:493-512.

————. 1964. "The origin of the abnormalities of the inner ear in Dreher mice." J. Emb. Exp. Morphol. 12:727-733.

————. 1964. "The abnormalities of the inner ear in Kreisler mice." J. Emb. Exp. Morphol. 12:475-490.

————. 1966. "Influence of the neural tube on the differentiation of the inner year in the mammalian embryo." Nature (Lond.). 209:219-220.

————, and Margaret C. Green. 1966. "Snell's waltzer, a new mutation affecting behaviour and the inner ear in the mouse." Genet. Res. 8:339-345.

————, H. Grunberg, H. G. Searle, and G. M. Truslove. 1960. "How pure are inbred strains of mice." Genet. Res. 1:50-58.

————, and Priscilla W. Lane. 1966. "A new gene affecting the morphogenesis of the vestibular part of the inner ear in the mouse." J. Emb. Exp. Morphol. 16:543-558.

Detwiter, S. R. 1932. "Experimental observations upon the developing rat retina." J. Comp. Neur. 55:473-492.

Dewar, A. D. 1957. "Body weight changes in the mouse during the oestrous cycle and pseudopregnancy." J. Endocrin. 15:230-233.

Dickmann, Z. 1965. "Sperm penetration into and through the zona pellucida of the mammalian egg" in "Preimplantation Stages in Pregnancy." G. E. W. Wolstenholme & M. O'Connor, eds. p. 169-182, Little, Brown & Co., Boston.

————, and R. W. Noyes. 1960. "The fate of ova transport into the uterus of the rat." J. Reprod. Fert. 1:197-212.

————. 1961. "The zona pellucida at the time of implantation." Fert. & Steril. 12:310-318.

Dickson, A. D. 1963. "Trophoblastic giant cell transformation of mouse blastocysts." J. Reprod. Fert. 6:465-466.

————. 1964. "Delay of implantation in superovulated mice subjected to crowded conditions." Nature (Lond.). 201:839-840.

————. 1965. "The structure and size of the mouse blastocyst." Anat. Rec. 151:343.

————. 1966. "The form of the mouse blastocyst." J. Anat. 100:335-348.

————. 1966. "The form of the mouse blastocyst undergoing delay of implantation." Anat. Rec. 154:338.

————. 1966. "Induction of the trophoblastic giant cell transformation after ovariectomy in the mouse." (In press.)

————. 1966. "The size of the inner cell mass in blastocysts recovered from normal and ovariectomized mice." Int. J. Fert. 11:231-234.

————. 1966. "Observations on blastocysts recovered from ovariectomized mice." Int. J. Fert. 11:227-230.

————. 1967. "Variations in development of mouse blastocysts." J. Anat. (Lond.) in press.

Dickson, A. D., and H. B. Aranjo. 1966. "Dissociation of implantation and trophoblastic giant cell transformation of mouse blastocysts." (In press.)

_____, and D. Bulmer. 1960. "Observations on the placental giant cells of the rat."
J. Anat. 94:418-425.

_____. 1961. "Observations on the origin of metrial gland cells in the rat placenta."
J. Anat. 95:262-273.

Dietert, S. E. 1966. "Fine structure of the formation and fate of the residual bodies of
mouse spermatozoa with evidence for the participation of lysosomes." Anat.
Rec. 114:338.

Di Paola, J. A., H. Gatzek, and J. Pichren. 1964. "Malformations induced in the
mouse by thalidomide." Anat. Rec. 149:149-155.

Dominic, C. J. 1965. "The origin of the phermones causing pregnancy block in mice."
J. Reprod. Fert. 10:469-472.

Doyle, L. L., A. H. Gates, and R. W. Noyes. 1963. "Asynchronous transfer of mouse
ova." Fert. & Steril. 11:215-225.

_____, A. H. Gates, and R. W. Noyes. 1963. "Asynchronous transfer of mouse ova."
Fert. & Steril. 11:215-225.

Drasher, M. L. 1952. "Morphological and chemical observations on the mouse uterus
during the estrous cycle and under hormonal treatment." J. Exp. Zool. 119:
333-354.

_____. 1953. "Aging changes in nucleic acid and protein-forming systems of the vir-
gin mouse uterus." Proc. Soc. Exp. Biol. & Med. 84:596-601.

_____. 1953. "Uterine and placental nucleic acids and protein during pregnancy in the
mouse." J. Exp. Zool. 122:388-408.

_____. 1955. "Strain differences in the response of the mouse uterus to estrogens."
J. Heredity. 46:190-192.

Dronkert, A., M. Ota, and A. H. Gates. 1965. "Gonadotropin-inhibiting substances in
human urine." Proc. for VI Panamerican Congress of Endocrinology, Mexico
City, Excerpta Medica International Congress Series, 99:78.

Dry, F. W. 1926. "The coat of the mouse." J. Genet. 16:287-340.

Duboo, R. J., and R. W. Schaedler. 1960. "The effect of the intestinal flora on the
growth rate of mice, and on their susceptibility to experimental infections."
J. Exp. Med. 111:407-417.

Dunn, T. B. 1954. "Normal and pathologic anatomy of the reticular tissue in laboratory
mice." J. Nat. Cancer Inst. 14,6:1281-1433.

Duplan, J. F., and N. S. Wolf. 1962. "Age-related factors which influence the value
of the mouse embryo for post-irradiation restoration of the adult." Int. J.
Rad. Biol. 5:597-607.

Dzuick, P. J., and M. N. Runner. 1960. "Recovery of blastocysts and induction of
implantation following artificial insemination of immature mice." J. Reprod.
Fert. 1:321-333.

Eagle, H. 1956. "The salt requirements of mammalian cells in tissue culture." Arch.
Biochem. Biophys. 61:356.

Eaton, G. J., and L. D'Aloisio. 1966. "Effects of progesterone on embryo implantation
in the mouse." Abstr. Amer. Zool. 6:316.

Eaton, O. N. 1941. "Crosses between inbred strains of mice." J. Heredity. 32:393-
395.

_____, and M. M. Green. 1963. "Giant cell differentiation and lethality of homozygous
yellow mouse embryos." Genetics. 34:155-161.

Ebert, J. D. 1965. "Interacting systems in development." Holt, Rinehart & Winston,
N.Y. 227 pps.

Eckstein, P. 1959. "Implantation of ova." Mem. Soc. Endocrin. #6 Cambridge U.
Press.

Eddo, M. U. 1956. "Immunology and development." Univ. Chicago Press, 59 pps.

Edidin, M. 1964. "Transplantation antigen levels in the early mouse embryo." Transplantation. 2:627-637.

Edwards, R. G. 1954. "The experimental induction of pseudogamy in early mouse em-
         bryos." Experientia. 10:499.
————. 1954. "Colchicine-induced heteroploidy in early mouse embryos." Nature
         (Lond.). 174:276-277.
————. 1955. "Selective fertilization following the use of sperm mixture in the
         mouse." Nature (Lond.). 175:215.
————. 1955. "Colchicine-induced heteroploidy in the mouse. III. The induction of
         tetraploidy and other types of heteroploidy." J. Exp. Zool. 137:349.
————. 1957. "The experimental induction of gynogenesis in the mouse." Proc. Royal
         Soc. (Lond.) Ser. B. 146:469;488;149:117 (1958).
————, and R. E. Fowler. 1958. "The experimental induction of superfoetation in the
         mouse." J. Endocrin. 17:223-236.
————, and A. H. Gates. 1958. "Radioactive tracers and fertilization in mammals."
         Endeavor. 17:47.
————. 1959. "Timing of stages of maturation divisions, ovulation, fertilization and
         the first cleavage of eggs of adult mice treated with gonadotrophins." J.
         Endocrin. 18:272-304.
————. 1959. "Embryonic development in superovulated mice not receiving the coital
         stimulus." Anat. Rec. 135:291.
Edwards, R. G., and J. L. Sirlin. 1956. "Labelled pronuclei in mouse eggs fertilized
         by labelled sperm." Nature (Lond.). 177:429.
————. 1957. "Studies in gametogenesis, fertilization and early development in the
         mouse, using radioactive tracers." Int. J. Fert. 2:185,376.
————. 1959. "Identification of the C^{14} labelled male chromatin at fertilization in
         colchicine-treated mouse eggs." J. Exp. Zool. 140:19-27.
Edwards, R. G., E. D. Wilson, and R. E. Fowler. 1963. "Genetic and hormonal in-
         fluences on ovulation and implantation in adult mice treated with gonado-
         trophins." J. Endocrin. 26:389-399.
Eguchi, Y., and Y. Hashimoto. 1961. "Histological development of the testis of the
         mouse during embryonic stages." Bull. Univ. Osoha Prefecture Ser. B.
         11:77-83.
Ehling, U. H. 1965. "Dominant skeletal mutations induced by x-irradiation of the
         mouse spermatogonia." (Abstr.) Genetics. 52:441-442 (see also *ibid* 51:
         723-732)
Ellinger, F., J. E. Morgan, and F. W. Chambers. 1952. "The use of small laboratory
         animals in medical radiation biology." NMRI Research Report Proj. NM 006
         012.04.43.
Elliott, J. R., and C. W. Turner. "The mammary gland spreading factor in normal
         pregnant animals." Endocrin. 54:284-289.
Enders, A. C., and S. Schlafke. 1962. "The fine structure of the blastocyst." Anat.
         Rec. 142:338.
————. 1965. "The fine structure of the blastocyst: some comparative studies" in
         "Preimplantation Stages of Pregnancy." G. E. W. Wolstenholme & M.
         O'Connor, eds., p. 29-59, Little, Brown & Co., Boston.
Engle, E. T. 1927. "A quantitative study of follicular atresia in the mouse." Am. J.
         Anat. 39:187-203.
————. 1927. "Polyovular follicles and polynuclear ova in the mouse." Anat. Rec.
         35:341-343.
————. 1931. "Prepubertal growth of the ovarian follicle in the albino mouse." Anat.
         Rec. 48:341-350.
————. 1942. "Female mating behavior shown by male mice after treatment with dif-
         ferent substances." Endocrin. 30:623.
————, and J. Rosasco. 1927. "The age of the albino mouse at normal sexual matur-
         ity." Anat. Rec. 36:383-388.
Enzmann, E. V. 1933. "Milk-production curve of the albino mouse." Anat. Rec. 56:
         345-358.

Enzmann, E. V. 1935. "Intrauterine growth of albino mice in normal and in delayed pregnancy." Anat. Rec. 62:31-45.

————, N. R. Sapkin, and G. Pincus. 1932. "Delayed pregnancy in mice." Anat. Rec. 54:325-342.

Epifanova, O. I. 1963. "A radiographic analysis of the mitotic cycle and kinetics of a cell population in the uterine epithelium of mice." Dokl. Acad. Nauk. USSR 149:424-427.

Espinasse, P. G. 1935. "The oviduccal epithelium of the mouse." J. Anat. 69:363-368.

Evans, E. P., G. Breckon, and C. E. Ford. 1964. "An air-drying method for meiotic preparations from mammalian testes." Cytogenetics. 3:289-294.

Everett, N. B. 1943. "Observational and experimental evidences relating to the origin and differentiation of the definitive germ cells in mice." J. Exp. Zool. 92:49-91.

Fainstat, T. D. 1951. "Hereditary differences in ability to conceive following coitus in mice." Science. 114:524.

Falconer, D. S. 1955. "Patterns of response in selection experiments with mice." Cold Spring Harbor Symp. Quant. Biol. 20:178-196.

————. 1960. "The genetics of litter-size in mice." J. Cell. Comp. Physiol. 56:153-168 (Supp. #1).

————, R. G. Edwards, R. E. Fowler, and R. C. Roberts. 1961. "Analysis of differences in the number of eggs shed by the two ovaries of mice during natural oestrus or after superovulation." J. Rep. Fert. 2:418.

————, and R. C. Roberts. 1960. "Effect of inbreeding on ovulation rate and foetal mortality." Genet. Res. 1:422-430.

Faris, E. J. 1950. "The care and breeding of laboratory animals." John Wiley and Sons, N.Y., 515 pps.

Fawcett, D. W. 1950. "The development of mouse ova under the capsule of the kidney." Anat. Rec. 108:71-92.

————. 1965. "The anatomy of the mammalian spermatozoon with particular reference to the guinea pig." Zeit. f. Zellforsch. 67:279-296.

————, and R. D. Hollenberg. 1963. "Changes in the acrosome of guinea pig spermatozoa during passage through the epididymis." Zeit. f. Zellforsch. 60:276-292.

————, and S. Ito. 1965. "The fine structures of bat spermatozoa." Am. J. Anat. 116:567-610.

————, G. B. Wislocki, and C. M. Waldo. 1947. "The development of mouse ova in the anterior chamber of the eye and in the abdominal cavity." Am. J. Anat. 81:413-443.

Fekete, E. 1940. "Observations on three functional tests in a high-tumor and low-tumor strain of mice." J. Cancer. 38:234-238.

————. 1947. "Differences in the effect of uterine environment upon development in the dba and C57 black strains of mice." Anat. Rec. 98:409-415.

————. 1950. "Polyovular follicles in the C58 strain of mice." Anat. Rec. 108:699.

————. 1954. "Gain in weight of pregnant mice in relation to litter size." J. Hered. 45:88-98.

————, O. Bartholemew, and G. D. Snell. 1940. "A technique for the preparation of sections of early mouse embryos." Anat. Rec. 76:441-447.

————, and A. B. Griffin. 1954. "Significance of recent developments in nuclear cytology and cytogenetics of the mouse." J. Nat. Cancer Inst. 15:801-808.

————, and C. C. Little. 1942. "Observations on the mammary tumors incidence in mice born from transferred ova." Cancer Res. 2:525-530.

————, and L. B. Newman. 1944. "A case of hermaphroditism in the mouse." Yale J. Biol. & Med. 17:395-396.

Fell, H. B., and A. F. Hughes. 1949. "Mitosis in the mouse: a study of living and fixed cells in tissue cultures." Quart. J. Mic. Sci. 90:355-380.

Feller, W. F., and J. Boretos. 1967. "Semiautomatic apparatus for milking mice." Jour. Nat. Cancer Inst. 38:11-17.

Fenner, F. 1949. "Mouse pox (infections ectromelia) in mice. A review." Jour. Immunology. 63:641.

Finkel, M. P. 1947. "The transmission of radio-strontium and plutonium from mother to offspring in laboratory animals." Physiol. Zool. 20:405-421.

———, and G. M. Hirsch. 1952. "The influence of low, continuous doses of aureoymycin on CF-1 female mice." ANL. 4745:48.

Finn, C. A., and J. R. Hinckliffe. 1964. "Reaction of the mouse uterus during implantation and deciduous formation as demonstrated by changes in the distribution of alkaline phosphatase." J. Reprod. Fert. 8:331-338.

Firlit, C. F., and J. R. Davis. 1965. "Morphogenesis of the residual body of the mouse testis." Quart. J. Mic. Sci. 106:93-98.

Fischberg, M., and R. A. Beatty. 1950. "Aufange einer genetischen Analyse der spontanen Heteroploidie bei Mausen." Arch. Klaus. Stift. Vereb. Forsch. 25:22-27.

———. 1950. "Experimentelle Herstellung von polyploiden Mausblastulae." Arch. Klaus. Stift. Vereb. Forsch. 25:54-55.

———. 1951. "Spontaneous heteroploidy in mouse embryos up to mid-term." J. Exp. Zool. 118:321-335.

———. 1952. "Heteroploidy in mammals. II. Induction of triploidy in pre-implantation mouse eggs." J. Genet. 50:455-470.

———. 1952. "Heteroploidy in the mouse embryo due to crossing of inbred strains." Evolution. 6:316-324.

Fitch, M. 1957. "A mutation in mice producing dwarfism, brachycephaly, cleft palate, and micromelia." J. Morphol. 109:141-149.

———. 1957. "An embryological analysis of two mutants in the house mouse, both producing cleft palate." J. Exp. Zool. 136:329-361.

Fitzgerald, M. J. T. 1966. "Perinatal changes in epidermal innervation in rat and mouse." J. Comp. Neurol. 126:37-41.

Flax, M. H. 1953. "Ribose nucleic acid and protein during oögenesis and early embryonic development." Ph. D. Thesis, Columbia U. 44 pps.

Flexner, B., and A. Gellhorn. 1900. "The transfer of water and sodium to the amniotic fluid of the guinea pig." Am. J. Physiol. 136:757-761.

Flynn, R. J. 1955. "Ectoparasites of mice." Proc. Animal Care Panel. 6:75-91.

———, L. Greco, and P. B. Jinkins. 1963. "A disease of mice characterized by lung congestion." Lab. An. Care. 13:499-501 (1962 UAC-6762).

Fogg, L. C., and R. F. Cowing. 1952. "Cytologic changes in the spermatagonial nuclei correlated with increased radio-resistance." Exp. Cell. Res. 4:107-115.

Forbes, T. R. 1957. "Progestin in mouse embryos placenta and amniotic fluid." Endocrin. 61:593-594.

———, and C. W. Hooker. 1957. "Plasma levels of progestin during pregnancy in the mouse." Endocrin. 61:281-286.

Ford, C. E., and G. L. Woollam. 1963. "A colchicine, hypotonic citrate, air drying sequence for fetal mammalian chromosomes." Stain Techn. 38:271.

———. 1964. "Selection pressure in mammalian cell populations." Symp. of the Int. Soc. for Cell Biology. Vol. 3. Academic Press, Inc., New York City.

Forsberg, J. G. 1965. "Origin of vaginal epithelium." Obstet. & Gynec. 25:787-791.

———. 1965. "Mitotic rate and auto-radiographic studies in the derivation and differentiation of the epithelium in the mouse vaginal anlagé." Acta Anat. (Basel). 62:266-282.

———, and H. Olivicrona. 1965. "Further studies on the differentiation of the epithelium in the mouse vaginal anlagé." Z. Zellforsch. 66:867-877.

Forsthoefel, P. F. 1958. "The embryological development of the skeletal effects of the luxoid gene in the mouse, including its interactions with the luxate gene." J. Morphol. 104:81-142.

———. 1963. "The embryological development of the effects of Strongs Luxoid gene in the mouse." J. Morphol. 113:427-452.

———. 1963. "Observations on the sequence of blastemal condensations in the limbs of the mouse embryo." Anat. Rec. 147:129-138.

Fowler, R. E., and R. G. Edwards. 1957. "Induction of superovulation and pregnancy in mature mice by gonado-trophins." J. Endocrin. 15:374-384.

Fowler, R. E., and R. G. Edwards. 1960. "The fertility of mice selected for large or small body size." Genet. Res. 1:393-407.

Francke, C. 1948. "Some observations on the morphological structure of explanted immature ovaries and on 'ovariohypophyses'." Acta Neer. Morphol. Pathol. 6:129-140.

Frankenberger, Z. 1926. "Sur la morphologie et le développement des voies biliaires chez le genre Mus." Arch. Anat. Histol. et Embryol. 6:201-216.

Fraser, F. C., T. D. Fainstat, and H. Kalter. 1953. "The experimental production of congenital defects with particular reference to cleft palate" in "Neo-natal Studies." Int. Children's Center. 2:43-58. McGill University.

Freye, H. 1954. "Anatomische und entwicklungs geschicht-liche Untersudningen und oligs dactyler Mause." Z. Martin-Luther-Univ. Math. Naturw. Reike 3 (1+4) 801-824.

Fridhandler, L., S. E. Hafez, and G. Pincus. 1956. "Respiratory metabolism of mammalian eggs." Proc. Soc. Exp. Biol. & Med. 92:127-129.

Friedrich, F. 1964. "The development of the so-called yolk sac diverticulum in the placenta of white mice." Z. Znat. Entwickl. 124:153-170.

Fritze, C. 1956. "Statistical contributions to the study of human fertility." Fert. & Steril. 87:88-95.

Friz, M., and R. May. 1959. "Early embryonal death before implantation." Int. J. Fert. 4:306.

Frommer, J. 1964. "Prenatal development of the mandibular joint in mice." Anat. Rec. 150:449-461.

Froud, M. D. 1959. "Studies on the arterial system of three inbred strains of mice." J. Morphol. 104:441-478.

Fruhman, G. J. 1966. "Shunting of erythropoiesis in mice." Anat. Rec. 154:346.

Fujita, S. 1963. "Matrix cell and cytogenesis of the developing central nervous system. J. Comp. Neur. 120:37-40.

———, 1964. "Analysis of neuron differentiation in the central nervous system by tritiated thymidine autoradiography." J. Comp. Neur. 122:311-327.

Fuller, John L. 1967. "Effect of drinking schedule upon alcohol preference in mice." Quart. J. Studies Alcohol. 28:22-26.

Fulton, J. D., A. C. Arnold, and R. B. Mitchell. "The antibody response of animals exposed to X-radiation. III. The protective effect of chemotherapeutic agents on a specific immune status of X-radiated mice." USAF School of Aviation Medicine, Project No. 21-47-002, Report No. 3.

Fuxe, K., and O. Nilsson. 1963. "The mouse uterine surface epithelium during the estrous cycle." Anat. Rec. 145:541-548.

Galton, M., and S. F. Holt. 1965. "Asynchronous replication of the mouse sex chromosomes." Exp. Cell. Res. 37:111-116.

Gardner, P. J. 1966. "Fine structure of the seminiferous tubule of the Swiss mouse. The spermatid." Anat. Rec. 155:235-250.

———, and E. A. Holyoke. 1963. "Observations on the fine structure of the seminiferous tubules of the Swiss mouse." Anat. Rec. 145:320.

———. 1964. "Fine structure of the seminiferous tubule of the Swiss mouse. I. The limiting membrane, Sertoli cell, spermatagonia, and spermatocytes." Anat. Rec. 150:391-404.

Gates, Allen. 1956. "Viability and developmental capacity of eggs from immature mice treated with gonadotrophins." Nature (Lond.). 177:754-5.

Gates, A. H. 1959. "Early embryology of the mouse as studied by transplantation of ova." Ph. D. Thesis, University of Edinburgh.

———. 1963. "Postnatal growth following asynchronous development of the egg and endometrium." Proc. XVI. Int. Cong. Zool. 2:94.

———. 1965. "Rate of ovular development as a factor in embryonic survival." Ciba Found. Symp. on "Preimplantation Stages of Pregnancy." p. 270-297. Ed. G. E. W. Wolstenholme & M. O'Connor. Churchill Ltd., London.

Gates, A. H., and R. A. Beatty. 1954. "Independence of delayed fertilization and spontaneous triploidy in mouse embryos." Nature (Lond.). 174:356-357.

———, L. L. Doyle, and R. W. Noyes. 1961. "A physiological basis for heterosis in hybrid mouse fetuses." (Abstr.). Am. Zool. 1:449.

———, and A. Dronkert. 1965. "Gonadotropin preparations and supervulation in the mouse." Am. Zool. 5:(Abstr.). #148.

———, and M. Karasek. 1965. "Hereditary absence of sebaceous glands in the mouse." Science. 148:1471-1473.

———, and M. N. Runner. "Factors affecting survival of transplanted ova of the mouse." Anat. Rec. 113:555.

———. 1957. "Influence of prepuberal age on number of ova that can be superovulated in the mouse." Anat. Rec. 128:554.

Gates, R. R. 1953. "Polyploidy and sex chromosomes." Acta Biochem. (Leiden). 11: 27-44.

Gates, W. H. 1925. "Litter size, birth weight, and early growth rate of mice." Anat. Rec. 29:183-193.

———. 1930. "The effect of polygamy on the sex ratio in mice." J. Exp. Biol. 7:235-240.

Gaunt, W. A. 1963. "An analysis of the growth of the cheek teeth of the mouse." Acta Anat. 54:220-259.

———. 1964. "Changes in the form of the jaws of the albino mouse during ontogeny." Acta Anat. (Basel). 58:37-61.

———. 1965. "Growth of the facial region of the albino mouse as revealed by the mesh diagram." Acta Anat. (Basel). 61:574-588.

Gaunt, W. S. 1956. "The development of enamel and dentin on the molars of the mouse, with an account of the enamel-free areas." Acta Anat. 28:111-134.

Geyer-Duszynska, I. 1964. "Cytological investigations on the T-locus in Mus musculus L." Chromosoma. 15:478-502.

Gihys, R. 1959. "Comparative study of the lethal effects of cobalt-60 gamma rays and 200 Kv X-rays on C57 mice." Onocologia. 12:279-94 (French).

Glass, L. 1963. "Transfer of native and foreign serum antigens to oviduccal mouse eggs." Am. Zool. 3:135-156.

Glass, L. E., and T. P. Lin. 1961. "Development of x-irradiated and non-irradiated mouse oöcytes transplanted to x-irradiated and non-irradiated recipient females." J. Cell. Comp. Physiol. 61:53-60.

Gluecksohn-Waelsch, S. 1953. "Lethal factors in development." (y, Sd, T. ki, Fu). Quart. Rev. Biol. 28:115-135.

———. 1954. "Some genetic aspects of development." Cold Spring Harbor Symp. 19: 41-49.

———. 1954. "Genetic control of embryonic growth and differentiation." J. Nat. Cancer Inst. 15:629-634.

———. 1965. "Genetic control of mammalian differentiation." Proc. XI. Int. Cong. Genet. 2:209-219.

Goodman, J. W., and L. H. Smith. 1961. "Erythrocyte life span in normal mice and in radiation bone marrow chimeras." Am. J. Physiol. 200:764-770.

Goss, C. M. 1940. "First contractions of the heart without cytological differentiation." Anat. Rec. 76:19-27.

Graff, Ralph J., Willys K. Silvers, Rupert E. Billingham, W. H. Hildemann, and George D. Snell. 1966. "The cumulative effect of histocompatibility antigens." Transplantation. 4:605-617.

Gray, A. P. 1954. "Mammalian hybrids: A check list with bibliography." Tech. Com. #11 Common. Bur. An. Breed, Gen. Edinburgh.

Green, E. L. ed. 1966. "Biology of the laboratory mouse." McGraw-Hill, N.Y.

———, and M. C. Green. 1946. "The effect of the uterine environment on the skeleton of the mouse." J. Morphol. 78:105.

Green, E. L., and M. C. Green. 1953. "Modification of difference in skeletal types tween reciprocal hybrids by transplantation of ova in mice." Genetics. 38: 666.

———. 1959. "Transplantation of ova in mice." J. Heredity. 50:109-114.

Green, J. A. "Ovarian weight and responsiveness to gonadotrophins throughout the estrous cycle of mice." Proc. Soc. Exp. Biol. & Med. 95:504-506.

Green, M. C. 1952. "A rapid method for clearing and straining specimens for the demonstrations of bone." Ohio J. Science. 52:31-33.

———. 1955. "Luxoid-a new hereditary leg and foot abnormality in the house mouse." J. Heredity. 46:90-99.

Green, Margaret C. 1966. (Jackson Lab., Bar Harbor). "Genes and development," p. 329-336. In E. L. Green (ed.) "Biol. Lab. Mouse," 2nd ed. N.Y., Mc-Graw-Hill.

———. 1967. "A defect of the splanchnic mesoderm caused by the mutant gene dominant hemimelia in the mouse." Develop. Biol. 15:62-89.

Green, M. C., and R. L. Sidman. 1962. "Tottering, a new neurological mutant in the mouse." J. Heredity. 53:233-237.

Greenwald, G. S. 1956. "The reproductive cycle of the field mouse." J. Mammology. 37:213.

———, and N. B. Everett. 1959. "The incorporation of S^{35} methionine by the uterus and ova of the mouse." Anat. Rec. 134:171-184.

Gresson, R. A. R. 1933. "A study of the cytoplasmic inclusions and nuclear phenomena during oögenesis of the mouse." Quart. J. Mic. Sci. 75:697-721.

———. 1940. "Presence of the sperm middle-piece in the fertilized egg of the mouse." Nature (Lond.). 145:425.

———. 1940. "A cytological study of the centrifuged oöcyte of the mouse." Quart. J. Mic. Sci. 81:569-583.

———. 1941. "A study of the cytoplasmic inclusions during the maturation, fertilization and first cleavage divisions of the egg of the mouse." Quart. J. Mic. Sci. 83:35-59.

———. 1948. "Fertilization, parthenogenesis, and the origin of the primitive germ cell of some animals" in "Essentials of General Cytology." p. 64-75. Edinburgh U. Press.

Griffen, A. B., and M. C. Bunker. 1964. "Three cases of trisomy in the mouse." Proc. Nat. Acad. Sci. 52(5):1194-1198.

Grillo, T. A. T. 1964. "The occurrence of insulin in the pancreas of foetuses of some rodents." J. Endocrin. 31:67-73.

Grobstein, C. 1949. "Behavior of components of the early embryo of the mouse in culture and in the anterior chamber of the eye." Anat. Rec. 105:490.

———. 1953. "Morphogenetic interaction between embryonic mouse tissues separated by a membrane filter." Nature (Lond.). 172:869-871.

———. 1955. "Inductive interaction in the development of the mouse metanephros." J. Exp. Zool. 130:319-339.

———. 1956. "Trans-filter induction of tubules in mouse metanephrogenic mesenchyme." Exp. Cell. Res. 10:424-440.

Grüneberg, H. 1937. "The relations of endogenous and exogenous factors in bone and tooth development. The teeth of the gray-lethal mouse." J. Anat. (Lond.). 71:246-244.

———. 1941. "The growth of the blood of the suckling mouse." J. Path. Bact. 52: 323-329.

———. 1942. "Inherited macrocytic anaemias of the house mouse. II. Dominance relationships." J. Genet. 43:285-293.

———. 1943. "The development of some external features in mouse embryos." J. Heredity. 34:88-92.

———. 1950. "Embryology of the mammalian genes." Rev. suisse Zool. 57. Suppl. 1:729-739.

Gruneberg, H. 1952. "The genetics of the mouse." 2nd ed. Martinus Nizhoff The Hague (Bibliogrophia Genet. Vol. 15 complete)

——. 1954. "Genetical studies on the skeleton of the mouse." XII. The development of undulated." J. Genet. 52:441-455.

——. 1956. "Hereditary lesions of the labyrinth in the mouse." Brit. Med. Bull. 12:153-157.

——. 1956. "A ventral ectodermal ridge of the tail in mouse embryos." Nature (Lond.). 177:787-788.

——. 1960. "Developmental genetics in the mouse, 1960." J. Cell. Comp. Physiol. Suppl. Vol. 56:49-60.

——. 1963. "The pathology of development." John Wiley & Sons, N. Y. 301 pps.

Guttenberg, I. 1961. "Plasma levels of 'Free' progestin during the estrous cycle in the mouse." Endocrin. 68:1006-1009.

Gwatkin, R. B. A. 1964. "Effect of enzyme and acidity on the zona pellucida of the mouse egg before and after fertilization." J. Reprod. Fert. 7:99-105.

Halberg, F., and M. B. Visscher. 1952. "A difference between the effects of dietary calorie restriction on the estrous cycle and on the 24-hour adrenal cortical cycle in rodents." Endocrin. 51:329-335.

Hall, B. U. 1935. "The reactions of rat and mouse eggs to hydrogen ions." Proc. Soc. Exp. Biol. & Med. 32:747-748.

——. 1936. "Variations in acidity and oxidation reduction potentials of rodent uterine fluids." Physiol. Zool. 9:471.

Hamburgh, M., L. Nebel, and G. Greenhouse. 1966. "Penetration and uptake of trypan blue in the yolk sac placenta of the mouse." Am. Zool. 6:

Hammond, J. 1949. "Survival of mouse ova *in vitro* and induced multiple pregnancies in cattle." Proc. 1st. Nat. Egg Transfer Breed Conf. Texas. p. 22.

——. 1949. "Recovery and culture of tubal mouse ova." Nature (Lond.). 163:28-29.

Hampton, J. C. 1966. "The effects of ionizing radiation on absorptive and secretory cells in the intestinal epithelium of the mouse." Anat. Rec. 154:353.

Hancock, R. L. 1966. "S-adenosylmethionine-synthesizing activity of normal and neoplastic mouse tissues." Cancer Res. 26:2425-2430.

Hanna, C. 1965. "Changes in DNA, RNA and protein synthesis in the developing lens." Invest. Ophthal. 4:480-495.

Hargitt, C. T. 1926. "The formation of the sex glands and germ cells of mammals. II. The history of the male germ cells in the albino rat." J. Morphol. 42: 253-305.

——. 1930. "The formation of the sex glands and germ cells of mammals. III. The history of the female germ cells in the albino rat to the time of sexual maturity." J. Morphol. 49:277-331.

Haring, O. M. 1965. "Effects of prenatal hypoxia on the cardiovascular system in the rat." A. M. A. Arch. Path. 80:351-356.

——, and F. J. Lewis. 1961. "The etiology of congenital developmental anomalies." Surgery Gynec. & Obstet. 113:1-18.

Harkness, R. A., A. McLaren, and E. J. Roy. 1964. "Oestrogens in mouse placenta." J. Rep. Fert. 8:411-413.

Harper, M. J. K. 1965. "Transport of eggs in cumulus through the ampulla of the rabbit oviduct in relation to day of pseudopregnancy." Endocrin. 77:114-123.

Harrington, F. E. 1965. "Transportation of ova and zygotes through the genital tract of immature mice treated with gonadotrophins." Endocrin. 77:635-640.

Harris, R. G. 1927. "Effect of bilateral ovariectomy upon the duration of pregnancy in mice." Anat. Rec. 37:83.

Harvey, E. B., R. Yanagimachi, and M. C. Chang. 1961. "Onset of estrus and ovulation in the golden hamster." J. Exp. Zool. 146:231-236.

Harvey, S. C., and Y. Clermont. 1962. "The duration of the cycle of the seminiferous epithelium of normal, hypophysectomized and hypophysectomized hormone-treated albino rats." Anat. Rec. 142:

Hashima, H. 1956. "Studies on the prenatal growth of the mouse with special references to the site of implantation of the embryo." Tohoku J. Agric. Res.
6:307.

Haushka, T. S. 1959. "The chromosomes in ontogeny and oncology." Cancer Res.
21:957-974.

Healy, M., A. McLaren, and D. Michie. 1960. "Foetal growth in the mouse." Proc.
Roy. Soc. (Lond.) B. 153:367.

Heinecke, H., and H. Grimm. 1958. "Untersuchungen zur Offnungszeit der Vaginal-
membran bei verschiedenen Mausestammen." Endokrinologie. 35:205-213.

Hemmingsen, A. M., and N. B. Krareys. 1937. "Rhythmic diurnal variations in the
oestrous phenomena of the rat and their susceptibility to light and dark."
Levin and Munksgaard, Kobenhaven.

Henderson, N. D. 1964. "Behavioural effects of manipulation during different stages
in the development of mice." J. Comp. & Physiol. Psych. 57:284-289.

Henin, A. 1941. "Etude des modification de l'oviducte au cours du cycle oestral (souris)."
Arch. Biol. 52:97-115.

Henricson, B., and A. Nilsson. 1964. "Chromosome investigations on the embryo
progeny of male mice treated with ^{90}Sr." Royal Veterinary Coll., Stockholm
& Res. Inst. Nat'l Defence, Sunndbyberg, Sweden. Acta Radiol., Therapy,
Phys. Biol. (N.S.) 2:315-320.

Herrmann-Erlee, M. P. 1964. "Quantitative histochemistry of the embryonic mouse
radius: influence of parathyroid extract on the activity of lactic dehydrogenase." J. Histochem. Cytochem. 12:481-482.

Hinricksen, K. 1959. "Morphologische Untersuchungen zum Topagenese der Mandi-
bularen Nogezakneder Maus." Anat. Anz. 107:59-74.

Hitzerman, Sister J. W. 1962. "Development of enzyme activity in the Leydig cells of
the mouse testis." Anat. Rec. 143:351-361.

Hoag, W. G. 1961. "Oxyuriosis in laboratory mouse colonies." Am. J. Vet. Res. 22:
150-153.

———. 1964. "Animal health control for inbred mouse colonies of the Jackson Laboratory." Laboratory & Animal Care. 14:253-259.

———, and M. M. Dickie. 1962. "Studies of the effect of various dietary protein fat
levels on inbred laboratory mice." Proc. Anim. Care Panel. 12:7-10.

———, and J. Rogers. 1961. "Techniques for the isolation of Salmonella tryphim-
curicum from laboratory mice." Jour. Bact. 82:153-154.

Hollander, W. F. 1959. "The problem of superfetation in the mouse." Heredity. 50:
71-73.

———. 1959. "Sperm abnormality of a mutant type involving the "p" locus in the
mouse." Proc. X Int. Cong. Gen. Vol. 2, Toronto. p. 123.

———. 1960. "Genetics in relation to reproductive physiology in mammals." J. Cell.
Comp. Phys. Vol. 56, Suppl. p. 61-72.

———, J. W. Gowen, and J. Stadler. 1956. "A study of 25 gynandromorphic mice of
the Bagg albino mice." Anat. Rec. 124:223-243.

———, and J. W. Gowen. 1959. "A single-gene antagonism between mother and fetus
in the mouse." Proc. Soc. Exp. Biol. & Med. 101:425-428.

———, and L. C. Strong. 1950. "Intra-uterine mortality and placental fusions in the
mouse." J. Exp. Zool. 115:131-150.

Holmes, R. L. 1953. "Nuclear studies on the thalamus of the mouse." J. Comp.
Neural. 99:377-414.

Hooker, C. H., and W. L. Williams. 1940. "Retardation of mammary involution in the
mouse by irritation of the nipples." Yale J. Biol. Med. 12:559-564.

Hoshino, K. 1962. "Influences of estrogen upon pregnancy in mice." Anat. Rec. 142:
p. 242. Gardner through Nat'l. Cancer Inst. U.S.P.H.S. C 343-C14 and
Jane Coffin Childs Memorial Fund.

———. 1964. "Regeneration and growth of quantitatively transplanted mammary
glands of normal female mice." Anat. Rec. 150:221-235.

Hoshino, K. 1965. "Development and function of mammary glands of mice prenatally exposed to testosterone proprionate." Endocrin. 76:789-794.

———. 1966. "Development and growth of mammary glands of CBA mice prenatally exposed to progesterone." Anat. Rec. 154:360.

———. 1967. "Transplantability of mammary gland in brown fat pads of mice." Nature (Lond.). 213:194-195.

———, and W. U. Gardner. 1967. "Transplantability and life span of mammary gland during serial transplantation in mice." Nature (Lond.). 213:193-194.

Howard, A. , and S. R. Pelc. 1950. "p^{32} autoradiographs of mouse testis. Preliminary observations of the timing of sperm at ogenic stages." Brit. Jour. Radiol. 33:634-641.

Hummel, Katharine P. , Margaret M. Dickie, and Douglas L. Coleman. 1966. "Diabetes, a new mutation in the mouse." Science. 163:1127-1128.

Hungerford, D. A. 1955. "Chromosome number of ten day fetal mouse cells." J. Morphol. 97:497-509.

Hunter, R. L. 1951. "Distribution of esterase in the mouse embryo." Proc. Exp. Biol. & Med. 78:56-57 (A).

Hupp, E. W. , H. B. Pace, E. Furchtgott, and R. L. Murphree. 1960. "Effect of fetal irradiation on mating activity in male rats." Psychological Reports. 7:289-294.

Hussey, K. L. 1957. "Syphacia muris vs. Sobvelata in laboratory rats and mice." J. Paristoloty. 43:555-559.

Ibery, P. L. T. 1958. "Evidence for a direct mechanism in leukaemogenesis." Australian Atomic Energy Symposium. 681-4.

Ingalls, Th. , E. F. Ingenito, and F. J. Curley. 1964. "Acquired chromosomal anomalies induced in mice by known teratogens." J. A. M. A. 187:836-838.

———, G. Keleman, and F. J. Curley. 1957. "Development of the inner ear after maternal hypoxia." A. M. A. Arch. Otolaryngology. 65:558-566.

Jackson, R. C. 1964. "Genotype and sex drive in intact and in castrated male mice." Science. 145:514-515.

Jacobs, R. M. 1964. "S^{35} - liquid scintillation count analysis of morphogenesis and teratogenesis of the palate in mouse embryos." Anat. Rec. 150:271-277.

———. 1964. "Histochemical study of morphogenesis and teratogenesis of the palate in mouse embryos." Anat. Rec. 149:691-697.

Jagrillo, G. M. 1965. "A method for meiotic preparations of mammalian ova." Cytogenetics. 4:245-250.

Johnson, M. L. 1933. "The time and order of appearance of ossification centers in the albino mouse." Am. J. Anat. 52:241-271.

Jollie, W. P. 1961. "The incidence of experimentally produced abdominal implantations in the rat." Anat. Rec. 141:159.

Jolly, J. , and M. Ferester-Tadie. 1935. "1. Sur la disposition de l'embryon dans l'oeuf et ses rapports avec les membranes ovulaires chez le rat et souris. 2. La formation du mesoderme dans l'oeuf de la souris." Comp. Rend. Soc. Biol. 119:1055-1058.

———. 1936. "Recherches sur l'oeuf du rat et de la souris." Arch. Anat. Micr. 32: 323-390.

Jones, E. C. , and P. L. Krohn. 1961. "The relationships between age, numbers of oöcytes and fertility in virgin and multiparous mice." J. Endocrin. 21:469-496.

Jones, G. E. S. , and E. B. Astwood. 1942. "The physiological significance of the estrogen: progesterone ratio on vaginal cornification in the rat." Endocrin. 30:295-300.

Jones, N. , and G. A. Harrison. 1958. "Genetically determined obesity and sterility in the mouse." Proc. Soc. Study Fert. 9:51-64.

Jones-Seaton, A. 1950. "A study of cytoplasmic basophily in the egg of the rat and some other mammals." Ann. Soc. Roy. Zool. (Belgium). 80:76-86.

Jones-Seaton, A. 1950. "Etude de l'organization cytoplasmique de l'oeuf des rongeurs principalment quant a la basophilie ribonucleique." Arch. Biol. 61:291-444.

Kallen, B. 1953. "Notes on the development of the neural crest in the head of *Mus musculus*." J. Embryol. Exp. Morphol. 1:393-398.

———. 1953. "Formation and disappearance of neuromery in *Mus musculua*." Acta Anat. 18:273-282.

Kalter, H. 1954. "The inheritance of susceptibility to teratogenic action of cortisone in mice." Genetics. 39:185-196.

Kaneko, K. 1940. "Ueber die Entwicklung der Thalamuskerne der Maus." Fol. Anat. Japan. 19:557-596.

Keeley, K. 1962. "Prenatal influence in behaviour of offspring of crowded mice." Science. 135:44-45.

Keighley, G. H., P. Lowy, Elizabeth S. Russell, and Margaret W. Thompson. 1966. "Analysis of erythroid homeostatic mechanisms in normal and genetically anaemic mice." Brit. Jour. Haematol. 12:461-477.

Kelemen, G. 1947. "The junction of the nasal cavity and the pharyngeal tube in the rat." Arch. Otolaryngol. 45:159-168.

———. 1955. "Experimental defects in the ear and the upper airways induced by radiation." Arch. Otolaryngol. 61:405-418.

———. 1955. "Aural changes in the embryo of a diabetic mother." A.M.A. Arch. Otolaryngol. 62:357-363.

———. 1963. "Hemorrhage: a specific poison to tissue of the ampullar cupulae." A.M.A. Arch. Otolaryngol. 4:365-379.

———. 1963. "Radiation and ear." Acta-Oto-Laryngologia Suppl. 184:5-48.

Kent, H. A. 1960. "Polyovular follicles and multinucleate ova in the ovaries of young mice." Anat. Rec. 137:521.

Kerr, T. 1946. "The development of the pituitary of the laboratory mouse." Quart. J. Micr. Sci. 87:3-29.

Kile, J. C. 1950. "An improved method for the artificial insemination of mice." O.R.N.L.-808., Anat. Rec. 109:109-117, 1951.

King, J. W. B. 1950. "Pigmy, a dwarfing gene in the house mouse." J. Heredity. 41:249-252.

———. 1955. "Observations of the mutant 'pigmy' in the house mouse." J. Genet. 53:487-497.

Kingery, H. M. 1914. "So-called parthenogenesis in the white house." Biol. Bull. 27:240.

———. 1917. "Oögenesis in the white mouse." J. Morphol. 30:261-315.

Kirby, D. R. S. 1960. "Development of mouse eggs beneath the kidney capsule." Nature (Lond.). 187:707-708.

———. 1962. "Reciprocal transplantation of blastocysts between rats and mice." Nature (Lond.). 194:785.

———. 1962. "The influence of the uterine environment on the development of the mouse egg." J. Emb. Exp. Morphol. 10:496-506.

———. 1962. "The development of mouse blastocysts transplanted to the scrotal and cryptorchid tĕstis." J. Anat. (Lond.). 97:119-130.

———. 1963. "Development of the mouse blastocyst transplanted to the spleen." J. Reprod. Fert. 5:1.

———. 1965. "The role of the uterus in the early stages of mouse development" in "Preimplantation Stages in Pregnancy." pps. 325-344, Little, Brown & Co., Boston.

———, W. D. Billington, S. Bradbury, and D. J. Goldstein. 1964. "Antigen barrier of the mouse placenta." Nature (Lond.). 204:548-549.

———, and S. K. Malhotra. 1964. "Cellular nature of the invasive mouse trophoblast." Nature (Lond.). 201:520.

Kirkham, W. B. 1906. "The maturation of the mouse egg." Biol. Bull. 12:259-265.

———. 1910. "Ovulation in mammals with special reference to the mouse and rat." Biol. Bull. 18:245-251.

_____. 1916. "The germ cell cycle in the mouse." Anat. Rec. 10:217-219.

_____. 1916. "The prolonged gestation period in suckling mice." Anat. Rec. 11:31-40.

Kliman, B., and H. A. Salhanick. 1952. "Relaxation of public symphysis of the mouse during the estrous cycle and pseudopregnancy." Proc. Soc. Exp. Biol. Med. 81:201-202.

Knowlton, N. P., Jr., and W. R. Widner. 1950. "The use of x-rays to determine the mitotic and intermitotic time of various mouse tissues." Cancer Res. 10:59-63.

Knudsen, P. A. 1964. "Mode of growth of the choroid plexus in mouse embryos." Acta Anat. 57:172-182.

_____. 1964. "The surface area of choroid plexus in normal mouse embryos." Acta Anat. 58:355-367.

_____. 1965. "Congenital malformations of upper incisors in exencephalic mouse embryos, induced by hypervitaminosis A. Types and frequency." Acta Odont. (Scand.) 23:71-89.

_____. 1965. "Congenital malformations of upper incisors in exencephalic mouse embryos, induced by hypervitaminosis A. II. Morphology of fused upper incisors." Acta Odont. (Scand.) 23:391-408.

_____. 1965. "Fusion of upper incisors at bud or cap stage in mouse embryos with exencephaly induced by hypervitaminosis A." Acta Odont. (Scand.) 23:549-565.

Koch, W. E. 1965. "*In vitro* development of tooth rudiments in embryonic mice." Anat. Rec. 152:513-524.

_____. 1965. "The interaction of embryonic tooth tissues growing *in vitro*." Anat. Rec.

_____. 1966. "*In vitro* studies of developmental associations in the embryonic mouse incisor." Anat. Rec. 154:370.

Kochi, T. 1936. "Ueber die Entwicklungstudien bei der Hypophysis cerebri von Mus musculus (in Japanese)." Akayama-Igakkai-Zasshi. 48:2213-2239.

Koller, P. C., and C. A. Auerback. 1941. "Chromosome breakage and sterility in the mouse." Nature (Lond.). 148, p. 501.

Konigsmark, B. W., and R. N. Sidman. 1963. "Origin of brain macrophages in the mouse." J. Neuropath. Exp. Neurol. 22:643-676.

Krabbe, K. H. 1944. "Studies on the morphogenesis of the brain of Rodentia, Prosimiae, and Edentates." Munksgaard, (Copenhagen).

Krebhiel, R. H., and J. C. Plagge. 1962. "Distribution of ova in the rat uterus." Anat. Rec. 143:239-241.

Kremer, J. 1924. "Das Verhalten der Vorkerne in befruckteten Eider Ratte und der Mause mit besonderer Beruchsichtgung ihren Nucleolen." Z. Mikr. Anat. Forsch. 1:353.

Kroc, R. L., B. G. Steinetz, and V. L. Beach. 1959. "The effect of estrogens progestrogens, and relaxin in pregnant and non-pregnant laboratory rodents." Am. N. Y. Acad. Sci. 75:942.

Krzanowska, H. 1960. "Studies on heterosis. II. Fertilization rate in inbred lines of mice and their crosses." Folia Biol. 8:269-279.

_____. 1960. "Early embryonal mortality in inbred lines of mice and their crosses." Bull. Soc. Roy. Belge de Gynec. et Obstetr. 30:719-728.

_____. 1962. "Sperm quantity and quality in inbred lines of mice and their crosses." Acta Biologica (Cracoviensia). 5:279-291.

_____. 1964. "Studies on Heterosis. III. The course of the sexual cycle and the establishment of pregnancy in mice, as affected by the type of mating." Folia Biologica. 12:415-426.

Kuhl, W., and H. Friedrich-Freksa. 1936. "Richtungs korperbildung und Furchung des Eies sourie das verholten des das Trophoblasten der weiben maus." Zool. Anz. 9:187 (Suppl. 2).

Ladman, A. J., and M. N. Runner. 1951. "Comparison of sensitivities of the immature and pregnant mouse for estimation of gonadotropin." Endocrin. 48:358-364.

———. 1959. "Correlation of the maternal pituitary weight with the number of uterine implantation sites in pregnant mice." Endocrin. 65:580-585.

———. 1960. "Induction of ovulation in normal and hypophysectomized immature mice with purified pituitary extracts of F. S. H. and LH." 1st Int. Cong. Endocrin. Abst. #100.

Laguchev, S. S. 1959. "Comparison of the estrous cycles in mice of high and low cancer lines (English trans.)." Bull. Exp. Biol. Med. 48:1149-1152.

Laird, A. K. 1966. "Dynamics of embryonic growth." Growth. 30:263-275.

Lamond, D. R. 1958. "Infertility associated with extirpation of the olfactory bulbs in female albino mice." Austral. J. Exp. Biol. Med. Sci. 36:103-108.

———. 1959. "Effect of stimulation derived from other animals of the same species on oestrous cycles in mice." J. Endocrin. 18:343-349.

———, and C. W. Emmens. 1959. "The effect of hypophysectomy on the mouse uterine response to gonadotrophins." J. Endocrin. 18:251-261.

Lams, H., and J. Doorme. 1907. "Nouvelles recherches sur la maturation et la fecondation de l'oeuf des mammiferes." Arch. Biol. 23:259-363.

Lane, P. W. 1959. "The pituitary - gonad response of genetically obese mice in parabiosis with thin and obese siblings." Endocrin. 65:863-868.

Larrson, K. S. 1960. "Studies on the closure of the secondary palate. II. Occurrence of sulpho-mucopolysaccharides in the palatine processes of the normal mouse embryo." Exp. Cell. Res. 21:498-503.

———, H. Bostrom, and S. Carlsoo. 1959. "Studies on the closure of the secondary palate. I. Autoradiographic study in the normal mouse embryo." Exp. Cell. Res. 16:379-383.

———, et al. 1966. (Dept. Ped. Pathol., Univ. Uppsala) "A microradiographic study of salicylate-induced skeletal anomalies in mouse embryos." Acta Pathol. Microbiol. Scand. 66:560.

Lash, J. W. 1966. "Chemical embryogenesis of skeletal tissues." Birth Defects, Nat'l. Foundation. 11:56-57.

Lataste, F. 1887. "Recherches de Zooethique sur les Mammiferes de l'orde des Rongeuro." Acta Soc. Linneus Bordeau. 40:202.

Leblond, C. P., and Y. Clermont. 1952. "Spermiogenesis of rat, mouse, hamster and guinea-pig as revealed by the periodic acid-fuchsin sulfurous acid technique." Am. J. Anat. 90:167-216.

———. 1952. "Definition of the stages of the cycle of the seminiferous epithelium in the rat." Ann. N. Y. Acad. Sci. 55:548-573.

Leduc, E. H., J. W. Wilson, and D. H. Winston. 1949. "The production of biotin deficiency in the mouse." J. Nutrition. 38:73-86.

Lee, S. van der., and L. M. Boot. 1955. "Spontaneous pseudopregnancy in mice." Acta Physiol. Pharmac. Neerland. 4:442-444.

Lenz, W. 1962. "How can the physician lessen a hazard to offspring?" (Universitat, Hamburg) Med. Welt. 48:2554-8 (in German).

Leuchtenberger, C. 1960. "The relation of the deoxyribose-nucleic acid (DNA) of sperm cells to fertility." J. Dairy Sci. Suppl. 43:31-53.

———, and F. Schrader. 1950. "The chemical nature of the acrosome in the male germ cells." Proc. Nation. Acad. Sci. Washington. 36:677-683.

Lewis, W. H., and E. S. Wright. 1935. "On the early development of the mouse egg." Contrib. to Embryol. pub. #429, no. 148, Carnegie Inst. pps. 113-143.

Leziak, K. 1958. "Studies on retarded pregnancy in mice from inbred matings (sib-matings) I. Effect of inbreeding on the course of the sexual cycle in mice." Folia Biol. 6:63-70.

———. 1959. "Studies on retarded pregnancy in mice from inbred matings (sib-matings) II. Resorption of foetuses." Folia Biol. 7:267-275.

Lin, T. P. 1956. "Dl-methionine (S[35]) for labelling unfertilized mouse eggs in transplantation." Nature (Lond.) 178:1175-1176.

Lin, T. P. 1966. "Microinjection of mouse eggs." Science. 151:333-337.

———, and D. W. Bailey. 1965. "Difference between two inbred strains of mice in ovulatory response to repeated administration of gonadotrophins." J. Reprod. Fert. 10:253-253-259.

———, and L. A. Glass. 1962. "Cause of pre-implantation death of mouse oöcytes x-irradiated *in vitro*." Anat. Rec. 142:253.

———, J. K. Sherman, and E. L. Willett. 1957. "Survival of unfertilized mouse eggs in media containing glycerol and glycine." J. Exp. Zool. 134:275.

Lindop, P. J. 1961. "Growth rate, life span, and causes of death in SAS/4 mice." Gerontologia. 5:193-208.

Lipkow, J. 1959. "Die Bedentung des Vaginal-propfes bei der weissen Maus." Naturwiss. 49:63.

Lloyd, C. W. (ed.). 1959. "Recent progress in the endocrinology of reproduction." Academic Press, N.Y.

Locke, M. 1964. "The Role of chromosomes in development." 290 pps. Academic Press, N.Y.

Loevy, H. 1962. "Developmental changes in the palate of normal and cortisone-treated strong A mice." Anat. Rec. 142:375-589.

Loewenstein, J. E., and A. I. Cohen. 1964. "Dry mass, lipid content and protein content of the intact and zona-free mouse ovum." J. Emb. Exp. Morphol. 12: 113-121.

Long, J. A. 1912. "The living eggs of rats and mice with a description of apparatus for obtaining and observing them." Minn. Col. Publ. Zool. 9:105-136.

———. 1912. "Studies on early stages of development in rats and mice." Univ. Calif. Pub. Zool. 9:105.

———, and E. L. Mark. 1911. "The maturation of the egg of the mouse." Carnegie Inst. Wash. #142:1-72.

Lugo, F. P. 1959. "The effect of a diet supplemented with hens' eggs upon the estrus cycle of mice." Anat. Rec. 133:408. (Abstr.)

Lyon, M. F. 1966. "Lack of evidence that inactivation of the mouse X-chromosome is incomplete." Genetic Res., Camb. 8:197-203.

———, and R. Meredith. 1966. "Autosomal translocations causing male sterility and viable aneuploidy in the mouse." Cytogenetics. 5:335-354.

Macaluso, M. C. 1965. "The fine structure of the corpus luteum of the Swiss mouse after parturition." Anat. Rec. (Abstr.).

MacDowell, E. C. 1924. "A method of determining the prenatal mortality in a given pregnancy of a mouse without affecting its subsequent reproduction." Anat. Rec. 27:329-336.

———. 1928. "Alcohol and sex ratios in mice." Am. Nat. 62:48-54.

———, and E. Allen. 1927. "Weight of mouse embryos 10-18 days after conception, a logarithmic function of embryo age." Proc. Soc. Exp. Biol. & Med. 24:672-674.

———, E. Allen, and C. G. MacDowell. 1927. "The prenatal growth of the mouse." J. Gen. Physiol. 11:57-70.

———. 1929. "The relation of parity, age, and body weight to the number of corpora lutea in mice." Anat. Rec. 41:267-272.

MacDowell, E. C., and E. M. Lord. 1925. "Data on the primary sex ratio in the mouse." Anat. Rec. 31:143-148.

———. 1926. "The relative viability of male and female mouse embryos." Am. J. Anat. 37:127-140.

———. 1927. "Reproduction in alcohol mice." Arch. Entwickl. Org. 109:549-583. (Quoted by Strong and Fuller, 1958).

Makino, S. 1941. "Some attempts to induce chromosome doubling in germ cells of mice." Bot. & Zool., Tokyo. 9:424-426.

———. 1941. "Studies on the murine chromosomes. I. Cytological investigations of mice, included in the genus Mus." J. Fac. Sci. Hokkaido Univ. 7:305.

Makino, S. 1951. "An atlas of chromosome numbers in animals." Iowa State College Press.

Mandl, A. 1963. "Pre-ovulatory changes in the oöcyte of the adult rat." Proc. Roy. Soc. B. 158:105-118.

Mann, S. J. 1912. "Prenatal formation of hair follicle types." Anat. Rec. 144:135-141.

Mark, F. L., and J. A. Long. 1912. "Studies in early stages of development in rats and mice." Univ. Calif. Pub. Zool. 9:105.

Markert, C. L. 1959. "Biochemical embryology and genetics." N.C.I. Monog. #2 Symp. on "Normal and Abnormal Differentiation and Development."

_____, and W. K. Silvers. 1956. "The effects of geno-type and cell environment on melanoblast differentiation in the house mouse." Genetics. 41:429-450.

Marsden, H. M., and F. H. Bronson. 1964. "Estrous synchrony in mice" in "Alteration by exposure to male urine." Science. 144:1469.

_____. 1965. "The synchrony of oestrus in mice: relative roles of the male and female environments." J. Endocrin. 32:313-319.

_____. 1965. "Strange male block to pregnancy: its absence in inbred mouse strains." Nature (Lond.). 207:878.

Marston, J. H., and M. C. Chang. 1964. "The fertilizable life of ova and their morphology following delayed insemination in mature and immature mice." J. Exp. Zool. 155:237-252.

_____. 1964. "Action of intra-uterine foreign bodies in the rat and rabbit." Excerpta Med. Int. Congress Ser. #86.

Martin, L., and P. J. Claringbold. 1960. "Sensitive oestrogen assay in mice." J. Endocrin. 20:173.

Martinoosteh, P. W. 1939. "The effect of subnormal temperature on the differentiation and survival of cultivated *in vitro* embryonic and infantile rat and mouse ovaries." Proc. Royal Soc. (Lond.) B. 128:138-143.

Matthey, R. 1951. "Chromosomes in muridae." Experientia. 7:340-341.

_____. 1952. "Chromosomes de Muridae." Chromosoma. 5:113-118.

_____. 1953. "Les chromosomes des muridae." Rev. Suisse Zool. 60:225-283.

_____. 1954. "Nouvelles recherches sur les chromosomes des muridae." Caryologia. 6:1-44.

_____. 1954. "Un cas nouveau de chromosomes sexuels multiples dans le genre Gerbillus." Experientia. 10:464-465.

Mayer, T. C. 1965. "The development of piebold spotting in mice." Develop. Biol. 11:319-334.

_____, and E. L. Maltby. 1964. "An experimental investigation of pattern development in lethal spotting and belted mouse embryos." Develop. Biol. 9:269-286.

McCafferty, R. E., and H. P. Mack. 1964. "Tissue porphyrin in pregnant and non-pregnant mice injected with hematoporphyrin." Quart. J. Exp. Physiol. 49:394-407.

_____, and M. L. Wood. 1963. "Intra-amniotic pressure of the mouse." Anat. Rec. 145:285-289. (Abstr.).

_____, M. L. Wood, and W. H. Knisley. 1964. "Uterine contractions and intraamniotic pressures of gravid mice." Am. J. Obstet. & Gynec. 90:120-127.

_____. 1965. "Morphological and physiological effects of thalidomide and trypan blue on uteri and concepti of gravid mice." Am. J. Obstet. & Gynec. 91:260-269.

McCarthy, J. C. 1965. "Effects of concurrent lactation on litter size and prenatal mortality in an inbred strain of mice." J. Reprod. Fert. 9:29-39.

_____. 1965. "Genetic and environmental control of foetal and placental growth in the mouse." Animal Produc. 7:347-361.

McLaren, A. 1963. "The distribution of eggs and embryos between sides in the mouse." J. Endocrin. 27:157-181.

_____. 1965. "Genetics and environmental effects on foetal and placental growth in mice." J. Reprod. Fert. 9:79-98.

McLaren, A. 1965. "Maternal factors in nidation" in "Symposium on the Early Conceptus, Normal and Abnormal," ed. W. W. Park, Dundee.

———. 1965. "Placental weight loss in late pregnancy." J. Reprod. Fert. 9:343-346.

———, and J. D. Biggers. 1958. "Successful development and birth of mice cultivated *in vitro* as early embryos." Nature (Lond.). 182:877-878.

———, and D. Michie. 1954. "Transmigration of unborn mice." Nature (Lond.). 174: 844.

———. 1956. "The spacing of implantations in the mouse uterus" in "Implantation of Ova." P. Echstein, ed. p. 65-75. Cambridge Univ. Press.

———. 1956. "Studies on the transfer of fertilized mouse eggs to uterine foster-mothers. I. Factors affecting the implantation and survival of native and transferred eggs." J. Exp. Biol. 33:394-416.

———. 1958. "An effect of the uterine environment upon skeletal morphology in the mouse." Nature (Lond.). 181:1147.

———. 1958. "Factors affecting vertebral variation in mice. IV. Experimental proof of the uterine basis of a maternal effect." J. Emb. Exp. Morphol. 6:645-659.

———. 1959. "The spacing of implantations in the mouse uterus." Endocrin. 6:65.

———. 1959. "Experimental studies on placental fusion in mice." J. Exp. Zool. 141: 47-73.

———. 1959. "Superpregnancy in the mouse. I. Implantation and the foetal mortality after induced superovulation in females of various ages." J. Exp. Biol. 36: 281.

———. 1959. "Superpregnancy in the mouse. II. Weight and gain during pregnancy." J. Exp. Biol. 36:301.

———. 1959. "Studies on the transfer of fertilized mouse eggs to uterine foster-mothers. II. The effect of transferring large numbers of eggs." J. Exp. Biol. 36:40.

———. 1960. "Control of pre-natal growth in mammals." Nature (Lond.). 187:363.

———. 1960. "Congenital runts." Cibia Edition Symp. Congen. Malform. p. 178-194.

———. 1963. "Nature of the systemic effect of litter size on gestation period in mice." J. Reprod. Fert. 6:139-141.

McLaren, A., and A. K. Tarkowski. 1963. "Implantation of mouse eggs in the peritoneal cavity." J. Reprod. Fert. 6:385-392.

McChere, T. J. 1962. "Infertility in female rodents caused by temporary inanition at or about the time of implantation." J. Reprod. Fert. 4:241.

McPhail, M. K., and H. G. Read. 1942. "The mouse adrenal. I. Development, degeneration and regeneration of the x-zone." Anat. Rec. 84:51-73.

Meier, Hans. 1967. "The neuropathy of teetering, a neurological mutation in the mouse." Arch. Neurol. 16:59-66.

Melissinos, K. 1907. "Die Entwicklung des Eies der mause von den ersten Furchungsphenomenen bis zur Festoetzung der Allantois an der Ectoplacentorplatte." Arch. Miki. Anat. 70:577-628.

Meller, K., W. Breipohl, and P. Glees. 1966. "Early cytological differentiation in the cerebral hemispheres of mice." Zeits. Zellforsch. 72:525-553.

Menefee, M. S. 1955. "The differentiation of keratin-containing cells in the epidermis of embryo mice." Anat. Rec. 122:181-191.

Menzies, J. I. 1957. "Gene-controlled sterility in the African mouse (Mastomys)." Nature (Lond.). 179:1142.

Merritt, G. C. 1959. "The histochemical demonstration of nucleic acid with pyronin-methyl green." Med. Techn. 1:36-41.

Merklin, R. J. 1957. "Pregnancy in mice immediately after parturition." Anat. Rec. 127:333.

Merton, H. 1938. "Studies on reproduction in the albino mouse. I. The period of gestation and the time of parturition." Proc. Roy. Soc. (Edinburgh). 58:80-96.

Merton, H. 1939. "Reproduction in the albino mouse. III. Duration of life of sperm in the female reproduction tract." Proc. Roy. Soc. (Edinburgh). 59:207.

Miale, I. L., and R. L. Sidman. 1961. "An autoradiographic analysis of histogenesis in the mouse cerebellum." Exptl. Neurol. 4:277-296.

Michie, D., and A. McLaren. 1955. "The importance of being cross-bred." New Biol. 19:48.

Michie, D., and M. E. Wallace. 1953. "Affinity: a new genetic phenomenon in the house mouse." Nature (Lond.). 171:26.

Midgley, A. R., and G. B. Pierce. 1963. "Immunohistochemical analysis of basement membranes of the mouse." Am. J. Anat. 63:929-944.

Milaire, J. 1963. "Etude morphologique et cytochimique du development des membres chez la souris et chez la taupe." Arch. Biol. 74:129-317.

Miller, J. F., and J. S. Davies 1964. "Embryological development of the immune mechanism." Am. Rev. Med. 15:23-36.

Mintz, B. 1957. "Embryological development of primordial germ cells in the mouse. Influence of a new mutation." J. Emb. Exp. Morphol. 5:396-406.

————. 1957. "Interaction between two allelic series modifying primordial germ cell development in the mouse embryo." Anat. Rec. 128:591.

Mintz, B. 1957. "Germ cell origin and history in the mouse: genetic and histochemical evidence." Anat. Rec. 127:335-6.

————. 1958. "Environmental influences on prenatal development." 87 pps. ed. B. Mintz, N. A. S. - N. R. C. Univ. Chicago Press.

————. 1959. "Continuity of the female germ cell line from embryo to adult." Arch. Anat. Mic. Morphol. Exptl. 48, Suppl. 155-172.

————. 1960. "Embryological phases of mammalian gametogenesis." J. Cell. Comp. Phys. 56, Suppl. 1:31-48.

————. 1962. "Experimental study of the developing mammalian egg. Removal of the zona pellucida." Science. 138:594-595.

————. 1962. "Formation of genotypically mosaic mouse embryos." Am. Zool. 2:432.

————. 1962. "Incorporation of nucleic acid and protein precursors by developing mouse eggs." Am. Zool. 2:432.

————. 1962. "Experimental recombination of cells in the developing mouse egg normal and lethal mutant genotypes." Am. Zool. 2:541-542.

————. 1963. "Growth *in vivo* of t^{12}/t^{12} lethal mutant mouse eggs." Am. Zool. 3:550-551.

————. 1964. "Synthetic processes and early development in the mammalian egg." J. Exp. Zool. 157:85-100.

————. 1964. "Gene expression in the morula stage of mouse embryos, as observed during development of T^{12}/T^{12} lethal mutants *in vitro*." J. Exp. Zool. 157:267-272.

————. 1964. "Formation of genetically mosaic mouse embryos, and early development of lethal (T^{12}/T^{12}) normal mosaics." J. Exp. Zool. 157:273-292.

————. 1965. "Genetic mosaicism in adult mice of quadri-parental lineage." Science. 148:1232-3.

————. 1965. "Nucleic acid and protein synthesis in the developing mouse embryo" in "Preimplantation Stages in Pregnancy." G. E. W. Wolstenholme & O'Connor, eds. p. 145-168, Little, Brown & Co., Boston.

————, and E. S. Russell. 1955. "Developmental modifications of primordial germ cells, induced by the W-series genes in the mouse embryo." Anat. Rec. 122:443.

————. 1957. "Gene-induced embryological modifications of primordial germ cells in the mouse." J. Exp. Zool. 134:207-230.

Mirskaia, L., and F. A. E. Crew. 1930. "On the genetic nature of the time of attainment of puberty in the female mouse." Quart. J. Exp. Physiol. 20:299-304.

————. 1930. "Maturity in the female mouse." Proc. Roy. Soc. (Edinburgh). 50:179-186.

Mirskaia, L., and F. A. E. Crew. 1931. "On the pregnancy rate in the lactating mouse and the effect of suckling on the duration of pregnancy." Proc. Roy. Soc. (Edinburgh). 51:1-7.

Mitchison, N. A. 1952. "The effect on the offspring of maternal immunization in mice." J. Genet. 51:406-420.

Miyazaki, T. 1940. "Uber die Entwicklung der Lymphknoten bei Maus." Soc. Path. Jap. Trans. 30:29-34.

Monesi, V. 1962. "Autoradiographic study of DNA synthesis and the cell cycle in spermatogonia and spermatocytes of mouse testis using tritiated thymidine." J. Cell. Biol. 14:1-18.

Moog, F. 1951. "The functional differentiation of the small intestine. II. The differentiation of alkaline phosphomonesterase in the duodenum of the mouse." J. Exp. Zool. 118:187-207.

Morgan, W. 1964. "Bipaternity in mice." Proc. S. D. Acad. Sci. 43:81-84.

Mori, A. 1961. "The difference in sperm morphology in different strains of mice." Tohoku J. Agric. Res. 12:107-118.

Mowry, R. W., and R. C. Millican. 1952. "A histochemical study of the distribution and fate of dextran in tissues of the mouse." Am. J. Path. 28:522.

Muhlbock, O. 1947. "On the susceptibility of different strains of mice for oestrone." Acta Brev. Neer. 15:18-20.

Mukeyee, H., J. S. Ram, and G. B. Pierce. 1965. "Basement membranes. V. Chemical composition of neoplastic basement membrane muco-protein." Am. J. Path. 46:49-57.

Mulnard, J. 1955. "Contributions a la connaissance des enzymes dans l'ontogenese, les phosphomonesterases acide et alcoline dans le developpement du Rat et de la Souris." Arch. d. Biol. 66:525-688.

Mulnard, J. G. 1965. "Studies of regulation of mouse ova in vitro" in "Preimplantation Stages in Pregnancy." G. E. W. Wolstenholme and M. O'Connor, eds. p. 123-144, Little, Brown & Co., Boston.

Munford, R. E. 1963. "Changes in the mammary glands of rat and mice during pregnancy, lactation and biochemical changes." J. Endocrin. 28:35-44.

Murakami, U. 1963. "Developmental disturbances of the central nervous system-mechanisms of their formation in experimental teratology." Animal Rep. of The Research Institute of Environmental Medicine. 11:63-75. (Japan).

———. 1963. "Studies on mechanisms manifesting congenital anomalies." (Japan). J. Human Genetics. 8:202-226.

———, Y. Kameyama, and T. Kato. 1956. "A pathologic process in the initial phase of maldevelopments of the central nervous system." Am. Rep. Res. Inst. Environ. Med. Nagoya Univ. (Japan). 67-80.

Muthukkauppen, V. 1965. "Inductive tissue interaction in the development of the mouse lens in vitro." J. Exp. Zool. 159:269-287.

Nadamitsu, S. 1961. "Studies in vitro ovulation in vertebrates. IV. In vitro ovulation in the mouse." J. Sc. Hiroshima U. Ser. B. Div. 1. Vol. 20:27-32.

Naeye, R. L. 1966. "Organ and cellular development in mice growing at simulated high altitude." Lab. Invest. 15:700-706.

Nakum, L. H. 1964. "Science tools. VI. The lethal gene." Conn. Med. 28:163-164.

Nakamura, H. 1926. "Etudes experimentale sur la duree de gestation de la souris." Ann. Inst. Pasteur. 40:303-308.

Nakamura, T. 1957. "Cytological studies on abnormal ova in mature ovaries of mice observed at different phases of oestrous cycle." J. Fac. Fish. Anim. Husbandry, Hiroshima Univ. 1:343-362.

Nandi, S. 1959. "Hormonal control of mammogenesis and lactogenesis in the C_3H/HeCrgl mouse." Univ. Calif. Pub. Zool. 65:1-128.

Nebel, B. R., A. P. Amarose, and E. M. Hackett. 1961. "Calender of gametogenic development in the prepuberal mouse." Science. 134:832-833.

Nebel, B. R. , and E. Hackett. 1961. "Synaptinemal complexes in primary spermatocytes of the mouse. The effect of elevated temperatures and some obvations on the structure of these complexes in control material." Z. Zullforsch. 55:556-565.

Nebel, L. , and M. Hamburgh. 1966. "Observations on the penetration and uptake of trypan blue in embryonic membranes of the mouse." Z. Zullforsch. 75:129-137.

Nelson, A. , S. Ullberg, H. Kristoffersson, and C. Ronnback. 1962. "Distribution of radioruthenium in mice." Acta Radiologica. 58:353-360.

Nelson, J. B. , and G. R. Collins. 1961. "The establishment and maintenance of a specific pathogen-free colony of Swiss mice. Proc. Animal Care Panel. 11:65-72.

New, D. A. 1963. "Effects of excess vitamin A on cultures of skin and buccal epithelium of embryonic rat and mouse." Brit. Jour. Derm. 75:320-325.

_____, and K. F. Stein. 1963. "Cultivation of mouse embryos *in vitro*. " Nature (Lond.). 199:279-299.

_____. 1964. "Cultivation of post-implantation mouse and rat embryos on plasma dots." J. Emb. Exp. Morphol. 12:101-111.

Newton, W. H. 1935. "Pseudo-parturition in the mouse and the relation of the placenta to post partem oestrus." J. Physiol. 84:196.

_____, and N. Beck. 1939. "Placental activity in the mouse in the absence of the pituitary gland." J. Endocrin. 1:65.

Nicholas, J. S. 1934. "Experiments on developing rats. I. Limits of foetal regeneration; behaviour of embryonic material in abnormal environments." Anat. Red. 58:387.

_____. 1934. "Mechanisms affecting embryonic growth." Cold Spring Harbor Symp. Quart. Biol. 19:36-40.

_____. 1949. "The problems of organization" in "The Chemistry and Physiology of Growth." A. K. Parpart, ed. Princeton U. Press.

Niimi, K. , and I. Harada. 1957. "On the ontogenetic development of the massa intermedia of the mouse (in Japanese)." Arb. II. Abt. Anat. Inst. Tokushima 2:97-128.

_____, I. Harada, Y. Kusaka, and S. Kishi. 1961. "The ontogenetic development of the diencephalon of the mouse." Tokushima J. Exp. Med. 8:203-238.

Nogami, H. 1964. "Digital malformations in the mouse foetus caused by x-radiation during pregnancy." J. Emb. Exp. Morphol. 12:637-650.

Noyes, R. W. 1953. "The fertilizing capacity of spermatozoa." West. J. Surg. 61:342.

_____, and Z. Dickmann. 1960. "Relationship of ovular age to endometrial development." J. Reprod. Fert. 1:186-196.

_____, L. L. Doyle, A. H. Gates, and D. L. Bentley. 1961. "Ovular maturation and fetal development." Fert. & Steril. 12:405-416.

_____, Z. Dickmann, L. L. Doyle, and A. H. Gates. 1963. "Ovum transfers, synchronous and asynchronous, in the study of implantation." pps. 197-211, A. C. Enders, (Ed.) "Delayed Implantation." Univ. Chicago Press, Chicago.

Oakberg, E. F. 1956. "A description of spermiogenesis in the mouse and its use in analysis of the cycle of the seminiferous epithelium and germ cell renewal." Am. J. Anat. 99:391-413.

_____. 1956. "Duration of spermatogenesis in the mouse and timing of stages of the cycle of the seminiferous epithelium." Am. J. Anat. 99:507-516.

_____. 1957. "Duration of spermatogenesis in the mouse." Nature (Lond.). 180:1137-1139, 1497.

_____. 1965. "The mammalian oöcyte." W. H. O. Conf. Chemistry & Physiology of the Gametes, Geneva, Switzerland.

Odor, D. L. 1955. "The temporal relationship of the first maturation division of rat ova to the onset of heat." Am. J. Anat. 97:461-492.

Ohno, S. , L. C. Christian, and C. Stenius. 1963. "Significance in mammalian oogenesis of non-homologous association of bivalents." Exp. Cell. Res. 32:590-592.

Okuda, H., B. Haga, T. Kawachi, S. Fujii, and Y. Yamamura. 1960. "Studies on liver catalase, beta-glucuromidose and plasma iron during development of mice." Gann. 51:231-234.

Orsini, M. W. 1962. "Study of ova-implantation in the hamster, rat, mouse, guinea-pig, and rabbit in cleared uterine tracts." J. Reprod. Fert. 3:288-293.

_____. 1963. "Morphological evidence on the intrauterine career of the ovum" (ed. Enders) in "Delayed Implantation." Univ. Chicago Press.

Otis, E. M. 1949. "Intra-uterine death-time in semisterile mice." Anat. Rec. 105:533.

_____, and R. Brent. 1952. "Equivalent ages in mouse and human embryos." U.R.-194 and Anat. Rec. 120:33-64. (1954)

Overton, J. 1965. "Fine structure of the free cell surface in developing mouse intestinal mucosa." J. Exp. Zool. 159:195-202.

Padykula, H. A., J. J. Deren, and T. H. Wilson. 1966. "Development of structure and function in the mammalian yolk sac. I. Developmental morphology and vitamin B_{12} uptake of the rat yolk sac." Dev. Biol. 13:311-348.

_____, and D. Richardson. 1963. "A correlated histochemical and biochemical study of glycogen storage in the rat placenta." Am. J. Anat. 112:215-242.

Pai, A. C. 1965. "Developmental genetics of a lethal mutation, muscular dysgenesis, in the mouse. II. Developmental analysis." Dev. Biol. 11:93-109.

Parkes, A. S. 1924. "Studies on the sex ratio and relayed phenomena. I. Foetal retrogression in mice." Proc. Royal Soc. (Lond.) 95:551-8.

_____. 1925. "The age of attainment of sexual maturity of the albino mouse." J. Roy. Microscop. Soc. 315-319. (Quoted by Engle and Rosasco, 1927).

_____. 1926. "Studies on the sex-ratio and related phenomena: observations on fertility and sex ratio in mice." Brit. Jour. Exp. Biol. 4:93-104.

_____. 1926. "Observations on the oestrous cycle of the albino mouse." Proc. Royal Soc. (Lond.) B. 100:151-170.

_____. 1928. "The length of the oestrous cycle in the unmated normal mouse, records of 1,000 cycles." Brit. Jour. Exp. Biol. 5:371-377.

_____. 1929. "The internal secretions of the ovary." Longmans Green & Co., London.

_____. 1929. "The functions of the corpus luteum. II. The experimental production of placentomata in the mouse." Proc. Royal Soc. (Lond.) B. 104:183-188.

_____. 1953. "Prevention of fertilization by hyaluronidase inhibitor." Lancet. 265:1285-1287.

_____. 1960. "The biology of spermatozoa and artificial insemination" in "Marshall's physiology of reproduction." pps. 161-263. A. S. Parkes (ed.). 3rd ed. Vol. 1, Part 2, Longmans Green, London.

_____, and C. W. Bellerby. 1926. "The mammalian sex-ratio." Biol. Rev. 2:1-51.

_____, and H. M. Bruce. 1961. "Olfactory stimuli in mammalian reproduction." Science. 134:1049-1054.

_____. 1962. "Pregnancy block in female mice placed in boxes soiled by males." J. Reprod. Fertil. 4:303-308.

Parkes, A. S., W. Fielding, and F. W. R. Brambell. 1927. "Ovarian regeneration in the mouse after complete double ovariotomy." Proc. Royal Soc. (Lond.) B. 101:328-354.

Patten, B. M. 1957. "Varying developmental mechanisms in teratology." Pediatrics. 19:734-748.

_____. 1964. "Foundations of Embryology." McGraw-Hill Book Co. 622 pps.

Penchez, R. I. 1929. "Experiments concerning ovarian regeneration in the white rat and white mouse." J. Exp. Zool. 54:319-339.

Pennycink, R. R. 1965. "The effects of acute exposure to high temperatures on prenatal development in the mouse with particular reference to secondary vibrissae." Austr. J. Biol. Sci. 18:97-113.

Perrotta, C. A. 1962. "Initiation of cell proliferation in the vaginal and uterine epithelia of the mouse." Am. J. Anat. 111:195-204.

Perrotta, C. A. 1966. "Effect of x-irradiation on DNA synthesis in the uterine epithelium." Rad. Res. 28:232-242.

Pesonen, S. 1946. "Abortive egg cells in the mouse." Hereditas. 32:93-96.

————. 1949. "On abortive eggs. III. On the cytology of fertilized ova in the mouse." Ann. Clin. Gynec. Fenn. Suppl. 3 Vol. 38:337-352.

Peters, H., and K. Borum. 1961. "The development of mouse ovaries after low-dose irradiation at birth." Int. J. Rad. Biol. 3:1-16.

————, E. Levy, and M. Crane. 1962. "Deoxy-ribonucleic acid synthesis in oöcytes of mouse embryos." Nature (Lond.). 195:915-916.

Pfeiffer, C. A., and C. W. Hooker. 1942. "Early and late effects of daily treatment with pregnant mare serum upon the ovary of mice of the A strain." Anat. Rec. 84:311-330.

Pierce, E. T. 1965. "An autoradiographic study of mouse brain stem histogenesis." Anat. Rec. (Abstr.) #151, p. 400.

————. 1966. "Histogenesis of the nuclei griseum pontis, corporis pontobulbaris and reticularis tegmenti pointis (Bechterew) in the mouse." J. Comp. Neurol. 126:219-240.

Pierce, G. B., and T. F. Beals. 1964. "The ultrastructure of primordial germinal cells of the fetal testes and of embryonal carcinoma cells of mice." Cancer Res. 24:1553-1567.

————, A. R. Midgley, J. Sri Ram, and J. D. Feldman. 1962. "Parietal yolk sac carcinoma: due to the histogenesis of Reicherts' membrane of the mouse embryo." Am. J. Path. 41:549-566.

Pierce, L. J. 1965. "Hereditary eye defects in the mouse." (Abstr.). Genet. 52:467.

Pincus, G. 1936. "The eggs of mammals." The Macmillan Co., N.Y.

————. 1951. "Fertilization in mammals." Scientific American. 184:44-47.

Pinsky, L., and A. M. DiGeorge. 1965. "Cleft palate in the mouse. A teratogenic index of glucocorticoid potency." Science. 147:402-403.

Porter, David G. 1966. "Observations on the yolk sac and Reichert's membrane of ectopic mouse embryos." Anat. Rec. 154:847-860.

Potter, R. G. 1958. "Artificial insemination by donors." Fert. & Steril. 9:37-53.

Price, D. 1963. "Comparative aspects of development and structure in the prostate." Nat. Cancer Inst. Monogr. 12:1-27.

Purdy, D. M., and H. Hillemann. 1950. "Prenatal growth in the golden hamster." Anat. Rec. 106:591-598.

Purshottam, N., M. M. Mason, and G. Pincus. 1961. "Induced ovulation in the mouse and the measurement of its inhibition." Fert. & Steril. 12:346-352.

————, and G. Pincus. 1961. "*In vitro* cultivation of mammalian eggs." Anat. Rec. 140:51.

Ravn, E. 1894. "Ueber die Arteria omphalomesenterica der Ratten und Mause." Anat. Anz. 9:420-424.

————. 1894. "Zur Entwicklung des Nobelstranges der weissen Maus." Arch. Anat. u. Physiol. Anat. Abt. 293-312.

————. 1895. "Ueber das Proamnion, besonders bei der Maus." Arch. Anat. u. Physiol. Anat. Abt. 189-224.

Rawles, M. E. 1947. "Origin of pigment cells from the neural crest in the mouse embryo." Physiol. Zool. 20:248-266.

Raymond, J. 1960. "Controles hormonal de la glande sous-maxillaire de la souris." Bull. Biol. 94:399-523.

Raynaud, A. 1941. "Reaction du sinus urogenital des embryons de souris aux hormones genitales injectees a la mere en gestation." Compt. Rend. Acad. Sci. 213: 187-189.

————. 1942. "Developpement des glandes annexes du tractus genital de la souris." Compt. Rend. Soc. Biol. 136:292-294.

————. 1948. "Retards de developpement, observes chez des foetus de souris, au voisenage du terme de la gestation." Notes et Rev. Arch. Zool. Exp. et Gen. 85:83-99.

Raynaud, A. 1950. "Recherches expérimentales sur le developpement de l'appareil endocrines et le fonctionnement des glandes endocrines des foetus de souris et de mulot." Arch. d'Anat. Mic. et de Morphol. Exp. 39:518-576.

_____. 1957. "Sur le developpement et la differenciation sexuelle de l'appareil gubernaculaire du foetus de souris." C. R. Acad. Sci. 245:2101-2123.

Reading, A. J. 1966. "Effects of parity and litter size on the birth weight of inbred mice." J. Mammology. 47:111-114.

Reamer, G. R. 1963. "The quantity and distribution of nucleic acids in the early cleavage stages of the mouse embryo." Ph. D. Thesis, Brown University. 108 pps.

Reed, S. C. 1933. "An embryological study of harelip in mice." Anat. Rec. 56:101-110.

_____. 1938. "Uniovular twins in mice." Science. 88:13.

Reinius, S. 1965. "Morphology of the mouse embryo, from the time of implantation to mesoderm formation." Zeits. Zellforsch. 68:711-723.

_____. 1967. "Ultrastructure of epithelium in mouse oviduct during egg transport." (In press, Excerpta Medica).

_____. 1967. "Ultrastructure of blastocyst attachment in the mouse." Z. Zellforsch. 77:257-266.

Ressler, R. H. "Parental handling in two strains of mice reared by foster parents." Science. 137:129-130.

Reynaud, J., and A. Reynaud. 1947. "Observations sur la structure du tractus genital des souris femelles castrees a la naissance." Ann. Endocrin. 8:81-86.

Richardson, F. 1953. "The mammary gland development in normal and castrate male mice at nine weeks of age." Anat. Rec. 117:449-465.

Rietsckel, P. E. 1929. "Zur Morphologie der Genital-ausfukrungs gange in Individual cyclus der weissen Maus." Z. Wissensch. Zool. 135:428-494.

Ring, J. R. 1944. "The estrogen-progesterone induction of sexual receptivity in the spayed female mouse." Endocrin. 34:269-275.

Ritter, W., and K. H. Degenhardt. 1963. "Clefts of the lips, jaws and palate induced in mice by means of x-rays." Int. Dental J. 13:489-494.

Roberts, R. C. 1960. "The effect of litter size of crossing lines of mice inbred without selection." Genetic Res. 1:239-252.

Robertson, G. G. 1940. "Ovarian transplantations in the house mouse." Proc. Soc. Exp. Biol. & Med. 44:302-304.

_____. 1942. "An analysis of the development of homozygous yellow mouse embryos." J. Exp. Zool. 89:197-231.

Robson, J. M. 1934. "Uterine reactivity and activity in the mouse at various stages of the sex cycle." J. Physiol. 82:105.

_____. 1935. "The effect of oestrin on the uterine reactivity and its relation to experimental abortion and parturition. J. Physiol. 84:21 and 86:171.

Roosen-Runge, E. C. 1962. "The process of spermatogenesis in mammals." Biol. Rev. 37:343-377.

Ross, L. 1965. "*In vivo* palatine shelf movement in mice after maternal treatment with several teratogens." Anat. Rec. (Abstr.).

Rothschild, L. 1954. "Polyspermy." Quart. Rev. Biol. 29:332.

_____. 1965. "Fertilization." Methuen, London.

Rowe, W. P. 1961. "The epidemiology of mouse polyoma virus infection." Bact. Rev. 25:18.

Rudali, G., and J. Reverdy. 1959. "Action of very weak doses (5r) of x-rays given at birth on the leukemogenesis of AKR mice." Compt. Rend. Soc. Biol. 248:1248-9.

Rudeberg, S. I. 1964. "Topographic distribution of non-specific esterase during cerebellar development in mouse." Z. Anat. Entwicklungs gesch. 124:226-233.

Rudkin, G. T., and A. A. Griech. 1962. "On the persistance of oöcyte nuclei from fetus to maturity in the laboratory mouse." J. Cell. Biol. 12:169-176.

Rugh, R. 1964. "The mouse: a discoid placentate," p. 236-303, in R. Rugh, "Verte-brate embryology; the dynamics of development." Harcourt, Brace & World, N.Y.

Runner, M. N. 1947. "Attempts at *in vitro* semination of the mouse eggs." Anat. Rec. 99:564.

————. 1947. "Development of mouse eggs in the anterior chamber of the eye." Anat. Rec. 98:1-17.

————. 1949. "Limitation of litter size in the mouse following transfer of ova from artificially induced ovulations." Anat. Rec. 103:585.

————. 1951. "Differentiation of intrinsic and maternal factors governing intrauterine survival of mammalian young." J. Exp. Zool. 116:1-20.

————. 1954. "Ovulation in the prepuberal mouse: a delicate bioassay." Anat. Rec. 128:514.

————. 1954. "Inheritance of susceptibility to congenital deformity-embryonic insta-bility." J. Nat. Cancer Inst. 15:637-649.

————. 1959. "Embryocidal effect of handling pregnant mice and its prevention with progesterone." Anat. Rec. 133:330-331. (Abstr.).

————, and A. J. Ladman. 1950. "The time of ovulation and its diurnal regulation in the post-parturitional mouse." Anat. Rec. 108:343-361.

————, and A. H. Gates. 1954. "Conception in prepuberal mice following artificially induced ovulation and mating." Nature (Lond.). 174:222-223.

————. 1954. "Sterile, obese mothers." J. Heredity. 45:51.

Runner, M. N., and J. Palm. 1952. "Length of life of the unfertilized ovum of the mouse." Anat. Rec. 112:383.

————. 1953. "Transplantation and survival of unfertilized ova of the mouse in rela-tion to post-ovulatory age." J. Exp. Zool. 124:303-316.

Russell, E. S., and E. Fekete. 1958. "Analysis of W-series pleiotropism in the mouse: Effect of W W substitution on definitive germ cells and on ovarian tumorigen-esis." J. Nat. Cancer Inst. 21:365-381.

————, and F. A. Lawson. 1959. "Selection and inbreeding for longevity of a lethal type." J. Heredity. 50:19-25.

————, and E. C. McFarland. 1965. "Erythrocyte populations in fetal mice with and without two hereditary anaemias." Fed. Proc. 24:240 (Abstr.).

Russell, L. B., S. K. Badgett, and C. L. Saylors. 1959. "Comparison of the effect of acute continuous, and fractionated irradiation during embryonic develop-ment." from "Immediate and Low Level Effects of Ionizing Radiations." Int. J. Rad. Biol. Suppl. 343-359.

————, and W. L. Russell. 1954. "An analysis of the changing radiation response of the developing mouse embryos." J. Cell. Comp. Physiol. 43:104-145.

Russell, Liane B., and Florence N. Woodiel. 1966. "A spontaneous mouse chimera formed from separate fertilization of two meiotic products of oögenesis." Cytogenetics. 5:106-119.

Russell, W. L. 1963. "The effect of radiation dose rate and fractionation on mutation in mice." from Sobels "Repair from Genetic Radiation." Pergamon Press.

Rutter, W. J., N. K. Wessells, and C. Grobstein. 1964. "Control of specific synthesis in the developing pancreas." Nat. Cancer Inst. Monogr. 13:51-65.

Sanel, F. T., and W. M. Copenhaver. 1965. "Histogenesis of mouse thymus studied with the light and electron microscope." Anat. Rec. 151:410.

Sapsford, C. S. 1957. "The development of the Sertoli cell." J. Endocrin. Proc. 15:lv, lvi.

————. 1962. "Changes in the cells of the sex cords and seminiferous tubules during the development of the testis of the rat and mouse." Austral. J. Zool. 10: 178-192.

Sato, K. 1936. "Uber die Entwicklungs geschichte des Maus eies. I. Die intratubase Entwicklung derselben." Okayama-Igakkai-Zosski. 48:423-441.

————. "Uber die Entwicklungs gechichte des Maus eies. II. Die intrauterine Ent-wicklung derselben, besonders der Emostetekungs-mechanismus des Am-mions." Okayama-Igakkai-Zosaki. 48:792-832.

Sawada, T. 1957. "An electron microscope study of spermatid differentiation in the mouse." Okayamas Fol. Anat. Japan. 30:73-80.

Schlafke, S., and A. C. Enders. 1963. "Observations on the fine structure of the rat blastocyst." J. Anat. 97:353-360.

Schlager, Gunther. 1966. "Systolic blood pressure in eight inbred strains of mice." Nature (Lond.). 212:519-520.

Schlesinger, M. 1964. "Serologic studies of embryonic and trophoblastic tissues of the mouse." J. Immun. 93:253-263.

_____. 1965. "Immune lysis of thymus and spleen cells of embryonic and neonatal mice." J. Immun. 94:358-364.

Searle, A. G. 1954. "The influence of maternal age on development of the skeleton of the mouse." Ann. N.Y. Acad. Sci. 57:558-563.

_____. 1964. "Effects of low-level irradiation on fitness in an inbred mouse strain." Genetics. 50:1159-1178.

Selye, H., and T. McKeown. 1934. "The effect of mechanical stimulation of the nipple on the ovary and the sexual cycle." Surg. Gynec. & Obstet. 59:886-890.

_____. 1934. "Production of pseudo-pregnancy by mechanical stimulation of the nipples." Proc. Soc. Exp. Biol. & Med. 31:683-687.

Sharma, K. N. 1960. "Genetics of gametes. IV. The phenotype of mouse spermatozoa in four inbred strains and their F_1 crosses." Proc. Royal Soc. (Edinburgh) B. 68:54.

Shelesnyak, M. C., and A. M. Davies. 1953. "Relative ineffectiveness of electrical stimulation of the cervix for inducing pseudopregnancies in the mouse." Endocrin. 52:362-363.

Sherman, J. K., and T. P. Lin. 1958. "Survival of unfertilized mouse eggs during freezing and thawing." Proc. Soc. Exp. Biol. & Med. 98:902-905.

_____. 1959. "Temperature shock and cold-storage of unfertilized mouse eggs." Fert. & Steril. 10:384.

Shintani, Y. K. 1959. "The nuclei of the prectectal region of the mouse brain." J. Comp. Neur. 113:43-60.

Shoji, R., and E. Ohzu. 1965. "Breeding experimental of white rats and mice. XI. Notes on implantation rate, prenatal mortality and spontaneous abnormality in eight strains of inbred mice." (Jap., Eng. summ.) Zool. Mag. (Dobutsugaku Sasshi). 74:115-118.

Sidman, R. L. 1961. "Histogenesis of mouse retina studies with thymidine-H^3" in "The Structure of the Eye." pps. 487-506, ed. G. Smelser, Academic Press, N.Y.

_____. 1963. "Organ culture analysis of inherited retinal degeneration in rodents." J. Nat. Cancer Inst. 11:227-246.

_____, and J. B. Angevine, Jr. 1962. "Audoradiographic analysis of time of origin of nuclear versus cortical components of mouse telencephalon." (Abstr.). Anat. Rec. 142:326.

_____, S. H. Appel., and J. F. Fuller. 1965. "Neurological mutants of the mouse." Science. 150:513-516.

_____, M. M. Dickie, and S. H. Appel. 1964. "Quaking and Jumpy, mutant mice with deficient myclination in the central nervous system." Science. 144:309-311.

_____, and M. C. Green. 1965. "Retinal degeneration in the mouse. Location of the rd locus in linkage group XXII." J. Heredity. 56:23-29.

_____, P. Lane, and M. Dickie. 1962. "Stagger, a new mutation in the mouse affecting the cerebellum." Science. 137:610-612.

_____, I. L. Miale, and N. Feder. 1959. "Cell proliferation migration in the primitive ependymal zone. An autoradiographic study of histogenesis in the nervous system." Exp. Neur. 1:322-333.

_____, P. A. Mottla, and N. Feder. 1961. "Improved polyester wax embedding for histology." Stain Techn. 36:279-284.

_____, and G. B. Wislocki. 1954. "Histochemical observations on rods and cones in retinas of vertebrate." J. Histochem. & Cytochem. 2:413-433.

Silagi, S. 1963. "Some aspects of the relationship of RNA metabolism to development in normal and mutant mouse embryos cultivated *in vitro*." Exp. Cell. Res. 32:149-152.

Silvers, W. K. 1958. "Origin and identity of clear cells found in hair bulbs of albino mice." Anat. Rec. 130:135-144.

Simkins, C. S. 1923. "Origin and migration of the so-called primordial germ cells in the mouse and rat." Acta Zool. 4:241-278.

Simmons, R. L., and P. S. Russell. 1962. "The antigenicity of mouse trophoblast." Ann. N.Y. Acad. Sci. 99:717-732.

_____, and J. Weintraub. 1965. "Transplantation experiments on placental ageing." Nature (Lond.). 208:82-83.

Simonds, J. P. 1925. "The blood of normal mice." Anat. Rec. 30:99-101.

Sirlin, J. L., and R. G. Edwards. 1959. "Timing of DNA synthesis in ovarian oöcyte nuclei and pronuclei of the mouse." Exp. Cell. Res. 18:190-198.

Sisken, B. F., and S. Gluechoohn-Waelsch. 1959. "A developmental study of the mutation 'phocomelia,' in the mouse." J. Exp. Zool. 142:623-642.

Skalko, R. G. 1963. "Deoxyribonucleic acid synthesis in the irradiated rat embryo." Thesis, Univ. of Florida. 89 pps.

Skoje, R., Ohzu, E. 1965. "Breeding experiments of white rats and mice. XI. Notes on implantation rate, prenatal mortality and spontaneous abnormality in eight strains of inbred mice." Zool. Mag. (Dobutsugaki-Zosski). 74:115-118.

Slizynski, B. M. 1949. "A preliminary pachytene chromosome map of the house mouse." J. Genetics. 49:242-244.

Smith, C. 1965. "Studies on the thymus of the mammal. XIV. Histology and histochemistry of embryonic and early postnatal thymuses of C57BL/6 and AKR strain mice." Am. J. Anat. 116:611-629.

_____, and M. J. Waldron. 1956. "Glycogen in the thymus of the fetal mouse." Anat. Rec. (Abstr.). 108:113.

Smith, L. J. 1956. "A morphological and histochemical investigation of a pre-implantation lethal (T^{12}) in the house mouse." J. Exp. Zool. 132:51-84.

_____. 1964. "The effects of transection and extirpation on axis formation and elongation in the young mouse embryo." J. Emb. Exp. Morphol. 12:787-803.

_____. 1966. "The changing pattern of basophilia in the mouse uterus from mating through implantation." Am. J. Anat. 119:1-14.

_____. 1966. "Metrial gland and other glycogen containing cells in the mouse uterus following mating and through implantation of the embryo." J. Anat. 119:15-23.

Smith, P. E., and E. T. Engle. 1927. "Experimental evidence regarding the role of the anterior pituitary in the development and regulation of the genital system." Am. J. Anat. 40:159-217.

_____. 1927. "Induction of precocious sexual maturity in the mouse by daily homeo and heterotransplants." Proc. Soc. Exp. Biol. Med. 24:561-562.

Smithberg, M. 1953. "The effect of different proteolytic enzymes on the zona pellucida of mouse ova." Anat. Rec. 117:554.

_____, and M. N. Runner. 1956. "The induction and maintenance of pregnancy in prepuberal mice." J. Exp. Zool. 133:441-457.

_____. 1957. "Pregnancy induced in genetically sterile mice." J. Heredity. 48:97-100.

_____. 1960. "Retention of blastocysts in non-pregestational uteri of mice." J. Exp. Zool. 143:21-30.

Smitten, N. A. 1963. "Cytological analysis of catechalamine synthesis in the ontogenesis of vertebrates and problems of melanogenesis." Gen. Comp. Endocrin. 3:362-377.

Snell, G. D. 1944. "Antigenic differences between the sperm of different inbred strains of mice." Science. 100:272-273.

_____, ed. 1941. "Biology of the Laboratory Mouse." Blakiston, Philadelphis. 497 pps.

Snell, G. D., E. Fekete, K. P. Hummel, and L. W. Law. 1940. "The relation of mat-
    ing, ovulation, and estrous smear in the house mouse to time of day." Anat.
    Rec. 76:39-54.

———, K. P. Hummel, and W. H. Abelmann. 1944. "A technique for the artificial
    insemination of mice." Anat. Rec. 87:473 & Anat. Rec. 90:243-253.

Sobel, E. H., M. Hamburgh, and R. Koblin. 1960. "Development of the fetal thyroid
    gland." First Intern. Congr. Endocrinology, Copenhagen, Session XIIIc,
    No. 608 - Thyroid Exper.

Sobotta, J. 1895. "Die Befruchtung and Furchung des Eies der Maus." Arch. Mikr.
    Anat. 45:15-93.

———. 1903. "Die Entwichlung des Eies du Maus vom Schlusse der Furchungsperiode
    bis zum Auftreten der Amniosfolten." Arch. Mikr. Anat. 61:274-330.

———. 1911. "Die Entwicklung des Eies du Maus vom Ersten Auftreten des Meso-
    derms an bis zur Ausbildung den Embryonanlage und dem Auftretern der
    Allantois." Arch. Mikr. Anat. 78:271-352.

Solomon, J. B. 1964. "Deoxyribonuclease II in the developing mouse embryo." Nature
    (Lond.). 201:618-619.

Soper, E. H. 1963. "Ovarian and uterine responses to gonadotrophin in immature mice
    as related to age." Anat. Rec. 145:352-353 (Abstr.).

Soriano, L. 1965. "Differenciation des epitheliums du tube digestif in vitro." Jour.
    Emb. Exp. Morphol. 14:119-128.

Southard, J. L. 1965. "Artificial insemination of dystrophic mice with mixture of
    spermatazoa." Nature (Lond.). 208:1126-1127.

Staats, J. 1964. "Standardized nomenclature for inbred strains of mice, third listing."
    Cancer Research. 24:147-168.

Stafford, E. S. 1930. "The origin of the blood of the placental sign." Anat. Rec. 47:
    43-57.

Stanley, N. F., D. C. Dorman, and J. Ponsford. 1953. "Studies on the pathogenesis of
    a hitherto underscribed virus (hepato-encephalo myelitis) producing unusual
    symptoms in suckling mice." Austral. J. Exp. & Med. Sci. 31:147-160.

Staugaard, Burton Christian. 1965. "Enzyme activities in the developing kidney of the
    normal mouse and of Sd heterozygotes and homozygotes." Abstr. Ph.D.
    Thesis, Univ. Connecticut, 1964.

Steinetz, B. G., V. L. Bead, and R. L. Kroc. 1957. "The influence of progesterone,
    relaxin and estrogen on some structure and functional changes in the pre-
    parturient mouse." Endocrin. 61:271.

Stevens, J. C., and J. A. Mackensen. 1958. "The inheritance and expression of a mu-
    tation in the mouse affecting blood formation, the axial skeleton, and body
    size." J. Heredity. 49:153-160.

Stevens, L. C. 1964. "Experimental production of testicular teratomas in mice."
    Proc. Nat. Acad. Sci. 52:645-661.

Stevens, W. L. 1937. "Significance of grouping and a test for uniovular twins in mice."
    Ann. Eugenics. 8:57-73.

Stoner, R. D., and W. M. Hale. 1953. "A method for eradication of the mite 'Myocop-
    tes musculinus' from laboratory mice." J. Econ. Entomal. 46:692.

Stotsenburg, J. M. 1915. "The growth of the fetus of the albino rat from the thirteenth
    to the twenty-second day of gestation." Anat. Rec. 9:667-682.

Stowell, R. E. 1941. "A case of probable superfetation in the mouse." Anat. Rec. 81:
    215-220.

Strong, L. C. 1942. "The origin of some inbred mice." Cancer Res. 2 No. 8:531.

———. 1961. "The Springville mouse, further observations on a new 'luxoid' mouse."
    J. Heredity. 52:122-124.

———, and C. A. Fuller. 1958. "Maternal age at time of first litters in mice." J.
    Gerontol. 13:236-240.

Sugahara, T. 1964. "Genetic effects of chronic irradiation given to mice through three
    successive generations." Genetics. 50:1143-1158.

Sugiyama, M. 1959. "A comparative cytoarchitectural study on the diencephalon of the mouse (in Japanese)." Arb. II. Abt. Anat. Inst. Tokushima. 7:49-104.

Sugiyama, T. 1961. "Morphological studies on the placenta of mice of various ages and strains. I. Variations in fetal and placental weight at term" Acta Med. Med. Univ. Kioto. 37:139.

Suntzeff, V., E. L. Burns, M. Moskop, and L. Loeb. 1938. "On the proliferative changes taking place in the epithelium of vagina and cervix of mice with advancing age and under the influence of experimentally administered estrogenic hormones." Amer. J. Cancer. 32:256-289.

Swyer, G. I. M. 1947. "The release of hyaluronidase from spermatozoa." Biochem. J. 41:413-417.

Szollosi, D. 1965. "Development of "yolky substance" in some rodent eggs." Anat. Rec. (Abstr.). 151:424.

Taber, E. 1963. "Histogenesis of brain stem neurons studied autoradiographically with thymidine H^3 in the mouse." Anat. Rec. 145:291 and Anat. Rec. 148:344.

Takasugi, N., and H. A. Bern. 1962. "Crystals and concretions in the vaginae of persistent-estrous mice." Proc. Soc. Exp. Biol. Med. 109:662-624.

Talbert, G. B., and P. L. Krohn. 1965. "Effect of maternal age on the viability of ova and on the ability of the uterus to support pregnancy." Anat. Rec. (Abstr.).

Tarkowski, A. K. 1955. "Experiments in the development of isolated blastomeres of mouse eggs." Nature (Lond.). 184:1286-1287.

_____. 1959. "Experimental studies on regulation in the development of isolated blastomeres of mouse eggs." Acta Theriologica. 3:191.

_____. 1959. "Experiments on the transplantation of ova in mice." Acta Theriologica. 2:251.

_____. 1960. "The effects of transplantation on the early development of rat eggs." Symp. on "Germ Cells and Development." Inst. Int. d. Emb. & Fondozioni, A., Baselli.

_____. 1961. "Mouse chimeras developed from fused eggs." Nature (Lond.). 190: 857-860.

_____. 1962. "Interspecific transfers of eggs between rat and mouse." J. Emb. Exp. Morphol. 10:476-495.

_____. 1963. "Studies on mouse chimeras developed from eggs fused in vitro." Nat. Cancer Inst. Monog. 11:51-67.

_____. 1964. "True hermaphroditism in chimaeric mice." J. Emb. Exp. Morphol. 12:735-757.

_____. 1964. "Patterns of pigmentation in experimentally produced mouse chimaerae." J. Emb. Exp. Morphol. 12:575-585.

_____. 1965. "Embryonic and postnatal development of mouse chimeras" in "Preimplantation Stages in Pregnancy." G. E. W. Wolstenholme & M. O'Connor, eds. pps. 183-193, Little, Brown & Co., Boston.

Taylor, R. B. 1965. "Pluripotential stem cells in mouse embryo liver." Brit. J. Exp. Pathol. 46:376-383.

Tedeschi, C. G., and T. H. Ingalls. 1956. "Vascular anomalies of mouse fetuses exposed to anoxia during pregnancy." Am. J. Obstet. & Gynec. 71:16-28.

Tennant, Judith R., and George D. Snell. 1966. "Some experimental evidence for the influence of genetic factors on viral leukemogenesis." Nat. Cancer Inst. Monogr. 22:61-72.

Theiler, K. 1954. "Die entetehung von spaltwirbeln bei Danforth's short-tail maus." Acta Anatomica. 21:259-283.

Theiler, K. 1957. "Über die differenzierung der rumpfmyotome beim menschen und die herkunft der bauchwandmuskeln." Acta Anat. 30:842-864.

_____. 1958. "Zelluntergang in den histersten Rumpfsomiten bei der Maus." Zeits. Anat. Extwickl. 120:274-278.

_____. 1959. "Anatomy and development of the 'Truncate' (Boneless) mutation in the mouse." Am. J. Anat. 104:319-343.

Theiler, K., and Salome Gluecksohn-Waelsch. 1956. "The morphological effects and the development of the fused mutation in the mouse." Anat. Rec. 125:83-104.

———, and L. C. Stevens. 1960. "The development of rib fusions, a mutation in the house mouse." Am. J. Anat. 106:171183.

Thiery, M. 1960. "Les variations de la teneur en acid desoxyribonucleique (DNA) des noyaux de l'epithelium vaginal de la souris au cours du cycle oestral." Arch. Biol. 71:389-406.

Thomas, L. J. 1926. "Ossification centers in the petrosal bone of the mouse." Anat. Rec. 33:59-68.

Thomson, J. L., and J. D. Biggers. 1966. "Effect of inhibitors of protein synthesis on the development of preimplantation mouse embryos." Exp. Cell. Res. 41:411-427.

Thompson, W. R., and S. Olian. 1961. "Some effects on offspring behavior of maternal adrenalin injection during pregnancy in three inbred mouse strains." Psychol. Rep. 8:87-90.

Thung, P. J., L. M. Boot, and O. Muhlbock. 1956. "Senile changes in the oestrous and in ovarian structure in some inbred strains of mice." Acta Endocrin. 23:8-32.

Tijo, J. H., and A. Levan. 1954. "Some experiences with acetic orcein in animal chromosomes." An. Estoc. Exp. Anla. Dei. 3:225-228.

Togari, C. 1927. "On the ovulation of the mouse." Nagoya J. Med. (Japan). 2:17-50.

Torrey, T. W. 1945. "The development of the urino-genital system of the albino rat. II. The gonads." Am. J. Anat. 76:375-400.

Trasler, D. G. 1960. "Influence of uterine site on occurrence of spontaneous cleft palate in mice." Science. 152:420-421.

———. 1965. "Aspiring-induced cleft lip and other malformations in mice." Lancet. 606-607.

Traurig, H. H., and C. F. Morgan. 1964. "Autoradiographic studies of the epithelium of mammary gland as influenced by ovarian hormones." Proc. Soc. Exp. Biol. & Med. 115:1076-1080.

Truslove, G. M. 1956. "The anatomy and development of the fidget mouse." J. Genet. 54:64-86.

Turner, C. D., and H. Asakawa. 1964. "Experimental reversal of germ cells in ovaries of fetal mice." Science. 143:1344-1345.

Turner, C. W., and E. T. Gomez. 1932. "The normal development of the mammary gland of the male and female albino mouse." Univ. Miss. Res. Bull. 182.

Tutikawa, Kiyosi and Akira Akahori. 1965. "Strain difference of susceptibility to the teratogenic action of ethylurethane in mice." Abstr. Ann. Rep. Nat. Inst. Genet. Japan (1964).

Tyan, M. L. 1964. "Thymus: role in maturation of fetal lymphoid precursors." Science. 145:934-935.

Tyan, M. L., and L. J. Cole. 1962. "Development of transplantation isoantigens in the mouse embryo plus trophoblast." Transplantation Bull. 30:526-529.

Tyler, A. 1961. "The fertilization process." Sterility - Vol. pp. 25-26.

Umansky, R. 1966. "The effect of cell population density on the developmental fate of reaggregating mouse limb bud mesenchyme." Dev. Biol. 13:31-56.

Uzman, L. 1960. "The histogenesis of the mouse cerebellum as studied by its tritiated thymidine uptake." J. Comp. Neur. 114:137-159.

Valverde, F., and R. L. Sidman. 1965. "Successful Golgi impregnations in brains of mutant mice with deficient myelination." Anat. Rec. 151:479-480.

Van der Lee, S., and L. M. Boot. 1955. "Spontaneous pseudopregnancy in mice." Acta Physiol. Pharmacol. Neer. 4:442-444.

Van der Stricht, O. 1901. "L'atresie ovulaire et l'atresie folliculaire du follicle de De Graaf dans l'ovaire de chauve-souris." Verh. Anat. Ges., Jena 15:108-121.

———. 1902. "Le spermatozoi de dans l'oeuf de chauve-souris." Verh. Anat. Ges. 16:163.

Van Ebbenhorst Tengbergen, W. J. P. R. 1955. "The morphology of the mouse anterior pituitary during the oestrous cycle." Acta Endocrin. 18:213-218.

Velardo, J. T. 1958. "The endocrinology of reproduction." Oxford Univ. Press. p. 340.

Venable, J. H. 1945. "Pre-implantation stages in the golden hamster." Anat. Rec. 94:105-120.

_____. 1946. "Volume changes in the early development of the golden hamster." Anat. Rec. 94:129-138.

Veneroni, G., and A. Bianchi. 1957. "Correcting the genetically determined sterility of W W male mice." J. Emb. Exp. Morphol. 5:422-427.

Vivien, J. H. 1950. "Epoque de la differenciation hypophysaire chez la souris albinos." Compt. Rend. Soc. Biol. 144:284-287.

Von Heyningen, H. E. 1961. "The initiation of thyroid function in the mouse." Endocrin. 69:720-727.

Wada, T. 1923. "Anatomical and physiological studies on the growth of the inner ear of the albino rat." Wistar Mem. 10, Philadelphis.

Waddington, C. H. 1956. "Principles of embryology." Macmillan Co. 510 pps.

Walker, B. E. 1954. "Genetics - embryological studies on normal and cleft palates in mice." Ph. D. Thesis, McGill Univ., Montreal.

_____. 1958. "Polyploidy and differentiation in the transitional epithelium of mouse urinary bladder." Chromosoma. 9:105-118.

_____. 1960. "A special component of embryonic mesenchyme." Anat. Rec. 136:298.

_____. 1961. "The association of muco-polysaccharides with morphogenesis of the palate and other structures in mouse embryos." J. Emb. Exp. Morphol. 9:22-31.

_____, and B. Crain. 1959. "The lethal effect of cortisone on mouse mbryos with spontaneous cleft lip-cleft palate." Texas Rep. Biol. Med. 17:637-644.

_____. 1960. "Effects of hypervitaminosis A on palate development in two strains of mice." Am. J. Anat. 107:49-58.

_____. 1961. "Abnormal palate morphogenesis in mouse embryos induced by ribo-flavin deficiency." Proc. Soc. Exp. Biol. & Med. 107:404-406.

Walker, B. E., and F. C. Fraser. 1956. "Closure of the secondary palate in three strains of mice." J. Emb. Exp. Morphol. 4:176-189.

_____. 1957. "The embryology of cortisone induced cleft palate." J. Emb. Exp. Morphol. 5:201-209.

Ward, M. C. 1946. "A study of the estrous cycle and the breeding of the golden hamster." Anat. Rec. 94:139-162.

_____. 1948. "The early development and implantation of the golden hamster and the associated endometrial changes." Am. J. Anat. 82:231-276.

Waring, H. 1935. "The development of the adrenal gland of the mouse." Quart. J. Mier. Sci. 78:329-366.

Washburn, W. W. 1951. "A study of the modification in rat eggs observed *in vitro* following tubal retention." Arch. Biol. 62:439.

Wegelius, O. 1959. "The dwarf mouse - an animal with secondary myxedema." Proc. Sn. Exp. Biol. & Med. 101:225-227.

Weir, J. A. 1958. "Sex ratio related to sperm source in mice." J. Heredity. 49:223-227.

Weir, M. W., and J. C. De Fries. 1963. "Blocking of pregnancy in mice as a function of stress." Psychol. Rep. 13:365-366.

_____. 1964. "Prenatal maternal influence on behaviour in mice: Evidence of a genetic basis." J. Cell. Comp. Phys. 58:412-417.

Weitlauf, H. M., and G. C. Greenwold. 1965. "Comparisons of S^{35} methionine incorporation by the blastocysts of normal and delayed implanting mice." J. Rep. Fert. 10:203-208.

Wessells, N. K., and K. D. Roessner. 1965. "Nonproliferation in dermal condensations of mouse vibrissae and pelage hairs." Develop. Biol. 12:419-433.

West, W. T., H. Meier, and W. G. Hoag. 1966. "Hereditary mouse muscular dystro-phy with particular emphasis on pathogenesis and attempts at therapy." Ann. N.Y. Acad. Sci. 138:4-13.

Whitten, W. K. 1956. "Modification of the oestrous cycle of the mouse by external stimuli associated with the male." J. Endocrin. 13:399-404.

———. 1956. "The effect of removal of the olfactory bulbs on the gonads of mice." J. Endocrin. 14:160-163.

———. 1956. "Culture of tubal mouse ova." Nature (Lond.). 177:96. Nature (Lond.). 179:1081-1082, 1957.

———. 1957. "The effect of progesterone on the development of mouse eggs *in vitro*." J. Endocrin. 16:80-85.

———. 1957. "Effect of exteroceptive factors on the oestrous cycle of mice." Nature (Lond.). 180:1436.

———. 1958. "Endocrine studies on delayed implantation in lactating mice: Role of the pituitary in implantation." J. Endocrin. 16:435-440.

———. 1959. "Occurrence of anoestrus in mice caged in groups." J. Endocrin. 18:102-107.

———, and C. P. Dagg. "Influence of spermatozoa on the cleavage rate of mouse eggs." J. Exp. Zool. 148:173-183.

Wilson, E. D., and M. X. Zarrow. 1958. "Induction of superovulation with HCG in immature mice primed with PMS." Proc. Am. Soc. Zool. #19.

Wilson, I. B. 1960. "Implantation of tissues in the uteri of pseudopregnant mice." Nature (Lond.). 185:553-554.

———. 1963. "New factor associated with the implantation of the mouse egg." J. Reprod. Fert. 5:281-282.

———. 1963. "A tumour tissue analogue of the implanting mouse embryo." Proc. Zool. Soc. (Lond.). 141:137-151.

Wilson, J. W., C. S. Gwat, and E. H. Leduc. 1963. "Histogenesis of the liver." Ann. N.Y. Acad. Sci. 111:8-24.

———, and E. H. Leduc. 1948. "The occurrence and formation of binucleate and multinucleate cells and polyploid nuclei in the mouse liver." Am. J. Anat. 82:3, 353-392.

———. 1950. "Abnormal mitosis in mouse liver." Am. J. Anat. 86:51-74.

———, and H. Winston. 1949. "The production of biotin deficiency in the mouse." J. Nutrition, v. 38: no. 1.

Wimsatt, W. A., and C. M. Waldo. 1945. "The normal occurrence of a peritoneal opening in the bursa ovarii of the mouse." Anat. Rec. 93:47-57.

Winick, M., and R. G. Greenberg. 1965. "Appearance and localization of a nerve growth-promoting protein during development." Pediatrics. 35:221-228.

Wirsen, C. 1964. "Histochemical heterogeneity of muscle spindle fibers." J. Histo-chem. Cytochem. 12:308-309.

———, and K. S. Larsson. 1964. "Histochemical differentiation of skeletal muscle in foetal and newborn mice." J. Emb. Exp. Morphol. 12:759-767.

Wirtschafter, Z. T. 1960. "Genesis of the mouse skeleton." C. C. Thomas, Springfield.

Wischnitzer, S. 1966. "The maturation of the ovum and growth of the follicle in the mouse ovary; a phase contrast microscope study." Growth. 30:239-255.

Wislocki, G. B., H. W. Deane, and E. W. Dempsey. 1964. "The histochemistry of the rodent's placenta." Am. J. Anat. 78:281-345.

———, and R. L. Sidman. 1954. "Chemical morphology of the retina." J. Comp. Neur. 101:53-100.

Witschi, E. 1956. "Development of Vertebrates." W. B. Saunders, Phila. 588 pps.

Wolf, M. K. 1964. "Differentiation of neuronal types and synapses in myelinating cul-tures of mouse cerebellum." J. Cell. Biol. 22:259-279.

Wolfe, H. Glenn. 1966. "Plasma proteins in fetal mice." Abstr. Genetics. 54:369.

Wolstenholme, G. E. W., and M. O'Connor. 1965. "Preimplanation stages of preg-nancy." (Ciba Foundation Symposium) Little, Brown & Co., Boston, 430 pps.

Wood, M. L. 1967. "*In-vivo* observations on normal and experimentally induced varia-
    tions in the electrical activity of the uterus of the mouse." (in press)

_____, and R. E. McCafferty. 1964. "Relationship of intra-amniotic pressure changes
    to electrical activity of surrounding uterine muscle." Anat. Rec. 148:351-
    352. (Abstr.).

_____. 1966. "*In-vivo* observations of spontaneous electrical activity in uteri of nor-
    mally cycling, pregnant and ovariectomized mixe." Anat. Rec. 154:443
    (Abstr.).

Woollam, D. H. M. 1964. "The effect of environmental factors on the foetus." Jour.
    Col. Gen. Pract. Suppl. #2, 8:35-46.

Yamada, E. 1955. "The fine structure of the gall bladder epithelium of the mouse." J.
    Biophys. Biochem. Cytol. 1:445-458.

_____. 1955. "The fine structure of the renal glomerulus of the mouse." J. Biophys.
    & Biochem. Cytol. 1:551.

_____, T. Muta, and A. Matamura. 1957. "The fine structure of the oöcyte in the
    mouse ovary studied with electron microscope." Kurume Med. J. 4:148-171.

Yanagimachi, R., and M. C. Chang. 1961. "Fertilizable life of golden hamster ova and
    their morphological changes at the time of losing fertilizability." J. Exp.
    Zool. 148:185-197.

_____. 1962. "Fertilizable life of the golden hamster ova and the cortical change at
    the time of losing fertilizability." Anat. Rec. 142:334.

Yoon, C. H. 1955. "Homeostasis associated with heterozygosity in the genetics of time
    of vaginal opening in the house mouse." Genetics. 40:297-309.

Young, H. B. 1917. "Some phases of spermatogenesis in the mouse." Univ. Calif. Pub.
    Zool. 16:371-380.

Young, W. C. 1933. "Die Resoystron in den Ductuli efferentes der Maus und ihre
    Bedentung fur das Problem der Unterbindung un Hoden-Nebenhodensystem."
    Z. Zellforsch. U. Miki. Anat. 17:729-759.

Zarrow, M. X., and E. D. Wilson. 1961. "The influence of age on superovulation in
    superovulation in the immature rat and mouse." Endocrin. 69:851-855.

Zeman, W., and J. R. McInnes. 1963. "Craigies Neuroanatomy of the rat." Academic
    Press, N.Y., 230 pps.

Zimmerman, L. E., and A. B. Eastham. 1959. "Acid mucopolysaccharide in the ret-
    inal pigment in the primitive apendymal zone: An autoradiographic study of
    histogenesis in the nervous system." Exp. Neurol. 1:322-333.

ADDITIONAL REFERENCES

Albert S., et al. 1966. Observations on the origin of lymphocyte-like cells in mouse
    bone marrow. Nature. 212:1577-1579.

Alescio, Tommaso, and Emilia Colombo Piperno. 1967. A quantitative assessment of
    mesenchymal contribution to epithelial growth rate in mouse embryonic lung
    developing *in vitro*. J. Embryol. Exp. Morphol. 17:213-227.

Aldred, John Phillip. 1963. Climatic environmental influences on growth and fertility
    in the mouse. Abstr. Diss. Abstr. 23:2962-2963.

Baccarini, Iracema M., et al. 1967. An autoradiographic study of vaginal epithelium
    of mice by serial biopsy. Abstr. Anat. Rec. 157:207-208.

Blackburn, Will R., and J. F. A. P. Miller. 1967. Electron microscopic studies of
    thymus graft regeneration and rejection I. Syngeneic grafts. Lab. Invest.
    16:66-83.

Borum, Kirstine. 1967. Oögenesis in the mouse; a study of the origin of the mature
    ova. Exp. Cell Res. 45:39-47.

Browning, Henry C., and M. Perley. 1966. Effect of single prenatal dosage of androgen on female mice. _Abstr_. Amer. Zool. 6:569.

Browning, Henry C., and Wilma D. White. 1967. Relation between the size of ovarian isografts and abnormal reproductive cycles in the mouse. Anat. Rec. 157: 155-162.

Burnet, F. M. 1966. Mast cells in the mouse thymus, p. 335-340. _In_ G. E. W. Wolstenholme & R. Porter (ed.) The thymus. Boston; Little & Brown.

Caruso, R., and N. L. Petrakis. 1966. Studies of the coagulation and prothrombin time in the mouse embryo. Thromb. Diath. Haemorrh. 16:732-737.

Chaudhry, Anand P., and Susan Siar. 1957. _In vitro_ study of fusion of palatal shelves in A/Jax mouse embryos. J. Dent. Res. 46:257-260.

Clark, Sam L., Jr. 1966. Cytological evidences of secretion in the thymus, p. 3-30. _In_ G. E. W. Wolstenholme & R. Porter (ed.). The thymus. Boston; Little & Brown.

Daems, W. Th., and E. Wisse. 1966. Shape and attachment of the cristae mitochondriales in mouse hepatic cell mitochondria. J. Ultrastruct. Res. 16:123-140.

Disher, Lenore. 1967. Histogenesis of mouse submandibular salivary gland. _Abstr_. Anat. Rec. 157:235.

Flower, Michael, and Clifford Grobstein. 1967. Interconvertibility of induced morphogenetic responses of mouse embryonic somites to notochord and ventral spinal cord. Develop. Biol. 15:193-205.

Godowicz, Barbara, and Halina Krzanowska. 1966. DNA content of mouse spermatozoa from inbred strain KE of low male fertility. Folia Biol. (Warsaw) 14:235-242.

Heath, Trevor, and Steven L. Wissig. 1966. Fine structure of the surface of mouse hepatic cells. Amer. J. Anat. 119:97-128.

Hoshino, K. 1967. Comparative study on the skeletal development in the fetus of rat and mouse. Congen. Anomalies (Japan). 7:32-38.

Izard, Jacques. 1967. A class of dense reticular cells with long processes in the mouse thymus. _Abstr_. Anat. Rec. 157:264.

Jacobs, Richard M. 1966. Effects of cortisone acetate upon hydration of embryonic palate in two inbred strains of mice. Anat. Rec. 156:1-4.

Knudsen, P. A. 1966. Congenital malformations of lower incisors and molars in exencephalic mouse embryos, induced by hypervitaminosis A. Acta Odontol. Scand. 24:55-90.

Krzanowska, Halina. 1966. Fertilization rate in mice after artificial insemination with epididymal or "capacitated" sperm from inbred and crossbred males. Folia Biol. (Warsaw) 14:171-175.

————. 1966. Inheritance of reduced male fertility, connected with abnormal spermatozoa, in mice. Acta Biol. Cracoviensia (Zool.) 9:61-70.

Laird, Anna Kane, and Alma Howard. 1967. Growth curves in inbred mice. Nature. 213:786-787.

Ogawa, T. 1967. Comparative study on development in the stage of organogenesis in the mouse and rat. Congen. Anomalies (Japan). 7:27-31.

Reading, Anthony J. 1966. Influence of room temperature on the growth of house mice. J. Mannal. 47:694-697.

Richardson, Flavia L. 1967. The acinar pattern in the mammary glands of virgin mice at different ages. J. Nat. Cancer Inst. 38:305-315.

Schlesinger, Michael, and Zeev Koren. 1967. Mouse trophoblastic cells in tissue culture. Fertil. Steril. 18:95-101.

Shelton, Emma. 1966. Differentiation of mouse thymus cultured in diffusion chambers. Amer. J. Anat. 119:341-358.

Simnett, J. D., and A. G. Heppleston. 1966. Cell renewal in the mouse lung; the influence of sex, strain, and age. Lab. Invest. 15:1793-1801.

————. 1956. Factors controlling organ growth; a comparison of mitotic activity of newborn and adult mouse lung in organ culture. Exp. Cell Res. 45:96-105.

Smiley, G. R. 1967. A profile cephalometric appraisal of normal growth parameters in embryonic mice. <u>Abstr</u>. Anat. Rec. 157:323.

Smiley, Gary R., and Andrew D. Dixon. 1966. Fine structure of midline epithelium in the developing palate. <u>Abstr</u>. J. Cell Biol. 31:162A.

Stevens, Leroy C. 1967. The development of teratomas from intratesticular grafts of 2-cell mouse eggs. <u>Abstr</u>. Anat. Rec. 157:328.

Stoeckel, M. E., and A. Porte. 1966. Observations ultrastructurales sur la parathyroide de souris. I. Etude chez la souris normale. Zeits. Zellforsch. 73:488-502.

Tarkowski, A. K. 1966. An air-drying method for chromosome preparations from mouse eggs. Cytogenetics. 5:394-400.

Wakasugi, Noboru, et al. 1967. Differences of fertility in reciprocal crosses between inbred strains of mice: DDK, KK and NC. J. Reprod. Fertil. 13:41-50.

Wessells, Norman K., and Julia H. Cohen. 1967. Early pancreas organogenesis: morphogenesis, tissue interactions, and mass effects. Develop. Biol. 15:237-270.

Index*

*Underscored page numbers refer to illustrations.

411